GREENSPEC®
DIRECTORY

GREENSPEC®
DIRECTORY

Product Listings & Guideline Specifications   7th Edition

EDITORS

**Alex Wilson, Nadav Malin,
Mark Piepkorn & Jennifer Atlee**

MANAGING EDITOR

Angela Battisto

AUTHORS, GUIDELINE SPECIFICATIONS

John Boecker, Scot Horst, Brian Toevs, P.E., Marcus B. Sheffer, Nadav Malin

BuildingGreen's corporate mission is to inspire and empower the North American building industry to create buildings and communities that nurture human and ecological well-being while protecting and restoring the local, regional, and global environment. In pursuing this mission, it promotes the health and prosperity of its employees, owners, associates, and customers.

Authoritative Information on Environmentally Responsible Building Design and Construction

GreenSpec® Directory: Product Listings & Guideline Specifications
Seventh Edition, April 2007

Front cover photos:

RetroPlate concrete polishing, Advanced Floor Products, Inc.
from *GreenSource* magazine, Issue 2, p. 40

Timbron molding, Timbron International

3form Varia wall panels, 3form, Inc.

EcoWorx carpet tiles, Shaw Contract Group
from *GreenSource* magazine, Issue 3, p. 29

Back cover photos:

Bamboo molding, JMX International
from *GreenSource* magazine, Issue 1, p. 35

AVX400 Turbine, AV Inc.
from *GreenSource* magazine, Issue 2, p. 38

Earthtex wall coverings, Design Tex
from *GreenSource* magazine, Issue 2, p. 36

ISBN: 1-929884-18-4

For information about permission to reprint selections from this book, please contact:

BuildingGreen, Inc.
122 Birge Street, Suite 30
Brattleboro, VT 05301
802/257-7300

Production notes:

Text design: Joy Wallens-Penford
Layout: Julia Jandrisits
Cover design: Julia Jandrisits

Text printed with vegetable-based ink on recycled Opaque Rolland/Cascade 30% post-consumer, processed chlorine-free (EcoLogo approved)

Printed in the United States of America by Edwards Brothers, Inc., Ann Arbor, Michigan

Table of Contents

GUIDELINE SPECIFICATIONS

01 00 00 GENERAL REQUIREMENTS

02 00 00 EXISTING CONDITIONS

03 00 00 CONCRETE

04 00 00 MASONRY

05 00 00 METALS

06 00 00 WOOD, PLASTICS, & COMPOSITES

07 00 00 THERMAL & MOISTURE PROTECTION

08 00 00 OPENINGS

09 00 00 FINISHES

10 00 00 SPECIALTIES

11 00 00 EQUIPMENT

26 00 00 ELECTRICAL

27 00 00 COMMUNICATIONS

28 00 00 ELECTRONIC SAFETY & SECURITY

31 00 00 EARTHWORK

32 00 00 EXTERIOR IMPROVEMENTS

33 00 00 UTILITIES

34 00 00 TRANSPORTATION

35 00 00 WATERWAY & MARINE CONSTRUCTION

Contents by Builder Product Categories

The product listings in this Directory are organized according to the CSI MasterFormat™ numbering system. This table of contents organizes the numbered CSI sections in product categories that may be more familiar to builders and contractors. Some CSI sections appear under more than one builder category. Page numbers for the first listing in each CSI section are provided.

STRUCTURAL SYSTEMS & COMPONENTS

SHEATHING

EXTERIOR FINISH & TRIM

ROOFING

WINDOWS

DOORS

INSULATION

FLOORING & FLOORCOVERINGS

INTERIOR FINISH & TRIM

PAINTS & COATINGS

CAULKS & ADHESIVES

MECHANICAL SYSTEMS/HVAC

PLUMBING

LIGHTING

ELECTRICAL

APPLIANCES

FURNITURE & FURNISHINGS

RENEWABLE ENERGY

MISCELLANEOUS

DISTRIBUTORS & RETAILERS

Acknowledgments

GreenSpec Directory Acknowledgments

Thanks to the many manufacturers, product managers, technical experts, and customer support staff who provided information about the products and companies included in this book.

Special thanks to:

Kalin Associates, Inc., publishers of an earlier guide to green building product specifications titled *Green Spec*, for the rights to the *GreenSpec* name.

BuildingGreen intern Frank Richter, for help with updating records in the *GreenSpec* database in preparation for this print edition.

BuildingGreen Residential Program Manager Peter Yost for consulting on product selections and CSI section introductions.

BuildingGreen Director of Web Applications Ethan Goldman for exporting the information from our database in amazing ways.

All other BuildingGreen staff for picking up slack while this book was being assembled.

Guideline Specifications Acknowledgments

The following persons and organizations provided invaluable support, expertise, criticism, and review:

Chris Long and Peter Schubert from U.S. Environmental Protection Agency's Research Triangle Park campus.

Bob Thompson, Chief, Indoor Environments Management Branch, U.S. EPA

Jim Newman, Jennifer Atlee and Peter Yost of BuildingGreen, Inc.

Bill Hoffman, Austin Water Utility

Disclaimers

GreenSpec *Disclaimer*

GreenSpec is intended to serve as a resource to architects, builders, designers, developers, government officials, planners, and building owners to make it as easy as possible for them to find environmentally preferable building products. Products are selected for inclusion in *GreenSpec* based in whole or in part on the representations of the manufacturers and suppliers. Many of the criteria for selection are, by nature, subjective; and a product may perform well in one situation but poorly in another.

BuildingGreen, Inc. advises all users of *GreenSpec* to obtain complete current product information and specifications directly from the manufacturer in order to determine independently the appropriateness of the product for their particular project or use. BuildingGreen, Inc. assumes no responsibility as to the accuracy, completeness, or usefulness of the information included in *GreenSpec* with respect to your individual needs.

BUILDINGGREEN, INC. MAKES NO WARRANTIES AS TO ANY PRODUCT LISTED OR DESCRIBED IN *GreenSpec.*, INCLUDING, WITHOUT LIMITATION, WARRANTIES AS TO ANY PROPERTIES OR CAPABILITIES AND ANY IMPLIED WARRANTIES OF MERCHANTABILITY OR FITNESS FOR A PARTICULAR PURPOSE. BUILDINGGREEN, INC. MAKES NO REPRESENTATIONS AS TO THE COMPLIANCE OF ANY PRODUCT WITH APPLICABLE LAWS OR REGULATIONS OR NON-INFRINGEMENT OF INTELLECTUAL PROPERTY RIGHTS.

BuildingGreen, Inc. shall have no liability to any party for any direct, indirect, incidental, punitive, or consequential damages, including without limitation, lost profits, or loss of use of property as a result of the use, application, or adaptation of the products, information or opinions contained in *GreenSpec*. Without limiting the effect of the foregoing, in no case will BuildingGreen, Inc.'s liability exceed the purchase price of this directory or the price printed hereon, whichever is less. If any statement in this Disclaimer is held to be invalid, unenforceable, or illegal, such holding will not invalidate, impair, or render unenforceable any other statement that is part of this Disclaimer.

Guideline Specifications Disclaimer

These Specifications are general guidelines as to product selection and installation and may not be appropriate for your particular project. This document provides no guaranty as to product performance, merchantability, or fitness for a particular purpose. BuildingGreen, Inc. makes no representation as to the particular products or materials identified in this document and makes no endorsement of any product, material, or construction method so identified. BuildingGreen, Inc. disclaims any warranties, expressed or implied, relating to these specifications.

Some of the materials and construction methods are new and have not yet been fully tested. The user should consult with the manufacturer of each product before using that product and carefully review any product information available to determine the fitness of the material for the project or use contemplated. Recommendations contained in this document, such as minimum recycled-content percentage, are based on current information; availability may change at any time, check with manufacturer.

The user should independently determine that the construction methods are appropriate for the particular project. BuildingGreen, Inc. makes no representation as to the particular construction methods identified in the Guidelines Specifications and makes no endorsement of any construction method so identified.

BuildingGreen, Inc. shall have no liability to any party for any direct, indirect, incidental, punitive, or consequential damages, including without limitation, lost profits, or loss of use of property as a result of the use, application, or adaptation of the guidelines or specifications. Without limiting the effect of the foregoing, in no case will BuildingGreen, Inc.'s liability exceed the purchase price of this directory or the price printed hereon, whichever is less. If any statement in this Disclaimer is held to be invalid, unenforceable, or illegal, such holding will not invalidate, impair, or render unenforceable any other statement that is part of this Disclaimer.

Introduction to GreenSpec®

Welcome to *GreenSpec*, your comprehensive guide to environmentally responsible building products and materials from the editors of *Environmental Building News*. More than 2,100 listings are included in these pages. Additional information, newly added products, and updated listings are available with a subscription to the *BuildingGreen Suite* of online resources (see the end of this book or visit **www.BuildingGreen. com/ecommerce**).

Using the most environmentally sound materials is an important step in the overall goal of improving the environmental performance of any building. *GreenSpec* helps you locate the greenest materials available.

How to Use GreenSpec

GreenSpec is organized according to the Construction Specifications Institute (CSI) *MasterFormat*™ (2004) structure for organizing products. If you are used to seeing building products organized according to *building components* (foundations, wall systems, etc.)—as is common with residential construction—the Contents by Builder Product Categories (pages *xi–xvi*) may prove useful. Specific companies and specific products can also be found by looking them up in the Company Index or Product Index.

While earlier editions of the *GreenSpec Directory* have included guideline specifications at the beginning of each *MasterFormat* division, this edition replaces that language with Division 1 specifications at the beginning of the book that address greening of an overall project.

The product listings in each division are divided into separate sections, following—to the extent possible—the *MasterFormat* system. Each section begins with a quick summary of environmental considerations relating to products in that section. The products are then listed (alphabetically by company name) with full contact information and brief descriptions. In some cases, the *MasterFormat* numbering was modified slightly to better fit the green products covered.

Products marked with this icon **New** are new listings added since the 6th edition was published. Some product category descriptions and individual product listings include references to more detailed articles in *Environmental Building News*. These articles are available through an online subscription to *BuildingGreen Suite*. Information on these and other BuildingGreen resources is found at the end of this book.

How Products Are Selected for GreenSpec

GreenSpec editors identify potential products from company press releases, trade shows, articles in other publications, e-mail discussion groups, *Environmental Building News* (EBN) subscribers, and general research.

Once a potential product is identified for *GreenSpec*, that product is carefully assessed for its "greenness." Over 15 years of publishing *EBN*, the editorial staff has developed comprehensive criteria for environmental performance. All products included in the *GreenSpec Directory* are screened using these criteria, which are described on pages xxi-xxvi. These criteria are regularly revised, reflecting new understanding about environmental impacts of manufacturing or new developments in the manufacturing industry, and new performance standards for specific product areas (appliances, for example). The most up-to-date version of the *GreenSpec* criteria is posted on the BuildingGreen. com website and available for downloading free. Because the editorial staff is constantly reexamining these criteria, you are invited to send in comments and suggestions. Please send any comments by e-mail addressed to **greenspec@BuildingGreen.com**.

Our goal with *GreenSpec* is to include only the greenest products. In areas where the industry has evolved over the past few years or energy efficiency standards have increased substantially, our *GreenSpec* criteria have become more selective than they were in previous editions. For example, engineered wood products have now become mainstream for many applications, so we've included them here only if they have other environmental features, such as being produced from certified wood from well-managed forests or using non-formaldehyde-emitting binders. In the case of appliances and mechanical equipment, our energy-efficiency standards for most product categories are quite a bit more stringent than those required for an Energy Star rating from EPA and DOE, and some are more stringent now than they were just a year ago.

We are rely on "life-cycle thinking" in our product screening. This is an abbreviated process that borrows from—but is less coprehensive than—life-cycle assessment (LCA). You can learn more about LCA through *BuildingGreen Suite*.

Thanks for Doing Your Part!

In spite of our best efforts, we have inevitably omitted many products that should have been included. We hope that you, the user, will help us find and include these products for the next edition. In addition, we would appreciate your feedback on the information included here, the criteria we use for product approval, and our organization of the material. If you have used products listed here and found them unsatisfactory for some reason, we would like to hear that feedback. Please e-mail any comments to **greenspec@BuildingGreen.com**, or call us at 802/257-7300, extension 107.

We trust that you will find *GreenSpec* helpful in your efforts to make environmentally sound buildings, and we look forward to your feedback. Thank you for your commitment to improving the world that our children will inherit.

Alex Wilson, Nadav Malin,
Mark Piepkorn and Jennifer Atlee
Editors, *GreenSpec Directory*

Selection Criteria: What Makes a Product Green?

Quite a bit of attention has been focused on the issue of green building materials and what makes a given product "green." How do you evaluate the relative greenness of different products? How do you find green products? More important, perhaps, manufacturers are asking, "How can we make our products greener?"

In compiling any directory of green building products, the editors have to figure out what qualifies a product for inclusion. Here we articulate the current listing criteria for the *GreenSpec® Directory*, now in its 7th year of production. Our criteria and thresholds for *GreenSpec* have evolved over time, and will continue to change. As they do, the products included in future editions of *GreenSpec* will also change. We welcome input in this ongoing process of determining just what is green.

The Challenges in Defining What is Green

The Holy Grail of the green building movement would be a database in which the life-cycle environmental impacts of different materials were fully quantified and the impacts weighted so that a designer could easily see which material was better from an environmental standpoint. Though efforts are afoot along these lines, we are still not close to realizing that goal. Very often, we are comparing apples to oranges. We are trying to weigh, for example, the resource-extraction impacts of one product with the manufacturing impacts of another, and the indoor-air-quality impacts of a third.

It is also critical to remember that a green building is not merely the sum of the green products included in the project. In building a house or office building, a great many materials and products will be used. Even in the greenest of projects it is likely that many products will be used that are not themselves green—but they are used in a manner that helps reduce the overall environmental impacts of the building. A particular window may not be green, but the way it is used maximizes collection of low winter sunlight and blocks the summer sun. So even a relatively conventional window can help make a house green. Creating a green building means matching the products and materials to the specific design and site to minimize the overall environmental impact.

GreenSpec addresses products in isolation—what makes a certain product green, but not how to use a product to make a building green. Even the greenest products, including virtually all of those found in *GreenSpec*, could be used in dumb ways that result in buildings that are far from environmentally responsible. In a well-thought-out building design, however, substituting green products for conventional products can make the difference between a good building and a great one.

Defining Measurable Criteria When Feasible

Our tactic with the *GreenSpec* directory is to identify quantifiable, easily verifiable, criteria where those can be defined, then base other decisions about what should be included on the collective wisdom of our editorial staff. In some product categories, such as energy-consuming appliances and VOC-emitting paints, specific thresholds can be established relatively easily. But for many criteria, the lines are much fuzzier and judgment calls are required.

It is important also to note that multiple criteria often apply—in other words, a product may be considered green for more than one reason. Take recycled plastic lumber, for example: it's made from recycled waste, it's highly durable, and it can obviate the need for pesticide treatments. Straw particleboard products are made from agricultural waste materials, and they are free from formaldehyde offgassing. A product with multiple benefits could qualify for *GreenSpec* on the basis of its overall environmental performance, even if it doesn't meet a threshold in any one category alone. Conversely, a product with one or more green attributes might not qualify if it also carries significant environmental burdens. For example, wood treated with toxic preservatives has advantages in terms of durability, but it would not be listed in *GreenSpec* due the health and environmental hazards it represents.

This article reviews the criteria—not listed in any order of priority—used to designate building products as green and therefore suitable for inclusion in our *GreenSpec Directory*.

1. Products Made with Salvaged, Recycled, or Agricultural Waste Content

The materials used to produce a building product—and where those materials came from—is a key determinant of green.

1a. Salvaged products — Whenever we can reuse a product instead of producing a new one from raw materials—even if those raw materials are recycled—

we save on resource use and energy. Many salvaged materials used in buildings (bricks, millwork, framing lumber, plumbing fixtures, and period hardware) are sold on a local or regional basis by salvage yards. Fewer salvaged materials are marketed widely, and it is generally only these that are profiled in a national directory such as *GreenSpec*. Local and regional green product directories can really shine when it comes to finding salvaged materials.

1b. Products with post-consumer recycled content
— Recycled content is an important feature of many green products. From an environmental standpoint, post-consumer is preferable to pre-consumer recycled content, because post-consumer recycled materials are more likely to be diverted from landfills. For many product categories, there is currently no set threshold for the percentage of recycled content required to qualify for inclusion in *GreenSpec*, but such thresholds will increasingly be developed in the future.

In some cases, products with recycled content are included with caveats regarding where they should be used. Rubber flooring made from recycled automobile tires is a good example——the caveat is that these products should not be used in most fully enclosed indoor spaces due to offgassing concerns.

In certain situations, from a life-cycle perspective, recycling has downsides. For example, energy consumption or pollution may be a concern with some collection programs or recycling processes. Also, closed-loop recycling is generally preferable to downcycling, in which a lower-grade material is produced. As more complete life-cycle information on recycled materials—and the process of recycling—becomes available, we intend to scrutinize recycled products more carefully.

1c. Products with pre-consumer recycled content — Pre-consumer (also called "post-industrial") recycling refers to the use of industrial by-products, as distinguished from material that has been in consumer use. Iron-ore slag used to make mineral wool insulation, fly ash used to make concrete, and PVC scrap from pipe manufacture used to make shingles are examples of post-industrial recycled materials. Usually excluded from this category is the use of scrap within the same manufacturing process from which it was generated—material that would typically have gone back into the manufacturing process anyway. While post-consumer recycled content is preferable to pre-consumer recycled content, the latter can still qualify a product for inclusion in *GreenSpec* in many product categories—especially those where there are no products available with post-consumer recycled content.

1d. Products made from agricultural waste material
— A number of products are included in *GreenSpec* because they are derived from agricultural waste products. Most of these are made from straw—the stems left after harvesting cereal grains. Citrus oil, a waste product from orange and lemon juice extraction, is also used in some green products, but such products usually include other agricultural oils as well and are lumped under 2d – Rapidly renewable products.

2. Products That Conserve Natural Resources

Aside from salvaged or recycled content, there are a number of other ways that products can contribute to the conservation of natural resources. These include products that serve a function using less material than the conventional solution, products that are especially durable and therefore won't need replacement as often, products made from FSC-certified wood, and products made from rapidly renewable resources.

2a. Products that reduce material use — Products meeting this criteria may not be distinctly green on their own but are included in *GreenSpec* because of resource efficiency benefits that they make possible. For example, drywall clips allow the elimination of corner studs, engineered stair stringers reduce lumber waste, pier foundation systems minimize concrete use, and concrete pigments can turn concrete slabs into attractive finished floors, eliminating the need for conventional finish flooring.

2b. Products with exceptional durability or low maintenance requirements — These products are environmentally attractive because they need to be replaced less frequently, or their maintenance has very low impact. Sometimes, durability is a contributing factor to the green designation but not enough to distinguish the product as green on its own. This criterion is highly variable by product type. Included in this category are such products as fiber-cement siding, fiberglass windows, slate shingles, and vitrified-clay drainage pipe.

2c. Certified wood products — Third-party forest certification, based on standards developed by the Forest Stewardship Council (FSC), is the best way to ensure that wood products come from well-managed forests. Wood products must go through a chain-of-custody certification process to carry an FSC stamp. Manufactured wood products can meet the FSC certification requirements with less than 100% certified wood content through percentage-based claims. With a few special-case exceptions, any nonsalvaged solid-wood product and most other wood products must be FSC-certified to be included in *GreenSpec*. A few manufactured wood products, including engineered lumber and particleboard or MDF, can be included

if they have other environmental advantages—such as non-formaldehyde-emitting binders. Engineered wood products in *GreenSpec* do not qualify by virtue of their resource efficiency benefits alone (for more on this, see *EBN* Vol. 8, No. 11).

2d. Rapidly renewable products — Rapidly renewable materials are distinguished from wood by the shorter harvest rotation—typically 10 years or less. They are biodegradable, often (but not always) low in VOC emissions, and often produced from agricultural crops. Because sunlight is generally the primary energy input (via photosynthesis), these products may be less energy-intensive to produce—though transportation and processing energy use must be considered. Examples include linoleum, bamboo flooring, form-release agents made from plant oils, natural paints, geotextile fabrics from coir and jute, cork, and such textiles as organic cotton, wool, and sisal. Note that not all rapidly renewable materials are included in *GreenSpec*—non-organic cotton, for example, is highly pesticide-intensive. In some cases, even though a product qualifies for *GreenSpec* by virtue of its natural raw materials, it may have negatives that render it inappropriate for certain uses—such as high VOC levels that cause problems for people with chemical sensitivities.

---

3. Products That Avoid Toxic or Other Emissions

Some building products are considered green because they have low manufacturing impacts, because they are alternatives to conventional products that contain chemicals considered problematic, or because they facilitate a reduction in polluting emissions from building maintenance. In the *GreenSpec* criteria, a few product components were singled out for avoidance in most cases: substances that deplete stratospheric ozone, and those associated with ecological or health hazards including mercury and halogenated compounds. In a few cases, these substances may be included in a "green" product if that product has significant environmental benefits (for example, low energy or water use).

These substitutes for products made with environmentally hazardous components may not, in themselves, be particularly green (i.e., they may be petrochemical-based or relatively high in VOCs), but relative to the products being replaced they can be considered green. Most of the products satisfying this criterion are in categories that are dominated by the more harmful products—such as foam insulation categories in which most products contain HCFCs. We have created several subcategories here for green products:

3a. Natural or minimally processed products — Products that are natural or minimally processed can be green because of low energy use and low risk of chemical releases during manufacture. These can include wood products, agricultural or nonagricultural plant products, and mineral products such as natural stone and slate shingles.

3b. Alternatives to ozone-depleting substances — Included here are categories where the majority of products still contain or use HCFCs: rigid foam insulation and compression-cycle HVAC equipment.

3c. Alternatives to hazardous products — Some materials provide a better alternative in an application dominated by products for which there are concerns about toxic constituents, intermediaries, or by-products. Fluorescent lamps with low mercury levels are included here, along with form-release agents that won't contaminate water or soils with toxicants. Also included here are alternatives to products made with chlorinated hydrocarbons such as polyvinyl chloride (PVC) and brominated fire retardants.

3d. Products that reduce or eliminate pesticide treatments — Periodic pesticide treatment around buildings can be a significant health and environmental hazard. The use of certain products can obviate the need for pesticide treatments, and such products are therefore considered green. Examples include physical termite barriers, borate-treated building products, and bait systems that eliminate the need for broad-based pesticide application.

3e. Products that reduce stormwater pollution — Porous paving products and green (vegetated) roofing systems result in less stormwater runoff and thereby reduce surface water pollution. Stormwater treatment systems reduce pollutant levels in any water that is released.

3f. Products that reduce impacts from construction or demolition activities — Included here are various erosion-control products, foundation products that eliminate the need for excavation, and exterior stains that result in lower VOC emissions into the atmosphere. Fluorescent lamp and ballast recyclers and low-mercury fluorescent lamps reduce environmental impacts during demolition (as well as renovation).

3g. Products that reduce pollution or waste from operations — Alternative wastewater disposal systems reduce groundwater pollution by decomposing organic wastes or removing nutrients more effectively. Masonry fireplaces burn fuel-wood more completely with fewer emissions than conventional fireplaces and wood stoves. Recycling bins and compost systems enable occupants to reduce their solid waste production.

4. Products That Save Energy or Water

The ongoing environmental impacts that result from energy and water used in operating a building often far outweigh the impacts associated with building it. Many products are included in *GreenSpec* because they save energy or water. There are several quite distinct subcategories:

4a. Building components that reduce heating and cooling loads

— Examples include structural insulated panels (SIPs), insulated concrete forms (ICFs), autoclaved aerated concrete (AAC) blocks, and high-performance windows and glazings. As these energy-saving products gain market acceptance, our threshold for inclusion in *GreenSpec* may become more stringent. For example, we may begin including only SIPs and ICFs with steady-state R-values above a certain threshold or with other environmental features, such as recycled-content foam insulation. Some products, such as insulation, clearly offer environmental benefits but are so common that they need other environmental features to qualify for *GreenSpec*.

In the case of windows, the base criteria for energy performance of windows is an NFRC-rated unit U-factor of 0.25 or lower for at least one product in a listed product line. If the windows are made from an environmentally attractive material (e.g., high recycled content or superb durability, such as fiberglass frames), the energy criteria is less stringent: unit U-factor of 0.30 or lower. If the frame material is nongreen, such as PVC (vinyl), the energy criteria is more stringent: unit U-factor of 0.20 or lower. There are a few exceptions to these criteria, such as high-recycled-content windows made for unheated buildings and daylighting-optimized glazing for interior applications.

4b. Equipment that conserves energy and manages loads

— With energy-consuming equipment, such as water heaters and refrigerators, we have good data on energy consumption and can set clear criteria accordingly. In most product categories—e.g., refrigerators, dishwashers, and clothes washers—we set higher thresholds than ENERGY STAR®: for example, exceeding those criteria by 10% or 20%. With lighting and lighting control equipment, certain generic products qualify, such as compact fluorescent lamps and occupancy/daylighting controls, while in other categories only a subset of products qualify. (See table for *GreenSpec* criteria for certain types of equipment.) In some cases, products that meet the energy efficiency requirements are excluded, because of evidence of poor performance or durability. Microturbines are included here because of the potential for cogeneration (combined heat and power) that they offer. Ice- or chilled-water thermal energy storage (TES) equipment is also included because it helps reduce peak loads, which in turn can reduce energy costs and lower the impact of electricity generation.

4c. Renewable energy and fuel cell equipment

— Equipment and products that enable us to use renewable energy instead of fossil fuels and conventional electricity are highly beneficial from an environmental standpoint. Examples include solar water heaters, photovoltaic systems, and wind turbines. Fuel cells are also included here, even though fuel cells today nearly always use natural gas or another fossil fuel

Sample *GreenSpec* Standards for Selected Equipment

Product Type	GreenSpec Standard
Domestic water heaters	Energy Factor = 0.80 or higher
Residential clothes washers	Minimum modified Energy Factor of 1.8 and maximum Water Factor of 5.5
Residential refrigerators	Exceed 2004 National Energy Standard by 20% (full-size) or 25% (compact)
Residential dishwashers	Energy Factor = 0.67 or higher
Central AC and heat pumps	Product line must have at least one model with a SEER rating of 16 or greater.

as the hydrogen source—they are considered green because emissions are lower than combustion-based equipment and because the use of fuel cells will help us eventually move beyond fossil fuel dependence.

4d. Fixtures and equipment that conserve water

— All toilets and most showerheads today meet the federal water efficiency criteria, but not all of these products perform satisfactorily. With toilets and showerheads we include products that meet the federal standards and have dependably good performance. We include in GreenSpec only toilets that offer at least 20% water savings, compared with the federal limit of 1.6 gallons per flush (gpf), and we have adopted the Maximum Performance (MaP) criteria for the performance of most toilets—requiring a minimum rating of 250 grams of test media removal per flush. Some other products, such as rainwater catchment systems, are also included.

5. Products That Contribute to a Safe, Healthy Built Environment

Buildings should be healthy to live or work in, and product selection is a significant determinant of indoor environment quality. Green building products that help to ensure a healthy built environment can be separated into several categories:

5a. Products that do not release significant pollutants into the building

— Included here are zero- and low-VOC paints, caulks, and adhesives, as well as products with very low emissions, such as non-formaldehyde manufactured wood products. Just how low the VOC level needs to be for a given product to qualify for inclusion in *GreenSpec* depends on the product category. Ideally, those criteria should be based not on simple VOC content, but on resultant VOC concentrations in the space after a given period of time—the EPA has worked on such an approach for paints (including a way to factor in higher impacts for more toxic VOCs), but results from such research are not yet available.

5b. Products that block the introduction, development, or spread of indoor contaminants

— Certain materials and products are green because they prevent the production or introduction of pollutants—especially biological contaminants—into occupied space. Duct mastic, for example, can block the entry of mold-laden air or insulation fibers into a duct system. "Track-off" systems for entryways help to remove pollutants from the shoes of people entering. Coated ductboard—compared with standard rigid fiberglass ductboard—prevents fiber shedding and helps control mold growth. And linoleum helps to control microbial growth because of the ongoing process of linoleic acid oxidation.

5c. Products that remove indoor pollutants

— Qualifying for inclusion here are certain ventilation products, filters, radon mitigation equipment, and other equipment and devices that help to remove pollutants or introduce fresh air. Because ventilation equipment is now fairly standard, only products that are particularly efficient or quiet, or that have other environmental benefits are included.

5d. Products that warn occupants of health hazards in the building

— Included here are carbon monoxide (CO) detectors, lead paint test kits, and other IAQ test kits. Because CO detectors are so common, other features are needed to qualify these products for *GreenSpec*, such as evidence of superb performance.

5e. Products that improve light quality

— There is a growing body of evidence that natural daylight is beneficial to our health and productivity (see *EBN* Vol. 8, No. 9). Products that enable us to bring daylight into a building, including tubular skylights, specialized commercial skylights, and fiber-optic daylighting systems, are included in *GreenSpec*. Some other products, such as full-spectrum lighting systems and highly reflective ceiling panels, could also be included in *GreenSpec* under this criterion.

5f. Products that help control noise

— Noise, both from indoor and outside sources, adds to stress and discomfort. A wide range of products are available to help absorb noise, prevent it from spreading, masking it, and even reducing it with sound-cancellation technologies.

5g. Products that enhance community well-being

— Looking beyond the walls of a building, many products can contribute to safer neighborhoods, more pedestrian-friendly areas, and more appealing and livable communities.

Final Thoughts

The primary intent with any green building products directory is to simplify the product selection process. Such directories, including *GreenSpec*, are designed to save you time. For a directory to properly serve your needs, you must be able to trust it—you need to have confidence that the process used to select products for inclusion is logical and based on good information and careful analysis. Here, we have attempted to lay out our process for selecting products for the *GreenSpec Directory*.

We are also providing this information so that you can critique it. We print updated editions of *GreenSpec* on a regular basis, and we update the online version every week. In addition to adding, deleting, and updating product listings, we also periodically reexamine our criteria for what should (and should not) be included as green building products. In the next edition of *GreenSpec* certain products will be removed—not because they have gotten worse from an environmental standpoint, but because we have reevaluated our criteria for inclusion. As more low-VOC paints reach the market, we will tighten our criteria because we want to include only the very best products. As we consider modifying our criteria, we'd like to hear from users of this information. Are our thresholds too tight in a given area? Are they too lax? What other criteria should we consider adding to our product-evaluation process? We welcome your suggestions and comments by e-mail at: greenspec@BuildingGreen.com.

Finally, we have laid out our criteria for *GreenSpec* to advance the development of new, greener products. We want to make it as easy as possible for manufacturers to understand what we consider to be green—so that they can strive to meet those criteria. Doing so will make more green building products available to us all and help to reduce the overall impacts of construction.

Summary of Product Criteria for GreenSpec

1. Products Made with Salvaged, Recycled, or Agricultural Waste Content
1a. Salvaged products
1b. Products with post-consumer recycled content
1c. Products with pre-consumer recycled content
1d. Products made with agricultural waste material

2. Products That Conserve Natural Resources
2a. Products that reduce material use
2b. Products with exceptional durability or low maintenance requirements
2c. Certified wood products
2d. Rapidly renewable products

3. Products That Avoid Toxic or Other Emissions
3a. Natural or minimally processed products
3b. Alternatives to ozone-depleting substances
3c. Alternatives to hazardous products
3d. Products that reduce or eliminate pesticide treatments
3e. Products that reduce stormwater pollution
3f. Products that reduce impacts from construction or demolition activities
3g. Products that reduce pollution or waste from operations

4. Products That Save Energy or Water
4a. Building components that reduce heating and cooling loads
4b. Equipment that conserves energy and manages loads
4c. Renewable energy and fuel cell equipment
4d. Fixtures and equipment that conserve water

5. Products That Contribute to a Safe, Healthy Built Environment
5a. Products that do not release significant pollutants into the building
5b. Products that block the introduction, development, or spread of indoor contaminants
5c. Products that remove indoor pollutants
5d. Products that warn occupants of health hazards in the building
5e. Products that improve light quality
5f. Products that help noise control
5g. Products that enhance community well-being

Abbreviations Used in This Directory

AAC	autoclaved aerated concrete
AASHTO	American Association of State Highway and Transportation Officials
ABS	acrylonitrile butadiene styrene
AC	air conditioner
AC	alternating current
ACA	ammoniacal copper arsenate
ACQ	ammoniacal copper quaternary
ADA	Americans with Disabilities Act
AFUE	annual fuel utilization efficiency
ANSI	American National Standards Institute
APA	APA–The Engineered Wood Association
ASHRAE	American Society of Heating, Refrigerating, and Air-Conditioning Engineers, Inc.
ASTM	American Society for Testing and Materials
Btu	British thermal unit
CCA	chromated copper arsenate
C&D	construction and demolition
CDDC	copper dimethyldithiocarbamate
CFC	chlorofluorocarbon
CFL	compact fluorescent lamp
cfm	cubic feet per minute
CMU	concrete masonry unit
CPSC	Consumer Products Safety Commission
CO	carbon monoxide
CO_2	carbon dioxide
CRI	Carpet and Rug Institute
CRI	color rendering index
CWPA	Certified Wood and Paper Association
DC	direct current
DEHP	Di (2-ethylhexyl) phthlate
DWV	drain, waste, and vent
EBN	Environmental Building News
EPDM	ethylene propylene diene monomer
EIFS	exterior insulation and finish system
EPA	U.S. Environmental Protection Agency
EPS	expanded polystyrene
ERV	energy recovery ventilator
FSC	Forest Stewardship Council
gpf	gallons per flush
gpm	gallons per minute
HCFC	hydrochlorofluorocarbon
HDPE	high-density polyethylene
HFC	hydrofluorocarbon
HID	high-intensity discharge
HRV	heat-recovery ventilator
HSPF	heating season performance factor
IAQ	indoor air quality
ICF	insulating concrete form
IEQ	indoor environmental quality
IG	insulating glass
LDPE	low-density polyethylene
LEED	Leadership in Energy and Environmental Design Rating System
LPG	liquified propane gas
LSL	laminated-strand lumber
LVL	laminated-veneer lumber
MDF	medium-density fiberboard
MDI	methyl diisocyanate
NFPA	National Fire Protection Association
NFRC	National Fenestration Rating Council
NO_2	nitrogen dioxide
NO_x	nitrogen oxides
ODP	ozone depletion potential
OSB	oriented-strand board
PCA	Portland Cement Association
PCB	polychlorinated biphenyl
PCI	Precast Concrete Institute
PEM	proton exchange membrane
PET	polyethylene terephthalate
PF	phenol formaldehyde
PS	polystyrene
PS	product standard of National Bureau of Standards
psi	pounds per square inch
PV	photovoltaic
PVA	polyvinyl acetate (white glue)
PVC	polyvinyl chloride
SBS	styrene-butadiene-styrene
SCS	Scientific Certification Systems
SEER	seasonal energy efficiency ratio
SIGMA	Sealed Insulating Glass Manufacturers' Association
SIP	structural insulated panel
SMACNA	Sheet Metal and Air Conditioning Contractors'National Association
SO_2	sulfur dioxide
SO_x	sulfur oxides
TPO	thermoplastic olefin
UBC	Uniform Building Code
UF	urea formaldehyde
UL	Underwriters Laboratories, Inc.
UV	ultraviolet
VOC	volatile organic compound
W	watt
Wp	peak watt
XPS	extruded polystyrene

Introduction to Guideline Specifications

The seventh edition of *GreenSpec* introduces an entirely new approach to guideline specifications. The guideline specifications for a range of sections throughout the various divisions that appeared in previous editions have been replaced with a much more comprehensive set of guideline specifications for four sections in Division 1 only. These sections are organized in the new MasterFormat 2004 structure.

These Division 1 sections are adapted from drafts of specifications that were developed by green building consultants 7group and BuildingGreen for the U.S. Environmental Protection Agency's Research Triangle Park Campus. While these new specifications lack some of the detail for specific technical sections that existed in the previous version of *GreenSpec's* Guideline Specifications, they include a lot of new material and product specific guidance, in addition to updated language on other topics.

These guideline specifications are designed to be modified as needed for new development, retrofits, and maintenance. They are organized into four Division 01 sections:

- 01 74 19 Construction Waste Management
- 01 81 09 Testing for Indoor Air Quality
- 01 81 13 Sustainable Design Requirements
- 01 91 00 General Commissioning Requirements

Together, these four sections provide an overview of sustainable design requirements that might be appropriate in a wide variety of projects. When these sections are used in actual project specifications, specific requirements must be inserted throughout the construction documents to ensure compliance with the sustainable design intent.

Topics relating to sustainable design that are not directly reflected in the specifications (because they are determined by design or siting decisions, for example) are identified below as a support to project designers.

Notes are included throughout these specifications describing the rationale for product- or material-specific guidelines in the specification. A separate set of notes describe how those guidelines relate to the requirements in current versions of the LEED Rating System.

General Information About LEED

The U.S. Green Building Council's LEED® Rating Systems are used as the basis for many of these sustainable design requirements. LEED is the predominant framework for implementing sustainable design in commercial and institutional buildings in North America. For projects pursuing LEED certification, or that wish to track their performance against LEED, the specifications include details on how LEED's requirements relate to the expressed requirements.

There are currently four official LEED Rating Systems:

- LEED for New Construction and Major Renovations (LEED-NC). LEED-NC is the original LEED Rating System, and forms the basis for the others. It was developed primarily for office buildings, but has been used successfully for a wide range of building types.

- LEED for Commercial Interiors (LEED-CI). LEED-CI applies to tenant improvements in preexisting (new or renovated) buildings. It accommodates the limited control that tenants typically have over the site and base building.

- LEED for Existing Buildings (LEED-EB). LEED-EB addresses the operations and maintenance of existing facilities, along with minor retrofits or upgrades to those facilities. Unlike the other LEED Rating Systems, in which certification is provided based on the design and construction of a building, LEED-EB certification is based on documentation of actual building performance in terms of energy use, water use, maintenance practices, and procurement policies, over a defined period of performance (which can range from 1 to 5 years).

- LEED for Core & Shell (LEED-CS). LEED-CS applies to spec buildings, in which a developer provides the base building and leaves the fit-out to the tenants.

Two additional rating systems, LEED for Homes (LEED-H) and LEED for Neighborhood Developments (LEED-ND) are currently being pilot-tested.

There are also several "Application Guides" that describe how to apply these rating systems (primarily LEED-NC, as it has the longest track record) to specific project types and conditions. These include LEED for Schools, LEED for Retail, and LEED for Healthcare.

Projects seeking LEED certification must be registered with the U.S. Green Building Council, and must be submitted for review by USGBC. A web-based tool, LEED Online, is available for submitting project documentation. More detail on the relationship between LEED and these Guideline Specifications appears below.

Information specific to each of the four sections follows.

Construction Waste Management

Commercial construction typically generates between 2 and 2.5 pounds of solid waste per square foot, the majority of which can be recycled. Salvaging and recycling C&D waste reduces demand for virgin resources and the associated environmental impacts. Effective construction waste management, including appropriate handling of non-recyclables, can reduce contamination from and extend the life of existing landfills. Whenever feasible, reducing initial waste generation is environmentally preferable to reuse or recycling. Section 01 74 19, "Construction Waste Management," defines terms and lays out general procedures and requirements for waste management on construction and renovation projects.

The Construction Waste Management Plan should recognize project waste as an integral part of overall materials management. The premise that waste management is a part of materials management, and the recognition that one project's wastes are materials available for another project, facilitates efficient and effective waste management.

Waste management requirements should be the topic of discussion at both preconstruction and ongoing regular job meetings, to ensure that contractors and appropriate subcontractors are fully informed of the implications of these requirements on their work prior to and throughout construction.

Waste management should be coordinated with or part of the standard quality assurance program and waste management requirements should be addressed regularly throughout the project. Any topical application of processed clean wood waste and ground gypsum board as a soil amendment must be done in accordance with local and state regulations. If possible, adherence to the plan would be facilitated by tying completion of recycling documentation to one of the payments for each trade contractor.

Indoor Air Quality Management

Section 01 81 13, "Sustainable Design Requirements," includes general requirements for managing and protecting indoor air quality during construction. It is written to conform with the requirements in LEED-NC EQ credit 3.1 and LEED-EB EQ credit 3. More detailed requirements for testing indoor air prior to occupancy, and for testing products that are to be installed, are included in section 01 81 09, "Testing for Indoor Air Quality."

Section 01 81 09 is intended to define terms and lay out general procedures and requirements for testing to ensure adequate indoor air quality prior to occupancy

of a new or refurbished facility. The scope of this document is limited to testing procedures and performance thresholds for those tests, including both testing of indoor air prior to occupancy, and testing of products and materials to be used in construction.

Threshold values in Section 01 81 09 have been determined largely based on interviews with indoor air researchers at U.S. Environmental Protection Agency. This document cites California Department of Health Services protocols for testing of materials, and California's chronic reference exposure levels (CRELs) for compounds of concern in establishing indoor air performance thresholds.

The sampling and analytical methods for speciating fungi have evolved significantly in the last decade. Based on consultations with EPA researchers, this specification calls for DNA detection using quantitative polymerase chain reaction (QPCR). The QPCR method is more reliable and consistent than conventional morphology using visual identification, which is highly dependent on the experience of the technician.

This method allows for accurate detection and speciation of more fungi that typical morphology. Given the relative dearth of experience with comparative indoor-outdoor fungal tests in new construction, the threshold of 10% differential in species between indoors and out is not well established, and should be revisited over time.

Sustainable Design Requirements

Section 01 81 13, "Sustainable Design Requirements," sets the stage for all sustainable design goals and demands that are expressed throughout the construction documents. Significant parts of this section are devoted to submittals and guidelines for product selection. Technically, this information may not belong in a "Part 2" of the specification, since no products should actually be purchased and installed based solely on these requirements. But for common usage it is more intuitive to retain this as "Part 2." While those requirements would be repeated in the appropriate technical sections, collecting them in this Division 1 section provides an important reference for the project team.

Ideally, product and material selection decisions would be based on a comprehensive, reliable life-cycle assessment to determine the most environmentally preferable choice for each application. Such a selection process is not feasible for most construction and renovation projects at this time. However, the Building for Environmental and Economic Sustainability software tool from the National Institute for Standards and Technology contains information that makes such comparisons feasible for at least one product category—carpets. The comments in the specifications document include a suggestion for using BEES as part of a carpet selection process. In addition the Athena Environmental Impact Estimator software from the Athena Sustainable Materials Institute (www.athenasmi.ca) provides useful guidance in comparing major building structural systems. That software is not referenced in this specification, however, as it is more appropriate for use by designers than by contractors working on the construction of a building.

Commissioning

Section 01 91 00, "Commissioning" is intended to define terms and lay out general procedures and requirements for commissioning. It is to be supplemented by a detailed commissioning plan, and, if appropriate depending on the complexity of the project, specific commissioning sections detailing requirements for commissioning pluming, HVAC, electrical, and other systems. Additional requirements regarding the commissioning of specific systems should be described in the appropriate sections in Divisions 22, 23, 26, and elsewhere in the specification.

Although the requirements in this specification are only binding for parties that are contracted to carry out the specified work, the owner and other members of the project may be expected to support the commissioning process by sharing information and participating in meetings. Therefore, information is provided regarding the roles of other members on the design team to ensure successful coordination of the commissioning process.

There are many sources of additional guidance on commissioning. The following organizations have programs for certifying commissioning practitioners:

AABC Commissioning Group (ACG), a subsidiary organization of the Associated Air Balance Council (AABC), offers "Certified Commissioning Authority" designation: http://www.commissioning.org/

Building Commissioning Association offers "Certified Commissioning Professional" designation: http://www.bcxa.org

Measurement and Verification

An additional related credit is not addressed in the specifications because it exceeds the temporal scope of the document. LEED-NC EA credit 5 for "Measurement and Verification" credit requires development and implementation of a measurement and verification (M&V) plan for at least one year of post-construction occupancy.

The measurement and verification protocols in this specification are based on the parts of the International Performance Measurement and Verification Protocol documents that are most relevant to new (Volume III) and existing (Volume I) buildings.

LEED and these Guidelines Specifications

Many LEED credits are not addressed directly in these Guideline Specifications because the achievement of those credits is determined by choices made in site-selection or design, and it is not affected by product choices or other activities governed by these sections. The designer will need to ensure that any such credits have been addressed appropriately in the design and construction process.

Early versions of LEED have required the submittal of extensive documentation from contractors and subcontractors to verify compliance with credit requirements. Recently, in conjunction with the shift to online submissions, the documentation requirements have been reduced dramatically. However, the owner or designer is required to vouch for the fact that the requirements have been met, so it is good practice to require documentation as a way of ensuring that they have, indeed, been met.

Section 01 81 13 includes some guidance regarding plumbing, mechanical and electrical components such as wiring, piping, and ductwork. However, it should be noted that such materials are generally excluded from the materials and resources credits in LEED version 2.

Most of the submittals requested in these Guideline Specifications are documents that might be required as part of LEED submission for an early version of LEED, and are still worth requiring for verification purposes whether or not they are needed for a LEED application.

For projects pursuing LEED certification, a "LEED Submittal Form" should be provided to the contractor for each LEED credit for which the contractor will be providing documentation. The contractor would then be expected to complete that form and attach any additional documentation to it. The project manager may wish to consider linking receipt of the completed forms to payment requests from the contractor at appropriate points in the process. There may however, also be submittals required for LEED or for the client that are not typically within the scope of the specifications document.

The commissioning requirements outlined in this specification are those that involve the contractor.

This specification includes requirements that should be sufficient to meet the LEED-NC and LEED-EB commissioning prerequisites. The LEED-NC EA credit 3 for "Enhanced Commissioning" includes additional requirements that exceed the scope of this specification. The primary task that is not included in this section is design-phase commissioning, which would have to have been met before the construction documents are finalized. Along these lines, both the LEED-NC commissioning prerequisite and credit 3 require an "Owner's Project Requirements" (OPR) document and a Basis of Design (BOD) document to be completed prior to the mid construction document phase.

To meet the additional LEED credit, the commissioning process would have had to start during the design phase, and include additional requirements. This specification can be considered as one part of this larger commissioning process.

The requirement in Section 01 74 19, "Construction Waste Management" to divert 75% of construction and demolition waste from landfills and incinerators meets the advanced requirements in LEED-NC MR credit 2 and LEED-EB MR credit 1, which provide one point for a 50% diversion and a second point for 75% diversion. Greater diversion rates have been shown to be feasible in certain locations.

Because of the decision to cite the California-based protocol for product testing and performance thresholds, the "Testing for Indoor Air Quality" specification is significantly more stringent in its requirements than LEED for New Construction version 2.2, with the exception of certain compounds that are referenced in LEED but omitted from this specification because it was deemed unnecessary to test for them. Those tests can be added, however, if needed to conform with LEED's requirements.

Quality Assurance

Sustainable design requirements, including construction waste management, commissioning, and any other special procedures that may not be familiar to all players, should be the subject of a special meeting dedicated to the topic. This meeting should fully inform contractors and appropriate subcontractors, prior to construction, about the implications of these requirements on their work. In addition, in coordination with standard quality assurance program, sustainable design requirements should be addressed regularly throughout the project.

Guideline Specifications

SECTION 01 74 19 - CONSTRUCTION WASTE MANAGEMENT

*Guidance for designers and specifiers, with suggested language
to be modified and incorporated into project specifications.*

PART 1 - GENERAL

1.1 RELATED DOCUMENTS

    A. Drawings and general provisions of the Contract, including General Conditions and Division 1 Specification Sections, apply to this Section.

1.2 SUMMARY

    A. This Section includes administrative and procedural requirements for the following:

        1. Salvaging non-hazardous demolition and construction waste

        2. Recycling non-hazardous demolition and construction waste

        3. Disposing of non-hazardous demolition and construction waste

    B. Related Sections include the following:

        1. Section 01 12 00 "Summary of Multiple Contracts" for coordination of responsibilities for waste management

        There should be language in the Summary of Multiple Contracts to explain that each of the prime contractors and subs have obligations in meeting the Construction & Management Waste specifications.

        2. Division 1 Section "Sustainable Design Requirements"

        3. Division 1 Section "Temporary Facilities and Controls" for environmental-protection measures during construction

        There should be language in the "Temporary Facilities and Controls" to provide a staging area for separation of staging waste.

        4. Sections within 02 41 00 "Demolition" for disposition of waste resulting from demolition of buildings, structures, and site improvements.

        Depending on how the Project documents are being assembled, there may be other Division 1 sections that should be listed here. Note that there are myriad technical sections in Divisions 2 and beyond that could be cited here, but it is generally more useful to cite this Division 1 section as a Related Section in each of those sections.

1.3   DEFINITIONS

A.   Clean: Untreated and unpainted; not contaminated with oils, solvents, caulk, paint, or the like

B.   Construction Waste: Building and site improvement materials and other solid waste resulting from construction, remodeling, renovation, or repair operations. Construction waste includes packaging.

> *Land clearing is excluded because it is no longer considered construction waste and generally is not landfilled, so is no longer included in the LEED calculation.*

C.   Demolition Waste: Building and site improvement materials resulting from demolition or selective demolition operations

D.   Disposal: Removal off-site of demolition and construction waste and subsequent sale, recycling, reuse, or deposit in landfill or incinerator acceptable to authorities having jurisdiction

E.   Diversion: Avoidance of demolition and construction waste **sent** to landfill or incineration. Diversion does not include using materials for landfill, alternate daily cover on landfills, or materials used as fuel in waste-to-energy processes

F.   Hazardous: Exhibiting the characteristics of hazardous substances, i.e., ignitability, corrosiveness, toxicity or reactivity

G.   Recycle: Recovery of demolition or construction waste for subsequent processing in preparation for reuse

H.   Recycling: The process of sorting, cleansing, treating, and reconstituting solid waste and other discarded materials for the purpose of using the altered form. Recycling does not include burning, incinerating, or thermally destroying waste.

I.   Salvage: Recovery of demolition or construction waste and subsequent reuse or sale in another facility

J.   Reuse: Recovery of demolition or construction waste and subsequent incorporation into the Work

K.   Source Separation: The act of keeping different types of waste materials separate beginning from the first time they become waste

L.   Toxic: Poisonous to humans either immediately or after a long period of exposure

M.   Trash: Any product or material unable to be reused, returned, recycled, or salvaged

N.   Waste: Extra material or material that has reached the end of its useful life in its intended use. Waste includes salvageable, returnable, recyclable, and reusable material.

1.4   PERFORMANCE REQUIREMENTS

A.   The Owner has established that this Project shall generate the least amount of waste possible and that processes that ensure the generation of as little waste as possible due to error, poor planning, breakage, mishandling, contamination, or other factors shall be employed.

B.   Of the waste that is generated, as many of the waste materials as economically feasible shall be reused, salvaged, or recycled. Waste disposal in landfills or incinerators shall be minimized, thereby reducing disposal costs.

C. Develop a construction waste management plan that results in end-of-Project rates for salvage/recycling of 95% (by weight) of construction and demolition waste.

> **The requirement to divert 75% of construction and demolition waste from landfills and incinerators meets the advanced requirement of the LEED-NC and LEED-EB construction waste management credits, which provide one point for a 50% diversion and a second point for 75% diversion. In some locations, significantly higher diversion has been shown to be feasible.**

D. Salvage/Recycle Requirements: Salvage and recycle as much non-hazardous demolition and construction waste as possible, including the following materials:

1. Demolition Waste:

    a. Asphaltic concrete paving

    b. Concrete

    c. Concrete reinforcing steel

    d. Brick

    e. Concrete masonry units

    f. Wood studs

    g. Wood joists

    h. Plywood and oriented strand board

    i. Wood paneling

    j. Wood trim

    k. Structural and miscellaneous steel

    l. Rough hardware

    m. Roofing

    n. Insulation

    o. Doors and frames

    p. Door hardware

    q. Windows

    r. Glazing

    s. Metal studs

    t. Gypsum board

    u. Acoustical tile and panels

    v. Carpet

    w. Carpet pad

    x. Demountable partitions

    y. Equipment

    z. Cabinets

    aa. Plumbing fixtures

    bb. Piping

    cc. Supports and hangers

    dd. Valves

    ee. Sprinklers

    ff.   Mechanical equipment

    gg. Refrigerants

    hh. Electrical conduit

    ii.   Copper wiring

    jj.   Lighting fixtures

    kk. Lamps

    ll.   Ballasts

    mm. Electrical devices

    nn. Switchgear and panelboards

    oo. Transformers

2. Construction Waste:

    a.   Masonry and CMU

    b.   All untreated wood, including lumber and finish materials

    c.   Wood sheet materials

    d.   Wood trim

    e.   Metals

    f.   Roofing

    g.   Insulation

    h.   Carpet and pad

    i.   Gypsum board

    j.   Unused (leftover) paint

    k.   Piping

    l.   Electrical conduit

    m. Packaging: Regardless of salvage/recycle goal indicated above, salvage or recycle 100 percent of the following uncontaminated packaging materials:

        1) Paper
        2) Cardboard
        3) Boxes
        4) Plastic sheet and film
        5) Polystyrene packaging
        6) Wood crates
        7) Plastic pails

    n.   Beverage and packaged food containers

1.5   SUBMITTALS

A.   Construction Waste Management Plan (CWMP): It is the intent of this specification to maximize the diversion of demolition and construction waste from landfill disposal. Accordingly, not more than 30 days after receipt of Notice to Proceed and prior to the generation of any waste, prepare and submit a draft Construction Waste Management Plan in accordance with Section 01 74 19 including, but not limited to, the following:

   1.   Procedures for Recycling/Reuse Program to divert a minimum of 95% (by weight) of construction and demolition waste from landfill disposal, including waste resulting from demolition of any existing building and site paving scheduled for demolition; any site paving is required to be ground on site and reused as granulated fill on site.

   2.   Approval of the Contractor's CWMP shall not relieve the Contractor of responsibility for adequate and continuing control of pollutants and other environmental protection measures.

B.   Submit a 3-ring binder with calculations on end-of-project recycling rates, salvage rates, and landfill rates itemized by waste material, demonstrating that a minimum of 75% of construction wastes were recycled or salvaged and diverted from landfill. Include documentation of recovery rate (if commingled), waste hauling certificates or receipts, and a brief narrative explaining how and to where each waste type has been diverted.

C.   Construction Waste Management Plan: Submit four copies of plan within 45 days of date established for the Notice to Proceed.

D.   Waste Reduction Progress Reports: Concurrent with each Application for Payment, submit four copies of report. Include separate reports for demolition and construction waste. Include the following information:

   1.   Material category

   2.   Generation point of waste

   3.   Total quantity of waste in tons

   4.   Quantity of waste salvaged, both estimated and actual in tons

   5.   Quantity of waste recycled, both estimated and actual in tons

   6.   Total quantity of waste recovered (salvaged plus recycled) in tons

   7.   Total quantity of waste recovered (salvaged plus recycled) as a percentage of total waste

   8.   Include up-to-date records of donations, sales, recycling and landfill/incinerator manifests, weight tickets, hauling receipts, and invoices.

E.   Waste Reduction Calculations: Before request for Substantial Completion, submit four copies of calculated end-of-project rates for salvage, recycling, and disposal as a percentage of total waste generated by the Work. Complete a table similar to the example below.

Recycled/Recycled/Salvaged/ Diverted Materials	Hauler or Location	Quantity of Material (tons)
Total Construction Waste Diverted		
Landfilled Materials		
Total Construction Waste Landfilled		
Total Construction Waste		Total Construction Waste Diverted + Total Construction Waste Landfilled
Percentage of Construction Waste Diverted from Landfill		(Total Construction Waste Diverted / Total Construction Waste)*100

F. Records of Donations: Indicate receipt and acceptance of salvageable waste donated to individuals and organizations. Indicate whether organization is tax-exempt.

G. Records of Sales: Indicate receipt and acceptance of salvageable waste sold to individuals and organizations. Indicate whether organization is tax-exempt.

H. Recycling and Processing Facility Records: Indicate receipt and acceptance of recyclable waste by recycling and processing facilities licensed to accept them. Include manifests, weight tickets, receipts, and invoices.

I. Landfill and Incinerator Disposal Records: Indicate receipt and acceptance of waste by landfills (or transfer stations) and incinerator facilities licensed to accept them. Include manifests, weight tickets, receipts, and invoices.

1.6 QUALITY ASSURANCE

B. Waste Management Meetings: Conduct an initial conference at Project Site to comply with requirements in Division 1 Section "Project Management and Coordination." Contractor shall include discussions on construction waste management requirements in the preconstruction meeting. Contractor shall include discussions on construction waste management requirements in the regular job meetings conducted during the course of the Project; at these meetings, review methods and procedures related to waste management including, but not limited to, the following:

1. Review and discuss waste management plan including responsibilities of the Waste Management Coordinator.

2. Review requirements for documenting quantities of each type of waste and its disposition.

3. Review and finalize procedures for materials separation and verify availability of containers and bins needed to avoid delays.

4. Review procedures for periodic waste collection and transportation to recycling and disposal facilities.

5. Review waste management requirements for each trade.

1.7   CONSTRUCTION WASTE MANAGEMENT PLAN

A. General: Develop and implement a CWMP consisting of waste identification, waste reduction work plan, and cost/revenue analysis. Include separate sections in plan for demolition and construction waste. Indicate quantities by weight or volume, but use the same units of measure throughout the CWMP.

B. Draft Construction Waste Management Plan: Within 30 days after receipt of Notice to Proceed, or prior to any waste removal, whichever occurs sooner, the Contractor shall submit to the Owner and Architect a Draft Waste Management Plan.

C. Final Construction Waste Management Plan: Once the Owner has determined which of the recycling options addressed in the draft Waste Management Plan are acceptable, the Contractor shall submit, within 10 calendar days, a Final Waste Management Plan.

D. Waste Identification: Indicate anticipated types and quantities of demolition, site-clearing, and construction waste generated by the Work. Include estimated quantities and assumptions for estimates.

E. Landfill Options: Indicate the name of the landfill(s) and/or transfer station(s) and/or incinerator(s) where trash will be disposed of, the applicable landfill tipping fee(s), and the projected cost of disposing of all Project waste in the landfill(s).

F. Waste Reduction Work Plan: List each type of waste and whether it will be salvaged, reused, recycled, or disposed of in landfill or incinerator. Include points of waste generation, total quantity of each type of waste, quantity for each means of recovery, and handling and transportation procedures.

1. Salvaged Materials for Reuse: For materials that will be salvaged and reused in this Project, describe methods for preparing salvaged materials before incorporation into the Work.

2. Salvaged Materials for Sale: For materials that will be sold to individuals and organizations, include list of their names, addresses, and telephone numbers.

3. Salvaged Materials for Donation: For materials that will be donated to individuals and organizations, include list of their names, addresses, and telephone numbers.

4. Recycled Materials: Include list of local receivers and processors and type of recycled materials each will accept. Include names, addresses, and telephone numbers.

5. Disposed Materials: Indicate how and where materials will be disposed of. Include name, address, and telephone number of each landfill and incinerator facility.

6. Handling and Transportation Procedures: Describe method that will be used for separating recyclable waste, including sizes of containers, container labeling, and designated location on Project Site where materials separation will be located.

G. Materials: The following list of required materials, at a minimum, must be included for salvaging/recycling:

1. Cardboard

2. Clean dimensional wood

3. Beverage and food containers

4. Paper

5. Concrete

6. Concrete Masonry Units (CMUs)

7. Asphalt: Include the approximate weight of the asphalt paving to be crushed and utilized as granulated fill from the existing paving as a component of waste material diverted from the landfill.

8. Ferrous and non-ferrous metals (banding, stud trim, ductwork, piping, rebar, roofing, other trim, steel, iron, galvanized sheet steel, stainless steel, aluminum, copper, zinc, lead, brass, and bronze)

9. Stretch and shrink wrap

10. Gypsum wallboard

11. Paint containers and other clean, empty plastic containers

The specifications writer may want to customize this list based on what is easily recycled or salvaged for resale or reuse at the Project and in local markets.

H. Meetings: Provide a description of the regular meetings to be held to address waste management.

I. Materials Handling Procedures: Provide a description of the means by which any waste materials identified will be protected from contamination, and a description of the means to be employed in recycling the above materials consistent with requirements for acceptance by designated facilities.

J. Transportation: Provide a description of the means of transportation of the recyclable materials (whether materials will be site-separated and self-hauled to designated centers, or whether mixed materials will be collected by a waste hauler and removed from the site) and destination of materials.

1.8   CONSTRUCTION WASTE MANAGEMENT RESOURCES

A. General information contacts regarding construction and demolition waste:

1. EPA Construction and demolition (C&D) debris website: http://www.epa.gov/epaoswer/non-hw/debris-new/bytype.htm

2. Directory of Wood-Framed Building Deconstruction and Reused Building Materials Companies: http://www.fpl.fs.fed.us/documnts/fplgtr/fpl_gtr150.pdf

3. Additional resources to be developed by Contractor with assistance from Owner and Architect, as requested.

The specifications writer could include a list of acceptable local entities and transfer stations for recycling, incineration, and landfilling.

PART 2 - PRODUCTS (Not Used)

PART 3 - EXECUTION

3.1 PLAN IMPLEMENTATION

A. General: Implement waste management plan as approved by Architect and Owner. Provide handling, containers, storage, signage, transportation, and other items as required to implement waste management plan during the entire duration of the Contract.

   1. Comply with Division 1 Section "Temporary Facilities and Controls" for operation, termination, and removal requirements.

B. Waste Management Coordinator: Engage a waste management coordinator to be responsible for implementing, monitoring, and reporting status of waste management work plan. Coordinator shall be present at the Project Site full-time for duration of Project.

C. Training: Train workers, subcontractors, and suppliers on proper waste management procedures, as appropriate for the Work occurring at Project Site.

   1. Distribute waste management plan to everyone concerned within three days of submittal return.

   2. Distribute waste management plan to entities when they first begin work on-site. Review plan procedures and locations established for salvage, recycling, and disposal.

D. Site Access and Temporary Controls: Conduct waste management operations to ensure minimum interference with roads, streets, walks, walkways, and other adjacent occupied and used facilities.

   1. Designate and label specific areas on Project Site necessary for separating materials that are to be salvaged, recycled, reused, donated, and sold.

   2. Recycling and waste bin areas are to be kept neat, and clean, and clearly marked in order to avoid contamination of materials.

   3. Comply with Division 1 Section "Temporary Facilities and Controls" for controlling dust and dirt, environmental protection, and noise control.

E. Hazardous Wastes: Hazardous wastes shall be separated, stored, and disposed of according to local regulations and should not be included in Construction Waste Management Plan's calculations of waste.

3.2 SALVAGING DEMOLITION WASTE

A. Salvaged Items for Reuse in the Work:

    1. Clean salvaged items.

    2. Pack or crate items after cleaning. Identify contents of containers.

    3. Store items in a secure area until installation.

    4. Protect items from damage during transport and storage.

    5. Install salvaged items to comply with installation requirements for new materials and equipment. Provide connections, supports, and miscellaneous materials necessary to make items functional for use indicated.

B. Salvaged Items for Owner's Use:

    1. Clean salvaged items.

    2. Pack or crate items after cleaning. Identify contents of containers.

    3. Store items in a secure area until delivery to Owner.

    4. Transport items to Owner's storage area designated by Owner.

    5. Protect items from damage during transport and storage.

C. Doors and Hardware: Brace open end of door frames. Except for removing door closers, leave door hardware attached to doors.

3.3 RECYCLING DEMOLITION AND CONSTRUCTION WASTE, GENERAL

A. General: Recycle paper and beverage containers used by on-site workers.

B. Recycling Receivers and Processors: List below is provided for information only; available recycling receivers and processors include, but are not limited to, the following:

    1. List to be developed by Contractor.

C. Recycling Incentives: Revenues, savings, rebates, tax credits, and other incentives received for recycling waste materials shall accrue to Contractor.

D. Procedures: Separate recyclable waste from other waste materials, trash, and debris. Separate recyclable waste by type at Project Site to the maximum extent practical.

    1. Provide appropriately marked containers or bins for controlling recyclable waste until they are removed from Project Site. Include list of acceptable and unacceptable materials at each container and bin.

        a. Inspect containers and bins for contamination and remove contaminated materials if found.

2. Stockpile processed materials on-site without intermixing with other materials. Place, grade, and shape stockpiles to drain surface water. Cover to prevent windblown dust.

3. Stockpile materials away from construction area. Do not store within drip line of remaining trees.

4. Store components off the ground and protect from the weather.

5. Remove recyclable waste off Owner's property and transport to recycling receiver or processor.

3.4   RECYCLING DEMOLITION WASTE

A.   Asphaltic Concrete Paving: Break up and transport paving to asphalt-recycling facility or recycle on-site into new paving.

B.   Concrete: Remove reinforcement and other metals from concrete and sort with other metals.

1. Pulverize concrete to maximum 4-inch (100-mm) size.

2. Crush concrete and screen to comply with requirements in Division 2 Section "Earthwork" for use as satisfactory soil for fill or subbase.

C.   Masonry: Remove metal reinforcement, anchors, and ties from masonry and sort with other metals.

1. Pulverize masonry to maximum 1-1/2-inch (38-mm) size.

   a.   Crush masonry and screen to comply with requirements in Division 2 Section "Earthwork" for use as general fill or subbase.

   b.   Crush masonry and screen to comply with requirements in Division 2 Section "Exterior Plants" for use as mineral mulch.

2. Clean and stack undamaged, whole masonry units on wood pallets.

D.   Wood Materials: Sort and stack members according to size, type, and length. Separate lumber, engineered wood products, and panel products for reuse and/or recycling. Separate wood material treated with heavy metal preservatives for reuse or landfill disposal.

E.   Metals: Separate metals by type.

1. Structural Steel: Stack members according to size, type of member, and length.

2. Remove and dispose of bolts, nuts, washers, and other rough hardware.

F.   Asphalt Shingle Roofing: Separate organic and glass-fiber asphalt shingles and felts for recycling into asphalt paving or by other recycling entities.

G.   Gypsum Board: Stack large, clean pieces on wood pallets and store in a dry location for recycling off-site. Remove edge trim and sort with other metals. Remove and dispose of fasteners.

1. Moisture-damaged gypsum board with evidence of significant mold growth shall be disposed of in accordance with New York City's "Guidelines on Assessment and Remediation of Fungi in Indoor Environments": http://www.nyc.gov/html/doh/html/epi/moldrpt1.shtml

H. Acoustical Ceiling Panels and Tile: Stack large, clean pieces on wood pallets and store in a dry location.

1. Separate suspension system, trim, and other metals from panels and tile and sort with other metals.

I. Carpet and Pad: Roll large pieces tightly after removing debris, trash, adhesive, and tack strips.

1. Store clean, dry carpet and pad in a closed container or trailer provided by a carpet recycler or manufacturer-related carpet reclamation agency.

J. Equipment: Drain tanks, piping, and fixtures. Seal openings with caps or plugs. Protect equipment from exposure to weather.

K. Plumbing Fixtures: Separate by type and size.

L. Piping: Reduce piping to straight lengths and store by type and size. Separate supports, hangers, valves, sprinklers, and other components by type and size.

M. Lighting Fixtures: Separate lamps by type and protect from breakage.

N. Electrical Devices: Separate switches, receptacles, switchgear, transformers, meters, panelboards, circuit breakers, and other devices by type.

O. Conduit: Reduce conduit to straight lengths and store by type and size.

3.5 RECYCLING CONSTRUCTION WASTE

A. Packaging:

1. Cardboard and Boxes: Break down packaging into flat sheets. Bundle and store in a dry location.

2. Polystyrene Packaging: Separate and bag materials.

3. Pallets: As much as possible, require deliveries using pallets to remove pallets from Project Site. For pallets that remain on-site, break down pallets into component wood pieces and comply with requirements for recycling wood.

4. Crates: Break down crates into component wood pieces and comply with requirements for recycling wood.

B. Site-Clearing Wastes: Chip brush, branches, and trees on-site.

1. Comply with requirements in Division 2 Section "Exterior Plants" for use of chipped organic waste as organic mulch.

C. Wood Materials:

1. Clean Cut-Offs of Lumber: Grind or chip into material appropriate for mulch or erosion control.

2. Lumber Treated with Heavy-Metal Preservatives: Do not grind, chip, or incinerate; must be reused or landfilled.

D. Gypsum Board: Stack large, clean pieces on wood pallets and store in a dry location for recycling and/or reuse on-site or off-site.

1. Moisture-damaged gypsum board with evidence of significant mold growth shall be disposed of in accordance with New York City's "Guidelines on Assessment and Remediation of Fungi in Indoor Environments": http://www.nyc.gov/html/doh/html/epi/moldrpt1.shtml

2. Clean Gypsum Board: Grind scraps of clean gypsum board using small mobile chipper or hammer mill. Screen out paper after grinding.

    a. Comply with requirements in Division 2 Section "Exterior Plants" for use of clean ground gypsum board as inorganic soil amendment.

E. Miscellaneous: Anything called out to be ground and used on site should utilize an on-site grinder.

1. Grinder should be able to accommodate a variety of materials including masonry, asphalt shingles, wood, and drywall.

3.6   DISPOSAL OF WASTE

A. General: Except for items or materials to be salvaged, recycled, or otherwise reused, remove waste materials from Project Site and legally dispose of them in a landfill or incinerator acceptable to authorities having jurisdiction.

1. Except as otherwise specified, do not allow waste materials that are to be disposed of to accumulate on site.

2. Remove and transport debris in a manner that will prevent spillage on adjacent surfaces and areas.

3. Do not burn or bury waste materials on or off site. Appropriate on-site topical application of ground gypsum or wood, or use of site paving as granulated fill is considered reuse, not waste.

SECTION 01 81 09 - TESTING FOR INDOOR AIR QUALITY

Guidance for designers and specifiers, with suggested language
to be modified and incorporated into project specifications.

PART 1 - GENERAL

1.1 RELATED DOCUMENTS

A. Drawings and general provisions of Contract, including General and Supplementary Conditions, other Division 1 Specification Sections, and specifications of materials mentioned in this section, apply to this Section.

1.2 SUMMARY

A. General: This section provides requirements for Baseline Indoor Air Quality (IAQ) Testing for maximum indoor pollutant concentrations for acceptance of the facility.

1.3 RELATED SECTIONS

A. All work shall comply with Division 1 Section 01 81 13.

B. Coordinate with Commissioning activities specified in Section 01 91 00.

C. All work shall comply with Division 23, the section on "Testing, Adjusting and Balancing."

1.4 SUBMITTALS

A. Baseline IAQ Testing: Submit a report for each test site specified for IAQ baseline testing as prescribed herein below and in Division 23, in the section on "Testing, Adjusting, and Balancing." Report on air concentrations of targeted pollutants identified in Subsection 3.1 of this section.

1.5 SEQUENCING AND SCHEDULING

A. Identify, program, and schedule all IAQ testing well in advance of construction in a manner to prevent delays to the performance of the work of this Contract in order to perform and complete all testing after the completion of construction activities and prior to occupancy.

PART 2 - PRODUCTS (Not Used)

PART 3 - EXECUTION

3.1   BASELINE IAQ TESTING

A.   HVAC System Verification: To assure compliance with recognized standards for indoor air quality including ASHRAE Standard 62.1-2004, the Contractor's independent testing and balancing agency shall verify the performance of each HVAC system prior to Indoor Air Quality testing, including space temperature and space humidity uniformity, outside air quantity, filter installation, drain pan operation, and any obvious contamination sources.

B.   Indoor Air Quality Testing: Upon verification of HVAC system operation, the Contractor shall hire an independent contractor, subject to approval by the Contracting Officer's Representative, with a minimum of 5 years experience in performing the types of testing specified herein, to test levels of indoor air contaminants for compliance with specified requirements.

1.   Conduct baseline IAQ testing using testing protocols consistent with the United States Environmental Protection Agency Compendium of Methods for the Determination of Air Pollutants in Indoor Air.

2.   A test plan shall be submitted for the approval of the Contracting Officer's Representative. The plan shall specify procedures, times, instrumentation, and sampling methods that will be employed.

3.   Perform IAQ testing for at least the minimum number of required sampling locations, determined as follows: For each portion of the building served by a separate ventilation system, the number of sampling points shall not be less than one per 25,000 sq. ft., or for each contiguous floor area, whichever is larger, and include areas with the least ventilation as calculated by Ventilation Rate Procedure of ASHRAE Standard 62.1-2004 and greatest presumed source strength as identified by Owner. Collect air samples on three consecutive days and average the results of each three-day test cycle to determine compliance or non-compliance of indoor air quality for each air handling zone tested.

The sampling area of not less than one sampling point per 25,000 sq. ft. meets the requirements for LEED-NC Construction Air Quality Management credit.

Note that the 2004 version of Standard 62.1 determines allowable ventilation based not only on occupancy but also on assumed pollutant emissions from furnishings, so the "areas with least ventilation" will have to be determined accordingly.

a.   Verify areas to be tested with the Contracting Officer's Representative. Areas with 100% outside air ventilation rates such as laboratories are excluded from these testing requirements. The Contracting Officer's Representative is the sole judge of areas exempt from testing.

4.   Perform IAQ testing following the completion of all interior construction activities and prior to occupancy. The building shall have all interior finishes installed including, but not limited to, millwork, doors, paint, carpet, and acoustic tiles. Perform testing prior to installation of furniture, workstation components, and casework.

Performing initial testing prior to upfit activities ensures that construction and ventilation meet IAQ requirements and also provides a measurement baseline. Because systems furniture and other owner upfit activities may be a source, it is also wise to test after installation of furniture. This allows for allocation of accountability for any problems.

5. Perform IAQ testing within the breathing zone, between 3'–0" and 6'–0" above the finished floor and over a minimum 4-hour period.

The 4-hour minimum requirement is the same as required in the LEED-NC credit for a construction IAQ management plan before occupancy.

6. Collect air samples during normal occupied hours (prior to occupancy) with the building ventilation system starting at the daily normal start times and operated at the minimum outside air flow rate for the occupied mode throughout the duration of the air testing.

7. Sample and record outside air levels of formaldehyde and TVOC contaminants at three outside air locations (as determined by Owner) simultaneously with indoor tests to establish basis of comparison for these contaminant levels by averaging the three outdoor readings for each contaminant.

8. Perform airborne mold and mildew air sampling and speciation with simultaneous indoor and outdoor readings.

   a. Samples are to be collected using a 12 liter-per-minute pump and a 0.45 micron polycarbonate filter, with a 4-hour duration for each sample.

   b. Speciation shall be done with DNA detection using the quantitative polymerase chain reaction (QPCR) method. To ensure that filters are not precontaminated with mold, a field blank filter cartridge shall be tested after every eighth sample is tested.

Four-hour sample collection periods are a minimum requirement—to ensure the collection of representative samples, an 8-hour period could be specified. The QPCR method is more reliable and consistent than conventional morphology using visual identification, which is highly dependent on the experience of the technician.

9. Acceptance of respective portions of the building by the Owner is subject to compliance with specified limits of indoor air quality contaminant levels.

C. Indoor air quality shall conform to the following standards and limits:

   1. Formaldehyde: <20 microgram/m^3 (16.3 ppb)

   2. Sum of VOCs: <200 microgram/m^3

   3. Carbon Monoxide: Not to exceed 9 ppm

   4. Other compounds found on the California Office of Environmental Health Hazard Assessment's list of chronic inhalation Reference Exposure Levels (RELs) are not to exceed those levels, as published on: http://www.oehha.ca.gov/air/chronic_rels/AllChrels.html

Use of the California CREL levels is supported by EPA IAQ research. The formaldehyde level is higher than the CREL (which is at a level that is often exceeded in outdoor air) but lower than the 27 ppb level that was selected for enforcement in California. The sum of VOCs level was retained from previous versions of this specification as a check against combinations of VOCs that individually are under the limit but may collectively constitute a problem.

Allowable Air Concentration Levels meet or exceed the requirements of LEED-NC credit for a construction IAQ management plan before occupancy, with the exception of particulates (PM10), which are unlikely to be found in unoccupied buildings, and 4PC, which was once a common pollutant associated with carpet but is no longer a concern, particularly since any carpet to be installed will be certified as Green Label Plus. However, it may be necessary to include those pollutants in the specification to conform to the requirements of the LEED credit.

5. Airborne Mold and Mildew: The species identified in indoor air cannot vary by more than 10% from those identified in the exterior samples.

Air sampling for mold and mildew is a rapidly changing science, and the 10% threshold represents a rough estimate of an acceptable differential, but a tighter threshold could also be applied.

D. Test Reports: Prepare test reports showing the results and location of each test, a summary of the HVAC operating conditions, and a listing of any discrepancies and recommendations for corrective actions, if required.

   1. Include certification of test equipment calibration with each test report.

E. For each sampling point where the maximum concentration limits are exceeded, the Contractor is responsible for conducting additional flush-out with outside air and retesting the specific parameter(s) exceeded to indicate the requirements are achieved. Repeat procedure until all requirements have been met. When retesting non-complying building areas, take samples from the same locations as in the first test. Retesting shall be performed at no additional expense to the Owner.

F. For each sampling point where the airborne mold and mildew indoor species distribution varies by more than 10% from exterior sampling speciation, Contractor shall identify the source of the mold and/or mildew and remediate with corrective action, then retest in accordance with section 3.1.B above until compliant results are attained.

G. In the event that any non-compliant test results occur, Contractor must provide a written report to the Owner describing the source(s) of the non-compliant condition(s) and the corrective action(s) implemented.

3.2 INDEPENDENT MATERIALS TESTING:

A. Materials That Must Be Tested: All materials listed below that are proposed for use on this project shall be tested for permanent, in-place indoor air quality performance in accordance with requirements of these specifications. Results shall be furnished to the Contracting Officer's Representative. Materials meeting the criteria for independent testing are as follows:

   1. Field-applied paint systems on appropriate substrate. Paint primers and intermediate coats (if used) should be applied with a typical drying time allowed between coats (not to exceed 7 days).

   2. Wallcoverings

   3. Carpet including manufacturer's recommended adhesive. The carpet will be applied to the appropriate flooring per manufacturer's instructions so that the testing is of the "carpet assembly."

   4. Ceiling tile

   5. Interior furnishings

   6. Any fireproofing material that may be exposed to indoor air, directly or in a plenum, applied to appropriate substrate

B. Materials for Testing: Only test representative samples of actual products selected for use on this project. Tests of products generically and/or technically similar but produced by a manufacturer other than that of the product selected for use on this project are invalid.

C.   Materials Testing and Evaluation Protocol: California Department of Health Services' "Standard Practice for the Testing of Volatile Organic Emissions from Various Sources Using Small-Scale Environmental Chambers," July 2004. available online: http://www.dhs.ca.gov/ps/deodc/ehlb/iaq/VOCS/

> *This protocol, commonly known as California's "Section 01350 Specification," is becoming accepted nationally as a standard for emissions testing. It is used in California for state facilities and by the Collaborative for High Performance Schools, and it is the basis for much of the Carpet and Rug Institute's Green Label Plus program and the Greenguard Environmental Institute's "Children & Schools" product certification.*

D.   Performance Thresholds: All compounds detected that have chronic reference exposure levels listed in the California DHS Standard Practice document shall be analyzed and compared to the allowable concentration levels.

E.   Materials Test Reports: Submit test reports to the Contracting Officer's Representative. The report shall include raw emission levels, as well as the calculated resulting concentrations and the assumptions (loading, volume of space, ventilation rates) used to determine those resulting concentrations.

> *For projects for which it is impractical to analyze all the parameters needed to predict resulting concentrations, the protocol includes default assumptions for offices and schools that may be used. Based on these default assumptions, there are lists of pre-approved products for which testing may not be necessary. Products on those lists have not been tested in combination with their substrates, however.*

F.   Product/Material Evaluation: All products/materials shown by testing to comply with emissions limits and other criteria specified in this section will be approved for use on this project subject to compliance with all other specified requirements of the Project Manual. Products/materials shown to exceed specified emission limits shall be discussed, test results interpreted, and a determination made as to alternative product uses or selections.

SECTION 01 81 13 – SUSTAINABLE DESIGN REQUIREMENTS

*Guidance for designers and specifiers, with suggested language
to be modified and incorporated into project specifications.*

PART 1 - GENERAL

1.1   SUMMARY

    A.   This Section includes general requirements and procedures for achieving the most environmentally conscious Work possible within the limits of the Construction Schedule, Contract Sum, and available materials, equipment, and products.

1.2   OBJECTIVES

    A.   To obtain acceptable Indoor Air Quality (IAQ) for the completed project and minimize the environmental impacts of the construction and operation, the Contractor during the construction phase of this project shall implement the following procedures singly or in combination:

        1.   Select products that minimize consumption of non-renewable resources, consume reduced amounts of energy and minimize amounts of pollution to produce, and employ recycled and/or recyclable materials. To help purchasers incorporate environmental considerations into purchasing decisions, it is the intent of this project to conform with EPA's Five Guiding Principles on environmentally preferable purchasing. The five principles are:

            a.   Include environmental considerations as part of the normal purchasing process.

            b.   Emphasize pollution prevention early in the purchasing process.

            c.   Examine multiple environmental attributes throughout a product's or service's life cycle.

            d.   Compare relevant environmental impacts when selecting products and services.

            e.   Collect and base purchasing decisions on accurate and meaningful information about environmental performance.

        2.   Control sources for potential IAQ pollutants by controlled selection of materials and processes used in project construction in order to attain superior IAQ.

        3.   Products and processes that achieve the above objectives to the extent currently possible and practical have been selected and included in these Construction Documents. The Contractor is responsible to maintain and support these objectives in developing means and methods for performing the work of this Contract and in proposing product substitutions and/or changes to specified processes.

1.3   RELATED DOCUMENTS

    A.   Drawings and general provisions of the Contract, including General Conditions and other Division 1 Specification Sections, apply to this Section.

B.   Related Sections include the following:

    1.   Divisions 2 through 48 Sections for Sustainable Design Requirements specific to the Work of each of those Sections.

    2.   01 74 19 Construction Waste Management

    3.   01 81 09 Testing for Indoor Air Quality

    4.   01 91 00 Commissioning

1.4   DEFINITIONS

A.   Agrifiber Products: Composite panel products derived from agricultural fiber

B.   Biobased Product: As defined in the 2002 Farm Bill, a product determined by the Secretary to be a commercial or industrial product (other than food or feed) that is composed, in whole or in significant part, of biological products or renewable domestic agricultural materials (including plant, animal, and marine materials) or forestry materials

C.   Biobased Content: The weight of the biobased material divided by the total weight of the product and expressed as a percentage by weight

D.   Certificates of Chain-of-Custody: Certificates signed by manufacturers certifying that wood used to make products has been tracked through its extraction and fabrication to ensure that is was obtained from forests certified by a specified certification program

E.   Composite Wood: A product consisting of wood fiber or other plant particles bonded together by a resin or binder

F.   Construction and Demolition Waste: Includes solid wastes, such as building materials, packaging, rubbish, debris, and rubble resulting from construction, remodeling, repair and demolition operations. A construction waste management plan is to be provided by the Contractor as defined in Section 01 74 19.

G.   LEED: The Leadership in Energy & Environmental Design green building rating systems developed and adopted by the U.S. Green Building Council (USGBC). The systems certify levels of environmental achievement based on a point and credit scoring system.

H.   LEED NC: The Leadership in Energy & Environmental Design green building rating system developed and adopted by the USGBC for new construction and major renovations of buildings

I.   LEED EB: The Leadership in Energy & Environmental Design green building rating system developed and adopted by the USGBC for operating and maintaining existing buildings

J.   Light Pollution: Light that extends beyond its source such that the additional light is wasted in an unwanted area or in an area where it inhibits view of the night sky

K.   Recycled Content Materials: Products that contain pre-consumer or post-consumer materials as all or part of their feedstock

L.   Post-Consumer Recycled Content: The percentage by weight of constituent materials that have been recovered or otherwise diverted from the solid-waste stream after consumer use

M. Pre-Consumer Recycled Content: Materials that have been recovered or otherwise diverted from the solid-waste stream during the manufacturing process. Pre-consumer content must be material that would not have otherwise entered the waste stream as per Section 5 of the FTC Act, Part 260 "Guidelines for the Use of Environmental Marketing Claims": www.ftc.gov/bcp/grnrule/guides980427

N. Regional Materials: Materials that are extracted, harvested, recovered, and manufactured within a radius of 250 miles (400 km) from the Project site

O. Salvaged or Reused Materials: Materials extracted from existing buildings in order to be reused in other buildings without being manufactured

P. Sealant: Any material that fills and seals gaps between other materials

Q. Volatile Organic Compounds (VOCs): Any compound of carbon, excluding carbon monoxide, carbon dioxide, carbonic acid, metallic carbides or carbonates, and ammonium carbonate, which participates in atmospheric photochemical reactions. Compounds that have negligible photochemical reactivity, listed in EPA 40 CFR 51.100(s), are also excluded from this regulatory definition.

1.5 SUBMITTALS

A. General: Additional Sustainable Design submittal requirements are included in other sections of the Specifications.

B. Sustainable Design Submittals:

1. Alternative Transportation: Provide manufacturer's cut sheets for all bike racks installed on site, including the total number of bicycle storage slots provided. Also, provide manufacturer's cut sheets for any alternative-fuel refueling stations installed on site, including fueling capacity information for an 8-hour period.

2. Heat Island Effect:

   a. Site Paving: Provide manufacturer's cut sheets for all impervious paving materials, highlighting the Solar Reflectance Index (SRI) of the material. Also, provide cut sheets for all pervious paving materials.

   b. Roofing Materials: Submittals for roofing materials must include manufacturer's cut sheets or product data highlighting the Solar Reflectance Index (SRI) of the material.

3. Exterior Lighting Fixtures: Submittals must include cut sheets with manufacturer's data on initial fixture lumens above 90° from nadir for all exterior lighting fixtures, and, for parking lot lighting, verification that the fixtures are classified by the IESNA as "full cutoff" (FCO); OR provide documentation that exterior luminaires are IDA-Approved as Dark-Sky Friendly by the International Dark Sky Association (IDA) Fixture Seal of Approval Program.

4. Irrigation Systems: Provide manufacturer's cut sheets for all permanent landscape irrigation system components and for any rainwater harvesting system components, such as cisterns.

5. Water Conserving Fixtures: Submittals must include manufacturer's cut sheets for all water-consuming plumbing fixtures and fittings (toilets, urinals, faucets, showerheads, etc.) highlighting maximum flow rates and/or flush rates. Include cut sheets for any automatic faucet-control devices.

6. Process Water Use: Provide manufacturer's cut sheets for all water-consuming commercial equipment (clothes washers, dishwashers, ice machines, etc.), highlighting water consumption performance. Include manufacturer's cut sheets or product data for any cooling towers, highlighting water consumption estimates, water use reduction measures, and corrosion inhibitors.

7. Elimination of CFCs AND HCFCs: Provide manufacturer's cut sheets for all cooling equipment with manufacturer's product data, highlighting refrigerants; provide manufacturer's cut sheets for all fire-suppression equipment, highlighting fire-suppression agents; provide manufacturer's cut-sheets for all polystyrene insulation (XPS) and closed-cell spray foam polyurethane insulation, highlighting the blowing agent(s).

8. Appliances and Equipment: Provide copies of manufacturer's product data for all Energy Star eligible equipment and appliances, including office equipment, computers and printers, electronics, and commercial food service equipment (excluding HVAC and lighting components), verifying compliance with EPA's Energy Star program.

9. On-Site Renewable Energy Systems: Provide cut sheets and manufacturer's product data for all on-site renewable energy generating components and equipment, including documentation of output capacity.

10. Measurement and Verification Systems: Provide cut sheets and manufacturer's product data for all controls systems, highlighting electrical metering and trending capability components.

11. Salvaged or Reused Materials: Provide documentation that lists each salvaged or reused material, the source or vendor of the material, the purchase price, and the replacement cost if greater than the purchase price.

12. Recycled Content: Submittals for all materials with recycled content (excluding MEP systems equipment and components) must include the following documentation:

    a. Cost of each material or product, excluding cost of labor and equipment for installation

    b. Manufacturer's product data, product literature, or a letter from the manufacturer verifying the percentage of post-consumer and pre-consumer recycled content (by weight) of each material or product

    c. An electronic spreadsheet that tabulates the Project's total materials cost and combined recycled content value (defined as the sum of the post-consumer recycled content value plus one-half of the pre-consumer recycled content value) expressed as a percentage of total materials cost. This spreadsheet shall be submitted every third month with the Contractor's Certificate and Application for Payment. It should indicate, on an ongoing basis, line items for each material, including cost, pre-consumer recycled content, post-consumer recycled content, and combined recycled content value.

    The submittal frequency suggestion of every third month is not based on LEED or any other requirement, and should be revised to reflect the needs of the specific Project.

13. Regional Materials: Submittals for all products or materials expected to contribute to the regional calculation (excluding MEP systems equipment and components) must include the following documentation:

    a. Cost of each material or product, excluding cost of labor and equipment for installation

b.   Location of product manufacture and distance from point of manufacture to the Project Site

c.   Location of point of extraction, harvest, or recovery for each raw material in each product and distance from the point of extraction, harvest, or recovery to the Project Site

d.   Manufacturer's product data, product literature, or a letter from the manufacturer verifying the location and distance from the Project Site to the point of manufacture for each regional material

e.   Manufacturer's product data, product literature, or a letter from the manufacturer verifying the location and distance from the Project Site to the point of extraction, harvest, or recovery for each regional material or product, including, at a minimum, gravel and fill, planting materials, concrete, masonry, and GWB

f.   An electronic spreadsheet that tabulates the Project's total materials cost and regional materials value, expressed as a percentage of total materials cost. This spreadsheet shall be submitted every third month with the Contractor's Certificate and Application for Payment. It should indicate on an ongoing basis, line items for each material, including cost, location of manufacture, distance from manufacturing plant to the Project Site, location of raw material extraction, and distance from extraction point to the Project Site.

The submittal frequency suggestion of every third month is not based on LEED or any other requirement, and should be revised to reflect the needs of the specific Project.

---

14. Biobased Products:

a.   Rapidly Renewable Products: Submittals must include written documentation from the manufacturer declaring that rapidly renewable materials are made from plants harvested within a 10-year or shorter cycle and must indicate the percentage (by weight) of these rapidly renewable components contained in the candidate products, along with the costs of each of these materials, excluding labor and delivery costs.

The Project Team should determine if it wants to follow LEED guidance regarding rapidly renewable materials or consider an alternative approach. This is a highly controversial issue. As an introduction to the contention, please refer to 'Dealing with Wood and Biobased Materials in the LEED Rating System' – a White Paper to the USGBC board by Alex Wilson, President of BuildingGreen, Inc.

This requirement is consistent with the LEED-NC rapidly renewable materials credit.

---

b.   Certified Wood: Submittals for all wood-based materials must include a statement indicating the cost of each product containing FSC Certified wood, exclusive of labor and delivery costs, and certificates of chain-of-custody from manufacturers certifying that specified certified-wood products were made from wood obtained from forests certified by an FSC-accredited certification body to comply with FSC 1.2 "Principles and Criteria."

15. Outdoor Air Delivery Monitoring: Provide manufacturer's cut sheets highlighting the installed carbon dioxide monitoring system components and sequence of controls shop drawing documentation, including CO_2 differential set-points and alarm capabilities.

16. Interior Adhesives and Sealants: Submittals for all field-applied adhesives and sealants, which have a potential impact on indoor air, must include manufacturer's MSDSs or other Product Data highlighting VOC content.

a.   Provide manufacturers' documentation verifying all adhesives used to apply laminates, whether shop-applied or field-applied, contain no urea-formaldehyde.

17. Interior Paints and Coatings: Submittals for all field-applied paints and coatings, which have a potential impact on indoor air, must include manufacturer's MSDSs or other Product Data highlighting VOC content

18. Exterior Paints and Coatings: Submittals for all field-applied paints and coatings, which have a potential impact on ambient air quality, must include manufacturer's MSDSs or other manufacturer's Product Data highlighting VOC content.

19. Floorcoverings:

a.   Carpet Systems: Submittals for all carpet must include the following:

1) A copy of an assessment from the Building for Environmental and Economic Sustainability (BEES) software model, either Version 3.0 or 4.0, with parameters of the model set as described by this specification section.

BEES analysis is frequently a task completed by the designer; however, it is preferable to obtain a BEES assessment from the product manufacturer. The process of acquiring the BEES analysis serves an educational purpose for the manufacturer and is driven by manufacturer motivation to win the bid.

---

2) Manufacturer's product data verifying that all carpet systems meet or exceed the testing and product requirements of the Carpet and Rug Institute Green Label Plus program.

b.   Resilient Flooring: Submittals for all resilient floorcovering must include manufacturer's product data verifying certification under either the Greenguard for Children & Schools or FloorScore indoor emissions testing program.

c.   Engineered Wood Flooring and Bamboo Flooring: Submittals for all engineered wood flooring and bamboo flooring must include manufacturer's product data verifying certification under either the Greenguard or FloorScore indoor emissions testing program.

20. Composite Wood and Agrifiber Binders: Submittals for all composite wood and agrifiber products (including but not limited to particleboard, wheatboard, strawboard, agriboard products, engineered wood components, solid-core wood doors, OSB, MDF, and plywood products) must include manufacturer's product data verifying that these products contain no urea-formaldehyde resins.

21. Systems Furniture and Seating: Provide manufacturer's product data verifying that all systems furniture and seating products meet the requirements of one of the following:

a.   Greenguard certification

b.   SCS Indoor Advantage certification

c.   SCS Indoor Advantage Gold certification

d.   BIFMA Standard X7.1-2005, as tested to BIFMA method M7.1-2005 and as verified by an independent laboratory

e.   Calculated indoor air concentration limits for furniture systems and seating determined by the U.S. EPA's Environmental Technology Verification Large Chamber Test Protocol for Measuring Emissions of VOCs and Aldehydes (September 1999) testing protocol as conducted in an independent air quality testing laboratory

22. Entryway Systems: Provide manufacturer's cut sheets for all walk-off systems installed

to capture particulates, including permanently installed grates, grilles, slotted systems, direct glue-down walk-off mats, and non-permanent roll-out mats.

23. Air Filtration: Provide manufacturer's cut sheets and product data highlighting the following:

   a.   Minimum Efficiency Reporting Value (MERV) for filtration media in all air handling units (AHUs)

   b.   Minimum Efficiency Reporting Value (MERV) for filtration media installed at return air grilles during construction if permanently installed AHUs are used during construction

24. Mercury in Lighting: Provide manufacturer's cut sheets or product data for all fluorescent or HID lamps highlighting mercury content.

25. Lighting Controls: Provide manufacturer's cut sheets and shop drawing documentation highlighting all lighting controls systems components.

26. Thermal Comfort Controls: Provide manufacturer's cut sheets and shop drawing documentation highlighting all thermal comfort-control systems components.

27. Blended Cement: It is the intent of this specification to reduce CO_2 emissions and other environmentally detrimental effects resulting from the production of portland cement by requiring that all concrete mixes, in aggregate, utilize blended cement mixes to displace 40% of the portland cement typically included in conventional construction. Provide the following submittals:

   a.   Copies of concrete design mixes for all installed concrete

   b.   Copies of typical regional baseline concrete design mixes for all compressive strengths used on the Project

   c.   Quantities in cubic yards of each installed concrete mix

28. Gypsum Wall Board: Provide manufacturer's cut sheets or product data verifying that all gypsum wallboard products are moisture and mold-resistant.

29. Fiberglass Insulation: Provide manufacturer's cut sheets or product data verifying that fiberglass batt insulation contains no urea-formaldehyde.

30. Duct Acoustical Insulation: Provide manufacturer's cut sheets or product data verifying that mechanical sound insulation materials in air distribution ducts consists of an impervious, non-porous coatings that prevent dust from accumulating in the insulating materials.

31. Green Housekeeping: Provide documentation that all cleaning products and janitorial paper products meet the VOC limits and content requirements of this specification section.

C.   Project Materials Cost Data: Provide a spreadsheet in an electronic file indicating the total cost for the Project and the total cost of building materials used for the Project, as follows:

1.   Not more than 60 days after the Preconstruction Meeting, the General Contractor shall provide to the Owner and Architect a preliminary schedule of materials costs for all materials used for the Project organized by specification section. Exclude labor costs and all mechanical, electrical, and plumbing (MEP) systems materials and labor costs. Include the following:

a. Identify each reused or salvaged material, its cost, and its replacement value.

b. Identify each recycled-content material, its post-consumer and pre-consumer recycled content as a percentage the product's weight, its cost, its combined recycled content value (defined as the sum of the post-consumer recycled content value plus one-half of the pre-consumer recycled content value), and the total combined recycled content value for all materials as a percentage of total materials costs.

c. Identify each regional material, its cost, its manufacturing location, the distance of this location from the Project site, the source location for each raw material component of the material, the distance of these extraction locations from the Project site, and the total value of regional materials as a percentage of total materials costs.

d. Identify each biobased material, its source, its cost, and the total value of biobased materials as a percentage of total materials costs. Also provide the total value of rapidly renewable materials (materials made from plants that are harvested in less than a 10-year cycle) as a percentage of total materials costs.

e. Identify each wood-based material, its cost, the total wood-based materials cost, each FSC Certified wood material, its cost, and the total value of FSC Certified wood as a percentage of total wood-based materials costs.

2. Provide final versions of the above spreadsheets to the Owner and Architect not more than 14 days after Substantial Completion.

D. Construction Waste Management: See Section 01 74 19 "Construction Waste Management" for submittal requirements.

E. Construction Indoor Air Quality (IAQ) Management: Submittals must include the following:

1. Not more than 30 days after the Preconstruction Meeting, prepare and submit for the Architect and Owner's approval, an electronic copy of the draft Construction IAQ Management Plan in an electronic file including, but not limited to, descriptions of the following:

a. Construction procedures for meeting or exceeding the minimum requirements of the Sheet Metal and Air Conditioning National Contractors Association (SMACNA) IAQ Guidelines for Occupied Buildings Under Construction, 1995, Chapter 3, including procedures for HVAC Protection, Source Control, Pathway Interruption, Housekeeping, and Scheduling

b. Construction procedures for protecting absorptive materials stored on-site or installed from moisture damage

c. Schedule of submission to Architect of photographs of on-site construction IAQ management measures such as protection of ducts and on-site stored oil installed absorptive materials

d. Construction procedures if air handlers must be used during construction, including a description of filtration media to be used at each return air grille

e. Construction procedure for replacing all air-filtration media immediately prior to occupancy after completion of construction, including a description of filtration media to be used at each air handling or air supply unit

2. Not more than 30 days following receipt of the approved draft CIAQMP, submit an electronic copy of the approved CIAQMP in an electronic file, along with the following:

       a.   Manufacturer's cut sheets and product data highlighting the Minimum Efficiency Reporting Value (MERV) for all filtration media to be installed at return air grilles during construction if permanently installed AHUs are used during construction.

       b.   Manufacturer's cut sheets and product data highlighting the Minimum Efficiency Reporting Value (MERV) for filtration media in all air handling units (AHUs).

   3. Not more than 14 days after Substantial Completion provide the following:

       a.   Documentation verifying required replacement of air filtration media in all air handling units (AHUs) after the completion of construction and prior to occupancy and, if applicable, required installation of filtration during construction.

       b.   A minimum of 18 Construction photographs: Six photographs taken on three different occasions during construction of the SMACNA approaches employed, along with a brief description of each approach, documenting implementation of the IAQ management measures, such as protection of ducts and on-site stored or installed absorptive materials.

   4. A copy of the report from testing and inspecting agency documenting the results of IAQ testing, demonstrating conformance with IAQ testing procedures and requirements defined in Section 01 81 09 "Testing for Indoor Air Quality."

> *Note: This requirement that the Contractor provide IAQ testing results is only applicable if the Contractor is responsible for getting the IAQ testing done. In some cases it may be more appropriate for the Owner to contract separately for this testing.*

  F. Commissioning: See Section 01 91 00 "General Commissioning Requirements" for submittal requirements.

  G. Sustainable Design Progress Reports: Concurrent with each Application for Payment, submit reports for the following:

   1. Construction Waste Management: Waste reduction progress reports and logs complying with the requirements of Section 01 74 19 "Construction Waste Management."

   2. Construction IAQ Management: See details below under Section 3.2 Construction Indoor Air Quality Management for Construction IAQ management progress report requirements.

1.6 QUALITY ASSURANCE

  A. General: Perform the work of this Section as a supplement and in accordance with applicable requirements of Division 1 "Contractor Quality Control Program."

  B. Preconstruction Meeting: After award of Contract and prior to the commencement of the Work, schedule and conduct meeting with Owner, Architect, and all Subcontractors to discuss the Construction Waste Management Plan, the required Construction Indoor Air Quality (IAQ) Management Plan, and all other Sustainable Design Requirements. The purpose of this meeting is to develop a mutual understanding of the Project's Sustainable Design Requirements and coordination of the Contractor's management of these requirements with the Contracting Officer and the Construction Quality Manager.

  C. Construction Job Conferences: The status of compliance with the Sustainable Design Requirements of these specifications will be an agenda item at all regular job meetings conducted during the course of work at the site.

PART 2 - PRODUCTS

2.1   PRODUCT ENVIRONMENTAL REQUIREMENTS

A. Site Clearing: Topsoil shall be provided by the Contractor from on-site material which has been stockpiled for reuse. Off-site borrow should only be used when on-site sources are exhausted. Chip and/or compost on site all vegetated material identified for removal.

> *Site Clearing: Using topsoil from the site and chipping woody material on site for mulch reduces transportation impacts and avoids the effect of producing topsoil and mulch at remote sites. During site-selection and design, any ecologically sensitive areas should be identified and addressed via protection and/or mitigation. Plant rescue should be carried out if appropriate.*

> **Managing landscape waste can be part of a green site management plan for the LEED-EB Green Site and Building Exterior Management credit.**

B. Do not burn rubbish, organic matter, etc. or any material on the site. Dispose of legally in accordance with Specifications Sections 01 74 19.

> *Burning of rubbish, organic material, and other material on-site contributes to air pollution.*

C. Site Paving: All site impervious paving must be light colored, with a Solar Reflectance Index (SRI) of at least 29.

> *Site Paving: Light-colored, high-reflectance paving is a way of reducing the localized heat build-up around paved surfaces that contributes to the urban heat island effect. Asphalt paving is not desirable in a cooling climate due to its tendency to absorb and reradiate heat, and the potential for emissions and runoff of petroleum byproducts during its installation and use. During design, consider using porous pavement to manage stormwater and reduce urban heat islands.*

> **This requirement exceeds the requirement for achieving the LEED-NC and LEED-EB heat island reduction credits.**

D. Roofing Materials: All roofing systems, other than vegetated roof systems, must comply with the following requirements:

1. Low-Sloped roofing less than or equal to 2:12 slope must have an SRI of at least 78.

2. Steep-Sloped roofing greater than 2:12 slope must have an SRI of at least 29.

> *Roofing Materials: Light-colored, reflective, and high-emissivity roofing helps to reduce localized heat build-up from roof surfaces that contribute to the urban heat island effect.*

> **This requirement significantly exceeds the requirement for achieving the LEED-NC and LEED-EB heat island reduction credits; exceeding LEED's requirement here is appropriate in urban areas and hot climates, but may not be appropriate elsewhere.**

E. Exterior Lighting Fixtures:

1. All exterior luminaires must emit 0% of the total initial designed fixture lumens at an angle above 90° from nadir and/or meet the requirements of the Dark Sky certification program.

2. Exterior lighting cannot exceed 80% of the lighting power densities defined by ASHRAE/IESNA Standard 90.1-2004, Exterior Lighting Section, without amendments.

3. No lighting of building facades or landscape features is permitted.

Exterior Lighting Fixtures: Light trespass represents wasted energy, diminishes views of the night sky, creates potentially unsafe visual conditions, and interferes with critical functions of nocturnal wildlife.

Exterior lighting should be designed in accordance with IESNA RP-33 and RP-20. The International Dark-Sky Association's Fixture Seal-of-Approval program, and a list of approved fixtures, can be found at http://www.darksky.org.

This requirement is consistent with the LEED-NC light pollution reduction credit.

F. Herbicides and Pest Control: Herbicides shall not be permitted, and pest control measures shall utilize EPA-registered biopesticides only.

Herbicides and Pest Control: Herbicides should be avoided because they can have unwanted side-effects and may accumulate in water and soils. Unwanted plants can be removed or managed manually. Biopesticides are usually inherently less toxic than chemical pesticides, are highly targeted, and are not usually persistent. Integrated pest management provides the effective management of pests using the least-toxic available strategies; for more, see http://www.epa.gov/pesticides/ipm.

G. Irrigation Systems: Any permanent landscape irrigation systems must be supplied entirely by collected rainwater or graywater and must be comprised of below-grade drip emitters controlled by moisture sensors. Timer controls shall not be permitted.

Irrigation systems: Use of potable water to irrigate is a poor use of resources and infrastructure. Even when landscape irrigation is supplied by rainwater and/or graywater, irrigation systems should be as efficient as possible to minimize the need for back-up potable water and make those alternative sources available for other uses, such as toilet flushing.

This specification meets the requirements for two points under the LEED-NC and LEED-EB water efficiency credits.

H. Water-Conserving Fixtures: Plumbing fixtures and fittings shall use in aggregate at least 40% less water than the water use baseline calculated for the building after meeting the Energy Policy Act of 1992 fixture performance requirements. Flow and flush rates shall not exceed the following:

1. Toilets: no more than 1.3 gallons per flush, otherwise be dual flush 1.6/0.8 gallons per flush, and have documented bowl evacuation capability per MaP testing of at least 400 grams

2. Urinals: no more than 0.125 gallons per flush or use

3. Lavatory Faucets: 0.5 gpm with automatic faucet controls

4. Kitchen Sink Lavatories: 2.2 gpm

5. Showerheads: no more than 1.5 gpm

Water Conserving Fixtures: Required flow rates are based on readily available technologies; collectively they should achieve the specified 40% water savings requirement, but that needs to be verified. The calculation may vary based on gender distribution and occupancy.

The 40% water use reduction level does not, on its own, meet the requirements of the LEED-NC innovative wastewater treatment credit. That credit can be achieved by using graywater to flush toilets, by installing composting toilets, or by providing on-site wastewater treatment.

The 40% level exceeds the requirements for two points under the LEED-NC water efficiency credit and can be used to request an innovation point.

I. Process Water Use: Employ strategies that in aggregate result in 20% less water use than the process water use baseline for the building after meeting the commercial equipment and HVAC performance requirements as listed in the Table below. For equipment not addressed by EPACT 2005 or the list below, additional equipment performance requirements may be proposed provided documentation supporting the proposed benchmark or industry standard is submitted.

1. Clothes Washer: 7.5 gallons/cubic foot/cycle

Consistent with LEED for Schools ballot draft, which cites Consortium for Energy Efficiency standards: Commercial CEE Tier 3a – Residential CEE Tier 1.

---

2. Dishwasher with Racks: 1.0 gallons/rack

Consistent with LEED for Schools ballot draft.

---

3. Ice Machine: 20 gallons/100 pounds ice for machines making over 175 pounds of ice per day; 30 gallons/100 pounds ice for machines making less than 175 ice per day. Avoid water-cooled machines.

Consistent with LEED for Schools ballot draft, which cites Consortium for Energy Efficiency Tier 3 standard.

---

4. Food Steamer: 2 gallons/hour. Use only boilerless steamers.

Consistent with LEED for Schools ballot draft.

---

5. Pre-Rinse Spray Valves: 1.4 gallons/minute

Consistent with LEED for Schools ballot draft.

---

6. Kitchen Pot-Washing Sinks: 2.2 gallons/minute

7. Cooling Towers: 2.3 gallons/ton-hr. water loss

   a. Use atrazine-based corrosion inhibitors and reducing bleed-off by increasing cycles of concentration (at least 5, or with water quality problems limit to 4).

   b. Install meters on make-up water and discharge blow-down.

   c. Install conductivity controller for blow-down.

   d. Provide overflow alarm connected to central building controls.

   e. Install drift eliminators.

   f. Provide makeup water from sources other than potable water supply.

Cooling Tower Water Use: Threshold of 2.3 gallons per ton assumes reasonably aggressive water management and moderate-mineral-content in replacement water. Note that some chemicals used to treat cooling tower water are toxic, and their use should be minimized.

In all cases: Prohibit once-through cooling systems and non-recirculating evaporative coolers.

J. Elimination of CFCs AND HCFCs:

1. Ozone Protection: Base building cooling equipment shall contain no refrigerants other than the following: HCFC-123, HFC-134a, HFC-245fa, HFC-407c, or HFC 410a.

    CFC Reduction; Ozone Depletion

    Selected refrigerants are low in both ozone-depletion potential and global warming potential. Their conformance with the LEED requirement depends on leakage rates and other parameters of the equipment, so this specification does not ensure conformity with LEED's requirements.

2. Fire suppression systems may not contain ozone-depleting substances.

3. Extruded polystyrene insulation (XPS) and closed-cell spray foam polyurethane insulation shall not be manufactured with hydrochlorofluorocarbon (HCFC) blowing agents.

    Extruded polystyrene (XPS) is the only rigid insulation material that is currently made with ozone-depleting compounds. The use of these blowing agents is slated for phase-out by 2010; in the meantime, XPS made without them is available from select manufacturers.

    Spray foam closed-cell polyurethane insulation is also still often blown with HCFCs; open-cell (low density) foams do not use CFCs.

K. Appliances and Equipment: All Energy Star eligible equipment and appliances, including office equipment, computers and printers, electronics, and commercial food service equipment (excluding HVAC and lighting components), shall be qualified by EPA's Energy Star program.

    Energy Star qualification ensures reasonable levels of energy efficiency.

L. HVAC Distribution Efficiency:

1. All duct systems shall be constructed of galvanized sheet metal, aluminum, or stainless steel as deemed appropriate based on the application requirements. No fiberglass duct board shall be permitted.

2. All medium- and high-pressure ductwork systems shall be pressure-tested in accordance with the current SMACNA standards.

3. All ductwork shall be externally insulated. No interior duct liner shall be permitted.

4. Where possible, all air terminal connections shall be hard-connected with sheet metal ductwork. If flexible ductwork is used, no flexible duct extension shall be more than six feet in length.

5. All HVAC equipment shall be isolated from the ductwork system with flexible duct connectors to minimize the transmittance of vibration.

6. All supply and return air branch ducts shall include the appropriate style of volume damper. Air terminal devices such as grilles, registers, and diffusers shall be balanced at duct branch dampers, not at terminal face.

M. Measurement and Verification: Install controls and monitoring devices as required by division 15 and 16 in order to comply with International Performance Measurement & Verification Protocol (IPMVP), Volume III: Concepts and Options for Determining Energy Savings in New Construction, April 2003, Option D.

The IPMVP provides guidance on situation-appropriate application of measurement and verification strategies.

This specification is consistent with the LEED-NC Energy and Atmosphere credit for Measurement and Verification.

N. Salvaged or Reused materials: There shall be no substitutions for specified salvaged and reused materials and products.

Salvaged materials: Use of salvaged materials reduces impacts of disposal and manufacturing of replacements.

This specification is consistent with the LEED-NC materials reuse and LEED-EB alternative materials credits in recognizing salvaged materials as those coming from other buildings. While other materials are commonly referred to as "salvaged," no consistent and defensible definition has been developed that would include other materials while excluding ones that are not consistent with the intent of this document, hence the decision to follow LEED in this language.

O. Recycled Content of Materials:

1. Provide building materials with recycled content such that post-consumer recycled content value plus half the pre-consumer recycled content value constitutes a minimum of 30% of the cost of materials used for the Project, exclusive of all MEP equipment, labor, and delivery costs. The Contractor shall make all attempts to maximize the procurement of materials with recycled content.

    a. The post-consumer recycled content value of a material shall be determined by dividing the weight of post-consumer recycled content by the total weight of the material and multiplying by the cost of the material.

    b. The pre-consumer recycled content value of a material shall be determined by dividing the weight of pre-consumer recycled content by the total weight of the material and multiplying by the cost of the material.

    c. Do not include mechanical and electrical components in the calculations.

    d. Do not include labor and delivery costs in the calculations.

    e. Recycled content of materials shall be defined according to the Federal Trade Commission's "Guide for the Use of Environmental Marketing Claims," 16 CFR 260.7 (e).

    f. Utilize all on-site existing paving materials that are scheduled for demolition as granulated fill, and include the cost of this material had it been purchased in the calculations for recycled content value.

    g. At a minimum, the materials in the following list must contain the minimum recycled content indicated:

Category	Minimum Recycled Content
Compost/mulch	100% post-consumer
Asphaltic Concrete Paving	25% post-consumer
Cast-in-Place Concrete	6% pre-consumer
CMU: Gray Block	20% pre-consumer
Steel Reinforcing Bars	90% combined
Structural Steel Shapes	90% combined
Steel Joists	75% combined
Steel Deck	75% combined
Steel Fabrications	60% combined
Steel Studs	30% combined
Steel Roofing	30% post-consumer
Aluminum Fabrications	35% combined
Rigid Insulation	20% pre-consumer
Batt insulation	30% combined
Cellulose Insulation	90% combined
Rock Wool Insulation	75% pre-consumer
Fireproofing	20% combined
Steel Doors and Frames	35% combined
Gypsum Wallboard	100% combined
Carpet	40% combined
Ceramic Tile Flooring	60% combined
Rubber Flooring and Base	60% combined
Acoustical Ceiling Tile (ACT)	40% post-consumer
ACT Suspension System	90% post-consumer
Toilet Partitions	60% post-consumer

Recycled content thresholds listed in this table are largely derived from EPA's Comprehensive Procurement Guidelines selected to balance embodied energy with solid-waste impacts and are based on availability.

Even though manufacturers must follow the reporting guidelines from the Federal Trade Commission, claims should be certified by an independent third party whenever possible.

Following this requirement is likely to earn 2 points under the LEED-NC credit for recycled content, but achievement will depend on the results of LEED's recycled content value calculation. Similarly, it can contribute to achieving one or more points under the LEED-EB credit for optimizing use of alternative materials depending on the total value of environmentally preferable products purchased in the performance period.

P.   Regional Materials: Provide a minimum of 20 percent of building materials (by cost) that are manufactured and extracted/harvested within a 500 mile radius of the project site, exclusive of abor and delivery costs. The Contractor shall make all attempts to maximize the procurement of materials within this specified 500 mile radius.

The specification exceeds the requirements of the LEED-NC credit for regional materials, and may qualify for an exemplary performance innovation credit.

The 500-mile radius conforms with LEED's requirement, but in industrialized areas it may be feasible to reduce it further.

Q. Biobased Products:

1. Use only biobased concrete form-release products.

2. Solid Wood Products: All new solid-wood-based materials will be certified as "FSC 100%" by an independent third party in accordance with FSC Forest Stewardship Council "Principles and Criteria" and will have received Chain-of-Custody Certification as certified by an accredited certification group such as Smartwood or Scientific Certification Systems (SCS).

3. Other Wood Products: All other new wood-based materials will be certified by an independent third party in accordance with any of the following standards:

    a. FSC: Forest Stewardship Council "Principles and Criteria" and has received Chain-of-Custody Certification as certified by an accredited certification group such as Smartwood or Scientific Certification Systems (SCS)

    FSC labels new-wood-based material as either "FSC 100%" or "FSC Mixed." Products with the FSC 100% label come entirely from FSC certified forests. Products with the FSC mixed label come from company controlled sources and recycled material as well as FSC certified forests. Company controlled sources exclude illegally harvested timber, among other requirements.

4. Preservative-treated lumber with chromated copper arsenate (CCA) treatments is not permitted, and lumber with copper-based treatments (such as ACQ) is permitted only for ground-contact applications.

    For preservative treatments, chromated copper arsenate (CCA) is no longer allowed for many building applications but is still used in other applications. It should be avoided whenever possible. Nontoxic options are now available, including borates for protected applications and sodium-silicate mineralization treatment for all applications. The latter is quite new, however, and has limited track record in the field. For ground-contact, copper-based preservatives may still be considered, as long as they are not used in situations in which the copper could leach into surface waters (copper is highly toxic to fish).

5. Wood-based materials include but are not limited to the following materials (when made from wood), engineered wood products, or wood-based panel products:

    a. Rough carpentry

    b. Miscellaneous carpentry

    c. Heavy timber construction

    d. Wood decking

    e. Particleboard

    f. Plywood

    g. Metal-plate-connected wood trusses

    h. Structural glued-laminated timber

    i. Finish carpentry

    j. Architectural woodwork

k.   Wood paneling

l.   Wood veneer wall covering

m.   Wood flooring

n.   Wood lockers

o.   Wood cabinets

p.   Wood doors

q.   Non-rented temporary construction, including bracing, concrete formwork, pedestrian barriers, and temporary protection

---

Biobased Materials: There are now USDA-designated biobased products in some emerging (as opposed to mature) markets, which have been screened using the BEES LCA software. As very few biobased materials have been designated as preferable by USDA, the specifier may want to include additional materials. It is the intent of these specifications to encourage the use of biobased materials such as agricultural byproducts, linoleum, bamboo, cork, insulation from recycled cotton, PLA, and wool. Alternatively, the designer may seek to specify any material that is available as an alternative for comparison in the Building for Environmental and Economic Sustainability (BEES), either Version 3.0 or 4.0, and whose score is better (lower) than any chosen alternative in the BEES software available at http://www.bfrl.nist.gov/oae/software/bees/scores.html

---

R.   Brominated Flame Retardants: For new furniture, do not utilize cushioned office seating, and for lounge seating, do not utilize cushioned seating with brominated flame retardants.

Brominated Flame Retardants: These compounds, and especially polybrominated diphenyl ethers (PBDEs), are persistent and bioaccumulative in the environment and are suspected of varying degrees of toxicity.

S.   Outdoor Air Delivery Monitoring:

1.   All spaces with an occupant density greater than 1 person per 40 square feet must include at least one CO_2 monitor located between 3 feet and 6 feet above the finished floor.

2.   All spaces with occupant density less than 1 person per 40 square feet must include a direct outdoor airflow monitor, capable of measuring the minimum outdoor airflow rate within 15% accuracy.

3.   Monitoring equipment must be configured to generate a building automation system alarm and a visual or audible alert when CO_2 concentrations vary by 10% or more from set point.

Outdoor Air Delivery Monitoring: Carbon dioxide (CO_2) is used as an indicator of fresh air delivery to occupied areas—high CO_2 concentrations indoors relative to outdoors indicate a lack of adequate air change. Set points for CO_2 concentration differentials should comply with ASHRAE Standard 62.1-2004 "Effective Ventilation Rates" which vary by occupancy and activity.

This section has the same requirements as the LEED-NC outdoor air delivery monitoring credit, which is also based on ASHRAE Standard 62.1-2004.

T.   Adhesives and Sealants:

1.   All adhesives and sealants used inside the building's thermal envelope must be third-party certified under one of the following programs:

a.   Indoor Advantage Plus from Scientific Certification Systems, Inc.

b.   Greenguard Children and Schools from Greenguard Environmental Institute

    c.   Collaborative for High Performance Schools

All these programs reference California's chronic reference exposure levels (CRELs) for occupant exposure likely to result from use of the materials, which are being adopted widely as a standard for IAQ performance.

2. All adhesives and sealants, regardless of where they are used, must comply with the following limits for VOC content when calculated according to 40 CFR 59, Subpart D (EPA method 24):

    a.   Concrete Curing Compound: 60 g/L

    b.   Concrete Sealer: 10 g/L

    c.   Concrete Form Release Agents: 0g/L

    d.   Garage Deck Sealer: 50g/L

    e.   Wood Glues: 20 g/L

    f.   Millwork and Casework Adhesives: 20g/L

    g.   Metal to Metal Adhesives: 30 g/L

    h.   Adhesives for Porous Materials (Except Wood): 50 g/L

    i.   Subfloor Adhesives: 50 g/L

    j.   Plastic Foam Adhesives: 50 g/L

    k.   Carpet Adhesives: 50 g/L

    l.   Carpet Pad Adhesives: 50 g/L

    m.   Carpet Seam Sealer: 50g/L

    n.   VCT and Sheet Vinyl Adhesives: 50 g/L

    o.   Cove Base Adhesives: 50 g/L

    p.   Rubber Floor Adhesives: 60 g/L

    q.   Wood Flooring Adhesives: 100 g/L

    r.   Ceramic Tile Adhesives: 65 g/L

    s.   Gypsum Board and Panel Adhesives: 50 g/L

    t.   Gypsum Drywall Joint Compound: 20 g/L

    u.   Portland Cement Plaster: 20 g/L

    v.   Multipurpose Construction Adhesives: 70 g/L

    w.   Cast Resin Countertop Silicone Sealant: 20g/L

    x.   Plastic Laminate Adhesives: 20 g/L

    y.   General Contact Adhesive: 80 g/L

    z.   Structural Glazing Adhesives and Compounds: 100 g/L

    aa. Silicone Sealant: 50 g/L

    bb. Pipe Thread Sealant: 50 g/L

    cc. Duct Sealant: 10 g/L

    dd. Plastic Cement Welding Compounds: 250 g/L

ee.   ABS Welding Compounds: 400 g/L

ff.   CPVC Welding Compounds: 270 g/L

gg.   PVC Welding Compounds: 150 g/L

hh.   Adhesive Primer for Plastic: 250 g/L

ii.   Architectural Sealants: 250 g/L

jj.   Single-Ply Roofing Membrane Adhesives: 250 g/L

3.   Interior sealants shall not contain: mercury, butyl rubber, neoprene, SBR (styrene butadiene rubber), or nitrile.

4.   Sealants and glazing compounds formulated with aromatic solvents (organic solvent with a benzene ring in its molecular structure) fibrous talc or asbestos, formaldehyde, halo-genated solvents, mercury, lead, cadmium, hexavalent chromium, or their components shall not be used.

5.   Adhesives used to apply laminates, whether shop-applied or field-applied, shall contain no urea-formaldehyde.

Adhesives and Sealants: The thresholds for allowable VOCs in this specification are not limited to interior field-applied applications (even though LEED's requirements are limited to those applications) because VOCs emitted on the exterior, at fabrication sites, and at factories also adversely affect ambient air quality. The specific thresholds and restrictions represent the most restrictive of the following sources: EPA Spec Section 01120 from the First Environments Early Learning Center project; Green Seal standard GS-36; Bay Area Air Quality Management District Regulation 8, Rule 51; South Coast Air Quality Management District Rule #1168; and LEED.

Meeting this specification should at least meet the requirements of the LEED-NC low-emitting materials credit and the LEED-EB credit for optimizing use of IAQ compliant products.

U.   Paints and Coatings:

1.   Interior Paints and Coatings: For interior field-applied applications, use paints and coatings that comply with the following limits for VOC content when calculated according to 40 CFR 59, Subpart D (EPA method 24) and the chemical restrictions (Restricted Components listed below) of Green Seal Standard GS-11, Paints, First Edition, May 20, 1993; Green Seal Standard GC-03, Anti-Corrosive Paints, Second Edition, January 7, 1997; and South Coast Air Quality Management District Rule 1113, Architectural Coatings, rules in effect on January 1, 2004, as follows:

a.   Flat Paints and Coatings: Not more than 10 grams of VOC per liter of coating less water and exempt compounds, including pigments

b.   Non-Flat Paints and Coatings Except High Gloss: Not more than 50 grams of VOC per liter of coating less water and exempt compounds, including pigments.

Including pigments in the calculation for allowable VOCs makes this standard much more stringent, especially for more saturated colors, but this level is justifiable because several major manufacturers offer paints with VOC-free pigment systems for their zero-VOC paint lines.

---

c.   High Gloss Paints and Coatings: Not more than 150 grams of VOC per liter of coating less water and exempt compounds, including pigments. High Gloss Coatings are coatings that register a gloss of 70 or above on a 60-degree meter according to ASTM Test Method D 523 as specified in paragraph (e)(6).

d.   Water-Based Polychromatic Finish Coatings: Not more than 150 g/L (150 g/L for primer and flat polychromatic paint)

e. Anti-Corrosive Coatings: Not more than 100 grams of VOC per liter of coating less water and exempt compounds

f. Sanding Sealers: Not more than 50 grams of VOC per liter of coating less water and exempt compounds

g. Waterproofing Sealers: Not more than 100 grams of VOC per liter of coating less water and exempt compounds

h. Concrete Slab Sealers: Not more than 10 grams of VOC per liter of coating less water and exempt compounds

The choice of 10 g/L VOCs for concrete sealers is much lower that the California Air Quality management district's limit of 100 VOCs but is justified based on the widespread availability of complying materials.

i. Polyurethanes: Not more than 100 grams of VOC per liter of coating less water and exempt compounds

j. Stains: Not more than 250 grams of VOC per liter of coating less water and exempt compounds

2. Interior field applied varnishes and lacquers are not permitted.

3. Interior paints shall not contain antimicrobial additives (such as fungicides and biocides).

Fungicides and biocides are banned from interior paints because those are needed primarily to extend shelf life. Instead paint should be used promptly and any remaining paint should be recycled.

4. Exterior Paints and Coatings: For exterior applications, use paints and coatings that comply with the following limits for VOC content when calculated according to 40 CFR 59, Subpart D (EPA method 24) and the chemical restrictions (Restricted Components listed below) of Green Seal's Standard GS-11:

a. Flat Paints and Coatings: Not more than 50 grams of VOC per liter of coating less water and exempt compounds, including pigments

b. Non-Flat Paints and Coatings: Not more than 150 grams of VOC per liter of coating less water and exempt compounds, including pigments

c. High Gloss Paints and Coatings: Not more than 150 grams of VOC per liter of coating less water and exempt compounds, including pigments. High Gloss Coatings are coatings that register a gloss of 70 or above on a 60-degree meter according to ASTM Test Method D 523 as specified in paragraph (e)(6)

d. Anti-Corrosive Coatings: Not more than 100 grams of VOC per liter of coating less water and exempt compounds

e. Varnishes and Sanding Sealers: Not more than 275 grams of VOC per liter of coating less water and exempt compounds

f. Stains: Not more than 250 grams of VOC per liter of coating less water and exempt compounds

5. Aromatic Compounds: Paints and coatings shall not contain more than 1% (by weight) total aromatic compounds (hydrocarbon compounds containing one or more benzene rings).

6. Restricted Components: Paints and coatings shall not contain any of the following:

a. Acrolein

b. Acrylonitrile

c.   Analine dyes

d.   Antimony

e.   Benzene

f.   Butyl benzyl phthalate

g.   Cadmium

h.   Di (2-ethylhexyl) phthalate

i.   Di-n-butyl phthalate

j.   Di-n-octyl phthalate

k.   1,2-dichlorobenzene

l.   Diethyl phthalate

m.   Dimethyl phthalate

n.   Ethylbenzene

o.   Formaldehyde

p.   Hexavalent chromium

q.   Isophorone

r.   Lead

s.   Mercury

t.   Methyl ethyl ketone

u.   Methyl isobutyl ketone

v.   Methylene chloride

w.   Naphthalene

x.   Toluene (methylbenzene)

y.   1,1,1-trichloroethane

z.   Vinyl chloride

aa. Xylene

The list of banned ingredients closely follows Green Seal's Standard GS-11, with the addition of xylene.

---

7. Coordinate with paint manufacturers for implementing a "take-back program" for all unused paint. Set aside scrap and unused paint to be returned to the manufacturer for recycling into new product. Close and seal all partially used containers of paint to maintain quality as necessary for reuse.

Paint consists of substances that represent valuable resources and are best reused by the original manufacturer. For optimum indoor air quality, the above requirements can be replaced with a requirement that all paints used indoors be third-party certified for compliance with a standard based on California's chronic reference exposure levels (CRELs), such as Greenguard Children & Schools, Indoor Air Advantage Gold, or Collaborative for High Performance Schools.

Meeting this specification should meet or exceed the requirements of the LEED-NC and LEED-EB credits for VOC levels in paint and coatings.

V. Floorcoverings:

1. Carpet shall achieve an Environmental Performance Score of 0.0200 as determined through an assessment in the Building for Environmental and Economic Sustainability (BEES) software model, either Version 3.0 or 4.0. The parameters of the model must be set in the following way for this assessment:

    a. "Environmental vs. Economics Performance Weights" shall be set at 100% Environmental Performance.

    b. "Environmental Impact Category Weights" shall be set using the EPA Scientific Advisory Board weights.

    c. "Transportation from "Manufacture to Use" shall be set at the lowest distance possible.

    d. In the "Nylon Carpet Parameters" dialogue box, set "Carpet Type" as "Carpet Tile" and "Installation Glue" as "Low VOC Glue."

    Floorcoverings: BEES—Building for Environmental and Economic Sustainability—is a software tool from the National Institute for Standards and Technology that contain life-cycle assessment data for a range of generic and some proprietary building products. The one category in which there are sufficient products to consider using BEES results as a selection method is carpet. The threshold score of 0.0200 was selected to differentiate the best-performing carpets in BEES 3.0. BEES 4.0 will have more carpet products, some of which should also achieve this threshold (although it will be necessary to check that the scoring system hasn't shifted and adjust the threshold for BEES 4.0 use).

    Low-Emitting Materials–Carpet Systems: Self-adhering carpet tile is the adhesive method that requires the least adhesive and the lowest associated VOC emissions.

2. All carpet systems, including adhesives, must meet or exceed the Carpet and Rug Institute Green Label Plus Indoor Air Quality Test Program.

3. Carpet cushion shall not contain brominated flame retardants.

4. Carpet tile applications shall be self-adhering.

5. All resilient floorcovering must be certified under the Greenguard or FloorScore indoor emissions testing programs.

    FloorScore is a third-party certification program for floorcoverings other than carpet that is based on the State of California's chronic reference exposure levels (CRELs) for allowable concentrations of selected compounds. Polished concrete is a good option for indoor air quality, where acoustical requirements are not too stringent, because no adhesives or potentially volatile materials are added to the space, and cleaning is possible with low-impact cleaning agents. Other hard surface flooring options are similarly attractive.

6. Engineered wood flooring and bamboo flooring must be certified under the Greenguard or FloorScore indoor emissions testing programs.

    Bamboo products should be certified as low-emitting under FloorScore or Greenguard to confirm that formaldehyde has not been added during manufacturing, due to confusion from some suppliers on this matter.

W. Composite Wood and Agrifiber Binders: All composite wood, agrifiber products, and wood doors shall contain no added urea-formaldehyde resins.

    Formaldehyde has been classified as a human carcinogen. Of the available formaldehyde-based binders, urea-formaldehyde offgasses at the highest levels. Agrifiber products are not made with urea-formaldehyde, as it is not effective as a binder on those materials.

> The LEED-NC low-emitting materials credit, and the LEED-EB credit for optimizing use of IAQ compliant products both require the avoidance of composite wood products made with urea-formaldehyde, so this specification conforms with those requirements.

X. Systems Furniture and Seating:

    1. All systems furniture and seating meet the requirements of one of the following:

        a. Greenguard certification

        b. SCS Indoor Advantage certification

        c. SCS Indoor Advantage Gold certification

        d. BIFMA Standard X7.1-2005, as tested to BIFMA method M7.1-2005 and as verified by an independent laboratory

        e. Calculated indoor air concentration limits for furniture systems and seating determined by the U.S. EPA's Environmental Technology Verification Large Chamber Test Protocol for Measuring Emissions of VOCs and Aldehydes (September 1999) testing protocol as conducted in an independent air quality testing laboratory

Systems Furniture and Seating: These products often contain contaminants that are harmful to occupants. Several certification programs and testing programs are available to limit, reduce, or eliminate such contaminants. The specification allows five such programs and protocols.

    2. Systems furniture and seating made with coatings or sealants that contain any of the following solvents are not permitted: naptha, benzene, toluene, xylene, hexavalent chromium.

Y. Entryway Systems: Walk-off systems to capture particulates shall be installed at least 12 feet long in the direction of entry travel at all entryways directly connected to the outdoors that are used as regular entry points by building users. Acceptable entryway systems include:

    1. Permanently installed grates, grilles, or slotted systems that allow for cleaning beneath them

    2. Permanently installed direct glue-down walk-off mats

    3. Non-permanent roll-out mats, but only if a service organization is contracted for maintenance on a weekly basis

Entryway Systems: Pollutants tracked in on the shoes of people entering a building are a significant source of contamination.

> The LEED-NC credit for indoor chemical and pollutant source control requires a 6-foot-long walk-off system to contain these pollutants, but studies indicate that less than 50% of pollutants are captured in that distance. This specification requires a 12-foot-long walk-off system, which should capture 80% of the pollutants.

Z. Air Filtration: Install air filtration media that provides a Minimum Efficiency Reporting Value (MERV) of 13 or better in all air handling units for processing both return and outside air that is delivered to the air supply system. Replace all filtration media after the completion of construction and prior to occupancy.

Air Filtration: MERV 13 filters are equivalent to an 85% to 90% efficiency, helping to control airborne contaminants. Replacing these filters between construction and occupancy is important to ensure that contaminants from the construction process do not adversely affect occupants.

AA. Mercury in Lighting:

1. Provide only low-mercury fluorescent or HID lamps with mercury content limited to the following:

   a.   T-5 and T-8 fluorescent lamps: 80 picograms per lumen hour

   ---

   Performance parameters for Compact Fluorescent Lamps and HID Lamps should be generally in alignment with the requirements stated above, but applicable to those lamps.

   ---

2. Measurement Standards: Lumens to be measured according to IES LM9 for linear fluorescent lamps, IES LM66 for compact fluorescent lamps, and LM51 for HID lamps; mercury content to be measured according to U.S. EPA "Total Mercury by Cold Vapor Absorption Method" 7471A.

   Mercury in Lighting: Fluorescent and high-intensity discharge lamps are a significant source of mercury in buildings. All such lamps should be recycled by a qualified service.

   In addition to the requirements here, LEED-EB requires (as a prerequisite for participating in LEED-EB) that, on average over the facility, mercury-containing lamps not exceed 100 picograms per lumen hour. The LEED-EB additional toxic material reduction credit restricts that further to 80 picograms per lumen hour. The Green Guide to Health Care restricts mercury in fluorescent lamps to 5 milligrams of mercury per lamp—in a typical T-8 or T-5 fluorescent lamp this should be consistent with the 80 picogram limit in the specification. Major lamp manufacturers have recently started offering data on their lamps for verifying compliance with the LEED-EB requirement.

BB. Lighting Controls: Install and calibrate controls as specified by Division 26 – Electrical in order to comply with LEED IAQ lighting controllability requirements.

   It is the responsibility of the designers to design a system of lighting and controls that meets the Owner's requirements (and LEED's requirements, if desired). The Contractor must ensure that all specified controls are installed and tested, and respond to any concerns or problems that emerge from commissioning.

CC. Thermal Comfort: Install and calibrate controls as specified in Division 23 – Heating, Ventilation, and Air-Conditioning.

   This approach meets the LEED v2.1 EQ 7.2 credit for thermal comfort. LEED v2.2 no longer includes this requirement.

DD. Blended Cement Concrete:

1. Cementitious Materials: Provide composite mix of portland cement and ground granulated blast-furnace slag or fly ash or blended hydraulic cement and limit percentage (by weight) of portland cement (ASTM C150) in aggregate (total weighted average of cementitious material weight for all mixes and pours) to 40% less than standard regional concrete mix designs.

2. Limit percentage (by weight) of standard portland cement (C-150), to the following maximum percentages of the cementitious portion of the mix while maintaining the above-40% required reduction in portland cement across the Project's total quantity of concrete:

---

     a.   Footings: 50%

     b.   Slab on Grade: 60%, except for cold-weather pours

     c.   Insulated Concrete Form Concrete: 40%

     d.   Elevated Slabs: 60%, except for cold-weather pours

     e.   Exterior Concrete: 75%

The purpose of this requirement is to reduce the CO_2 emissions associated with cement production. Care should be taken to coordinate with the structural engineer and the concrete supplier or installing subcontractor to verify needs or modifications for cold weather pores including an assessment of setup times and duration required to achieve specified target strength.

The 40% average reduction in portland cement is consistent with an establishing innovation point threshold in LEED for New Construction.

EE. Gypsum Wallboard: Standard paper-faced gypsum wallboard can be used only in dry climates, where wetting during or after construction is not anticipated. In humid climates, where dampness and condensation are a concern, use only non-paper-faced gypsum wallboard. In wet locations a cementitious wallboard, made of portland or magnesium oxide cement, must be used.

These guidelines are based on best practices for managing moisture damage in buildings.

FF. Fiberglass Insulation: Fiberglass batt insulation shall contain no formaldehyde-based binders or shall be third-party certified for conformance with Greenguard Children & Schools or Indoor Advantage Gold.

Most fiberglass batts are bonded with a phenol formaldehyde resin, which can contribute to unwanted indoor emissions.

GG. Duct Acoustical Insulation: Mechanical sound insulation materials within the duct shall consist of an impervious, non-porous coating that prevents dust from accumulating in the insulating materials.

HH. Green Housekeeping:

1. Utilize cleaning products that meet the requirements of the Green Seal GS-37 standard or comply with the requirements and maximum VOC limits of Title 17, California Code of Regulations, Division 3, Chapter 1, Subchapter 8.5, Article 2, Regulation for Reducing VOC Emissions from Consumer Products (September 2001).

2. Utilize janitorial paper products and trash bags that meet the minimum percentages of post-consumer recycled content and recovered content requirements of EPA's Comprehensive Procurement Guidelines.

The requirements in this section are intended to reduce the environmental impacts of housekeeping operations and reduce exposure of maintenance personnel and building occupants to harmful VOC emissions.

This specification meets the requirements for the LEED-EB materials credit for sustainable cleaning products and materials.

PART 3 - EXECUTION

3.1 CONSTRUCTION WASTE MANAGEMENT

A. Develop and implement a Construction Waste Management Plan (CWMP), as defined in Section 01 74 19 "Construction Waste Management," quantifying material diversion by weight in order to re-cycle, reuse, and/or salvage at least 95% (by weight) of construction, demolition, and land-clearing waste.

B. Clean materials which are contaminated prior to placing in collection containers. Deliver materials free of dirt, adhesives, solvents, petroleum contamination, and other substances deleterious to the recycling process.

C. Utilize any on-site existing paving materials that are scheduled for demolition as granulated fill or subbase material, and include the weight of this material in the calculations for material diverted from landfill disposal.

D. Arrange for materials collection by or materials delivery to the appropriate recycling or reuse facility.

E. Tax credits and other savings obtained or revenue generated for recycled or reused materials accrue to the Contractor.

F. Discuss CWMP procedures and measures as an agenda item at all regular job meetings conducted during the course of work at the site, and record progress in meeting minutes.

G. Submit monthly progress reports with Applications for Payment in accordance with Section 01 74 19, documenting the status of the CWMP and current diversion percentage rates.

3.2 CONSTRUCTION INDOOR AIR QUALITY MANAGEMENT

A. Develop and implement a Construction IAQ Management Plan (CIAQMP) to prevent indoor air quality problems resulting from construction activities, including, at minimum, the following:

1. Construction activities must meet or exceed the minimum requirements of the SMACNA IAQ Guideline for Occupied Buildings under Construction, 1995.

2. During construction, protect all absorptive materials stored on-site or installed from moisture damage as described in the Construction IAQ Management Plan (CIAQMP) defined above. Specifically:

    a. Exercise special care at all times in the storage of materials to prevent exposure to moisture.

    b. Avoid installation of gypsum wallboard and other porous materials until the building is weather-tight.

    c. All standing water which accumulates on interior floors shall be removed on the day that it is observed.

    d. Any drywall that has retained more than 20% moisture after 48 hours following exposure to moisture, or that has evidence of mold, must be disposed of in accordance with Specification Section 01 74 19 "Construction Waste Management."

    e. The contractor shall identify and remove all porous building materials that become wet or damaged by moisture within 7 calendar days of such exposure.

These measures are intended to minimize the opportunity for moisture damage and mold growth within the building.

---

3. During construction and HVAC system installation, provide the Architect with photographs of IAQ management measures (such as protection of ducts and on-site or installed absorptive materials), including six photographs on three different occasions depicting implemented SMACNA approaches.

B. Air Filtration:

1. Install air filtration media that provides a Minimum Efficiency Reporting Value (MERV) of 13 or better in all air handling units for processing both return and outside air that is delivered to the air supply system; replace all filtration media after the completion of construction and prior to occupancy.

2. Install air filtration media that provides a Minimum Efficiency Reporting Value (MERV) of 8 or better for filtration media installed at return air grilles during construction if permanently installed AHUs are used during construction. Inspect weekly and replace as required.

C. Discuss CIAQMP procedures and measures as an agenda item at all regular job meetings conducted during the course of work at the site, and record progress in meeting minutes.

D. Engage an independent testing and inspecting agency to conduct a baseline indoor air quality testing program after the completion of construction and prior to occupancy in accordance with Section 01 81 09 "Testing for Indoor Air Quality."

This section spells out the requirements for managing and protecting indoor air quality during construction. It is written to conform with the construction IAQ management plan credit in LEED-EB and the first credit in LEED-NC for the management plan during construction. For details on a testing plan to meet the requirements of the second LEED-NC credit for the construction IAQ management plan before occupancy, see related Section 01 81 09 "Indoor Air Quality Testing."

3.3 COMMISSIONING

A. Commissioning: All building energy-related systems and building envelope components shall be commissioned in accordance with the requirements of Specification Section 01 91 00 "Commissioning Requirements" and related commissioning sections in other divisions in order to verify and ensure that fundamental building elements and systems are installed, constructed, calibrated to operate, and perform according to the Owner's Project Requirements, Basis of Design, and Construction Documents.

3.4 MEASUREMENT & VERIFICATION

A. For new construction, comply with the requirements of the International Performance Measurement & Verification Protocol (IPMVP), Volume III: Concepts and Options for Determining Energy Savings in New Construction, April 2003, Option B or D.

B. For existing buildings, comply with the requirements of the International Performance Measurement & Verification Protocol (IPMVP), Volume I: Concepts and Options for Determining Energy and Water Savings, 2001, Option B or D.

SECTION 01 91 00 – GENERAL COMMISSIONING REQUIREMENTS

*Guidance for designers and specifiers, with suggested language
to be modified and incorporated into project specifications.*

PART 1 - GENERAL

1.1 RELATED DOCUMENTS

A. Drawings and general provisions of the Contract, including General and Supplementary Conditions and other Division 1 Specification Sections, apply to this Section.

B. Section 22 08 00 – Commissioning of Plumbing

C. Section 23 08 00 – Commissioning of HVAC

D. Section 26 08 00 – Commissioning of Electrical Systems

1.2 SUMMARY

A. This section includes:

1. Commissioning: Commissioning is a systematic process of ensuring that all building systems perform interactively according to the design intent and the Owner's operational needs. This is achieved by beginning in the design phase and documenting design intent and continuing through construction, acceptance, and the warranty period with actual verification of performance. The commissioning process shall encompass and coordinate the traditionally separate functions of system documentation, equipment startup, control system calibration, testing and balancing, performance testing and training.

2. Commissioning during the construction phase is intended to achieve the following specific objectives according to the Contract Documents:

    a. Verify that applicable equipment and systems are installed according to the manufacturer's recommendations and to industry accepted minimum standards and that they receive adequate operational checkout by installing contractors.

    b. Verify and document proper performance of equipment and systems.

    c. Verify that O&M documentation left on site is complete.

    d. Verify that the Owner's operating personnel are adequately trained.

This section addresses those commissioning activities that involve the Contractor and are completed during and after the construction phase. The commissioning process should also involve activities that are beyond the scope of this specification document.

This specification includes requirements that should be sufficient to meet the LEED-NC and LEED-EB commissioning prerequisites. The LEED-NC credit 3 for "Enhanced Commissioning" includes additional requirements, notably design-phase commissioning, that exceed the scope of this specification.

3. The commissioning process does not take away from or reduce the responsibility of the Contractor to meet the Contract Documents.

B. Related Sections include the following:

1. Contract drawings and specifications, general provisions of the contract, including general and supplementary conditions, architectural, electrical, and mechanical provisions, and Division 1 Specification Sections apply to work of this Section.

1.3 ABBREVIATIONS

A. Abbreviations: The following are common abbreviations used in this *Specification* and in the *Commissioning Plan*.

A/E	Architect and design engineers	GC	General Contractor
CA	Commissioning authority	IC	Installing Contractor
CC	Construction checklist	MC	Mechanical Contractor
CT	Commissioning Team	RTF	Resolution Tracking Form
Cx	Commissioning	Subs	Subs to Prime Contractors
Cx Plan	Commissioning Plan document	TAB	Test and balance Contractor (If independent)
EC	Electrical Contractor	TCC	Temperature Controls Contractor
FT	Functional performance test		

1.4 COORDINATION

A. Commissioning Team: The members of the commissioning team consist of the CA, the GC, the Architect and Design Engineers (particularly the Mechanical Engineer), the MC, the EC, the TAB representative, the TCC, and any other installing subs or suppliers of equipment. If known, the Owner's building or plant operator/engineer is also a member of the commissioning team.

B. Management: The CA directs and coordinates the commissioning activities and reports to the Owner. All members work together to fulfill their contracted responsibilities and meet the objectives of the Contract Documents. The CA's responsibilities are the same regardless of who hired the CA.

C. Scheduling: The CA will work with the GC according to established protocols to schedule the commissioning activities. The CA will provide sufficient notice (generally two weeks' notice) to the GC for scheduling commissioning activities. The GC will integrate all commissioning activities into the master schedule. All parties will address scheduling problems and make necessary notifications in a timely manner in order to expedite the commissioning process.

D. The CA will provide the initial schedule of primary commissioning events, or commissioning milestones, at the initial commissioning meeting. The Commissioning Plan provides a format for this schedule. As construction progresses and more detailed schedules are available from the GC, the CA will adjust the commissioning schedule accordingly.

1.5 COMMISSIONING PROCESS

A. Commissioning Plan: The Commissioning Plan, provided as part of the bid documents, is binding on the Contractor. The commissioning plan provides guidance in the execution of the commissioning process. The Specifications will take precedence over the Commissioning Plan.

B. Commissioning Process: The following narrative provides a brief overview of the typical commissioning tasks during construction and the general order in which they occur.

1. Commissioning during construction begins with an initial Commissioning meeting conducted by the CA where the commissioning process is reviewed with the commissioning team members.

2. Additional meetings will be required throughout construction, scheduled by the CA with necessary parties attending, to plan, coordinate, schedule future activities and resolve problems.

3. Equipment documentation is distributed by the A/E to the CA during the normal submittal process, including detailed start-up procedures.

4. The CA works with the Contractor in each discipline in developing startup plans and startup documentation formats, including providing the Contractor with construction checklists to be completed during the installation and startup process.

5. In general, the checkout and performance verification proceeds from simple to complex; from component level to equipment to systems and intersystem levels with construction checklists being completed before functional testing occurs.

6. The Contractors, under their own direction, will execute and document the completion of construction checklists and perform startup and initial checkout. The CA documents that the checklists and startup were completed according to the approved plans. This may include the CA witnessing start-up of selected equipment.

7. The CA develops specific equipment and system functional performance test procedures.

8. The functional test procedures are reviewed with the A/E, CA, and Contractors.

9. The functional testing and procedures are executed by the Contractors under the direction of, and documented by, the CA.

10. During initial functional tests and for critical equipment, the Engineer will witness the testing.

11. Items of non-compliance in material, installation, or setup are corrected at the Contractor's expense, and the system is retested.

12. The CA reviews the O&M documentation for completeness.

13. The project will not be considered substantially complete until the conclusion of Commissioning functional testing procedures as defined in the Commissioning Plan.

14. The CA reviews and coordinates the training provided by the Contractors and verifies that it was completed.

15. Deferred testing is conducted as specified or required.

1.6 RESPONSIBILITIES

A. The responsibilities of various parties in the commissioning process are provided in this section. The responsibilities of the MC, TAB and TCC are in Divisions 22 and 23, those of the EC in Division 26, and those of the GC related to the building envelope and LEED-related credits and prerequisites in Division 1. It is noted that the services for the A/E and CA are not provided for in this Contract.

That is, the Contractor is not responsible for providing their services. Their responsibilities are listed in the Commissioning Plan.

B.　All Parties:

    1.　Follow the Commissioning Plan.

    2.　Attend an initial commissioning meeting and additional meetings, as necessary.

C.　General Contractor (GC)

    1.　Construction and Acceptance Phase:

       a.　Facilitate the coordination of the commissioning work by the CA, and with the GC and CA, ensure that commissioning activities are being scheduled into the master schedule.

       b.　Include the cost of commissioning in the total contract price.

       c.　Furnish a copy of all construction documents, addenda, change orders, and approved submittals and shop drawings related to commissioned equipment to the CA.

       d.　In each purchase order or subcontract written, include requirements for submittal data, O&M data, commissioning tasks, and training.

       e.　Ensure that all Contractors execute their commissioning responsibilities according to the Contract Documents and schedule.

       f.　A representative shall attend the initial commissioning meeting and other necessary meetings scheduled by the CA to facilitate the Cx process.

       g.　Coordinate and schedule the training of owner personnel.

          1)　Prepare O&M manuals, according to the Contract Documents, including clarifying and updating the original sequences of operation to as-built conditions.

       h.　Provide all requested submittal data, including detailed start-up procedures and specific responsibilities of the Owner to keep warranties in force.

       i.　Assist in equipment testing per agreements with sub-contractors.

       j.　Include all special tools and instruments (only available from vendor, specific to a piece of equipment) required for testing equipment according to these Contract Documents in the base bid price to the Contractor, except for stand-alone data logging equipment that may be used by the CA.

       k.　Through the Contractors they supply products to, analyze specified products and verify that the Designer has specified the newest most updated equipment reasonable for this project's scope and budget.

       l.　Provide information requested by CA regarding equipment sequence of operation and testing procedures.

          1)　Review test procedures for equipment installed by factory representatives.

    2.　Warranty Period:

       a.　Ensure that Subcontractors execute seasonal or deferred functional performance testing, witnessed by the CA, according to the specifications.

D.　Ensure that Subcontractors correct deficiencies and make necessary adjustments to O&M manuals and as-built drawings for applicable issues identified in any seasonal testing.

1.7   DEFINITIONS

A.   Acceptance Phase: Phase of construction after startup and initial checkout when functional performance tests, O&M documentation review, and training occur

B.   Approval: Acceptance that a piece of equipment or system has been properly installed and is functioning in the tested modes according to the Contract Documents

C.   Architect / Engineer (A/E): The prime consultants who comprise the design team, generally the HVAC mechanical designer/engineer and the electrical designer/engineer

D.   Owner's Project Requirements: The Owner's Project Requirements is the documentation of the primary thought processes and assumptions behind design decisions that were made to meet the design intent. The Owner's Project Requirements describes the systems, components, conditions, and methods chosen to meet the intent. Some reiterating of the design intent may be included.

E.   Commissioning Authority (CA): An independent authority, not otherwise associated with the A/E team members or the Contractor, though he/she may be hired as a subcontractor to them. The CA directs and coordinates the day-to-day commissioning activities. The CA does not take an oversight role.

> **This definition meets LEED EA prerequisite 1, but is slightly less stringent than LEED EA Credit 3, which requires that the individual serving as the Commissioning Authority is neither an employee of, nor contracted through, a Contractor or Construction Manager holding construction contracts.**

F.   Commissioning Plan: An overall plan, developed before or after bidding that provides the structure, schedule, and coordination planning for the commissioning process

G.   Construction Checklist (CC): A list of items to inspect and elementary component tests to conduct to verify proper installation of equipment, provided by the CA to the Sub. Construction checklists are primarily static inspections and procedures to prepare the equipment or system for initial operation (e.g., belt tension correct, oil levels OK, labels affixed, gages in place, sensors calibrated, etc.). However, some construction checklist items entail simple testing of the function of a component, a piece of equipment, or system (such as measuring the voltage imbalance on a three phase pump motor of a chiller system). The word construction refers to before functional testing. Construction checklists augment and are combined with the manufacturer's start-up checklist. Even without a commissioning process, Contractors typically perform some, if not many, of the construction checklist items a commissioning authority will recommend. However, few Contractors document in writing the execution of these checklist items. Therefore, for most equipment, the Contractors execute the checklists on their own. The Commissioning Authority only requires that the procedures be documented in writing and does not witness much of the completion of construction checklists, except for larger or more critical pieces of equipment.

H.   Contract Documents: The documents binding on parties involved in the construction of this Project (drawings, specifications, change orders, amendments, contracts, Cx Plan, etc.)

I.   Contractor: The general contractor or authorized representative

1.   Control system: The central building energy management control system

J.   Data Logging: Monitoring flows, currents, status, pressures, etc. of equipment using stand-alone data loggers separate from the control system

K.   Deferred Functional Tests: FTs that are performed later, after substantial completion, due to partial occupancy, equipment, seasonal requirements, design, or other site conditions that prevent the test from being performed

L. Deficiency: A condition in the installation or function of a component, piece of equipment or system that is not in compliance with the Contract Documents

M. Design Intent: A dynamic document that provides the explanation of the ideas, concepts, and criteria that are considered to be very important to the owner. It is initially the outcome of the programming and conceptual design phases.

N. Factory Testing: Testing of equipment on-site or at the factory by factory personnel with a Project Manager present

O. Functional Performance Test (FT): Test of the dynamic function and operation of equipment and systems using manual (direct observation) or monitoring methods. Functional testing is the dynamic testing of systems (rather than just components) under full operation (e.g., the chiller pump is tested interactively with the chiller functions to see if the pump ramps up and down to maintain the differential pressure setpoint). Systems are tested under various modes, such as during low cooling or heating loads, high loads, component failures, unoccupied, varying outside air temperatures, fire alarm, power failure, etc. The systems are run through all the control system's sequences of operation, and components are verified to be responding as the sequences state. Traditional air or water test and balancing (TAB) is not functional testing, in the commissioning sense of the word. TAB's primary work is setting up the system flows and pressures as specified, while functional testing is verifying that which has already been set up. The Commissioning Authority develops the functional test procedures in a sequential written form, coordinates, oversees, and documents the actual testing, which is usually performed by the installing Contractor or vendor. FTs are performed after construction checklists and startup are complete.

P. General Contractor (GC): The Contractor for this project. Generally refers to all the GC's subs as well. Also referred to as the Contractor, in some contexts.

Q. Indirect Indicators: Indicators of a response or condition, such as a reading from a control system screen reporting a damper to be 100% closed

R. Installing Contractor: Contractor who installs specific equipment and/or systems

S. Manual Test: Using hand-held instruments, immediate control system readouts, or direct observation to verify performance (contrasted to analyzing monitored data taken over time to make the "observation")

T. Monitoring: The recording of parameters (flow, current, status, pressure, etc.) of equipment operation using data loggers or the trending capabilities of control systems

U. Non-Compliance: See Deficiency

V. Non-Conformance: See Deficiency

W. Over-written Value: Writing over a sensor value in the control system to see the response of a system (e.g., changing the outside air temperature value from 50°F to 75°F to verify economizer operation). See also "Simulated Signal."

X. Owner-Contracted Tests: Tests paid for by the Owner outside the GC's contract and for which the CA does not oversee. These tests will not be repeated during functional tests if properly documented.

Y. Phased Commissioning: Commissioning that is completed in phases (by floors, for example) due to the size of the structure or other scheduling issues, in order minimize the total construction time

Z. Sampling: Functionally testing only a fraction of the total number of identical or near-identical pieces of equipment. Refer to Part 3.4 F for details.

AA. Seasonal Performance Tests: FTs that are deferred until the system(s) will experience conditions closer to their design conditions

BB. Simulated Condition: Condition that is created for the purpose of testing the response of a system (e.g., applying a hair blower to a space sensor to see the response in a VAV box)

CC. Simulated Signal: Disconnecting a sensor and using a signal generator to send an amperage, resistance, or pressure to the transducer and DDC system to simulate a sensor value

DD. Specifications: The construction specifications of the Contract Documents

EE. Startup: The initial starting or activating of dynamic equipment, including executing construction checklists

FF. Subs: The subcontractors to the Prime Contractor who provide and install building components and systems

GG. Test Procedures: The step-by-step process that must be executed to fulfill the test requirements. The CA develops the test procedures.

HH. Test Requirements: Requirements specifying what modes and functions, etc. shall be tested. The test requirements are not the detailed test procedures. The test requirements for each system are specified in the respective section of the Contract Documents.

II. Trending: Monitoring using the building control system

JJ. Vendor: Supplier of equipment

KK. Warranty Period: Warranty period for entire project, including equipment components. Warranty begins at Substantial Completion and extends for at least one year, unless specifically noted otherwise in the Contract Documents and accepted submittals.

1.8 SYSTEMS TO BE COMMISSIONED

A. The following checked systems are to be commissioned.

HVAC Equipment and System

(_) Variable Speed Drives
(_) Hydronic Piping systems
(_) HVAC Pumps
(_) Boilers
(_) Chemical Treatment System
(_) Air Cooled Condensing Units
(_) Makeup Air Systems
(_) Air Handling Units
(_) Underfloor Air Distribution
(_) Centrifugal Fans
(_) Ductwork
(_) Fire/Smoke Dampers
(_) Automatic Temperature Controls – Including an intentional sequence of operation
(_) Laboratory Fume Hoods
(_) Testing, Adjusting, and Balancing
(_) Building / Space Pressurization
(_) Ceiling Radiant Heating
(_) Underfloor Radiant Heating

Electrical Equipment and System

(_) Power Distribution System
(_) Lighting Control Systems
(_) Lighting Control Programs
(_) Engine Generators
(_) Transfer Switches
(_) Switchboard
(_) Panelboards
(_) Grounding
(_) Fire Alarm and Interface Items with HVAC
(_) Security System

Plumbing System

(_) Domestic Water Heater
(_) Air Compressor & Dryer
(_) Storm Water Oil / Grit Separators

Building Envelope

(_) Building Insulation Installation
(_) Building Roof Installation Methods
(_) Doors & Windows Installation Methods
(_) Water Infiltration / Shell Drainage Plain

Commissioning needs may differ by project; however, commissioning the building envelope systems, domestic water heating, power distribution, ductwork, and any hydronic piping systems is strongly recommended for any project.

To meet the LEED EA prerequisite 1 or the LEED-NC credit 3, commissioning must be completed, at a minimum, for: 1. HVAC&R systems; 2. Lighting and daylighting controls; 3. Domestic hot water systems; 4. Renewable energy systems. Commissioning of water-using systems, building envelope systems, and others is recommended but not required.

PART 2 - PRODUCTS

2.1 TEST EQUIPMENT

A. All standard testing equipment required to perform startup and initial checkout and required functional performance testing shall be provided by the ICI for the equipment being tested. For example, the MC of Division 23 shall ultimately be responsible for all standard testing equipment for the HVAC system and controls system in Division 23, except for equipment specific to and used by TAB in their commissioning responsibilities. The Installing Contractor shall provide two-way radios.

B. Special equipment, tools and instruments (only available from vendor, specific to a piece of equipment) required for testing equipment, according to these Contract Documents, shall be included in the base bid price to the Contractor and left on site, except for stand-alone data logging equipment that may be used by the CA.

C. Temporary Data logging equipment and software required to test equipment will be provided by the CA but shall not become the property of the Owner.

D. All testing equipment shall be of sufficient quality and accuracy to test and/or measure system performance with the tolerances specified in the Specifications. If not otherwise noted, the following minimum requirements apply: Temperature sensors and digital thermometers shall have a certified calibration within the past year to an accuracy of 0.5°F and a resolution of + or - 0.1°F. Pressure sensors shall have an accuracy of + or - 2.0% of the value range being measured (not full range of meter) and have been calibrated within the last year. All equipment shall be calibrated according to the manufacturer's recommended intervals and when dropped or damaged. Calibration tags shall be affixed or certificates readily available.

E. Refer to Part 3 for details regarding equipment that may be required to simulate required test conditions.

PART 3 - EXECUTION

3.1 MEETINGS

A. Commissioning Meeting: Within 60 days of commencement of construction, the CA will schedule, plan and conduct a commissioning meeting with the entire commissioning team in attendance. Meeting minutes will be distributed to all parties by the CA. Information gathered from this meeting will allow the CA to revise the Commissioning Plan, which will be distributed to all parties.

B. Miscellaneous Meetings: Other meetings will be planned and conducted by the CA as construction progresses. These meetings will cover coordination, deficiency resolution and planning issues with particular contractors. The CA will plan these meetings and will minimize unnecessary time being spent by contractors. For large projects, these meetings may be held monthly, until the final 3 months of construction when they may be held as frequently as one per week.

3.2 STARTUP, CONSTRUCTION CHECKLISTS, AND INITIAL CHECKOUT

A. The following procedures apply to all equipment to be commissioned. Some systems that are not comprised so much of actual dynamic machinery, e.g., electrical system power quality, may have very simplified CCs and startup.

B. General: Construction checklists are important to ensure that the equipment and systems are hooked up correctly and operational. Checklists also ensure that functional performance testing (in-depth system checkout) may proceed without unnecessary delays. Each piece of equipment receives full construction checkout. No sampling strategies are used. The construction testing for a given system must be successfully completed prior to formal functional performance testing of equipment or subsystems of the given system.

C. Startup and Initial Checkout Plan: The CA will assist the commissioning team members responsible for startup of any equipment in developing detailed startup plans for all equipment. The primary role of the CA in this process is to ensure that there is written documentation that each of the manufacturer-recommended procedures has been completed. Parties responsible for construction checklists and startup are identified in the initial commissioning meeting and in the checklist forms.

1. The CA adapts, if necessary, the representative construction checklists and procedures from the related sections. These checklists indicate required procedures to be executed as part of startup and initial checkout of the systems and the party responsible for their execution.

2. The CA provides these checklists and tests to the Contractor. The Contractor determines which trade is responsible for executing and documenting each of the line item tasks and notes that trade on the form. Each form will have more than one trade responsible for its execution.

3. The Contractor responsible for the purchase of the equipment develops the full startup plan by combining (or adding to) the CA's checklists with the manufacturer's detailed startup and checkout procedures from the O&M manual and the normally used field checkout sheets. The plan will include checklists and procedures with specific boxes or lines for recording and documenting the checking and inspections of each procedure and a summary statement with a signature block at the end of the plan.

    a. The full startup plan could consist of something as simple as:

        1) The CA's construction checklists
        2) The manufacturer's standard written startup procedures copied from the installation manuals with check boxes by each procedure and a signature block added by hand at the end
        3) The manufacturer's normally used field checkout sheets

4. The contractor submits the full startup plan to the CA for review and approval.

5. The CA reviews and approves the procedures and the format for documenting them, noting any procedures that need to be added.

D. Sensor and Actuator Calibration

1. All field-installed temperature, relative humidity, CO, CO_2 and pressure sensors and gages, and all actuators (dampers and valves) on all equipment shall be calibrated using the methods described below. Alternate methods may be used if approved by the CA beforehand. All test instruments shall have had a certified calibration within the last 12 months. Sensors installed in the unit at the factory with calibration certification provided need not be field-calibrated.

2. All procedures used shall be fully documented on the construction checklists or other approved forms, clearly referencing the procedures followed and written documentation of initial, intermediate, and final results.

3. Sensor Calibration Methods

    a. All Sensors: Verify that all sensor locations are appropriate and away from causes of erratic operation. Verify that sensors with shielded cable are grounded only at one end. For sensor pairs that are used to determine a temperature or pressure difference, make sure they are reading within 0.2°F of each other for temperature and within a tolerance equal to 2% of the reading of each other for pressure. Tolerances for critical applications may be tighter.

    b. Sensors Without Transmitters--Standard Application: Make a reading with a calibrated test instrument within 6 inches of the site sensor. Verify that the sensor reading (via the permanent thermostat, gage, or building automation system (BAS)) is within the tolerances in the table below of the instrument-measured value. If not, install offset in BAS, calibrate or replace sensor.

    c. Sensors With Transmitters--Standard Application: Disconnect sensor. Connect a signal generator in place of sensor. Connect ammeter in series between transmitter and BAS control panel. Using manufacturer's resistance-temperature data, simulate minimum desired temperature. Adjust transmitter potentiometer zero until the ammeter reads 4 mA. Repeat for the maximum temperature matching 20 mA to the potentiometer span or maximum and verify at the BAS. Record all values and recalibrate controller as necessary to conform to specified control ramps, reset schedules, proportional relationship, reset relationship, and P/I reaction. Reconnect sensor. Make a reading with a calibrated test instrument within 6 inches of the site sensor. Verify that the sensor reading (via the permanent thermostat, gage, or building automation system [BAS]) is within the tolerances in the table below of the instrument-measured value. If not, replace sensor and repeat. For pressure sensors, perform a similar process with a suitable signal generator.

    d. Critical Applications: For critical applications (process, manufacturing, etc.) more rigorous calibration techniques may be required for selected sensors. Describe any such methods used on an attached sheet.

4. Tolerances, Standard Applications

Sensor	Required Tolerance (+/-)	Sensor	Required Tolerance (+/-)
Cooling coil, chilled and condenser water temps	0.4°F	Flow rates, water Relative humidity	4% of design 4% of design
AHU wet bulb or dew point	2.0°F	Combustion flue temps	5.0°F
Hot water coil and boiler water temp	1.5°F	Oxygen or CO_2 monitor	0.1 % pts
Outside air, space air, duct air temps	0.4°F	CO monitor	0.01 % pts
Watthour, voltage and amperage	1% of design	Natural gas and oil flow rate	1% of design
Pressures, air, water and gas	3% of design	Steam flow rate	3% of design
Flow rates, air	10% of design	Barometric pressure	0.1 in. of Hg

5. Valve and Damper Stroke Setup and Check

   a. EMS Readout: For all valve and damper actuator positions checked, verify the actual position against the BAS readout.

   b. Set pumps or fans to normal operating mode. Command valve or damper closed, visually verify that valve or damper is closed and adjust output zero signal as required. Command valve or damper open, verify position is full open and adjust output signal as required. Command valve or damper to a few intermediate positions. If actual valve or damper position doesn't reasonably correspond, replace actuator or add pilot position indicator (for pneumatics).

   c. Closure for heating coil valves (NO): Set heating setpoint 20°F above room temperature. Observe valve open. Remove control air or power from the valve and verify that the valve stem and actuator position do not change. Restore to normal. Set heating setpoint to 20°F below room temperature. Observe the valve close. For pneumatics, by override in the EMS, increase pressure to valve by 3 psi (do not exceed actuator pressure rating) and verify valve stem and actuator position does not change. Restore to normal.

   d. Closure for cooling coil valves (NC): Set cooling setpoint 20°F above room temperature. Observe the valve close. Remove control air or power from the valve and verify that the valve stem and actuator position do not change. Restore to normal. Set cooling setpoint to 20°F below room temperature. Observe valve open. For pneumatics, by override in the EMS, increase pressure to valve by 3 psi (do not exceed actuator pressure rating) and verify valve stem and actuator position does not change. Restore to normal.

E. Execution of Construction Checklists and Startup

   1. Four weeks prior to startup, the contractors and vendors schedule startup and checkout with the GC and CA. The performance of the construction checklists, startup and checkout are directed and executed by the contractor or vendor. When checking off construction checklists, signatures may be required of other contractors for verification of completion of their work.

   2. The CA will, at their own discretion, observe, at minimum, the procedures for each piece of primary equipment unless there are multiple units. In no case will the number of units witnessed be less than four on any one building, nor less than 20% of the total number of identical or very similar units.

   3. For lower-level components of equipment, (e.g., VAV boxes, sensors, controllers), the CA shall observe a sampling of the construction and startup procedures. The sampling procedures are identified in the Commissioning Plan.

   4. The contractors shall execute startup and provide the CA with a signed and dated copy of the completed startup and construction tests and checklists.

   5. Only installing individuals who have direct knowledge that a line item task on the construction checklist was actually performed shall initial or check off that item.

F. Deficiencies, Non-Conformance and Approval in Checklists and Startup

   1. The contractors shall clearly list any outstanding items of the initial startup and construction procedures that were not completed successfully, at the bottom of the procedures form or on an attached sheet. The procedures form and any outstanding deficiencies are provided to the CA within two days of test completion.

2. The CA reviews the report and submits either a non-compliance report or an approval form to the contractors. The CA shall work with the Prime contractors to correct and retest deficiencies or uncompleted items. The CA will involve the contractors and others as necessary. The installing contractors shall correct all areas that are deficient or incomplete in the checklists and tests in a timely manner, and shall notify the CA as soon as outstanding items have been corrected and resubmit an updated startup report and a Statement of Correction on the original non-compliance report. When satisfactorily completed, the CA recommends approval of the execution of the checklists and startup of each system to the A/E using a standard form.

3. Items left incomplete, which later cause deficiencies or delays during functional testing, may result in back charges to the responsible party.

3.3 PHASED COMMISSIONING

A. The project will require startup and initial checkout to be executed in phases. This phasing will be planned and scheduled in a coordination meeting of the CA, MC, TAB, TCC and the GC. Results will be added to the master and commissioning schedule.

3.4 FUNCTIONAL PERFORMANCE TESTING

A. This subsection applies to all commissioning functional testing for all divisions.

B. The general list of equipment to be commissioned is found in this Section. The specific equipment and modes to be tested for each system are found in the respective sections.

C. The parties responsible to execute each test are listed with each test in the respective sections.

D. Objectives and Scope: The objective of functional performance testing is to demonstrate that each system is operating according to the Contract Documents. Functional testing facilitates bringing the systems from a state of substantial completion to full dynamic operation. Additionally, during the testing process, areas of deficient performance are identified and corrected, improving the operation and functioning of the systems.

1. In general, each system should be operated through all modes of operation (seasonal, occupied, unoccupied, warm-up, cool-down, part- and full-load) where there is a specified system response. Verifying each sequence in the sequences of operation is required. Proper responses to such modes and conditions as power failure, freeze condition, low oil pressure, no flow, equipment failure, etc. shall also be tested. Specific modes required in this project are given in Divisions 22, 23, and 26, and other parts of the specification.

E. Development of Test Procedures: Before test procedures are written, the CA shall obtain all requested documentation and a current list of change orders affecting equipment or systems, including an updated points list, program code, control sequences and parameters. Using the testing parameters and requirements in Divisions 22, 23, 26, and elsewhere, the CA shall develop specific test procedures and forms to verify and document proper operation of each piece of equipment and system. Each contractor or vendor responsible to execute a test shall provide limited assistance to the CA in developing the procedures review (answering questions about equipment, operation, sequences, etc.). Prior to execution, the CA shall provide a copy of the test procedures to the contractors, who shall review the tests for feasibility, safety, equipment, and warranty protection.

1. The CA shall review Owner-contracted factory testing or required Owner acceptance tests which the CA is not responsible to oversee, including documentation format, and shall determine what further testing or format changes may be required to comply with the Specifications. Redundancy of testing shall be minimized.

2. The purpose of any given specific test is to verify and document compliance with the stated criteria of acceptance given on the test form.

3. Representative test formats and examples (not designed for this facility) are found in the appendices to Divisions 22, 23, and 26. The test procedure forms developed by the CA shall include (but not be limited to) the following information:

   a. System and equipment or component name(s)

   b. Equipment location and ID number

   c. Unique test ID number, and reference to unique construction checklist and start-up documentation ID numbers for the piece of equipment

   d. Date

   e. Project name

   f. Participating parties

   g. A copy of the specification section describing the test requirements

   h. A copy of the specific sequence of operations or other specified parameters being verified

   i. Formulas used in any calculations

   j. Required pre-test field measurements

   k. Instructions for setting up the test

   l. Special cautions, alarm limits, etc.

   m. Specific step-by-step procedures to execute the test, in a clear, sequential, and repeatable format

   n. Acceptance criteria of proper performance with a Yes / No checkbox to allow for clearly marking whether or not proper performance of each part of the test was achieved

   o. A section for comments

   p. Signatures and date block for the CA

F. Test Methods

1. Functional performance testing and verification may be achieved by manual testing (persons manipulate the equipment and observe performance) or by monitoring the performance and analyzing the results using the control system's trend log capabilities or by stand-alone data loggers. Division 23 Sections and other Sections specify which methods shall be used for each test. The CA may substitute specified methods or require an additional method to be executed other than what was specified. The CA will determine which method is most appropriate for tests that do not have a method specified.

2. Simulated Conditions: Simulating conditions (not by an overwritten value) shall be allowed, though timing the testing to experience actual conditions is encouraged wherever practical.

3. Overwritten Values: Overwriting sensor values to simulate a condition, such as overwriting the outside air temperature reading in a control system to be something other than it really is, shall be allowed, but shall be used with caution and avoided when possible. Such testing methods often can only test a part of a system, as the interactions and responses of other systems will be erroneous or not applicable. Simulating a condition is preferable, e.g., for the above case, by heating the outside air sensor with a hair dryer rather than overwriting the value or by altering the appropriate setpoint to see the desired response. Before simulating conditions or overwriting values, sensors, transducers, and devices shall have been calibrated.

4. Simulated Signals: Using a signal generator which creates a simulated signal to test and calibrate transducers and DDC constants is generally recommended over using the sensor to act as the signal generator via simulated conditions or overwritten values.

5. Altering Setpoints: Rather than overwriting sensor values, and when simulating conditions is difficult, altering setpoints to test a sequence is acceptable. For example, to see the AC compressor lockout work at an outside air temperature below 55°F, when the outside air temperature is above 55°F, temporarily change the lockout setpoint to be 2°F above the current outside air temperature.

6. Indirect Indicators: Relying on indirect indicators for responses or performance shall be allowed only after visually and directly verifying and documenting, over the range of the tested parameters, that the indirect readings through the control system represent actual conditions and responses. Much of this verification is completed during construction testing.

7. Setup: Each function and test shall be performed under conditions that simulate actual conditions as close as is practically possible. The contractor executing the test shall provide all necessary materials, system modifications, etc. to produce the necessary flows, pressures, temperatures, etc. necessary to execute the test according to the specified conditions. At completion of the test, the contractor shall return all affected building equipment and systems, due to these temporary modifications, to their pre-test condition.

8. Sampling: Multiple identical pieces of non-life-safety or otherwise non-critical equipment may be functionally tested using a sampling strategy. Significant application differences and significant sequence of operation differences in otherwise identical equipment invalidates their common identity. A small size or capacity difference, alone, does not constitute a difference. The specific recommended sampling rates are specified with each type of equipment in Divisions 22, 23, and 26. It is noted that no sampling by contractors is allowed in construction checklist execution.

   a. A common sampling strategy referenced in the Specifications as the "xx% Sampling—yy% Failure Rule" is defined by the following example.

      1) xx = the percent of the group of identical equipment to be included in each sample
      2) yy = the percent of the sample that if failing, will require another sample to be tested

   b. The example below describes a 20% Sampling—10% Failure Rule.

      1) Randomly test at least 20% (xx) of each group of identical equipment. In no case test less than three units in each group. This 20%, or three, constitute the "first sample."
      2) If 10% (yy) of the units in the first sample fail the functional performance tests, test another 20% of the group (the second sample).
      3) If 10% of the units in the second sample fail, test all remaining units in the whole group.
      4) If at any point, frequent failures are occurring and testing is becoming more troubleshooting than verification, the CA may stop the testing and require the contractor to perform and document a checkout of the remaining units, prior to continuing with functionally testing the remaining units.

G. Coordination and Scheduling: The contractors shall provide sufficient notice to the CA regarding their completion schedule for the construction checklists and startup of all equipment and systems. The CA will schedule functional tests through the A/E, GC and other contractors. The CA shall direct, witness and document the functional testing of all equipment and systems. The contractors shall execute the tests.

　　1. In general, functional testing is conducted after construction testing and startup has been satisfactorily completed. The control system is sufficiently tested and approved by the CA before it is used for TAB or to verify performance of other components or systems. The air balancing and water balancing is completed and debugged before functional testing of air-related or water-related equipment or systems. Testing proceeds from components to subsystems to systems. When the proper performance of all interacting individual systems has been achieved, the interface or coordinated responses between systems is checked.

H. Problem Solving: The CA will recommend solutions to problems found; however, the burden of responsibility to solve, correct, and retest problems is with the GC, contractors, and A/E.

> **The requirements of this section meet LEED-NC EA prerequisite 1 requirements for both System Performance Testing (or Functional Performance Testing) and Installation Inspections.**

3.5   DOCUMENTATION, NON-CONFORMANCE AND APPROVAL OF TESTS

A. Documentation: The CA shall witness and document the results of all functional performance tests using the specific procedural forms developed for that purpose. Prior to testing, these forms are provided to the contractors for review. The CA will include the filled-out forms in the O&M manuals.

B. Non-Conformance

　　1. The CA will record the results of the functional test on the procedure or test form. All deficiencies or non-conformance issues shall be noted and reported to the A/E on a standard non-compliance form.

　　2. Corrections of minor deficiencies identified may be made during the tests at the discretion of the CA. In such cases the deficiency and resolution will be documented on the procedure form.

　　3. Every effort will be made to expedite the testing process and minimize unnecessary delays, while not compromising the integrity of the procedures. However, the CA will not be pressured into overlooking deficient work or loosening acceptance criteria to satisfy scheduling or cost issues, unless there is an overriding reason to do so at the request of the Owner.

　　4. As tests progress and a deficiency is identified, the CA discusses the issue with the executing contractor.

　　　　a. When there is no dispute on the deficiency and the contractor accepts responsibility to correct it:

　　　　　　1) The CA documents the deficiency and the Prime contractor's response and intentions, and they go on to another test or sequence. After the day's work, the CA submits the non-compliance reports to the A/E for signature, if required. A copy is provided to the contractor and CA. The contractor corrects the deficiency, signs the statement of correction at the bottom of the non-compliance form certifying that the equipment is ready to be retested, and sends it back to the CA.

2) The contractor reschedules the test and coordinates with CA to establish a time and date that the test is to be repeated.

b. If there is a dispute about a deficiency, regarding whether it is a deficiency or who is responsible:

1) The deficiency shall be documented on the non-compliance form with the contractor's response and a copy given to the A/E and to the contractor representative assumed to be responsible.

2) Resolutions are made at the lowest management level possible. Other parties are brought into the discussions as needed. Final interpretive authority is with the A/E. Final acceptance authority is with the A/E.

3) The CA documents the resolution process.

4) Once the interpretation and resolution have been decided, the appropriate party corrects the deficiency, signs the statement of correction on the non-compliance form and provides it to the CA. The contractor reschedules the test and notifies the CA of the date and time the test is to be repeated. This will occur until satisfactory performance is achieved.

5. Cost of Retesting

a. The cost for the contractor to retest a construction or functional test, if they are responsible for the deficiency, shall be theirs. If they are not responsible, any cost recovery for retesting costs shall be negotiated with the responsible parties.

b. For a deficiency identified, not related to any construction checklist or startup fault, the following shall apply: The CA will direct the retesting of the equipment once at no "charge" to the contractor for their time. However, the CA's time for a second retest will be charged to the contractor, who may choose to recover costs from the responsible Sub.

c. The time for the CA to direct any retesting required because a specific construction checklist or start-up test item, reported to have been successfully completed, but determined during functional testing to be faulty, will be back charged to the contractor, who may choose to recover costs from the party responsible for executing the faulty construction test.

d. Refer to the sampling section of Section 01810, for requirements for testing and retesting identical equipment.

6. The contractor shall respond in writing to the CA at least as often as commissioning meetings are being scheduled concerning the status of each apparent outstanding discrepancy identified during commissioning. Discussion shall cover explanations of any disagreements and proposals for their resolution.

7. The CA retains the original non-conformance forms until the end of the project.

8. Any required retesting by any contractor shall not be considered a justified reason for a claim of delay or for a time extension by the contractor.

C. Failure Due to Manufacturer Defect: If 10%, or three, whichever is greater, of identical pieces (size alone does not constitute a difference) of equipment fail to perform to the Contract Documents (mechanically or substantively) due to manufacturing defect, not allowing it to meet its submitted performance spec, all identical units may be considered unacceptable by the Owner. In such case, the contractor shall provide the Owner with the following:

1. Within one week of notification from the A/E, the contractor shall examine all other identical units making a record of the findings. The findings shall be provided to the A/E within two weeks of the original notice.

2. Within two weeks of the original notification, the contractor shall provide a signed and dated, written explanation of the problem, cause of failures, etc. and all proposed solutions, which shall include full equipment submittals. The proposed solutions shall not significantly exceed the specification requirements of the original installation.

3. The A/E will determine whether a replacement of all identical units or a repair is acceptable.

4. Two examples of the proposed solution will be installed by the contractor and the CA will be allowed to test the installations for up to one week, upon which the CA will decide whether to accept the solution.

5. Upon acceptance, the contractor and/or manufacturer shall replace or repair all identical items, at their expense and extend the warranty accordingly, if the original equipment warranty had begun. The replacement/repair work shall proceed with reasonable speed beginning within one week from when parts can be obtained.

D. Approval: The CA notes each satisfactorily demonstrated function on the test form. Formal approval of the functional test is made later after review by the CA. The CA recommends acceptance of each test to the Owner and A/E using a standard form. The A/E gives final approval on each test using the same form, providing a signed copy to the CA and the contractor.

3.6　OPERATION AND MAINTENANCE MANUALS

A. Standard O&M Manuals.

1. Special requirements for the TCC and TAB contractor are found in Sections 22 08 00 and 23 08 00.

This document requires that the CA review O&M manuals, whereas the LEED-NC credit 3 requires that the CA and CT develop a Systems Manual in addition to the contractor's O&M Manuals. The LEED-NC prerequisite 1 does not have this requirement.

3.7　TRAINING OF OWNER PERSONNEL

A. The GC shall be responsible for training coordination and scheduling and ultimately for ensuring that training is completed.

B. The CA shall be responsible for overseeing and approving the content and adequacy of the training of Owner personnel for commissioned equipment.

1. The CA shall interview the facility manager and lead engineer to determine the special needs and areas where training will be most valuable. The Owner and CA shall decide how rigorous the training should be for each piece of commissioned equipment. The CA shall communicate the results to the contractor and vendors who have training responsibilities.

2. In addition to these general requirements, the specific training requirements of Owner personnel by contractor and vendors is specified in Divisions 22, 23, and 26.

3. Each contractor and vendor responsible for training will submit a written training plan to the CA for review and approval prior to training. The plan will cover the following elements:

a. Equipment (included in training)

b. Intended audience

c. Location of training

d. Objectives

e. Subjects covered (description, duration of discussion, special methods, etc.)

f. Duration of training on each subject

g. Instructor for each subject

h. Methods (classroom lecture, video, site walk-through, actual operational demonstrations, written handouts, etc.)

i. Instructor and qualifications

4. For the primary HVAC equipment, the TCC shall provide a short discussion of the control of the equipment during the mechanical or electrical training conducted by others.

5. The CA develops an overall training plan and coordinates and schedules, with the Owner and contractor, the overall training for the commissioned systems. The CA develops criteria for determining that the training was satisfactorily completed, including attending some of the training, etc. The CA recommends approval of the training to the A/E using a standard form. The A/E also signs the approval form.

6. At one of the training sessions, the CA presents a presentation discussing the use of the blank functional test forms for re-commissioning equipment.

7. The GC will provide videotaping of the training sessions, with tapes cataloged by the GC, and added to the O&M manuals.

8. The mechanical design engineer shall at the first training session present the overall system design concept and the design concept of each equipment section. This presentation shall include a review of all systems using the simplified system schematics (one-line drawings) including chilled water systems, heat rejection systems, heating systems, fuel oil and gas supply systems, supply air systems, exhaust system, and outside air strategies.

This requirement meets or exceeds requirements for the LEED-NC credit 3, which requires only that the CA verify that operational personnel training requirements were completed according to the Contract Documents, but does not outline the training required. The LEED-NC prerequisite 1 does not have this requirement.

3.8   DEFERRED TESTING

A. Unforeseen Deferred Tests: If any check or test cannot be completed due to the building structure, required occupancy condition, or other deficiency, execution of checklists and functional testing may be delayed upon approval of the A/E.

B. Architect: These tests will be conducted in the same manner as the seasonal tests as soon as possible. Services of necessary parties will be negotiated.

C. Seasonal Testing: During the warranty period, seasonal testing (tests delayed until weather conditions are closer to the system's design) specified in Division 23 shall be completed as part of this contract. The CA shall coordinate this activity. Tests will be executed and documented. and any deficiencies corrected by the appropriate contractor, with facilities staff and the CA witnessing. Any final adjustments to the O&M manuals and as-builds due to the testing will be made.

> **This requirement differs from, but could meet, the LEED-NC credit 3 requirements for delayed testing and post-occupancy review 8-10 months from completion. The LEED-NC prerequisite 1 does not have this requirement.**

3.9 WRITTEN WORK PRODUCTS

A. The commissioning process generates a number of written work products described in various parts of the Specifications. The Commissioning Plan lists all the formal written work products, describes briefly their contents, who is responsible to create them, their due dates, who receives and approves them, and the location of the specification to create them. In summary, the written products are:

Product	Developed By
Commissioning plan	CA
Commissioning meeting minutes	CA
Commissioning schedules	GC and CA with other contractors
Equipment documentation submittals	Contractors
Sequence clarifications	Contractors and A/E as needed
Construction checklists	CA (Preliminary in Spec. Revised based on Approved Submittals)
Startup and initial checkout plan	Contractors and CA (Compilation of existing documents)
Startup and initial checkout forms filled out	Contractors
Final TAB report	TAB
Issues log (deficiencies)	CA with responses provided by contractors
Commissioning Progress Record	CA
Deficiency reports	CA
Functional test forms	CA
Filled-out functional tests	CA
O&M manuals	Contractors with review by CA
Commissioning record books and CD's	CA
Overall training plan	CA, GC, and Contractors
Specific training agendas	Contractors
Final commissioning report	CA
Miscellaneous approvals	CA

01 00 00 General Requirements

PRODUCT LISTINGS

01 62 01
Distributors/Retailers, Green Building Materials

Certain green building materials can be found in most lumberyards and home centers; a few building supply centers in the U.S. specialize in green products. Among the broad selection of products offered by these companies are low-toxic paints and finishes, cabinets, flooring products, formaldehyde-free panels, and FSC-certified lumber. In most cases, online or print catalogs are available with listings of the products offered. In addition to sourcing products, these companies have knowledgeable sales experts. A few have buildings that serve as demonstrations of high-performance green building. (See feature article EBN Vol. 10, No. 4.)

Amicus Green Building Center

Amicus Green Building Center
4080A Howard Ave.
Kensington, MD 20895-2465 **New**

Phone: 301-571-8590
Fax: 301-571-8597
www.amicusgreen.com

The Amicus Green Building Center offers a wide range of environmentally responsible building and finishing materials, including paints, panel products, water conservation products, and flooring materials. Design support is also available through their sister company, Amicus Design and Build.

BC Energy

BC Energy
357 Warbler Pl.
Nanaimo, BC V9R 6Y8 Canada

Toll-free: 888-714-4545
Phone: 250-714-4545
www.bcenergy.net

BC Energy provides energy-efficient, environmentally preferable products for home builders, including ICFs, SIPs, engineered wood, HVAC, water heaters, windows, lighting, and finishes. In addition to selling products, the company offers design, certification, and supply of energy-optimized home packages.

Bettencourt Green Building Supplies

Bettencourt Green Building Supplies
70 N. 6th St.
Brooklyn, NY 11211

Toll-free: 800-883-7005
Phone: 718-218-6737
Fax: 866-848-0392
www.bettencourtwood.com

Bettencourt Green Building Supplies provides sheet goods such as Plyboo®, Kirei Board, Environ®, Dakota Burl™, Durapalm®, and FSC-certified hardwood plywood to designers, architects, contractors and homeowners on the East Coast. Bettencourt is based in Brooklyn, NY with an office outside Boston. In late 2005, the company planned to begin stocking eco-friendly and low-VOC finishes soon.

BigHorn Materials

BigHorn Materials
1221 Blue River Pkwy.
Silverthorne, CO 80498

Phone: 970-513-1575
Fax: 970-513-1555
www.bighornace.com

In business for 18 years and offering green building products for four years, BigHorn Materials supplies general building materials and hardware, sustainable forest products, CFLs, and set-back thermostats. The company caters mainly to contractors but serves the general public as well.

Most recently mentioned in EBN 10:3, 10:4, 10:5

Building For Health Materials Center

Building For Health Materials Center
102 Main St.
P.O. Box 113
Carbondale, CO 81623

Toll-free: 800-292-4838
Phone: 970-963-0437
Fax: 970-963-3318
www.buildingforhealth.com

The Building For Health Materials Center is a centrally located, nationwide supplier of healthy, environmentally conscious building products for consumers and contractors. The company states that each product is evaluated in relationship to environmental impact and human health effects. Catalogs are available upon request.

Most recently mentioned in EBN 10:4

ECO of NY

ECO of NY
901 E. 134th St.
Bronx, NY 10454

Toll-free: 800-238-5008
Phone: 718-292-0626
Fax: 718-742-5140
www.environmentaldepot.com

Environmental Construction Outfitters of NY offers a full line of environmental and hypoallergenic building products. They cater to the needs of the chemically sensitive. Home inspections and consultations on greening homes and workplaces are available.

Most recently mentioned in EBN 10:4

Green Building Finishing Materials

New

EcoHome Improvement
2619 San Pablo Ave.
Berkeley, CA 94702

Phone: 510-644-3500
www.ecohomeimprovement.com

Ecohome Improvement offers environmentally responsible finishing materials including flooring, cabinetry, countertops, tiles, paints, stains, and sealants. Ecohome Improvement also offers design services.

01 00 00
General Requirements

Eco-Products, Inc.

Eco-Products, Inc.
3655 Frontier Ave.
Boulder, CO 80304

Phone: 303-449-1876
Fax: 303-449-1877
www.ecoproducts.com

Eco-Products primarily supplies exterior and interior finish materials, composite decking, and household items and equipment. The company currently serves Colorado and neighboring states but is expanding to serve the national market.

Most recently mentioned in EBN 10:4

Eco-wise Building Supplies

Eco-Wise
110 W. Elizabeth St.
Austin, TX 78704

Phone: 512-326-4474
Fax: 512-326-4496
www.ecowise.com

Eco-wise Building Supplies carries a wide variety of green building materials, including such items as rainwater catchment systems, cotton insulation, recycled-glass tiles, reclaimed woods, plant-based finishes, milk paint, recycled-content carpeting, bamboo flooring, and Energy Star® appliances.

Most recently mentioned in EBN 10:4

Environmental Building Supplies

Environmental Building Supplies
819 S.E. Taylor St.
Portland, OR 97214

Phone: 503-222-3881
Fax: 503-222-3756
www.ecohaus.com

Environmental Building Supplies, which recently merged with Environmental Home Center (EHC), sells environmental building materials and interior finishes to trade professionals and to both residential and commercial end-users. Products include flooring and floorcoverings, FSC-certified and salvaged wood, finishes, cabinetry, tiles, and furniture. The company distributes to retailers as well as offers products to the public from their showroom location in Portland, Oregon. Environmental Building Supplies also has a second retail location in Bend, Oregon.

Most recently mentioned in EBN 7:8 & 10:4

Environmental Home Center

Environmental Home Center
4121 1st Ave. S
Seattle, WA 98134

Toll-free: 800-281-9785
Phone: 206-682-7332
Fax: 206-682-8275
www.environmentalhomecenter.com

Environmental Home Center sells a wide variety of environmental building products to trade professionals, dealers, and commercial and residential customers across the country through their showroom and call center in Seattle, as well as through the company's website. Wholesale pricing is available to trade professionals.

Most recently mentioned in EBN 10:4 & 13:9

Green Building Supply

Green Building Supply
508 N. 2nd St.
Fairfield, IA 52556

Toll-free: 800-405-0222
Phone: 641-469-5558
Fax: 641-469-5601
www.greenbuildingsupply.com

Green Building Supply offers hundreds of name-brand, sustainable, and energy-efficient construction products for residential and commercial projects, including non-toxic paints, stains, sealers, cleaners, furniture and cabinetry; air and water purification equipment; water-efficient toilets and non-water-using urinals; linoleum, cork and bamboo flooring; wool carpeting; cotton insulation. Contact the company for a catalog.

Hayward Corporation

Hayward Corporation
10 Ragsdale Dr., Ste. 100
Monterey, CA 93940

Phone: 831-643-1900
Fax: 831-644-7630
www.haywardlumber.com

Hayward Corporation, formerly Hayward Lumber, with six building supply centers in California, is reported to have the largest stock of certified lumber in the country. They also carry an expanding stock of other green building materials, including high-performance windows, ACQ- and borate-treated lumber, cotton insulation, and wood alternatives. In 2000, the company began producing its own line of FSC-certified roof trusses, now manufactured in a solar-powered facility soon to be LEED®-certified.

Most recently mentioned in EBN 7:1, 8:11, 10:4, 13:3

Livingreen

Livingreen
218 Helena Ave.
Santa Barbara, CA 93101

Toll-free: 866-966-1319
Phone: 805-966-1319
Fax: 805-966-1309
www.livingreen.com

Livingreen offers environmentally sustainable building and finishing materials, accessories, and retail products highlighting natural and recycled alternatives to standard building materials. The company's two stores provide product samples for both homeowners and trade professionals. As a resource center, Livingreen maintains a green bookstore and provides consultation and information on design, energy and water conservation, and product searches for home, work, and marine environments.

Most recently mentioned in EBN 10:4

Maine Green Building Supply

Maine Green Building Supply
111 Fox St.
Portland, ME 04101

Phone: 207-780-1500
Fax: 207-780-1510
www.mainegreenbuilding.com

Maine Green Building Supply offers a range of hand-chosen heating systems, solar thermal, insulation, finishing products, and other green building materials that meet high environmental standards for commercial and residential applications.

Natural Home Products.com

Natural Home Products.com
461 Sebastopol Ave
Santa Rosa, CA 95401

Toll-free: 800-373-4548
Phone: 707-571-1229
Fax: 707-571-1711
www.naturalhomeproducts.com

Natural Home Products.com carries an extensive line of natural floor coverings and flooring. The company also sells organic paints and wood finishes, as well as organic-cotton sheets and wool bedding.

Planetary Solutions

Planetary Solutions
2030 17th St.
P.O. Box 1049
Boulder, CO 80302

Phone: 303-442-6228
Fax: 303-442-6474
www.planetearth.com

Planetary Solutions caters to contractors, the design professions, and the general public in the Rocky Mountain region with a range of environmentally sound products including cork flooring, linoleum, 100% natural wool and recycled PET plastic carpet, reclaimed and FSC-certified wood flooring, bamboo flooring, recycled-glass tile, and natural paints and finishes.

Most recently mentioned in EBN 10:4

Refuge Sustainable Building Center

Refuge Sustainable Building Center
714 E. Mendenhall
Bozeman, MT 59715

Phone: 406-585-9958
Fax: 406-585-9730
www.refugebuilding.com

Refuge Sustainable Building Center offers a wide range of environmental building materials as well as non-toxic household products and sustainable building books. Products include FSC-certified and salvaged wood; siding, sheathing, and flooring; bamboo and cork flooring; recycled roofing and glass tiles; caulking; plasters; cotton insulation; dual-flush toilets; and low-VOC finishes and adhesives. Refuge also hosts environmental building workshops.

SolSource

New

SolSource, Inc.
5919 N. Broadway
Denver, CO 80216

Phone: 303-297-1874
Fax: 303-296-1261
www.solsourceinc.com

SolSource is a distributor of high-performance green building materials and systems through a network of dealers in the Rocky Mountain region. Lines include a range of renewable energy, roofing, SIP, and ICF products, as well as finishes.

Truitt & White Lumber Company

Truitt & White Lumber Company
642 Hearst Ave.
Berkeley, CA 94710

Toll-free: 877-600-1470
Phone: 510-841-0511
Fax: 510-845-2604
www.truittandwhite.com

Since 1946, builder's supply store Truitt & White has committed to developing and promoting green products and practices. Environmentally preferable products, such as FSC-certified wood, low-VOC paints and caulks, and energy-efficient items, are

clearly labeled throughout the store, making them easy to find. Truitt & White is a founding member and sponsor of educational nonprofit Bay Area Build It Green.

01 62 02
Distributors/Retailers, Used Building Materials

Clearly, reusing building materials can be environmentally advantageous. The companies listed here commonly have varying selections of doors, windows, cabinets, brick, stone, wood flooring, and plumbing fixtures. Also check the Yellow Pages under "salvage" for local suppliers. Avoid the use of old, inefficient windows in exterior envelopes, plumbing fixtures that don't meet current water conservation standards, or appliances such as refrigerators with poor efficiencies. In these cases, new products will save more than the environmental costs of their manufacture. Testing for lead paint is recommended for items such as salvaged doors and millwork. Raw, unsealed wood can be a source of lead dust in a building even if lead paint has been removed. If lead paint residue is found or suspected, the wood should be sealed after paint is stripped. (See also 02 42 00 - Removal and Salvage of Construction Materials.) (See feature articles EBN Vol. 9, No. 5 & Vol. 10, No. 4.)

Used Building Materials

1st Saturday Construction Salvage
7010 S.R. 43
Spencer, IN 47460

Phone: 812-876-6347

1st Saturday deconstructs small buildings and carries everything from lumber to doors to stained glass. Open Saturdays.

Used Building Materials

American Salvage
7001 N.W. 27th Ave.
Miami, FL 33147

Phone: 305-691-7001
Fax: 305-691-0001
www.americansalvage.com

A source for general home furnishing items, American Salvage carries a wide variety of finished building components such as paneled doors and specialty windows.

Used Building Materials

Austin Habitat for Humanity Re-Store
310 Comal, Ste. 101
Austin, TX 78702

Phone: 512-478-2165
Fax: 512-478-9477
www.re-store.com

The Austin Re-Store carries a broad range of salvaged building materials in part supplied by deconstruction activities of the local Habitat for Humanity affiliate.

Bent Nail

New

Bent Nail
31255 Wheel Ave.
Abbotsford, BC V2T 6H1 Canada

Toll-free: 877-850-2691
Phone: 604-850-2691
Fax: 604-850-3337
www.bentnail.org

Bent Nail offers 60,000 sf of salvaged and new construction and renovation stock including lumber, doors, plumbing, windows, bathtubs, and lighting. All salvaged lumber is denailed and resawn as needed.

Used Building Materials

Building Materials Resource Center
100 Terrace St.
Boston, MA 02120

Phone: 617-442-8917
Fax: 617-427-2491
www.bostonbmrc.org

The Building Materials Resource Center (BMRC) is a nonprofit organization that accepts donations of good quality used and surplus building materials and offers them for a modest fee to the general public. A generous discount is offered to low- to moderate-income homeowners (proof of income is required) and nonprofit organizations. BMRC maintains a 6,000 ft² retail location and also offers workshops, in-home consults, a lending library, and other homeowner-assistance services. Donations to the BMRC are tax-deductible on the estimated fair market value of the item.

Industry Representation

Building Materials Reuse Association
545 Ridge Ave.
State College, PA 16803

Fax: 800-990-2672
www.ubma.org

01 00 00
General Requirements

01 00 00
General Requirements

The Building Materials Reuse Association (formerly the Used Building Materials Association) is the nonprofit North American organization representing firms that deconstruct buildings, retail used building materials, or both. Its website gives current contact information for all members nationwide.
Most recently mentioned in EBN 9:5 & 14:3

Used Building Materials

Caldwells
195 Bayshore Blvd.
San Francisco, CA 94124

Phone: 415-550-6777
Fax: 415-550-0349
www.caldwells.com

Caldwell Building Wreckers salvages a wide variety of building products including lumber, beams, timbers, doors, windows, bricks, and cobblestones. The company also offers custom remilling.

Used Building Materials

Center for ReSource Conservation
1702 Walnut St.
Boulder, CO 80302

Phone: 303-441-3278
Fax: 303-441-4367
www.conservationcenter.org

ReSource is a program of the Center for ReSource Conservation to salvage and resell building materials from construction and demolition projects. Available materials include lumber, door, window, and cabinet packages as well as architectural artifacts including timbers, hardwood flooring, and other items of significance. ReSource also now offers a complete line of millwork and flooring from reclaimed timbers.

Jack's New & Used Building Materials

 New

Jack's New & Used
4912 Still Creek Ave.
Burnaby, BC V5C 4E4 Canada

Phone: 604-299-2967
Fax: 604-299-1383
www.jacksused.com

Jack's New & Used Building Materials offers thousands of items, including new and used doors, windows, cabinets, plumbing, electrical, lumber, stained glass, skylights, architectural antiques, and more.

Liz's Antique Hardware

New

Liz's Antique Hardware
453 S. La Brea
Los Angeles, CA 90036

Phone: 323-939-4403
Fax: 323-939-4387
www.lahardware.com

Liz's Antique Hardware refurbishes and sells salvaged door, cabinet, and window hardware, lighting, and other building materials. Their Los Angeles showroom has over 1 million pieces of original hardware circa 1850 to 1970. The company also offers a hardware matching service for hard-to-find original hardware.

Salvaged Architectural Antiques

North Shore Architectural Antiques
616 - 2nd Ave.
Two Harbors, MN 55616

Phone: 218-834-0018
www.north-shore-architectural-antiques.com

North Shore Architectural Antiques salvages antique residential and commercial building materials. The company operates a retail showroom and will deliver regionally and ship anywhere.

Used Building Materials

Odom Reusable Building Materials
5555 Brentwood Ave.
Grawn, MI 49637

Phone: 231-276-6330
www.odomreuse.com

Odom salvages and deconstructs commercial and residential buildings and sells lumber, cabinets, doors, windows, and a variety of fixtures to the public at a retail warehouse.

Used Building Materials

Rejuvenation
1100 S.E. Grand Ave.
Portland, OR 97214

Phone: 503-238-1900
Fax: 503-230-2656
www.rejuvenation.com

Encompassing over 5,000 ft², the Salvage Department of the Rejuvenation store in Portland, OR offers a wide variety of salvaged architectural products. The company's Restoration Department refurbishes, repairs, and sells antique lighting fixtures. Rejuvenation is also a manufacturer of period lighting fixtures, including a line equipped with energy-efficient CFLs and small electronic ballasts. The company has taken a number of steps to reduce its environmental impact.

Used Building Materials

Rejuvenation Seattle
2910 1st Ave. S
Seattle, WA 98134

Toll-free: 888-401-1900
Phone: 206-382-1901
Fax: 800-526-7329
www.rejuvenation.com

Rejuve Seattle, a branch of Rejuvenation in Portland, OR, offers a wide variety of salvaged architectural products at its 6,000 ft² facility. The company's Restoration Department refurbishes, repairs, and sells antique lighting fixtures. Rejuvenation is also a manufacturer of period lighting fixtures, including a line equipped with energy-efficient CFLs and small electronic ballasts. The company has taken a number of steps to reduce its environmental impact.

ReNew Building Materials & Salvage

ReNew Building Materials & Salvage, Inc.
16 Town Crier Dr. #2   **New**
Putney Rd. (opposite Shell)
Brattleboro, VT 05301

Phone: 802-246-2400
www.renewsalvage.org

ReNew Building Materials & Salvage is a non-profit, environmentally-driven store offering used, surplus, and salvaged building materials including doors, windows, kitchen cabinets, hardware, plumbing, electrical, lumber, appliances, and tools. Stock is derived from donations and deconstruction projects. They also offer an expanding selection of new green products and materials. Profits support other local initiatives and organizations.

Used Building Materials

Renovators ReSource
6040 Almon St.
Halifax, NS B3K 1T8 Canada

Toll-free: 877-230-7700
Phone: 902-429-3889
Fax: 902-425-6795
www.renovators-resource.com

Renovators ReSource stocks a wide variety of quality used building materials, including entire dismantled buildings, and carries a line of furniture and household items elegantly designed from used building materials.
Most recently mentioned in EBN 10:4

Used Building Materials

Reuse Development Organization
2 N. Kresson St.
c/o The Loading Dock
Baltimore, MD 21224

Phone: 410-558-3625
Fax: 410-558-1888
www.redo.org

Reuse Development Organization is a national nonprofit organization providing technical assistance in reuse, deconstruction, and building materials salvaging. It's a great information resource for all types of secondhand consumer products as well as building materials, office equipment, and furniture.

Green Building Resource Guide

Salvaged Building Materials Exchange
P.O. Box 3808
Redwood City, CA 94064

www.greenguide.com/exchange/

The salvaged building materials exchange section of this website is set up for sellers and buyers to connect by way of free listings.

Used Building Materials

Second Use Building Materials
7953 Second Ave. S
Seattle, WA 98108

Phone: 206-763-6929
Fax: 206-763-6021
www.seconduse.com

Second Use salvages and sells reusable building materials from their well-stocked retail yard in Seattle, WA.

Used Building Materials

South Puget Sound Habitat for Humanity
210 Thurston Ave.
Olympia, WA 98501

Phone: 360-753-1575
Fax: 360-753-5402
www.spshabitat.org

South Puget Sound Habitat for Humanity is a nonprofit organization donating all profits from the sale of a wide variety of used building supplies to Habitat for Humanity. The company operates a 5,500 sq. ft. retail space known as the Builders' ReStore in downtown Olympia stocked with everything from vintage, one-of-a-kind items to new and surplus materials. Purchases help to fund the construction of safe, decent, affordable homes for Habitat for Humanity's partner families in Thurston County.

Surrey New & Used Building Materials

Surrey New & Used Building Materials, Inc.
17861-64th Ave.
Surrey, BC V3S 1Z3 Canada

New

Toll-free: 877-570-8733
Phone: 604-576-8488
Fax: 604-576-8489
www.surreynewandused.com

For over 40 years, Surrey New & Used has offered salvaged windows, doors, hardware, plumbing, woodwork, cupboards and cabinets, appliances, lighting, electrical, lumber and structural materials, commercial and industrial salvage.

Used Building Materials

The Brass Knob and The Back Doors Warehouse
2311 18th St. NW
Washington, DC 20009

Phone: 202-332-3370
Fax: 202-332-5594
www.thebrassknob.com

The Brass Knob and The Back Doors Warehouse offer salvaged building supplies, carrying everything from salvaged antique hardware to chandeliers, stained glass, and radiators. The two locations are within walking distance of each other, with The Back Doors Warehouse carrying larger items in greater volume.

Used Building Materials

The Rebuilding Center of Our United Villages
3625 N. Mississippi Ave.
Portland, OR 97227

Phone: 503-331-1877
Fax: 503-331-9291
www.rebuildingcenter.org

The Rebuilding Center accepts and carries lumber, doors, windows, cabinets, sinks, tubs, toilets, carpets, and more. The Rebuilding Center also offers deconstruction services for commercial and residential structures.

Used Building Materials

The ReUse Center
2801 21st Ave. S
Minneapolis, MN 55407

Phone: 612-724-2608
Fax: 612-724-2288
www.greeninstitute.org

Run by the Green Institute, The ReUse Center supplies its retail operations through a partner deconstruction business and as a donation-based resale business.

Used Building Materials

Urban Ore, Inc.
900 Murray St.
Berkeley, CA 94710

Phone: 510-841-7283
Fax: 510-548-4460
www.urbanore.citysearch.com

One of the oldest used building materials retail operations in the country, Urban Ore carries large quantities of a wide variety of exterior and interior building materials.

Used Building Materials

Used Building Materials Exchange
RecycleNet Corporation
P.O. Box 24017
Guelph, ON N1E 6V8 Canada

Phone: 519-767-2913
build.recycle.net/exchange/index.html

Used Building Materials Exchange (UBM) is a free worldwide information exchange for those companies and individuals who buy/sell/trade used building materials.

Materials Exchange

Vermont Business Materials Exchange
1580 Barber Pond Rd.
Pownal, VT 05261

Toll-free: 800-895-1930
Phone: 802-823-9399
Fax: 802-823-5228
www.vbmx.org

Vermont Business Materials Exchange (VBMeX) is a free service that connects businesses or institutions that have surplus commercial materials with other businesses or individuals who can put the materials to good use. VBMeX maintains a database of available and wanted materials, and publicizes the listings in the form of "classified ads" through their website, specialized listserves and Vermont Business magazine. The database normally contains about 150 active listings of materials offered free or at low cost, updated daily. Materials include surplus wood and plastic materials, construction salvage, and containers, among other items.

Used Building Materials

Whole House Building Supply
1955 Pulgas Ave.
E. Palo Alto, CA 94303

Phone: 650-856-0634
Fax: 650-327-1933
www.driftwoodsalvage.com

**01 00 00
General
Requirements**

01 00 00
General Requirements

Whole House Building Supply offers a complete range of used building materials, fixtures, cabinetry, and architectural elements, including virgin growth redwood. Their website pictures these quality materials as well as uses of salvaged building materials.

Salvaged and Sustainably Harvested Wood Search Engine

Woodfinder
P.O. Box 493
Springtown, PA 18081

Toll-free: 877-933-4637
www.woodfinder.com

Woodfinder can be used to locate both salvaged and sustainably harvested wood.

01 62 03
Distributors/Retailers, FSC-Certified Wood

Distributors of FSC-certified wood products are subject to the same rigor of inspections as manufacturers and land managers. "Chain-of-custody certification" is the term used to describe the documentation of certified-wood product sourcing, processing, handling, and distribution. Accurate paperwork and careful separation of certified and noncertified wood must be maintained for compliance with FSC standards. (See also 06 05 70 - Wood Products Certification and Information.)

AltruWood Certified Wood Products

AltruWood, Inc.   *For full listing, see CSI section 09 64 01 - FSC-Certified Wood Flooring*

Craftmark Reclaimed Wood

Craftmark Reclaimed Wood, Inc.
P.O. Box 237
McMinnville, OR 97128

Phone: 503-472-6929
Fax: 503-472-5150
www.craftmarkinc.com

Craftmark Reclaimed Wood, Inc. is a distributor of flooring, decking, paneling, wainscoting, timbers, and specialty wood products such as architectural moldings produced from a wide variety of FSC-certified species. Custom-milling is a specialty. The company is also a manufacturer of wood products from reclaimed timber.

Canadian Eco-Lumber Co-op

Eco-Lumber Coop
150 - 14480 Knox Way
Richmond, BC V6V 2Z5 Canada

Toll-free: 866-827-4352
Phone: 604-278-4300
Fax: 604-278-4398
www.ecolumber.ca

The Canadian Eco-Lumber Co-op carries only wood products that are FSC-certified, or reclaimed from buildings slated for demolition. Sheet products include CD fir sheathing plywood, MDO (medium density overlay) concrete-forming plywood, and B2 maple Europly cabinet plywood. Flooring products include plywood-back, 6mm Douglas-fir solid-surface engineered flooring, and Douglas-fir 3/4" solid-wood flooring. Cedar lumber products include common dimensions, fencing & landscaping, and T&G paneling. Custom cedar profiles, sizes, and grades can be ordered.

EcoTimber

EcoTimber
1611 4th St.
San Rafael, CA 94901

Toll-free: 888-801-0855
Phone: 415-258-8454
Fax: 415-258-8455
www.ecotimber.com

EcoTimber® offers a wide range of domestic and tropical wood flooring from ecologically sound sources. EcoTimber products include reclaimed and FSC-certified woods, as well as a full line of bamboo flooring products. Prefinished, floating and formaldehyde-free floors are available.

Most recently mentioned in EBN 3:5, 4:4, 8:11, 10:11

Edensaw Woods

Edensaw Woods Ltd.
211 Seton Rd.
Port Townsend, WA 98368

Toll-free: 800-745-3336
Phone: 360-385-7878
Fax: 360-385-5215
www.edensaw.com

Edensaw Woods' selection of FSC-certified wood includes alder, ash, cherry, Honduras mahogany, maple, poplar, and red and white oak as well as many species of FSC-certified domestic hardwood plywood. Edensaw also has a location in Kent, Washington.

Most recently mentioned in EBN 10:4

Endura Wood Products

Endura Wood Products, Ltd.
1303 S.E. 6th Ave.
Portland, OR 97214

Phone: 503-233-7090
Fax: 503-233-7091
www.endurawood.com

Endura offers FSC-certified hardwood and softwood flooring, lumber, and decking in a wide variety of exotic and domestic species. Endurawood butcher blocks and countertops are produced from certified woods such as rock maple. Endura also sells reclaimed wood products as well as straw particleboard and agrifiber composite sheet goods.

J. E. Higgins Lumber Company

J. E. Higgins Lumber Company, Purchasing Division
6999 S. Front Rd.
Livermore, CA 94550

Toll-free: 800-241-1883
Phone: 925-245-4300
Fax: 877-241-1883
www.higlum.com

J. E. Higgins Lumber sells FSC-certified hardwood, plywood, and flooring.

North American Wood Products

North American Wood Products, Inc.
7204 Durham Rd. #800
Portland, OR 97224

Phone: 503-620-6655
Fax: 503-598-7959
www.nawpi.com

North American Wood Products, chain-of-custody certified according to FSC standards, matches wood suppliers with buyers requiring specific species, grades, colors dimensions, or cuts. Products include hardwood and softwood lumber, veneers, dimension stock, and panels.

Northland Forest Products

Northland Forest Products
16 Church St.
P.O. Box 369
Kingston, NH 03848

Phone: 603-642-3665
Fax: 603-642-8670
www.northlandforest.com

Northland Forest Products carries FSC-certified kiln-dried Northern and Appalachian hardwood lumber for flooring and architectural millwork, as well as fixed widths, special widths, and figured woods. Species include cherry, maple, ash, yellow birch, red oak, mahogany, eastern white pine, white oak, eucalyptus grandis and others, depending on availability.

Pittsford Lumber and Woodshop

Pittsford Lumber and Woodshop
50 State St.
Pittsford, NY 14534

Phone: 585-586-1877
Fax: 585-586-1934
www.northfieldcommon.com/
pittsford%20lumber.htm

Pittsford Lumber and Woodshop stocks FSC-certified tropical hardwoods for cabinet and furniture construction. They also carry Tried & True nontoxic oil finishes.

EarthSource Forest Products

Plywood and Lumber Sales, Inc.
1618 28th St.
Earth Source Forest Products
Oakland, CA 94608

Toll-free: 866-549-9663
Phone: 510-208-7257
Fax: 510-547-2511
www.earthsourcewood.com

EarthSource Forest Products, a division of Plywood and Lumber Sales, Inc., sells FSC-certified hardwood plywood and lumber of the following species: maple, cherry, red oak, white oak, ash, Honduras mahogany, walnut, machiche, amapola, and many more. EarthSource also sells salvaged and rediscovered lumber such as fir, redwood, and hickory.

Windfall Lumber and Milling

Windfall Lumber and Milling
404 Jefferson Street St. NE
Olympia, WA 98501

Phone: 360-352-2250
Fax: 360-352-8294
www.windfalllumber.com

Windfall Lumber is a manufacturer and distributor of FSC-certified and Smartwood Rediscovered hardwoods, flooring, millwork, countertops, and timbers.

01 62 04
Distributors/Retailers, Energy Conservation

The companies listed here specialize in energy conservation products, including lighting, weatherization materials, and specialized energy-conserving products. (See feature article EBN Vol. 10, No. 4.)

Weatherization and Energy-Conservation Products

AM Conservation Group, Inc.
430 Sand Shore Rd., Ste. 7
Hackettstown, NJ 07840

Toll-free: 800-777-5655
Phone: 908-852-6464
Fax: 908-852-6444
www.amconservationgroup.com

AM Conservation Group, Inc. introduces, manufactures, markets, and distributes a wide array of products for weatherization, as well as water and energy conservation.

Lighting, Ventilation, and Weatherization

Energy Federation Incorporated
40 Washington St., Ste. 2000
Westborough, MA 01581

Toll-free: 800-876-0660
Phone: 508-870-2277
Fax: 508-870-9933
www.efi.org

Energy Federation Incorporated (EFI) is a retailer and wholesaler of energy-efficient lighting, ventilation, and weatherization products.

Energy-Efficient Lighting

Fred Davis Corp.
93 West St.
Medfield, MA 02052

Toll-free: 800-497-2970
Phone: 508-359-3610
Fax: 508-359-3644

Fred Davis Corporation is a national wholesaler of energy-efficient lighting. The company offers thousands of products including: compact, low-mercury, and T8/T5 fluorescent lamps; electronic ballasts; energy-efficient fixtures; and LED exit signs.

Most recently mentioned in EBN 3:3 & 8:2

Renewable Energy & Energy-Conservation

Gaiam Real Goods

For full listing, see CSI section 01 62 05 - Distributors/Retailers, Renewable Energy Equipment

Weatherization and Energy-Conservation Products

Positive Energy
P.O. Box 7568
Boulder, CO 80306

Toll-free: 800-488-4340
Fax: 303-444-4340
www.positive-energy.com

Positive Energy publishes a catalog of hard-to-find energy saving products at wholesale prices. The selection includes products for ventilation, sealing, lighting, water saving, and water and air purification.

Ventilation and Energy-Conserving Products

Shelter Supply, Inc.
151 E. Cliff Rd., Ste. 30
Burnsville, MN 55337

Toll-free: 800-762-8399
Phone: 952-516-3400
Fax: 952-736-3370
www.sheltersupply.com

Shelter Supply offers products for better indoor air quality and greater energy efficiency. Shelter Supply specializes in residential building ventilation products.

Most recently mentioned in EBN 7:7

Renewable Energy Equipment

Solardyne.com

For full listing, see CSI section 01 62 05 - Distributors/Retailers, Renewable Energy Equipment

01 00 00
General Requirements

01 00 00
General
Requirements

01 62 05
Distributors/Retailers, Renewable Energy Equipment

Most of these companies supply a wide range of renewable energy equipment, including photovoltaic systems, solar water-heating equipment, batteries, and inverters. A few also supply wind-energy and micro-hydro equipment. (See feature article EBN Vol. 10, No. 4.)

Renewable Energy Equipment

AEE Solar
1155 Redway Dr.
P.O. Box 339
Redway, CA 95560

Toll-free: 800-777-6609
Phone: 707-923-2277
Fax: 707-923-3009
www.aeesolar.com

AEE Solar offers solar, wind, hydro, and balance-of-system products for renewable energy systems, as well as pumps, lighting, and appliances. AEE Solar sells only to resale-licensed dealers, contractors, and installers.

Renewable Energy Equipment

Backwoods Solar Electric Systems
1589 Rapid Lightning Creek Rd.
Sandpoint, ID 83864

Phone: 208-263-4290
Fax: 208-265-4788
www.backwoodssolar.com

A company of six solar-electric technicians who own and operate solar-electric homes powered by the products in their catalog, Backwoods Solar Electric Systems has been in business since 1978. The company is catalog-based (web and print) and is dedicated to serving remotely located homeowners/builders.

Renewable Energy Equipment

Carmanah Technologies Corporation
Building 4, 203 Harbour Rd.
Victoria, BC V9A 3S2 Canada

Toll-free: 877-722-8877
Phone: 250-380-0052
Fax: 250-380-0062
www.carmanah.com

Carmanah's Solar Power Systems Group was formed through the purchase of Soltek Powersource, Ltd. in July 2005. A wide range of photovoltaic equipment and systems is offered, including remote, grid-connected, and emergency backup power for industry, commercial, and residential installations. Carmanah packages and integrates PV and balance-of-systems components, such as their Green Gridtie™ Solar Power System for residential applications. The company also manufacturers and markets solar LED hazard lighting and LED illuminated signs.

Renewable Energy Equipment

Creative Energy Technologies
2872 State Rte. 10
Summit, NY 12175

Phone: 518-287-1428
www.cetsolar.com

Founded in 1999, Creative Energy Technologies (CET) offers a wide range of renewable and energy-efficient equipment through its online catalog. The company operates a store in Summit, New York, from which they also offer workshops and an energy audit weatherization service. According to CET, they test all the products they offer to verify the claims of the manufacturers and will provide free technical support for the life of a purchased product.

Renewable Energy Equipment

EA Energy Alternatives Ltd.
5-4217 Glanford Ave.
Victoria, BC V8Z 4B9 Canada

Toll-free: 800-265-8898
Phone: 250-727-0522
Fax: 250-727-2286
www.energyalternatives.ca

Energy Alternatives offers solar, wind, hydro, and balance-of-systems products for renewable energy systems, as well as pumps, lighting, appliances, and books.

Renewable Energy Equipment

Electron Connection
P.O. Box 203
Hornbrook, CA 96044

Toll-free: 800-945-7587
Fax: 530-475-3401
www.electronconnection.com

In business and producing its own power since 1976 (with its owner utilizing renewable energy since 1970), Electron Connection designs, sells, installs, and maintains renewable energy systems. The company does not publish a paper catalog but provides information about some products on its website. Manufacturers' literature is also provided on products determined to be suitable for a specific customer's needs. Electron Connection is fully licensed, bonded, and insured to install and service renewable energy systems in California and Oregon. The company also maintains a worldwide network of Electron Connection dealer/installers.

Renewable Energy Equipment

Energy Outfitters, Ltd.
543 N.E. "E" St.
Grants Pass, OR 97526

Toll-free: 800-467-6527
Phone: 541-476-4200
Fax: 541-476-7480
www.energyoutfitters.com

In business since 1991, Energy Outfitters is a renewable energy distributor supplying products either as components or assembled systems, and offering technical design services for a wide range of renewable energy products and systems including PV, wind, and micro-hydro. The company also distributes a variety of photovoltaic modules from BP, GE, Isofoton, and Mitsubishi.

Renewable Energy & Energy-Conservation

Gaiam Real Goods
13771 South Highway 101
Hopland, CA 95449

Toll-free: 888-507-2561
Phone: 303-222-3500
Fax: 303-222-8702
www.realgoods.com

Gaiam Real Goods sells a broad range of energy-conserving, alternative energy, and environmental-living products through its catalogs and retail stores. Real Goods catalogs are available by mail upon request or can be accessed on their website. Real Goods and Jade Mountain merged in 2001 to become the largest provider of renewable energy systems (solar, wind, and hydro) in the world. These companies have been involved with solarizing more than 50,000 homes since 1978.

Most recently mentioned in EBN 10:4

Solar Energy Solutions

groSolar
(formerly Global Resource Options)
Corporate Headquarters
White River Junction, VT 05001

Toll-free: 800-374-4494
Fax: 802-295-4417
www.grosolar.com

groSolar, previously Global Resource Options, sells and installs solar electric systems for residential and commercial markets in locations across the country. In late 2006, groSolar acquired Oregon-based Energy Outfitters, with distribution offices in Grants Pass Oregon as well as Calgary, Alberta and Barrie, Ontario, making groSolar one of North America's largest solar energy distribution and installation companies.

Renewable Energy Equipment

Mr.Solar.com
P.O. Box 1506
Cockeysville, MD 21030

Phone: 410-308-1599
Fax: 410-561-7813
www.mrsolar.com

Mr.Solar.com designs and sells PV systems using BP, Siemens, Kyocera, Trace, and Solarex components for residential and commercial use. Small wind systems, water pumps, fans, appliances, and balance-of-systems equipment are also available.

Renewable Energy Equipment

New England Solar Electric, Inc.
401 Huntington Rd.
P.O. Box 435
Worthington, MA 01098

Toll-free: 800-914-4131
Fax: 413-238-0203
www.newenglandsolar.com

New England Solar Electric, formerly Fowler Solar Electric, offers renewable energy equipment and systems from a 96-page catalog and product guide. The company also publishes the *Solar Electric Independent Home Book*.

Renewable Energy Equipment

Northern Arizona Wind & Sun, Inc.
4091 East Huntington Dr.
Flagstaff, AZ 86004

Toll-free: 800-383-0195
Phone: 928-526-8017
Fax: 928-527-0729
www.solar-electric.com

In business selling and installing solar electric systems since 1979, Northern Arizona Wind & Sun offers renewable energy equipment through its catalog, an online store, and a retail location in Flagstaff.

Renewable Energy Equipment

RWE Schott Solar, Inc.
2260 Lava Ridge Ct., Ste. 102
U.S. Sales & Marketing
Roseville, CA 95661

Toll-free: 888-457-6527
Phone: 916-774-3000
Fax: 916-784-9781
www.us.schott.com

RWE Schott Solar Inc. (RSS), formerly Schott Applied Power, is a leading manufacturer and distributor of solar power components and systems. RSS produces the world's largest solar power module available, the ASE 300. RSS serves a diverse market including grid-connected residential and commercial systems, and grid-independent agricultural, governmental and utility applications. RWE Scott Solar Inc. is a joint venture of the RWE Group, a global multi-utility concern with core businesses in electricity, gas, water, waste management, and recycling.

Most recently mentioned in EBN 13:11

Renewable Energy Equipment

SBT Designs
25581 IH-10 W
San Antonio, TX 78257

Toll-free: 800-895-9808
Phone: 210-698-7109
Fax: 210-698-7147
www.sbtdesigns.com

SBT Designs' Alternative Energy Catalog includes design guides, product descriptions, and prices on solar modules, wind generators, and a variety of renewable energy products.

Renewable Energy Equipment

Solar Energy, Inc.

For full listing, see CSI section 23 56 16 - Packaged Solar Heating Equipment

Renewable Energy Equipment

Solar Works, Inc.
64 Main St.
Montpelier, VT 05602

Phone: 802-223-7804
Fax: 802-223-8980
www.solar-works.com

Solar Works, Inc. is a renewable energy systems integrator and contractor providing solar electric (photovoltaic), solar thermal and wind power systems for clients worldwide. Founded in 1980, Solar Works is also active in commercializing new technologies and developing renewable energy programs for both public and private sector clients. The company's corporate headquarters are located in Montpelier, VT.

Renewable Energy Equipment

Solardyne.com
Solar Dynamics LLC
5806 N. Williams Ave.
Portland, OR 97217

Phone: 503-830-8739
Fax: 503-286-0847
www.solardyne.com

Solardyne is an online retailer of renewable energy equipment and high-efficiency appliances including solar and wind power systems and components, solar lighting, solar water pumps, tankless water heaters, and super efficient refrigerators, freezers, and washers.

Renewable Energy Equipment

Southwest Photovoltaic Systems, Inc.
212 E. Main
Tomball, TX 77375

Toll-free: 800-899-7978
Phone: 281-351-0031
Fax: 281-351-8356
www.southwestpv.com

In business since 1986, Southwest PV Systems designs and supplies PV, wind, and hybrid-power systems. The company offers training seminars on-site and maintains a large in-stock distribution warehouse.

01 00 00
General Requirements

Renewable Energy Equipment

Sunnyside Solar, Inc.
1014 Green River Rd.
Guilford, VT 05301

Phone: 802-254-4670
Fax: 802-254-4670
www.sunnysidesolar.com

Sunnyside Solar, Inc., founded in 1979, is a small, family-owned firm specializing in photovoltaic electric systems. The company provides design, engineering, sales, installation, service, and education in the field of off- and on-grid residential and commercial photovoltaic installations.

Renewable Energy Equipment

 New

TerraTek Environmental Solutions
P.O. Box 3303
Courtenay, BC V9N 5N5 Canada

Toll-free: 877-335-1415
Phone: 250-335-1444
www.terratek.ca

TerraTek Environmental Solutions sells and installs renewable energy systems for grid-connected and off-grid systems, specializing in solar, wind and micro-hydro on Vancouver Island, the Gulf Islands, and the Coastal Mainland area of western Canada. Lighting and off-grid appliances are also offered.

Solar Street Lighting

Quality Solar Concepts Inc.

For full listing, see CSI section 26 56 00 - Exterior Lighting

01 93 16 Recycling Programs

Rechargeable nickel-cadmium (Ni-Cad) batteries have become ubiquitous on building sites. Despite their durability, they do wear out; the health and environmental risks posed by the heavy-metal content of Ni-Cad batteries makes their recycling a very high priority, so programs for recycling them are included here. (See also 11 82 00 - Recycling and Solid Waste Handling Equipment, 09 69 26 - Carpet Recycling, 26 01 51 - Electrical Component Recycling.)

Ni-Cad Battery Recycling

Inmetco
One Inmetco Dr.
Ellwood City, PA 16117

Phone: 724-758-2800
Fax: 724-758-2845
www.inmetco.com

Inmetco maintains a nationwide battery recycling program for nickel-cadmium, nickel-metal-hydride, zinc, alkaline, lithium-ion, and nickel-iron batteries.

Most recently mentioned in EBN 2:2

Charge Up to Recycle Program

Rechargeable Battery Recycling Corporation (RBRC)
1000 Parkwood Cir., Ste. 450
Atlanta, GA 30339

Toll-free: 877-723-1297
Phone: 678-419-9990
Fax: 678-419-9986
www.rbrc.org

The RBRC is a nonprofit, public service organization serving business and public agencies throughout North America. Through their Charge Up to Recycle® program, the company sells chemical-specific or all-in-one collection containers to facilitate the recycling of portable rechargeable batteries. Each container holds about 40 lbs. and includes prepaid shipping label, safety instructions, and plastic bags. Appropriate non-RBRC collection containers can also be shipped to consolidation centers. In Canada, a single shipment weight limit of 500 kg applies. The RBRC accepts Ni-Cd, Ni-MH, Li-ion, and small sealed lead rechargeable batteries (up to 2 lbs/1 kg each). Registration is required.

This Space is Available for Your Notes

02 00 00 Existing Conditions

PRODUCT LISTINGS

02 42 00
Removal and Salvage of Construction Materials

Service companies that recycle C&D waste on- or off-site not only keep usable and recyclable materials from being landfilled, they can save money on tipping fees. Companies listed here handle either or both the recycling or the salvage of construction materials during the demolition of existing buildings and structures. (See also 01 62 02 - Distributors/Retailers, Used Building Materials.)

Construction and Demolition Waste Management

Institution Recycling Network
7 S. State St.
Concord, NH 03301

Phone: 603-229-1962
Fax: 603-229-1960
www.ir-network.com

Institution Recycling Network (IRN) is the most experienced recycler of construction and demolition wastes in the northeast. The IRN markets and manages the recycling of more than 20 different C&D materials, from site work to roof, and routinely achieves recycling rates over 85 percent. In almost all cases, aggressive C&D recycling is less expensive than disposal, without interfering with project flow or schedules. IRN provides a single point of contact to handle everything related to C&D recycling: planning, training, on-site management, hauling, marketing, recordkeeping, and documentation.

The IRN Surplus Network

Institution Recycling Network
7 S. State St.
Concord, NH 03301

Phone: 603-229-1962
Fax: 603-229-1960
www.ir-network.com

The Surplus Network, a service of The Institution Recycling Network (IRN), manages the removal and donation of almost any items of surplus property, including fixed assets, to a network of charitable organizations

that will distribute these materials to needy individuals and organizations in the U.S. and abroad. The 'specification' for surplus property handled by the IRN includes office furniture and furnishings, medical and laboratory equipment and supplies, classroom furnishings, reception/lounge furnishings, dormitory furniture, mattresses. Also, removable fixed assets like doors and windows, bathroom partitions, cabinets, and kitchen equipment.

02 80 00
Facility Remediation

Asbestos and lead are among the most common hazardous materials encountered in older buildings. Use of asbestos as an insulating and fireproofing material, and lead as a primary ingredient in paint, ended in the 1970s as awareness of these dangers grew. Lead and asbestos remediation in buildings should generally be done by professionals, through either removal or encapsulation. Fluorescent lighting products—lamps as well as older ballasts—should also be disposed of only through specialized recycling facilities, some of which are listed here. All fluorescent lamps (as well as mercury-vapor and other high-intensity-discharge-HID-lamps) contain elemental mercury, which is a very serious environmental contaminant. Fluorescent lighting ballasts made prior to 1979 contain significant quantities of PCB (polychlorinated biphenyls)—each ballast containing 0.6 to 1 ounce—which is highly toxic and bioaccumulates in natural systems. Before sending fluorescent lamps and ballasts to out-of-town recycling facilities, check with your local solid-waste agency; many handle lamps and ballast disposal through toxic waste collection programs. Products listed here aid in managing lead and asbestos with minimal additional environmental and health risks. (See also 28 30 00 - Electronic Detection and Alarm, 31 21 13 - Radon Mitigation, 23 40 13 - Air Quality Monitoring and Assessment.)

AeRO 30 Dry Ice Blasting System

Cold Jet, LLC
455 Wards Corner Rd.
Loveland, OH 45140

Toll-free: 800-337-9423
Phone: 513-831-3211
Fax: 513-831-1209
www.coldjet.com

Cold Jet's AeRO 30 system is configured specifically for disaster remediation contractors and used for removing mold and fire-damage from building surfaces. The dry ice evaporates immediately, greatly reducing the clean-up and disposal costs compared with sandblasting. It is more energy intensive to produce and handle, however. The AeRO 30 uses 1.5 pounds of dry ice per minute, along with 50 to 150 cfm of compressed air at 80 psi, depending on the nozzle used. Dry ice for the system can be purchased from a regional supplier (prices range from 35 to 45 cents per pound, according to Cold Jet) or manufactured on site using Cold Jet's dry ice production equipment. (The company's P325 dry ice maker draws about 17 kW to make 300 lbs. of dry ice per hour, or about 18 lbs. per kWh.)

A-B-C and L-B-C

Fiberlock Technologies, Inc.
150 Dascomb Rd.
Andover, MA 01810

Toll-free: 800-342-3755
Phone: 978-623-9987
Fax: 978-475-6205
www.fiberlock.com

A-B-C® (Asbestos Binding Compound) is a high-solids asbestos encapsulant. This product can be used for effective in-place management of asbestos hazards.

L-B-C® (Lead Barrier Compound) is an elastomeric-thermoplastic water-based copolymer paint for lead encapsulation. L-B-C is available for indoor and outdoor applications in 1-, 5-, and 55-gallon containers.

02 00 00
Existing
Conditions

LeadLock and AsbestoSafe

Global Encasement, Inc.
711 Lehigh Ave.
Union, NJ 07083

Toll-free: 800-266-3982
Phone: 201-902-9770
Fax: 201-902-9835
www.encasement.com

AsbestoSafe® and LeadLock™ are water-based, low-VOC, protective acrylic coatings for long-term, in-place management of asbestos and lead-based paint. Both products provide waterproofing yet allow water vapor to pass through the protective coating, and both are highly impact- and seismic-resistant. One of the most impressive characteristics of Global Encasement's Prep-LESS Primer is that it can eliminate and/or minimize surface preparation prior to the application of TopCoats.

Most recently mentioned in EBN 5:6

LeadCheck

HybriVet Systems, Inc.
P.O. Box 1210
Framingham, MA 01701

Toll-free: 800-262-5323
Phone: 508-651-7881
Fax: 508-651-8837
www.leadcheck.com

HybriVet Systems offers several tests for lead in paint, soil, and water, as well as tests for other heavy metal pollutants. LeadCheck® swabs are a quick means of detecting lead in paint and other materials.

Most recently mentioned in EBN 2:2

Safe Encasement Systems

SAFE Encasement Systems
7860 Dana Point Ct.
Las Vegas, NV 89117

Toll-free: 888-277-8834
Phone: 702-360-6111
Fax: 888-277-8835
www.safeencasement.com

Safe Encasement Systems manufactures a two-step encasement process for in-place abatement of lead-based paint and asbestos-fibers. SE-110 Penetrating Stabilizer, also available with corrosion inhibitors or mold-resisting additive, is a clear primer suitable for penetrating and sealing friable fibrous insulation materials and damaged paint

surfaces. SE-110 can be used for interior and exterior applications on a variety of surfaces. When dry, SE-110 is followed by the application of SE-120 Protective Skin, a high-solids, 100% acrylic coating available with or without a mold-resisting additive. Both the Stabilizer and Protective Skin are water-based, nontoxic, nonflammable, zero-VOC formulations that clean up with soap and water.

02 81 00
Transportation and Disposal of Hazardous Materials

Absorbent materials can be used to clean up fuel spills or absorb pollutants in vehicle-maintenance areas. Products listed here manage these fuel spills and pollutants and are made from recycled or natural, rapidly-renewable materials. (See feature article EBN Vol. 8, No. 3.)

ReEweSorb

Appleseed Wool Corp.
55 Bell St.
Plymouth, OH 44865

Toll-free: 800-881-9665
Phone: 419-687-9665
Fax: 419-687-8272
www.appleseedwoolcorp.com

ReEweSorb is a wool-needlefelt oil sorbent that is both reusable (up to 12 times) and highly effective at absorbing oil. Available in 18" squares and 3' x 50' rolls.

ProSorb

Tascon, Inc.
7607 Fairview St.
P.O. Box 41846
Houston, TX 77241

Toll-free: 800-937-1774
Phone: 713-937-0900
Fax: 713-937-1496
www.tasconindustries.com

ProSorb is a recycled-paper absorbent made into small granules for use in and around garage areas for absorbing drips and spills.

03 00 00 Concrete

PRODUCT LISTINGS

03 01 00
Maintenance of Concrete

Concrete is a long-lasting material, but can require maintenance and repair—particularly when it is exposed to severe weather conditions and in structure-as-finish applications where appearance is almost as important as structural integrity. Covering up concrete with additional cosmetic layers can increase maintenance needs significantly over the life of the structure. Products listed here include concrete maintenance and cleaning agents made with biodegradable, biobased materials; and concrete-repair mortars with high fly-ash content. (See also 03 35 00 - Concrete Finishing, 07 19 00 - Water Repellents, 09 97 23 - Concrete and Masonry Coatings, 09 01 93 - Paint Removers.)

Emaco T415 and Emaco T430

BASF Corporation
889 Valley Park Dr.
Shakopee, MN 55379

Toll-free: 800-433-9517
Fax: 800-496-6067
www.corporate.basf.com

Emaco T415 and Emaco T430 are concrete-repair mortars with high levels of fly ash content, an industrial waste product from coal-fired power plants. These products were formerly produced by Degussa Building Systems acquired by BASF in March of 2006.

Orange Peel

Conspec
4226 Kansas Ave.
Kansas City, KS 66106

Toll-free: 800-348-7351
Phone: 913-279-4800
Fax: 913-371-3330
www.conspecmkt.com

Orange Peel is a heavy-duty, biodegradable, citrus-based degreaser and stripper for specialized concrete cleaning and preparation for sealers.

Concrete & Masonry Cleaner and Sealer

Envirosafe Manufacturing Corporation
7634-B Progress Cir.
W. Melbourne, FL 32904

Toll-free: 866-874-8070
Fax: 321-733-0439
www.envirosafemfg.com

Envirosafe Nu Look Concrete & Masonry Cleaner #40-44 is a fluid-applied cleaner that removes dirt, oil, and stains from concrete. Nu Look is biodegradable, noncarcinogenic, and water-soluble with a pH of less than 1.0. Nu Look Gel is slightly more viscous for vertical surfaces. Trojan Masonry Sealer, a penetrating sealer for permanently waterproofing masonry, is a water-dispersed polyester polymer that dries to form a monolithic barrier filling voids and coating the interior particles of concrete to block moisture transmission. Trojan Masonry Sealer releases no VOCs, is nontoxic, nonflammable, noncaustic, and is suitable for use indoors or out on concrete, cement, brick, stucco, plaster, mortar, terrazzo, and most natural stones.

K Pro CD Grease Remover for Concrete Surfaces **New**

Kaufman Products, Inc.
3811 Curtis Ave.
Baltimore, MD 21226

Toll-free: 800-637-6372
Phone: 410-354-8600
Fax: 410-354-1122
www.kaufmanproducts.net

K Pro CD from Kaufman Products is a biodegradable, citrus-based cleaning formulation for removing deposits of grease, oil, and other contaminants from concrete surfaces. K Pro CD, which has zero VOC content and is water-soluble, penetrates surfaces, dissolving rubber tire marks, fats, and greases on floors in garages, plants, restaurants, and kitchens.

03 05 13
Coal Fly Ash

Coal fly ash is a waste product of coal-fired power plants and can be used as a substitute for some of the portland cement in a concrete mixture—up to 60% is common, but even higher levels of substitution are possible. It makes the concrete stronger and gives it improved workability compared with a conventional mix. The environmental advantages include reducing the use of high-embodied-energy portland cement and reusing an otherwise landfilled waste product. Other industrial and agricultural waste products, including ground blast-furnace slag and rice-hull ash, can also be used to replace some of the portland cement in concrete. At low levels (up to about 20% substitution) fly can be used instead of concrete with little or no impact on curing and finishing. At higher levels, care must be used to ensure that mixtures are properly engineered for the application and that appropriate finishing procedures are applied. Fly ash is generally supplied in bulk to ready-mix plants, which do the custom-mixing. (See also 03 30 00 - Cast-in-Place Concrete.) (See feature article EBN Vol. 8, No. 6.)

Industry Representation

American Coal Ash Association
15200 E. Girard Ave., Ste. 3050
Aurora, CO 80014

Phone: 720-870-7897
Fax: 720-870-7889
www.acaa-usa.org

The American Coal Ash Association's (ACAA's) mission is to advance the management and use of coal combustion products (CCPs) in ways that are environmentally responsible, technically sound, and commercially competitive.

Boral Material Technologies

Boral Material Technologies Inc.
45 N.E. Loop 410 Ste. 700
San Antonio, TX 78216

Toll-free: 800-964-0951
Phone: 210-349-4069
Fax: 210-349-8512
www.boral.com

Boral Material Technologies, Inc. is a supplier of coal fly ash.

Full Circle Solutions

Full Circle Solutions Inc.
665 Molly Ln., Ste. 100
Woodstock, GA 30189

Phone: 770-517-7017
Fax: 770-517-9689
www.fcsi.biz

Full Circle Solutions, Inc. is a supplier of coal fly ash.

Headwaters Resources

Headwaters Resources, Inc.
10653 S. Riverfront Pkwy., Ste. 300
South Jordan, UT 84095

Toll-free: 888-236-6236
Phone: 801-984-9400
Fax: 801-984-9410
www.flyash.com

Headwaters Resources, Inc., formerly ISG Resources, is a supplier of coal fly ash.

Lafarge North America

Lafarge North America
12950 Worldgate Dr.,Ste. 500
Herndon, VA 20170

Toll-free: 800-323-5949
Phone: 703-480-3600
Fax: 703-796-2218
www.lafargenorthamerica.com

Lafarge North America, formerly Mineral Solutions, Inc., is a supplier of coal fly ash.

Nebraska Ash Co.

Nebraska Ash Co.
1815 Y St.
P.O. Box 80268
Lincoln, NE 68501

Phone: 402-434-1776
Fax: 402-434-1799
www.nebraskaash.com

Nebraska Ash Co. is a supplier of coal fly ash.

03 00 00
Concrete

Recyclospheres and Bionic Bubble

Sphere Services, Inc.
123 Leinart St., Ste. 205
Clinton, TN 37716

Toll-free: 800-314-8613
Phone: 865-388-3827
Fax: 865-463-2491
www.sphereservices.com

Recyclospheres (also known as cenospheres) are coal combustion byproducts that can be used as fillers in plastics, sealants, adhesives, caulks, paints, coatings, etc. to improve low-density flowability and strength. Cenospheres are currently being evaluated for the EPA's Comprehensive Procurement Guidelines list for use in concrete products. Available in 50-lb. bags, 2,000-lb. pallets, and bulk bags, as well as by the bulk tanker truckload.

SEFA Group

The SEFA Group
217 Cedar Rd.
Lexington, SC 29073

Toll-free: 888-339-7332
Phone: 803-520-9000
www.sefagroup.com

The SEFA Group is a supplier of coal fly ash.

Trans-Ash

Trans-Ash
617 Shepherd Dr.
P.O. Box 15396
Cincinnati, OH 45215

Phone: 513-733-4770
Fax: 513-554-6147
www.transash.com

Trans-Ash is a supplier of coal fly ash.

---

03 05 14
Concrete Pigments

Coloring pigments in concrete add architectural interest using very little additional material—turning concrete into finished surfaces, which avoids the need for additional products and coatings, eliminating the environmental impacts associated with manufacturing and maintaining those materials. Products listed here include recycled materials and mineral byproducts of industry.

Recycled Glass Aggregates and Powders

American Specialty Glass, Inc.

For full listing, see CSI section 09 66 03 - Terrazzo Flooring Aggregate

Davis Colors

Davis Colors
3700 E. Olympic Blvd.
Los Angeles, CA 90023

Toll-free: 800-356-4848
Phone: 323-269-7311
Fax: 323-269-1053
www.daviscolors.com

Davis Colors produces color additives for portland cement-based concrete paving and finished floor surfaces, concrete products, and structures. Made from recycled or reclaimed steel and iron, Davis Colors are added to the concrete mix with the company's Chameleon™ computer-operated automatic dosing system or with Mix-Ready® bags that dissolve when tossed directly into an operating ready-mix truck. With integral color, the high embodied energy of concrete is offset by the dual structural and finish floor role of the colored concrete.

EnvironOxide Pigments

Hoover Color Corporation
2170 Julia Simpkins Rd.
P.O. Box 218
Hiwassee, VA 24347

Phone: 540-980-7233
Fax: 540-980-8781
www.hoovercolor.com

Hoover Color Corporation, in partnership with Iron Oxide Recovery, Inc. (IOR), produces a range of earth-tone pigments made with EnvironOxide™, a natural iron oxide product recovered from abandoned coal mine drainage. Settling ponds and constructed wetlands are used in a patented process to contain the mine runoff. The process yields a premium quality pigment that is nontoxic, nonbleeding, and weather-resistant while cleaning water that would otherwise pollute the receiving stream. The product can be used as a colorant in a wide range of building products, including concrete, cement block, paint, wood stain, and brick. For general information, contact IOR at 412-571-2204; for sales, contact Hoover Color at 540-980-7233. Iron oxide pigments made from EnvironOxide must be specifically requested.

03 05 15
Curing Agents

Concrete curing agents are coatings or admixtures that aid the set and cure of freshly poured concrete. They generally use coalescing agents to retard evaporation. Conventional products use a petroleum hydrocarbon resin base. Products listed here are made with biobased materials, are low-solvent, low-VOC (50 gpl or less), water-based, or some combination of those.

Quantum-Cure

Atlas Construction Supply, Inc.
4640 Brinell St.
San Diego, CA 92111

Phone: 858-277-2100
Fax: 858-277-0585
www.atlastechproducts.com

Atlas Quantum-Cure™ is a water-based, zero-VOC, concrete curing compound that forms a moisture-retaining membrane for proper cement hydration. The ready-to-use, non-staining cure is spray-applied on freshly placed concrete and does not need to be removed prior to application of subsequent materials. Quantum-cure is NSF/ANSI certified to be safe for potable water containment projects.

Kure 200W

BASF Corporation
889 Valley Park Dr.
Shakopee, MN 55379

Toll-free: 800-433-9517
Fax: 800-496-6067
www.corporate.basf.com

Kure 200W is a water-based, zero-VOC concrete curing compound formerly manufactured by Degussa Building Systems acquired by BASF in March of 2006.

Concrete Curing Compounds

Kaufman Products, Inc.
3811 Curtis Ave.
Baltimore, MD 21226

Toll-free: 800-637-6372
Phone: 410-354-8600
Fax: 410-354-1122
www.kaufmanproducts.net

Kaufman Products offers several low-VOC industrial concrete curing and sealing compounds. Thinfilm 422 Wax Base is a zero-VOC water-emulsion membrane compound formulated especially for highways, but also appropriate for driveways, sidewalks, curbs, and gutters; available pigmented or clear in pails, drums, and bulk. Krystal 15 emulsion and Krystal 25 emulsion are water emulsion acrylic polymer curing and sealing compounds with 9 g/l VOC, available in drums and pails. Cure 100 is a water-emulsion, resin-based membrane compound with 14 g/l VOC, available in drums and pails. Cure & Seal 309 emulsion is a water-emulsion, acrylic-modified resin curing and sealing compound with 60 g/l VOC.

Cure and Seal

Natural Soy, LLC
2 Liberty St.
Watkins, IA 52354

Toll-free: 888-655-0039
Phone: 319-227-7418
Fax: 319-227-7428
www.naturalsoyprod.com

Natural Soy's Cure and Seal, made from soy oil and other natural ingredients, is designed to retain the hydration water in freshly worked concrete. It also repels water and assists in the prevention of surface scaling of concrete induced by freeze-thaw cycles and the impact of deicing salts. Cure and Seal will not prevent the penetration of motor or other heavier oils. It is available in 5-, 55-, and 250-gallon containers and should be applied at a rate of 1 gal/200 ft².

SOYsolv Concrete Curing Agent

SOYsolv
6154 N. CR 33
Tiffin, OH 44883

Toll-free: 800-231-4274
Phone: 419-992-4570
Fax: 419-992-4595
www.soysolv.com

SOYsolv® Concrete Curing Agent, made from soybean oil, is nontoxic, nonflammable, ASTM C-309-compliant, and cleans up with water.

03 05 16
Waterproofing Admixtures

Water-repelling admixtures for site-cast and precast concrete can produce better results than surface-applied waterproofing. Products listed here have VOC contents of less than 50 grams per liter. (See also 07 16 00 - Cementitious and Reactive Waterproofing.)

Hycrete

Hycrete
250 Newark Ave.
Jersey City, NJ 07302

Phone: 201-386-8110
Fax: 201-386-8155
www.hycrete.com

Hycrete's zero VOC water- and corrosion-proofing admixture chemically reacts with concrete to shut down capillary absorption and make the concrete hydrophobic, eliminating the need for an external waterproofing membrane. Hycrete's polar molecule also forms a protective coating on rebar. In third-party corrosion tests, Hycrete significantly outperformed other high-performance concrete additives. Hycrete is Cradle to Cradle™ (C2C) certified as a 'biological nutrient', meeting McDonough Braungart Design Chemistry (MBDC) requirements for human and environmental health. Sold by the gallon, tote, or tanker, Hycrete is cost competitive with other concrete waterproofing methods for commercial construction.

Most recently mentioned in EBN 16:2

03 11 00
Concrete Forming

Cement production requires about 6 million Btus per ton of cement produced; most of that energy is used in coal-fired cement kilns, resulting in high carbon dioxide, nitrous oxide, and sulfur emissions. It's been calculated that producing a ton of cement releases a ton of CO2 into the atmosphere. Judicious use of concrete is an important green-building consideration. Concrete pier foundations greatly reduce concrete use compared with full-height frost walls; while most commonly used for decks, outdoor stairs, and the like, they are also used for entire buildings and can be particularly appropriate on ecologically fragile sites. Products listed here are less resource-intensive than conventional concrete-forming products, permit the construction of foundations using less concrete, or are made from recycled-content materials or plywood certified according to the standards of the Forest Stewardship Council (FSC). Concrete construction tubes made from recycled paper, in conjunction with recycled-plastic or fabric footing forms, offer a quick, resource-efficient means of pouring structural piers. (See also 03 11 19 - Insulating Concrete Forming, 03 51 00 - Cast Roof Decks, 03 11 33 - Form-Release Agents.)

03 00 00
Concrete

Bigfoot System Footing Forms

Bigfoot Systems Inc.
6750 Hwy. #3
Martin's Point, NS B0J 2E0 Canada

Toll-free: 800-934-0393
Phone: 902-627-1600
Fax: 902-627-1700
www.bigfootsystems.com

The Bigfoot System® is a one-piece, lightweight, recycled, high-density polyethylene (HDPE) form for site-forming pier footings. The funnel-shaped form replaces site-built solid-wood footings. The construction tube and the footing pour as one unit. Bigfoot Systems will accept all 6", 8", 10", 12", 14", 16", and 18" cardboard construction tubes. Tubes are attached to the Bigfoot Systems using four screws.

Most recently mentioned in EBN 7:2

Caraustar Concrete Column Forms

Caraustar ICPG Corp.
100 Forest Ln.
Evergreen Industrial Park
Beardstown, IL 62618

Phone: 217-323-5225
Fax: 217-323-1994
www.caraustar.com

Caraustar (formerly Smurfit) Concrete Column Forms are recycled-paper concrete forms with a polyethylene-impregnated virgin kraft interior layer (to aid release) and a waxed exterior. The recycled-paper content is estimated to be 90% from mixed, post-industrial, and post-consumer sources, according to the company. Caraustar Concrete Column Forms are available from 6" to 48" in diameter (2" increments up to 24").

Fastfoot, Fastbag, and Fast-Tube Fabric Forms

Fab-Form Industries Ltd.
Unit #212, 6333 148th St.
Surrey, BC V3S 3C3 Canada

Toll-free: 888-303-3278
Phone: 604-596-3278
Fax: 604-501-6090
www.fab-form.com

Fastfoot® is a fabric concrete footing form system for linear foundations. Specially designed steel "yokes" hold pairs of 2x4s, which hold the fabric in a trough formation. After the 2x4s are leveled, the trough is filled with concrete. The 2x4s can be nailed to the partially cured concrete as bracing for the foundation forms or removed for reuse. Fastfoot is well suited to rocky or uneven ground. Fastfoot Lite is a simplified version,

03 00 00
Concrete

which uses the same fabric with 2x4s and stakes. Fastbag®, for pier footings, is a nonwoven polypropylene "pillowcase" with a hole in the top that is nailed to the ground and filled with concrete. As the plastic fabric forms are not removed, there may be some indoor air quality benefits from the capillary break between footings and soil. The company also now offers Fast-Tube™ for forming concrete columns.

Most recently mentioned in EBN 10:1

Geotube Reusable Plastic Column Forms

Geoproducts Corp.
11-110 Jardin Dr.
Concord, ON L4K 4R4 Canada

Toll-free: 877-GEOTUBE
Phone: 905-760-2256
Fax: 905-760-0491
www.geoproductscorp.com

Geotube reusable plastic forms for square, rectangular, and round columns are made with recycled polypropylene. Since concrete doesn't stick to plastic, these forms do not require release agents, lubricants, or cleaning detergents. The modular formworks, which can be stored in damp environments without damage, connect together with nylon handles. The manufacturer guarantees 100 reuses.

GreenCore Plyform

ROMEX World Trade Company, LLC - sales agent for ROM
P.O. Box 1110
Alexandria, LA 71309

Toll-free: 800-299-5174
Phone: 318-445-1973
Fax: 318-443-0159
www.martco.com

GreenCore Plyform® FSC-certified concrete forming panels are available in BB grade and 19/32" and 23/32" thicknesses. These panels are edge-sealed and oiled with NOX-CRETE Concrete Forming Oil, a petroleum-based product made by Chemtrec in Omaha, Nebraska. The mill also produces industrial plywood. GreenCore Plyform is certified using partial-content rules for certification (some fiber used in the mill comes from land not owned by the company), but 100% FSC-certified product can be provided. Roy O. Martin Lumber Management, LLC (ROM) is the first company to receive FSC-certification in the state of Louisiana, and they offer the first FSC-certified OSB and FSC-certified utility poles.

Most recently mentioned in EBN 11:6

SONOTUBES

Sonoco Products Co.
1 North Second St.
Hartsville, SC 29550

Toll-free: 888-875-8754
Phone: 843-383-7000
Fax: 843-339-6803
www.sonoco.com

Sonotube® fiber forms are cylindrical recycled paperboard forms available from 6" to 60" in diameter. These are the most widely used concrete column forms; in fact, the brand name is often used generically.

Recycled-Paper Formworks/ Brick Ledger Void Forms

SureVoid Products, Inc.
1895 W. Dartmouth Ave.
Englewood, CO 80110

Toll-free: 800-458-5444
Phone: 303-762-0324
Fax: 303-762-9931
www.surevoid.com

SureVoid® produces a range of corrugated paper construction products, referred to commonly as "void forms" or "carton forms." These forms create a space between concrete structures and expansive soils (soils high in clay content that expand when wet) to isolate the concrete from the swelling ground. They can also provide a temporary support platform until the grade beam or structural slab has set and can support itself across drilled piers, pads, or intermittent footings. As the corrugated paper eventually absorbs ground moisture and loses strength, it creates a space for wet soil to expand into without causing damage. An alternative use for these products is to displace concrete volume as a means of reducing weight and cost.

The Footing Tube

The Footing Tube
28 Amberwood Ln.
Fredericton, NB E3C 1L7 Canada

Toll-free: 888-929-2011
Phone: 506-452-8919
Fax: 506-457-2543
www.foottube.com

The Footing Tube™ is a tapered, one-piece, 100% recycled polyethylene footing and pier form primarily for decks and additions. The 62"-high form, which can hold a volume of 4.8 ft³ of concrete, has a diameter of 24" at the base of the footing and 8" at the top of the pier. According to the company, the taper and smooth plastic of the sides of a properly installed tube increases resistance to frost uplift in comparison to typical cylindrical formwork. The Footing Tube works in frost-prone areas to 5' depths.

03 11 19 Insulating Concrete Forming

Insulating concrete forms (ICFs) provide a labor-efficient means of making insulated poured-concrete walls, floors, and roof decks. ICFs are permanent forms—they aren't disassembled after the concrete has cured. Most of these products are made from expanded polystyrene (EPS) foam produced with a non-ozone-depleting blowing agent; a couple are made from a composite of wood waste or EPS beads and portland cement. To protect against potential damage from wood-boring insects, some EPS foam used in ICFs contains borates, which are benign to humans and the environment; however, the brominated flame retardants used in most EPS foam have health and environmental risks that are generating significant concern. The environmental advantages of ICF walls include higher R-values, and their use can result in reduced concrete content compared with conventionally formed concrete walls. Be aware that the R-values claimed by ICF manufacturers are not always arrived at in a consistent manner and may be misleading. For comparison purposes, "steady-state" R-values should be used when that information is available. Mass-enhanced or "effective" R-values are only relevant in certain climates or under certain conditions, but they're often listed in product literature in a way that fails to distinguish them clearly from steady-state R-values. (See also 06 12 13 - Cementitious Reinforced Panels, 31 60 00 - Special Foundations and Load-Bearing Elements, 04 22 20 - Autoclaved Aerated Concrete Masonry Units.) (See feature article EBN Vol. 9, No. 3.)

R-Control ICF System

Advance Foam Plastics, Inc. - California Division
Maquiladoras #331 Interior A y B
Cd. Industrials Nueva Tijuana
Tijuana, BC 22500 Mexico

Phone: 626-334-5358
Fax: 626-969-3978
www.afprcontrol.com

Advance Foam Plastics is a licensed manufacturer of AFM Corporation's R-Control® ICF System. The R-Control system consists of 1' x 8' R-Control PerformGuard® insect-resistant EPS foam panels joined by plastic form ties on 12" centers. Ties vary in length to create 4", 6", 8", and 10" walls with a nominal R-value of 20.

R-Control ICF System

Advance Foam Plastics, Inc. - Colorado Division
5250 N. Sherman St.
Denver, CO 80216

Toll-free: 800-525-8697
Phone: 303-297-3844
Fax: 303-292-2613
www.afprcontrol.com

Advance Foam Plastics is a licensed manufacturer of AFM Corporation's R-Control® ICF System. The R-Control system consists of 1' x 8' R-Control PerformGuard® insect-resistant EPS foam panels joined by plastic form ties on 12" centers. Ties vary in length to create 4", 6", 8", and 10" walls with a nominal R-value of 20.

R-Control ICF System

Advance Foam Plastics, Inc. - Nevada Division
920 Kleppe Ln.
Sparks, NV 89431

Toll-free: 800-444-9290
Phone: 775-355-7655
Fax: 775-355-7615
www.afprcontrol.com

Advance Foam Plastics is a licensed manufacturer of AFM Corporation's R-Control® ICF System. The R-Control system consists of 1' x 8' R-Control PerformGuard® insect-resistant EPS foam panels joined by plastic form ties on 12" centers. Ties vary in length to create 4", 6", 8", and 10" walls with a nominal R-value of 20.

R-Control ICF System

Advance Foam Plastics, Inc. - Utah Division
111 W. Fireclay Ave.
Murray, UT 84107

Toll-free: 877-775-8847
Phone: 801-265-3465
Fax: 801-265-3542
www.afprcontrol.com

Advance Foam Plastics is a licensed manufacturer of AFM Corporation's R-Control® ICF System. The R-Control system consists of 1' x 8' R-Control PerformGuard® insect-resistant EPS foam panels joined by plastic form ties on 12" centers. Ties vary in length to create 4", 6", 8", and 10" walls with a nominal R-value of 20.

Amazon Grid-Wall ICFs

Amazon Forms One, Inc.
19068 Marbach Ln.
San Antonio, TX 78266

Toll-free: 866-651-3322
Phone: 210-651-3322
Fax: 210-651-3238
www.amazongridwall.com

Amazon Grid-Wall™ is an insulated concrete form system made from polystyrene (85% by volume, 100% of which is post-consumer recycled) and cement. The standard form measures 4' long x 10" thick x 16" tall with 6" diameter voids running horizontally and vertically 16" o.c. Grid-Wall forms are dry stacked but must be spot glued with a polystyrene-compatible adhesive to keep the forms from shifting during the concrete pour. Grid-Wall does not require drywall on the interior; stucco can be applied to the exterior using only one coat and no wire lath. Grid-Wall forms are termite- and fire-resistant and can be molded with power tools or a rasp.

PolySteel Forms

American PolySteel, LLC
6808 Academy Pkwy. East, NE
Building C-2
Albuquerque, NM 87109

Toll-free: 800-977-3676
Phone: 505-345-8153
Fax: 505-345-8154
www.polysteel.com

American PolySteel manufactures a variety of ICF products utilizing expanded polystyrene foam form pieces and steel connectors/attachment studs rather than the much more common plastic ties. In 2002 the company reconfigured its forms so that the steel connectors are now recessed 1/2" below the surface of the form, thereby improving thermal performance. PolySteel manufactures both a "waffle-grid" and "flat-wall" form, as well as an insulated concrete deck form. The company also incorporates AFM Corporation's Perform Guard® borate treatment in their forms to protect against insect damage.

Most recently mentioned in EBN 11:6

Arxx Walls & Foundations

Arxx Building Products
800 Division St.
Cobourg, ON K9A 5V2 Canada

Toll-free: 800-293-3210
Phone: 905-373-0004
Fax: 905-373-8301
www.arxxwalls.com

03 00 00
Concrete

Arxx standard 6" ICFs are comprised of two 2-3/8"-thick EPS panels separated by 99% post-industrial recycled polypropylene plastic webbing on 8" centers. The webbing serves as strapping for attachment of interior and exterior finishes and as support for steel reinforcing rods within the wall. Each standard interlocking Arxx block is 4' long, 16-3/4" high, and 11-1/2" thick with a steady-state R-value of 22.1. Other thicknesses (4", 8", and 10") and configurations are available, as are a number of accessories that facilitate construction.

R-Control ICF System

Big Sky Insulations, Inc.
P.O. Box 838
Belgrade, MT 59714

Toll-free: 800-766-3626
Phone: 406-388-4146
Fax: 406-388-7223
www.bsiinc.com

Big Sky Insulations is a licensed manufacturer of AFM Corporation's R-Control® ICF System. The R-Control system consists of 1' x 8' R-Control PerformGuard® insect-resistant EPS foam panels joined by plastic form ties on 12" centers. Ties vary in length to create 4", 6", 8", and 10" walls with a nominal R-value of 20.

Baleblock System

Celestial Construction, Inc.
1599 Luisa St.
Santa Fe, NM 87505

Phone: 505-820-2818
Fax: 505-820-0861
www.birkaniarchitects.com

The Baleblock™ system uses straw bales with two predrilled 4" holes to form an insulating straw-bale wall with a "post-and-beam" reinforced-concrete structure. This technique was developed by Erem Birkan, an architect in Sante Fe, New Mexico.

Cempo Form

Cempo Forms, Inc.
P.O. Box 9300
Pahrump, NV 89060

Phone: 775-727-6565
Fax: 775-727-1347
www.cempo.com

Cempo Form is a 100% recycled EPS and cement-composite permanent form system. The standard forms are available in 8", 10", and 12" thicknesses in a 32" x 48" block (approximately 150 lbs. and most often chosen by owner-builders) and a 32" x 96" block (300 lbs. and more commonly used by contractors). Cempo Form can be easily worked with hand tools, and can be cut and

shaped for a variety of details. The company is in the process of testing for R-value.

SmartBlock

ConForm Pacific Inc.
1376 W. 8040 S, Ste. 2
West Jordan, UT 84088

Toll-free: 800-266-3676
Phone: 801-562-9050
Fax: 801-562-9053
www.smartblock.com

SmartBlocks, made from EPS, are available to form a solid concrete wall in 4", 6", 8", 10", and 12" nominal sizes or as a screen concrete wall measuring 40" x 10" x 10" with a 6-1/2" wide (standard size) post-and-beam concrete-core structure. SmartBlock walls possess superior acoustic insulation and use plastic connectors with 100% recycled content. ConForm Pacific Inc. claims R-22 to R-24 insulation values.

Durisol Wallforms

Durisol Building Systems Inc.
67 Frid St.
Hamilton, ON L8P 4M3 Canada

Phone: 905-521-0999
Fax: 905-521-8658
www.durisolbuild.com

Durisol Wallforms are the original stay-in-place concrete forms introduced in 1945. They are made from a composite of mineralized wood chips and portland cement. Each wallform provides approximately 3 ft² of wall. Mineral wool insulation inserts are available in several sizes to provide steady-state R-values up to R-21. The structural design permits use in multistory buildings. The Durisol material can also be specified in custom shapes for use as precast noise-absorption panels, retaining walls, floor forms, and roof panels.

Most recently mentioned in EBN 7:3 & 9:3

ECO-Block ICFs

ECO-Block, LLC
11220 Grader St., Ste. 700
Dallas, TX 75238

Toll-free: 800-503-0901
Phone: 214-503-1644
Fax: 214-342-5322
www.eco-block.com

ECO-Block® EPS ICFs have embedded HDPE webs that serve as recessed furring strips on the exterior and as attachment points on the interior. Connectors (4", 6", 8", and 10") can be used singly or spliced together, allowing for concrete thicknesses from 4" to 24" or greater. With 5" of EPS in the wall profile, ECO-Blocks have an R-value of 22. The ECO-Block system includes straight

panels, 90-degree corners (4", 6", and 8"), 45-degree corners, and brick ledge panels, and is amenable to tilt-up construction with insulation on one side only. ICF blocks are shipped unassembled (to save freight) and assembled on-site. The total recycled content by weight is approximately 40%, per the manufacturer. The ECO-Block team offers support for installation, code compliance, design assistance, and building science.

Most recently mentioned in EBN 11:6

Fox Blocks

New

Fox Blocks
6110 Abbott Dr.
Division of Airlite Plastics Company
Omaha, NE 68110

Toll-free: 877-369-2562
Fax: 402-408-5099
www.foxblocks.com

Fox-Blocks™ is an ICF block system including reversible, pre-assembled ICF blocks with interlocking key-way block connections, ties, and corner brackets designed to add strength and facilitate application of veneer finishes. The ties are 100% recycled material. The EPS foam core has a steady-state R-value of 4.55 per inch, and the manufacturer claims a total R-value for the block of 35 or greater.

Greenblock

Greenblock Worldwide Corp.

P.O. Box 749
Woodland Park, CO 80866

Toll-free: 800-216-1820
Phone: 719-687-0645
Fax: 719-687-7820
www.greenblock.com

Greenblock™ is an insulating concrete form made from EPS and held together by plastic webs for structural integrity and minimal thermal bridging. Greenblock's 6" core and 8" core blocks have 2-5/8" of foam on the interior side of the block and 2-5/8" on the exterior side. Greenblock forms have been used for over 30 years.

ICF Block System

ICF Industries, Inc.
570 S. Dayton - Lakeview Rd.
New Carlisle, OH 45344

Toll-free: 877-423-4800
Phone: 937-845-8347
Fax: 937-845-9837
www.iceblock.net

The ICF Block™ System utilizes 16" x 48" x 9-1/4"-wide (or 11"-wide) EPS foam blocks with 6" (or 8") concrete cores. Steel studs are embedded on 12" centers within the blocks to facilitate attachment of interior and exterior finishes. Thermal bridging is minimized because the studs are not exposed on the exterior of the EPS block.

Insul-Deck ICFs for Floors, Roofs, and Walls

Insul-Deck
7000 Houston Rd., Bldg. 100, Ste. 3
Florence, KY 41042

Toll-free: 800-475-6720
Phone: 859-525-6720
Fax: 859-525-1167
www.insul-deck.org

Insul-Deck® is an interlocking ICF for joisted concrete floors, roofs, tilt-walls, and precast walls. Molded from EPS with integral steel functioning as support beams and receptors for drywall attachment, Insul-Deck can span up to 30' or more, allowing for clear-span basements. Integral channels (approximately 4-3/4" in diameter) for utility lines enable ducting within the insulated space and improved energy performance. Panels are available in any length, with variable thicknesses for R-values from 16 to 34. According to the manufacturer, the finished Insul-Deck system is 30-40% lighter than comparable poured-in-place slab floor systems and provides the same load capacity.

Insulating Concrete Form Association

Insulating Concrete Form Association
1730 Dewes St., Ste. 2
Glenview, IL 60025

Toll-free: 888-864-4232
Phone: 847-657-9730
Fax: 847-657-9728
www.forms.org

The Insulating Concrete Form Association (ICFA) is primarily involved in promoting the use of ICF construction. They also work on drafting building codes and standards, research, and the education of its members.

Premier ICFs

Insulfoam (Division of Premier Industries, Inc.)
1019 Pacific Ave., Ste. 1501
Tacoma, WA 98402

Toll-free: 800-248-5995
Phone: 253-572-5111
Fax: 253-387-7100
www.insulfoam.com

Insulfoam manufactures interlocking insulated concrete forms from expanded polystyrene (EPS) containing up to 15% post-consumer recycled content. The forms are borate-treated for insect resistance. No assembly of individual forms is required. The company claims an average R-value of 27 (minimum R-20, but with 30% of the wall a solid 9-1/2" of EPS at R-45, Insulfoam calculates an average of approximately R-27). The company manufactures ICFs at their plants in Alaska, California, Washington, and Nebraska and accepts EPS scrap from its larger customers.

Faswall Wallforms

K-X Faswall Corp.
P.O. Box 88
Windsor, SC 29865

Toll-free: 800-491-7891
Phone: 803-642-8142
Fax: 803-642-9346
www.faswall.com

Faswall® is a fiber-cement block ICF. These ICFs are made of cement with optional fly ash content and K-X Aggregate (waste wood chips treated with mineral solutions to improve durability and cementitious bonding). A standard wallform block measures 16" x 8" x 11-1/2" with a 6"-deep core and weighs 22 lbs. Split-double, large-core, and corner wallforms are also available.

Most recently mentioned in EBN 1:3, 7:3, 9:3

Lite-Form and Fold-Form

Lite-Form
1950 W. 29th St.
South Sioux City, NE 68776

Toll-free: 800-551-3313
www.liteform.com

Lite-Form ICFs are comprised of two EPS rigid-foam planks measuring 4' x 8" x 2" held together by plastic spacer ties that can be sized to offer concrete thicknesses from 4" to 24" (in 2" increments). Lite-Form is available in EPS or XPS foam. Only the EPS is being specified here. Fold-Form is an interlocking, foldable ICF. The forms are made from two 1' x 4' x 2" sheets of rigid EPS foam insulation held together with plastic spacer ties. Fold-Form folds flat for more compact shipping and storage. Form widths are available to create concrete thicknesses of 4" to 16" (also in 2" increments). Both Lite-Form and Fold-Form have calculated R-values of 26 for finished walls. In-Wall bracing is available for all walls over 4' in height.

NUDURA Integrated Building Technology

NUDURA Corporation
27 Hooper Rd., Unit 10
Barrie, ON L4N 9S3 Canada

Toll-free: 866-468-6299
Phone: 705-726-9499
Fax: 705-726-2110
www.nudura.com

Nudura ICF's hinged plastic webs allow compact pre-assembled shipping. The modular, interlocking, reversible EPS units are unfolded at the site and stacked. Standard form size is 8' x 18", in five widths ranging from 9.25" to 17.25". Foam width is 2-5/8" on each side. The webbed polypropylene cross-ties are on 8" centers, with integral hangers for steel reinforcement. The webs are embedded in the foam, providing attachment strips for wall coverings. A variety of specialized forms and accessories are available, including end caps, tapers, corners, height adjusters, T-junctions, and lintels. Factory-cut radius walls are also available. The cross-tie and fastening strip components are made with 100% recycled HDPE from post-consumer and post-industrial sources. Hinge pins in the webbing are made with 100% recycled post-industrial steel alloy. Recycled content, by weight, ranges from 57% to 63% depending on overall width.

03 00 00
Concrete

Pentstar Concrete Form Masonry Units

Pentstar, Corp.
7308 Aspen Ln. N, Ste. 114
Minneapolis, MN 55428

Toll-free: 877-645-9704
Phone: 763-315-9342
Fax: 763-315-9351
www.pentstar.com

Pentstar® Concrete Form Masonry Units, a hybrid of unit masonry and ICF construction, are comprised of two masonry faces tied together by post-industrial recycled reinforced nylon connectors. Between the two masonry faces (starting on the outside) is a 1" dead-air space weep cavity and 2" of rigid foam (EPS or Celotex) that creates a 5-1/2" cavity for the concrete pour. The units are designed to be laid up with mortar, creating a hollow form that works like an ICF. With the insulation to the outside of the concrete pour and inner masonry, thermal mass effects are a significant part of the wall's thermal performance. An additional benefit is that the forms can also serve as the finish on both exterior and interior surfaces.

Most recently mentioned in EBN 10:7

Perform Wall Panel System

Perform Wall, LLC
5776 N. Mesa St.
El Paso, TX 79912

Toll-free: 888-727-8725
Phone: 915-587-8885
Fax: 915-587-8555
www.performwall.com

Perform Wall Panels are made from 85% (by volume) post-consumer EPS and 15% portland cement molded into 8.5"-, 10"-, 12"-, and 14"-thick blocks. Flat stock is available in 2" or 4" thicknesses. Because of the insulating beads, the insulating value is considerably higher than that for concrete alone.

03 00 00
Concrete

IntegraSpec ICF

Phil-Insul Corp o/a IntegraSpec ICF
11U - 735 Arlington Park Place
Kingston, ON K7M 8M8 Canada

Toll-free: 800-382-9102
Phone: 613-634-1319
Fax: 613-634-2291
www.integraspec.com

IntegraSpec® ICF consists of two 2-1/2"-thick interlocking expanded polystyrene form panels (48" long x 12-1/4" high interlocked) held together with High Impact Polystyrene (HIPS) plastic spacers of 4", 5", 6", 8", 10", or 12" to create insulated concrete walls with corresponding concrete core thicknesses. The spacers can be combined to increase core thickness and also function as furring strips/studs. The patented, completely reversible panels are shipped flat. IntegraSpec ICF has an R-value of 22+ per ASHRAE Fundamentals (1997) and is manufactured in both Canada and the U.S.

QUAD-LOCK Insulating Concrete Forms

QUAD-LOCK Building Systems Ltd.
7398 - 132nd St.
Surrey, BC V3W 4M7 Canada

Toll-free: 888-711-5625
Phone: 604-590-3111
Fax: 604-590-8412
www.quadlock.com

QUAD-LOCK® is a system of interlocking expanded polystyrene (EPS) panels connected with HDPE plastic ties. The panels are 12" high, 48" long, and either 2-1/4" or 4-1/4" thick; the HDPE connectors come in different lengths to create walls of nominal 4", 6", 8", 10", or 12" thickness. The manufacturer claims R-values of 22, 32, or 40.

Reddi Form

Reddi Form, Inc.
10 Park Pl., Ste. 5-B
Butler, NJ 07405

Toll-free: 800-334-4303
Phone: 973-283-0055
Fax: 973-283-9505
www.reddiform.com

Reddi Form is a one-piece, screen-grid block insulating concrete form made entirely from expanded polystyrene (EPS). Available in two basic sizes, the 6" concrete-core form with 5 vertical cells (9.6" W x 48" L x 12" H) weighs 3 lbs. and can be used for most residential buildings. The 8" concrete-core form with 4 vertical cells (12" W x 48" L x 12" H) is used for commercial applications. Both foam forms have an R-value of 21. Reddi-Form warrants pours of up to 10' of wall height to be free of blow-outs.

Reddi-Deck Floor and Roof-Deck ICFs

Reddi Form, Inc.
10 Park Pl., Ste. 5-B
Butler, NJ 07405

Toll-free: 800-334-4303
Phone: 973-283-0055
Fax: 973-283-9505
www.reddiform.com

Reddi-Deck™ is a stay-in-place, self-supporting insulating concrete forming system for joisted concrete floor and roof decks. The Reddi-Deck panels are produced by a continuous molding production line integrating the insulating capabilities of EPS with the structural strength of metal inserts. According to the manufacturer, the systems are half the weight of comparable hollow-core, precast systems, which in turn reduces the load on walls and foundations.

iForm

Reward Wall Systems, Inc.
9931 S. 136th St., #100
Omaha, NE 68138

Toll-free: 800-468-6344
Phone: 402-592-7077
Fax: 402-592-7969
www.rewardwalls.com

Reward Wall Systems manufactures the iForm™ flat wall form used in residential and commercial structures including large-scale high-rise projects. Reward's iForm is made from two 2.4"-thick premolded 48" x 16" slabs of EPS held together with plastic ties that are embedded in the EPS. The ties provide strength while the concrete is poured and serve as a nailing surface for interior and exterior finishes such as drywall and siding. The forms remain in place and become part of the wall providing a steady-state R-value of 22 and, according to the manufacturer, an effective R-value of more than 32.

Most recently mentioned in EBN 10:4

I.C.E. Block Insulated Concrete Forms

Southwest I.C.E. Block
501 East Plaza Cir., Ste. F
Litchfield Park, AZ 85340

Toll-free: 800-423-2557
Phone: 623-935-5428
Fax: 623-935-3568
www.iceblockinc.com

The I.C.E. Block™ System utilizes 16" x 48" x 9-1/4"-wide (or 11"-wide) tongue-and-groove EPS foam blocks with 6" (or 8") concrete cores. Steel studs are embedded on 12" centers within the blocks to facilitate attachment of interior and exterior finishes. Thermal bridging is minimized because the studs are not exposed. Concrete Capacity: one yard fills 13 blocks of 6" core; or 10 blocks of 8" core; or 12 blocks of 6-8" Super Duty.

Standard ICFs

Standard ICFs
425 Second Ave. SW
Oronoco, MN 55960

Toll-free: 800-925-3676
Phone: 507-367-2183
Fax: 507-367-2275
www.standardicf.com

Standard ICF Corporation®, formerly Therm-O-Wall, manufactures the 895 ICFs™ System. The system consists primarily of two forms; a standard form made from two 2-3/8"-thick EPS panels separated by recycled-HDPE plastic brackets; and a corner form of the same materials. Standard panels are 48" L x 16" H x 11-1/4" W, providing for a concrete thickness of 6-1/2". The imbedded brackets are placed 12" on center and also function as furring strips for finish material attachment. The company claims an R-value of 26.

Tech Block

Tech Block International, LLC
PO Box 9954
Denver, CO 80209

Phone: 720-308-8815
Fax: 303-777-4514
www.techblock.com

Tech Blocks are patented exterior wall blocks composed of a mixture of polystyrene beads and cement. Bonded to the blocks is OSB sheathing, which becomes the inside surface of the wall and acts as an attachment surface for drywall. Underneath the drywall, the OSB acts as backing for hanging cabinetry, drape hardware, base, casing, etc. The exterior of the blocks is ready for stucco without the need for wire mesh. The Tech Block Wall System resists fire, sound, water, and termites. Each Tech Block weighs about 85 lbs. and measures 48" x 16" x 11" thick, with a steady-state R-value of 47.5, according to the manufacturer. Tech Block International, LLC, is an Energy Star® Partner with plants in Arizona, California, and Georgia, and has plans for plants in Texas and New Mexico.

Most recently mentioned in EBN 10:5

Thermal Foams TF ICF

Thermal Foams, Inc.
2101 Kenmore Ave.
Buffalo, NY 14207

Phone: 716-874-6474
Fax: 716-874-8180
www.thermalfoams.com

Thermal Foams Inc. is an authorized manufacturer/distributor of the TF Insulated Concrete Building System. The TF ICF system is a vertical plank system that consists of Thermal Foams EPS foam panels joined together with PVC or metal I-beams that vary in height and are available in widths to create 4", 6", 8", 10", and 12" walls with a nominal R-value of 22.

VariantHouse ICFs

New

VariantHouse LLC
6625 Miami Lakes Dr. #243
Miami Lakes, FL 33014

Phone: 305-777-3849
Fax: 305-777-3850
www.varianthouse.com

VariantHouse uses BASF's Neopor® EPS to manufacture lightweight, thin, fire-retardant, ICF blocks that are targeted to the do-it-yourself market. VariantHouse's ICF blocks have naps and grooves that click together to create an insulating wall without thermal bridges that can be assembled and concrete-filled by a novice. VariantHouse provides a versatile set of blocks that can accommodate almost any architectural design and conventional finish (such as brick, stone, stucco, wood, and vinyl siding). VariantHouse is currently the only company in North America to use BASF's Neopor. The black Neopor beads contain microscopic flakes of graphite that reflect heat radiation, reducing the foam's thermal conductivity. Products made of silver-grey Neopor® can achieve the same insulating performance as products using BASF's Styropor® with up to 20% less thickness and 50% less raw material. Neopor has an R-value of 5 per inch, which for Variant blocks of 9.8", 13.7", and 17.7" thicknesses, results in R-values of approximately 20, 38, and 57, respectively.

TF System Vertical ICFs

Wisconsin Thermo-Form, Inc.
185 E. Walnut
Sturgeon Bay, WI 54235

Toll-free: 800-360-4634
Phone: 920-746-9100
Fax: 920-743-3811
www.tfsystem.com

Wisconsin Thermo-Form, an Energy Star® Homes Ally, manufactures the TF System™ of unique, vertically oriented insulated concrete forms. This system utilizes a standard 2-1/2" x 12" x 8' expanded polystyrene plank (or custom planks variable in height up to 12') and preformed corner planks. The planks are joined by 26-gauge galvanized steel I-Beam studs, which enable planks to slide up to allow access to the inside of the forms until a top cap is installed. Wall thicknesses of 4", 6", 8", 10", and 12" are possible, with the company claiming an R-value of 25. Forms are shipped flat. Bracing requirements are minimal, and compressive strength allows for the installation of floor systems before pouring.

03 11 33
Form-Release Agents

Conventional form-release oils can be a major source of VOCs, soil contamination, and human health risks. Increasingly, biodegradable, nonpetroleum alternatives are available. These products contain just a fraction of the federally permitted VOC limit for concrete form-release agents. Many of these products produce a smoother finished surface with fewer "bug holes." Products listed here are made with agricultural crops, are typically water-based and biodegradable, and have less than 60 grams per liter VOC. (See also 03 05 15 - Curing Agents.)

BioGuard Form Release Agent

New

Atlas Construction Supply, Inc.
4640 Brinell St.
San Diego, CA 92111

Phone: 858-277-2100
Fax: 858-277-0585
www.atlastechproducts.com

Atlas Bio-Guard is a water-borne, zero-VOC, biodegradable, soy-derived form-release agent that can be used on many types of concrete forms and liners, including plywood, steel, aluminum, polystyrene, fiberglass, etc. It is available in ready-to-use 5-, 55-, and 275-gallon containers. Atlas offers 100% guaranteed satisfaction.

Enviroform and Aquastrip

Conspec
4226 Kansas Ave.
Kansas City, KS 66106

Toll-free: 800-348-7351
Phone: 913-279-4800
Fax: 913-371-3330
www.conspecmkt.com

Enviroform is a 100% biodegradable, plant-oil-based, zero-VOC form-release agent. Aquastrip is a water-based, solvent-containing, VOC-compliant release agent.

Crete-Lease 20-VOC

Cresset Chemical Company
One Cresset Center, Box 367
Weston, OH 43569

Toll-free: 800-367-2020
Phone: 419-669-2041
Fax: 419-669-2200
www.cresset.com

Crete-Lease 20-VOC is a water-based form-release agent. Available in 5- and 55-gallon containers and 275-gallon totes.

Asphalt Release

Franmar Chemical, Inc.
P.O. Box 5565
Bloomington, IL 61702

Toll-free: 800-538-5069
Phone: 309-452-7526
Fax: 309-827-9308
www.franmar.com

Franmar makes soy-based asphalt and concrete form-release agents.

**03 00 00
Concrete**

Greenplus Form Release Agent ES

Greenland Corporation
7016-30 St. SE
Calgary, AB T2C 1N9 Canada

Toll-free: 800-598-7636
Phone: 403-720-7049
Fax: 403-720-4951
www.greenpluslubes.com

Greenland Corporation manufactures the Greenplus line of rapidly biodegradable, vegetable oil-based lubricants suitable for a wide variety of lubricating applications. Customized products are also available, as well as technical support for the proper product choice, and ongoing support. Included in the line is Greenplus Form Release Agent ES for use with metal, wood, plastic, and fiberglass forms. Greenplus Form Release Agent does not react with portland cement or its common admixtures.

FormKote Emulsion

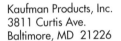

Kaufman Products, Inc.
3811 Curtis Ave.
Baltimore, MD 21226

Toll-free: 800-637-6372
Phone: 410-354-8600
Fax: 410-354-1122
www.kaufmanproducts.net

FormKote Emulsion is a water-based, freeze-thaw-stable, low-VOC (5 g/l), emulsified-chemical form-release agent offering a high coverage rate. Available in 55-gallon drums and five-gallon pails, this biodegradable product applies white and dries clear.

Soy Form Release and Natural Form Oil

Natural Soy, LLC
2 Liberty St.
Watkins, IA 52354

Toll-free: 888-655-0039
Phone: 319-227-7418
Fax: 319-227-7428
www.naturalsoyprod.com

Natural Soy produces Soy Form Oil form-release agent containing soy oil, surfactant, and water. It prevents the adhesion of concrete to forms and molds and can be used to clean forms for reuse. It is sprayable, cleans up with water, and has no VOCs or other hazards. It is available in 5-, 55-, and 250-gallon containers. 1 gallon covers approximately 300 ft². Natural Form Oil is a nonwater-based version for use in freezing conditions.

SOYsolv Concrete Form Release Agent

SOYsolv
6154 N. CR 33
Tiffin, OH 44883

Toll-free: 800-231-4274
Phone: 419-992-4570
Fax: 419-992-4595
www.soysolv.com

Water-based, nonflammable, nontoxic SOYsolv® Concrete Form Release is made from soybean oil and cleans up with soap and water.

Formshield WB

The Euclid Chemical Company
3835 State Rte. 72
Kirkland, IL 60146

Toll-free: 800-862-2667
Phone: 815-522-3394
Fax: 815-522-2323
www.tamms.com

Formshield WB (formerly Aquaform) is a water-based form-release agent available in 5- and 55-gallon containers.

Farm Fresh Form Release Agent

Unitex
3101 Gardner
Kansas City, MO 64120

Toll-free: 800-821-5846
Phone: 816-231-7700
Fax: 816-483-3149
www.unitex-chemicals.com

Farm Fresh is a water-borne, zero-VOC, biodegradable, soybean oil, form-release agent for plywood, steel, aluminum, polystyrene and fiberglass forms and liners. Farm Fresh Plus is a solvent-borne version, also made from soybean oil, for use in sub-freezing conditions. Both are available in 5-gallon pails, 55-gallon drums, and 275-gallon totes. The manufacturer offers 100% guaranteed satisfaction.

Bio-Form

Universal Building Products Inc.
840 25th Ave.
Bellwood, IL 60104

Phone: 708-544-4255
Fax: 708-544-0104
www.universalbuildingproducts.com

Bio-Form® is a biodegradable, zero-VOC concrete form-release agent made primarily from rapeseed oil (in food-grade form known as Canola oil). It can be used below freezing point and covers 2,000 ft²/gal

on pretreated high-density overlay forms. Bio-Form is available in 5- and 55-gallon containers and 275-gallon tanks. Though more expensive than conventional products, it has been reported to perform better.

Most recently mentioned in EBN 6:1

Ezkote Green

US Mix Products Company
112 S. Santa Fe Dr.
Denver, CO 80223

Toll-free: 800-397-9903
Phone: 303-778-7227
Fax: 303-722-8426
www.usmix.com

Ezkote Green is a non-petroleum based, biodegradable form release agent made from agricultural oils. Ezkote Green contains zero VOCs and is part of the US SPEC line of concrete products from US Mix Co.

Duogard II

W. R. Meadows, Inc.
300 Industrial Dr.
P.O. Box 338
Hampshire, IL 60140

Toll-free: 800-342-5976
Phone: 847-214-2100
Fax: 847-683-4544
www.wrmeadows.com

Duogard II, a water-emulsion concrete form-release agent with a VOC content of 55 g/l, is available in 5- and 55-gallon containers.

03 15 00
Concrete Accessories

Concrete accessories include such items as anchors, inserts, expansion joints, waterstops, and products that prevent soil contamination from truck overages. Filling the expansion joints in concrete construction is a good use of panels made from recycled newspaper or waste agricultural materials, because the strength requirements are minimal (though for radon control, less permeable joint sealants may be preferable). Waterstops must be highly durable and corrosion resistant; plasticized PVC is the most common waterstop material, though alternatives are available to a limited degree. Rebar supports for concrete formwork hold rebar in place during pours; they have minimal structural requirements, making them good candidates for manufacturing with

03 00 00
Concrete

recycled waste plastic. Products listed here have high recycled content or some other significant attribute.

Rebar Supports

Eclipse Plastic, Inc.
12504 Roosevelt Rd.
Snohomish, WA 98290

Toll-free: 800-278-4276
Phone: 360-863-9213
Fax: 360-863-1703
www.eclipseplastic.com

Eclipse Plastic manufactures and sells directly a variety of rebar support devices made from 100% recycled engineering-grade plastic.

EnviroSac Bag

New

Enviro-Systems, Inc.
1869 S. Cobb Industrial Blvd.
Smyrna, GA 30082

Toll-free: 800-851-3082
Phone: 770-333-0206
Fax: 770-319-7870
www.envirosys.us

EnviroSac™ woven polypropylene bags collect overage waste during clean-out of concrete ready-mix trucks, concrete pump rigs, and hoppers. The concrete can be left to cure for pick-up by loader, forklift, crane, or hoist. Lightweight EnviroSac bags come in several sizes, include high-strength lifting straps, and fold for compact storage. Bags may be made of lined, urethane coated, or uncoated material. Moisture will bleed through the uncoated material; waterproof liners are recommended for applications in which the alkaline runoff is not acceptable. EnviroSystems also has a program for recycling EnviroSac™ bags and provides customers with a national list of concrete recyclers for the excess concrete.

Homex 300

Homasote Company
932 Lower Ferry Rd.
P.O. Box 7240
West Trenton, NJ 08628

Toll-free: 800-257-9491
Phone: 609-883-3300
Fax: 609-883-3497
www.homasote.com

Homex® 300 can be used both as an expansion joint filler and a clean, curvable light-duty forming material for concrete slabs. This non-bituminous 98% post-consumer waste paper material with weather- and termite-resistant additives conforms to ASTM D-1751, and is available in a variety of lengths, widths, and thicknesses.

Earth Shield Chemical Resistant Waterstop

J P Specialties, Inc.
551 Birch St.
Lake Elsinore, CA 92530

Toll-free: 800-821-3859
Phone: 951-674-6869
Fax: 951-674-1315
www.jpspecialties.com

Earth Shield is a thermoplastic vulcanizate, an alloy of EPDM rubber for flexibility and polypropylene for processability and weldability. It contains no additives, such as fillers, stabilizers, or plasticizers, and is designed to withstand highly demanding conditions. The company claims that Earth Shield is the only embedded waterstop that has been certified to meet NSF Standard 61 for direct contact with drinking water.

03 30 00
Cast-in-Place Concrete

Cement production is energy-intensive and polluting; concrete mixtures incorporating recycled-content, performance-enhancing, portland-cement-reducing admixtures such as fly ash are desirable. Recycled materials used in place of mined stone aggregate—such as slag, a byproduct of steel production—ease landfill burdens and can improve the concrete's strength-to-weight ratio and thermal properties. Products listed here incorporate recycled content or have other desirable environmental qualities. (See also 03 05 13 - Coal Fly Ash, 03 05 14 - Concrete Pigments, 03 05 15 - Curing Agents, 03 05 16 - Waterproofing Admixtures.) (See feature article EBN Vol. 9, No. 3.)

GranCem Cement

Holcim (US), Inc.
201 Jones Rd., Ste. 200
Waltham, MA 02451

Toll-free: 866-465-2460
Phone: 781-647-2501
www.holcim.us

GranCem® cement is a finely ground granulated blast-furnace slag (GGBFS) that typically replaces a portion of the portland cement in mixtures. Concrete made with GranCem as part of the mix design is typically whiter, and the colors are brighter than concrete made with portland cement. GranCem cement used with portland cement produces more calcium silicate hydrate binder than portland cement alone, which

can increase the concrete's compressive strength and durability. The cement blend can be designed to be more resistant to sulfate attack and alkali-silica reaction than pure portland cement. GranCem is listed as a recyclable material by the U.S. Environmental Protection Agency.

Lafarge Lightweight Concrete Aggregate

Lafarge North America
(Chicago and Hamilton Slag)
139 Windermere Rd.
Hamilton, ON L8H 3Y2 Canada

Phone: 219-378-1193
Fax: 219-378-1191
www.lafargenorthamerica.com

Lafarge Lightweight Concrete Aggregate is blast furnace slag aggregate—the recovered nonmetallic mineral components from iron blast furnaces. It can reduce portland cement concrete's weight while improving its compressive strength. The slag is inert and is otherwise typically landfilled. A finer grind of this slag has properties similar to fly ash.

Lightweight Concrete Aggregate

Persolite Products, Inc.
P.O. Box 505
Florence, CO 81226

Toll-free: 800-873-1972
Phone: 719-784-6531
Fax: 719-784-4855
www.persoliteproducts.com

Persolite Products manufactures lightweight concrete aggregates of volcanic materials (perlite) for use in insulating roof decks or producing lightweight concrete. Loose perlite can also be used to insulate concrete masonry units.

Stable Air

Stable Air Inc.
4020 Calle Sonora Este, Unit N
Laguna Woods, CA 92637

Phone: 949-587-1087
Fax: 949-587-1093
www.stableair.com

Stable Air is a cellular concrete system that reduces the weight of cementitious mixes by replacing heavier materials with a durable, preformed foam bubble. Compressive strengths of over 3,000 psi are obtainable within 24 hours, rising to over 6,000 psi in 28 days (maximum compressive strength achieved at 125 pcf is 8,400 psi). The durable foam bubble resists breakage during the pumping action of concrete mixes, thus maintaining designed unit volume. The reduced friction of pumped mixes allows

03 00 00
Concrete

filling ICF block structures without blowout. The Stable Air bubble resists breakage in high-water-content slurry used in reinforced soil projects. The ball-bearing action of the small bubbles improves drilling production and reduces freeze/thaw damage. Benefits include lower water-cement ratio mixes, lower-cost lightweight concrete, lighter-weight structures that reduce other material costs, less costly seismic code compliance, reduced thermal conductivity, and improved acoustic insulation.

03 35 00
Concrete Finishing

03 00 00
Concrete

Covering concrete with cosmetic layers can increase environmental and financial costs significantly over the lifespan of a structure as compared with using concrete in a structure-as-finish capacity. Polished and densified concrete floors (old or new) combine diamond stone-polishing technology with silicate chemical treatment to provide a significantly better alternative to film and wax coatings—highly durable, nearly maintenance-free, noncombustible... and the improved reflectivity can also reduce lighting requirements. (See also 03 01 00 - Maintenance of Concrete & 07 19 00 - Water Repellents.)

RetroPlate Concrete Polishing System

Advanced Floor Products, Inc.
P.O. Box 80533
Provo, UT 84605

Toll-free: 888-942-3144
Phone: 801-812-3420
Fax: 801-812-3400
www.retroplatesystem.com

The RetroPlate system grinds, polishes, and densifies old or new concrete floors using grinding machines and sodium silicate treatment to achieve a finished floor. The sodium silicate hardens the concrete, reducing its porosity and contributing to a lasting surface. A uniform finish or a terrazzo look is possible. Coloring can be achieved with acid dyes and, with new concrete, with pigments and colored aggregate.

Most recently mentioned in EBN 15:2 & 15:12

SureHard Colorless Silcate Liquid

New

Kaufman Products, Inc.
3811 Curtis Ave.
Baltimore, MD 21226

Toll-free: 800-637-6372
Phone: 410-354-8600
Fax: 410-354-1122
www.kaufmanproducts.net

SureHard is a clear, colorless blend of liquid silicates chemically engineered to react with the lime in concrete, forming an insoluble gel in its pores. On a concrete slab, SureHard provides dustproofing, densifying, sealing, and hardening, as well as waterproofing and increased reflectance. Concrete surfaces treated with SureHard may be diamond polished for a polished concrete floor. SureHard is applied with a water-based solution with no VOC content. It is also non-flammable, low-odor, and non-toxic.

Most recently mentioned in EBN 15:2

FGS PermaShine Polished Concrete System

L&M Construction Chemicals, Inc.
14851 Calhoun Rd.
Omaha, NE 68152

New

Toll-free: 800-362-3331
www.lmcc.com

The FGS PermaShine System is a patented dry method of concrete floor or concrete surface restoration using the process of grinding a concrete surface to be resurfaced while extracting and retaining dust during the grinding process. FGS Hardener Plus, a water-based, VOC compliant, odorless, penetrating alkaline siliconate solution is applied to the concrete surface after it has been ground to the predetermined degree of smoothness. FGS PermaShine renews existing concrete floors as well as improving new floors. Polishing new concrete should be done after a 28-day curing process. The FGS PermaShine System is patented and is available exclusively through L&M Construction Chemicals, Inc, and only through its dealers and its certified, trained and approved installers.

Most recently mentioned in EBN 15:2

Certified Green System

VIC International Corporation
231 E. Emory Rd.
Powell, TN 37849

New

Toll-free: 800-423-1634
Phone: 865-947-2882
Fax: 800-242-1141
www.vicintl.com

VIC International produces concrete grinding and polishing equipment and components for use in producing polished concrete floors. The system uses VIC's grinding machines and specialized densifiers that react with the calcium hydroxide in concrete to achieve a finished floor. Applicable to both new and old concrete slab floors. VIC International provides technical support and complete polishing services along with diamond-grinding/polishing and vacuum machines.

WerkMaster Concrete Polishing System

New

Werk Industries /
Fab-u-Floors Refinishing Services
1448 Charlotte Rd.
North Vancouver, BC V7J 1H2 Canada

Toll-free: 866-373-WERK
Phone: 604-629-8705
Fax: 604-904-9597
www.fab-u-floors.com

The WerkMaster system grinds and polishes concrete, creating a high-gloss floor surface. The system can be used with concrete hardening/densifying compounds, such as sodium silicate, available from other suppliers. Werkmaster Octi-Disc Technology incorporates eight counter-rotating diamond grit discs to achieve a polished surface within 1/8-inch of walls. Together with the WerkMaster HEPA vacuum system, the process is 100% dust free, according to the company. The tools are available in both do-it-yourself and contractor sizes, and work on wood, granite, and marble, as well as terrazzo and concrete. The WerkMaster system is available in North America from Fab-u-Floors Refinishing Services.

Most recently mentioned in EBN 15:2

03 40 00
Precast Concrete Panels

Precast structural and architectural concrete products tend to have optimized geometries, can speed construction, and can contribute to reduced environmental damage on the construction site as compared with pouring concrete on-site. Waste from overage is also eliminated through precasting at a plant. Through aeration, the weight of precast concrete components can be reduced by up to a third while improving its insulation value; substitution of fly ash or other post-industrial waste materials can further improve environmental performance. Some panels are cast with integral foam insulation. Products listed here contain recycled materials, contribute to ap-

propriate thermal design, or have other compelling environmental features. (See feature article EBN Vol. 9, No. 3.)

VersaCore Plus

Fabcon, Inc.
6111 W. Hwy. 13
Savage, MN 55378

Toll-free: 800-727-4444
Phone: 952-890-4444
Fax: 952-890-6657
www.fabcon-usa.com

VersaCore Plus™ foam-core concrete wall panel is a precast using expanded polystyrene (EPS) billet instead of gravel to form the panel "voids" (whereas the gravel would subsequently be removed, the EPS is left in place). The VersaCore process enables window and door openings to be precast in a hollow-core type of panel. These panels range from 8" to 12" thick, with R-values of up to 33, according to the manufacturer. Fabcon has manufacturing plants in Minnesota, Pennsylvania, Indiana, and Ohio, which serve the Midwest and Eastern regions of the U.S.

Superior Walls

Superior Walls of America, Ltd.
937 East Earl Rd.
New Holland, PA 17557

Toll-free: 800-452-9255
Fax: 717-351-9263
www.superiorwalls.com

Superior Walls™ is a custom precast foundation wall system with integrated footer, concrete "studs," and bond beam that is insulated at the factory with extruded polystyrene (currently made with ozone-depleting HCFC-141b). Superior Wall Panels are lifted by crane into place and locked together. The R-5 line has 1" of rigid insulation to achieve an R-value of 5, which may be increased with additional insulation to R-24. The Xi line has 2-1/2" of rigid insulation for R-12.5, which may be increased with additional insulation to R-31.5.

Most recently mentioned in EBN 9:3

03 51 00
Cast Roof Decks

Permanent, insulating concrete forms for roof decks are made from expanded polystyrene (EPS) foam produced with a non-ozone-depleting blowing agent. This labor-efficient approach provides improved thermal resistance and reduced concrete use. (See also 03 40 00 - Pre-

cast Concrete Panels.)

Reddi-Deck Floor and Roof-Deck ICFs

Reddi Form, Inc.

For full listing, see CSI section 03 11 19 - Insulating Concrete Forming

03 52 00
Lightweight Concrete Roof Insulation

Cast-in-place concrete roof insulation—aerated or containing insulating aggregate—can be installed over most old or new substrates, and used to overcome dips and negative slopes in the roof plane.

Elastizell

Elastizell Corporation of America
P.O. Box 1462
Ann Arbor, MI 48106

Phone: 734-761-6900
Fax: 734-761-8016
www.elastizell.com

The Elastizell Roof Deck System consists of lightweight foamed cement slurry with optional embedded sheets of EPS insulation up to 12" thick. The slurry is air-entrained on-site using a foaming machine and proprietary protein-stabilized surfactants. The use of other additives and aggregates may be specified; densities from 30-110 pcf may be achieved, with R-values ranging from 0.86 to 1.8 per inch. Elastizell can be applied over metal, concrete, or wood decking, filling depressions and flutes on the roof's surface to eliminate potential air and water channels. The product is positively sloped during installation to achieve proper drainage and eliminate ponding. Then a built-up or single-ply roofing membrane is applied directly on the finished installation. The optional embedded EPS insulation is protected during future roofing tear-offs. The Elastizell system must be installed by certified applicators.

03 54 00
Cast Underlayment

Self-leveling and troweled cementitious underlayments are generally a blend of portland cement and gypsum, typically augmented with VOC-containing polymers and plasticizers, that are used to create a flat, smooth, new surface for subsequent flooring applications. When applied in existing, closed structures, these products can introduce significant moisture as they cure, requiring ventilation. Products listed here include recycled content (such as fly ash), and have very low VOC content.

Fritz Underlayments

Fritz Industries, Inc.
500 Sam Houston Road
Mesquite, TX 75149

Toll-free: 800-955-1323
Phone: 972-285-5471
Fax: 972-270-0179
www.fritztile.com

Fritz Industries manufactures non-toxic, zero-VOC, pozzolanic cementitious underlayment products for use in leveling and patching subfloor surfaces before installing floorcoverings. They are made from 45-70% fly ash, sand, and a small amount of proprietary ingredients including polymer material. F-10 is self-leveling underlayment, Poz-Patch® I is a fast-setting (non self-leveling) underlayment, Poz-Patch® II is a underlayment for use on flexible substrates such as plywood, and Poz-Patch® III is a fast-setting skim-coating patch product.

Level-Right

Maxxon Corporation
920 Hamel Rd.
P.O. Box 253
Hamel, MN 55340

Toll-free: 800-356-7887
Phone: 763-478-9600
Fax: 763-478-2431
www.level-right.com

Level-Right® self-leveling, thin-topping cementitious underlayment from Maxxon® (formerly the Gyp-Crete Corporation) is not polymer-modified, resulting in nearly zero VOCs. It also contains over 51% fly ash (which improves certain qualities of the product, but in this case does not reduce the amount of portland cement content). Note that these green attributes do not apply to the entire Level-Right line of products.

03 00 00
Concrete

This Space is Available for Your Notes

03 00 00
Concrete

04 00 00 Masonry

PRODUCT LISTINGS

04 05 13
Masonry Mortaring

The portland cement content of conventional masonry mortar is high, making most masonry mortars high in embodied energy. Products listed here have some or all of their portland cement content substituted with industrial and agricultural waste products, such as fly ash, ground blast-furnace slag, or rice-hull ash. (See feature article EBN Vol. 8, No. 6.)

MRT Blended Hydraulic Cement

Mineral Resource Technologies, LLC Inc.
2700 Research Forest Dr., Ste. 150
The Woodlands, TX 77381

Toll-free: 800-615-1100
Phone: 281-362-1060
Fax: 281-362-1809
www.mrtus.com

MRT Blended Hydraulic Cement, an alternative to portland cement, is made from Class C fly ash and other ingredients. It is available in bulk for ready-mix plants or in bags for mixing on-site.

Most recently mentioned in EBN 11:4

St. Astier Natural Hydraulic Lime

TransMineral USA, Inc.

For full listing, see CSI section 09 25 00 - Other Plastering

04 05 23
Masonry Accessories

Forces affecting the durability and performance of masonry wall systems include bulk water penetration, wicking of moisture, and solar-driven moisture movement. Products listed here are designed to improve the durability and performance of masonry wall systems. Masonry accessories that improve the durability and performance of masonry

wall systems can include two-piece adjustable brick ties, brick veneer venting and clear cavity components. Note that clear cavity components represent a product solution that should be considered along with techniques for keeping the cavity space clear, such as loose sand and mortar cleanouts in the first course of the veneer.

CavClear Masonry Mat

Archovations, Inc.
P.O. Box 241
Hudson, WI 54016

Toll-free: 888-436-2620
Phone: 715-381-5773
Fax: 715-381-9883
www.cavclear.com

CavClear Masonry Mat is an airspace maintenance and drainage material designed to be installed full-height behind brick or stone. The matting prevents obstruction of the cavity drainage airspace and also prevents formation of energy-conducting mortar bridges. CavClear is a nonwoven plastic mesh made from 100% recycled plastic (25% minimum post-consumer content) and is available in thicknesses of 1/2", 3/4", 1", 1-1/4" and 1-3/4". It is also available bonded to EPS insulation.

CavClear Weep Vents

Archovations, Inc.
P.O. Box 241
Hudson, WI 54016

Toll-free: 888-436-2620
Phone: 715-381-5773
Fax: 715-381-9883
www.cavclear.com

CavClear® Weep Vents are 100% recycled-plastic, nonwoven mesh vents with a flame-retardant binder designed for use in the vertical joints between brick masonry units in masonry cavity wall construction. When installed as intended, CavClear Weep Vents help provide moisture drainage and airflow. The vents come in light gray and manilla colors, with other colors subject to availability, and are part of a complete line of products that aid in keeping cavity airspaces clear.

Mortar Net Masonry Drainage Products

Mortar Net USA, Ltd.
541 S. Lake St.
Gary, IN 46403

Toll-free: 800-664-6638
Fax: 219-939-3877
www.mortarnet.com

Mortar Net is a 90%-open, fibrous-mesh wall drainage system used to maintain airflow and allow moisture migration from behind masonry veneer facades. 2"-thick Mortar Net for Brick, Mortar Net Block, and Mortar Net Weep Vents are made from 50% recycled 200-dernier polyester; at least 17% is post-consumer and up to 33% is post-industrial polyester. Mortar Net is designed to keep mortar droppings from blocking weep holes.

CavityRock

Roxul Inc.
551 Harrop Dr.
Milton, ON L9T 3H3 Canada

Toll-free: 800-265-6878
Phone: 905-878-8474
Fax: 905-878-8077
www.roxul.com

CavityRock® is a non-combustible, lightweight, water repellent, semi-rigid, insulating drainage board for cavity wall applications. This mineral fiber product provides effective water drainage, and maintains its thermal resistance even when damp. A fire stop is not required because CavityRock® is a non-combustible insulation. According to the manufacturer, this product is compatible with all air/vapor barrier systems, adhesives, and wall ties. Roxul's mineral wool is made from approximately equal amounts of natural basalt rock and recycled slag (with 1%-6% urea extended phenolic formaldehyde binder).

04 21 00
Clay Unit Masonry

Bricks are typically fired in large kilns at very high temperatures, which results in significant embodied energy. Reusing bricks is good because it saves that embodied energy. High temperature firing also enables waste materials—even

04 00 00
Masonry

toxic materials such as oil-contaminated soils—to be safely incorporated into certain brick products. Products listed here are salvaged for reuse in new brick veneer. Note that not all salvaged brick is suitable for reuse in new brick veneer—the salvaged brick's surface condition (residual mortar film), structural integrity (so-called "salmon" brick can be too soft and fragile for reuse in brick veneers) and water absorbancy need to be considered.

Cunningham Bricks

Cunningham Brick Co., Inc.
701 N. Main St.
Lexington, NC 27292

Toll-free: 800-672-6181
Phone: 336-248-8541
Fax: 336-224-0002
www.cunninghambrick.com

Cunningham Brick manufactures bricks that incorporate 1.3% manganese dioxide by weight, a toxic metal waste from battery production. Vitrified manganese imparts a darker color to the bricks and is considered safe after firing. The product may not be widely available.

Most recently mentioned in EBN 5:4

Salvaged Brick

Gavin Historical Bricks

For full listing, see CSI section 32 14 16 - Brick Unit Paving

Thin-Sliced Salvaged Chicago Brick

Vintage Brick Salvage LLC.

For full listing, see CSI section 09 63 00 - Masonry Flooring

04 22 00
Concrete Masonry Units

Like many conventional products, CMUs can be used in "green" ways—for example, using a decorative type of block that eliminates additional finish materials. Products listed here exhibit superior energy performance (innovative web designs with specially designed expanded polystyrene insulation inserts), reduced material use by way of a finished exterior face (such as split-faced block), or post-industrial recycled content (such as fly ash or ground blast-furnace slag). (See also 03 11 19 - Insulating Concrete

Forming, 03 40 00 - Precast Concrete Panels, 04 05 13 - Masonry Mortaring, 04 22 20 - Autoclaved Aerated Concrete Masonry Units.) (See feature article EBN Vol. 9, No. 3.)

Omni Block

Omni Block, Inc.
15125 N. Hayden Rd. #123
Scottsdale, AZ 85260

Phone: 480-661-9009
Fax: 480-778-0818
www.omniblock.com

Omni Block is a uniquely molded concrete block (not foam) available in 8" and 12" sizes designed to minimize thermal bridging and to receive molded EPS insulation inserts. Omni Block is reinforced with rebar and grout in some of the interior cells as determined per structural engineering. All electrical and plumbing are run within the block so no furring or sheetrock is required for a finished wall.

Astra-Glaze-SW+

Trenwyth Industries
One Connelly Rd.
Emigsville, PA 17318

Toll-free: 800-233-1924
Phone: 717-767-6868
Fax: 717-764-6774
www.trenwyth.com

Astra-Glaze-SW+ and Verastone are concrete masonry units that include 38% pre-consumer slag from steel-making. Astra-Glaze-SW+ features a glazed facing that makes this product highly weather-resistant and provides an integral finish layer. Verastone is an integrally colored product with a prefinished, ground face. Additional cladding is not needed with these products (provided appropriate detailing is incorporated in the wall system to deal with thermal and moisture transmission). EPS inserts are available to improve the blocks thermal performance. Note that the lightweight blocks manufactured in Pennsylvania and Illinois have better thermal performance than the medium weight blocks made in Arizona.

04 22 20
Autoclaved Aerated Concrete Masonry Units

Commercial production of autoclaved aerated concrete (AAC) began in 1930 in Europe, where it has been widely used for decades. Concrete masonry units (CMUs) made from AAC are lighter

than conventional CMUs, generally have no cores, and provide higher insulation levels (R-values of up to 1.25 per inch, an order of magnitude higher than standard concrete). The insulating value of AAC allows it to function simultaneously as structure and insulation system. It has about 20% of the density—though only about 10% of the compressive strength—of regular concrete. Manufacturers may increase the product's strength by including reinforcing steel rods or mesh. Structural applications of unreinforced AAC are limited to low-rise buildings; in high-rise buildings it may be used in partition and curtain walls. AAC has very good sound-absorbing characteristics and can be worked with conventional carpenter's tools, making site modifications relatively easy. It's also nontoxic, fire-resistant, insect-proof, and can be produced using coal fly ash as a substitute for some of the sand in conventional AAC. But because AAC is a porous material, it must be protected from moisture with claddings or coatings. AAC is not a 1:1 substitution for conventional CMU in terms of installation; greater care must be taken in installation because the shallow mortar bed does not allow for alignment adjustments easily made with the deeper mortar beds of conventional CMUs. (See also 03 11 19 - Insulating Concrete Forming.) (See feature article EBN Vol. 2, No. 2.)

ACCOA

ACCOA Aerated Concrete Corporation of America
3351 W. Orange Blossom Trl.
Apopka, FL 32712

Phone: 407-884-0051
Fax: 407-884-5111
www.accoaac.com

ACCO AAC blocks, lintels, and panels are made by Aerated Concrete Corporation of America.

Most recently mentioned in EBN 10:6

E-Crete

E-Crete
2151 E. Broadway Rd. #115
Tempe, AZ 85282

Toll-free: 888-432-7383 x11
Phone: 480-596-3819 x11
www.e-crete.com

E-Crete has been producing autoclaved aerated concrete (AAC) blocks in a plant near Phoenix, Arizona since December 2000. The company uses sterile mine tailings from

04 00 00
Masonry

an adjacent closed copper mine to substitute for the silica content, which represents 25% of the dry weight content. E-Crete reports a steady-state insulating value of approximately R-1.04 per inch for their most common block (density of 32 lbs/ft³). E-Crete has a UL Classified 4-hour fire rating and is mold resistant.

Most recently mentioned in EBN 10:10

SafeCrete AAC

SafeCrete AAC
7638 Nashville St.
PO Box 1129
Ringgold, GA 30736

Phone: 706-965-4587
Fax: 706-965-4597
www.safecrete.com

In June 2001, Babb International acquired Matrix (a licensee of the Hebel AAC process). SafeCrete, a Babb Company, offers many block and panel sizes of AAC, including blocks larger than standard CMU-size, larger "jumbo" units, panels, and a variety of specially manufactured shapes and pre-assembled wall sections—with integral reinforcement. AAC products are made from a mixture of poured concrete, fly ash, and sand. Babb products can be used for interior and exterior applications. In exterior wall applications, they must not be exposed but can be painted with a textured paint, coated with a stucco finish specially made for AAC, or clad with standard siding.

Most recently mentioned in EBN 5:2, 8:11, 9:7, 10:6, 15:3

Contec AAC

Texas Contec, Inc.
1535 Brady Blvd., Ste. 2
San Antonio, TX 78237

Toll-free: 877-926-6832
Phone: 210-402-3223
Fax: 210-402-6390
www.texascontec.com

Contec AAC, formed in 1995, manufactures AAC at its plant in Monterrey, Mexico. Texas Contec is their U.S. distributor and offers a full line of AAC products, accessories, and technical services.

04 24 00
Adobe Unit Masonry

Adobe is a natural building material common to the U.S. Southwest. It can be very durable if protected from erosion; many Native American adobe structures built hundreds of years ago are still standing. Made from soil that has suitable sand and clay content and then air-dried in the sun, adobe bricks typically have extremely low greenhouse gas emissions and embodied energy. Most commercially available adobe bricks are "stabilized" with cement or asphalt additives, but adobe bricks are commonly made on site without stabilizers. Walls made of adobe bricks are most often protected from the weather with a parge coat of stucco or plaster, or large overhangs.

Adobe Factory

Adobe Factory
P.O. Box 510
Alcalde, NM 87511

Phone: 505-852-4131
Fax: 505-852-4055
www.adobefactory.com/

Adobe Factory is northern New Mexico's main adobe manufacturer and supplier.

Adobe and Earth Plasters

Clay Mine Adobe, Inc.
6401 W. Old Ajo Hwy.
Tucson, AZ 85735

Phone: 520-578-2222
Fax: 520-578-1721
www.claymineadobe.com

Clay Mine Adobe, founded in 1996, manufactures adobe block with a custom portland cement stabilizer, wheat straw (optional), and washed coarse aggregate admixture. Clay Mine adobe block requires no sealing and retains the authentic look of unstabilized adobe. It is available in a variety of standard as well as custom sizes and natural custom colors including a burnt adobe look. Clay plaster, cement-stabilized and unstabilized in a variety of earth tones, is also available in 95-pound bags.

New Mexico Earth Adobes

New Mexico Earth Adobes
P.O. Box 10506
Albuquerque, NM 87184

Phone: 505-898-1271
Fax: 505-898-1271
www.newmexicoearth.com

New Mexico Earth Adobes is an adobe block supplier serving the central and northern New Mexico, and southern Colorado regions. Blocks are 4" x 10" x 14" and weigh approximately 30 lbs. each.

Old Pueblo Adobe

Old Pueblo Adobe Company
9353 N. Casa Grande Hwy.
Tucson, AZ 85743

Toll-free: 800-327-4705
Phone: 520-744-9268
Fax: 520-744-8057
www.oldpuebloadobe.com

Old Pueblo Adobe Company manufactures adobe and Southwestern building supplies as well as offering a variety of antique Mexican Ranchero furnishings, accessories, and building products for sale in their Tucson showroom.

Rio Abajo Adobe

Rio Abajo Adobe
7 Industrial Park Ln.
Belen, NM 87002

Phone: 505-864-6191

Rio Abajo Adobe manufactures adobe brick and offers consulting services for small to large adobe block manufacturing startups or people building adobe homes.

04 00 00
Masonry

04 57 00
Masonry Fireplaces

Burning wood creates significant pollution. Emissions of particulates, carbon monoxide, VOCs, and methane are significantly greater from wood stoves than from any other common heating fuel. However, when wood is locally available and can be harvested sustainably, it has no net impact on global warming—because the carbon emissions from combustion are more than compensated for by growing trees. Thus, if wood is burned in a manner that minimizes pollution, it can be a good fuel choice. Products listed here have superior burning efficiencies and reduced particulate emissions in comparison even the best wood stoves. The high thermal mass of masonry heaters and biomass-fueled boiler systems can more effectively capture, store, and release heat over time. The downside of a high-mass masonry heater is that the heat of a freshly lit fire may not be felt in the living space until several hours later. In passive solar homes this may make temperature regulation difficult.

Moberg Fireplaces

Moberg Fireplaces, Inc.
Cellar Building
1124 N.W. Couch St. Ste. 300
Portland, OR 97209

Phone: 503-227-0547
Fax: 503-227-0548
www.mobergfireplaces.com

FireSpaces is a dealer and manufacturer of masonry fireplaces. They also manufacture the masonry Moberg MRC and the Modern Rumford Masonry Fireplace Kit.

Temp-Cast Enviroheat Masonry Heater Kits

Temp-Cast
3409 Yonge St.
P.O. Box 94059
Toronto, ON M4N 3R1 Canada

Toll-free: 800-561-8594
Phone: 416-322-5197
Fax: 416-486-3624
www.tempcast.com

Temp-Cast is a modular masonry heater core kit featuring corner, 'see through,' and bake-oven models. Temp-Cast provides manuals detailing appropriate chimney construction with each masonry heater kit. Masonry materials for the chimney and the heater's exterior are sourced separately.

Tulikivi

Tulikivi U.S., Inc.
P.O. Box 7547
Charlottesville, VA 22906

Toll-free: 800-843-3473
www.tulikivi.com

Tulikivi's masonry heaters, available in over 25 different models, are made from soapstone quarried in Finland. Tulikivi masonry heaters produce a hot, clean-burning fire and efficiently transfer the fire's heat to the living space.

04 00 00
Masonry

04 73 00
Manufactured Stone Masonry

Simulated stone products typically contain a high percentage of portland cement, a material with high embodied energy. As with all cementitious claddings adhered to the structural exterior wall, two layers of building paper or housewrap should be used, the first to serve as the bond break, and the latter to function as the weather-resistive barrier. Products listed here have significant or total replacement of the portland cement content with agricultural or industrial waste materials, such as fly ash.

LodeStone

LodeStone Companies
2708 Glenwood
Denton, TX 76209

Phone: 940-483-1761
Fax: 940-591-9778
www.lodestoneproducts.com

LodeStone is designed to achieve the appearance of natural stone. These veneer blocks are 3" thick at the mortar joint and come in nominal sizes ranging from 12" x 8" to 32" x 16". A handful of trim profiles and end pieces are also available. LodeStone uses Class C coal fly ash to replace most the portland cement typically used in cast stone; portland cement accounts for 20% of the cement blend, while Class C fly ash constitutes 65%, and other industrial recycled materials comprise most of the remaining 15%.

Most recently mentioned in EBN 12:3 & 12:5

This Space is Available for Your Notes

05 00 00 Metals

PRODUCT LISTINGS

05 12 00
Structural Steel Framing

Steel is both the most energy-intensive framing material, on a pound-for-pound basis, and the most recyclable. Overall, the steel industry's recycling rate is over 60%. Heavy-gauge structural steel framing members from almost all sources commonly have greater than 90% recycled content. The embodied energy of steel averages about 19,200 Btu/lb; manufacture of structural steel from recycled materials conserves 5,450 Btu/lb. In addition to having lower embodied energy, high-recycled-content steel results in lower impact associated with mining waste and pollution. Products listed here contain at least 90% recycled content. (See feature article EBN Vol. 9, No. 3.)

SmartBeam

CMC Steel Products
4365 Hwy. 278 W
P.O. Box 2099
Hope, AR 71802

Toll-free: 800-308-9925
Phone: 972-772-0769
Fax: 972-772-0882
www.cmcsteelproducts.com

SmartBeam® is a 100% recycled steel I-beam with either round or hexagonal holes in the web. The openings in the web make for a lighter beam that allows electrical and mechanical systems to occupy the same space as the floor structure. SmartBeam is a resource-efficient I-beam that enables additional resource savings by reducing building heights and weights.

Most recently mentioned in EBN 9:3

Industry Representation

Steel Recycling Institute
680 Andersen Dr.
Pittsburgh, PA 15220

Toll-free: 800-937-1226
www.recycle-steel.org

The Steel Recycling Institute (SRI) is an industry association that promotes and sustains the recycling of all steel products. The SRI educates the solid waste industry, govern-

ment, the business sector, and consumers about the benefits of recycling steel and using high-recycled-content steel products.

Delta Stud and Mega-Joist

Steelform Building Products, Inc.
4104 69th Ave.
Edmonton, AB T6B-2V2

New

Toll-free: 866-440-4499
Phone: 780-440-4499
www.steelform.ca

Delta Studs and Mega-Joists from Steelform Building Products offer a lightweight alternative to conventional steel studs and joists for steel-frame construction. Regular stamped openings in the stud and joist webs reduce weight and use of raw materials, as well as reducing the need for cutting and drilling to accommodate electrical and piping installation. Flanges around each opening increase the product's strength-to-mass ratio. When used in insulated building-envelope applications, the openings in the web reduce thermal and acoustical transference.

Vulcraft Steel Joist and Girder

Vulcraft
P.O. Box 637
Brigham City, UT 84302

Phone: 435-734-9433
Fax: 435-723-5423
www.vulcraft.com

Vulcraft Steel Joist and Girder fabricates structural steel members of at least 90% recycled steel supplied by Vulcraft's parent company Nucor Corporation.

05 21 00
Steel Joist Framing

Commonly used for interior partitioning of commercial buildings, light-gauge steel framing is increasingly being used in residential construction. Compared to solid wood, steel studs are lightweight, dimensionally stable, resistant to insect damage, and of consistent quality. Cold-rolled steel framing typically contains 20-25% recycled material (10-15% post-consumer content), though some manu-

facturers have in excess of 90% recycled content. Steel studs are also recyclable at the end of the building's useful life. Despite the advantages of light-gauge steel, its use can cripple a building's energy performance when improperly used in exterior wall applications because of thermal bridging through the highly conductive steel. Foam insulation is often recommended on the inside or outside surface of a wall to address this problem. Products listed here have high recycled content or are designed to help minimize thermal bridging. (See feature article EBN Vol. 3, No. 4.)

Tri-Chord

Tri-Chord Steel Systems, Inc.
3639 E. Superior
Phoenix, AZ 85040

Toll-free: 877-426-7100
Phone: 602-426-8700
Fax: 602-426-8200
www.tri-chordsteel.com

The Tri-Chord Stud and Truss Systems were designed to minimize thermal bridging. They have triangular sections at each edge, and discrete webs spanning the wall cavity instead of a solid heat-conducting steel web (90% of the stud webbing is removed leaving 10% for thermal transference). The manufacturer claims to have the highest thermal, seismic, acoustic and fire ratings for steel framing, and that it will meet the thermal transference of wood. Tri-Chord EESI Thermal Steel Studs are structural; 18 gauge will carry just under 7,000 lbs each. Tri-Chord also manufactures wide-spanning, open-web floor trusses. These studs and trusses contain up to 66% post-consumer recycled content.

Tri-Steel

Tri-Steel Homes
5400 S. Stemmons Fwy.
Denton, TX 76210

Toll-free: 800-874-7833
Phone: 940-497-7070
Fax: 940-497-3505
www.tri-steel.com

Tri-Steel Homes fabricates steel framing for residential construction. Over 66% of the steel content in the studs is recycled scrap material, such as from automobiles.

05 00 00
Metals

Delta Stud and Mega-Joist

Steelform Building Products, Inc.

For full listing, see CSI section 05 12 00 - Structural Steel Framing

This Space is Available for Your Notes

05 00 00
Metals

06 00 00 Wood, Plastics, & Composites

PRODUCT LISTINGS

06 05 23
Wood, Plastic, and Composite Fastenings

Adhesives are a significant potential source of indoor air quality concerns, so these products should be selected with care. Water-based adhesives have lower VOC emissions than solvent-based products. While some are sold as multipurpose, others are specific to particular applications. If a manufacturer recommends a low- or zero-VOC, water-based product for use with its material, then use that product; otherwise consider one known to minimize indoor air pollution. Products included here have VOC levels of 50 grams per liter or less. With mechanical fasteners, look for recycled content.

Titebond Solvent Free Construction Adhesive

Franklin International
2020 Bruck St.
Columbus, OH 43207

Toll-free: 800-877-4583
Phone: 614-443-0241
Fax: 614-445-1501
www.titebond.com

Titebond® is a solvent-free, nonflammable construction adhesive that contains 6.6 g/l VOCs. Its performance is equivalent to conventional adhesives and can be used on most common building materials. Titebond complies with the requirements of the APA, AFG-01 test for subfloors as well as ASTM C557. It costs about 10% more than conventional solvent-based adhesives. Titebond is available in 10.5-ounce and 29-ounce sizes. The company also produces specialized solvent-free adhesives for such applications as subflooring, drywall, cove-base, and acoustical ceiling tile.

Speed Grip

Geocel Corporation
P.O. Box 398
Elkhart, IN 46515

Toll-free: 800-348-7615
Phone: 574-264-0645
Fax: 800-348-7009
www.geocelusa.com

Speed Grip construction adhesive—with a 100% VOC-free, chemically reactive formula—is suitable for use on a variety of porous and nonporous surfaces including plastic, wood, concrete, brick, plasterboard, carpet, and metal. This adhesive is intended for applications such as panel installation, sheathing, windows, and other building components. Speed Grip cleans up with water.

Henkel Consumer Adhesives & Sealants

Henkel Consumer Adhesives

For full listing, see CSI section 07 92 13 - Caulk Joint Sealants

Construction Adhesives

ITW TACC
56 Air Station Industrial Pk.
Rockland, MA 02370

Toll-free: 800-503-6991
Fax: 800-231-8222
www.itwtacc.com

ITW TACC offers waterbased construction adhesive, duct sealant, and lag seal. T1168 is a multipurpose, nonflammable, synthetic-latex-emulsion, mastic-type construction adhesive particularly formulated for field-gluing subflooring; also appropriate for wallboard, paneling, and drywall, according to the manufacturer. (One surface must be porous.) It is also sold as Job Site Brand Miracle SFA-1168 Water Base, it contains 22.9 g/l of VOCs.

Maze Nails

Maze Nails
100 Church St.
Peru, IL 61354

Toll-free: 800-435-5949
Fax: 815-223-7585
www.mazenails.com

Maze Nails are made from domestic remelted steel in all standard and most specialty nail styles and sizes. Maze's Stormguard line of nails is galvanized with a double hot-dipped zinc coating for extra durability.

06 05 70
Wood Products Certification and Information

Forest certification in North America is conducted primarily by two third-party certifying organizations: SmartWood and Scientific Certification Systems (SCS). SmartWood and SCS certify forest lands and chain-of-custody forest products based on Forest Stewardship Council (FSC) standards. (See feature articles EBN Vol. 6, No. 10 & Vol. 12, No. 4.)

Forest Stewardship Council

Forest Stewardship Council - US
1155 30th St. NW, Ste. 300
Washington, DC 20007

Toll-free: 877-372-5646
Phone: 202-342-0413
Fax: 202-342-6589
www.fscus.org

The Forest Stewardship Council (FSC) is a nonprofit international organization committed to the conservation, restoration, and protection of the world's working forests through standards setting and accreditation. Founded in 1993, FSC is comprised of more than 600 members from 70 countries, including major environmental groups like Greenpeace and World Wildlife Fund, social organizations representing indigenous peoples and forest workers, and progressive forest-management and wood-products companies. The FSC checkmark-and-tree logo indicates that wood and wood products bearing the logo came from a well-managed forest. The FSC is the only forest certification standards program recognized in evaluating wood products for *GreenSpec*.

Most recently mentioned in EBN 1:3, 6:10, 10:9, 11:4, 12:4, 12:6, 12:9

Scientific Certification Systems

Scientific Certification Systems
2000 Powell St., Ste. 1350
Emeryville, CA 94608

Phone: 510-452-8000
Fax: 510-452-8001
www.scscertified.com

06 00 00
Wood, Plastics, & Composites

Scientific Certification Systems (SCS) is an independent certification organization that offers a range of services. SCS certifies manufacturers' claims of building product attributes such as recycled and recovered content and absence of added formaldehyde. The company also conducts life-cycle impact assessments and the certification of environmentally preferable products such as paints, carpets, technologies, services, and electricity. In addition, SCS is accredited by the FSC to certify well-managed forests and conduct chain-of-custody certification for forest products based on FSC standards.

Most recently mentioned in EBN 3:5, 3:6, 5:6, 6:10, 11:4, 12:4

SmartWood

SmartWood
65 Millet St., Ste. 201
Goodwin-Baker Bldg.
Richmond, VT 05477

Phone: 802-434-5491
Fax: 802-434-3116
www.smartwood.org

SmartWood is the sustainable forestry program of the Rainforest Alliance, an international conservation organization that works to protect ecosystems and the people and wildlife that depend on them by transforming land use practices, business practices, and consumer behavior. Established in 1989, SmartWood was the first certification program in the world and is accredited by the Forest Stewardship Council. SmartWood's headquarters is located in Richmond, Vermont.

Most recently mentioned in EBN 5:4, 6:10, 8:2, 11:4, 12:4

**06 00 00
Wood,
Plastics, &
Composites**

06 05 73
Wood Treatment

Extending the service life of wood products reduces the demands on forests for replacement timber. Site-applied treatments can contribute to wood longevity as well as mold and insect prevention. Products listed here are low-toxic and low-VOC. (See feature articles EBN Vol. 2, No. 1, Vol. 6, No. 3, Vol. 15, No. 8.)

American MoldGuard

American MoldGuard, Inc.

For full listing, see CSI section 09 96 14 - Mold-Resistant Coatings

Bora-Care and Tim-Bor Professional

Nisus Corporation
100 Nisus Dr.
Rockford, TN 37853

Toll-free: 800-264-0870
Phone: 865-577-6119
Fax: 865-577-5825
www.nisuscorp.com

Bora-Care® is a liquid borate-based termiticide, insecticide, and fungicide concentrate applied directly to wood and concrete. Treatment prevents termites from tubing across treated areas; it kills and prevents subterranean, Formosan, and drywood termites; wood boring beetles; carpenter ants; and fungal decay. Wood is removed as a food source. Bora-Care contains ethylene glycol and patented penetrants. Tim-bor® Professional is a water soluble, glycol-free borate powder that acts as a wood preservative, fungicide, and insecticide to control and prevent wood decay fungi, drywood termites, wood boring beetles, and carpenter ants. Borate products are not effective in damp or wet areas, and will leach from wet wood.

Most recently mentioned in EBN 2:1, 3:3, 9:9

LifeTime Wood Treatment

Valhalla Wood Preservatives, Ltd.
P.O. Box 328
Salt Spring Island, BC V8K 2R7 Canada

Phone: 250-538-5516
Fax: 250-538-5517
www.valhalco.com

Valhalla claims LifeTime wood treatment as a nontoxic family recipe that outperforms pressure-treated wood. LifeTime, which can also be used as a wood stain, is packaged as a powder for mixing with water to create an acidic solution that can be applied by roller, brush, or sprayer. Some prominent green building experts have reported good success with LifeTime, though comprehensive test results have not been made available.

06 10 13
Rough Carpentry Accessories

Especially when structural requirements are minimal, look for recycled-content products.

EZ-Shim

EZ-Shim
P.O. Box 4820
Santa Barbara, CA 93140

Toll-free: 800-772-0024
Phone: 805-682-2155
Fax: 805-682-2155
www.ezshim.com

EZ-Shim™ is a load-bearing, injection-molded shim made from recycled ABS plastic with prescored grooves for breaking off excess shim stock after installation. EZ-Shim measures 1-3/16" x 7-7/8" x 5/16" at its thick end. There are 10 shims per sheet.

06 11 01
FSC-Certified Wood Framing Lumber

Certified wood products are verified by a third party as originating from well-managed forests. GreenSpec recognizes the Forest Stewardship Council (FSC) standards as the most rigorous and the only certification system with well-established chain-of-custody certification. Some companies listed here sell both certified and noncertified wood products, or products that have been certified according to different, less stringent environmental standards. To make certain that you get environmentally responsible wood products, be sure to specify your interest in FSC-certified wood. (See also 06 05 70 - Wood Products Certification and Information.)

Certified Hardwood Lumber

Allard Lumber Company
354 Old Ferry Rd.
Brattleboro, VT 05301

Phone: 802-254-4939
Fax: 802-254-8492
www.allardlumber.com

Allard Lumber is a manufacturer and wholesaler of FSC-certified northern hardwood lumber, including white hard maple, red oak, and cherry.

AltruWood Certified Wood Products

AltruWood, Inc.

For full listing, see CSI section 09 64 01 - FSC-Certified Wood Flooring

Certified Redwood Lumber

Big Creek Lumber Company
3564 Hwy. 1
Davenport, CA 95017

Phone: 831-457-5023
Fax: 831-423-2800
www.big-creek.com

Big Creek harvests FSC-certified timber on its 6,800 acres of second- and third-growth forestland in the Santa Cruz Mountains of coastal California. They were the first wood products company operating a redwood forest to be awarded "Well Managed Forest" Certification by the Forest Conservation Program of Scientific Certification Systems (SCS). The family-owned lumber company runs five retail lumber yards on California's central coast; they also wholesale a wide variety of redwood Douglas-fir grades and dimensions, including 2x4 through 2x12, 4x4, 4x6 and 6x6. Larger timbers can be custom cut by special order.

Most recently mentioned in EBN 5:4, 5:6, 6:4, 6:7, 13:2

Certified Wood Products

Cascadia Forest Goods, LLC
38083 Wheeler Rd.
Dexter, OR 97431

Phone: 541-485-4477
Fax: 541-485-1852
www.cascadiaforestgoods.com

Cascadia Forest Goods (CFG) is a supplier of FSC-certified and recycled forest products, including hardwood and softwood veneers, dimensional lumber and decking, timbers and beams, siding, flooring, paneling, and trim. CFG's woods come from the Pacific Northwest and British Columbia, and include the following species: douglas fir, incense and western red cedar, sitka and englemann spruce, ponderosa and sugar pine, and regional hardwoods (madrone, white and black oak, broadleaf maple, alder, chinkapin, and myrtlewood). FSC-certified and recycled-forest-product flooring species include madrone, white oak, clear vertical grain (CVG) Douglas fir, birch, big-leaf maple, and myrtlewood. CFG also supplies FSC-certified flooring and decking from Central and South America, including Santa Maria, catalox, chechen negro, jobillo, machiche, ramon blanco, sauche, ipe, pucte (ironwood), and others. CFG offers both solid and engineered wood flooring. CFG also supplies both FSC-certified hardwood and softwood veneers and lumber to window and door manufacturers.

Certified Iron Woods Lumber

Cecco Trading, Inc.

For full listing, see CSI section 06 15 01 - FSC-Certified Wood Decking

SmartChoice Wood Products

Certified Forest Products, LLC.
7 Los Conejos
Orinda, CA 94563

Phone: 925-258-4372
Fax: 925-258-4373
www.certifiedforestproducts.com

Certified Forest Products (CFP) is a distributor of SmartChoice, a collection of FSC-certified and reclaimed wood products from a variety of species including hardwoods, cedar, and redwood. Products include lumber, plywood, decking, siding, flooring, interior and exterior millwork.

CollinsWood FSC-Certified Wood Products

Collins Companies

For full listing, see CSI section 07 46 43 - Composition Siding

FSC-Certified Wood Products

Dwight Lewis Lumber / Lewis Lumber Products

For full listing, see CSI section 09 64 01 - FSC-Certified Wood Flooring

F.D. Sterritt Certified-Wood Building Products

F.D. Sterritt Lumber Co.

For full listing, see CSI section 06 22 01 - FSC-Certified Millwork

Harmonized Tropical Wood

Harmonized Wood Products
5500 Prytania St., #143
New Orleans, LA 70115

Toll-free: 877-635-3362
Phone: 504-342-4250
Fax: 504-324-1988
www.harmonizedwood.com

Harmonized Wood Products offers a wide range of FSC-certified tropical hardwood products, specializing in Latin American hardwoods. Products include lumber, timber, decking, flooring, doors, veneer, and custom furniture.

Harrop-Procter Certified-Wood Building Products

Harrop-Procter Watershed Protection Society
101 3rd Ave.
P.O. Box 5
Procter, BC V0G 1V0 Canada

Phone: 250-229-2221
Fax: 250-229-2332
www.hpcommunityforest.org

The Harrop-Procter Community Forest in southeastern British Columbia, stewarded by The Harrop-Procter Watershed Protection Society and managed by The Harrop-Procter Community Co-operative, is FSC-certified. Species include Douglas fir, lodgepole pine, birch, aspen, larch, hemlock, balsam fir, and spruce. Rough green, tight-knot, cedar lumber and timbers are available in common dimensions. T&G indoor paneling is available in fir, pine, cedar, and larch. Fir and larch flooring, fir interior decking, cedar and larch exterior decking, and various profiles of cedar siding are offered. Custom orders over 1000 board feet can be quoted.

Certified Lumber and Timbers

Harwood Products
P.O. Box 224
Branscomb, CA 95417

Toll-free: 800-441-4140 (CA only)
Phone: 707-984-6181
Fax: 707-984-6631
www.harwoodp.com

Harwood Products offers certified redwood decking and timbers, Douglas fir lumber and timbers, and white fir lumber.

Horse- and Biodiesel-Harvested Hardwood and Softwood Lumber

JH Lumber & Wood Products
1701 Chase Rd.
Montpelier, VT 05602

Phone: 802-229-4148
Fax: 802-223-3192
www.jhlumber.net

JH Lumber & Wood Products mills kiln-dried North American hardwood and softwood lumber. Logging is done with horses and biodiesel-powered equipment and soon will occur on over 1,400 acres of forest land.

06 00 00
Wood, Plastics, & Composites

Certified Hardwood and Softwood Lumber

Lashway Lumber, Inc.
22 Main St.
Williamsburg, MA 01096

Phone: 413-268-7685
Fax: 413-268-7697
www.lashwaylumber.com

Lashway Lumber mills FSC-certified North American hardwood and softwood lumber.

Certified Hardwood Building Products

Maine Woods Company, LLC
Fish Lake Rd.
P.O. Box 111
Portage, ME 04768

Phone: 207-435-4393
Fax: 207-435-6714
www.mainewoods.net

Maine Woods Company, LLC, owned in part by Seven Islands Land Company, operates a state-of-the-art sawmill in northern Maine producing primarily hard maple and yellow birch lumber and flooring. Smaller quantities of American beech, red maple, and white ash are also produced. A portion of the mill output is FSC-certified.

Certified Red Cedar

Mary's River Lumber Co.
4515 N.E. Elliott Cir.
Corvallis, OR

Toll-free: 800-523-2052
Phone: 541-752-0122
Fax: 541-752-5143
www.marysrvr.com

Mary's River Lumber offers FSC-certified, second-growth, tight-knotted, western red cedar products, including boards, decking, fencing, paneling, and siding in T&G, channel, bevel, and square-end.

Certified Spruce-Pine-Fir (SFP) Lumber

Materiaux Blanchet, Inc.
5055 W. Hamel Blvd., Ste. 225
Quebec City, QC G2E 2G6 Canada

Phone: 418-871-2626
Fax: 418-871-9755

Materiaux Blanchet, Inc. produces a full range of graded, kiln-dried, FSC-certified spruce-pine-fir dimensional lumber from Seven Islands Land Company timber.

Most recently mentioned in EBN 3:6

Certified Lumber, Flooring, Wainscoting, and Veneer

McDowell Lumber Company, Inc.

For full listing, see CSI section 09 64 01 - FSC-Certified Wood Flooring

FSC-Certified Wood Products

Menominee Tribal Enterprises
Hwy. 47 N
P.O. Box 10
Neopit, WI 54150

Phone: 715-756-2311
Fax: 715-756-2386
www.mtewood.com

Menominee Tribal Enterprises (MTE) offers a full line of certified wood products harvested from the 220,000-acre Menominee Forest. MTE is continuing its development of value-added products from the 16 wood species harvested. Menominee forest lands were the first certified to FSC standards in North America.

Most recently mentioned in EBN 1:2 & 3:5

Certified Lumber

Midwest Hardwood Corporation
9540 83rd Ave. N
Maple Grove, MN 55369

Phone: 763-425-8700
Fax: 763-391-6740
www.midwesthardwood.com

Midwest Hardwood Corporation's Sawmill Division offers some varieties of FSC-certified northern hardwood lumber. The wood is harvested from forests in Wisconsin, Michigan, and Minnesota.

EarthSource Forest Products

Plywood and Lumber Sales, Inc.

For full listing, see CSI section 01 62 03 - Distributors/Retailers, FSC-Certified Wood

FSC-Certified Lumber, Plywood, and Products

Potlatch Corporation
W. 201 North River Dr., Ste. 380
Spokane, WA 99201

Phone: 509-328-0930
Fax: 509-327-9409
www.potlatchcorp.com

In 2004, Potlatch Corporation became the first publicly traded U.S. timber company to certify timberland according to Forest Stewardship Council (FSC) standards. Potlatch is producing chain-of-custody FSC-certified Hem-Fir and Douglas Fir/Larch framing lumber, inland red cedar decking and siding, and Douglas fir and white fir plywood from three chain-of-custody-certified mills in Idaho. Potlatch has recently added over 400,000 acres of FSC certified timber in Arkansas which supports a chain-of –custody sawmill in Warren, Arkansas. Warren produces dimensional Southern Yellow Pine framing lumber. These products are stamped with the FSC logo when required for specific sales.

Most recently mentioned in EBN 13:12, 14:6, 14:10

Certified Wood Products

Randall Custom Lumber, Ltd.
3530 S.E. Arcadia Rd.
Shelton, WA 98584

Phone: 360-426-8518
Fax: 360-426-8518

Randall Custom Lumber manufactures FSC-certified decking, flooring, hard and softwood lumber, and stair parts. Some of their certified species are ash, red cedar, red alder, Douglas fir, madrone, and maple.

Certified Hardwood Lumber and Timbers

ROMEX World Trade Company, LLC - sales agent for ROM
P.O. Box 1110
Alexandria, LA 71309

Toll-free: 800-299-5174
Phone: 318-445-1973
Fax: 318-443-0159
www.martco.com

Roy O. Martin Lumber Management, LLC has received certification of its 585,000 acres of forestland and four mills according to standards of the Forest Stewardship Council (FSC). This is the first FSC certification of any forest management operation in Louisiana. Roy O. Martin produces FSC-certified lumber in red oak, white oak, ash, hackberry, pecan, sap gum (sweet gum), cypress, and several other species at the company's hardwood lumber mill in LeMoyen. While the majority of the mill's output is red oak, ROM has become one of the largest suppliers of southern ash and cypress. Lumber accounts for 75% of production, with the rest in timbers, railroad ties, and pallet cants.

Most recently mentioned in EBN 11:6

06 00 00
Wood, Plastics, & Composites

06 11 02
Reclaimed-Wood Framing Lumber

As the demands on forest resources have increased, nonforest sources of wood have grown in importance. Reclaimed wood is usually salvaged from buildings slated for demolition, abandoned railroad trestles, and "sinker logs" that sank decades ago during river-based log drives. It can also be obtained from trees that have been recently harvested from urban or suburban areas (such as disease-killed trees). Reclaimed wood is often available in species, coloration, and wood quality that is no longer available in newly harvested timber. In some cases, reclaimed wood suppliers have only limited quantities with matching coloration or weathering patterns; ample lead time and accurate materials estimates can help ensure the availability of the desired wood. Lowering the uniformity standards for finished wood can also increase the potential for use of reclaimed wood. As with other resources, the supply of reclaimed wood is limited. Efficient and appropriate use of reclaimed wood is important for its long-term availability. (See also 01 62 02 - Distributors/Retailers, Used Building Materials & 06 13 02 - Reclaimed-Wood Heavy Timber.) (See feature article EBN Vol. 9, No. 5.)

Reclaimed-Wood Lumber and Products

A Reclaimed Lumber Co.

For full listing, see CSI section 06 22 02 - Reclaimed-Wood Millwork

Used Building Materials

Caldwells

For full listing, see CSI section 01 62 02 - Distributors/Retailers, Used Building Materials

Wood Materials from Urban Trees

CitiLog

For full listing, see CSI section 09 64 02 - Reclaimed-Wood Flooring

Reclaimed-Wood Products

Crossroads Recycled Lumber

For full listing, see CSI section 06 13 02 - Reclaimed-Wood Heavy Timber

D. Litchfield Reclaimed Wood

D. Litchfield & Co. Ltd.
3046 Westwood St.
Port Coquitlam, BC V3C 3L7 Canada

Toll-free: 888-303-2222
Phone: 604-464-7525
Fax: 604-944-1674
www.dlitchfield.com

Litchfield carries a large, steady supply of all types of reclaimed lumber and beams salvaged through their deconstruction operations.

Most recently mentioned in EBN 9:5

Reclaimed-Wood Building Products

Endura Wood Products, Ltd.

For full listing, see CSI section 09 64 02 - Reclaimed-Wood Flooring

Georgian Bay Wetwood

Georgian Bay Wetwood Inc.

For full listing, see CSI section 06 40 26 - Wood Veneer

Heartwood Reclaimed-Wood Flooring

Heartwood Industries

For full listing, see CSI section 09 64 02 - Reclaimed-Wood Flooring

M. Fine Lumber Company

M. Fine Lumber Company
1301 Metropolitan Ave.
P.O. Box 37 701
Brooklyn, NY 11237

Phone: 718-381-5200
Fax: 718-366-8907
www.mfinelumber.com

M. Fine Lumber Company is a leading supplier of salvaged heavy timber and dimension lumber. Inventory is salvaged from buildings being demolished throughout the U.S. Species include longleaf yellow pine, oak, and Douglas fir.

Pinocchio's

Pinocchio's

For full listing, see CSI section 06 13 02 - Reclaimed-Wood Heavy Timber

Reclaimed Lumber and Timbers

R. W. Rhine Inc.

For full listing, see CSI section 06 13 02 - Reclaimed-Wood Heavy Timber

Resource Woodworks

Resource Woodworks, Inc.

For full listing, see CSI section 06 13 02 - Reclaimed-Wood Heavy Timber

Reclaimed-Wood Building Products

TerraMai

For full listing, see CSI section 09 64 02 - Reclaimed-Wood Flooring

Trestlewood

Trestlewood

For full listing, see CSI section 09 64 02 - Reclaimed-Wood Flooring

Triton Underwater Wood

Triton Logging Inc.
6675 Mirah Rd.
Saanichton, BC V8M 1Z4 Canada

New

Phone: 250-652-4033
Fax: 250-483-1955
www.tritonlogging.com

Triton Logging harvests underwater, old-growth standing forests submerged decades ago by man-made lakes behind hydroelectric dams. Using its proprietary Sawfish™ unmanned logging submarine, Triton recovers Douglas Fir, Western Red Cedar, Western White Pine, Lodgepole Pine, Hemlock, and other species year-round in British Columbia, which is estimated to have five billion board feet of standing timber preserved in reservoirs. All Triton's product is certified SmartWood Rediscovered by the Rainforest Alliance.

Most recently mentioned in EBN 15:7 & 15:12

**06 00 00
Wood, Plastics, & Composites**

Underwater Timber Salvage

Underwater Timber Salvage
1550 Railroad Ave.
St. Helens, OR 97051

Toll-free: 888-366-5353
Phone: 503-366-5353
Fax: 503-366-5454

Underwater Timber Salvage Corp. retrieves century-old "sinker logs" from the Columbia River Basin waterways for its custom mill. The company started out with removal of navigational hazards, but recognized the value of what they were removing. UTS offers clear, finished wood in standard dimensions, as well as rough-cut widths 24 inches (300 mm) and more, in lengths up to 20 feet (6 m). Trim packages cut entirely from a single log are available to ensure consistent quality and appearance. Species include fir, hemlock, cedar, ash, maple, alder, oak, pine, and others. Some of these woods are available in coloration and quality no longer available from today's second- and third-growth forests. Stock is dependent on what's come out of the water lately. UTS has applied for FSC certification through the "FSC Recycled" label, using the third-party certification organization SCS.

Most recently mentioned in EBN 14:4

Reclaimed-Wood Building Products

Vintage Material Supply Co.

For full listing, see CSI section 09 64 02 - Reclaimed-Wood Flooring

06 00 00
Wood, Plastics, & Composites

Reclaimed-Wood Building Products

West Wind Hardwood, Inc.

For full listing, see CSI section 09 64 02 - Reclaimed-Wood Flooring

Reclaimed-Wood Building Products

What Its Worth, Inc.

For full listing, see CSI section 09 64 02 - Reclaimed-Wood Flooring

06 11 04
Preservative-Treated Framing Lumber

The durability of preservative-treated wood is the most important advantage to its use. Extending the service life of wood products reduces the demands on forests for replacement timber. Sales of lumber treated with the preservative CCA (chromated copper arsenate) are banned for consumer applications. Disposal by incineration is the most significant environmental concern associated with the billions of board feet already in use that were treated with this preservative: toxins such as arsenic may become airborne, and those that don't get into the air end up in the ash, where they're highly leachable. Copper-based wood treatments such as ACQ (ammoniacal copper quaternary) and copper azole have replaced CCA as the standard product. Wood treated with copper should be avoided near aquatic ecosystems, since copper is highly toxic to many aquatic organisms. Copper-treated wood is also corrosive to steel fasteners; follow manufacturers' recommendations for fastener selection. Silica-based treatments are available that are not actually preservatives, but that have the same effect by rendering the wood inedible to insects and fungi. Borate treatments effectively protect wood from insects while offering low mammalian and environmental toxicity, however, most borate-treated products are only suitable in interior applications because the borates do not stay fixed in the wood when exposed to weather. Organic (carbon-based) pesticides, used in various combinations, also appear in treated wood, in both surface and pressure treatments. These pesticides, relatively new to wood preservation, offer a less-toxic alternative to copper-based treatments. Treated wood should not be chipped for mulch, or burned.

FrameGuard

Arch Wood Protection, Inc.
1955 Lake Park Dr., Ste. 100
Smyrna, GA 30080

Phone: 866-789-4567
Fax: 770-801-1990
www.wolmanizedwood.com

FrameGuard framing lumber, trusses, and sheathing components are factory-treated against mold, rot, fungus, and wood-destroying insects with a surface coating of borate (disodium octaborate tetrahydrate) and a mix of three low-toxic organic fungicides. The borate component protects against decay and insects, while the organic compounds provide surface protection against mold. Green-dyed FrameGuard lumber is appropriate in climates where houses are normally framed with treated wood. It is not appropriate for ground contact, exterior applications, internal sill plates, or any other application where outdoor-exposure or ground-contact pressure-treated wood should be used. FrameGuard has been certified by Greenguard for low chemical emissions.

SillBor Borate-Treated Wood

Arch Wood Protection, Inc.
1955 Lake Park Dr., Ste. 100
Smyrna, GA 30080

Phone: 866-789-4567
Fax: 770-801-1990
www.wolmanizedwood.com

SillBor framing lumber is factory-treated against mold, rot, fungus, and wood-destroying insects with a borate DOT (Disodium Octaborate Tetrahydrate) wood preservative. SillBor is appropriate in climates where houses are normally framed with treated wood, as an alternative to more toxic copper treatments. The bluish-dyed wood is appropriate for interior framing and applications not exposed to the elements or ground contact, and it does not corrode galvanized steel plates and fasteners. The wood is sold at two retention levels, with the lower level not effective against the Formosan termite. The warranty requires termiticide soil treatment for the duration of the lifetime warranty, including prior to construction, though *GreenSpec* does not endorse such treatments. The wood should be covered at job sites.

SafeLumber

Babb Technologies   New
7638 Nashville St.
Ringgold, GA 30736

Phone: 706-965-4587
Fax: 706-965-4597
www.babb.com

SafeLumber from Babb Technologies, a wood treater distributing wood through the southeast and midwest, is factory-treated against mold, rot, fungus, and wood-destroying insects using a borate DOT (Disodium Octaborate Tetrahydrate) wood preservative and a mold inhibitor. SafeLumber is appropriate in climates where houses are normally framed with treated wood, as an alternative to more toxic copper treatments. The blue-dyed wood is appropriate for interior framing and applications without exterior exposure or ground contact, and it does not corrode galvanized steel plates and fasteners. The warranty requires termiticide soil treatment for the duration of the lifetime warranty, including prior to construction, though *GreenSpec* does not endorse such treatments. The wood should be covered at job sites.

Advance Guard Borate Pressure-Treated Wood

Osmose Wood Preserving, Inc.
P.O. Box O
Griffin, GA 30224

Toll-free: 800-585-5161
Fax: 770-229-5225
www.osmose.com

Osmose introduced Advance Guard® lumber and plywood pressure-treated with Tim-Bor® sodium-borate in 1998. The product was developed to deal with the growing problem of termites and fungal decay in the southern U.S. and Hawaii. Advance Guard® is used for sill plate, furring strips, and other code driven applications. Advance Guard can be used for framing houses, though it costs significantly more than untreated lumber. Advance Guard treated lumber is offered with a lifetime residential limited warranty.

Most recently mentioned in EBN 9:9, 13:2, 15:8

TimberSIL Nontoxic Pressure-Treated Wood

Timber Treatment Technologies
7481 Huntsman Blvd., Suite 520
Springfield, VA 22153

Phone: 703-644-0391
www.timbersilwood.com

TimberSIL is a sodium-silicate-based treatment process for wood that relies on a micro-manufacturing technology rather than toxins to prevent infestations and decay. The patented process uses heat to change a proprietary formula from a soluble solution that is infused into the wood and turn it into a microscopic layer of amorphous glass throughout the wood, providing a permanent treatment with no dusting or leaching. The treated wood is non-toxic, odorless and nonvolatile, is not corrosive to fasteners, does not cause excessive wear on tools, and has a natural clear color. TimberSIL Decking and other exterior products carry a 40-year warranty and TimberSIL interior products can be stored for up to one year of outdoor exposure with no negative consequences. As of October 2005, this product was not yet listed with the International Code Council; approval for use is granted by local jurisdictions.

Most recently mentioned in EBN 13:10, 13:12, 14:11, 14:12, 15:8, 15:10, 16:1

EnviroSafe Plus

Wood Treatment Products, Inc.
P.O. Box 950445
Lake Mary, FL 32795

Toll-free: 800-345-8102
Phone: 407-330-0177
Fax: 407-330-3243
www.eswoodtreatment.com

ES+Wood is pressure-treated with Disodium Octaborate Tetrahydrate (DOT Borates) and EnviroSafe Plus, a proprietary polymer binder that fixates the borates in the wood. According to the manufacturer, it is effective against such pests as termites (including Formosan), carpenter ants, beetles, silverfish, fleas, and cockroaches, in addition to antifungal properties. ES+Wood pressure treated wood is non-corrosive, retains natural color characteristics and won't affect indoor air quality. It is approved for interior and exterior, code compliant applications and has a 40-year transferable warranty. As of May 2006, ES+Wood is completing testing for submission to the International Code Council (ICC) to receive their NER Number.

Most recently mentioned in EBN 15:8

BluWood

New

WoodSmart Solutions, Inc.
3500 NW Boca Raton Blvd.,
Ste 701 & 702
Boca Raton, FL 33431

Phone: 561-416-1972
www.perfectbarrier.com

BluWood® framing lumber, trusses, and sheathing components are factory-treated against mold, rot, fungus, and wood-destroying insects with the WoodSmart Solutions two-part Perfect Barrier System: a water-repellant, vapor permeable, mold-resistant subsurface infusion film using a proprietary blend of fungicides, and a borate DOT (Disodium Octaborate Tetrahydrate) wood preservative. BluWood is appropriate in climates where houses are normally framed with treated wood. It is not for ground contact, or for use in exterior applications unless protected by paint, stain, or sealer. The blue-dyed BluWood can be stored uncovered at job sites for up to six months. The warranty against insect infestation requires soil treatment for the duration of the lifetime warranty. (The warranty is transferable within a 30-year initial period.)

06 11 13
Engineered Wood Framing Products

While not free from ecological concerns, engineered lumber products can provide a significant environmental advantage over solid wood by efficiently utilizing fast-growing, small-diameter trees. Products listed here are limited to those that do not include formaldehyde binders; or, if they do, offer other green features such as FSC-certified content.

Phenol-formaldehyde binders, while not emitting as much formaldehyde as urea-formaldehyde binders, still may pose an indoor air quality concern. (See feature article EBN Vol. 8, No. 11.)

TimberStrand LSL Studs, Headers, and Rim Board

iLevel by Weyerhaeuser
2910 E. Amity Rd.
Boise, ID 83716

Toll-free: 888-453-8358
Phone: 208-364-1200
Fax: 208-364-1300
www.ilevel.com

Laminated Strand Lumber (LSL) is manufactured from fast-growing aspen and poplar trees that are debarked and shredded into strands. The strands are coated with a form-aldehyde-free MDI (methyl diisocyanate) binder and pressed into huge billets that are milled into dimensional lumber. LSL lumber is very consistent and stable; it does not warp and twist like solid wood. TimberStrand® LSL Studs and Headers are available in 2x4 and 2x6; Rim Boards are 2x10. Lengths up to 22' are available.

Most recently mentioned in EBN 1:3, 2:6, 5:2, 5:3, 8:11

Insul-Beam

Premier Building Systems - Division of Premier Industries, Inc.
4609 70th Ave. E
Fife, WA 98424

Toll-free: 800-275-7086
Phone: 253-926-2020
Fax: 253-926-3992
www.pbspanel.com

Insul-Beam is an insulated header with laminated veneer lumber facings and a core of EPS foam insulation. EPS may contain up to 15% recycled content. Insul-Beam can be used in place of site-fabricated headers and will improve building envelope energy performance. This product is available for 2x4, 2x6, and 2x8 framing in lengths up to 24'. Engineering data is available from the company.

Certified Engineered Wood

Standard Structures, Inc.
P.O. Box K
Santa Rosa, CA 95402

Toll-free: 877-980-7732
Phone: 707-836-8100
Fax: 707-838-8377
www.standardstructures.com

Standard Structures was the first manufacturer of certified engineered wood products.

**06 00 00
Wood, Plastics, & Composites**

The company can provide FSC-certified glulam beams, wood I-joists, and open-web trusses. Conventional phenol resorcinol formaldehyde binders are used in the manufacturing process. With some products, special orders may be required for certified-wood fabrication.

Most recently mentioned in EBN 8:2 & 8:11

SWII, SWIII Headers

Superior Wood Systems
1301 Garfield Ave.
P.O. Box 1208
Superior, WI 54880

Toll-free: 800-375-9992
Phone: 715-392-1822
Fax: 715-392-3484
www.swi-joist.com

Superior Wood Systems SWII and SWIII headers are engineered, insulated headers that deliver superior thermal performance when compared to solid-wood, site-fabricated headers. SWII headers consist of solid 2" thick wood top and bottom chords and dual OSB web members that encase an EPS foam core. The SWIII headers have three OSB web members. The 5-1/2" wide headers insulate to R-18.

Most recently mentioned in EBN 2:6

06 11 22
Wood Framing Fasteners

Let-in metal wall bracing, which provides racking resistance, can eliminate or reduce the need for wall sheathing in light-frame construction. Follow structural requirements carefully, and obtain a design review by a structural engineer if uncertain. Also check with a building official before substituting let-in bracing for structural sheathing.

06 00 00
Wood, Plastics, & Composites

TWB and RCWB Wall Bracing

Simpson Strong-Tie Connectors
5956 W. Las Positas Blvd.
P.O. Box 10789
Pleasanton, CA 94588

Toll-free: 800-999-5099
Phone: 925-560-9000
Fax: 925-833-1496
www.strongtie.com

Simpson TWB and RCWB Wall Bracing are let-in metal bracing products available in both T and L cross-sections requiring 15/16" and 9/16" deep kerf cuts, respectively. They are designed to fulfill the same code bracing requirements as 1x4 let-in bracing. TWB and RCWB are available in lengths of 9'9", 11'4", and 14'2".

S365, S366, S367 Wall Bracing

USP Structural Connectors
14305 Southcross Drive - Suite 200
Burnsville, MN 55306

Toll-free: 800-328-5934
Fax: 952-898-8683
www.uspconnectors.com

S365, S366, and S367 Wall Bracing requires a shallow (1/2"-deep) kerf cut.

06 12 13
Cementitious Reinforced Panels

Site-stuccoed insulation-core panels can be appropriate where the need for good R-values meets the need for extreme structural requirements where earthquake, hurricane, and tornado resistance are required. Products listed here provide superior energy performance, or use FSC-certified wood and other green materials. (See also 03 11 19 - Insulating Concrete Forming.)

Green Sandwich

Green Sandwich Technologies
8125 Lankershim Blvd.
North Hollywood, CA 91605

Phone: 818-771-5200
Fax: 818-771-5215
www.greensandwichtech.com

Green Sandwich Panels are site-finished structural concrete insulating panels consisting of an EPS core with a pre-engineered reinforcing cage surrounding and penetrating it. The panels are fastened together in the field, and a minimum 1.5" thickness of portland cement finish is machine- or hand-applied on both sides of the panel. The manufacturer specifies a 40% coal fly ash concentration for the skins. The EPS core is made with BASF's Greenguard-certified Styropor®. Locally-harvested biomass, such as straw, may be specified in place of EPS. The wire mesh contains 40% recycled steel. Panels are available up to 12' x 48', in 3" to 20" thicknesses.

Tridipanel

Hadrian Tridi-Systems
909 W. Vista Way, Ste D
Vista, CA 92083

Phone: 760-643-2307
Fax: 760-643-2305
www.tridipanel.com

The Tridipanel consists of a rigid EPS core with 11-gauge steel welded wire 2" x 2" fabric mesh on both sides, held together with 9-gauge steel truss wires. The panels are fastened together in the field, and a minimum 1.5" thickness of portland cement finish is machine- or hand-applied on both sides of the panel. The standard panels are 4' x 8', but may be manufactured up to 40' in length in 8" increments. The EPS core is available in either 1- or 2-lb. density, in thicknesses ranging from 1.5" to 5" by half-inch increments. Polyisocyanurate foam may be specified in place of EPS. Wire gauges are available in 11, 12.5, and 14, in bright or galvanized. This building system is appropriate where extreme structural requirements for earthquake, hurricane, and tornado resistance are required.

06 12 16
Stressed Skin Panels

Most structural insulated panels (SIPs) consist of oriented strand board (OSB) sandwiching an insulating foam core. SIPs are gaining market share in the residential and light commercial building market because they're quick to assemble and provide excellent energy performance. The insulating core of SIPs is most commonly made from expanded polystyrene (EPS), though in some cases polyurethane foam, or even compressed straw or mineral wool, is used. SIPs are manufactured in a range of thicknesses providing different R-values. In response to problems with insects burrowing in SIP foam cores, look for products that incorporate borate compounds; without the borate treatment, it's sometimes necessary to use insecticides or special termite trap systems on an ongoing basis. SIP buildings can be quickly assembled, particularly when panels are factory-cut for door and window openings. (See feature article EBN Vol. 7, No. 5.)

R-Control Panels

ACH Foam Technologies, LLC -
Headquarters
90 Trowbridge Dr.
P.O. Box 669
Fond du Lac, WI 54936

Toll-free: 800-236-5377
Phone: 920-924-4050
Fax: 920-924-4042
www.achfoam.com

ACH Foam Technologies, LLC is a licensed manufacturer of AFM Corporation's R-Control® Structural Insulated Panels made from R-Control Perform Guard® EPS cores and OSB skins. Panel dimensions range from 4' x 8' to 8' x 24' in thicknesses of 4-1/2" to 12-1/4". AFM has gone through full structural and fire testing of its system, including relevant building code listings.

R-Control Panels

ACH Foam Technologies, LLC - Newton Division
1418 Cow Palace Rd.
Newton, KS 67114

Toll-free: 800-835-2161
Phone: 316-283-1100
Fax: 316-283-3732
www.achfoam.com

AFM Corporation's R-Control® Structural Insulated Panels are made from R-Control Perform Guard® EPS cores and OSB skins. Panel dimensions range from 4' x 8' to 4' x 24' in thicknesses of 4-1/2" to 12-1/4". AFM has gone through full structural and fire testing of its system, including relevant building code listings. For sales information, contact the company's Kansas City Division.

R-Control Panels

Advance Foam Plastics, Inc. - California Division
Maquiladoras #331 Interior A y B
Cd. Industrials Nueva Tijuana
Tijuana, BC 22500 Mexico

Phone: 626-334-5358
Fax: 626-969-3978
www.afprcontrol.com

Advance Foam Plastics is a licensed manufacturer of AFM Corporation's R-Control® Structural Insulated Panels made from R-Control Perform Guard® EPS cores and OSB skins. Panel dimensions range from 4' x 8' to 8' x 24' in thicknesses of 4-1/2" to 12-1/4". AFM has gone through full structural and fire testing of its system, including relevant building code listings.

R-Control Panels

Advance Foam Plastics, Inc. - Colorado Division
5250 N. Sherman St.
Denver, CO 80216

Toll-free: 800-525-8697
Phone: 303-297-3844
Fax: 303-292-2613
www.afprcontrol.com

Advance Foam Plastics is a licensed manufacturer of AFM Corporation's R-Control® Structural Insulated Panels made from R-Control Perform Guard® EPS cores and OSB

skins. Panel dimensions range from 4' x 8' to 8' x 24' in thicknesses of 4-1/2" to 12-1/4". AFM has gone through full structural and fire testing of its system, including relevant building code listings.

R-Control Panels

Advance Foam Plastics, Inc. - Nevada Division
920 Kleppe Ln.
Sparks, NV 89431

Toll-free: 800-444-9290
Phone: 775-355-7655
Fax: 775-355-7615
www.afprcontrol.com

Advance Foam Plastics is a licensed manufacturer of AFM Corporation's R-Control® Structural Insulated Panels made from R-Control Perform Guard® EPS cores and OSB skins. Panel dimensions range from 4' x 8' to 8' x 24' in thicknesses of 4-1/2" to 12-1/4". AFM has gone through full structural and fire testing of its system, including relevant building code listings.

R-Control Panels

Advance Foam Plastics, Inc. - Utah Division
111 W. Fireclay Ave.
Murray, UT 84107

Toll-free: 877-775-8847
Phone: 801-265-3465
Fax: 801-265-3542
www.afprcontrol.com

Advance Foam Plastics is a licensed manufacturer of AFM Corporation's R-Control® Structural Insulated Panels made from R-Control Perform Guard® EPS cores and OSB skins. Panel dimensions range from 4' x 8' to 8' x 24' in thicknesses of 4-1/2" to 12-1/4". AFM has gone through full structural and fire testing of its system, including relevant building code listings.

R-Control Panels

AFM Corporation
211 River Ridge Cir. #102A
Burnsville, MN 55337

Toll-free: 800-255-0176
Phone: 952-474-0809
Fax: 952-474-2074
www.r-control.com

R-Control® SIPs are made from R-Control Perform Guard® EPS cores and OSB skins. The panel dimensions range from 4' x 8' to 8' x 24' in thicknesses of 4-1/2" to 12-1/4". AFM has gone through full structural and fire testing of its system, including relevant building code listings. AFM also licenses several dozen manufacturers throughout the U.S. to produce these and several other EPS products.

Most recently mentioned in EBN 4:1 & 7:5

Agriboard

Agriboard Industries, L.C.
8301 E. 21st St. N
Suite 320
Wichita, KS 67206

Toll-free: 866-247-4267
Phone: 316-630-9223
Fax: 316-636-9255
www.agriboard.com

After being purchased by one of the original investors in the company, Agriboard™ Industries is back in business manufacturing an engineered insulated panel construction system; its straw core is bound only with high heat and pressure. 4" cores are laminated single- or double-ply between two sheets of OSB using a polyurethane adhesive, though Agriboard has plans to switch to a soy-based adhesive, as well as straw-based outer panels. According to the company, the structural wall panels offer excellent thermal and acoustical insulation, have up to a 2-hour fire transmission rating, and are lower in cost and two to three times stronger than conventional wood-frame construction in compressive load, racking, and bending. Agriboard also offers a new ceramic and fiberglass composite, water- and UV-resistant, factory-applied exterior coating.

Most recently mentioned in EBN 4:3, 4:4, 7:1, 7:4, 7:5, 8:4, 8:7, 11:7, 14:5

R-Control Panels

Allied Foam Products, Inc.
2731 White Sulphur Rd.
Gainesville, GA 30501

Toll-free: 800-533-2613
Phone: 770-536-7900
Fax: 770-532-8123
www.alliedfoamprod.com

Allied Foam Products is a licensed manufacturer of AFM Corporation's R-Control® Structural Insulated Panels made from R-Control Perform Guard® EPS cores and OSB skins. Panel dimensions range from 4' x 8' to 8' x 24' in thicknesses of 4-1/2" to 12-1/4". AFM has gone through full structural and fire testing of its system, including relevant building code listings.

R-Control Panels

Big Sky Insulations, Inc.
P.O. Box 838
Belgrade, MT 59714

Toll-free: 800-766-3626
Phone: 406-388-4146
Fax: 406-388-7223
www.bsiinc.com

Big Sky Insulation is a licensed manufacturer of AFM Corporation's R-Control® Structural Insulated Panels made from R-Control

06 00 00
Wood, Plastics, & Composites

Perform Guard® EPS cores and OSB skins. Panel dimensions range from 4' x 8' to 8' x 24' in thicknesses of 4-1/2" to 12-1/4". AFM has gone through full structural and fire testing of its system, including relevant building code listings.

R-Control Panels

Branch River Foam Plastics, Inc.
15 Thurber Blvd.
Smithfield, RI 02917

Toll-free: 800-336-3626
Phone: 401-232-0270
Fax: 401-231-3434
www.branchriver.com

Branch River Foam Plastics is a licensed manufacturer of AFM Corporation's R-Control® Structural Insulated Panels made from R-Control Perform Guard® EPS cores and OSB skins. Panel dimensions range from 4' x 8' to 8' x 24' in thicknesses of 4-1/2" to 12-1/4". AFM has gone through full structural and fire testing of its system, including relevant building code listings.

Enercept Super Insulated Building System

Enercept, Inc.
3100 Ninth Ave. SE
Watertown, SD 57201

Toll-free: 800-658-3303
Phone: 605-882-2222
Fax: 605-882-2753
www.enercept.com

Enercept SIPs consist of a core of expanded polystyrene laminated between two sheets of oriented strand board (OSB).

06 00 00
Wood, Plastics, & Composites

Structural Insulated Panels

Extreme Panel Technologies, Inc.
475 E. Fourth St. N
P.O. Box 435
Cottonwood, MN 56229

Toll-free: 800-977-2635
Phone: 507-423-5530
Fax: 507-423-5531
www.extremepanel.com

Extreme Panel Technologies, Inc. manufactures structural insulated panels for residential, commercial, and agricultural applications. Panels are made with oriented strand board manufactured to APA standards for maximum strength and durability, and are available with expanded polystyrene cores.

Structural Insulated Panels

FischerSIPs, Inc.
1843 Northwestern Pkwy.
Louisville, KY 40203

Toll-free: 800-792-7477
Phone: 502-778-5577
Fax: 502-778-0508
www.fischersips.com

A FischerSIP® is made by laminating an expanded polystyrene foam core between two sheets of 7/16" oriented strand board (OSB). Panels can be manufactured in sizes ranging from 4' x 8' to 8' x 24'.

Structural Insulated Panels

Foam Laminates of Vermont
P.O. Box 102
Hinesburg, VT 05461

Toll-free: 800-545-6290
Phone: 802-453-3727
Fax: 802-453-2339
www.foamlaminates.com

Foam Laminates of Vermont started manufacturing structural insulated panels in 1982 in conjunction with their sister company, Vermont Frames. Exterior skins are generally plywood or OSB. Insulating cores are either expanded polystyrene (EPS) or polyisocyanurate. Only products with an EPS core are being specified here.

Foard Structural Insulated Panels

Foard Panel
P.O. Box 185
West Chesterfield, NH 03466

Toll-free: 800-644-8885
Phone: 603-256-8800
Fax: 603-256-6902
www.foardpanel.com

Foard Panel, Inc. makes structural insulated panels (SIPs) with expanded polystyrene foam cores, which are ozone-safe (not to be confused with extruded polystyrene, which is not ozone safe). Foard SIPs are four feet wide, and eight to 24 feet long with nominal 4", 6", or 8" thick insulation cores. In addition to the structural panels, Foard also makes a curtainwall panel, with drywall on one side an oriented-strand board (OSB) on the other, and nailbase roof insulation panel, with OSB on one side only.

Structural Insulated Panels

General Panel Corporation
106 Perma R Rd.
Johnson City, TN 37604

Toll-free: 800-647-6130
Fax: 423-929-7271
www.generalpanel.com

General Panel Corporation, formerly Perma R and previously listed as Apache Products Company, produces an EPS-core SIP system.

Polyurethane Structural Insulated Panels

Insulated Component Structures Rocky Mountain, Inc. (ICS-RM)
5858 Wright Dr.
Loveland, CO 80538

Phone: 970-427-7477
Fax: 800-427-7477
www.ics-rm.net

ICS-Rocky Mountain produces structural insulated panels (SIPS) with polyurethane foam cores that provide above R-6 per inch and have ASTM Class 1 fire resistance rating. The foam is blown without ozone depleting substances and is injected between the skins, resulting in strong surface bonding. Products include corner, wall, roof, and specially shaped panels, as well as cladding (for adding insulation to the outside of an existing building). Panels include metal camlocks for ease of installation and are available in a variety of sizes and thicknesses. Wall and roof panels come in 4 1/2" (R-28+), and 6 1/2" (R-42+) thicknesses. Surface options include fiber-cement, OSB, fiber re-enforced plastic laminate, metal, and custom. ICS-Rocky Mountain, with its affiliate companies in Florida and North Carolina, manufactures and distributes nationally.

Insulspan SIPs

Insulspan
9012 E. U.S. Hwy. 223
P.O. Box 38
Blissfield, MI 49228

Toll-free: 800-726-3510
Phone: 517-486-4844
Fax: 517-486-2056
www.insulspan.com

Insulspan's SIPs are produced with EPS foam cores laminated between OSB sheathing.

kama Energy Efficient Building Systems

kama Energy Efficient Building Systems, Inc.
6012 Topaz St., Ste. 6
Las Vegas, NV 89120

Phone: 702-451-7155
Fax: 702-446-0445
www.kama-eebs.com

kama Energy Efficient Building Systems™ panels consist of EPS boardstock inside structural galvanized steel framing designed to have no thermal breaks. kama-eebs™ panels can be used as a structural wall, floor, or roof system and can be used with any roof system and any interior and exterior finish. Panels are available in all dimensional lumber sizes and custom thicknesses and are built to meet project specifications.

R-Control SIP

Noark Enterprises
10101 Highway 70 E
N. Little Rock, AR 72117

Toll-free: 800-632-4586
Phone: 501-945-1114
Fax: 501-945-2583
www.noarkrcontrol.com

Noark Enterprises is a licensed manufacturer of AFM Corporation's R-Control® Structural Insulated Panels made from R-Control Perform Guard® EPS cores and OSB skins. Panel dimensions range from 4' x 8' to 8' x 24' in thicknesses of 4-1/2" to 12-1/4". AFM has gone through full structural and fire testing of its system, including relevant building code listings.

Structural Insulated Panels

Pacemaker Building Systems
126 New Pace Rd.
P.O. Box 279
Newcomerstown, OH 43832

Toll-free: 800-551-9799
Phone: 740-498-4181
Fax: 740-498-4184
www.pacemakerbuildingsystems.com

Pacemaker Building Systems is a manufacturer of Structural Insulated Panels with full fire and structural testing, and related UL and building code listings. The panels are made with EPS cores and OSB skins. Dimensions range from 4' x 8' to 8' x 24' in thicknesses of 4-9/16" (R-16) to 12-9/16" (R-45).

R-Control SIP Panels

Pacific Allied Products, Ltd.
91-110 Kaomi Loop
Kapolei, HI 96707

Toll-free: 888-824-3626
Phone: 808-864-8990
Fax: 808-595-4277
www.pacificalliedproducts.com

Pacific Allied Products is a licensed manufacturer of AFM Corporation's R-Control® Structural Insulated Panels made from R-Control Perform Guard® EPS cores and OSB skins. Panel dimensions range from 4' x 8' to 8' x 24' in thicknesses of 4-1/2" to 12-1/4". AFM has gone through full structural and fire testing of its system, including relevant building code listings.

Structural Insulated Panels

PORTERCorp
4240 N. 136th Ave.
Holland, MI 49424

Toll-free: 800-354-7721
Phone: 616-399-1963
Fax: 616-928-0076
www.portersips.com

PORTERCorp (formerly W. H. Porter) SIPs are made with an EPS foam core and come in any size that can be cut from a 4' x 8' or 8' x 24' sheet of oriented strand board. Panels with custom angles and/or cut-outs are also available. Panels are available in thicknesses of 4-1/2", 6-1/2", 8-1/4", 10-1/4", and 12-1/4" and provide R-values ranging from 15.8 to 45.7.

Structural Insulated Panels

Premier Building Systems - Division of Premier Industries, Inc.
4609 70th Ave. E
Fife, WA 98424

Toll-free: 800-275-7086
Phone: 253-926-2020
Fax: 253-926-3992
www.pbspanel.com

Premier Building Systems manufactures SIPs with borate-treated EPS foam insulation and OSB skins. Other substrates are available upon request. EPS may contain up to 15% recycled content. Panels are available in sizes of 4' x 8' up to 8' x 24' and range in thickness from 4" to 12" (with R-values of 15, 23, 30, 37, and 45). The company has SIP manufacturing plants in Fife, Washington, and Phoenix, Arizona.

Structural Insulated Panels

Shelter Enterprises, Inc.
8 Saratoga St.
P.O. Box 618
Cohoes, NY 12047

Toll-free: 800-836-0719
Phone: 518-237-4101
Fax: 518-237-0125
www.shelter-ent.com

Shelter custom-builds stress skin panels and interior wall panels in sizes up to 8' x 40'. Shelter produces their own EPS foam for the core. 98% of the EPS waste is recycled into other products. Other core materials are available upon request.

Industry Representation

Structural Insulated Panel Association
P.O. Box 1699
Gig Harbor, WA 98335

Phone: 253-858-7472
Fax: 253-858-0272
www.sips.org

The Structural Insulated Panel Association (SIPA) represents the industry in promoting the advantages of SIPs to designers, contractors, and homeowners.

Most recently mentioned in EBN 4:2 & 7:5

R-Control SIP Panels

Team Industries, Inc.
4580 Airwest Dr. SE
P.O. Box 888691
Grand Rapids, MI 49588

Toll-free: 800-356-5548
Phone: 616-698-2001
Fax: 616-698-0605
www.teamindustries.com

Team Industries is a licensed manufacturer of AFM Corporation's R-Control® Structural Insulated Panels made from R-Control Perform Guard® EPS cores and OSB skins. Panel dimensions range from 4' x 8' to 8' x 24' in thicknesses of 4-1/2" to 12-1/4". AFM has gone through full structural and fire testing of its system, including relevant building code listings.

R-Control SIP Panels

Team/IBS, Inc.
326 McGhee Rd.
Winchester, VA 22603

Phone: 540-662-0882
Fax: 540-662-9104
www.rcontrolibs.com

Team/IBS is a licensed manufacturer of AFM Corporation's R-Control® Structural Insulated Panels made from R-Control Perform Guard® EPS cores and OSB skins. Panel dimensions range from 4' x 8' to 8' x 24' in thicknesses of 4-1/2" to 12-1/4". AFM has gone through full structural and fire testing of its system, including relevant building code listings.

Murus EPS and Polyurethane SIPs

New

The Murus Company
3234 Rte. 549
P.O. Box 220
Mansfield, PA 16933

Phone: 570-549-2100
Fax: 570-549-2101
www.murus.com

**06 00 00
Wood,
Plastics, &
Composites**

Murus produces structural insulated panels with OSB skins and non-ozone depleting polyurethane or EPS foam cores. Both panel types are available in a variety of sizes, thicknesses, and application-specific configurations. The EPS SIPs are available with system R-Values of 16, 23, 30, 38, and 45 (the latter 12-1/8" thick), and are manufactured by cutting and laminating the pre-molded EPS core to the OSB skin with a urethane adhesive. The Polyurethane SIPs have a tongue and groove edge and unique cam-lock connectors. The Polyurethane SIPs are available with system R-values of 26, 33, and 40, and are manufactured by foaming the self-adhering expanding foam between the OSB skins.

R-Control Panels

Therma Foam, Inc.
P.O. Box 161128
Fort Worth, TX 76161

Toll-free: 800-333-3626
Phone: 817-624-7204
Fax: 800-999-6729
www.thermafoam.com

Therma Foam is a licensed manufacturer of AFM Corporation's R-Control® Structural Insulated Panels made from R-Control Perform Guard® EPS cores and OSB skins. Panel dimensions range from 4' x 8' to 8' x 24' in thicknesses of 4-1/2" to 12-1/4". AFM has gone through full structural and fire testing of its system, including relevant building code listings.

Thermal Foam SIPs

Thermal Foams, Inc.
2101 Kenmore Ave.
Buffalo, NY 14207

Phone: 716-874-6474
Fax: 716-874-8180
www.thermalfoams.com

Thermal Foams Inc. is a manufacturer of structural insulated panels made from Thermal Foams EPS cores and OSB Skins. Panel sizes range from 4' x 8' to 8' x 24' in thicknesses of 4-1/2" to 12-1/4". Thermal Foams has gone through full structural and fire testing of its systems with an approved model code testing facility.

**06 00 00
Wood, Plastics, & Composites**

Thermapan Structural Insulated Panels

Thermapan Structural Insulated Panels Inc.
1380 Commerce Pkwy.
P.O. Box 429
Fort Erie, ON L2A 5M4 Canada

Toll-free: 877-443-9255
Phone: 905-994-7399
Fax: 905-994-7400
www.thermapan.com

Thermapan SIP, formerly known as The Wall™, is an EPS-core structural insulated panel system.

EPS and Polyurethane SIPs

Winter Panel Corporation
74 Glen Orne Dr.
Brattleboro, VT 05301

Phone: 802-254-3435
Fax: 802-254-4999
www.winterpanel.com

Winter Panel produces structural insulated panels with either EPS or polyisocyanurate (polyurethane) foam cores. EPS has always been blown with non-ozone-depleting, non-global-warming pentane. As of late 2003, Winter Panel's polyiso foam is also blown using pentane. The 4-1/2"- or 6-1/2"-thick panels are available in Structurewall™ (a direct substitute for 2x4 or 2x6 framing using OSB as the outer skins), Curtainwall panels (nonstructural with gypsum wallboard on interior side, OSB on outside), and Woodclad™ (Structurewall panels with 1x8 v-groove pine cladding on interior finish side). The EPS-core panels are less expensive, while the polyurethane panels have a higher R-value. Panels with custom skins, cores, and thicknesses are also available.

Most recently mentioned in EBN 7:5

06 13 01
FSC-Certified Heavy Timber

Certified wood products are verified by a third party as originating from well-managed forests. GreenSpec recognizes the Forest Stewardship Council (FSC) standards as the most rigorous and the only certification system with well-established chain-of-custody certification. Some companies listed here sell both certified and noncertified wood products, *or products that have been certified according to different, less stringent environmental standards. To make certain that you get environmentally responsible wood products, be sure to specify your interest in FSC-certified wood. (See also 06 05 70 - Wood Products Certification and Information.)*

AltruWood Certified Wood Products

AltruWood, Inc.

For full listing, see CSI section 09 64 01 - FSC-Certified Wood Flooring

Certified Redwood Lumber

Big Creek Lumber Company

For full listing, see CSI section 06 11 01 - FSC-Certified Wood Framing Lumber

Certified Wood Products

Cascadia Forest Goods, LLC

For full listing, see CSI section 06 11 01 - FSC-Certified Wood Framing Lumber

Harmonized Tropical Wood

Harmonized Wood Products

For full listing, see CSI section 06 11 01 - FSC-Certified Wood Framing Lumber

Harrop-Procter Certified-Wood Building Products

Harrop-Procter Watershed Protection Society

For full listing, see CSI section 06 11 01 - FSC-Certified Wood Framing Lumber

Certified Lumber and Timbers

Harwood Products

For full listing, see CSI section 06 11 01 - FSC-Certified Wood Framing Lumber

Certified Hardwood Lumber and Timbers

ROMEX World Trade Company, LLC - sales agent for ROM

For full listing, see CSI section 06 11 01 - FSC-Certified Wood Framing Lumber

Certified Wood Building Products

West Wind Hardwood, Inc.

For full listing, see CSI section 09 64 01 - FSC-Certified Wood Flooring

06 13 02
Reclaimed-Wood Heavy Timber

As the demands on forest resources have increased, nonforest sources of wood have grown in importance. Reclaimed wood is usually salvaged from buildings slated for demolition, abandoned railroad trestles, and "sinker logs" that sank decades ago during river-based log drives. It can also be obtained from trees that have been recently harvested from urban or suburban areas (such as disease-killed trees). Reclaimed wood is often available in species, coloration, and wood quality that is no longer available in newly harvested timber. In some cases, reclaimed wood suppliers have only limited quantities with matching coloration or weathering patterns; ample lead time and accurate materials estimates can help ensure the availability of the desired wood. Lowering the uniformity standards for finished wood can also increase the potential for use of reclaimed wood. As with other resources, the supply of reclaimed wood is limited. Efficient and appropriate use of reclaimed wood is important for its long-term availability. (See also 01 62 02 - Distributors/Retailers, Used Building Materials.) (See feature article EBN Vol. 9, No. 5.)

Reclaimed-Wood Lumber and Products

A Reclaimed Lumber Co.

For full listing, see CSI section 06 22 02 - Reclaimed-Wood Millwork

Reclaimed-Wood Products

Albany Woodworks, Inc.

For full listing, see CSI section 06 22 02 - Reclaimed-Wood Millwork

AltruWood Reclaimed-Wood Products

AltruWood, Inc.

For full listing, see CSI section 09 64 02 - Reclaimed-Wood Flooring

Appalachian Woods

Appalachian Woods, LLC

For full listing, see CSI section 09 64 02 - Reclaimed-Wood Flooring

Reclaimed-Wood Products

Architectural Timber and Millwork
49 Mt. Warner Rd.
P.O. Box 719
Hadley, MA 01035

Toll-free: 800-430-5473
Phone: 413-586-3045
Fax: 413-586-3046
www.atimber.com

Architectural Timber and Millwork specializes in custom architectural millwork fabricated from reclaimed wood. They source their materials from different parts of the country, providing a widely varied species inventory. Wide-plank flooring is produced from wood salvaged from existing structures slated for demolition. Species include heart pine, chestnut, and oak.

Barnstormers Reclaimed Hand-Hewn Beams

Barnstormers

For full listing, see CSI section 09 64 02 - Reclaimed-Wood Flooring

Reclaimed-Wood Materials

Black's Farmwood, Inc.

For full listing, see CSI section 09 64 02 - Reclaimed-Wood Flooring

Reclaimed-Wood Materials

BT Timberworks
1 Rabel Ln.
P.O. Box 368
Gallatin Gateway, MT 59730

Phone: 406-763-4639
Fax: 406-763-4818
www.bttimberworks.com

BT Timberworks offers custom-milled, reclaimed lumber and timbers in a variety of species. The company specializes in shipping timber frame houses all over the country for supervised construction but also sells custom-cut, reclaimed wood from their sawmill in Montana for residential and commercial applications such as siding, flooring, and millwork.

Used Building Materials

Caldwells

For full listing, see CSI section 01 62 02 - Distributors/Retailers, Used Building Materials

Reclaimed-Wood Products

Centre Mills Antique Floors

For full listing, see CSI section 09 64 02 - Reclaimed-Wood Flooring

Reclaimed-Wood Products

Chestnut Specialists, Inc.

For full listing, see CSI section 09 64 02 - Reclaimed-Wood Flooring

Wood Materials from Urban Trees

CitiLog

For full listing, see CSI section 09 64 02 - Reclaimed-Wood Flooring

Reclaimed-Wood Building Products

Conklin's Authentic Antique Barnwood
R.R. 1, Box 70
Susquehanna, PA 18847

Phone: 570-465-3832
Fax: 570-465-3835
www.conklinsbarnwood.com

Conklin's Authentic Antique Barnwood sells hand-hewn beams, barn boards, and flooring "as is" or remilled.

Reclaimed-Wood Products

Crossroads Recycled Lumber
57839 Rd. 225
P.O. Box 928
North Fork, CA 93643

Toll-free: 888-842-3201
Phone: 559-877-3645
Fax: 559-877-3646
www.crossroadslumber.com

Crossroads Recycled Lumber sells raw and remilled salvaged Douglas fir, sugar pine, ponderosa pine, cedar, and redwood lumber, timbers, flooring, paneling, and siding. They also offer doors made from this wood.

D. Litchfield Reclaimed Wood

D. Litchfield & Co. Ltd.

For full listing, see CSI section 06 11 02 - Reclaimed-Wood Framing Lumber

06 00 00
Wood, Plastics, & Composites

Reclaimed-Wood Products

Duluth Timber Co.
P.O. Box 16717
Duluth, MN 55816

Phone: 218-727-2145
Fax: 218-727-0393
www.duluthtimber.com

Duluth Timber reclaims and remills mainly Douglas fir and longleaf yellow pine, but also redwood and cypress. Demolition and salvage of warehouses and sheep-shearing sheds in Australia has yielded a supply of Australian hardwoods such as jarrah and Mountain ash. Duluth has mills in Minnesota, and Washington.

Most recently mentioned in EBN 10:4

Reclaimed-Wood Building Products

Endura Wood Products, Ltd.

For full listing, see CSI section 09 64 02 - Reclaimed-Wood Flooring

Reclaimed-Wood Building Products

General Woodcraft, Inc.

For full listing, see CSI section 09 64 02 - Reclaimed-Wood Flooring

Georgian Bay Wetwood

Georgian Bay Wetwood Inc.

For full listing, see CSI section 06 40 26 - Wood Veneer

06 00 00
Wood, Plastics, & Composites

River-Reclaimed Wood Products

Goodwin Heart Pine Company

For full listing, see CSI section 09 64 02 - Reclaimed-Wood Flooring

Reclaimed-Wood Building Products

J. Hoffman Lumber Co.
1330 E. State St.
Sycamore, IL 60178

Phone: 815-899-2260
Fax: 815-889-2460
www.hoffmanlumberco.com

J. Hoffman Lumber Co. is the Midwest's only sawmill company specializing in reclaimed antique heart pine, Douglas fir, and white pine. Reclaimed lumber is remilled into flooring, siding, and other millwork.

Logs End Reclaimed-Wood Building Products

Logs End Inc.

For full listing, see CSI section 09 64 02 - Reclaimed-Wood Flooring

Reclaimed-Wood Building Products

Longleaf Lumber

For full listing, see CSI section 09 64 02 - Reclaimed-Wood Flooring

M. Fine Lumber Company

M. Fine Lumber Company

For full listing, see CSI section 06 11 02 - Reclaimed-Wood Framing Lumber

Michael Evenson Natural Resources

Michael Evenson Natural Resources
P.O. Box 157
Petrolia, CA 95558

Phone: 707-826-2354
www.oldgrowthtimbers.com

Natural Resources dismantles buildings and remills salvaged lumber for resale. Available species include redwood, Douglas fir, and western red cedar.

Reclaimed-Wood Building Products

Mountain Lumber

For full listing, see CSI section 09 64 02 - Reclaimed-Wood Flooring

Pinocchio's

Pinocchio's
18651 Hare Creek Ter.
Fort Bragg, CA 95437

Phone: 707-964-6272
Fax: 707-964-0458
www.pinocchioredwood.com

Pinocchio's offers raw and remilled lumber from Douglas fir and redwood in both standard-dimension and custom sizes.

Reclaimed-Wood Building Products

Pioneer Millworks

For full listing, see CSI section 09 64 02 - Reclaimed-Wood Flooring

Reclaimed Lumber and Timbers

R. W. Rhine Inc.
1124 112th St. E
Tacoma, WA 98445

Toll-free: 800-963-8270
Phone: 253-537-5852
Fax: 253-531-9548
www.rwrhine.com

R. W. Rhine stocks a wide variety of reclaimed lumber and beams supplied by its extensive deconstruction operations.

Re-Tech Wood Products

Re-Tech Wood Products
1324 Russell Rd.
P.O. Box 215
Forks, WA 98331

Phone: 360-374-4141
Fax: 360-374-4141
www.retechwoodproducts.com

Re-Tech reclaims and remills timber for a wide variety of custom millwork and complete custom timber-frame packages for houses. They also make specialty cuts in timber to order.

Resource Woodworks

Resource Woodworks, Inc.
627 E. 60th St.
Tacoma, WA 98404

Phone: 253-474-3757
Fax: 253-474-1139
www.rwtimber.com

Resource Woodworks specializes in Douglas fir, cedar, and redwood timbers salvaged from demolition projects and remilled to custom specifications, including decking, flooring, lumber, timbers, siding, paneling, and millwork.

Reclaimed-Wood Building Products

Solid Wood Products

For full listing, see CSI section 09 64 02 - Reclaimed-Wood Flooring

Reclaimed-Wood Building Products

TerraMai

For full listing, see CSI section 09 64 02 - Reclaimed-Wood Flooring

Timeless Timber

Timeless Timber, Inc.
2200 E. Lake Shore Dr.
Ashland, WI 54806

Toll-free: 1-888-653-5647
Phone: 715-685-9663
Fax: 715-685-9620
www.timesstimber.com

Timeless Timber, Inc., formerly The Superior Water-Logged Lumber Company, harvests logs that sank during the log drives of the 1800s. Domestic species include red and white oak, maple, birch, white pine, basswood, elm, hickory, beech, ponderosa pine, and cypress. The company was certified in June of 2000 by Scientific Certification Systems as a producer of timber from 100% salvaged wood.

Trestlewood

Trestlewood

For full listing, see CSI section 09 64 02 - Reclaimed-Wood Flooring

Triton Underwater Wood

Triton Logging Inc.

For full listing, see CSI section 06 11 02 - Reclaimed-Wood Framing Lumber

Underwater Timber Salvage

Underwater Timber Salvage

For full listing, see CSI section 06 11 02 - Reclaimed-Wood Framing Lumber

Reclaimed-Wood Building Products

Vintage Log and Lumber, Inc.
Glen Ray Rd.
Rt. 1, Box 2F
Alderson, WV 24910

Toll-free: 877-653-5647
Phone: 304-445-2300
Fax: 304-445-2249
www.vintagelog.com

Vintage Log and Lumber salvages the materials in log cabins and timber-frame barns in Kentucky, Ohio, Pennsylvania, and West Virginia. The company's inventory includes salvaged redwood, chestnut, oak, pine, and poplar boards, beams, flooring, and split rails. They also sell complete hand-hewn log cabins and timber-frame barns.

Reclaimed-Wood Building Products

Vintage Material Supply Co.

For full listing, see CSI section 09 64 02 - Reclaimed-Wood Flooring

Reclaimed-Wood Building Products

Vintage Timberworks
47100 Rainbow Canyon Rd.
Temecula, CA 92592

Phone: 951-695-1003
Fax: 951-695-9003
www.vintagetimber.com

Vintage Timberworks offers a wide range of reclaimed products made with wood salvaged from buildings in the U.S., Canada, and Australia that are typically at least 70 years old. Typical species include Douglas fir, cedar, and redwood. Reclaimed timber, beams, and flooring are available in a variety of species and are offered "as is," remilled, and/or refinished (distressed, hand-hewed, sandblasted, etc.). Douglas fir and oak flooring can be milled in a wide variety of widths and lengths. Most other species are limited in width and length to available stock. The company also can arrange for building demolition and material reclamation in the U.S. and Canada.

Reclaimed-Wood Building Products

West Wind Hardwood, Inc.

For full listing, see CSI section 09 64 02 - Reclaimed-Wood Flooring

Reclaimed-Wood Building Products

What It's Worth, Inc.

For full listing, see CSI section 09 64 02 - Reclaimed-Wood Flooring

06 13 13
Log Construction

Log and heavy timber construction has appeal in North America for its rustic qualities. Though the embodied energy of wood can be relatively low, heavy timber construction—such as in log houses—is rarely environmentally preferable compared with more conventional building systems. Conventional framing is more wood-efficient, and in most cases, results in a more energy-efficient building envelope. Products listed here have environmental features that separate them from conventional timber and log products.

EcoLog Homes

Haliburton Forest: EcoLog Concepts
Box 202, Kennisis Lake Rd.
R.R. 1
Haliburton, ON K0M 1S0 Canada

Phone: 705-754-4663
Fax: 705-754-1179
www.haliburtonforest.com

EcoLog Homes are built of certified hemlock logs from the 60,000-acre Haliburton Forest and Wildlife Reserve. The company's annual capacity is limited by the sustainable yield of the forest to 20 building kits per year.

06 15 01
FSC-Certified Wood Decking

Certified wood products are verified by a third party as originating from well-managed forests. GreenSpec recognizes the Forest Stewardship Council (FSC) standards as the most rigorous and the only certification system with well-established chain-of-custody certification. Some companies listed here sell both certified and noncertified wood products, or products that have been certified according to different, less stringent environmental standards. To make certain that you get environmentally responsible wood products, be sure to specify your interest in FSC-certified wood. (See also 06 05 70 - Wood Products Certification and Information.) (See feature article EBN Vol. 6, No. 10.)

AltruWood Certified Wood Products

AltruWood, Inc.

For full listing, see CSI section 09 64 01 - FSC-Certified Wood Flooring

Certified Wood Products

Cascadia Forest Goods, LLC

For full listing, see CSI section 06 11 01 - FSC-Certified Wood Framing Lumber

06 00 00
Wood, Plastics, & Composites

Certified Iron Woods Lumber

Cecco Trading, Inc.
600 E. Vienna Ave.
Milwaukee, WI 53212

Phone: 414-445-8989
Fax: 414-445-9155
www.ironwoods.com

Iron Woods® is a brand of ipe decking and lumber from the Brazilian forest that is offered FSC-certified with an upcharge. Iron Woods' natural durability rating of 25+ years is the highest of woods tested by the U.S. Forest Products Lab. The product is available in all standard decking, porch flooring, and dimensional lumber sizes from 2x2 to 4x12 and up to 20' long in standard even lengths. Iron Woods decking is Class A fire-rated and comes with a 25-year fully transferable limited warranty.

SmartChoice Wood Products

Certified Forest Products, LLC.

For full listing, see CSI section 06 11 01 - FSC-Certified Wood Framing Lumber

Certified Decking

Disdero Lumber Company
12301 SE Carpenter Dr.
P.O. Box 469
Clackamas, OR 97015

Toll-free: 800-547-4209
Phone: 503-239-8888
www.disdero.com

Disdero Lumber Company offers FSC-certified decking made with wood from Collins Pine Company, the first privately owned timber management company in the U.S. to receive FSC certification.

F.D. Sterritt Certified-Wood Building Products

F.D. Sterritt Lumber Co.

For full listing, see CSI section 06 22 01 - FSC-Certified Millwork

Certified Decking

Forest World Group
P.O. Box 852
Bethany Beach , DE 19930

Phone: 302-541-4541
Fax: 302-541-4542
www.naturallydurable.com

Forest World Group, formerly Sylvania Certified, sells decking lumber of FSC-certified ipe and lesser-known naturally durable tropical species as alternatives for pressure-treated wood decking.

Most recently mentioned in EBN 8:7

Harmonized Tropical Wood

Harmonized Wood Products

For full listing, see CSI section 06 11 01 - FSC-Certified Wood Framing Lumber

Harrop-Procter Certified-Wood Building Products

Harrop-Procter Watershed Protection Society

For full listing, see CSI section 06 11 01 - FSC-Certified Wood Framing Lumber

Certified Lumber and Timbers

Harwood Products

For full listing, see CSI section 06 11 01 - FSC-Certified Wood Framing Lumber

Certified Red Cedar

Mary's River Lumber Co.

For full listing, see CSI section 06 11 01 - FSC-Certified Wood Framing Lumber

FSC-Certified Lumber, Plywood, and Products

Potlatch Corporation

For full listing, see CSI section 06 11 01 - FSC-Certified Wood Framing Lumber

Certified-Wood Products

Randall Custom Lumber, Ltd.

For full listing, see CSI section 06 11 01 - FSC-Certified Wood Framing Lumber

Certified Tropical Hardwood Decking

Sustainable Forest Systems LP
995 Castaway Blvd.
Vero Beach, FL 32963

Toll-free: 800-866-0795
Phone: 772-234-3482
Fax: 240-218-4002
www.sustainableforestsystems.com

Sustainable Forest Systems has operated tropical hardwood timberlands and associated processing since 1994. They offer a wide range of FSC-certified tropical hardwood products.

06 15 02
Reclaimed-Wood Decking

As the demands on forest resources have increased, nonforest sources of wood have grown in importance. Reclaimed wood is usually salvaged from buildings slated for demolition, abandoned railroad trestles, and "sinker logs" that sank decades ago during river-based log drives. It can also be obtained from trees that have been recently harvested from urban or suburban areas (such as disease-killed trees). Reclaimed wood is often available in species, coloration, and wood quality that is no longer available in newly harvested timber. In some cases, reclaimed wood suppliers have only limited quantities with matching coloration or weathering patterns; ample lead time and accurate materials estimates can help ensure the availability of the desired wood. Lowering the uniformity standards for finished wood can also increase the potential for use of reclaimed wood. As with other resources, the supply of reclaimed wood is limited. Efficient and appropriate use of reclaimed wood is important for its long-term availability. (See also 01 62 02 - Distributors/Retailers, Used Building Materials.) (See feature article EBN Vol. 9, No. 5.)

Reclaimed-Wood Lumber and Products

A Reclaimed Lumber Co.

For full listing, see CSI section 06 22 02 - Reclaimed-Wood Millwork

AltruWood Reclaimed-Wood Products

AltruWood, Inc.

For full listing, see CSI section 09 64 02 - Reclaimed-Wood Flooring

Used Building Materials

Caldwells

For full listing, see CSI section 01 62 02 - Distributors/Retailers, Used Building Materials

**06 00 00
Wood,
Plastics, &
Composites**

Wood Materials from Urban Trees

CitiLog

For full listing, see CSI section 09 64 02 - Reclaimed-Wood Flooring

D. Litchfield Reclaimed Wood

D. Litchfield & Co. Ltd.

For full listing, see CSI section 06 11 02 - Reclaimed-Wood Framing Lumber

Reclaimed-Wood Building Products

Endura Wood Products, Ltd.

For full listing, see CSI section 09 64 02 - Reclaimed-Wood Flooring

Logs End Reclaimed-Wood Building Products

Logs End Inc.

For full listing, see CSI section 09 64 02 - Reclaimed-Wood Flooring

Pinocchio's

Pinocchio's

For full listing, see CSI section 06 13 02 - Reclaimed-Wood Heavy Timber

Reclaimed-Wood Building Products

Pioneer Millworks

For full listing, see CSI section 09 64 02 - Reclaimed-Wood Flooring

Resource Woodworks

Resource Woodworks, Inc.

For full listing, see CSI section 06 13 02 - Reclaimed-Wood Heavy Timber

Reclaimed-Wood Building Products

TerraMai

For full listing, see CSI section 09 64 02 - Reclaimed-Wood Flooring

Trestlewood

Trestlewood

For full listing, see CSI section 09 64 02 - Reclaimed-Wood Flooring

06 15 04
Preservative-Treated Wood Decking

The durability of preservative-treated wood is the most important advantage to its use. Extending the service life of wood products reduces the demands on forests for replacement timber. Sales of lumber treated with the preservative CCA (chromated copper arsenate) are banned for consumer applications. Disposal by incineration is the most significant environmental concern associated with the billions of board feet already in use that were treated with this preservative: toxins such as arsenic may become airborne, and those that don't get into the air end up in the ash, where they're highly leachable. Copper-based wood treatments such as ACQ (ammoniacal copper quaternary) and copper azole have replaced CCA as the standard product. Wood treated with copper should be avoided near aquatic ecosystems, since copper is highly toxic to many aquatic organisms. Copper-treated wood is also corrosive to steel fasteners; follow manufacturers' recommendations for fastener selection. Silica-based treatments are available that are not actually preservatives, but that have the same effect by rendering the wood inedible to insects and fungi. Borate treatments effectively protect wood from insects while offering low mammalian and environmental toxicity, however, most borate-treated products are only suitable in interior applications because the borates do not stay fixed in the wood when exposed to weather. Organic (carbon-based) pesticides, used in various combinations, also appear in treated wood, in both surface and pressure treatments. These pesticides, relatively new to wood preservation, offer a less-toxic alternative to copper-based treatments. Treated wood should not be chipped for mulch, or burned. (See feature articles EBN Vol. 2, No. 1 & Vol. 6, No. 3.)

Wolmanized L3 Outdoor

Arch Wood Protection, Inc.
1955 Lake Park Dr., Ste. 100
Smyrna, GA 30080

Phone: 866-789-4567
Fax: 770-801-1990
www.wolmanizedwood.com

New

Wolmanized® L3 Outdoor® wood for residential use is pressure-treated against decay and termites with a metal-free, organic (carbon-based), waterborne preservative mixture of low-toxic tebuconazole, propiconazole, and imidacloprid. It is appropriate for above-ground uses, such as decks, fence boards, trim, and siding. The treatment is not corrosive to metal fasteners and hardware. The light-green dye used to differentiate this treated wood has little or no effect on the final color of paints or stains, according to the manufacturer, but it will help differentiate unpainted treated wood from untreated wood at the time of disposal.

TimberSIL Nontoxic Pressure-Treated Wood

Timber Treatment Technologies

For full listing, see CSI section 06 11 04 - Preservative-Treated Framing Lumber

EnviroSafe Plus

Wood Treatment Products, Inc.

For full listing, see CSI section 06 11 04 - Preservative-Treated Framing Lumber

06 16 00
Sheathing

Sheathing comprises a significant portion of the materials used with many building types. Careful consideration of product selection and use can reduce the environmental impacts of a project. Wall sheathing is often used only as an additional layer of weather protection, although it may also be required for racking resistance. When let-in diagonal bracing is used to provide racking resistance, wood-panel sheathing can sometimes be eliminated or replaced with more resource-efficient or insulative products. Phenol-formaldehyde (PF) binders are used in plywood, while OSB can be made with PF or the non-formaldehyde-emitting methyl diisocyanate (MDI), a polyurethane binder. Paradoxically, exterior-rated products using PF binders are less of an offgassing concern than interior-grade panels made with urea-formaldehyde. Oriented-strand board (OSB) can be an efficient use of forest resources because it can be produced from small-diameter or low-grade tree species. Wood products can carry the "FSC Mixed" label under a percentage-based standard based on the average certified and non-certified throughput

06 00 00
Wood, Plastics, & Composites

of the facility at which they are made. Products listed here have one or more of the following attributes: FSC-certification; nonformaldehyde binders; nontoxic (to humans) borate insect treatments; or other environmental advantages over conventional OSB and plywood. (See also 06 05 70 - Wood Products Certification and Information.) (See feature article EBN Vol. 1, No. 2.)

Viroc Cement-Bonded Particleboard

Allied Building Products Corp.
15 East Union Ave.
East Rutherford, NJ 07073

Toll-free: 800-541-2198
Fax: 201-507-3842
www.alliedbuilding.com

Viroc is a structural cement-bonded particleboard made with portland cement and mineralized wood particles (71% portland cement, 18.5% wood fibers). It can be machined and worked with typical carpentry tools. Viroc is available in 4x8 sheets from 5/16" to 1-5/8" thicknesses. 4x10 sheets come in 3 thicknesses of 5/16", 3/8", and 1/2". T&G, half-lap, and beveled edge are available. Due to the energy intensity of the cement content, this product should not be considered a green substitute for particleboard except where significant resistance to fire, moisture, termites, or vermin are required.

SmartChoice Wood Products

Certified Forest Products, LLC.

For full listing, see CSI section 06 11 01 - FSC-Certified Wood Framing Lumber

CollinsWood FSC-Certified Wood Products

Collins Companies

For full listing, see CSI section 07 46 43 - Composition Siding

FSC-Certified, Formaldehyde-Free Wood Panel Products

Columbia Forest Products
222 S.W. Columbia, Ste. 1575
Portland, OR 97201

Toll-free: 800-547-1791
Fax: 503-224-5294
www.columbiaforestproducts.com

Columbia Forest Products, the largest hardwood plywood producer in North America, offers FSC-certified plywood. Columbia manufactures both veneer-core panels and

particleboard panels, including particleboard made with agrifiber (wheat-straw). The PureBond™ brand refers to the company's panel products that are produced with a non-formaldehyde soy-based adhesive that was introduced in 2005. The company is converting all of its veneer-core plywood and veneered-agrifiber-core panel production to this PureBond process.

Most recently mentioned in EBN 8:2, 14:6, 14:12, 15:7

F.D. Sterritt Certified-Wood Building Products

F.D. Sterritt Lumber Co.

For full listing, see CSI section 06 22 01 - FSC-Certified Millwork

Green Board

GreenImports, LLC
P.O. Box 60
North Stonington, CT 06359

Phone: 860-887-5813
Fax: 860-887-5813
www.wwieinc.com

Green Board is made from recycled Tetra Pak beverage cartons and is composed of 75% paper, 20% polyethylene, and 5% aluminum. It is water resistant, termite and borer resistant, and provides insulative and sound proofing qualities. Green Board has a textured surface, and can be formed into curves and other shapes. Marketed as a direct replacement for plywood in any application (including "roofing, boats, cabinets, shipping crates, sheathing, underlayment, furniture"), it can be sawn, molded, cut, glued, screwed, or nailed. Available from the importer by the container-load in 4x8 sheets in 10, 12, or 18 mm thicknesses. Each container holds 676, 250, or 354 sheets of the respective board thicknesses.

4-Way Floor Deck, N.C.F.R., and Firestall Roof Deck

Homasote Company
932 Lower Ferry Rd.
P.O. Box 7240
West Trenton, NJ 08628

Toll-free: 800-257-9491
Phone: 609-883-3300
Fax: 609-883-3497
www.homasote.com

4-Way® Floor Deck, N.C.F.R.®, and Firestall® Roof Deck are structural high-density fiberboard panels made from 100% recycled newspaper, with paraffin binders and additives for pest and fire resistance. Panels are available in a variety of thicknesses. N.C.F.R. is a Class A fire-rated panel for interior and exterior use. 4-Way Floor Deck is a

tongue-and-groove multi-ply subfloor that is structural, sound deadening, and moderately insulative (R-2.5/in.). Firestall Roof Deck is a tongue-and-groove Class A fire-rated panel manufactured with 1 to 4 plies of Homasote® and a face ply of N.C.F.R..

AdvanTech OSB

J. M. Huber Wood Products
10925 David Taylor Dr., Ste. 300
One Resource Sq.
Charlotte, NC 28262

Toll-free: 800-933-9220
Phone: 704-547-0671
Fax: 704-547-0739
www.huberwood.com

AdvanTech™ OSB from Huber is an OSB made primarily with formaldehyde-free MDI resin (a small quantity of phenolic resin is added to improve certain properties). Due to its greater moisture resistance than conventional OSB, AdvanTech carries a 50-year warranty. This product has been certified by Greenguard for low emissions.

Most recently mentioned in EBN 8:11 & 12:10

PureKor Certified Plywood and Manufactured Panels

Panel Source International
18 Rayborn Cres., Ste. 101
St. Albert, AB T8N 5C1 Canada

New

Toll-free: 877-464-7246
Phone: 780-458-1007
Fax: 780-419-2345
www.panelsource.net

PureKor Certified Hardwood Plywood Plus is FSC-certified and contains no added urea formaldehyde. The binder used for both the plywood substrate and for adhering the face veneer, according to Panel Source, is polyvinyl acetate (PVA). This plywood is available in a number of grades and species, including alder, ash, birch, cherry, pine, cedar, hickory, maple, okoume, red and white oak, white maple, mahogany, poplar, and walnut. With most products, the core veneers are FSC-certified and the face veneers are not. Panel Source International also offers particleboard and PureKor Platinum Grade MDF panels made with FSC-certified, pre-consumer recycled wood fiber and formaldehyde-free resin. They are available from 4 x 8 to 5 x 12, in thicknesses ranging from 1/4" to 1-1/2" in mill grade, M1, M2, and premium. Standard density is 45 lbs.

EarthSource Forest Products

Plywood and Lumber Sales, Inc.

For full listing, see CSI section 01 62 03 - Distributors/Retailers, FSC-Certified Wood

FSC-Certified Lumber, Plywood, and Products

Potlatch Corporation

For full listing, see CSI section 06 11 01 - FSC-Certified Wood Framing Lumber

Certified Pine Plywood

ROMEX World Trade Company, LLC - sales agent for ROM
P.O. Box 1110
Alexandria, LA 71309

Toll-free: 800-299-5174
Phone: 318-445-1973
Fax: 318-443-0159
www.martco.com

Roy O. Martin Lumber Management, LLC (ROM) has received SmartWood certification for its 585,000 acres of forestland and four mills according to standards of the Forest Stewardship Council (FSC). This is the first FSC certification of any forest management operation in Louisiana. ROM's FSC-certified pine plywood, formerly under the name of SmartCore®, is produced by Martco Plywood in Chopin, Louisiana. Sanded plywood is available in AA, AB, AC, BC, and A-Flat grades in 4' x 8' panels standard thicknesses of 1/4", 11/32", 15/32", 19/32" and 23/32". As is true for the company's OSB plant, some fiber used in the Chopin mill comes from non-company-owned land, but 100% FSC-certified product can be provided. ROM's pine plywood is also available sided with a foil radiant barrier, or printed with the company's new "GRID" panel marking system.

Most recently mentioned in EBN 11:6

Tuff-Strand Certified OSB

ROMEX World Trade Company, LLC - sales agent for ROM
P.O. Box 1110
Alexandria, LA 71309

Toll-free: 800-299-5174
Phone: 318-445-1973
Fax: 318-443-0159
www.martco.com

Roy O. Martin Lumber Management, LLC (ROM) has gained FSC-certification of its 585,000 acres of forestland and four mills. In addition to this being the first FSC certification of any forest management operation in Louisiana, ROM has made available the first-ever FSC-certified oriented strand board (OSB). Tuff-Strand® is a fairly conventional OSB produced by the Martco Partnership plant in LeMoyen, Louisiana. The 4' x 8' panels are available in three standard thicknesses: 7/16", 15/32", and 19/32". The mill is fed by up to 70% company-owned timber, and while OSB is typically certi-

fied using FSC's partial-content rules, the company can provide 100% FSC-certified product. Tuff-Strand's binder is 100% phenol formaldehyde. FSC-certified Tuff-Strand is also now available sided with a foil radiant barrier, or printed with the company's new "GRID" panel marking system.

Most recently mentioned in EBN 11:6 & 11:12

SkyBlend UF-Free Particle Board

Roseburg Forest Products
P.O. Box 1088
Roseburg, OR 97470

Toll-free: 800-245-1115
Phone: 541-679-3311
Fax: 541-679-9543
www.rfpco.com

Roseburg SkyBlend™ is a general-use particleboard produced with phenol-formaldehyde (PF) binder instead of the industry-standard urea-formaldehyde (UF) binder. The company claims formaldehyde emissions of about 0.01 parts per million (ppm) under standard test conditions—comparable to natural levels in outdoor air. It is Green Cross-certified by Scientific Certification Systems (SCS) as being made from 100% recycled wood fibers (pre-consumer waste from lumber mills). The wood fiber is not FSC-certified. The particleboard core is tinted light blue for field identification. SkyBlend™ is available in industrial grade only, in seven thicknesses from 1/4" to 1-1/8". Standard dimensions for most thicknesses are 49" x 97", while the 3/4" and 1-1/8" panels are also available in larger sizes. Custom dimensions may be available for large orders.

Most recently mentioned in EBN 14:9

SierraPine Formaldehyde-free Fiberboard

SierraPine Ltd.
3010 Lava Ridge Ct. #220
Roseville, CA 95661

Toll-free: 800-676-3339
Phone: 916-772-3422
Fax: 916-772-3415
www.sierrapine.com

SierraPine's Medex MDF, for use in interior high-moisture applications, and Medite II MDF, for interior non-structural applications, are manufactured with a polyurethane binder, methyl diisocyanate(MDI), rather than conventional formaldehyde-based resins. (Medite FR2, a Class 1, fire-retardant MDF panel, is now manufactured with formaldehyde.) SierraPine's newest formaldehyde-free product, Arreis SDF (Sustainable Design Fiberboard), uses the same MDI binder more efficiently to lower cost premiums. SierraPine

has earned certification from Scientific Certification Systems (SCS) for using up to 100% recovered and recycled wood fiber for their MDF products.

Most recently mentioned in EBN 1:1, 3:5, 5:6, 6:1, 11:11, 13:2, 15:8

Versaroc Cement-Bonded Particleboard

U.S. Architectural Products
55 Industrial Cir.
Lincoln, RI 28730

Toll-free: 800-243-6677
Fax: 401-725-8540
www.architecturalproducts.com

Versaroc® from U.S. Architectural Products is a structural cement-bonded particleboard made with mineralized wood particles and portland cement. It can be worked with typical carpentry tools; fasteners should be treated for corrosion resistance. The formaldehyde-free, termite-resistant, non-combustible product is available in stock nominal ("uncalibrated") thicknesses of 10 mm (3/8"), 12 mm (1/2"), and 19 mm (3/4"); several other thicknesses may be special-ordered. "Calibrated" stock is sanded to more precise thicknesses for applications requiring tighter tolerances. These boards are available square-edged in 48" widths; or tongue-and-groove in 46-1/2" widths for thickness of 16 mm (5/8") or more. Stocked length is 96"; shorter or longer boards (up to 120") are available by special order, as are widths less than 48" square or 46-1/2" tongue-and-groove. All orders can be factory-sealed on all surfaces with an acrylic paint sealer. Due to the energy intensity of the cement content, this product should not be considered a green substitute for particleboard except where significant resistance to fire, moisture, termites, or vermin are required.

06 00 00
Wood, Plastics, & Composites

06 16 13 Insulating Sheathing

Products listed here provide insulating qualities, often through the incorporation of a radiant barrier. When they face a heat source, radiant barriers work by reflecting heat. When faced away from a heat source, radiant barriers function primarily by virtue of their low emissivity. This means that the surface does not radiate heat well. A radiant-barrier surface on roof sheathing, for example, heats up from the sunlight striking the roof, but that heat energy is not readily emitted into the attic space—so that attic remains cooler. This is why the radiant barrier seems to "reflect" heat back out of the building. An air space is required on at least one side of a radiant barrier in order for it to function as designed. Radiant barriers in attics are most beneficial in reducing cooling loads; their effectiveness in reducing heating loads is more limited. Radiant barrier products usually do not include significant recycled content, because of the lower reflectivity of recycled aluminum and the difficulty in producing very thin foils from recycled aluminum; the high embodied energy of virgin aluminum can be recovered through energy savings. When comparing products, look for the lowest emissivity (which corresponds to the highest reflectivity). Do not rely on "effective" or "equivalent" R-values, which are only relevant in certain climates or under certain conditions. (See also 06 16 29 - Acoustical Underlayment.)

Thermo Ply

Covalence Coated Products
700 Centreville Rd.
Constantine, MI 49042

Toll-free: 800-345-8881
Phone: 269-435-2425
Fax: 269-435-7510
www.covalencecoatedproducts.com

Thermo Ply® are thin, lightweight structural sheathing panels manufactured from 100% recycled cardboard and aluminum-foil facings. The plies are pressure-laminated with a special water-resistant, nontoxic adhesive. Thermo Ply is available in three grades: nonstructural, structural, and super strength. Although Thermo Ply structural is less than 1/8" thick, when properly secured with 3" fastener spacing on the perimeter and 6" spacing on intermediate studs, the racking strength meets building codes even in seismically active areas. Thermo Ply super strength is applicable with studs on 24" centers. All grades are available in the following sizes: 4' x 8', 4' x 9', 4'-3/4" x 8', and 4'-3/4" x 9'.

Most recently mentioned in EBN 1:2

EnerMax Radiant Barrier Sheathing

EMCO Building Products Corporation
9510 St. Patrick St.
LaSalle, QC H8R 1R9 Canada

Toll-free: 800-567-2726
Fax: 800-361-7011
www.emcobp.com

EnerMax™ is a 1/2"-thick, lightweight structural sheathing radiant barrier panel made from reclaimed sawdust and wood shavings with a nontoxic binder. The company claims that the product's vapor-resistant aluminum-foil skin can boost the wall R-value by 4.7 (this will depend on the application, however). EnerMax comes in 4' x 8' and 4.5' x 12' sizes with preprinted nailmarks at 8" intervals. The company also produces High Performance sheathing, which includes an asphalt coating on all six sides.

Fiberboard—Regular and High Density

Huebert Brothers Products, LLC
1545 E. Morgan St.
Boonville, MO 65233

Toll-free: 800-748-7147
Phone: 660-882-2704
Fax: 660-882-7991
www.huebertfiberboard.com

Huebert Fiberboard is made from waste wood chips and cellulose fiber with a carbon-based black emulsion surface coating. This insulating roof sheathing product for mopped roofs contains 40-60% recycled materials, of which 20% is post-consumer. The company claims R-values of roughly 2.78/in. for the 1/2"-, 1"-, and 2"-thick panels.

Fiberboard Insulating Sheathing

Knight-Celotex
One Northfield Plaza
Northfield, IL 60093

Phone: 847-716-8030
Fax: 847-716-8040
www.knightcelotex.com

Knight-Celotex Premium Insulating Sheathing is a vapor-permeable exterior sheathing alternative to plywood and OSB. It is made with 80% or more recovered fiber (hardwood or sugarcane, depending on which plant manufactures the product), and small percentages of starch, clay, paraffin, carbon black, and formaldehyde-free adhesive. SturdyBrace™ is a similar product with improved structural qualities; it contains 75% fiber, 22% asphalt, and small amounts of starch and wax. These 1/2" sheathing products cut with a knife, have a 1.3 R-value, and are most appropriate behind vented rainscreen and reservoir claddings. The high permeability is an important feature in climates where wall-cavity drying to the exterior is important.

BarrierPanel, TechShield Radiant Barrier, and BarrierFloor OSB

LP
414 Union St., Ste. 2000
Nashville, TN 37219

Toll-free: 877-744-5600
Fax: 877-523-7192
www.lpcorp.com

Part of the SmartGuard™ family, a venture between LP Corp. and Osmose, these products are treated with zinc borate for resistance to termites, carpenter ants, and fungal decay. LP's BarrierPanel™ is an OSB sheathing product suitable for wall, roof, and (double-layer) subfloor applications in residential and light commercial buildings. TechShield™ Radiant Barrier is an OSB roof sheathing with a radiant-foil overlay to minimize radiant heat gain. LP's BarrierFloor™ T&G OSB subflooring is edge-coated to reduce swelling. All carry a 20-year transferable warranty.

Most recently mentioned in EBN 9:9

Polar-Ply Radiant-Barrier

Superior Radiant Insulation
P.O. Box 247
San Dimas, CA 91773

Toll-free: 888-774-4422
Phone: 909-305-1450
Fax: 909-305-1448
www.superiorrb.com

Superior Radiant Insulation manufactures several radiant barrier and insulation products. Among them is Polar-Ply™ aluminum foil-faced OSB or plywood sheathing.

06 16 29
Acoustical Underlayment

Acoustical underlayment—which is distinct from flooring underlayment—helps prevent sound transmission through a structure. Use of a sound-deadening sheathing can reduce the need to further control sound transmission with carpeting or rugs. (See also 06 16 13 - Insulating Sheathing & 09 68 19 - Carpet Cushion.)

06 00 00
Wood, Plastics, & Composites

Homasote 440 SoundBarrier and ComfortBase

Homasote Company
932 Lower Ferry Rd.
P.O. Box 7240
West Trenton, NJ 08628

Toll-free: 800-257-9491
Phone: 609-883-3300
Fax: 609-883-3497
www.homasote.com

Homasote 440 Sound Barrier® and Comfort Base® panels are high-density fiberboard made from 100% recycled wastepaper and a formaldehyde-free paraffin binder, with an R-value of 1.2 for a 1/2" panel. Sound Barrier panels are available in a variety of sizes and thicknesses and are designed to provide sound control as a flooring underlayment and in wall assemblies. Comfort Base is designed for use as a floating underlayment over a concrete slab, has a grooved grid pattern on the underside to provide slab ventilation, and is 1/2" thick.

Homasote has been manufacturing building panels from waste papers since 1909.

SoundStop Interior Substrate

Knight-Celotex
One Northfield Plaza
Northfield, IL 60093

Phone: 847-716-8030
Fax: 847-716-8040
www.knightcelotex.com

SoundStop™ interior acoustical substrate from Knight-Celotex is a 1/2" fiberboard that can be used to achieve system STC ratings exceeding 42. Designed to be installed prior to wall or ceiling drywall or plywood underlayment, it is made with 96% recovered fiber (hardwood or sugarcane, depending on which plant manufactures the product), and small percentages of starch and wax. Knight-Celotex also produces SoundStop® Underlayment.

QuietWalk

MP Global Products LLC

For full listing, see CSI section 09 60 14 - Flooring Underlayment

QuietWood

Quiet Solution, Inc.
1250 Elko Dr.
Sunnyvale, CA 94089

Toll-free: 800-797-8159
www.quietsolution.com

QuietWood™ sound-control plywood for floors and walls is made with a thin layer of steel embedded in viscoelastic polymer and sandwiched between wood veneers. It provides impressive sound transmission reduction, installs quickly, and results in very little added thickness, relative to the sound control provided. QuietWood is available in thicknesses ranging from 5/8" to 1-3/8".

Most recently mentioned in EBN 14:3

06 16 37
Preservative-Treated Wood Panel Product Sheathing

The durability of preservative-treated wood is the most important advantage to its use. Extending the service life of wood products reduces the demands on forests for replacement timber. Sales of lumber treated with the preservative CCA (chromated copper arsenate) are banned for consumer applications. Disposal by incineration is the most significant environmental concern associated with the billions of board feet already in use that were treated with this preservative: toxins such as arsenic may become airborne, and those that don't get into the air end up in the ash, where they're highly leachable. Copper-based wood treatments such as ACQ (ammoniacal copper quaternary) and copper azole have replaced CCA as the standard product. Wood treated with copper should be avoided near aquatic ecosystems, since copper is highly toxic to many aquatic organisms. Copper-treated wood is also corrosive to steel fasteners; follow manufacturers' recommendations for fastener selection. Silica-based treatments are available that are not actually preservatives, but that have the same effect by rendering the wood inedible to insects and fungi. Borate treatments effectively protect wood from insects while offering low mammalian and environmental toxicity, however, most borate-treated products are only suitable in interior applications because the borates do not stay fixed in the wood when exposed to weather. Organic (carbon-based) pesticides, used in various combinations, also appear in treated wood, in both surface and pressure treatments. These pesticides, relatively new to wood preservation, offer a less-toxic alternative to copper-based treatments. Treated wood should not be chipped for mulch, or burned. (See feature articles EBN Vol. 2, No. 1 & Vol. 6, No. 3.)

FrameGuard

Arch Wood Protection, Inc.

For full listing, see CSI section 06 11 04 - Preservative-Treated Framing Lumber

Advance Guard Borate Pressure-Treated Wood

Osmose Wood Preserving, Inc.

For full listing, see CSI section 06 11 04 - Preservative-Treated Framing Lumber

EnviroSafe Plus

Wood Treatment Products, Inc.

For full listing, see CSI section 06 11 04 - Preservative-Treated Framing Lumber

BluWood

WoodSmart Solutions, Inc.

For full listing, see CSI section 06 11 04 - Preservative-Treated Framing Lumber

06 16 54
Fire-Resistant Sheathing Board

Products listed here have formaldehyde-free binders, are FSC-certified, or have other compelling environmental attributes.

4-Way Floor Deck, N.C.F.R., and Firestall Roof Deck

Homasote Company

For full listing, see CSI section 06 16 00 - Sheathing

Pyroblock Fire-Retardant Particleboard, MDF, and Plywood

Panel Source International
18 Rayborn Cres., Ste. 101
St. Albert, AB T8N 5C1 Canada

Toll-free: 877-464-7246
Phone: 780-458-1007
Fax: 780-419-2345
www.panelsource.net

Pyroblock® PB Plus Particleboard Pyroblock MDF Plus, and Plywood Plus Fire-Retardant Panels are urea formaldehyde-free. Unlike conventional fire-retardant panels, in which a fire-retardant chemical is incorporated throughout the product, Pyroblock Panels rely

06 00 00
Wood, Plastics, & Composites

on an intumescent coating. This coating expands and chars when subjected to heat and thereby insulates and protects the substrate from fire. According to the company, the product is inert when cured. Pyroblock meets applicable flame-spread standards (ASTM E-84(01) in the U.S., and CAN/ULC 102-M in Canada). Available sizes are 4' or 5' wide by 8', 9', or 10' long by 1/8" to 1-1/4" thick. Pyroblock FSC-certified fire-retardant composite panels are also available.

Most recently mentioned in EBN 12:4

06 17 36
Metal-Web Wood Joists

Metal-web wood joists are lightweight, high-strength framing members that can provide long, clear spans and don't require drilling for mechanical and electrical systems. Metal-web wood joists are also very resource-efficient. (See also 06 11 13 - Engineered Wood Framing Products.)

Open-Web T-Series Trusses

iLevel by Weyerhaeuser
2910 E. Amity Rd.
Boise, ID 83716

Toll-free: 888-453-8358
Phone: 208-364-1200
Fax: 208-364-1300
www.iLevel.com

Trus Joist's new T-Series open-web trusses have a top chord made from TimberStrand® LSL, which is manufactured with fast-growing aspen and poplar trees that are debarked and shredded into strands. The strands are coated with a formaldehyde-free MDI (methyl diisocyanate) binder and pressed into huge billets that are milled into dimensional lumber. LSL lumber is very consistent and stable; it does not warp and twist like solid wood. TimberStrand® LSL also resists splitting, which increases the allowable nailing options. The bottom chord of these trusses is made from solid lumber, and steel-tube web members are in between. All trusses are custom-engineered and manufactured for specific applications.

SpaceJoist

Jager Metal Products
2711 - 61st Ave SE
Calgary, AB T2V 2X5 Canada

Toll-free: 888-885-2437
Phone: 403-259-0714
Fax: 403-258-3191
www.jagermetalproducts.com

The Jager SpaceJoist™ is a truss for wood-framed construction with solid-wood top and bottom flanges and open-metal web members. SpaceJoists can have trimmable, I-joist-type ends.

Posi-Strut

MiTek Industries
14515 N. Outer 40 Dr., Ste. 300
Chesterfield, MO 63017

Toll-free: 800-325-8075
Phone: 314-434-1200
Fax: 314-434-5343
www.mii.com

Posi-Struts offer a high-strength 20-gauge steel alternative to wood webs for floor joists and roof rafters; their open-web configuration eliminates the need for cutting and drilling, and they feature standard 2' o.c. spacing to cut down on cost and labor over conventional webs.

TrimJoist

TrimJoist
5146 Hwy. 182 E
P.O. Box 2286
Columbus, MS 39704

Toll-free: 800-844-8281
Phone: 662-327-7950
Fax: 662-329-4610
www.trimjoist.com

TrimJoist's open-web trusses are manufactured with solid-wood top and bottom chords and solid-wood web members joined with metal plate connectors. TrimJoists have trimmable, I-joist-type ends.

06 17 53
Shop-Fabricated Wood Trusses

Roof and floor trusses are inherently more wood-efficient than dimension-lumber rafters and joists. Products listed here use FSC-certified wood or have other compelling environmental attributes.

FrameGuard

Arch Wood Protection, Inc.
For full listing, see CSI section 06 11 04 - Preservative-Treated Framing Lumber

Hayward Corporation

Hayward Corporation
For full listing, see CSI section 01 62 01 - Distributors/Retailers, Green Building Materials

BluWood

WoodSmart Solutions, Inc.
For full listing, see CSI section 06 11 04 - Preservative-Treated Framing Lumber

06 22 01
FSC-Certified Millwork

Certified wood products are verified by a third party as originating from well-managed forests. GreenSpec recognizes the Forest Stewardship Council (FSC) standards as the most rigorous and the only certification system with well-established chain-of-custody certification. Some companies listed here sell both certified and noncertified wood products, or products that have been certified according to different, less stringent environmental standards. To make certain that you get environmentally responsible wood products, be sure to specify your interest in FSC-certified wood. (See also 06 05 70 - Wood Products Certification and Information.) (See feature article EBN Vol. 6, No. 10.)

Certified Millwork

Anderson-Tully
1725 N. Washington St.
P.O. Box 38
Vicksburg, MS 39181

Phone: 601-629-3283
Fax: 601-629-3284
www.andersontully.com

Anderson-Tully Company (ATCO) received its FSC certification from SmartWood after years of uncertified but well-managed forestry practices. Anderson-Tully has long been offering an extensive number of species (with cottonwood and hackberry leading the list) due to its practice of finding markets for lesser-used tree species rather than eliminating them.

Most recently mentioned in EBN 2:4 & 9:11

Certified Paneling and Millwork

Architectural Millwork Mfg. Co.
2125 Cross St.
P.O. Box 2809
Eugene, OR 97402

Toll-free: 800-685-1331
Phone: 541-689-1331
Fax: 541-463-2068
www.archmillwork.com

Architectural Millwork produces finished and unfinished FSC-certified stock and custom molding and paneling (including radius paneling and millwork) for commercial and residential projects. Custom panels may utilize any available core. Moldings may be up to 11-1/4" wide; custom profiles and pattern-matching are achieved with in-house knife grinding. Paint-grade MDF millwork (from sawmill byproduct) is also available.

Certified Wood Products

Cascadia Forest Goods, LLC

For full listing, see CSI section 06 11 01 - FSC-Certified Wood Framing Lumber

CollinsWood FSC-Certified Wood Products

Collins Companies

For full listing, see CSI section 07 46 43 - Composition Siding

Certified Wood Moldings

Colonial Craft
501 Main St.
Luck, WI 54853

Toll-free: 800-289-6653
Phone: 715-472-2223
Fax: 715-472-8770
www.colonialcraft.com/
architecturalmouldings.html

Colonial Craft offers FSC-certified hardwood moldings. All other Colonial Craft products, including architectural moldings, can be produced from certified wood upon request.

FSC-Certified Wood Products

Dwight Lewis Lumber / Lewis Lumber Products

For full listing, see CSI section 09 64 01 - FSC-Certified Wood Flooring

F.D. Sterritt Certified-Wood Building Products   **New**

F.D. Sterritt Lumber Co.
110 Arlington St.
Watertown, MA 02472

Toll-free: 877-635-3362
Phone: 617-923-1480
Fax: 617-354-1698
www.sterrittlumber.com

F.D. Sterritt Lumber sells FSC-certified lumber, plywood, and hardwoods, including hardwood flooring. They have a variety of certified species in stock and additional material available by special order.

Certified Millwork

Les Produits Forestiers Becesco
2900, 95ieme Rue
St-Georges, QC G6A 1E3 Canada

Phone: 418-227-3671
Fax: 418-228-3672

Les Produits Forestiers Becesco is a certified hardwood lumber supplier milling oak, beech, birch, hard maple, and soft maple.
Most recently mentioned in EBN 3:6

Certified Lumber, Flooring, Wainscoting, and Veneer

McDowell Lumber Company, Inc.

For full listing, see CSI section 09 64 01 - FSC-Certified Wood Flooring

Windfall Lumber and Milling

Windfall Lumber and Milling

For full listing, see CSI section 01 62 03 - Distributors/Retailers, FSC-Certified Wood

06 22 02
Reclaimed-Wood Millwork

As the demands on forest resources have increased, nonforest sources of wood have grown in importance. Reclaimed wood is usually salvaged from buildings slated for demolition, abandoned railroad trestles, and "sinker logs" that sank decades ago during river-based log drives. It can also be from trees that have been recently harvested from urban or suburban areas (such as disease-killed trees). Reclaimed wood is often available in species, coloration, and wood quality not available in newly harvested timber. In some cases, reclaimed wood suppliers have only limited quantities with matching coloration or weathering patterns; ample lead time and accurate materials estimates can help ensure the availability of the desired wood. Lowering the uniformity standards for finished wood can also increase the potential for use of reclaimed wood. As with other resources, the supply of reclaimed wood is limited. Efficient and appropriate use of reclaimed wood is important for its long-term availability. Be aware that reclaimed wood may contain lead paint; testing is recommended if lead paint residue is suspected. (See also 01 62 02 - Distributors/Retailers, Used Building Materials.) (See feature article EBN Vol. 9, No. 5.)

Reclaimed-Wood Lumber and Products

A Reclaimed Lumber Co.
9 Old Post Rd.
Madison, CT 06443

Phone: 203-214-9705
Fax: 928-396-3425
www.woodwood.com

A Reclaimed Lumber Co. (formerly Armster) salvages wood from old water and wine tanks, mill buildings, bridge timbers, river-recovery log operations, and other sources and custom mills it into a variety of wood products including siding, plank flooring, millwork, paneling, shingles and shakes, stairs parts, and dimension lumber and timber. Available species include red cedar, redwood, beech, black cherry, chestnut, rock maple, red and white oak, Eastern hemlock, Douglas fir, mahogany and Longleaf heart pine. Wood is sourced from all over the country, much of it processed at their Connecticut mill; but the company makes an effort to provide wood that is local to the customer and will make arrangements to process it locally.

Reclaimed-Wood Flooring and Millwork

Aged Woods / Yesteryear Floorworks Company
2331 E Market St, Ste 6
York, PA 17402

Toll-free: 800-233-9307
Phone: 717-840-0330
Fax: 717-840-1468
www.agedwoods.com

Aged Woods® / Yesteryear Floorworks Company is a full-service mill that uses reclaimed, kiln-dried wood to produce flooring, stair parts, moldings, cabinetry, and paneling. They salvage their materials from barns that are typically between 75 and 200 years old. Available species include American chestnut, longleaf heart pine, maple, cherry, walnut, hemlock, hickory, poplar, pine, and oak. Most of the flooring is 3/4" tongue-and-groove and of random widths and lengths within given ranges. Matching stair parts are available in conjunction with flooring orders.

Reclaimed-Wood Products

Albany Woodworks, Inc.
P.O. Box 729
Albany, LA 70711

Toll-free: 1-800-551-1282
Phone: 225-567-1155
Fax: 225-567-5150
www.albanywoodworks.com

06 00 00
Wood, Plastics, & Composites

Albany Woodworks mills reclaimed woods, including heart pine and heart cypress, into various architectural woodwork products, including flooring, timber, and stair parts. Doors are also offered.

AltruWood Reclaimed-Wood Products

AltruWood, Inc.

For full listing, see CSI section 09 64 02 - Reclaimed-Wood Flooring

Appalachian Woods

Appalachian Woods, LLC

For full listing, see CSI section 09 64 02 - Reclaimed-Wood Flooring

Reclaimed-Wood Products

Architectural Timber and Millwork

For full listing, see CSI section 06 13 02 - Reclaimed-Wood Heavy Timber

Reclaimed-Wood Doors

Avision, LLC
3424 N. Canada Rd.
Nampa, ID 83687

New

Phone: 208-412-7823
Fax: 208-426-8988
www.avisionllc.com

Avision manufactures custom doors from reclaimed lumber salvaged from barns, old mills, and fences in the U.S. The company makes interior and exterior doors to any size and thickness, and in a variety of styles. Customers can also request particular reclaimed species from around the world, or FSC-certified wood. Dowels, wood glue, and weatherstripping are the only components not made of reclaimed lumber.

06 00 00
Wood, Plastics, & Composites

Reclaimed-Wood Materials

BT Timberworks

For full listing, see CSI section 06 13 02 - Reclaimed-Wood Heavy Timber

Reclaimed-Wood Products

Centre Mills Antique Floors

For full listing, see CSI section 09 64 02 - Reclaimed-Wood Flooring

Wood Materials from Urban Trees

CitiLog

For full listing, see CSI section 09 64 02 - Reclaimed-Wood Flooring

Craftmark Reclaimed Wood

Craftmark Reclaimed Wood, Inc.

For full listing, see CSI section 01 62 03 - Distributors/Retailers, FSC-Certified Wood

Reclaimed-Wood Products

Duluth Timber Co.

For full listing, see CSI section 06 13 02 - Reclaimed-Wood Heavy Timber

Reclaimed-Wood Building Products

Endura Wood Products, Ltd.

For full listing, see CSI section 09 64 02 - Reclaimed-Wood Flooring

River-Reclaimed Wood Products

Goodwin Heart Pine Company

For full listing, see CSI section 09 64 02 - Reclaimed-Wood Flooring

Reclaimed-Wood Millwork

J. L. Powell & Co., Inc.

For full listing, see CSI section 09 64 02 - Reclaimed-Wood Flooring

Reclaimed and Urban-Harvested Millwork

Jackel Enterprises

For full listing, see CSI section 09 64 02 - Reclaimed-Wood Flooring

Logs End Reclaimed-Wood Building Products

Logs End Inc.

For full listing, see CSI section 09 64 02 - Reclaimed-Wood Flooring

Reclaimed-Wood Building Products

Longleaf Lumber

For full listing, see CSI section 09 64 02 - Reclaimed-Wood Flooring

Reclaimed-Wood Building Products

Mayse Woodworking Co.

For full listing, see CSI section 09 64 02 - Reclaimed-Wood Flooring

Reclaimed-Wood Building Products

Mountain Lumber

For full listing, see CSI section 09 64 02 - Reclaimed-Wood Flooring

Pinocchio's

Pinocchio's

For full listing, see CSI section 06 13 02 - Reclaimed-Wood Heavy Timber

Reclaimed-Wood Building Products

Pioneer Millworks

For full listing, see CSI section 09 64 02 - Reclaimed-Wood Flooring

Re-Tech Wood Products

Re-Tech Wood Products

For full listing, see CSI section 06 13 02 - Reclaimed-Wood Heavy Timber

Resource Woodworks

Resource Woodworks, Inc.

For full listing, see CSI section 06 13 02 - Reclaimed-Wood Heavy Timber

Reclaimed-Wood Building Products

Solid Wood Products

For full listing, see CSI section 09 64 02 - Reclaimed-Wood Flooring

Reclaimed-Wood Building Products

TerraMai

For full listing, see CSI section 09 64 02 - Reclaimed-Wood Flooring

G. R. Plume Co.

The G. R. Plume Co.
1373 W. Smith Rd., Ste. A-1
Ferndale, WA 98248

Phone: 360-384-2800
Fax: 360-384-0335
www.grplume.com

The G. R. Plume Co. produces custom architectural millwork and timbers fabricated from reclaimed Douglas fir.

Reclaimed-Wood Flooring and Millwork

Treasured Timbers, Inc.

For full listing, see CSI section 09 64 02 - Reclaimed-Wood Flooring

Trestlewood

Trestlewood

For full listing, see CSI section 09 64 02 - Reclaimed-Wood Flooring

Reclaimed-Wood Building Products

Vintage Material Supply Co.

For full listing, see CSI section 09 64 02 - Reclaimed-Wood Flooring

Reclaimed-Wood Building Products

Vintage Timberworks

For full listing, see CSI section 06 13 02 - Reclaimed-Wood Heavy Timber

Reclaimed-Wood Building Products

What Its Worth, Inc.

For full listing, see CSI section 09 64 02 - Reclaimed-Wood Flooring

06 22 03
Fiberboard Millwork

Pressures on timber supply are especially acute for high-visibility, solid-wood products like window sash and molding, which have traditionally been produced from old-growth trees. Medium-density fiberboard (MDF) molding made from post-industrial wood wastes is an excellent substitute for paint-grade moldings. The consistent quality and economical price of MDF moldings is broadening its market share. Some MDF is available with a nonformaldehyde binder. (See also 06 22 04 - Agfiber Millwork, 06 46 03 - Fiberboard Trim, 06 46 04 - Wood-Alternative Trim.)

Certified Veneer-Faced Trim

S. J. Morse Company
Rte. 50
P.O. Box 600
Capon Bridge, WV 26711

Phone: 304-856-3423
Fax: 304-856-3073
www.sjmorse.com

The S. J. Morse Company offers custom-made, veneer-faced trim in eight FSC-certified species—three domestics: red oak, cherry, and maple; one European: steamed beech; and four relatively unknown Brazilian species: Amapa, Taurari Vermelho, Ucuuba, and Cupiuba. The trim is available in any specified width and can be provided with a clear finish (a water-based option is available) or be left unfinished for custom staining and finishing. FSC-certified, recycled-content, or agrifiber cores are offered, including formaldehyde-free options. Other custom veneer products are also available FSC-certified: window seats, wide window and door jambs, column wraps, ceiling panels, and cabinet door faces.

Medite II and Medex MDF Molding

SierraPine Ltd.
3010 Lava Ridge Ct. #220
Roseville, CA 95661

Toll-free: 800-676-3339
Phone: 916-772-3422
Fax: 916-772-3415
www.sierrapine.com

SierraPine's Medite Division produces MDF moldings made from Medite II, which uses a formaldehyde-free MDI binder. For high-moisture applications, the molding can be produced from Medex, which uses the same binder. SierraPine moldings are manufactured in knot-free, blemish-free, 16' lengths, factory-primed with a water-based paint. SierraPine has earned certification from Scientific Certification Systems (SCS) for using up to 100% recovered and recycled wood fiber for MDF.

Most recently mentioned in EBN 15:8

06 22 04
Agfiber Millwork

With similar qualities to wood particleboard and Medium Density Fiberboard (MDF), straw particleboard is made from the stems left over after harvesting the cereal grains, such as wheat, oats, and rice. This is a substitute for paint-grade moldings, offering consistent quality and

economy, though it is somewhat rougher and more porous than MDF and does not mill as smoothly. Straw particleboard is made using a non-formaldehyde PMDI binder. (See also 06 22 03 - Fiberboard Millwork, 06 46 03 - Fiberboard Trim, 06 46 04 - Wood-Alternative Trim.)

Wheatboard Millwork

CitiLog
370 Pittstown Rd.
P.O. Box 685
Pittstown, NJ 08867

Toll-free: 877-248-9564
Phone: 908-735-8871
Fax: 908-735-6893
www.citilogs.com

CitiLog™ offers custom millwork from formaldehyde-free wheatboard. The company also offers wheatboard cabinetry and doors.

06 25 00
Prefinished Paneling

The following products are an eclectic assortment of prefinished panels that offer an alternative to traditional prefinished paneling. Products listed here are made with recycled content, low-emitting binders, agricultural-waste fiber such as straw, and/or FSC-certified wood. (See also 06 40 23 - Interior Architectural Woodwork Substrate, 07 42 00 - Wall Panels, 06 05 70 - Wood Products Certification and Information.) (See feature article EBN Vol. 5, No. 4.)

FSC-Certified, Formaldehyde-Free Wood Panel Products

Columbia Forest Products

For full listing, see CSI section 06 16 00 - Sheathing

Bamboo Veneer and Paneling

DMVP Timber Bamboo Ltd.

For full listing, see CSI section 06 40 26 - Wood Veneer

06 00 00
Wood, Plastics, & Composites

Environ Biocomposite, Dakota Burl, and Biofiber Wheat

Environ Biocomposites, LLC
221 Mohr Dr.
Mankato, MN 56001

Toll-free: 800-324-8187
Phone: 507-388-3434
Fax: 507-388-3159
www.environbiocomposites.com

Environ® is a biocomposite panel containing recycled newsprint, soy flour, pigment, and a water-based catalyst that converts the soy flour into a resin. This tough material looks like granite and works like hardwood. It is not appropriate for moisture-prone applications. Dakota Burl™ composite panels are made primarily from post-process, sunflower-seed hulls. Biofiber™ panels are made from finely chopped post-harvest wheat straw combined with a high-performance urethane resin. All the panels come in standard 4' x 8' sheets in 1/2", 3/4", and 1" thicknesses.

Most recently mentioned in EBN 4:3, 5:4, 8:11, 13:2, 14:5, 15:11

DesignWall, NovaCork, and Burlap Panels

Homasote Company
932 Lower Ferry Rd.
P.O. Box 7240
West Trenton, NJ 08628

Toll-free: 800-257-9491
Phone: 609-883-3300
Fax: 609-883-3497
www.homasote.com

DesignWall®, NovaCork®, and Burlap Panels all consist of a Homasote 100% recycled newspaper fiber and paraffin binder substrate with various decorative coverings. DesignWall is a substrate of Class A fire-rated N.C.F.R. board wrapped in Class A fire-rated Guilford of Maine fabric covering. NovaCork is available as a Class A board and is covered with cork veneer. Burlap Panels are standard 440 Homasote covered with burlap. All three products are available in 4' x 8' and 4' x 10' panels.

Most recently mentioned in EBN 3:3

Kirei Board

Kirei USA
1805 Newton Ave.
San Diego, CA 92113

Phone: 619-236-9924
Fax: 240-220-5946
www.kireiusa.com

Kirei™ board, made with waste sorghum fiber, is a lightweight substitute for wood-panel products and is appropriate for use in cabinetry and furniture, store displays, restaurant and office interiors, wall treatments, and flooring for low-traffic areas. The nonformaldehyde MDI binder (similar to that used in most straw-particleboard panels) is more water-resistant than the common urea-formaldehyde binder. Though not friable, the product has a soft surface that may require wood-putty filling and sealing. The irregular pattern is very striking and popular with designers. Kirei board is 3' x 6' and comes in 10, 20 or 30 mm thicknesses.

Most recently mentioned in EBN 13:12

MeadowBoard Straw Panels

Meadowood Industries, Inc.
P.O. Box 257
Belmont, CA 94002

Phone: 650-637-0539
www.meadowoodindustries.com

MeadowBoard™ is a formaldehyde-free rye grass straw panel available in 4' x 8' sheets from 1/8" to 1" thick. This coarse-textured interior finish material can be custom-molded into various shapes. Meadowood is not an M3-rated structural panel product. Rye grass straw is an agricultural waste product from grass seed production.

Most recently mentioned in EBN 14:5

MOSO Bamboo Building Products

MOSO International NA, Ltd.

For full listing, see CSI section 09 62 23 - Bamboo Flooring

Unicor

National Shelter Products, Inc.
50 S.E. Bush St.
Issaquah, WA 98027

Toll-free: 800-552-7775
Phone: 425-557-7968
Fax: 425-557-8592
www.nationalshelter.com

Unicor™ wallboard is made from recycled corrugated containers and bottle carrier stock from the beverage industry bonded with PVA (white glue) adhesive. Unicor is mainly used as a sheathing panel in RV, manufactured housing, and residential construction applications. It is not rated for use as a shear panel.

Most recently mentioned in EBN 3:5

EarthSource Forest Products

Plywood and Lumber Sales, Inc.

For full listing, see CSI section 01 62 03 - Distributors/Retailers, FSC-Certified Wood

SkyBlend UF-Free Particle Board

Roseburg Forest Products

For full listing, see CSI section 06 16 00 - Sheathing

Plyboo Bamboo Paneling, Plywood, and Veneer

Smith & Fong Company
375 Oyster Point Blvd. #3
S. San Francisco, CA 94080

Toll-free: 866-835-9859
Fax: 650-872-1185
www.plyboo.com

Plyboo® tambour, fabric-backed, flexible paneling is available in a 3/16" x 48" x 96" size with either a sanded or "raw" surface. Sanded comes prefinished or unfinished in an amber or natural color. The "raw" paneling, which retains the outside skin of the bamboo and has a more rustic appeal, comes unfinished in a natural green/yellow, black, or amber color. Plyboo bamboo plywood is available in a variety of dimensions and sizes. 1/4" and 1/2" solid bamboo plywood comes in a 16" x 72" size; 3/4" plywood is available in both 30" x 72" and 48" x 96" sizes; and 1/8" plywood is 48" x 96" with plywood backing. All these sizes are available in either vertical or flat grain in an amber or natural color. Plyboo bamboo veneer has a vertical pattern in natural or amber color in a 0.6 mm x 12" x 98". There is also a 1/8" bamboo veneer in a 48" x 96" size with a plywood backing. Veneers are provided with either paper or fleece backing.

Teragren Bamboo Flooring, Panels, and Veneer

Teragren

For full listing, see CSI section 09 62 23 - Bamboo Flooring

Tricel Honeycomb

Tricel Corp.
2100 Swanson Ct.
Gurnee, IL 60031

Toll-free: 800-352-3300
Phone: 847-336-1321
Fax: 847-336-1311
www.tricelcorp.com

Tricel Honeycomb recycled-content paper core panels have either plywood, foil, or paper board exteriors bonded with phenolic resins.

06 00 00
Wood, Plastics, & Composites

06 26 01
FSC-Certified Board Paneling

Certified wood products are verified by a third party as originating from well-managed forests. GreenSpec recognizes the Forest Stewardship Council (FSC) standards as the most rigorous and the only certification system with well-established chain-of-custody certification. Some companies listed here sell both certified and noncertified wood products, or products that have been certified according to different, less stringent environmental standards. To make certain that you get environmentally responsible wood products, be sure to specify your interest in FSC-certified wood. (See also 06 05 70 - Wood Products Certification and Information.)

SmartChoice Wood Products

Certified Forest Products, LLC.

For full listing, see CSI section 06 11 01 - FSC-Certified Wood Framing Lumber

FSC-Certified Wood Products

Dwight Lewis Lumber / Lewis Lumber Products

For full listing, see CSI section 09 64 01 - FSC-Certified Wood Flooring

F.D. Sterritt Certified-Wood Building Products

F.D. Sterritt Lumber Co.

For full listing, see CSI section 06 22 01 - FSC-Certified Millwork

Harrop-Procter Certified-Wood Building Products

Harrop-Procter Watershed Protection Society

For full listing, see CSI section 06 11 01 - FSC-Certified Wood Framing Lumber

Certified Red Cedar

Mary's River Lumber Co.

For full listing, see CSI section 06 11 01 - FSC-Certified Wood Framing Lumber

06 26 02
Reclaimed-Wood Paneling

As the demands on forest resources have increased, nonforest sources of wood have grown in importance. Reclaimed wood is usually salvaged from buildings slated for demolition, abandoned railroad trestles, and "sinker logs" that sank decades ago during river-based log drives. It can also be obtained from trees that have been recently harvested from urban or suburban areas (such as disease-killed trees). Reclaimed wood is often available in species, coloration, and wood quality that is no longer available in newly harvested timber. In some cases, reclaimed wood suppliers have only limited quantities with matching coloration or weathering patterns; ample lead time and accurate materials estimates can help ensure the availability of the desired wood. Lowering the uniformity standards for finished wood can also increase the potential for use of reclaimed wood. As with other resources, the supply of reclaimed wood is limited. Efficient and appropriate use of reclaimed wood is important for its long-term availability. (See also 01 62 02 - Distributors/Retailers, Used Building Materials & 07 46 25 - Reclaimed-Wood Siding.) (See feature article EBN Vol. 9, No. 5.)

Reclaimed-Wood Lumber and Products

A Reclaimed Lumber Co.

For full listing, see CSI section 06 22 02 - Reclaimed-Wood Millwork

AltruWood Reclaimed-Wood Products

AltruWood, Inc.

For full listing, see CSI section 09 64 02 - Reclaimed-Wood Flooring

Antique Woods & Colonial Restorations

Antique Woods & Colonial Restorations, Inc.

For full listing, see CSI section 09 64 02 - Reclaimed-Wood Flooring

Appalachian Woods

Appalachian Woods, LLC

For full listing, see CSI section 09 64 02 - Reclaimed-Wood Flooring

Reclaimed-Wood Materials

Black's Farmwood, Inc.

For full listing, see CSI section 09 64 02 - Reclaimed-Wood Flooring

Reclaimed-Wood Materials

BT Timberworks

For full listing, see CSI section 06 13 02 - Reclaimed-Wood Heavy Timber

Reclaimed-Wood Products

Centre Mills Antique Floors

For full listing, see CSI section 09 64 02 - Reclaimed-Wood Flooring

Reclaimed-Wood Products

Chestnut Specialists, Inc.

For full listing, see CSI section 09 64 02 - Reclaimed-Wood Flooring

Wood Materials from Urban Trees

CitiLog

For full listing, see CSI section 09 64 02 - Reclaimed-Wood Flooring

Reclaimed-Wood Building Products

Conklin's Authentic Antique Barnwood

For full listing, see CSI section 06 13 02 - Reclaimed-Wood Heavy Timber

Reclaimed-Wood Products

Crossroads Recycled Lumber

For full listing, see CSI section 06 13 02 - Reclaimed-Wood Heavy Timber

D. Litchfield Reclaimed Wood

D. Litchfield & Co. Ltd.

For full listing, see CSI section 06 11 02 - Reclaimed-Wood Framing Lumber

**06 00 00
Wood,
Plastics, &
Composites**

Reclaimed-Wood Products

Duluth Timber Co.

For full listing, see CSI section 06 13 02 - Reclaimed-Wood Heavy Timber

Reclaimed-Wood Building Products

Endura Wood Products, Ltd.

For full listing, see CSI section 09 64 02 - Reclaimed-Wood Flooring

Reclaimed-Wood Building Products

General Woodcraft, Inc.

For full listing, see CSI section 09 64 02 - Reclaimed-Wood Flooring

Georgian Bay Wetwood

Georgian Bay Wetwood Inc.

For full listing, see CSI section 06 40 26 - Wood Veneer

Logs End Reclaimed-Wood Building Products

Logs End Inc.

For full listing, see CSI section 09 64 02 - Reclaimed-Wood Flooring

Reclaimed-Wood Building Products

Longleaf Lumber

For full listing, see CSI section 09 64 02 - Reclaimed-Wood Flooring

M. Fine Lumber Company

M. Fine Lumber Company

For full listing, see CSI section 06 11 02 - Reclaimed-Wood Framing Lumber

Michael Evenson Natural Resources

Michael Evenson Natural Resources

For full listing, see CSI section 06 13 02 - Reclaimed-Wood Heavy Timber

Pinocchio's

Pinocchio's

For full listing, see CSI section 06 13 02 - Reclaimed-Wood Heavy Timber

**06 00 00
Wood,
Plastics, &
Composites**

Reclaimed-Wood Building Products

Solid Wood Products

For full listing, see CSI section 09 64 02 - Reclaimed-Wood Flooring

Reclaimed-Wood Building Products

TerraMai

For full listing, see CSI section 09 64 02 - Reclaimed-Wood Flooring

06 40 23
Interior Architectural Woodwork Substrate

Medium-density fiberboard (MDF) is usually manufactured from sawmill waste and a urea-formaldehyde (UF) binder. Formaldehyde, a known human carcinogen, offgasses from UF binders and can be especially problematic for chemically sensitive individuals. Particleboard is made from larger wood fiber particles than MDF, has a lower density; and doesn't mill as cleanly. Products listed here are low- or zero-formaldehyde, contain FSC-certified wood content, or are made from recovered waste fiber. (See also 06 25 00 - Prefinished Paneling & 06 05 70 - Wood Products Certification and Information.)

PrimeBoard

PrimeBoard, Inc.
2441 N. 15th St.
Wahpeton, ND 58075

Phone: 701-642-1152
Fax: 701-642-1154
www.primeboard.com

PrimeBoard® was the first M3-rated particleboard made from wheat straw and a formaldehyde-free binder. Now made from a blend of agricultural-residue fibers, panels are available in a range of thicknesses, sizes, and grades. As of January, 2006, Masonite —the world's largest producer of doors—has purchased Primeboard, and is using most of the output as door core material.

Most recently mentioned in EBN 4:3, 6:3, 6:8, 14:5, 15:1

SierraPine Formaldehyde-free Fiberboard

SierraPine Ltd.

For full listing, see CSI section 06 16 00 - Sheathing

Maplex

Weidmann Electrical Technology, Inc.
One Gordon Mills Way
St. Johnsbury, VT 05819

New

Phone: 800-242-6748
www.weidmann-industrial.com

Maplex is a dense, strong, bendable, pressed wood fiberboard manufactured without the use of chemical binders. This nontoxic, biodegradable material provides an alternative to formaldehyde-emitting particleboard and MDF products for a variety of interior finish, furniture, and consumer product applications. Maplex can be machined, bent, rolled, formed, punched, and laminated—as well as painted, dyed, stained, and coated. Maplex C (Contour) provides maximum bending or forming, and Maplex P (Performance) provides maximum stability and strength. Weidmann has been manufacturing fiber products since 1877 and is ISO 9001 and ISO 14001 certified.

06 40 26
Wood Veneer

Products listed here come from FSC-certified sources. GreenSpec recognizes the Forest Stewardship Council (FSC) standards as the most rigorous and the only certification system with well-established chain-of-custody certification. (See also 06 05 70 - Wood Products Certification and Information.) (See feature article EBN Vol. 6, No. 10.)

FSC-Certified Veneer

Bohlke Veneer Corporation
8375 N. Gilmore Rd.
Fairfield, OH 45014

Phone: 513-874-4400
Fax: 513-682-1469
www.mbohlkeveneer.com

Bohlke Veneer sells FSC-certified veneers cut from bird's eye and figured maple logs as well as red oak and hard maple.

Certified Wood Products

Cascadia Forest Goods, LLC

For full listing, see CSI section 06 11 01 - FSC-Certified Wood Framing Lumber

Bamboo Veneer and Paneling

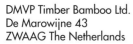

DMVP Timber Bamboo Ltd.
De Marowijne 43
ZWAAG The Netherlands

Phone: 0031-229-265732
Fax: 0031-229-267759
www.dmvpbamboo.com

DMVP's standard veneers have a cellulose fleece backing, which is bonded with a D3 water resistant PVAC glue. The cellulose backing can endure temperatures above 220 degrees Celsius.

In addition to single-ply veneers, DMVP produces multi-layer veneer panels by laminating multiple layers of veneer under high temperature, producing panels 1.5 mm or thicker.

DMVP also offers sandwich panels, with bamboo veneers laminated onto core panels, such as chipboard, plywood, MDF, or HDF.

DMVP is a joint venture between Hangzhou Liuzhuang floor Co., Ltd. and MVP International BV. MVP delivers veneer from the Netherlands to customers in Europe and the USA. DMVP distributes in the US, through various distributors, including M Bohlke Veneer Corporation of Fairfield, Ohio and General Woods & Veneers Ltd. of Québec, Canada.

FSC-Certified Hardwood Veneer

Freeman Corporation
415 Magnolia St.
P.O. Box 96
Winchester, KY 40392

Phone: 859-744-4311
Fax: 859-744-4363
www.freemancorp.com

Freeman Corporation is a producer of FSC-certified hardwood veneers.

Georgian Bay Wetwood

Georgian Bay Wetwood Inc.
8520 Highway 93
Midland, ON L4R 4K4 Canada

Phone: 705-526-6912
Fax: 705-526-5845
www.georgianbaywetwood.com

Georgian Bay Wetwood Inc. recovers submerged old-growth timber from Ontario's Georgian Bay of Lake Huron then mills it to produce veneers, flooring, and lumber. Birch, beech, birds-eye maple, and flame birch are typically recovered. Heritage Timber Veneers are available in two species, Flame Birch and Birds Eye Maple. Heritage Timber Engineered Flooring has a nominal 1/8" (3.2mm) sawn veneer of recovered Maple, Birch, or Oak in 4" wide, random length boards with tongue and groove sides, micro-bevel edges, and a 9mm, 7-ply, FSC-certified Birch plywood core. The flooring is pre-finished with an aluminum oxide, UV-cured, urethane coating. Overall, the product has greater than 70% FSC-certified wood. Georgian Bay Wetwood's wood products come with a certificate of authenticity that verifies that the product is genuine Georgian Bay Wet Wood.

Certified Lumber, Flooring, Wainscoting, and Veneer

McDowell Lumber Company, Inc.

For full listing, see CSI section 09 64 01 - FSC-Certified Wood Flooring

FSC-Certified Wood Products

Menominee Tribal Enterprises

For full listing, see CSI section 06 11 01 - FSC-Certified Wood Framing Lumber

MOSO Bamboo Building Products

MOSO International NA, Ltd.

For full listing, see CSI section 09 62 23 - Bamboo Flooring

Oak Hill Veneer

Oak Hill Veneer
Route 14 N
P.O. Box 304
Troy, PA 16947

Phone: 570-297-4137
Fax: 570-297-5082
www.oakhillveneer.com

All 2.1 million acres of Pennsylvania's state forest land are certified as sustainably managed according to FSC standards. Oak Hill Veneer produces FSC-certified veneer from this timber in a range of species, thickness, and dimensions for plywood, cabinetry, doors, flooring, and furniture.

Plyboo Bamboo Paneling, Plywood, and Veneer

Smith & Fong Company

For full listing, see CSI section 06 25 00 - Prefinished Paneling

Teragren Bamboo Flooring, Panels, and Veneer

Teragren

For full listing, see CSI section 09 62 23 - Bamboo Flooring

06 42 01
FSC-Certified Wood Paneling

Certified wood products are third-party verified as originating from well-managed forests based on Forest Stewardship Council (FSC) standards. Some companies listed here may sell both certified and noncertified products or carry other types of certification that don't qualify for GreenSpec. To ensure the use of environmentally responsible wood products, be sure to specify your interest in FSC-certified wood when contacting these companies. (See also 06 05 70 - Wood Products Certification and Information.) (See feature article EBN Vol. 6, No. 10.)

Certified Paneling and Millwork

Architectural Millwork Mfg. Co.

For full listing, see CSI section 06 22 01 - FSC-Certified Millwork

Certified Wood Products

Cascadia Forest Goods, LLC

For full listing, see CSI section 06 11 01 - FSC-Certified Wood Framing Lumber

CollinsWood FSC-Certified Wood Products

Collins Companies

For full listing, see CSI section 07 46 43 - Composition Siding

06 00 00
Wood, Plastics, & Composites

FSC-Certified Wood Products

Menominee Tribal Enterprises

For full listing, see CSI section 06 11 01 - FSC-Certified Wood Framing Lumber

Certified Paneling

Mt. Baker Plywood
2929 Roeder Ave.
Bellingham, WA 98225

Phone: 360-733-3960
Fax: 360-733-0803
www.mtbakerplywood.com

Mt. Baker Plywood manufactures FSC-certified paneling and panel products.

EarthSource Forest Products

Plywood and Lumber Sales, Inc.

For full listing, see CSI section 01 62 03 - Distributors/Retailers, FSC-Certified Wood

SkyBlend UF-Free Particle Board

Roseburg Forest Products

For full listing, see CSI section 06 16 00 - Sheathing

FSC-Certified Wood Wall and Ceiling Paneling

Wood Ceilings
25310 Jeans Rd.
Veneta, OR 97487

Toll-free: 866-935-9663
Phone: 541-935-9663
Fax: 541-935-1200
www.woodceilings.com

Wood Ceilings—formerly Pacific Wood Systems—crafts architectural suspended ceiling panel systems and wall paneling of FSC-certified woods including black cherry, western hemlock, red oak, maple, mahogany, and teak (when available).

06 42 02
Reclaimed-Wood Paneling

As the demands on forest resources have increased, nonforest sources of wood have grown in importance. Reclaimed wood is usually salvaged from buildings slated for demolition, abandoned railroad trestles, and "sinker logs" that sank decades ago during river-based log drives. It can also be from trees that have been recently harvested from urban or suburban areas (such as disease-killed trees). Reclaimed wood is often available in species, coloration, and wood quality not available in newly harvested timber. In some cases, reclaimed wood suppliers have only limited quantities with matching coloration or weathering patterns; ample lead time and accurate materials estimates can help ensure the availability of the desired wood. Lowering the uniformity standards for finished wood can also increase the potential for use of reclaimed wood. As with other resources, the supply of reclaimed wood is limited. Efficient and appropriate use of reclaimed wood is important for its long-term availability. Be aware that reclaimed wood may contain lead paint; testing is recommended if lead paint residue is suspected. (See also 01 62 02 - Distributors/Retailers, Used Building Materials.)

Reclaimed-Wood Flooring and Millwork

Aged Woods / Yesteryear Floorworks Company

For full listing, see CSI section 06 22 02 - Reclaimed-Wood Millwork

River-Reclaimed Wood Products

Goodwin Heart Pine Company

For full listing, see CSI section 09 64 02 - Reclaimed-Wood Flooring

Resource Woodworks

Resource Woodworks, Inc.

For full listing, see CSI section 06 13 02 - Reclaimed-Wood Heavy Timber

Trestlewood

Trestlewood

For full listing, see CSI section 09 64 02 - Reclaimed-Wood Flooring

Reclaimed-Wood Building Products

Vintage Log and Lumber, Inc.

For full listing, see CSI section 06 13 02 - Reclaimed-Wood Heavy Timber

Reclaimed-Wood Building Products

What Its Worth, Inc.

For full listing, see CSI section 09 64 02 - Reclaimed-Wood Flooring

06 42 16
Wood-Veneer Paneling

FSC-certified wood veneer panels are made with certified veneers on various cores. The greenest cores are made from certified wood, recovered wood, or straw particleboard. Wood products can carry the "FSC Mixed" label under a percentage-based standard based on actual product content or the average certified and non-certified throughput of the facility at which they are made. Urea-formaldehyde (UF), phenol-formaldehyde (PF), and methyl diisocyanate (MDI) binders are used in these materials, though UF is currently most common. UF binders can offgas significant concentrations of formaldehyde gas, a known carcinogen and an indoor air quality concern. (See also 06 05 70 - Wood Products Certification and Information.) (See feature article EBN Vol. 6, No. 10.)

FSC-Certified, Formaldehyde-Free Wood Panel Products

Columbia Forest Products

For full listing, see CSI section 06 16 00 - Sheathing

EarthSource Forest Products

Plywood and Lumber Sales, Inc.

For full listing, see CSI section 01 62 03 - Distributors/Retailers, FSC-Certified Wood

Certified Hardwood Veneer Panels

States Industries, Inc.
P.O. Box 7037
Eugene, OR 97401

Toll-free: 800-626-1981
Phone: 541-688-7871
Fax: 541-689-8051
www.statesind.com

06 00 00
Wood, Plastics, & Composites

States Industries manufactures hardwood-veneered plywood, MDF, and particleboard certified under Forest Stewardship Council and Sustainable Forest Initiative protocols. Most domestic and some imported species of veneers are available in panel thicknesses from 1/4" through 1-1/4". States will prefinish any of its hardwood panel products with Nova, a UV-cured epoxy acrylate topcoat containing or releasing no formaldehyde or VOCs during manufacturing or use. This product is available with clear finishes, translucent stains, solid colors, and printed wood grains. As an option, the panels can be manufactured with no added urea-formaldehyde adhesives.

Most recently mentioned in EBN 6:8

06 43 01
Certified-Wood Stairs and Railings

FSC-certified wood products are third-party verified as originating from well-managed forests based on Forest Stewardship Council (FSC) standards. Some companies listed here may sell both certified and noncertified products or products certified according to other, less stringent environmental standards. To ensure the use of environmentally responsible wood products, be sure to specify your interest in FSC-certified wood when contacting these companies.

Certified Stair Parts

B. W. Creative Wood Industries Ltd.
23282 River Rd.
Maple Ridge, BC V2W 1B6 Canada

Toll-free: 800-667-8247
Phone: 604-467-5147
Fax: 604-467-1197
www.creativerailing.com

B. W. Creative Wood specializes in stair parts fabricated of FSC-certified white fir.

ENVIROgt Handrail, Wall and Corner Guards

InPro Corporation

For full listing, see CSI section 10 26 00 - Wall and Door Protection

Certified-Wood Products

Randall Custom Lumber, Ltd.

For full listing, see CSI section 06 11 01 - FSC-Certified Wood Framing Lumber

06 43 02
Reclaimed-Wood Stairs and Railings

Reclaimed wood stair parts are environmentally attractive because new trees don't have to be cut and material is diverted from the waste stream. Often the quality of reclaimed wood is superior to newly milled wood because the reclaimed material is from old-growth trees that are no longer available for harvest. Be aware that reclaimed wood may contain lead paint; testing is recommended if lead paint residue is suspected.

Reclaimed-Wood Lumber and Products

A Reclaimed Lumber Co.

For full listing, see CSI section 06 22 02 - Reclaimed-Wood Millwork

Reclaimed-Wood Flooring and Millwork

Aged Woods / Yesteryear Floorworks Company

For full listing, see CSI section 06 22 02 - Reclaimed-Wood Millwork

Reclaimed-Wood Products

Albany Woodworks, Inc.

For full listing, see CSI section 06 22 02 - Reclaimed-Wood Millwork

Antique Woods & Colonial Restorations

Antique Woods & Colonial Restorations, Inc.

For full listing, see CSI section 09 64 02 - Reclaimed-Wood Flooring

Reclaimed-Wood Materials

BT Timberworks

For full listing, see CSI section 06 13 02 - Reclaimed-Wood Heavy Timber

Reclaimed-Wood Building Products

Endura Wood Products, Ltd.

For full listing, see CSI section 09 64 02 - Reclaimed-Wood Flooring

Reclaimed-Wood Building Products

General Woodcraft, Inc.

For full listing, see CSI section 09 64 02 - Reclaimed-Wood Flooring

River-Reclaimed Wood Products

Goodwin Heart Pine Company

For full listing, see CSI section 09 64 02 - Reclaimed-Wood Flooring

Reclaimed-Wood Millwork

J. L. Powell & Co., Inc.

For full listing, see CSI section 09 64 02 - Reclaimed-Wood Flooring

Reclaimed-Wood Building Products

Mayse Woodworking Co.

For full listing, see CSI section 09 64 02 - Reclaimed-Wood Flooring

Reclaimed-Wood Building Products

Mountain Lumber

For full listing, see CSI section 09 64 02 - Reclaimed-Wood Flooring

Reclaimed-Wood Building Products

Pioneer Millworks

For full listing, see CSI section 09 64 02 - Reclaimed-Wood Flooring

Reclaimed-Wood Building Products

Solid Wood Products

For full listing, see CSI section 09 64 02 - Reclaimed-Wood Flooring

Reclaimed-Wood Flooring and Millwork

Treasured Timbers, Inc.

For full listing, see CSI section 09 64 02 - Reclaimed-Wood Flooring

**06 00 00
Wood,
Plastics, &
Composites**

Reclaimed-Wood Building Products

Vintage Material Supply Co.

For full listing, see CSI section 09 64 02 - Reclaimed-Wood Flooring

Reclaimed-Wood Building Products

What Its Worth, Inc.

For full listing, see CSI section 09 64 02 - Reclaimed-Wood Flooring

06 44 33
Wood Mantels

Products listed here are from FSC-certified or reclaimed-wood sources. (See also 01 62 02 - Distributors/Retailers, Used Building Materials & 06 05 70 - Wood Products Certification and Information.)

Reclaimed-Wood Materials

BT Timberworks

For full listing, see CSI section 06 13 02 - Reclaimed-Wood Heavy Timber

Reclaimed-Wood Products

Centre Mills Antique Floors

For full listing, see CSI section 09 64 02 - Reclaimed-Wood Flooring

Reclaimed-Wood Products

Duluth Timber Co.

For full listing, see CSI section 06 13 02 - Reclaimed-Wood Heavy Timber

Reclaimed-Wood Building Products

General Woodcraft, Inc.

For full listing, see CSI section 09 64 02 - Reclaimed-Wood Flooring

Reclaimed-Wood Building Products

Mountain Lumber

For full listing, see CSI section 09 64 02 - Reclaimed-Wood Flooring

Reclaimed-Wood Building Products

Pioneer Millworks

For full listing, see CSI section 09 64 02 - Reclaimed-Wood Flooring

Urban Hardwoods

Urban Hardwoods

For full listing, see CSI section 09 64 02 - Reclaimed-Wood Flooring

Reclaimed-Wood Building Products

Vintage Log and Lumber, Inc.

For full listing, see CSI section 06 13 02 - Reclaimed-Wood Heavy Timber

Reclaimed-Wood Building Products

Vintage Material Supply Co.

For full listing, see CSI section 09 64 02 - Reclaimed-Wood Flooring

Reclaimed-Wood Building Products

Vintage Timberworks

For full listing, see CSI section 06 13 02 - Reclaimed-Wood Heavy Timber

06 46 03
Fiberboard Trim

Pressures on timber supply are especially acute for high-visibility, solid-wood products like window sash and molding, which have traditionally been produced from old-growth trees. Medium-density fiberboard (MDF) molding made from post-industrial wood wastes is an excellent substitute for paint-grade moldings. The consistent quality and economical price of MDF moldings is broadening its market share. Some MDF is available with nonformaldehyde binder. (See also 06 66 00 - Ornamental Simulated Woodwork, 06 22 03 - Fiberboard Millwork, 06 22 04 - Agfiber Millwork, 06 46 04 - Wood-Alternative Trim.)

Medite II and Medex MDF Molding

SierraPine Ltd.

For full listing, see CSI section 06 22 03 - Fiberboard Millwork

06 46 04
Wood-Alternative Trim

Pressures on timber supply are especially acute for high-visibility, solid-wood products like window sash and molding, which have traditionally been produced from old-growth trees. Molding made from plastic wastes is an excellent substitute for paint-grade moldings. (See also 06 66 00 - Ornamental Simulated Woodwork, 06 22 03 - Fiberboard Millwork, 06 22 04 - Agfiber Millwork, 06 46 03 - Fiberboard Trim.)

Timbron Molding

Timbron International, Inc.
1333 N. California Ave., Ste. 545
Walnut Creek, CA 94596

Phone: 925-943-1632
Fax: 925-943-1164
www.timbron.com

Timbron produces interior molding in a variety of profiles made from at least 90% recycled polystyrene, along with small quantities of a coloring agent, a UV stabilizer, and a foaming agent. Timbron has earned certification from Scientific Certification Systems (SCS) for using a minimum of 75% post-consumer and 15% pre-consumer recycled material in its molding products, and claims the products are low-VOC and recyclable. Timbron is highly durable, waterproof, termite-proof, paintable (though also suitable unpainted as white), and fully workable with carpentry tools.

Most recently mentioned in EBN 15:12 & 16:2

06 51 13
Plastic Lumber

In 2003, the EPA estimated that 26.7 million tons of the municipal U.S. solid waste stream was plastics. Just 1.4 million tons of it was recycled; the rest went to landfills, where it occupies about 25% of the overall landfill space. Plastic lumber makes good use of recycled plastic and is an effective replacement for pressure-treated lumber, protecting timber resources and preventing the use of chemical lumber treatments. Plastic lumber won't rot, absorb water, splinter, or crack; it's also resilient to shock, making it an extremely durable component in exterior and marine applications. It can accept most types of fasteners and is workable with standard saws and carbide blades. Plastic lumber usually isn't a suitable replacement for load-bearing structural components, however; the physical characteristics of plastic polymers, while durable, don't provide the rigidity necessary for primary structural support. Some companies have addressed this weakness by reinforcing their products with fiberglass or steel. In addition, plastic lumber experiences greater rates of thermal expansion and contraction, which can give rise to problems in certain applications.

Trimax

Trimax Building Products, Inc.
2600 W. Roosevelt Rd.
Chicago, IL 60608

Toll-free: 866-987-4629
www.trimaxbp.com

Trimax Decking consists of decking, rail, and stair parts containing 90% post-consumer HDPE by weight. Decking lumber and stair treads are also available in a knurled, non-skid finish. Trimax structural lumber and marine pilings contains 90% recycled material by weight, including post-consumer recycled HDPE (65%) and post-industrial recycled fiberglass. Trimax Structural Lumber comes in gray, and is available by special order in green, tan, redwood, and white; pilings come in gray and are available by special order in light gray, green, tan, redwood, and white.

Most recently mentioned in EBN 2:4, 2:6, 13:9, 15:2

06 53 13
Solid Plastic Decking

In 2003, the EPA estimated that 26.7 million tons of the municipal U.S. solid waste stream was plastics. Just 1.4 million tons of it was recycled; the rest went to landfills, where it occupies about 25% of the overall landfill space. Plastic lumber makes good use of recycled plastic and is an effective replacement for pressure-treated lumber, protecting

timber resources and preventing the use of chemical lumber treatments. Plastic lumber won't rot, absorb water, splinter, or crack; it's also resilient to shock, making it an extremely durable component in exterior and marine applications. It can accept most types of fasteners and is workable with standard saws and carbide blades. Plastic lumber usually isn't a suitable replacement for load-bearing structural components, however; the physical characteristics of plastic polymers, while durable, don't provide the rigidity necessary for primary structural support. Some companies have addressed this weakness by reinforcing their products with fiberglass or steel. In addition, plastic lumber experiences greater rates of thermal expansion and contraction, which can give rise to problems in certain applications. (See feature articles EBN Vol. 2, No. 4 & Vol. 5, No. 4.)

Aeolian Plastic Lumber & Fences

Aeolian Enterprises, Inc.
P.O. Box 888
Latrobe, PA 15650

Toll-free: 800-269-4672
Phone: 724-539-9460
Fax: 724-539-0572
www.aeo1.com

Aeolian Enterprises manufactures hollow and solid-profile plastic lumber made from recycled HDPE (recycled content varies with color). Solid-profile products are planed to achieve a uniform flat surface and texture during fabrication. Various dimensions offered include nominal 1x4, 1x6, and 5/4x6. Aeolian also fabricates corral, privacy, and picket fencing products made from recycled HDPE.

Most recently mentioned in EBN 2:4

Aztec Recycled-Plastic Lumber

Amazing Recycled Products, Inc.
P.O. Box 312
Denver, CO 80201

Toll-free: 800-241-2174
Phone: 303-699-7693
Fax: 303-699-2102
www.amazingrecycled.com

Amazing Recycled Products manufactures lumber, timber, parking stops and bollards with recycled HDPE. Their Aztec line of park furnishings includes benches, chairs, picnic tables, and trash receptacles.

Better Than Wood

American Ecoboard, LLC
200 Finn Ct.
Farmingdale, NY 11735

Toll-free: 800-567-9851
Phone: 631-753-5151
Fax: 631-753-5165
www.americanecoboard.com

American Ecoboard manufactures fiberglass-reinforced dimension lumber from recycled HDPE, LDPE, and PP plastics.

Most recently mentioned in EBN 2:4

Recycled-Plastic Products

American Recycled Plastic, Inc.
1500 Main St.
Palm Bay, FL 32905

Toll-free: 866-674-1525
Phone: 321-674-1525
Fax: 321-674-2365
www.itsrecycled.com

American Recycled Plastic manufactures a range of products from recycled HDPE, including lumber and timbers, car stops, speed bumps and humps, and vehicle barriers. They also offer a wide variety of recycled-HDPE site furnishings, including benches, outdoor tables, waste receptacles, mailboxes, planters, custom wildlife structures, and bicycle racks.

Bedford Technology Recycled-Plastic Products

Bedford Technology, LLC
2424 Armour Rd.
P.O. Box 609
Worthington, MN 56187

Toll-free: 800-721-9037
Phone: 507-372-5558
Fax: 507-372-5726
www.plasticboards.com

Bedford Technology offers plastic lumber and other products made with post-consumer recycled HDPE and LDPE. Their lumber is available in a variety of dimensions, including 5/4 decking, two-by, and large timbers up to 12x12, in black, brown, gray, and cedar with other colors available. Parking stops and speed bumps are also offered, as well as plastic paneling that can be used as a substitute for plywood. Bedford's ForeSite Designs(R) line of recycled-plastic site furnishings includes picnic tables, benches, and waste receptacles.

Most recently mentioned in EBN 2:4 & 11:11

06 00 00
Wood, Plastics, & Composites

Recycled-Plastic Products

BJM Industries, Inc.

*For full listing, see CSI section 12 93 43
- Site Seating and Tables, Plastic*

Perma-Deck

Cascades Re-Plast, Inc.
1350 chemin Quatre Saisons
Bon Conseil, QC J0C 1A0 Canada

Toll-free: 888-313-2440
Phone: 888-313-2440
Fax: 819-336-2442
www.cascadesreplast.com

Perma-deck® is 100% recycled HDPE decking and lumber available in light gray, sandstone brown, redwood, and beige.

Most recently mentioned in EBN 2:4

EPS Recycled-Plastic Building Products

Engineered Plastic Systems
740 Industrial Dr., Ste. B
Cary, IL 60013

Phone: 847-462-9001
Fax: 847-462-9002
www.epsplasticlumber.com

Environmental Plastic Systems (EPS) Bear Board plastic lumber is typically made from 100% post-consumer recycled HDPE and is available in a variety of sizes and colors, with a smooth or wood-grain finish. Fiberglass-reinforced structural plastic lumber is also available. Their plastic landscape timbers (from the same feedstock) are available in 3x4, 4x4, 4x6, and 6x6, smooth or wood-grain, in dark brown, black, and charcoal gray; other colors are available for an additional charge. Durapoly plastic "plywood" is available in white and gray, in thicknesses ranging from 3/8" to 1-1/8". All of these products are covered by a 50-year limited warranty.

Perma-Deck Plastic Lumber

Environmental Building Products, Inc.
P.O. Box 261310
Highlands Ranch, CO 80163

Toll-free: 888-313-2440
Phone: 303-470-7555
Fax: 303-470-7390
www.perma-deck.com

Environmental Building Products markets and distributes plastic lumber throughout the Rocky Mountain region and western United States. Perma-Deck is a wood-grained plastic lumber made from recycled HDPE, PP, and PS plastic, and it comes in sandstone brown, beige, redwood, and light gray. The product has a 50-year limited warranty against

splitting, warping, peeling, rot, and insect infestation. The manufacturer has certified the following recycled-content levels (by weight): total recovered material 100% typical, 90% guaranteed; post-consumer material 50% typical, 30% guaranteed.

Environmental Recycling Plastic Lumber

Environmental Recycling, Inc.
8000 Hall St #5
St. Louis, MO 63147

Phone: 314-382-7766
Fax: 314-382-7711

Environmental Recycling offers a full line of 100% recycled HDPE plastic lumber in common dimensions and gray, redwood, and black colors. They specialize in flooring systems for commercial trucks.

Most recently mentioned in EBN 2:4

Everlast Plastic Lumber

Everlast Plastic Lumber
1000 S. 4th St.
Hamburg, PA 19526

Phone: 610-562-8336
Fax: 610-562-8381
www.everlastlumber.com

Everlast nonstructural plastic lumber is made with 100% recycled HPDE (80% post-consumer). Nominal sizes include 1-1/2 x 1-1/2 x 8; 2 x 2 x 8; 5/4 x 6 x 8; 5/4 x 6 x 12; 2 x 4 x 12; 2 x 6 x 12; 4 x 4 x 12; 6 x 6 x 12. Conventional carpentry tools with carbide blades are used for cutting and routing. Nails are not sufficient for fastening due to expansion and contraction (1/4" per 8 board feet); screws must be used. This product has a 50-year warranty.

Everlasting Lumber

Great Lakes Specialty Products
206 Enterprise Rd.
Delafield, WI 53018

Toll-free: 800-505-7926
Phone: 262-646-9470
Fax: 800-962-3455
www.greatlakesspecialty.com

Everlasting Lumber™ is made with 95% recycled #2 HDPE from consumer and industrial sources, impregnated with UV inhibitors and non-metallic colorants. A foamless manufacturing process is claimed to significantly enhance the material's usable life. The solid, pultruded products are manufactured with a slight wood grain texture; a coarser anti-skid surface is also available. Its weight is comparable to oak. Floor and railing boards, spindles, posts, and fascia skirting are available in standard and spe-

cial sizes. Great Lakes Specialty Products supplies commercial and significant private enterprises including golf courses, theme parks, and campuses.

Inteq Plastic Lumber

Inteq Corp.
35800 Glen Dr.
Eastlake, OH 44095

Phone: 440-953-0550
Fax: 440-953-0564
www.4-inteqcorp.com

Inteq manufactures a variety of recycled HDPE plastic lumber. Nonstructural landscape timbers are available in multiple colors up to 12' in length in standard sizes of 4x4, 4x6, and 6x6. Decking and railing material is also made from recycled HDPE plastic and is available in multiple colors. Additionally, Inteq offers structural and nonstructural recycled plastic lumber in standard dimensions. Nonstructural is 100% HDPE, and structural contains 15% recycled fiberglass. Inteq asks customers to consult with them before utilizing the structural lumber.

VERDURA Deck

New Frontier Industries, Inc.
P.O. Box 1360
Milton, NH 03851

Toll-free: 866-637-7888
Phone: 603-652-7888
www.newfrontierindustries.com

VERDURA Deck is a strong, lightweight, engineered decking product made with 95% post-consumer mixed plastic (mostly ABS, polycarbonate and high impact polystyrene) with a thin, UV-protected PVC wear layer. The interlocking 6" x 1.5" tongue-and-groove engineered modules install onto joists using regular deck screws. The maintenance-free, slip-resistant, wood-textured surface is ribbed to channel water off the deck. A variety of colors and simulated wood tones are available. This product is re-usable and recyclable, according to the manufacturer, and comes with a 25-year transferable warranty. The "recyclable" claim is questionable, given the mix of polymer types going into the manufacture, especially the PVC topcoat.

Plasboard

Northern Plastic Lumber, Inc.
77 St. David St.
Lindsay, ON K9V 1N8

Toll-free: 888-255-1222
Phone: 705-878-5700
Fax: 705-878-5702
www.northernplasticlumber.com

**06 00 00
Wood,
Plastics, &
Composites**

Plasboard plastic lumber is made with commingled post-consumer recycled plastics (approximately 96% HDPE/LDPE/PP, 2% PET, 1% P.S., 1% other). A wide range of stock dimensions and profiles are available ranging from 7/8" x 3-3/8" to 4" x 4", and including round stock in 2" to 6" diameters. Custom-size orders can be quoted. The Premium Plus line is available in white, cedar, sandstone, orange, yellow, and red. The Premium consumer-quality line is available in brown, light gray, forest green, and blue. Plasboard Standard comes in range of gray only; and a low-priced Utility line is available for applications where function is more important than issues of color and visual quality.

PlasTEAK Plastic Lumber

PlasTEAK
3563 Copley Rd.
P.O. Box 4290
Akron, OH 44321

Toll-free: 800-320-1841
Phone: 330-668-2587
Fax: 330-666-0844
www.plasteak.com

PlasTEAK is made with 100% post-consumer recycled HDPE in a paraffin base the boards become more slip-resistant when wet. Stock material includes solid (molded) and hollow (extruded) dimension lumber in a variety of sizes and colors. Trim and sheet goods are also available. Landscape timbers of 6 x 6 x 8' have a structural ribbed design that allows them to weigh less than half as much as wood timbers while maintaining strength. Landscape timbers have pre-molded holes for rebar reinforcement to facilitate installation.

Recycled-Plastic Decking, Docks, and Timbers

Plastic Lumber Yard, LLC
220 Washington St.
Norristown, PA 19401

Phone: 610-277-3900
Fax: 610-277-3970
www.plasticlumberyard.com

Plastic Lumber Yard, LLC, manufactures recycled-plastic lumber. The Forever Deck and ForeverDock Floating Dock Kits are constructed with recycled plastic lumber made from 100% recycled HDPE. Landscape grade plastic lumber in various profiles and colors is also available.

Recycled-Plastic Lumber

Plastic Recycling of Iowa Falls, Inc.
10252 Hwy. 65
Iowa Falls, IA 50126

Toll-free: 800-338-1438
Phone: 641-648-5073
Fax: 641-648-5074
www.hammersplastic.com

Plastic Recycling of Iowa Falls, formerly Hammer's Plastic Recycling, manufactures a full line of recycled plastic lumber (in lengths up to 12') and assembled products (picnic tables, park benches, etc.) in a variety of colors of commingled recycled HDPE, LDPE, LLDPE, and miscellaneous plastics.

Most recently mentioned in EBN 2:4

Re-Source Plastic Lumber

Re-Source Building Products
1685 Holmes Rd.
Elgin, IL 60123

Toll-free: 800-585-4988
Phone: 847-931-4771
Fax: 847-931-1771
www.plastival.com

Re-Source Building Products manufactures plastic lumber from 98% recycled HDPE in 30 different profiles including deck and railing components.

Perma-Poly and Evolve Recycled-Plastic Lumber

Renew Plastics, Division of N.E.W. Plastics Corp.
110 Frontier Rd.
P.O. Box 480
Luxemburg, WI 54217

Toll-free: 800-666-5207
Phone: 920-845-2326
Fax: 920-845-2335
www.renewplastics.com

Perma-Poly™ and Evolve® contain 90% or more recycled HDPE plastic and are available in many profiles, including common dimensional sizes, tongue-and-groove decking, round stock, and custom-extruded shapes. The products come in black, white, earth tones, reds, blues, yellows, and greens. Custom color matching is also available.

Most recently mentioned in EBN 2:4

Renew Resources Plastic Lumber

New

Renew Resources Ltd.
81 Mack Ave.
Toronto, ON M1L 1M5 Canada

Toll-free: 800-439-5028
Phone: 416-335-4040
Fax: 416-335-4039
www.renewresources.com

Renew Resources offers solid plastic lumber manufactured from a blend of 100% pre-consumer recycled plastics (approximately 96% polyolefins [HDPE, LPDE, PP], 2% PET, 1% PS and 1% other). It is available in grey, tan, redwood, blue grey, and black in typical lumber dimensions. Color and appearance may vary slightly from board to board. Renew Resources also offers a semi-hollow, 100% recycled-content, HDPE-and-wood-fiber decking product in grey, taupe, and cedar.

Rumber Lumber

Rumber Materials Inc.
3420 Executive Center Dr., Ste. 200
Austin, TX 78731

Toll-free: 877-786-2371
Phone: 940-759-4181
Fax: 940-759-4011
www.rumber.com

Rumber® Lumber, made from recycled HDPE plastic and recycled-tire rubber, is available in 2x2, 2x4, 2x6, 2x8, 2x12, and 4x4 dimensions in standard lengths of 6' to 24'.

Syntal Altwood

New

Syntal Products (Victoria) Ltd.
6722 Bertram Pl.
Victoria, BC V8M 1Z6 Canada

Toll-free: 877-544-1677
Phone: 250-544-1676
Fax: 250-544-1756
www.syntalproducts.com

Syntal Altwood is made with 80% post- and 20% pre-consumer recycled, commingled thermoplastics. It is a solid plastic product that does not contain wood fiber or fiberglass reinforcement. Available in standard lumber dimensions in integral, UV-stabilized colors (tan, green, and grey), it can be worked with standard tools. It is manufactured using extreme pressure (not heat) to produce posts, poles, stakes, slats, and planks. This extrusion process was developed in Belgium more than 20 years ago; the Syntal facility is the first of its type in North America.

**06 00 00
Wood, Plastics, & Composites**

Plastic Lumber

Taylors Recycled Plastic Products Inc.
581 Hwy. 28
Bailieboro, ON K0L 1B0 Canada

Phone: 705-939-6072
Fax: 705-939-6256
www.taylorsplastic.com

Taylors Recycled Plastic Products, Inc. produces nonstructural recycled-plastic lumber primarily from post-consumer recycled plastic in a variety of sizes, with gray as the standard color. Other colors are available on volume orders.

The Plastic Lumber Company

The Plastic Lumber Company, Inc.
115 W. Bartges St.
Akron, OH 44311

Toll-free: 800-886-8990
Phone: 330-762-8989
Fax: 330-762-1613
www.plasticlumber.com

The Plastic Lumber Company offers approximately 20 different profiles of dimensional plastic lumber available in 12 different colors. Sizes range from 1/2" x 2-1/2" to 4x6. Commercial and residential decking is also available. Recycled content is 97% post-consumer.

Ecoboard Plastic Lumber

Trelleborg Engineered Products, Inc.
3470 Martinsburg Pike
P.O. Box 98
Clearbrook, VA 22624

Phone: 540-667-5191
Fax: 540-667-7987
www.trelleborg.com

Ecoboard lumber is manufactured in a wide array of dimensions and colors. These products contain recycled HDPE and LDPE, as well as UV-stabilization, flame-retardant, and strength additives. Landscape timbers in 4x4, 5x5, and 6x6 contain fiberglass reinforcing. Ecoboard marine pilings have been tested as a friction pile where load-bearing capability needed to exceed 15 tons of vertical loading with a minimum of "creep" or failure, according to the manufacturer; the pilings tested to a 60-ton load, at which time the test was stopped.

Trimax

Trimax Building Products, Inc.

For full listing, see CSI section 06 51 13 - Plastic Lumber

06 00 00 Wood, Plastics, & Composites

06 63 00
Plastic Railings

Plastic handrails are common in health care facilities and other public buildings. Products listed here avoid the use of PVC, have FSC-certified content, or other compelling environmental attributes.

EnviroGT Handrail, Wall and Corner Guards

InPro Corporation

For full listing, see CSI section 10 26 00 - Wall and Door Protection

06 64 00
Plastic Paneling

Recycled plastic paneling is an appropriate use for some of the various post-consumer plastic materials entering the waste stream in particular, high-density polyethylene (HDPE) from milk and detergent bottles. Plastic materials are resistant to water and microbial growth, making them appropriate for wet locations such as bathrooms and industrial or agricultural facilities. The plastic paneling products listed here have a recycled content value (equal to % post-consumer plus 1/2 % pre-consumer) of at least 45%, with many products using 100% post-consumer recycled plastic.

Bedford Technology Recycled-Plastic Products

Bedford Technology, LLC

For full listing, see CSI section 06 53 13 - Solid Plastic Decking

Phonotherm 200

BOSIG, Inc.
2125 Center Ave., Ste. 500
Fort Lee, NJ 07024

Phone: 201-302-6081
Fax: 201-302-6062
www.bosig.com

Phonotherm® 200 has the appearance of particleboard, but is made with compressed recycled residuals from the rigid polyurethane foam industry—resulting in a board product that is waterproof, free of swell and decay, and recyclable, and that offers better

insulation values than wood-based or solid plastic boards. Damp and wet applications such as bathrooms, kitchen, facades, doors, and windows are appropriate. Phonotherm may be used as a subfloor. It can be milled with normal carbide tools; contains no formaldehyde; and is vapor permeable.

Plastic Panels

Coon Manufacturing, Inc.
78 N.E. 115th St.
P.O. Box 108
Spickard, MO 64679

Toll-free: 800-843-1532
Phone: 660-485-6299
Fax: 660-485-6122
www.coonmfginc.com

Coon Manufacturing markets their recycled plastic products for agricultural construction applications. Their 100% plastic sheet goods are rugged, smooth or corrugated, recycled high-density polyethylene panels available in various sizes. Coon complements their white panels with plastic molding products and stainless steel hardware. Coon also manufactures 100% recycled septic tanks and trash containers.

Most recently mentioned in EBN 2:4

EPS Recycled-Plastic Building Products

Engineered Plastic Systems

For full listing, see CSI section 06 53 13 - Solid Plastic Decking

Plastic Panels

Iowa Plastics, Inc.
322 N. Main Ave.
Sioux Center, IA 51250

Phone: 712-722-0692
Fax: 712-722-0692

Iowa Plastics manufactures 4' x 8' panels in thicknesses from 1/16" to 1/2". Panels come in white and black and are made from 98% post-consumer recycled HDPE. Custom sizes are also available.

Most recently mentioned in EBN 2:4

Ny-Board

NYCORE
200 Galleria Pkwy., Ste. 2000
Atlanta, GA 30339

Phone: 770-980-0000
www.nycore.com

Ny-Board is a strong, flexible, skid-resistant sheeting made from 100% recycled nylon carpet waste from post-consumer and post-industrial sources. The flexible, waterproof sheets can be cut with standard saws, screwed, nailed, glued, and painted; they don't rot, deteriorate, or support mold or insects. According to the manufacturer, no waste is generated in the manufacturing process, and the product is recyclable. Ny-Board is available in 1/8", 1/4" or 3/8" thicknesses and in 4x4 or 4x8 sheets. Other sizes are available by special order. Uses are wide-ranging, including protective wall and floor liners, foundation guards, dock surfacing, and sign backing. Considerations include thermal expansion and possible cold-weather brittleness. The manufacturer offers a 30-year warranty.

Most recently mentioned in EBN 6:6

PlasTEAK Plastic Paneling

PlasTEAK
3563 Copley Rd.
P.O. Box 4290
Akron, OH 44321

Toll-free: 800-320-1841
Phone: 330-668-2587
Fax: 330-666-0844
www.plasteak.com

PlasTEAK is made with 100% post-consumer recycled HDPE in a paraffin base—the boards become more slip-resistant when wet. Boatboard extruded HDPE panels meet the requirements of marine and outdoor environments. Limarpa is a lightweight alternative to plywood, also appropriate for marine use. PlasTEAK also makes UV-stabilized, 1' x 4' x 1.25"-thick, recycled-plastic grates for such applications as boardwalks, dune walkovers, nature walks, and floating docks; these grates provide 60% light and visual penetration for such uses as boardwalks, dune walkovers, and nature walks. Trim and lumber goods are available as well.

Recycled-Plastic Panels

Plastic Lumber Yard, LLC
220 Washington St.
Norristown, PA 19401

Phone: 610-277-3900
Fax: 610-277-3970
www.plasticlumberyard.com

Plastic Lumber Yard, LLC manufactures plastic sheeting from 100% recycled plastic. The black or white panels come in 4' x 8' sheets in 1/8", 1/4", 3/8", and 1/2" thicknesses and 4' x 10' sheets in a 1/2" thickness.

Plastic Panels

Reprocessed Plastics, Inc.
609 County Rd. 82 NW
Garfield, MN 56332

Phone: 320-834-2293
Fax: 320-834-2290
www.gipo-rpi.com

RPI's plastic panels (formerly called EcoPanels) are extruded sheets made from 100% recycled HDPE. Depending upon specific color patterns, the sheets contain 0-50% post-industrial recycled HDPE, with the balance being post-consumer recycled. This product is available in 10 custom colors as well as black and white, and measure 4' x 8' in thicknesses from 1/8" to 3/4". They can be cut, sanded, routed, milled, drilled and otherwise handled with conventional wood and metal working tools and machines. In addition, the material can be shaped by thermoforming and welding.

Sandhill Plastics Sheeting

Sandhill Plastics
119 W. 19th St.
Kearney, NE 68847

Toll-free: 800-644-7141
Phone: 308-236-5025
Fax: 308-237-0602
www.sandhillplastics.com

Sandhill Plastics manufactures plastic sheeting of 100% post-consumer HDPE used primarily for agricultural applications. Standard sheets measure 4' x 8' in thicknesses ranging from 1/16" to 5/8".

Plastic Paneling

Taylors Recycled Plastic Products Inc.
581 Hwy. 28
Bailieboro, ON K0L 1B0 Canada

Phone: 705-939-6072
Fax: 705-939-6256
www.taylorsplastic.com

Taylors Recycled Plastic Products, Inc. produces 100% recycled plastic sheeting primarily from post-consumer recycled plastic as a direct replacement for plywood in nonstructural indoor and outdoor applications. It comes in square-edged 4' x 8' sheets with a smooth matt surface in off-white and gray. Available thicknesses range from 1/4" to 1-3/4". Custom colors and sizes are available on volume orders.

Origins

Yemm & Hart Ltd.
1417 Madison 308
Marquand, MO 63655

Phone: 573-783-5434
Fax: 573-783-7544
www.yemmhart.com

Yemm & Hart manufactures Origins, a recycled HDPE-plastic panel made from milk jugs and detergent bottles, available in 24 patterns and 30 solid colors. The panel sheets are 4' x 8' and 5' x 10', in thicknesses from 1/8" to 2". Yemm & Hart also manufactures toilet and shower partitions

and sign stock. Origins Restroom Partitions are available in three standard configurations, Floor Mounted Headrail Braced, Floor Mounted Ceiling Attached, and Ceiling Hung, specifically made in a thickness range to guarantee that panels and pilasters will fit easily into extruded aluminum or stainless steel hardware. Origins signage can be as simple as cut-out letters and shapes from various thicknesses of standard Origins material, or it can be made with laminated colors that are routed through to reveal an interior color.

06 66 00
Ornamental Simulated Woodwork

Pressures on timber supply are especially acute for high-visibility, solid-wood products like window sash and molding, which have traditionally been produced from old-growth trees. Molding made from plastic wastes is an excellent substitute for paint-grade moldings. (See also 06 22 03 - Fiberboard Millwork, 06 22 04 - Agfiber Millwork, 06 46 03 - Fiberboard Trim, 06 46 04 - Wood-Alternative Trim.)

Timbron Molding

Timbron International, Inc.

For full listing, see CSI section 06 46 04 - Wood-Alternative Trim

06 73 00
Composite Decking

Wood-plastic composite lumber incorporates some of the characteristics of wood with those of plastic lumber. Recycled plastic resin (usually polyethylene) is combined with wood or another plant fiber—which may be post-industrial recycled content or virgin fiber—to create a product that has various advantages over both solid wood and solid plastic. Like plastic lumber, it will not rot, crack, or splinter, while the wood fiber adds considerable strength. Wood-plastic composite materials generally have a more natural coloring and appearance than 100%-plastic materials. The wood fibers, however, may absorb water and fade in color over time. Some wood-plastic composite lumber is graded for structural

**06 00 00
Wood,
Plastics, &
Composites**

use, primarily as deck substructure and for marine use. This is not true of all wood-plastic composites, so check with the manufacturer for specific product indications. (See feature articles EBN Vol. 2, No. 4 & Vol. 5, No. 4.)

MoistureShield and ChoiceDek

AERT, Inc. (Advanced Environmental Recycling Technologies, Inc.)
P.O. Box 1237
Springdale, AR 72765

Toll-free: 800-951-5117
Phone: 479-756-7400
www.aertinc.com

AERT manufactures MoistureShield and ChoiceDek, decking products composed of an approximately 50/50 blend of recycled polyethylene and recycled wood fibers. These products are available in standard decking dimensions and lengths (20-ft lengths can be special ordered), and they work with standard tools. The MoistureShield line included CornerLoc composite trim and trim board. The ChoiceDek line is available only at Lowe's Home Centers. The manufacturer has certified the following recycled-content levels (by weight): total recovered material 100% typical, 95% guaranteed; post-consumer material 10-20% typical, 0% guaranteed.

Most recently mentioned in EBN 2:4, 6:6, 8:1, 8:7, 11:3

CorrectDeck

Correct Building Products
8 Morin St.
Biddeford, ME 04005

Toll-free: 877-332-5877
Phone: 207-284-5600
Fax: 207-284-1001
www.correctdeck.com

CorrectDeck™ biocomposite decking is made with a combination of virgin and reclaimed polypropylene (minimum 25% recycled, up to 50%), reclaimed hardwood fiber (up to 60% of the total composition), and UV-inhibited pigmenting. CorrectDeck Classic™ has a solid profile and fastens with decking screws; CorrectDeck Channeled has a side-grooved profile to accommodate a hidden fastener system that eliminates screw holes. Both profiles have embossed wood grain and are slightly crowned to shed water; come in 12', 16', and 20' lengths; and are available in Grey, Cedar, Acadia, and Mahogany integral colors. Posts, rails, fascia and other accessories are also available. CorrectDeck DCL (dimensional composite lumber) is the same material as the decking, available in several dimensions and lengths

including 2x4, 2x6, and 4x4. CorrectDeck offers a 25-year warranty.

WeatherBest Decking

LP
414 Union St., Ste. 2000
Nashville, TN 37219

Toll-free: 877-744-5600
Fax: 877-523-7192
www.lpcorp.com

WeatherBest™ Basic and WeatherBest Select are smooth-faced composite decking products that weather to varying shades of grey or ivory. WeatherBest Premium has a reversible, random wood-grained pattern over rough-sawn boards and is available in five colors with minimal fading. All three lines are made with 100% recycled wood and HDPE; the MSDS lists 55-90% wood flour, 5-35% HDPE, and less than 5% talc. These lines have a limited 10-year warranty. Available sizes include standard 8', 12', 16', and 20' lengths in a nominal 5/4x6 solid plank for 16" on-center installations. Fascia, post sleeves, post caps, balusters, and side rails are available in all colors.

Most recently mentioned in EBN 11:3 & 11:11

Rhino Deck

Master Mark Plastics
One Master Mark Drive
P.O. Box 662
Albany, MN 56307

Toll-free: 800-535-4838
Phone: 320-845-2111
Fax: 320-845-7093
www.mastermark.com

Rhino Deck® composite deck building components include lumber, posts, spindles, a rail system, and planks in 12', 16' and 20' lengths. Decking products are made from 50% recycled HDPE plastic and 50% recycled wood fibers from cabinet/furniture making operations.

EverGrain

TAMKO Building Products, Inc.
P.O. Box 1404
Joplin, MO 64802

Toll-free: 800-253-1401
www.evergrain.com

Epoch's EverGrain composite decking and railing products are made with post-consumer recycled HPDE, LPDE, and wood flour. Nominal sizes include 1/2x12, 1x6, 2x2, 2x4, and 2x6 in lengths ranging from 12' to 20'. Post sleeves and caps are also available. EverGrain has a 10-year warranty.

Trex

Trex Company, Inc.
160 Exeter Dr.
Winchester, VA 22603

Toll-free: 800-289-8739
Phone: 540-542-6300
Fax: 540-542-6890
www.trex.com

Trex® was the first wood-plastic composite product brought to market. Available in a number of common dimensions, seven colors, and three finishes, Trex is a wood-polymer lumber made from post-consumer and/or post-industrial reclaimed plastic and waste wood. According to the manufacturer, the reclaimed plastic comes primarily from grocery sacks and stretch film, and the waste wood is from woodworking manufacturers.

Most recently mentioned in EBN 2:2, 2:4, 3:1, 5:6, 6:6, 8:1, 8:4, 8:11, 11:3

This Space is Available for Your Notes

06 00 00
Wood, Plastics, & Composites

07 00 00 Thermal & Moisture Protection

PRODUCT LISTINGS

07 10 00
Dampproofing and Waterproofing

Products listed here help prevent moisture from penetrating the envelope.

QuickFlash Weatherproofing Products

QuickFlash Weatherproofing Products, Inc.
4129 Wagon Trail Ave.
Las Vegas, NV 89118   **New**

Phone: 702-614-6100
Fax: 702-614-4090
www.quickflashproducts.com

A line of products from QuickFlash offers prefabricated thermoplastic flashing for exterior wall protrusions on buildings, including plumbing, electrical, gas, and HVAC penetrations. The polyethylene or rubber panels friction fit around a protrusion, helping prevent moisture, air, and insect entry. A variety of products in QuickFlash's plumbing and HVAC lines accommodate 1/2- and 3/4-inch pipes, up to 4" and 6" sheet metal duct. The electrical line offers specific solutions for single-gang, pancake, and round boxes, as well as depth variations for different exterior cladding. The products carry a 10-year warranty.

07 13 00
Sheet Waterproofing

Sheet waterproofing is usually made from rubberized asphalt, isobutylene-isoprene rubber, or EPDM. Products listed here are manufactured using alternative materials, such as the more environmentally benign HDPE. (See also 07 14 00 - Fluid-Applied Waterproofing, 07 16 00 - Cementitious and Reactive Waterproofing, 09 97 23 - Concrete and Masonry Coatings.)

Delta-MS and Delta-Dry

Cosella Dörken Products Inc.

For full listing, see CSI section 07 25 00 - Weather Barriers

Underseal Termite-Resistant Membranes

Polyguard Products, Inc.
3801 S. Business 45
P.O. Box 755
Ennis, TX 75120

Toll-free: 800-541-4994
Phone: 972-875-8421
Fax: 972-875-9425
www.polyguardproducts.com

Underseal waterproofing membranes from Polyguard resist termites, radon, pesticide migration, soil fungi, puncture, and tearing while providing waterproofing and stress relief for slabs and concrete or IFC walls. Underseal Protected Wall Membrane is a peel-and-stick sheet membrane applied to the outside of finished flat concrete walls. Underseal Blindside has a nonwoven textile top layer that bonds with the concrete when monolithic walls are poured.

07 14 00
Fluid-Applied Waterproofing

Fluid-applied waterproofing is commonly made of polyurethane-based or hot rubberized-asphalt materials. Products listed here have low VOC content, recycled content, exceptional durability, or some combination of these product attributes. (See also 07 13 00 - Sheet Waterproofing, 07 16 00 - Cementitious and Reactive Waterproofing, 09 97 23 - Concrete and Masonry Coatings, 03 05 16 - Waterproofing Admixtures.)

DynoSeal Waterproofing Sealer

American Formulating & Manufacturing (AFM)
3251 Third Ave.
San Diego, CA 92103

Toll-free: 800-239-0321
Phone: 619-239-0321
Fax: 619-239-0565
www.afmsafecoat.com

DynoSeal is an asphaltic emulsion waterproof sealer with a VOC content of less than 100 g/l for use on foundations and other wet

applications. The product containers have over 90% post-consumer recycled-plastic content. The Dyno line of AFM coatings also includes driveway sealers and UV-stabilized rooftop coatings.

Rub-R-Wall Foundation Waterproofing

Rubber Polymer Corp.
1135 W. Portage Trl. Ext.
Akron, OH 44313

Toll-free: 800-860-7721
Phone: 330-945-7721
Fax: 330-945-9416
www.rpcinfo.com

Rub-R-Wall® foundation waterproofing is made from synthetic rubber. This product is spray-applied under high pressure (3,000 psi) and temperature (140 to 160 degrees F) by factory-certified professionals. The resulting rubber coating requires protection from backfilling with either 1/4" EPS foam or a woven geotextile. Rub-R-Wall has a lifetime limited warranty for residential applications and a 10-year warranty for commercial applications.

07 16 00
Cementitious and Reactive Waterproofing

While most conventional concrete sealers and waterproofing agents have very high VOCs, some products react with the concrete or otherwise provide a seal without resort to solvents that emit VOCs. Products listed here contain zero VOCs, either nominally or actually. (See also 07 13 00 - Sheet Waterproofing, 07 14 00 - Fluid-Applied Waterproofing, 07 19 00 - Water Repellents, 09 97 23 - Concrete and Masonry Coatings, 03 05 16 - Waterproofing Admixtures.)

Aquafin-IC Crystalline Waterproofing

Aquafin, Inc.
505 Blue Ball Rd., Bldg. 160
Elkton, MD 21921

Toll-free: 888-482-6339
Phone: 410-392-2300
Fax: 410-392-2324
www.aquafin.net

**07 00 00
Thermal &
Moisture
Protection**

Aquafin-IC is a penetrating, inorganic, cementitious material used to permanently waterproof and protect new or existing structurally sound concrete and concrete masonry by reacting with moisture and free lime in the concrete. Aquafin-IC resists strong hydrostatic pressure and can be used in both interior and exterior below-grade applications. It is "breathable," nontoxic, releases no VOCs, and is suitable for potable water storage applications. Aquafin-IC may take up to a month to reach full waterproofing potential.

Industraseal

US Mix Products Company

For full listing, see CSI section 09 97 23 - Concrete and Masonry Coatings

Xypex Concentrate

Xypex Chemical Corporation
13731 Mayfield Pl.
Richmond, BC V6V 2G9 Canada

Toll-free: 800-961-4477
Phone: 604-273-5265
Fax: 604-270-0451
www.xypex.com

Xypex Concentrate is a nontoxic powder consisting of portland cement, very fine treated silica sand, and various active proprietary chemicals. Mixed with water to form a slurry, it penetrates the pores of concrete and masonry structures, plugging them with a nonsoluble crystalline formation that becomes an integral part of the structure. This product is approved for use on potable water structures and contains no VOCs. Xypex Concentrate is available in powder form in 20-lb. pails, 60-lb. pails, and 50-lb. bags. Other formulations for the protection and waterproofing of concrete are available. Xypex products also protect reinforcing steel.

07 00 00
Thermal &
Moisture
Protection

07 17 00
Bentonite Waterproofing

Bentonite is a highly expansive natural clay. When exposed to moisture, it swells "shut," providing effective waterproofing. Products are available in sheets or panels.

Bentonite Waterproofing Systems

CETCO - Building Materials Group
1500 W. Shure Dr.
Arlington Heights, IL 60004

Toll-free: 800-527-9948
Phone: 847-392-5800
Fax: 847-506-6195
www.cetco.com

CETCO produces several waterproofing membranes using sodium bentonite, a natural clay with extremely low permeability and self-sealing properties. These membranes may be used beneath concrete slabs, against backfilled foundation walls, and for property line construction, such as lagging and metal sheet piling retention walls. Also, CETCO provides bentonite-based concrete joint waterstops that activate and swell to form a positive seal. CETCO claims that the products typically contain no VOCs and require no solvent-based primers or adhesives. Bentonite waterproofing can be installed on "green" concrete as soon as the forms are removed in a wide range of weather conditions, including freezing temperatures.

07 18 00
Traffic Coatings

Most traffic coatings are urethane- or epoxy-based and have high VOC content. Products listed here have VOC content well below the federal VOC content limit of 700 grams per liter.

DynoSeal Waterproofing Sealer

American Formulating & Manufacturing (AFM)

For full listing, see CSI section 07 14 00 - Fluid-Applied Waterproofing

07 19 00
Water Repellents

Water repellents are clear liquid products that are usually solvent- or water-based silicone, acrylic, silane or siloxane based. Products listed here have VOC content well below the federal VOC content limit of 700 grams per liter for this category of products. (See also 07 14 00 - Fluid-Applied Waterproofing, 07 16 00 - Cementitious and Reactive Waterproofing, 09 97 23 - Concrete and

Masonry Coatings, 03 05 16 - Waterproofing Admixtures.)

Penetrating Waterstop

American Formulating & Manufacturing (AFM)
3251 Third Ave.
San Diego, CA 92103

Toll-free: 800-239-0321
Phone: 619-239-0321
Fax: 619-239-0565
www.afmsafecoat.com

Safecoat® Penetrating WaterStop is a zero-VOC sealer that increases water-repellency and helps control the migration of free salts identified as efflorescence on brick walls, concrete foundations, stucco, stone, and most unglazed tile. It is nonflammable and free of formaldehyde and hazardous ingredients.

Enviroseal

BASF Corporation
889 Valley Park Dr.
Shakopee, MN 55379

Toll-free: 800-433-9517
Fax: 800-496-6067
www.corporate.basf.com

The Enviroseal® product line consists of single-component, water-based, water-repellent clear sealers. The VOC contents of these products is below 350 g/l. Enviroseal 20 and Enviroseal 40 are patented, penetrating silane sealers for concrete and masonry. Enviroseal 7 is an economical, blended silane/siloxane penetrating sealer for concrete, brick masonry, stucco, and many natural stones. Enviroseal Double 7 for Brick is a high-performance sealer developed for dense, vertical masonry surfaces such as hard-burnt brick, and also concrete, stone, and stucco. Enviroseal Surface Guard is a protective sealer designed to repel water and oils from horizontal interior masonry surfaces. The Enviroseal product line was formerly produced by Degussa Building Systems acquired by BASF in March of 2006.

Intraseal

Conspec
4226 Kansas Ave.
Kansas City, KS 66106

Toll-free: 800-348-7351
Phone: 913-279-4800
Fax: 913-371-3330
www.conspecmkt.com

Intraseal is a penetrating, water-based, reactive siliconate concrete sealer, hardener, and dustproofer. Its VOC content is below 100 g/l. This product is for use on concrete floors.

Ashford Formula

Curecrete Distribution, Inc.
1203 W. Spring Creek Pl.
Springville, UT 84663

Toll-free: 800-998-5664
Phone: 801-489-5663
Fax: 801-489-3307
www.ashfordformula.com

Ashford Formula is a permanent, penetrating concrete hardener, densifier, dustproofer, and sealer for new or existing concrete. As it progressively seals, the concrete becomes watertight but remains breathable and will develop a shine through use or by scrubbing. The product also locks in salts to eliminate the formation of concrete dust. Ashford Formula is water-based, nontoxic, nonflammable, and releases no VOCs. It is effective on concrete, stucco, terrazzo, concrete block, and similar materials. This product is particularly intended for flooring applications.

Concrete & Masonry Cleaner and Sealer

Envirosafe Manufacturing Corporation
For full listing, see CSI section 03 01 00 - Maintenance of Concrete

Concrete Sealing Compounds

Kaufman Products, Inc.
3811 Curtis Ave.
Baltimore, MD 21226

Toll-free: 800-637-6372
Phone: 410-354-8600
Fax: 410-354-1122
www.kaufmanproducts.net

Kaufman Products offers several industrial concrete sealing and curing compounds; the following low-VOC products are appropriate for sealing existing concrete. Krystal 15 emulsion is a water-emulsion, acrylic-polymer curing and sealing compound with 9 g/l VOC, available in drums and pails. Cure & Seal 309 emulsion is a water emulsion, acrylic-modified resin curing and sealing compound with 60 g/l VOC.

SoySeal

Natural Soy, LLC
2 Liberty St.
Watkins, IA 52354

Toll-free: 888-655-0039
Phone: 319-227-7418
Fax: 319-227-7428
www.naturalsoyprod.com

SoySeal is a water-based, nontoxic, nonflammable sealer suitable for exposed wood surfaces. It contains no VOCs or other known user hazards and cleans up with water. This product spreads water rather than beading it, which reduces the risk of UV magnification and damage, according to Natural Soy. Coverage is 150 to 300 ft². This product complies with ASTM C-672 and is also used to seal concrete. It is available in 1-, 5-, 55-, and 250-gallon containers.

Seal-Once

New Image Coatings, LLC
150 Dow St.
Manchester, NH 03101

Phone: 603-669-8786
Fax: 603-669-9048
www.seal-once.com

Seal-Once™ water-based waterproofers for wood, concrete, and masonry contain no heavy metals, or VOCs. It is colorless, UV-resistant, paintable, and stainable. The manufacturer claims that the compound will not leach and is safe for aquatic environments. Clear and tinted formulas are available, as well as marine and industrial grades.

9400 and 9400W Impregnant

Palmer Industries, Inc.
10611 Old Annapolis Rd.
Frederick, MD 21701

Toll-free: 800-545-7383
Phone: 301-898-7848
Fax: 301-898-3312
www.palmerindustriesinc.com

9400 Impregnant is a water-repellent, UV-protective coating for masonry, concrete, and other cementitious materials, formulated without solvents for minimal toxicity. 9400W is a variant for wood surfaces.

Seal-Krete Sealers

Seal-Krete, Inc.
306 Gandy Rd.
Auburndale, FL 33823

Toll-free: 800-323-7357
Phone: 863-967-1535
Fax: 863-965-2326
www.seal-krete.com

Seal-Krete Original Waterproofing Sealer (SKWPS) is a water-based, very-low-VOC (less than 8 g/l), strong-binding, clear acrylic, penetrating sealer/primer for interior and exterior concrete and masonry surfaces. The product is available in 10% solids and 25% solids formulations. Seal-Krete Masonry Sealer is a waterborne, nonyellowing, clear acrylic emulsion sealer that can be used on both concrete and wood floors. It has a VOC content below 100 g/l. These sealers are for above-grade applications.

SOYsolv Soy Seal

SOYsolv
6154 N. CR 33
Tiffin, OH 44883

Toll-free: 800-231-4274
Phone: 419-992-4570
Fax: 419-992-4595
www.soysolv.com

SOYsolv® Soy Seal, made from soybean oil, is a water-based, nontoxic, nonflammable, zero-VOC formulation for sealing cured concrete and wood. According to the company, testing in the upper Midwest shows sealing performance to last over a year outdoors.

Weather-Bos Sealers

Weather-Bos International
316 California Ave., Ste. 1082
Reno, NV 89509

Toll-free: 800-664-3978
Fax: 530-272-8098
www.weatherbos.com

Weather-Bos sealers are made from natural, nontoxic vegetable oils and resins as well as other natural ingredients. These sealers are low-odor, water-reducible, nonflammable, and free of harmful fungicides. The small amount of pigment in some formulas provides UV protection. Masonry Boss™ waterproofs and protects brick, adobe, concrete, tile, and stone.

07 21 00
Thermal Insulation

Thermal insulation products for buildings generally reduce the flow of heat by trapping air or some other gas in a matrix of loose-fill fibers or particles (glass, cellulose, mineral woo, cotton), sprayed in place foams, or rigid board products. Products listed here exhibit one or more of the following attributes: reduced off-gassing (particularly of formaldehydes), post-consumer recycled-content, less-processed formulations, post-industrial waste content, non-ozone depleting blowing agents, and reduced greenhouse gas emissions. Note that any product that manages conductive heat loss can also manage both energy loss by air infiltration and moisture flow; the selection process for insulation products should include consideration of these other hygrothermal properties. (See also 03 52 00 - Lightweight Concrete Roof Insulation, 07 21 13 - Board Insulation, 07 21 16 - Blanket Insulation, 07 21 19

07 00 00
Thermal & Moisture Protection

- Foamed-in-Place Insulation, 07 21 23 - Loose-Fill Insulation, 07 21 29 - Sprayed Insulation.) (See feature article EBN Vol. 2, No. 5.)

Industry Representation

Cellulose Insulation Manufacturers Association
136 S. Keowee St.
Dayton, OH 45402

Toll-free: 888-881-2462
Phone: 937-222-2462
Fax: 937-222-5794
www.cellulose.org

The Cellulose Insulation Manufacturers Association (CIMA) represents the technical, scientific, and professional interests of cellulose producers in the United States. CIMA is dedicated to fostering greater energy efficiency through environmentally sound insulation products. Cellulose insulation is made from recycled paper and cardboard.

Most recently mentioned in EBN 2:5, 3:1, 4:1, 4:3, 7:1, 14:1

Industry Representation

North American Insulation Manufacturers Association
44 Canal Center Plz., Ste. 310
Alexandria, VA 22314

Phone: 703-684-0084
Fax: 703-684-0427
www.naima.org

The North American Insulation Manufacturers Association (NAIMA) is the trade association of North American manufacturers of fiberglass, rock wool, and slag wool insulation products. Insulation often incorporates recycled glass and iron slag.

Most recently mentioned in EBN 2:5, 4:1, 5:6, 14:1

07 00 00
Thermal & Moisture Protection

Aerogel Insulation

New

Solar Components Corp.
121 Valley St.
Manchester, NH 03103

Phone: 603-668-8186
Fax: 603-668-1783
www.solar-components.com

Cabot's synthetic silica aerogel, Nanogel™, provides both high insulating value (R-8/inch) and high light transmissivity (53% with 1" thickness). The product is UV-stable, hydrophobic, and non-combustible. The lightweight microporous structure reduces sound transmission as well as heat conduction and convection. This aerogel provides diffuse daylighting without sacrificing energy performance, and has been used for a number of daylighting products. Solar

Components Corporation sells this Aerogel in one- and five-gallon containers.

Most recently mentioned in EBN 11:12 & 12:3

07 21 13
Board Insulation

Board insulation can be made up of glass fibers, mineral wool or rigid foam. Unlike most batt or blown-in insulation, rigid boards can be applied across the surface of walls, roofs, or foundations, reducing thermal bridging through the structure. Foam insulation products are all petroleum-derived with most foams require a blowing agent to create the foaming action. Extruded polystyrene (XPS) is still blown with HCFC-142b—although European manufacturers have converted to non-ozone-depleting blowing agents. Only a few specialized XPS insulation materials in the U.S. are currently produced without HCFCs. Mineral wool insulation is made from either molten slag—a waste product of steel production—or natural rock, such as basalt and diabase. Mineral wool has a higher density than fiberglass, so it has better sound-blocking properties. Note that board insulation products vary widely in terms of more than just their resistance to conductive heat loss; consideration of each product's air tightness and moisture performance may be important as well. Products listed here have post-consumer and/or post-industrial recycled-content, reduced off-gassing, reduced or eliminated ozone-depleting potential blowing agents. (See feature article EBN Vol. 1, No. 1.)

Perform and Perform Guard EPS

ACH Foam Technologies, LLC - Headquarters
90 Trowbridge Dr.
P.O. Box 669
Fond du Lac, WI 54936

Toll-free: 800-236-5377
Phone: 920-924-4050
Fax: 920-924-4042
www.achfoam.com

ACH Foam Technologies, LLC is a licensed manufacturer of AFM Corporation's Perform® EPS Insulation, a non-ozone-depleting foam insulation manufactured in various sizes for many insulation applications. Perform Guard® is Perform EPS formulated with a boron insect repellent. Contour Taper Tile® roof

insulation is Perform EPS shaped to achieve appropriate pitches for low-slope roofs.

Perform and Perform Guard EPS

ACH Foam Technologies, LLC - Illinois Division
3751 Sunset Ave.
Waukegan, IL 60087

Toll-free: 800-800-0359
Phone: 847-263-0200
Fax: 847-263-0350
www.achfoam.com

ACH Foam Technologies, LLC is a licensed manufacturer of AFM Corporation's Perform® EPS Insulation, a non-ozone-depleting foam insulation manufactured in various sizes for many insulation applications. Perform Guard® is Perform EPS formulated with a boron insect repellent. Contour Taper Tile® roof insulation is Perform EPS shaped to achieve appropriate pitches for low-slope roofs.

Perform and Perform Guard EPS

ACH Foam Technologies, LLC - Iowa Division
809 E. 15th St.
Washington, IA 52353

Toll-free: 888-633-6033
Phone: 319-653-6216
Fax: 319-653-6837
www.achfoam.com

ACH Foam Technologies, LLC is a licensed manufacturer of AFM Corporation's Perform® EPS Insulation, a non-ozone-depleting foam insulation manufactured in various sizes for many insulation applications. Perform Guard® is Perform EPS formulated with a boron insect repellent. Contour Taper Tile® roof insulation is Perform EPS shaped to achieve appropriate pitches for low-slope roofs.

Perform and Perform Guard EPS

ACH Foam Technologies, LLC - Newton Division
1418 Cow Palace Rd.
Newton, KS 67114

Toll-free: 800-835-2161
Phone: 316-283-1100
Fax: 316-283-3732
www.achfoam.com

AFM Corporation's Perform® EPS Insulation is a non-ozone-depleting foam insulation manufactured in various sizes for many insulation applications. Perform Guard® is Perform EPS formulated with a boron insect repellent. Contour Taper Tile® roof insulation is Perform EPS shaped to achieve appropriate pitches for low-slope roofs. For sales information, contact the company's Kansas City Division.

Perform and Perform Guard EPS

Advance Foam Plastics, Inc. - California Division
Maquiladoras #331 Interior A y B
Cd. Industrials Nueva Tijuana
Tijuana, BC 22500 Mexico

Phone: 626-334-5358
Fax: 626-969-3978
www.afprcontrol.com

Advance Foam Plastics is a licensed manufacturer of AFM Corporation's Perform® EPS Insulation, a non-ozone-depleting foam insulation manufactured in various sizes for many insulation applications. Perform Guard® is Perform EPS formulated with a boron insect repellent. Contour Taper Tile® roof insulation is Perform EPS shaped to achieve appropriate pitches for low-slope roofs.

Perform and Perform Guard EPS

Advance Foam Plastics, Inc. - Colorado Division
5250 N. Sherman St.
Denver, CO 80216

Toll-free: 800-525-8697
Phone: 303-297-3844
Fax: 303-292-2613
www.afprcontrol.com

Advance Foam Plastics is a licensed manufacturer of AFM Corporation's Perform® EPS Insulation, a non-ozone-depleting foam insulation manufactured in various sizes for many insulation applications. Perform Guard® is Perform EPS formulated with a boron insect repellent. Contour Taper Tile® roof insulation is Perform EPS shaped to achieve appropriate pitches for low-slope roofs.

Perform and Perform Guard EPS

Advance Foam Plastics, Inc. - Nevada Division
920 Kleppe Ln.
Sparks, NV 89431

Toll-free: 800-444-9290
Phone: 775-355-7655
Fax: 775-355-7615
www.afprcontrol.com

Advance Foam Plastics is a licensed manufacturer of AFM Corporation's Perform® EPS Insulation, a non-ozone-depleting foam insulation manufactured in various sizes for many insulation applications. Perform Guard® is Perform EPS formulated with a boron insect

repellent. Contour Taper Tile® roof insulation is Perform EPS shaped to achieve appropriate pitches for low-slope roofs.

Perform and Perform Guard EPS

Advance Foam Plastics, Inc. - Utah Division
111 W. Fireclay Ave.
Murray, UT 84107

Toll-free: 877-775-8847
Phone: 801-265-3465
Fax: 801-265-3542
www.afprcontrol.com

Advance Foam Plastics is a licensed manufacturer of AFM Corporation's Perform® EPS Insulation, a non-ozone-depleting foam insulation manufactured in various sizes for many insulation applications. Perform Guard® is Perform EPS formulated with a boron insect repellent. Contour Taper Tile® roof insulation is Perform EPS shaped to achieve appropriate pitches for low-slope roofs.

Perform and Perform Guard EPS

AFM Corporation
211 River Ridge Cir. #102A
Burnsville, MN 55337

Toll-free: 800-255-0176
Phone: 952-474-0809
Fax: 952-474-2074
www.r-control.com

Perform EPS Insulation is a non-ozone-depleting foam insulation manufactured in various sizes for many insulation applications. Contour Taper Tile® roof insulation is Perform EPS cut to achieve appropriate pitches for low-slope roofs. Perform Guard® is termite-resistant EPS formulated with a borate additive. AFM also makes use of Perform Guard to manufacture structural insulated panels (SIPs). AFM licenses several dozen manufacturers throughout the U.S. to produce these products as well.

Most recently mentioned in EBN 2:5 & 4:1

Perform and Perform Guard EPS

Allied Foam Products, Inc.
2731 White Sulphur Rd.
Gainesville, GA 30501

Toll-free: 800-533-2613
Phone: 770-536-7900
Fax: 770-532-8123
www.alliedfoamprod.com

Allied Foam Products is a licensed manufacturer of AFM Corporation's Perform® EPS

Insulation, a non-ozone-depleting foam insulation manufactured in various sizes for many insulation applications. Perform Guard® is Perform EPS formulated with a boron insect repellent. Contour Taper Tile® roof insulation is Perform EPS shaped to achieve appropriate pitches for low-slope roofs.

ACFoam

Atlas Roofing Corp.
2000 RiverEdge Pkwy., Ste. 800
Atlanta, GA 30328

Phone: 770-952-1442
Fax: 770-952-3170
www.atlasroofing.com

ACFoam® was the first North American polyisocyanurate foam insulation to be blown with hydrocarbons rather than HCFCs; it has zero ODP and zero GWP. ACFoam with ACUltra™ is sold under various brand names for both commercial and residential roofing and wall sheathing applications. This product also contains recovered materials and meets ASTM C-1289, UL, and FM standards. ACFoam-II (a roof insulation) contains between 16% and 43% recovered materials by weight, depending on thickness.

Most recently mentioned in EBN 7:5, 10:5, 10:7, 11:7, 14:1

EPS Foam Insulation Components

BASF Corporation
889 Valley Park Dr.
Shakopee, MN 55379

Toll-free: 800-433-9517
Fax: 800-496-6067
www.corporate.basf.com

BASF produces components for manufacturing low-pentane foam insulation.

Most recently mentioned in EBN 2:1 & 4:1

Perform and Perform Guard EPS

Big Sky Insulations, Inc.
P.O. Box 838
Belgrade, MT 59714

Toll-free: 800-766-3626
Phone: 406-388-4146
Fax: 406-388-7223
www.bsiinc.com

Big Sky Insulation is a licensed manufacturer of AFM Corporation's Perform® EPS Insulation, a non-ozone-depleting foam insulation manufactured in various sizes for many insulation applications. Perform Guard® is Perform EPS formulated with a boron insect repellent. Contour Taper Tile® roof insulation is Perform EPS shaped to achieve appropriate pitches for low-slope roofs.

07 00 00
Thermal & Moisture Protection

Perform and Perform Guard EPS

Branch River Foam Plastics, Inc.
15 Thurber Blvd.
Smithfield, RI 02917

Toll-free: 800-336-3626
Phone: 401-232-0270
Fax: 401-231-3434
www.branchriver.com

Branch River Foam Plastics is a licensed manufacturer of AFM Corporation's Perform® EPS Insulation, a non-ozone-depleting foam insulation manufactured in various sizes for many insulation applications. Perform Guard® is Perform EPS formulated with a boron insect repellent. Contour Taper Tile® roof insulation is Perform EPS shaped to achieve appropriate pitches for low-slope roofs.

Perform and Perform Guard EPS

Contour Products, Inc. - Kansas City Division
4001 Kaw Dr.
Kansas City, KS 66102

Toll-free: 800-638-3626
Phone: 913-321-4114
Fax: 913-321-8063
www.contourfoam.com

Contour Products is a licensed manufacturer of AFM Corporation's Perform® EPS Insulation, a non-ozone-depleting foam insulation manufactured in various sizes for many insulation applications. Perform Guard® is Perform EPS formulated with a boron insect repellent. Contour Taper Tile® roof insulation is Perform EPS shaped to achieve appropriate pitches for low-slope roofs.

Styrofoam High Performance Underlayment

Dow Chemical Co., Styrofoam Brand Products
200 Larkin Ctr.
Midland, MI 48674

Toll-free: 800-441-4369
Phone: 989-636-1000
Fax: 989-832-1465
www.styrofoam.com

Styrofoam® High Performance Underlayment from Dow is the first U.S.-manufactured extruded polystyrene (XPS) foam board with zero ODP. This product, blown with HFC-152a, is designed for residential wall-sheathing applications. It comes in 4' x 50' fanfold sections, several different facings, and in thicknesses of 1/4" (R-1) and 3/8" (R-1.5).

EPS Foam

Insulfoam (Division of Premier Industries, Inc.)
1019 Pacific Ave., Ste. 1501
Tacoma, WA 98402

Toll-free: 800-248-5995
Phone: 253-572-5111
Fax: 253-387-7100
www.insulfoam.com

Insulfoam manufactures a large variety of expanded polystyrene insulation products including the polyethylene-skinned R-TECH family of perimeter foundation, wall, and roof insulation (in standard sheathing and fanfold configurations); standard roof insulation and the custom-cut Insultaper Tapered Roof Drainage System; Insul-Lam and Insul-Vent, nailable deck panels for use on steel and wood roof systems; as well as their Garage Door Insulation Kit. Insulfoam insulation products are made from up to 15% post-consumer recycled EPS with the company accepting EPS scrap from its larger customers.

Perform and Perform Guard EPS

Noark Enterprises
10101 Highway 70 E
N. Little Rock, AR 72117

Toll-free: 800-632-4586
Phone: 501-945-1114
Fax: 501-945-2583
www.noarkrcontrol.com

Noark Enterprises is a licensed manufacturer of AFM Corporation's Perform® EPS Insulation, a non-ozone-depleting foam insulation manufactured in various sizes for many insulation applications. Perform Guard® is Perform EPS formulated with a boron insect repellent. Contour Taper Tile® roof insulation is Perform EPS shaped to achieve appropriate pitches for low-slope roofs.

Perform and Perform Guard EPS

Pacific Allied Products, Ltd.
91-110 Kaomi Loop
Kapolei, HI 96707

Toll-free: 888-824-3626
Phone: 808-864-8990
Fax: 808-595-4277
www.pacificalliedproducts.com

Pacific Allied Products is a licensed manufacturer of AFM Corporation's Perform® EPS Insulation, a non-ozone-depleting foam insulation manufactured in various sizes for many insulation applications. Perform Guard® is Perform EPS formulated with a borate insect repellent. Contour Taper Tile® roof insulation is Perform EPS shaped to achieve appropriate pitches for low-slope roofs.

Foamglas Sheet Insulation

Pittsburgh Corning Corporation (PCC)
800 Presque Isle Dr.
Pittsburgh, PA 15239

Toll-free: 800-359-8433
Fax: 724-325-9704
www.foamglasinsulation.com

Foamglas® cellular glass insulation from Pittsburgh Corning Corporation for commercial and industrial roofs, plazas, decks, and other architectural applications is 100% glass, made with sand (41%), feldspar (22%), limestone (17%), soda (17%), and trace minerals (3%). Production is free of HCFCs. Foamglas is moisture-impermeable and noncombustible, resists corrosion in any environment, is dimensionally stable, and has a high compressive strength. It is available in flat or tapered sheets. The manufacturer offers a 20-year warranty covering resistance to moisture absorption, retention of original insulation efficiency, and retention of compressive strength.

Polar Guard Rigid EPS

Polar Industries
32 Grammar Ave.
Prospect, CT 06712

Toll-free: 800-237-3763
Phone: 203-758-6651
Fax: 203-758-3162
www.polarcentral.com

Polar Industries manufactures Polar Guard, a standard 1-lb. density EPS board manufactured with the pulfusion process. Polar Guard is available in 3/4", 1", and 2" thicknesses.

Most recently mentioned in EBN 10:2

Perform and Perform Guard EPS

Poly-Foam, Inc.
116 Pine St. S
Lester Prairie, MN 55354

Phone: 320-395-2551
Fax: 320-395-2702
www.polyfoaminc.com

Poly-Foam is a licensed manufacturer of AFM Corporation's Perform® EPS Insulation, a non-ozone-depleting foam insulation manufactured in various sizes for many insulation applications. Perform Guard® is Perform EPS formulated with a boron insect repellent. Contour Taper Tile® roof insulation is Perform EPS shaped to achieve appropriate pitches for low-slope roofs.

**07 00 00
Thermal &
Moisture
Protection**

DrainBoard

Roxul Inc.
551 Harrop Dr.
Milton, ON L9T 3H3 Canada

Toll-free: 800-265-6878
Phone: 905-878-8474
Fax: 905-878-8077
www.roxul.com

Roxul offers DrainBoard™, a durable, rigid mineral wool insulation board that is water repellent and environmentally stable used as an insulating foundation drainage system. It is designed for use with a dampproofing layer on commercial applications up to 12' below grade. The non-directional fiber structure allows the system to be installed horizontally or vertically, providing an insulating drainage plane for foundation walls and structural concrete. Roxul's mineral wool is made from approximately equal amounts of natural basalt rock and recycled slag (with 1%-6% urea extended phenolic formaldehyde binder).

Most recently mentioned in EBN 4:6, 5:6, 14:1

Mineral Wool Insulation

Roxul Inc.
551 Harrop Dr.
Milton, ON L9T 3H3 Canada

Toll-free: 800-265-6878
Phone: 905-878-8474
Fax: 905-878-8077
www.roxul.com

Roxul offers the U.S. market commercial and industrial mineral wool products in faced and unfaced rigid and semi-rigid boards, blankets, and formed products for thermal, acoustical, and fireproofing insulation for wall, floor, curtain wall, pipe, and tank installations. Roxul's mineral wool—made from approximately equal amounts of natural basalt rock and recycled slag (with 1%-6% urea extended phenolic formaldehyde binder)—is vapor-permeable, water-repellant, and non-combustible. The dimensionally stable, chemically inert material doesn't degrade or support mold, and is made with CFC- and HCFC-free processes. Compressive strength of up to 877 psf (42 kPa) is available in rigid boards. R-values per inch range from 4 to 4.3. Roxul offers additional products for residential applications to the Canadian market.

Most recently mentioned in EBN 4:6 & 5:6

Perform and Perform Guard EPS

Team Industries, Inc.
4580 Airwest Dr. SE
P.O. Box 888691
Grand Rapids, MI 49588

Toll-free: 800-356-5548
Phone: 616-698-2001
Fax: 616-698-0605
www.teamindustries.com

Team Industries is a licensed manufacturer of AFM Corporation's Perform® EPS Insulation, a non-ozone-depleting foam insulation manufactured in various sizes for many insulation applications. Perform Guard® is Perform EPS formulated with a boron insect repellent. Contour Taper Tile® roof insulation is Perform EPS shaped to achieve appropriate pitches for low-slope roofs.

Perform and Perform Guard EPS

Team/IBS, Inc.
326 McGhee Rd.
Winchester, VA 22603

Phone: 540-662-0882
Fax: 540-662-9104
www.rcontrolibs.com

Team/IBS is a licensed manufacturer of AFM Corporation's Perform® EPS Insulation, a non-ozone-depleting foam insulation manufactured in various sizes for many insulation applications. Perform Guard® is Perform EPS formulated with a boron insect repellent. Contour Taper Tile® roof insulation is Perform EPS shaped to achieve appropriate pitches for low-slope roofs.

Perform and Perform Guard EPS

Therma Foam, Inc.
P.O. Box 161128
Fort Worth, TX 76161

Toll-free: 800-333-3626
Phone: 817-624-7204
Fax: 800-999-6729
www.thermafoam.com

Therma Foam is a licensed manufacturer of AFM Corporation's Perform® EPS Insulation, a non-ozone-depleting foam insulation manufactured in various sizes for many insulation applications. Perform Guard® is Perform EPS formulated with a boron insect repellent. Contour Taper Tile® roof insulation is Perform EPS shaped to achieve appropriate pitches for low-slope roofs.

Thermafiber Insulation Products

Thermafiber, Inc.

For full listing, see CSI section 07 21 29 - Sprayed Insulation

07 21 16
Blanket Insulation

Blanket insulation is typically made up of fiberglass, mineral wool, or cotton. Most fiberglass insulation is made primarily from silica spun into glass fibers and contains a phenol-formaldehyde (PF) binder— though formaldehyde-free products have been introduced. Most fiberglass insulation today has at least 30% recycled-glass content, with some plants using as much as 40% post-consumer recycled beverage glass as the raw material. Mineral wool insulation is made from either molten slag—a waste product of steel production—or natural rock, such as basalt and diabase. Mineral wool has a higher density than fiberglass, so it has better sound-blocking properties. It's also more fire-resistant than fiberglass. Cotton insulation is made from post-industrial recycled cotton textiles, such as denim, with synthetic fibers added to maintain loft. Nontoxic flame retardants similar to those used in clothing are added. Unlike fiberglass and mineral wool, there are no mineral microfibers as a potential cause of respiratory problems. Products listed here have high recycled content, reduced indoor air quality concerns, or superior performance in particular applications based on their air tightness or management of moisture.

UltraTouch Natural Fiber Insulation

Bonded Logic, Inc.
411 E. Ray Rd.
Chandler, AZ 85225

Phone: 480-812-9114
Fax: 480-812-9633
www.bondedlogic.com

Bonded Logic makes UltraTouch from post-industrial recycled denim and other cotton-fiber textile trimmings. This insulation contains no mineral fibers and carries no warning labels for installers or occupants. It is completely recyclable at the end of its useful life and has been ASTM tested for thermal resistance, surface-burning characteristics,

07 00 00
Thermal & Moisture Protection

water-vapor absorption, mold/fungi resistance, and odor emission. Available in batts that are either 16" or 24" wide, UltraTouch comes in 3-1/2" (R-13) or 5-1/2" (R-19) thicknesses.

Most recently mentioned in EBN 9:11 & 13:3

CertainTeed Batt Insulation

CertainTeed Corporation
750 E. Swedesford Rd.
P.O. Box 860
Valley Forge, PA 19482

Toll-free: 800-233-8990
Phone: 610-341-7000
Fax: 610-341-7777
www.certainteed.com

CertainTeed Building Insulation is manufactured with recycled glass cullet. CertainTeed uses an average of approximately 25% recycled glass depending on availability. These products carry the Greenguard certification for low emissions.

Most recently mentioned in EBN 7:6 & 12:10

Climatizer Plus and Enviro-Batt

Climatizer Insulation, Ltd.

For full listing, see CSI section 07 21 29 - Sprayed Insulation

Wool Insulation

Good Shepherd Wool Insulation
R.R. #3
Rocky Mountain House, AB T4T 2A3
Canada

Phone: 403-845-6705
Fax: 403-845-6705
www.goodshepherdwool.com

Good Shepherd Wool Insulation is sold in batts for frame houses (16" or 24" centers) and wool rope for log homes. The only additive is a boron-based fire retardant and vermin and insect repellent.

Inno-Therm Fiber Insulation

InnoTherm
1633 Shea Rd.
P.O. Box 226
Newton, NC 28658

Toll-free: 877-466-0612
Phone: 828-466-1147
Fax: 828-466-1498
www.innotherm.com

Inno-Therm is made of recycled cotton or custom-tailored thermal fibers. It contains no melamine or phenolic resins, can be installed without safety precautions, and is recyclable. Rolls are available in 15-1/2" and 23-1/2" widths; R11 and R13 are 3-1/2" thick, and R19 is 5-1/2" thick. This insulation meets or exceeds standards for thermal resistance, flame and smoke spread ratings, water vapor sorption, odor emission, and fungi resistance.

Most recently mentioned in EBN 14:1

InsulCot Cotton Insulation

Insulcot
411 S. Fox St.
Post, TX 79356

New

Phone: 806-777-2811
www.insulcot.com

InsulCot contains 75% cotton fibers and 25% polyester binder. Cotton fibers impregnated with a nontoxic phosphorous flame retardant is mixed with polyester and then heated, causing the polyester to melt. InsulCot, which has passed all federal tests for insulation, including fire and moisture resistance, is available in most standard widths and thickness in rolls or bats, with or without asphalted Kraft flanged facing. It is also available as a cellulose alternative for blow-in installations. InsulCot Cotton Insulation provides equivalent R-values to synthetic fibers per inch, but is lighter-weight. It meets the same Class 1 standards as fiberglass insulation.

Most recently mentioned in EBN 3:2, 3:3, 4:1

Formaldehyde-Free Insulation Batts

Johns Manville Corporation
P.O. Box 5108
Denver, CO 80217

Toll-free: 800-654-3103
Phone: 303-978-2000
Fax: 303-978-3661
www.jm.com

Johns Manville Corporation eliminated the use of formaldehyde in their insulation products in 2002. Their thermal- and sound-insulating fiberglass batts use an acrylic binder, and come in rolls either unfaced or with foil, FSK, or Kraft facing. ComfortTherm is a poly-encapsulated fiberglass insulation designed for metal- and wood-framing as well as for directly above suspended ceilings. Available in batts or rolls, R-values range from 11 to 38. ComfortTherm contains 20% post-consumer and 5% post-industrial recycled glass.

Most recently mentioned in EBN 14:1

Fiberglass Insulation

Ottawa Fibre, Inc.
1365 Johnston Rd.
Ottawa, ON K1V 8Z1 Canada

Phone: 613-247-7116
Fax: 613-736-7281
www.ofigroup.com

Ottawa Fibre L.P. fiberglass insulation is made from 65% recycled glass (typical), of which 100% is usually post-consumer content. Ottawa Fibre's Golden Glow Fiber Glass residential insulation is available in five configurations; unfaced, kraft-faced, foil-faced, FSK-faced, and flangeless. R-values range from R-8 to R-40, depending on density and thickness. The company also offers a wide range of fiberglass insulation products including commercial and industrial insulation and ceiling tiles for both residential and commercial markets.

PINK Fiberglas Building Insulation

Owens Corning
1 Owens Corning Pkwy.
Toledo, OH 43659

Toll-free: 800-438-7465
Phone: 419-248-8000
Fax: 419-248-6215
www.owenscorning.com

Owens Corning Pink fiber glass insulation products are certified by Scientific Certification Systems to contain at least 35% recycled glass (9% post-consumer and 26% post-industrial). A wide range of insulation products are manufactured by Owens Corning. This product carries the Greenguard certification for low emissions.

Most recently mentioned in EBN 12:10 & 14:4

Mineral Wool Insulation

Roxul Inc.

For full listing, see CSI section 07 21 13 - Board Insulation

07 21 19
Foamed-in-Place Insulation

With foamed-in-place insulation it is relatively easy (though not necessarily inexpensive) to fill wall and ceiling cavities completely, providing high R-values (3.6 to 6.5 per inch) and blocking air leakage very effectively. Installation requires special equipment, however, and must be done by licensed contractors. Most

07 00 00
Thermal & Moisture Protection

foamed-in-place insulation products are fairly high-density (2 lbs. per cubic foot) closed-cell polyurethanes—and some of these still use the ozone-depleting HCFC-141b blowing agent. Open-cell, low-density polyurethane foams have been produced with water or carbon dioxide as the blowing agent for some time. Compared with closed-cell polyurethane, open-cell products also use significantly less material, making them attractive from a resource standpoint, but also lower in R-value per inch. Some of the low-density foam products are made in part from bio-based raw materials in place of petrochemicals. Products listed use blowing agents that are non-ozone depleting. (See feature article EBN Vol. 1, No. 1.)

Air Krete Foam Insulation

Air Krete, Inc.
2710 E. Brutus St.
P.O. Box 380
Weedsport, NY 13166

Phone: 315-834-6609
Fax: 315-834-7420
www.airkrete.com

Air Krete is a lightweight, inorganic, cementitious foam insulation that is fireproof, non-toxic, pest-resistant, and moisture resistant. It does not support mold growth, and contains no fluorocarbons. Compressed air is mixed with an expanding agent, and the cement (magnesium oxide) is added to produce the final product. Air Krete, at standard density, has an R-value of 3.9/in. when tested at 75 degrees F. It is foamed in place in new or existing wall cavities by licensed Air Krete contractors. The foam density can be varied to withstand high-vibration environments, such as along busy roadways.

Most recently mentioned in EBN 4:1, 6:7, 14:1

BioBased 501

Bio-Based Systems
1315 N 13th St.
Rogers, AR 72756

Toll-free: 800-803-5189
Phone: 479-246-9523
Fax: 479-636-5810
www.biobased.net

BioBased 501 soybean-oil-based polyurethane spray foam insulation functions much like petroleum-based polyurethane foam. The polyol component of the two-part urethane consists of about 40% soy-derived oil. The open-cell foam is installed at a density of 0.5 lbs/ft^3 using CO2 as the blowing agent. It expands to 100 times its original liquid size. The product has an R-value of 3.7/in. (R-13

at 3-1/2") and is applied with customized equipment by certified installers. BioBased 501 was named "Outstanding Green Product of the Year" in 2003 by the National Association of Homebuilders (NAHB) Green Builders Conference in Baltimore.

Most recently mentioned in EBN 12:9 & 14:1

Sealection 500

Demilec USA, Inc.
2925 Galleria Dr.
Arlington, TX 76011

Toll-free: 877-336-4532
Phone: 817-640-4900
Fax: 817-633-2000
www.sealection500.com

Sealection™ 500 is a low-density polyurethane foam that is 100% water-blown and contains no HCFCs or hydrocarbon blowing agents. The product insulates to R-3.8/in. This product has passed the established offgassing tests and is approved by the Environmental Choice Program (a private ecolabeling program in Canada). Like all polyurethane foams, Sealection is hazardous during installation.

Most recently mentioned in EBN 6:5 & 10:7

SUPERGREEN FOAM

Foam-Tech, Division of Building Envelope Solutions, Inc.
P.O. Box 87, Rte. 5
N. Thetford, VT 05054

Phone: 802-333-4333
Fax: 802-333-4364
www.foam-tech.com

SuperGreen Foam™ is a closed-cell, high-density polyurethane foam containing no HCFCs. The blowing agent is HFC-134a. SuperGreen insulates to between R-6 and R-7/in. Like all polyurethane foams, SuperGreen is hazardous during installation. Foam-Tech is a foamed-in-place building insulation contractor that holds a patent license to produce SuperGreen using components manufactured by Preferred Foam Products.

Most recently mentioned in EBN 2:4, 4:1, 6:5, 11:1

The Icynene Insulation System

Icynene Inc.
6747 Campobello Rd.
Mississauga, ON L5N 2L7 Canada

Toll-free: 800-758-7325
Phone: 905-363-4040
Fax: 905-363-0102
www.icynene.com

The Icynene Insulation System® was the first water based, HCFC-free, low-density, open-cell polyurethane insulation to be introduced and is the most widely recognized brand in its kind. The foam is typically sprayed into open wall, ceiling, and floor cavities in a thin layer. It expands about 100 times its original volume to form an air barrier and is trimmed flush with the framing members before drywall is installed. With an R-value of about R-3.6/in., it can outperform fiberglass insulation with twice the R-value due to its air sealing capability. A slightly different formulation of Icynene can be poured into closed wall cavities in retrofit applications.

Most recently mentioned in EBN 4:1, 4:5, 10:7, 14:1

Air Krete Foam Insulation

Palmer Industries, Inc.
10611 Old Annapolis Rd.
Frederick, MD 21701

Toll-free: 800-545-7383
Phone: 301-898-7848
Fax: 301-898-3312
www.palmerindustriesinc.com

Air Krete is a lightweight, inorganic, cementitious foam insulation that is fireproof, non-toxic, pest-resistant, and moisture resistant. It does not support mold growth, and contains no fluorocarbons. Compressed air is mixed with an expanding agent, and the cement (magnesium oxide) is added to produce the final product. Air Krete, at standard density, has an R-value of 3.9/in. when tested at 75 degrees F. It is foamed in place in new or existing wall cavities by licensed Air Krete contractors. The foam density can be varied to withstand high-vibration environments, such as along busy roadways.

Most recently mentioned in EBN 4:1 & 6:7

RTC Polyurethane Insulation

Resin Technology Division of Henry Co.
2270 Castle Harbor Pl.
Ontario, CA 91761

Toll-free: 800-729-0795
Phone: 909-947-7224
Fax: 909-923-9617
www.resintechnology.com

Resin Technology formulates several water-blown, open-cell polyurethane foam insulation products with installed densities of 0.35 to 0.6 lbs/ft^3, depending on specific requirements. The company reports an R-value of close to 3.4/in. As with all polyurethane foams, this insulation requires appropriate, professional precautions during installation.

Most recently mentioned in EBN 4:1

07 00 00
Thermal & Moisture Protection

07 21 23
Loose-Fill Insulation

Loose-fill insulations include fiberglass, mineral wool or cellulose systems, among others. Cellulose insulation has several environmental advantages. Most contain 75-80% recycled newspaper (often post-consumer) and nontoxic borate and/or ammonium sulfate fire retardants. The energy performance is comparable to high-density fiberglass batts at roughly R-3.7 per inch, but cellulose insulation generally packs more tightly so is more effective at controlling air leakage. Health concerns with fiberglass have not been substantiated, but it is generally a good idea to install loose-fill fiberglass only if the fibers can be prevented from getting into occupied space or air distribution systems. Products listed here have recycled content, superior moisture or air leakage performance, or reduced indoor air quality concerns. (See feature article EBN Vol. 2, No. 5.)

Cellulose Insulation

Advanced Fiber Technology, Inc.
100 Crossroads Blvd.
Bucyrus, OH 44820

Phone: 419-562-1337
Fax: 419-562-9062
www.advancedfiber.com

Advanced Fiber Technology manufactures cellulose insulation from recycled wastepaper. The company would not disclose which fire retardant is used in this insulation. Advanced Fiber Technology is also a manufacturer of cellulose insulation processing equipment.

Most recently mentioned in EBN 2:5

07 00 00
Thermal & Moisture Protection

All-Weather Insulation

All-Weather Insulation Co., LLC
19 W. Industry Dr.
Springfield, KY 40069

Phone: 859-336-3651
Fax: 859-336-9631

All-Weather Cellulose Insulation contains recycled newspaper.

Applegate Loosefill and Stabilized Cellulose Insulation

Applegate Insulation Manufacturing

For full listing, see CSI section 07 21 29 - Sprayed Insulation

Benotherm

Benolec, Ltd.
1451 Nobel St.
Sainte-Julie, QC J3E 1Z4 Canada

Phone: 450-922-2000
Fax: 450-922-4333
www.benolec.com

Benotherm cellulose insulation contains recycled newspaper.

Cellulose Insulation

Can-Cell Industries, Inc.
14735 124th Ave.
Edmonton, AB T5L 3B2 Canada

Toll-free: 800-661-5031
Fax: 780-447-1034
www.can-cell.com

Can-Cell Industries manufactures Weathershield loose-fill cellulose, WallBAR stabilized cavity-fill cellulose, K-13 spray-applied thermal and acoustical insulation, and Sonaspray "fc" acoustical spray insulation from recycled newspaper. Typical post-consumer recycled content is 85%. Can-Cell Industries now manufactures K-13 and Sonaspray "fc" for the entire Canadian market.

Cell-Pak Advantage

Cell-Pak, Inc.
204 McIntire Ln.
Decatur, AL 35603

Toll-free: 800-325-5320
Phone: 256-260-2151
Fax: 256-301-9521
www.cellpak.com

Cell-Pak Advantage cellulose insulation, formerly Celluguard Light Wallboard, contains 85% recycled newspaper.

Most recently mentioned in EBN 2:5

Xcell Cellulose Insulation

Central Fiber Corp.
4814 Fiber Ln.
Wellsville, KS 66092

Toll-free: 800-654-6117
Phone: 785-883-4600
Fax: 785-883-4429
www.centralfiber.com

Clean and Xcell cellulose insulation is made from recycled newspaper with a boric acid fire-retardant.

Most recently mentioned in EBN 2:5 & 4:3

InsulSafe 4

CertainTeed Corporation
750 E. Swedesford Rd.
P.O. Box 860
Valley Forge, PA 19482

Toll-free: 800-233-8990
Phone: 610-341-7000
Fax: 610-341-7777
www.certainteed.com

InsulSafe® 4 is a formaldehyde-free, loose-fill, fiberglass insulation suitable for open-blow attic applications. InsulSafe 4 contains recycled glass cullet. This product carries the Greenguard certification for low emissions.

Most recently mentioned in EBN 2:1, 4:1, 7:6, 12:10

OPTIMA Fiberglass Insulation

CertainTeed Corporation
750 E. Swedesford Rd.
P.O. Box 860
Valley Forge, PA 19482

Toll-free: 800-233-8990
Phone: 610-341-7000
Fax: 610-341-7777
www.certainteed.com

Optima® is an insulation system composed of a nonwoven fabric facing behind which Optima is blown. Optima fiberglass is blown dry, without additives or moisture, and can be used in closed-cavity, retrofit applications. Some of the glass fibers are from recycled glass cullet. This product carries the Greenguard certification for low emissions.

Most recently mentioned in EBN 2:1, 4:1, 7:6, 12:10

Weather Blanket, House Blanket, Comfort Control, and Good News - Reused

Champion Insulation, Inc.
1249 S. Hickory St.
P.O. Box 1555
Fond du Lac, WI 54936

Phone: 920-322-8977
Fax: 920-322-8966
www.championinsulation.com

Champion Insulation's cellulose insulation products are manufactured using over 85% post-consumer recycled newsprint.

Cellulose Insulation

Clayville Insulation
P.O. Box 713
Burley, ID 83318

Toll-free: 800-584-9022
Phone: 208-678-9791
Fax: 208-678-9784

Clayville insulation is made from recycled newspaper.

Climatizer Plus and Enviro-Batt

Climatizer Insulation, Ltd.

For full listing, see CSI section 07 21 29 - Sprayed Insulation

Energy Control

Energy Control, Inc.
804 W. Mill St.
P.O. Box 327
Ossian, IN 46777

Toll-free: 800-451-6429
Phone: 260-622-7614
Fax: 260-622-7604

Manufactured under the brand names Energy Control II and Forest Wool, Energy Control cellulose insulation contains over 80% recycled newspaper.

Most recently mentioned in EBN 2:5

Therm Shield

Erie Energy Products, Inc.
1400 Irwin Dr.
Erie, PA 16505

Toll-free: 800-233-1810
Phone: 814-454-2828
Fax: 814-454-2820

Therm Shield cellulose insulation contains recycled newspaper.

Recycled-Content Cellulose Insulation

Fiberlite Technologies, Inc.
3605 E. 25th St.
Joplin, MO 64804

Toll-free: 800-641-4296
Phone: 417-781-6380
Fax: 417-781-8335
www.fiberlitetech.com

Fiberlite Technologies, Inc. offers several lines of cellulose insulation products containing recycled newsprint. Fiber-lite, Fiber-lite Plus, and In-Cide® PC are residential products; SATAC is for commercial use. Wal-Mat is a residential product made with recycled cardboard.

Thermolok and Thermospray

Hamilton Manufacturing, Inc.
901 Russet St.
Twin Falls, ID 83301

Toll-free: 800-777-9689
Phone: 208-733-9689
Fax: 208-733-9447
www.hmi-mfg.com

Thermolok and Thermospray cellulose insulation contain 100% boron and recycled newspaper.

Most recently mentioned in EBN 2:5

Igloo Cellulose Insulation

Igloo Cellulose, Inc.
195 Brunswick
Pointe Claire, QC H9R 4Z1 Canada

Toll-free: 800-363-7876
Phone: 514-694-1485
Fax: 514-694-3999
www.cellulose.com

Contains 85% recycled newspaper and special natural additives.

Climate Pro Blowing Wool

Johns Manville Corporation
P.O. Box 5108
Denver, CO 80217

Toll-free: 800-654-3103
Phone: 303-978-2000
Fax: 303-978-3661
www.jm.com

Climate Pro® Blowing Wool is a formaldehyde-free loose-fill fiberglass insulation containing 20% post-consumer and 5% post-industrial recycled glass. Climate-Pro can achieve an R-value of R-70 over 1/2" ceiling drywall without exceeding ceiling weight limits.

Most recently mentioned in EBN 11:3

Comfort-Zone

Mason City Recycling
P.O. Box 1534
Mason City, IA 50402

Toll-free: 800-373-1200
Phone: 641-423-1200
Fax: 641-424-8726
www.mcrecycling.com

Comfort-Zone cellulose insulation is manufactured from recycled newspaper.

Good News - Reused, House Blanket, Weather Blanket, and Comfort Control

Modern Insulation
1206 S. Monroe St.
Spencer, WI 54479

Phone: 715-659-2446
Fax: 715-659-4734

Modern Insulations' cellulose insulation products contain 80% post-consumer recycled newspaper.

Most recently mentioned in EBN 3:1

Good News - Reused

Mountain Fiber Insulation
1880 E. Anvil Blvd.
Hyrum, UT 84319

Toll-free: 800-669-4951
Phone: 435-245-6081
Fax: 435-245-4476
www.mtfiberinsulation.com/

Good News - Reused cellulose insulation is made from recycled newspaper.

Most recently mentioned in EBN 3:1

Thermo-Cel and Cel-Pak

National Fiber
50 Depot St.
Belchertown, MA 01007

Toll-free: 800-282-7711
Phone: 413-283-8747
Fax: 413-283-2462
www.nationalfiber.com

Thermo-Cel, Cel-Pak, and NuWool WallSeal cellulose insulation contain 85% recycled newspaper according to the manufacturer. Delivery is available to the 9 northeastern states.

Dry Pac Wall System

Par/PAC(TM)
53 Coveside Rd.
P.O. Box 153
South Bristol, ME 04568

Toll-free: 877-937-3257
Fax: 207-644-1503
www.parpac.com

The Par/PAC™ Dry Pac Wall System™ is a patented cellulose insulation in which a non-elastic, polyester-reinforced vapor retarder (Par/PAC poly) is stapled to wooden wall studs prior to drywalling and Good News-Reused™ cellulose insulation is dry-blown into the cavity at a high density. The poly layer allows inspection of the insulation to prevent voids. Cellulose insulation contains recycled newspaper.

AZ Energy Saver

Paul's Insulation
P.O. Box 115
Vergas, MN 56587

Toll-free: 800-627-5190
Phone: 218-342-2800
Fax: 218-342-3050

AZ Energy Saver is cellulose insulation made from 100% post-consumer recycled newspaper.

07 00 00
Thermal & Moisture Protection

Regal Wall Net and Insulweb

Regal Industries, Inc.
9564 E. County Rd. 600 S
Crothersville, IN 47229

Toll-free: 800-848-9687
Phone: 812-793-2214
Fax: 812-793-3432
www.regalind.com

Regal Industries offers two products that are stapled or glued to the interior face of stud framing to contain blown-in cellulose insulation prior to the installation of drywall. Regal Wall Insulweb is a clothlike product, while Regal Wall Net is a more expensive plastic netting. Glue is available either water-based latex by the gallon for warm weather, or solvent-based in a 5-gal. container for cold weather. The solvent-based adhesive has higher VOC emissions.

Most recently mentioned in EBN 3:1

EnviroPro, EnviroSmart, and Spray-On

Tascon, Inc.
7607 Fairview St.
P.O. Box 41846
Houston, TX 77241

Toll-free: 800-937-1774
Phone: 713-937-0900
Fax: 713-937-1496
www.tasconindustries.com

EnviroPro and EnviroSmart are residential insulation products for attic and wall applications. They are made from recycled paper and perform well to insulate and control sound. Spray-On, made from recycled paper, is applied to interior building walls and ceiling to insulate, prevent condensation, and control sound.

Most recently mentioned in EBN 3:1

Toc-Light

Therm-O-Comfort Co. Ltd.
75 S. Edgeware Rd.
St. Thomas, ON N5P 2H7 Canada

Toll-free: 877-684-3766
Phone: 519-631-3400
Fax: 519-631-9533

Therm-O-Comfort cellulose insulation is a fiberized product made of 100% recycled newspaper (80% post-industrial and 20% post-consumer) and boric acid/ammonium sulfate fire retardant. It is available in both loose fill and stabilized forms.

Most recently mentioned in EBN 2:5

Thermafiber Insulation Products

Thermafiber, Inc.

For full listing, see CSI section 07 21 29 - Sprayed Insulation

Weathershield

Thermo-Cell Industries, Ltd.
123 Clement Rd.
Vars, ON K0A 3H0 Canada

Toll-free: 800-267-1433
Fax: 613-837-5537
www.thermocell.com

Weathershield cellulose insulation contains 85% by weight recycled newspaper from a mix of post-consumer and post-industrial sources.

Mono-Therm

Thermo-Kool of Alaska
P.O. Box 230085
Anchorage, AK 99507

Phone: 907-563-3644
Fax: 907-561-2758

Mono-Therm insulation contains recycled newspaper.

Most recently mentioned in EBN 3:1

Fibre-Wool Cellulose

Tri-State Insulation Co.
1003 Valley View Dr.
Vermillion, SD 57069

Toll-free: 800-658-3531
Phone: 605-624-6405
Fax: 605-853-3022
www.tri-stateinsulation.com

Tri-State's Fibre-Wool cellulose insulation contains 100% recycled newspaper (minimum 80% post-consumer).

Cocoon Loose-Fill and Cocoon2 Stabilized Insulation

U.S. GreenFiber, LLC
2500 Distribution St.
Charlotte, NC 28203

Toll-free: 800-228-0024
Phone: 704-379-0644
Fax: 704-379-0685
www.us-gf.com

Cocoon® Loose-fill Insulation consists of 85% recycled paper fiber (at least 80% post-consumer paper content) that has been treated with borates to meet and exceed fire resistance requirements. Cocoon Insulation is blown into attics and is also used in retrofit sidewall applications. Cocoon2® products consist of 85% recycled paper fiber (at least 80% post-consumer paper content) and have an added adhesive for use in walls, attics, floors, ceilings, and other enclosed spaces.

Most recently mentioned in EBN 14:11 & 15:3

Walkote Mix II, Loose Fill, and Craftkote

Western Fibers, Inc.

For full listing, see CSI section 07 21 29 - Sprayed Insulation

07 21 29
Sprayed Insulation

Many insulation materials that are installed as loose-fill can also be sprayed when mixed with moisture or a binding agent. Some are sprayed into cavities and then covered, as with damp-spray cellulose, or fiberglass with a binder, while others are sprayed onto exposed surfaces. These applications are often effective at reducing air leakage, in addition to reducing conductive heat loss or gain. Installers must carefully manage the moisture content of damp-sprayed fiber products to ensure that they can dry quickly and avoid trapping moisture in building cavities. Products listed here have high recycled content and low-toxicity binders. (See feature article EBN Vol. 2, No. 5.)

Thermal-Pruf, Dendamix, and Sound-Pruf

American Sprayed Fibers, Inc.
P.O. Box 735
Crown Point, IN 46308

Toll-free: 800-824-2997
Phone: 219-690-0180
Fax: 219-690-01800
www.asfiusa.com

Thermal-Pruf™ is a blend of cellulose and premium rock wool insulation that can be spray-applied onto steel, aluminum, concrete, brick, block, or wood. In addition to achieving an R-value of 3.9/in., Thermal-Pruf also provides fireproofing and acoustical insulation. It can be applied to exterior as well as interior locations and be left textured, rolled to a smooth finish, or overcoated with approved weather-coating systems. American Sprayed Fibers also offers two additional spray-on systems that provide thermal insulation: Dendamix™, made specifically for fireproofing, and Sound-Pruf™ for soundproofing.

Applegate Loosefill and Stabilized Cellulose Insulation

Applegate Insulation Manufacturing
1000 Highview Dr.
Webberville, MI 48892

Toll-free: 800-627-7536
Phone: 517-521-3545
Fax: 517-521-3597
www.applegateinsulation.com

Applegate insulation is made from recycled paper.

Most recently mentioned in EBN 2:5

Fiberiffic 2000

Ark-Seal
2185 S. Jason St.
Denver, CO 80223

Toll-free: 800-525-8992
Phone: 303-934-7772
Fax: 303-934-2177
www.fiberiffic.com

Ark-Seal manufactures the Fiberiffic® 2000 spray equipment and supplies the latex binder to spray-on loose-fill insulation (cellulose is the greenest option) with a latex foam binder similar in composition to interior latex paint. This product contains no HCFCs. It can be troweled to a smooth surface or used in blown-in applications. R-values range from 4/in. with fiberglass to 3.6/in. with cellulose, to 3.5/in. with rockwool and cotton. It can be painted, waterproofed, or coated with stucco.

Cellulose Insulation

Can-Cell Industries, Inc.

For full listing, see CSI section 07 21 23 - Loose-Fill Insulation

Climatizer Plus and Enviro-Batt

Climatizer Insulation, Ltd.
120 Claireville Dr.
Etobicoke, ON M9W 5Y3 Canada

Toll-free: 866-871-5495
Phone: 416-798-1235
Fax: 416-798-1311
www.climatizer.com

Climatizer Plus thermal and acoustical cellulose insulation contains recycled newspaper. It may be hand-poured or pneumatically placed with a blowing machine and delivery

hose. Enviro-Batt™ contains less than 2% formaldehyde-free, no-VOC adhesive activated by a very small amount of water during pneumatic installation; moisture-loading is only 20% of that experienced with typical wet-cellulose applications. Both products contain at least 85% post-consumer recycled paper fibers.

Recycled-Content Cellulose Insulation

Fiberlite Technologies, Inc.

For full listing, see CSI section 07 21 23 - Loose-Fill Insulation

K-13 and SonaSpray "fc" Insulation

International Cellulose Corporation
12315 Robin Blvd.
P.O. Box 450006
Houston, TX 77245

Toll-free: 800-979-4914
Phone: 713-433-6701
Fax: 713-433-2029
www.spray-on.com

K-13 is designed for surface-spray applications. It gives a rough finish and can be applied up to 5" thick. SonaSpray® "fc" gives a finished ceiling and can be applied 1" thick. Fire resistance is obtained by adding Borax. Both products, made from recycled ONP, OCC, and other papers, are available in standard colors or custom tints. K-13 has an insulation R-value of 3.8 per inch. SonaSpray "fc" has an NRC (noise reduction) of 0.65 at 1/2" and 0.90 at 1".

Monoglass Spray-On Insulation

Monoglass, Inc.
922 - 1200 West 73rd Avenue
Vancouver, BC V6P 6G5 Canada

Toll-free: 888-777-2966
Phone: 604-261-7712
Fax: 604-261-1342
www.monoglass.com

Monoglass® Spray-On Insulation is a combination of elongated, recycled-cullet glass fibers and water-based, nontoxic adhesives that can be spray-applied to virtually any surface or configuration. Without additional support, Monoglass can be applied overhead to a maximum of 5" (R-20) and applied vertically to 7" (R-28). Monoglass is white in color, noncombustible, and can be applied over fireproofing. Monoglass contains no formaldehyde and does not support fungal growth or encourage infestation by pests.

Nu-Wool Engineered Cellulose Insulation

Nu-Wool Co., Inc.
2472 Port Sheldon St.
Jenison, MI 49428

Toll-free: 800-748-0128
Phone: 616-669-0100
Fax: 616-669-2370
www.nuwool.com

Nu-Wool cellulose insulation is made from recycled newspaper and contains an EPA Registered fungicide making it resistant to mold growth.

Most recently mentioned in EBN 3:1

EnviroPro, EnviroSmart, and Spray-On

Tascon, Inc.

For full listing, see CSI section 07 21 23 - Loose-Fill Insulation

Thermafiber Insulation Products

Thermafiber, Inc.
3711 W. Mill St.
Wabash, IN 46992

Toll-free: 888-834-2371
Phone: 260-563-2111
Fax: 800-294-7076
www.thermafiber.com

Thermafiber Firespan, Safing Insulation, Curtain Wall Insulation, FS15, FS25, and Sound Attenuation Fire Blankets (SAFBs), are mineral-fiber insulation products manufactured with high proportions of slag (80.6% post-industrial recycled content). The products come in a wide variety of densities, facings, thicknesses, and R-values, as rigid or blanket material. These products have been evaluated by an independent testing facility for low pollutant emissions. ThermaTech products, according to the manufacturer, contain no added chemical fire retardants, are noncombustible, odor-free, will not absorb moisture or support mildew or fungus, and will not rot or decay. Phenolic resin content is less than 5% by weight.

**07 00 00
Thermal &
Moisture
Protection**

Attic Insulation and Wall Cavity Spray

ThermoCon Manufacturing / Applegate Inc.
2500 Jackson St.
Monroe, LA 71202

Toll-free: 800-854-1907
Phone: 318-323-1337
Fax: 318-323-1338
www.thermocon.com

Attic Insulation and Wall Cavity Spray are cellulose insulations made from recycled newspaper.

Most recently mentioned in EBN 2:5

Isolite, Thermalite, and Isopro

Thermoguard Co.
125 N. Dyer Rd.
Spokane, WA 99212

Toll-free: 800-541-0579
Phone: 509-535-4600
Fax: 509-535-8519
www.service-partners.com

Thermoguard offers a loose-fill cellulose insulation and two different spray-on adhesive insulations, one with a mesh backing. Both are designed for wet-spray installation. Thermoguard is UL-approved. Thermoguard insulation contains recycled newspaper.

Most recently mentioned in EBN 3:1

Walkote Mix II, Loose Fill, and Craftkote

Western Fibers, Inc.
1601 E. Broadway
Hollis, OK 73550

Phone: 580-688-9223
Fax: 580-688-2766
www.westernfibers.com

Walkote Mix II, Loose Fill, and Craftkote cellulose insulation products contain recycled newspaper and cardboard.

07 21 30 Radiant Barriers

07 00 00 Thermal & Moisture Protection

When they face a heat source, radiant barriers work by reflecting heat. When faced away from a heat source, radiant barriers function primarily by virtue of their low emissivity, which reduces the amount of heat that radiates from them. Radiant barrier products can be foil-faced kraft paper, foil-faced polyethylene film, foil facings on rigid insulation or wood-fiber sheathing, or aluminized paints. If the radiant surface is touching another material it won't work—an air space is required on at least one side of a radiant barrier in order for it to function as designed. Radiant barriers in attics are most beneficial in reducing cooling loads; their effectiveness in reducing heating loads is more limited. Radiant barrier products usually do not include significant recycled content, because of the lower reflectivity

of recycled aluminum and the difficulty in producing very thin foils from recycled aluminum; the high embodied energy of virgin aluminum can be recovered through energy savings. Products listed here have below average emissivity (which corresponds to the highest reflectivity), recycled-content in non-aluminum components of the product, or low VOC levels in the case of paints. A word of caution: Do not rely on blanket "effective" or "equivalent" R-values; they are only relevant in certain climates or under certain conditions. (See also 06 16 13 - Insulating Sheathing.)

The Insulator

Bonded Logic, Inc.

For full listing, see CSI section 09 81 16 - Acoustic Blanket Insulation

Low-E Insulation

Environmentally Safe Products, Inc.
313 W. Golden Ln.
New Oxford, PA 17350

Toll-free: 800-289-5693
Phone: 717-624-3581
Fax: 717-624-7089
www.low-e.com

Low-E Insulation has a core of microcell polyethylene foam insulation, which has 40% recycled content, and facings of polished aluminum foil. The product is reported to reflect 97% of the radiant energy that strikes its surfaces. Based on the direction of heat flow, the company claims the following insulation performance (ASTM C-236) for the 1/4" version: down, R-10.74; up, R-7.55; and horizontal, R-7.75.

Most recently mentioned in EBN 4:1 & 14:1

Fi-Foil Radiant Barriers

Fi-Foil Company, Inc.   **New**
612 Bridgers Ave. W.
P.O. Box 800
Auburndale, FL 33823

Toll-free: 800-448-3401
Phone: 863-965-1846
Fax: 863-967-0137
www.fifoil.com

Fi-Foil produces a number of low- and high-perm radiant sheet barrier products using metalized polyethylene films, recycled paper materials, and PVA hot-melt adhesives. Some products contain metalized PVC backings; those are not specified here. Applications include wood, metal, and masonry wall, roof, and floor systems.

Astro-Foil

Innovative Energy
10653 W. 181 Ave.
Lowell, IN 46356

Toll-free: 800-776-3645
Phone: 219-696-3639
Fax: 800-551-3645
www.insul.net

Astro-Foil has two layers of polyethylene film with air bubbles sandwiched between layers of reflective aluminum foil. The company claims the following insulation performance, based on ASTM C-236 Hot Box testing procedures, depending on the direction of heatflow: down, R-15; up, R-5.4; and horizontal, R-7.3.

K Shield Reflective Barrier

Key Solutions Marketing
7529 E. Woodshire CV
Scottsdale, AZ 85258

Toll-free: 800-776-9765
Phone: 480-948-5150
Fax: 602-951-6811
www.paintwithceramic.com

The K Shield Reflective Barrier is made from aluminum-foil facings with a core of either 100# kraft paper or plastic film. Available in 500 and 1,000 ft² rolls, 25-1/2" and 51" wide.

Reflectix

Reflectix, Inc.
1 School St.
P.O. Box 108
Markleville, IN 46056

Toll-free: 800-879-3645
Phone: 765-533-4332
Fax: 765-533-2327
www.reflectixinc.com

Reflectix combines an aluminum-foil facing with bubble-wrap packaging to form a 5/16"-thick insulating radiant barrier. Reflectix comes in various roll widths and lengths.

Reflectix Foil/Bubble Insulation

Reflectix, Inc.
1 School St.
P.O. Box 108
Markleville, IN 46056

Toll-free: 800-879-3645
Phone: 765-533-4332
Fax: 765-533-2327
www.reflectixinc.com

Reflectix® reflective-foil, air-cellular insulation consists of one or two layers of air-cellular material laminated between layers of aluminum foil. The company claims up to 97% radiant heat reflection for this insulation. Reflectix insulation is a Class A/Class 1 fire-retardant product. Reflectix, Inc. is a subsidiary of Sealed Air Corp.

F-2, FSKF, and Type 4, 5, & 6

Superior Radiant Insulation
P.O. Box 247
San Dimas, CA 91773

Toll-free: 888-774-4422
Phone: 909-305-1450
Fax: 909-305-1448
www.superiorrb.com

Superior Radiant Insulation manufactures several radiant barrier and insulation products. F-2 is 100-lb. kraft paper-faced with foil on both sides. Similarly, FSKF has two foil facings on 30-lb. kraft with a nylon or fiberglass mesh scrim layer. Type 4, 5, and 6 are multilayer radiant barriers with chipboard stapling flanges for use in 2x4 and 2x6 framing. Superior Radiant Insulation also manufactures an aluminum foil-faced OSB or plywood sheathing.

07 22 17
Insulation Baffles

In vented roof and attic assemblies, insulation baffles ensure that a properly sized cavity is maintained between the top of the insulation and the roof decking. Proper ventilation in attics and roofs is essential to maintaining insulation performance unless other measures have been taken to prevent heat-transfer moisture problems. Insulation performance suffers when moisture, trapped under the roof sheathing, condenses on the insulation below, and escaping heat can cause ice-damming. The highly conductive nature of water renders wet insulation much less effective—and wet insulation can also result in rotting wood framing members and mold growth. Insulation baffles can be made from corrugated cardboard with sizing, foam, or plastic. Products listed here have recycled content and avoid extruded polystyrene produced with HCFC blowing agents.

DUROVENT and proVent

ADO Products
21800 129th Ave. N
P.O. Box 236
Rogers, MN 55374

Toll-free: 866-240-4933
Phone: 763-428-7802
Fax: 763-428-7806
www.adoproducts.com

Durovent is made from EPS foam with up to 40% recycled content; proVent is made from polystyrene plastic and has up to 80% recycled content. Both products are 48" long and available for 16" and 24" rafter spacings. Durovent is for new construction, while proVent is designed for remodeling applications. The thinner profile of proVent allows this product to be shipped more compactly, and its greater durability results in less breakage and other damage than occurs with EPS foam.

Perma-Vent

Cellofoam North America, Inc.
1917 Rockdale Industrial Blvd.
P.O. Box 406
Conyers, GA 30012

Toll-free: 800-241-3634
Phone: 770-929-3688
Fax: 770-929-3608
www.cellofoam.com

Perma-Vent is an EPS foam insulation baffle for 16" and 24" on-center rafter bays. This product is not known to contain recycled polystyrene.

StyroVent

DiversiFoam Products
9091 County Rd. 50
P.O. Box 44
Rockford, MN 55373

Toll-free: 800-669-0100
Phone: 763-477-5854
Fax: 763-477-5863
www.diversifoam.com

StyroVent Attic Ventilation Chute, made from RayLite brand EPS, comes in two sizes: StyroVent Mini is for 16" on-center construction and measures 15" W x 2-1/4" D x 48" L; StyroVent Maxi, for 24" on-center construction, measures 23-1/4" W x 2-1/2" D x 48" L.

Insul-Tray

Insulation Solutions, Inc.
401 Truck Haven Rd.
East Peoria, IL 61611

Toll-free: 866-698-6562
Phone: 309-698-0062
Fax: 309-698-0065
www.insulationsolutions.com

Insul-Tray insulation baffles are made from 100% recycled-content corrugated cardboard with or without a radiant-barrier foil facing for 16" and 24" on-center rafter bays and wall cavities. The radiant barrier reduces heat gain and heat loss through the roof as long as the baffles have an air space next to them.

PermaVent Attic Baffle

Perma "R" Products
2064 Sunset Dr.
P.O. Box 279
Grenada, MS 38902

Toll-free: 800-647-6130
Phone: 662-226-8075
Fax: 601-226-8088
www.leclairindustries.com

PermaVent Attic Baffles are insulation baffles for 16" and 24" on-center rafter bays. The product measures 3/8" x 22" x 48" for 24" o.c. rafters; break along center perforations for 16" o.c. installations.

Attic Vents Chutes

Plymouth Foam Incorporated
1800 Sunset Dr.
Plymouth, WI 53073

Toll-free: 800-669-1176
Phone: 920-893-0535
Fax: 920-892-4986
www.plymouthfoam.com

Attic Vents Chutes are insulation baffles made from EPS foam for 16" and 24" on-center rafter bays. They are not known to contain recycled polystyrene. Plymouth Foam operates manufacturing plants in Plymouth, Wisconsin; Becker, Minnesota; and Newcomerstown, Ohio.

TuffVENT and BaffleVENT

Weidmann Electrical Technology, Inc.
One Gordon Mills Way
St. Johnsbury, VT 05819

Phone: 800-242-6748
www.weidmann-industrial.com

**07 00 00
Thermal &
Moisture
Protection**

TuffVENT is made from 100% unbleached post-industrial recycled paper fibers (from box clippings), with a mild sizing agent added for moisture resistance. Appropriate for new construction and remodeling, the sturdy, recyclable material resists staple blow-through, ripping, and damage, but cuts easily to accommodate pipes and conduits. TuffVENT provides a 2" air-channel depth, and is available for 16" or 24" on-center rafters, in 43" or 120" lengths. BaffleVENT is a similar product (16" o.c. only) with an integrated baffle that extends from the roof decking past the top plate, preventing blown-in insulation from blocking the soffit.

07 25 00
Weather Barriers

Weather barriers form a secondary drainage plane (the first in most cases being the exterior cladding) to assist in keeping assembly components to the interior protected from bulk water. Note that the vapor permeability of concealed weather barrier products can vary widely and the desirability of low or high or no vapor permeability is always in the context of the primary direction of wetting, the primary direction of drying, and the vapor permeability of all the other components in the assembly. Products listed here contribute to durability (generally by creating an air space) and/or reduce the potential for indoor air quality problems associated with moisture and mold.

Home Slicker

Benjamin Obdyke Inc.
199 Precision Dr.
Horsham, PA 19044

Toll-free: 800-523-5261
Phone: 215-672-7200
Fax: 215-672-3731
www.benjaminobdyke.com

Home Slicker® is a ventilating and self-draining rainscreen for use under siding, which provides a thermal break and moisture protection for sidewalls. Home Slicker's 3-dimensional, 0.25"-thick matrix provides a continuous space for drying, drainage, and pressure equalization. For use under sidings such as wood, fiber-cement, EIFS, brick, and vinyl, Home Slicker comes with a 50-year limited warranty.

Delta-MS and Delta-Dry

Cosella Dörken Products Inc.
4655 Delta Way
Beamville, ON L0R 1B4 Canada

Toll-free: 888-433-5824
Phone: 905-563-3255
Fax: 905-563-5582
www.deltams.com

Delta-Dry is a stiff, egg-carton-textured, 5/16"-thick, vapor-impermeable housewrap made with 22-mil, virgin HDPE. When properly installed, the weather-resistive barrier creates a ventilated rainscreen, while blocking moisture migration through the wall assembly. Similarly, Delta-MS for subsurface use is an air-gap membrane constructed from 6 mm-thick HDPE, with a pattern of dimples molded into the surface. When installed, the membrane is held off the wall to allow any moisture in the concrete to migrate to the outer surface, condense on the inside surface of the membrane, and flow into the foundation drain. Because HDPE is impervious, soil moisture is unable to penetrate but will also flow to the foundation drain.

Most recently mentioned in EBN 15:11

Construction Film

Gempak
9611 James Ave. S
Bloomington, MN 55431

Toll-free: 800-328-4556
Phone: 952-881-8673
Fax: 952-881-9617

Gempak, formerly Strout Plastics, manufactures construction film that generally contains 100% recycled LDPE. With some production runs, contamination of recycled materials necessitates the addition of virgin resins to produce a quality product.

07 26 00
Vapor Retarders

Vapor retarders are generally sheet goods added to either the interior (cold climates) or exterior (hot and particularly hot humid climates) to restrict moisture moving by diffusion into wall, roof and foundation assemblies. Products listed here usually have superior performance in terms of variable vapor permeability based on their water content. Note that the placement of vapor retarders should always be done in the context of the vapor permeabilities of all the other components of the assembly and their vapor permeability, and the designated direction for drying of the assembly.

MemBrain Smart Vapor Retarder

CertainTeed Corporation
750 E. Swedesford Rd.
P.O. Box 860
Valley Forge, PA 19482

Toll-free: 800-233-8990
Phone: 610-341-7000
Fax: 610-341-7777
www.certainteed.com

MemBrain™ Smart Vapor Retarder is made from a transparent polyamide-based (Nylon-6) material, which changes permeability according to relative humidity and can increase the drying potential of closed building envelope systems. The 2-mil-thick, high-tensile-strength sheeting is as strong as a 6-mil sheet of polyethylene. Its moisture permeability varies from less than 1 perm at low relative humidity to more than 20 perms at high (95%) relative humidity. MemBrain is intended for use in heating and mixed climates, and is not suitable for cooling climates with high outdoor humidity or in buildings with high constant indoor relative humidity. Interior finish materials and cavity-fill insulation must also be highly permeable.

Most recently mentioned in EBN 12:7, 12:11, 13:3

07 27 00
Air Barriers

Products listed here are designed to limit air infiltration through discontinuities in the building envelope.

Fireplace DraftStopper

Battic Door Energy Conservation Products
P.O. Box 15
Mansfield, MA 02048

Phone: 508-320-9082
Fax: 508-339-4571
www.batticdoor.com

The Fireplace DraftStopper™ is an inflatable urethane pillow that is installed beneath the fireplace damper to stop drafts that occur even when the damper is shut. After installation, the filling tube hangs down into the fireplace with an orange warning label to prevent fires from being lit when the unit is installed. Significant energy savings can be achieved, up to 30% according to the manufacturer. Available in 2 sizes to fit any masonry fireplace with a rectangular damper (Large) or any metal or zero-clearance fireplace with a round damper (Small).

07 00 00
Thermal & Moisture Protection

The Battic Door Attic Stair Cover

Battic Door Energy Conservation Products
P.O. Box 15
Mansfield, MA 02048

Phone: 508-320-9082
Fax: 508-339-4571
www.batticdoor.com

The Battic Door is a simple and inexpensive product for weatherstripping attic hatches that have folding stairways. Essentially a heavy-duty cardboard box that embeds itself into foam weatherstripping installed on the top of the stairway frame, the unit allows easy access to the attic, while providing an airtight seal when dropped into place. Available in two sizes to fit 22" to 22-1/2" x 54" as well as 25" to 25-1/2" x 54" rough openings. A reflective insulation kit (R-7) and an encapsulated-fiberglass slip-on insulation kit (R-50) are also available.

The Energy Guardian

ESS Energy Products, Inc.
P.O. Box 400
Paoli, PA 19301

Phone: 610-993-9585
Fax: 610-640-1378
www.energysentrysolutions.com

Made from high-density EPS, The Energy Guardian™ is an insulating and air-sealing cover for attic hatches and pull-down ladders. These patent-pending units consist of a frame and a snug-fitting lid, which is simply put aside and then put in place again when entering and exiting the attic. The ladder-cover version fits any opening less than 35" x 63" and allows 7-1/2" clearance for a folded ladder. A second frame can be added for 16-1/2" total clearance. The attic hatch cover is designed to fit any opening measuring less than 28" x 32". For areas with little clearance, a 2" frame is available for 7" of total clearance; a 10" frame allows 15" of clearance. The manufacturer claims an R-value of 30 and offers a lifetime warranty. Significant energy savings can be achieved.

Energy Block

Pine Ridge Builders
613 2nd St. NE
Jamestown, ND 58401

Phone: 701-320-1111
www.energyblock.com

Energy Block is a 1.5 pound-density EPS block of foam insulation molded to fit tightly around electrical boxes, providing an air barrier around and behind. Installation with latex caulk can be quickly accomplished

without electricians. Energy Blocks are available in three sizes—for single boxes, multiple gang (up to 4), and a block for ceiling fixtures.

07 31 16
Metal Shingles

Metals are readily recyclable, and certain metal roofing products also have high recycled content. These products can be a part of a long-lasting roof when installed with appropriate fasteners and proper flashing. The use of dissimilar metals for roofing, flashing, and fastening isn't recommended because they're susceptible to galvanic corrosion in the presence of water. Metal is also a preferred material for roofs used in rainwater catchment systems. In northern climates, snow readily slides off metal roofs, avoiding the damage caused by ice dams. (See also 07 41 13 - Metal Roof Panels.)

Rustic Shingle

Classic Metal Roofing Systems
8510 Industry Park Dr.
P.O. Box 701
Piqua, OH 45356

Toll-free: 800-543-8938
Phone: 937-773-9840
Fax: 937-778-5116
www.classicroof.com

Rustic Shingle is made from an alloy with recycled-aluminum content (mostly beverage cans). The shingles are formed to resemble wood shakes and finished with a baked-on Kynar coating. The Rustic Shingle System consists of 12" x 24" interconnecting panels and matching preformed accessories. The shingles are available in 11 colors.

Most recently mentioned in EBN 4:4

MetalWorks Steel Shingles

Tamko Roofing Products, Inc.
220 W. 4th St.
P.O. Box 1404
Joplin, MO 64801

Toll-free: 800-641-4691
Fax: 417-624-8935
www.metalworksroof.com

MetalWorks (formerly AstonWood) Steel Shingles from Tamko are made from as much as 50% recycled material. The shingles consist of G90 galvanized steel with a Kynar 500® or Hylar 5000® coating. These wood and slate shingle look-alike products

are 12" x 40" and interconnect on all four sides. Shingles are available in a variety of colors. Because of their light weight, these steel shingles can be installed over two existing layers of asphalt shingles. MetalWorks shingles carry a 50 year warranty.

Recycled-Metal Shingles

Zappone Manufacturing
2928 N. Pittsburg St.
Spokane, WA 99207

Toll-free: 800-285-2677
Phone: 509-483-6408
Fax: 509-483-8050
www.zappone.com

Zappone shingles are made from either recycled copper or aluminum. Both products contain a concealed nailing flange and a four-way interlocking mechanism. Shingles measure 9-1/8" x 15" with an 8" x 14-1/2" exposure. Aluminum shingles have a Kynar 500 finish in a choice of 6 colors. Recycled aluminum fasteners and accessories are also available. The manufacturer has certified the following recycled-content levels for copper shingles (by weight): total recovered material 85% typical, 85% guaranteed; post-consumer material 75% typical, 75% guaranteed. The manufacturer has certified the following recycled-content levels for aluminum shingles (by weight): total recovered material 100% typical, 100% guaranteed; post-consumer material 100% typical, 100% guaranteed.

07 31 19
Mineral-Fiber Cement Shingles

Fiber-cement building materials earn green points for their durability. The new generation of fiber-cement doesn't contain asbestos; it's made from portland cement, sand, clay, and wood fiber. Environmental concerns with fiber-cement include the embodied energy of portland cement and the source of the wood fiber—some fiber-cement products use wood from such distant locations as New Zealand and Russia. Although newer fiber-cement products are not yet proven over the long haul, the material is quite stable and typically carries a 50-year warranty. Of particular concern with roof shingle products in cold climates are the effects of freeze-thaw cycling; some products have coatings or polymer constituents to minimize water absorption.

07 00 00
Thermal & Moisture Protection

FireFree Naturals

Re-Con Building Products, Inc.
4850 SW Scholls Ferry Rd, Ste 203
Portland, OR 97225

Toll-free: 877-276-7663
Phone: 604-850-7353
www.naturalsroofing.com

FireFree Naturals™ roofing is a polymer-modified fiber-cement product available in Rustic Shake™ or Quarry Slate™ styles. Both products have high recycled content. Rustic Shake is available in three colors; Quarry Slate is available in six colors. These products are Class A fire-rated, Class IV hail-rated, and backed by a 50-year warranty.

Most recently mentioned in EBN 4:4

07 31 26
Slate Shingles

Natural slate roofing is an excellent product from an environmental standpoint. Besides being a minimally processed material, slate also has superb durability: properly installed slate roofs last 70 to 100 or more years with only minor maintenance. Additionally, slates can easily be salvaged and reused on new building projects. However, they are heavy—proximity to slate quarries and adequately strong roof structures must be considered. Some recycled-plastic shingles are manufactured to look like slate shingles.

Salvaged Slate and Clay Tile Roofing

Alluvium Construction
200 Lake Shore Dr.
Marlton, NJ 08053

Phone: 856-767-2700
Fax: 856-768-7766
www.historicroofs.com

Alluvium Construction specializes in reclaimed slate and tile roofing in all quantities, types, and colors. Domestic or imported new slate may also be ordered. If purchasing new slate, domestic slate from nearby quarries is recommended.

Reclaimed Natural Salvaged Slate and Clay Tile Roofing

Durable Slate Co.
1050 N. Fourth St.
Columbus, OH 43201

Toll-free: 800-666-7445
Phone: 614-299-5522
Fax: 614-299-7100
www.durableslate.com

Durable Slate Co. stocks well over 600,000 pieces of salvaged slate and 400,000 pieces of salvaged clay tiles. Durable Slate is able to match colors and styles of slate and tile that are no longer produced.

Salvaged Slate Roofing

Echeguren Slate
1495 Illinois St.
San Francisco, CA 94107

Phone: 415-206-9343
Fax: 415-206-9353
www.echeguren.com

Echeguren Slate offers salvaged roofing slate in sizes from 8" x 12" to 12" x 24" and in thicknesses of 3/16" to 3/4". Domestic or imported new slate for roofing and flooring may also be ordered. If purchasing new slate, domestic slate from nearby quarries is recommended.

Salvaged Slate and Clay Tile Roofing

Emack Slate Company, Inc.
9 Office Park Cir., Ste. 120
Birmingham, AL 35223

Phone: 205-879-3424
Fax: 205-879-5420
www.emackslate.com

Emack Slate maintains an inventory of salvaged slate and clay tiles. Domestic or imported new slate may also be ordered. If purchasing new slate, domestic slate from nearby quarries is recommended.

Slate Roofing Shingles

Hilltop Slate Inc.
Rte. 22A
P.O. Box 201
Middle Granville, NY 12804

Phone: 518-642-2270
Fax: 518 642 1220
www.hilltopslate.com

Hilltop Slate, in business since 1948, is a producer of slate roofing shingles with six quarries in New York and Vermont. Hilltop Slate is part of the Slate Products division of the Alfred McAlpine Group and a sister company to Penrhyn, the largest producer of slate products in the world.

Nu-Lok Slate Roofing System

Nu-Lok Roofing Systems
711 S. Carson St., Ste. 4
Carson City, NV 89701

Toll-free: 800-946-8565
Phone: 802-287-9701
Fax: 802-287-5720
www.nu-lok.com

The Nu-Lok roofing system is a stainless-steel framework of battens, channels, and clips that holds natural slate or ceramic tile in place, reducing the amount of material needed for roofing installations. The system reduces the weight of the roof, reduces material use, and increases installation options while reducing labor costs. The system comes with a 50-year warranty and, according to the manufacturer, permits installation and repair of slate by standard roofing crews. The system is available with GreenStone Slate from a Vermont slate quarrier.

Salvaged Slate and Clay Tile Roofing

Reclaimed Roofs, Inc.
7454 Lancaster Pike #328
Hockessin, DE 19707

Phone: 302-369-9187
Fax: 302-397-2742
www.reclaimedroofs.com

Reclaimed Roofs provides salvaged roofing slates and tiles. Its owner sits on the Board of Directors for the National Slate Association.

Salvaged Slate and Clay Tile Roofing

Renaissance Roofing, Inc.

For full listing, see CSI section 07 32 13 - Clay Roof Tiles

Salvaged Slate and Clay Tile Roofing

The Roof Tile and Slate Company

For full listing, see CSI section 07 32 13 - Clay Roof Tiles

Slate Roofing Shingles

Vermont Structural Slate Co., Inc.
3 Prospect St.
P.O. Box 98
Fair Haven, VT 05743

Toll-free: 800-343-1900
Phone: 802-265-4933
Fax: 802-265-3865
www.vermontstructuralslate.com

07 00 00
Thermal & Moisture Protection

Vermont Structural Slate has been a producer of slate products since 1859. The company offers roofing shingles in several colors from their Vermont quarries as well as select top quality stones from around the world.

Slate Roofing Shingles

Virginia Slate Company
2471 Goodes Bridge Rd.
Richmond, VA 23224

Toll-free: 888-827-5283
Phone: 804-745-4100
Fax: 804-377-2545
www.virginiaslate.com

The Virginia Slate Company has been producing slate roofing shingles from its Buckingham County quarry since 1860. Slate can be purchased directly from their own quarry. Virginia Slate also offers slate from other producers in a variety of color choices. Their premium roofing slate carries a 100-year limited warranty.

07 31 29
Wood Shingles and Shakes

Wood shingles and shakes are traditionally and most commonly made from old-growth western red cedar. Although the embodied energy of this product is quite low, the harvesting of western red cedar is, in most cases, unsustainable. If a wood shingle roof is desired and fire-related concerns aren't prohibitive, using certified eastern white cedar shingles, commonly used as wall siding, is an option. Some recycled-plastic shingles are manufactured to look like wood shingles. (See feature article EBN Vol. 6, No. 7.)

Reclaimed-Wood Lumber and Products

A Reclaimed Lumber Co.
For full listing, see CSI section 06 22 02 - Reclaimed-Wood Millwork

Certified PR Shingles

Industries Maibec, Inc.
660 Lenoir St.
Sainte-Foy, QC G1X 3W3 Canada

Toll-free: 800-363-1930
Phone: 418-659-3323
Fax: 418-653-4354
www.maibec.com

PR® Shingles are made from eastern white cedar from the Seven Islands Land Company that is chain-of-custody certified by SCS.

Shingles are available in three options: unfinished (natural); kiln-dried and factory-stained in gray, beige, or an unlimited choice of colors; and factory-treated with an oil finish. While most commonly used on walls, they may be appropriate in some roofing applications if installed more thickly.
Most recently mentioned in EBN 3:6 & 6:7

07 31 33
Plastic and Rubber Shingles

Plastic roofing products, like plastic lumber, provide a use for plastics in the solid-waste stream. Products included here appear very durable, but as with plastic lumber, the long-term effects of UV light, and expansion and contraction of the material, are still unknown. Some of these products carry 50-year warranties—longer than those of asphalt shingles. Another environmental benefit of some of these products is their end-of-life recyclability. Rubber roofing shingles and tiles can provide exceptional durability without adding a lot of weight to the roof. Some products made from crumb rubber may use environmentally questionable binders.

Authentic Roof FR

Crowe Building Products Ltd.
116 Burris St.
Hamilton, ON L8M 2J5 Canada

Phone: 905-529-6818
Fax: 905-529-1755
www.authentic-roof.com

Authentic Roof™ was the first slate-look recycled polymer and rubber roofing material. This product's weight is only 25% that of slate and installs quickly. Authentic Roof FR is produced using a proprietary thermoplastic olefin (TPO) and is available in a choice of 5 colors and 3 slate patterns: full, mitered-edge, and beavertail. Authentic shingles have UL Class A, B, or C fire rating; Class 4 hail; pass 110 MPH wind tunnel; and carry a 50-year limited warranty.
Most recently mentioned in EBN 9:5

Majestic Slate Tiles

EcoStar
P.O. Box 7000
Carlisle, PA 17013

Toll-free: 800-211-7170
Fax: 888-780-9870
www.ecostar.carlisle.com

Majestic Slate Tiles are 98% post-industrial recycled and recyclable, lightweight shingles made from industrial rubber and plastics. The coloration of Majestic Slate varies slightly, imitating differences in color of natural slate. Preformed ridge slates are also available. EcoStar is a division of Carlisle SynTec, Inc.
Most recently mentioned in EBN 9:5

EuroSlate and EuroShake

GEM, Inc.
9330 48 St. SE
Calgary, AB T2C 2R2 Canada

Phone: 403-215-3333
Fax: 403-287-2012
www.euroslate.ca

EuroSlate and EuroShake are interlocking roofing systems with the look of slate tiles and cedar shakes. They are made with 60-70% recycled tire crumb rubber, plus another 15% of a recycled component that the manufacturer will not divulge. The materials are heat-formed with a binder, also proprietary. The system is lightweight (under 4 lbs/ft²) and recyclable, and the manufacturer is in the process of obtaining Class A fire-resistance certification at this writing. Available colors for EuroSlate include black, slate grey, copper, dark brown, leather, and terra cotta and for EuroShake colors include weathered, black, grey, and redwood. Colors are integral, so those other than black may reduce the overall recycled content of the product. A licensed installer is required. The manufacturer indicates that installation time is significantly reduced over more common options.

Infinity Roof System

Inteq Corp.
35800 Glen Dr.
Eastlake, OH 44095

Phone: 440-953-0550
Fax: 440-953-0564
www.4-inteqcorp.com

Inteq Corp. manufactures the Infinity Roof System in simulated slate, wood shake, and terra cotta tile profiles from recycled HDPE. All three styles have uniform color throughout and come with a 50-year warranty. Slate and wood shake styles have a UL Class A fire rating; Terra Cotta style are rated Class C. Recycled content is 60% pre-consumer, with up to 15% post-consumer content available.

**07 00 00
Thermal & Moisture Protection**

Mooroof Recycled-Tire Roofing

New

Moore Enviro Systems
Box 1459
Squamish, BC V0N 3G0 Canada

Phone: 604-898-5683

Mooroof roof tiles are made of post-consumer recycled tire rubber treads. The sidewalls are removed during the manufacturing process; the tread is installed as roofing tiles with screws, either inside-out or tread-side-up. The tiles, which can be painted if desired, have a class C fire rating and a 50-year warranty.

Most recently mentioned in EBN 4:4

Ny-Slate

NYCORE
200 Galleria Pkwy., Ste. 2000
Atlanta, GA 30339

Phone: 770-980-0000
www.nycore.com

Ny-Slate, made from 100% recycled post-consumer carpet, is a lightweight, mold- and bacteria-resistant replacement for slate, tile, cedar, or asphalt roofing. The proprietary manufacturing process generates a durable, extruded material that can be cut with standard saws, screwed, nailed, glued, and painted. It doesn't rot, deteriorate, or support mold or insects. According to the manufacturer, no waste is generated in the manufacturing process, and the product is recyclable. A 50-year manufacturer's warranty is offered. Considerations may include thermal expansion and cold-weather brittleness.

Most recently mentioned in EBN 6:6 & 9:5

Eco-shake

Re-New Wood, Inc.
104 N.W. Eighth St.
P.O. Box 1093
Wagoner, OK 74467

Toll-free: 800-420-7576
Phone: 918-485-5803
Fax: 918-485-1097
www.renewwood.com

Eco-shake® is a roofing shingle made from post-industrial recycled PVC (recycled content varies due to market availability) and 100% reclaimed wood fibers. The product has the look of a wood shake and is available in three standard colors: umber, teak, and charcoal. Custom colors are also available.

Most recently mentioned in EBN 5:3 & 9:5

07 00 00
Thermal & Moisture Protection

RoofRoc Synthetic Slate

New

RoofRoc Canada Ltd.
19483 Fraser Way
Pitt Meadows, BC V3Y 2V4 Canada

Toll-free: 877-465-5177
Phone: 604-465-5177
www.roofroc.com

RoofRoc is a roofing tile made with 15 – 20% post-consumer recycled HDPE and 80% calcium carbonate (limestone). Closely resembling natural slate in appearance and feel but with only one-third the weight (about 5.75 lbs/sf), it carries a Class A Fire Rating and a 50-year warranty. Its integral colors—black, grey, green, or brown—vary slightly, like natural slate. The standard tiles are approximately 10" x 16" inches, with four profiles to provide a random look. Hip and ridge caps are 5" x 16", with a beveled edge.

Enviroshake

Wellington Polymer Technology Inc.
650 Riverview Dr., Unit #1
P.O. Box 1462
Chatham, ON N7M 5W8 Canada

Toll-free: 866-423-3302
Phone: 519-380-9265
Fax: 519-380-0689
www.enviroshake.com

Enviroshake® Composite Engineered Roofing shakes are manufactured from 95% recycled material by weight. Approximately 90% of the shake is comprised of roughly equal parts post-industrial recycled plastics and agricultural fiber waste, plus a small percentage of recycled tire rubber. The remaining portion is comprised of proprietary binders. Enviroshake starts out dark brownish grey and ages to a silver-gray that resembles weathered cedar shakes within 3 to 9 months. The 20"-long shakes come in bundles of mixed widths of 12", 8", 7", 6", 5", and 4" and carry a 50-year limited warranty. Custom molded ridge caps are also available.

07 32 13
Clay Roof Tiles

Clay tiles are durable and made from abundant raw materials. As typically installed, roof tiles are also effective at preventing heat gain through the roof. In some climates and with some products, hail may be a concern. Some recycled-plastic shingles are manufactured to look like clay roof tiles.

Salvaged Slate and Clay Tile Roofing

Alluvium Construction

For full listing, see CSI section 07 31 26 - Slate Shingles

Salvaged Clay and Concrete Tile Roofing

Custom Tile Roofing, Inc.
2875 West Hampden Ave.
Englewood, CO 80110

Phone: 303-761-3831
Fax: 303-761-3839
www.customtileroofing.com

Custom Tile Roofing maintains an inventory of close to 400,000 pieces of reclaimed roofing tiles.

Reclaimed Natural Salvaged Slate and Clay Tile Roofing

Durable Slate Co.

For full listing, see CSI section 07 31 26 - Slate Shingles

Salvaged Slate and Clay Tile Roofing

Emack Slate Company, Inc.

For full listing, see CSI section 07 31 26 - Slate Shingles

Clay Roofing Tiles

Gladding, McBean & Co.
P.O. Box 97
Lincoln, CA 95648

Toll-free: 800-776-1133
Phone: 916-645-3341
Fax: 916-645-9538
www.gladdingmcbean.com

Gladding, McBean manufactures clay roofing tiles in a large variety of shapes, sizes, and fire-flashed blends, all of which are suitable for freeze/thaw climates.

Clay Roofing Tiles

Ludowici Roof Tile, Inc.
4757 Tile Plant Rd.
New Lexington, OH 43764

Toll-free: 800-945-8453
Phone: 740-342-1995
Fax: 740-342-0025
www.ludowici.com

Ludowici Clay Roof Tiles are available in 47 standard profiles and 43 standard colors in matte, gloss, weathered, sanded, and combed finishes. The company also offers an expanding lineup of larger, more affordable clay roofing tiles that reduce installation time and create less of a load for the roof deck. Recommended in freeze/thaw climates, all Ludowici standard grade tiles and fittings are covered by a 75-year limited warranty.

Clay Roofing Tiles

MCA Clay Tile
1985 Sampson Ave.
Corona, CA 92879

Toll-free: 800-736-6221
Fax: 951-736-6052
www.mca-tile.com

Among the tiles manufactured by MCA Clay Tile are a one-piece, S-shaped mission style tile in natural or glazed colors, the Corona Tapered Mission Tile available in standard and custom colors and blends, and an interlocking flat tile (MF 108 Flat) in Natural Red and glazed colors. MCA also manufactures Turret Tile®, which allows for a true turret- or fan-shaped installation. MCA's Oriental Style is an interlocking tile in the Japanese tradition. It is available in various glazed colors with many accessories and ornaments available. All MCA tiles have a limited 50-year warranty.

Nu-Lok Slate Roofing System

Nu-Lok Roofing Systems
For full listing, see CSI section 07 31 26 - Slate Shingles

Salvaged Slate and Clay Tile Roofing

Reclaimed Roofs, Inc.
For full listing, see CSI section 07 31 26 - Slate Shingles

Salvaged Slate and Clay Tile Roofing

Renaissance Roofing, Inc.
P.O. Box 5024
Rockford, IL 61125

Toll-free: 800-699-5695
Phone: 815-547-1725
Fax: 815-547-1425
www.claytileroof.com

Renaissance Roofing, Inc. is a supplier of salvaged clay tile and slate roofing materials.

Salvaged Slate and Clay Tile Roofing

The Roof Tile and Slate Company
1209 Carroll St.
Carrollton, TX 75006

Toll-free: 800-446-0220
Phone: 972-446-0005
Fax: 972-242-1923
www.claytile.com

The Roof Tile and Slate Company maintains a large inventory of salvaged slate and tile. New domestic slate and tile are also available.

Claylite and ClayMax

US Tile Company
909 W. Railroad St.
Corona, CA 92882

Toll-free: 800-252-9548
Phone: 909-737-0200
Fax: 951-734-9591
www.ustile.com

Claylite® and ClayMax® are over 40% lighter than standard roofing tile. Claylite is configured in the traditional "S" tile shape, while ClayMax is in the form of a twin "S." US Tile® (UST) also manufactures tiles of standard weight. All UST tiles are a true tapered mission style to provide a tight fit; they are offered in over 20 colors and have a transferable lifetime limited warranty ($50 transfer fee).

07 34 00
Building Integrated Photovoltaic Roofing

Photovoltaics (PV) enable the direct conversion of sunlight into electricity. Some PV modules are integrated into building components, such as roofing and wall glazings—these are often referred to as building-integrated photovoltaics (BIPV). (See feature article EBN Vol. 10, No. 3.)

Sunslates

Atlantis Energy Systems, Inc.
4517 Harlin Dr.
Sacramento, CA 95826

Phone: 916-438-2930
Fax: 916-438-2935
www.atlantisenergy.org

Atlantis Energy Systems produces Sunslates®, which serve as both a roofing product and a solar-electric power source. Sunslates are fiber-cement shingles into which PV cells have been laminated. Each shingle has a plug-in wiring connection.

Most recently mentioned in EBN 4:4 & 10:3

PowerGuard Interlocking Solar Roof Tiles

PowerLight Corporation
2954 San Pablo Ave.
Berkeley, CA 94702

Toll-free: 800-251-9728
Phone: 510-540-0550
Fax: 510-540-0552
www.powerlight.com

Founded in 1991, PowerLight produces PowerGuard, a UL-listed roof tile system that is comprised of PV modules laminated onto (vented) Dow Styrofoam® (HCFC-blown) insulation. Designed for low-slope roofs, the tiles insulate to R-10 and produce approximately 10 Wp/ft².

Most recently mentioned in EBN 10:3, 11:6, 13:2

UNI-SOLAR PV Shingles and Standing Seam Panels

United Solar Ovonic LLC
3800 Lapeer Rd.
Auburn Hills, MI 48326

Toll-free: 800-843-3892
Phone: 248-475-0100
Fax: 248-364-0510
www.uni-solar.com

Uni-Solar Ovonic LLC PV Shingles and Standing Seam Roofing Panels are installed much like conventional roofing products. They generate electricity while protecting the structure from weather. PV Shingles, measuring 86.4" x 12" with 7 tabs, are interspersed among conventional 3-tab shingles. Standing Seam Panels are available for laminating onto conventional roofing or as a PV-integrated, standing-seam product. Lead wires from each shingle or panel enter the structure through drilled holes in the roof decking. Uni-Solar roofing products use triple-junction amorphous silicon technology.

Most recently mentioned in EBN 10:3

**07 00 00
Thermal & Moisture Protection**

07 41 00
Roof Panels

Roof panels can be made of metal, a composition of fibers and asphalt, or other materials, but they must be durable enough to withstand the ultraviolet radiation and other elements experienced on a roof. Metal roofing, properly installed, is highly durable and readily recyclable at the end of its useful life. Using dissimilar metals for roofing, flashing, and fastening isn't recommended because they're susceptible to galvanic corrosion in the presence of water. Metal is also a preferred material for roofs used in rainwater catchment systems. In northern climates, snow readily slides off metal roofs, avoiding the damage caused by ice dams. In recent years, manufacturers have introduced low-slope metal roofing systems to complement more conventional steep-slope products. (See feature article EBN Vol. 7, No. 10.)

Met-Tile

Met-Tile
1745 E. Monticello Ct.
P.O. Box 4268
Ontario, CA 91761

Phone: 909-947-0311
Fax: 909-947-1510
www.met-tile.com

Met-Tile metal roofing is corrugated and detailed to give the appearance of clay roofing tiles. It is made from recycled steel with a "galvalume" (zinc-alloy) coating for durability and an additional water-based coating in a choice of 10 colors. It comes in lengths from 2' to 25'. Cool Roof panels that meet or exceed Energy Star requirements are available. Met-tile roofs are custom-designed to order.

Ondura

Tallant Industries, Inc.
4900 Ondura Dr.
Fredericksburg, VA 22407

Toll-free: 800-777-7663
Phone: 540-898-7000
Fax: 540-898-4991
www.ondura.com

Ondura corrugated asphalt roofing is composed of 50% asphalt and 50% cellulose fiber (by weight). The cellulose fiber is 100% post-consumer recycled mixed-paper waste.

Ondura claims that their product is safe for rainwater collection systems. Ondura sheets measure 48" x 79" (4.5 sheets per square). Ondura tiles measure 48" x 19-3/4" (24 tiles per square).

07 42 00
Wall Panels

Straw, a byproduct of agricultural production, is gaining acceptance as a building material. Although its use in straw-bale houses is perhaps more widely recognized, compressed-straw panels and particleboard are becoming a more significant presence. The straw panels listed here are formed under high temperature between heavyweight kraft paper similar to that used in drywall. The 2"- to 4"-thick panels listed here are nonstructural, appropriate for interior partition walls and ceilings. They offer excellent sound control and have been used for decades in parts of Europe and Australia.

Durra Panel

Durra Building Systems
2747 State Highway 160
Whitewright, TX 75491

Toll-free: 866-364-1198
Phone: 903-364-1198
Fax: 903-364-1108
www.durra.com

Durra Panel is designed to replace standard stud and drywall construction for interior walls. These 2-1/4"-thick straw panels, measuring 4' wide, are bound together with only high heat and pressure using straw that originated from within a 50-mile radius of the manufacturing plant. The panels are tapered at the vertical edges to 2" with slots to receive biscuit connector disks for fastening panels together with screws. Joints can be taped and finished just like drywall. Two preformed 3/4" channels per panel are available for wiring. Durra Panel comes with a recycled paperboard finish and is resistant to mold, termites, and fire—with a Class A fire rating possible for commercial use and a Class B rating for residential use. Straw panels bound in this way are exceptionally strong and do not offgas pollutants. This product was previously marketed as Prestowall™ by Affordable Building Systems. Durra also makes acoustical solutions with strawboard.

Most recently mentioned in EBN 10:4 & 14:5

07 42 16
Insulated Metal Wall Panels

With a thin metal skin and foam insulation for a core, insulated metal wall panels provide excellent thermal protection and efficient use of materials. The materials, themselves, however, have relatively high embodied energy.

Acsys Panel System

Acsys Inc.
1677 E. Miles Ave., Ste. 101
Hayden, ID 83835

Toll-free: 866-362-2797
Phone: 208-772-6422
Fax: 208-772-5942
www.acsys.net

The Acsys Building System is a structural insulated panel-type product employing an engineered 16- to 20-gauge corrugated galvanized steel endoskeletal core (rather than the more common exoskeleton of OSB). The steel is embedded in molded EPS, which offers R-values ranging from 25 to 50 (panel thicknesses of 6", 8", 10", and 12"). The EPS typically contains 7-10% recycled content from packaging waste, according to the manufacturer. Available in 2' and 4' widths up to 18' long, it may be used with steel framing or as a fully load-bearing system. The panels interconnect with ship-lap joints (secured by galvanized screws) and may be lifted into place by two people. 18-gauge galvanized steel top- and bottom-mounting tracks, as well as corner locater plates, are provided. Panels are typically finished on the exterior with acrylic stucco and on the interior with drywall.

Koretek

R-Steel Division of Butler Manufacturing
P.O. Box 248
Verona, VA 24482

Toll-free: 866-877-8335
Fax: 540-248-1173
www.koreteck.com

The Koretek™ Building System is a structural insulated panel-type product employing an engineered 16- to 20-gauge corrugated galvanized steel endoskeletal structural core (rather than the more common exoskeleton of OSB). The steel is embedded in molded EPS insulation, which offers R-values of R-25 (6" panel) and R-33 (8"). The EPS typically contains 7 to 10% recycled content from packaging waste, according to the manufacturer. Available in 2' and 4' widths up to 18' long, it may be used with steel framing or as a fully

07 00 00
Thermal & Moisture Protection

load-bearing system. The panels interconnect with ship-lap joints (secured by galvanized screws) and may be lifted into place by two people. 18-gauge galvanized steel top- and bottom-mounting tracks and corner locater plates are provided. Panels are typically finished on the exterior with acrylic stucco and on the interior with drywall.

07 46 24
FSC-Certified Wood Siding

Certified wood products are verified by a third party as originating from well-managed forests. GreenSpec recognizes the Forest Stewardship Council (FSC) standards as the most rigorous and the only certification system with well-established chain-of-custody certification to ensure that products used were derived from certified forests. Some companies listed here sell both certified and non-certified wood products, or products that have been certified according to different, less stringent environmental standards. To make certain that you get environmentally responsible wood products, be sure to specify your interest in FSC-certified wood. (See also 06 05 70 - Wood Products Certification and Information.)

Certified Wood Products

Cascadia Forest Goods, LLC

For full listing, see CSI section 06 11 01 - FSC-Certified Wood Framing Lumber

SmartChoice Wood Products

Certified Forest Products, LLC.

For full listing, see CSI section 06 11 01 - FSC-Certified Wood Framing Lumber

F.D. Sterritt Certified-Wood Building Products

F.D. Sterritt Lumber Co.

For full listing, see CSI section 06 22 01 - FSC-Certifed Millwork

Certified Red Cedar

Mary's River Lumber Co.

For full listing, see CSI section 06 11 01 - FSC-Certified Wood Framing Lumber

FSC-Certified Lumber, Plywood, and Products

Potlatch Corporation

For full listing, see CSI section 06 11 01 - FSC-Certified Wood Framing Lumber

07 46 25
Reclaimed-Wood Siding

Reclaimed-wood siding, though not commonly available, is environmentally attractive. It is generally milled from large timbers recovered from old buildings and other structures—not from wood that previously served as siding. Due to slower growth and straighter grain, quality, stability, and durability, reclaimed siding is often superior to new siding. However, the finite supply of reclaimed wood resources suggests that the material may be more suited to higher-visibility uses, such as furniture, interior trim, and flooring. (See also 01 62 02 - Distributors/Retailers, Used Building Materials.) (See feature articles EBN Vol. 6, No. 7 & Vol. 9, No. 5.)

Reclaimed-Wood Lumber and Products

A Reclaimed Lumber Co.

For full listing, see CSI section 06 22 02 - Reclaimed-Wood Millwork

AltruWood Reclaimed-Wood Products

AltruWood, Inc.

For full listing, see CSI section 09 64 02 - Reclaimed-Wood Flooring

Antique Woods & Colonial Restorations

Antique Woods & Colonial Restorations, Inc.

For full listing, see CSI section 09 64 02 - Reclaimed-Wood Flooring

Appalachian Woods

Appalachian Woods, LLC

For full listing, see CSI section 09 64 02 - Reclaimed-Wood Flooring

Reclaimed-Wood Materials

Black's Farmwood, Inc.

For full listing, see CSI section 09 64 02 - Reclaimed-Wood Flooring

Reclaimed-Wood Materials

BT Timberworks

For full listing, see CSI section 06 13 02 - Reclaimed-Wood Heavy Timber

Reclaimed-Wood Products

Centre Mills Antique Floors

For full listing, see CSI section 09 64 02 - Reclaimed-Wood Flooring

Reclaimed-Wood Products

Chestnut Specialists, Inc.

For full listing, see CSI section 09 64 02 - Reclaimed-Wood Flooring

Wood Materials from Urban Trees

CitiLog

For full listing, see CSI section 09 64 02 - Reclaimed-Wood Flooring

Reclaimed-Wood Building Products

Conklin's Authentic Antique Barnwood For full listing, see CSI section 06 13 02 - Reclaimed-Wood Heavy Timber

Reclaimed-Wood Products

Crossroads Recycled Lumber

For full listing, see CSI section 06 13 02 - Reclaimed-Wood Heavy Timber

D. Litchfield Reclaimed Wood

D. Litchfield & Co. Ltd.

For full listing, see CSI section 06 11 02 - Reclaimed-Wood Framing Lumber

Reclaimed-Wood Products

Duluth Timber Co.

For full listing, see CSI section 06 13 02 - Reclaimed-Wood Heavy Timber

07 00 00
Thermal & Moisture Protection

Reclaimed-Wood Building Products

Endura Wood Products, Ltd.

For full listing, see CSI section 09 64 02 - Reclaimed-Wood Flooring

River-Reclaimed Wood Products

Goodwin Heart Pine Company

For full listing, see CSI section 09 64 02 - Reclaimed-Wood Flooring

Poplar Bark Siding

Highland Craftsmen, Inc.
P.O. Box 2011
Blowing Rock, NC 28605

Phone: 828-295-0796
Fax: 828-295-0796
www.highlandcraftsmen.com

Highland Craftsmen offers Bark House™ chemical-free, kiln-sterilized siding made of tulip poplar or tulip tree (Liriodendron tulipifera) bark salvaged with hand tools during conventional logging practices. The "bark house" style was popular in the Appalachians a century ago. 75-year-old extant examples suggest good durability.

Reclaimed-Wood Building Products

J. Hoffman Lumber Co.
1330 E. State St.
Sycamore, IL 60178

Phone: 815-899-2260
Fax: 815-889-2460
www.hoffmanlumberco.com

J. Hoffman Lumber Co. is the Midwest's only sawmill company specializing in reclaimed antique heart pine, Douglas fir, and white pine. Reclaimed lumber is remilled into flooring, siding, and other millwork.

07 00 00
Thermal & Moisture Protection

Logs End Reclaimed-Wood Building Products

Logs End Inc.

For full listing, see CSI section 09 64 02 - Reclaimed-Wood Flooring

Reclaimed-Wood Building Products

Longleaf Lumber

For full listing, see CSI section 09 64 02 - Reclaimed-Wood Flooring

Michael Evenson Natural Resources

Michael Evenson Natural Resources
For full listing, see CSI section 06 13 02 - Reclaimed-Wood Heavy Timber

Pinocchio's

Pinocchio's

For full listing, see CSI section 06 13 02 - Reclaimed-Wood Heavy Timber

Reclaimed-Wood Building Products

Pioneer Millworks

For full listing, see CSI section 09 64 02 - Reclaimed-Wood Flooring

Resource Woodworks

Resource Woodworks, Inc.

For full listing, see CSI section 06 13 02 - Reclaimed-Wood Heavy Timber

Reclaimed-Wood Building Products

TerraMai

For full listing, see CSI section 09 64 02 - Reclaimed-Wood Flooring

Trestlewood

Trestlewood

For full listing, see CSI section 09 64 02 - Reclaimed-Wood Flooring

Reclaimed-Wood Building Products

Vintage Log and Lumber, Inc.

For full listing, see CSI section 06 13 02 - Reclaimed-Wood Heavy Timber

07 46 43
Composition Siding

Composition siding products are environmentally attractive because they utilize low-grade or waste wood fiber (such as newsprint or sawdust), or strands of fast-growing wood mixed with binding agents and finishes. Although composition siding is resource-efficient relative to solid wood, some products in the past have demonstrated poor dura-

bility. Quality composition siding products, if durable, can be affordable green products. (See also 06 05 70 - Wood Products Certification and Information.) (See feature article EBN Vol. 6, No. 7.)

CollinsWood FSC-Certified Wood Products

Collins Companies
1618 S.W. First Ave., Ste. 500
Portland, OR 97201

Toll-free: 800-329-1219
Phone: 503-417-7755
Fax: 503-417-1441
www.collinswood.com

The CollinsWood line includes FSC-certified western pine particleboard, FSC-certified TruWood engineered (hardboard) siding and trim, and FSC-certified hardwood and softwood lumber and millwork. TruWood products are made under FSC's partial-content rules (with an actual certified fiber content of 32%), and use a phenol formaldehyde binder. Millwork includes cherry, red oak, soft maple and poplar interior millwork, including casing, base, chair rail, crown, etc. In 1993, Collins Pine Company became the first privately owned timber management company to receive FSC certification in the U.S. CollinsWood has been a leader in the forest and wood products certification movement since its inception.

Most recently mentioned in EBN 2:4, 3:5, 6:8, 6:10, 8:11, 9:3

PaperStone Certified

KlipTech Composites

For full listing, see CSI section 12 36 00 - Countertops

LP SmartSide Siding and Exterior Trim Products

LP
414 Union St., Ste. 2000
Nashville, TN 37219

Toll-free: 877-744-5600
Fax: 877-523-7192
www.lpcorp.com

LP's SmartSide™ siding and exterior trim includes formaldehyde-free OSB-based (lap and panel), soffit, and fascia trim products treated during manufacture with zinc borate. A paint-based overlay enhances weather resistance. The 30-year transferable warranty includes 7-year 100% repair/replacement coverage, and a 30-year termite resistance guarantee is offered. Introduced in 1997, SmartSide Siding was joined in 2000 by other products in the LP SmartGuard® family of termite-resistant building products.

Most recently mentioned in EBN 9:9

07 46 46
Fiber Cement Siding

Fiber-cement building materials earn green points for durability. Fiber-cement, the new generation of what was once an asbestos-containing material, is today made from portland cement, sand, clay, and wood fiber. Environmental concerns include the embodied energy of portland cement and the source of the wood fiber—some products use wood from such distant locations as New Zealand and Russia. Although the current generation of fiber-cement products isn't yet proven over the long haul, the material is quite stable, and products carry up to 50-year warranties. Most fiber-cement siding is available factory primed. It takes paint very well, and proper painting is important for long-term durability. (See feature article EBN Vol. 6, No. 7.)

Cemplank and Cempanel

Cemplank, Inc.
26300 La Alameda, Ste. 250
Mission Viejo, CA 92691

Toll-free: 877-236-7526
www.cemplank.com

Cemplank lap siding and Cempanel vertical siding have cedar textures. Cemplank is 5/16" thick and 12' long and is available in widths from 6" (4-3/4" exposure) to 12" (10-3/4" exposure). Cemplank is a division of James Hardie Building Products, with manufacturing locations in Pennsylvania and South Carolina.

Most recently mentioned in EBN 6:7

Fiber-Cement Siding

CertainTeed Corporation
750 E. Swedesford Rd.
P.O. Box 860
Valley Forge, PA 19482

Toll-free: 800-233-8990
Phone: 610-341-7000
Fax: 610-341-7777
www.certainteed.com

CertainTeed WeatherBoards™ fiber-cement siding is available in lap, panel, and soffit products with smooth, cedar, or stucco (panel only) textures. Lap siding is available in widths from 6-1/4" to 12". Panel siding comes in 4' x 8', 9', or 10' sheets. According to CertainTeed, the manufacturing process provides 60% higher interlaminate bond strength for superior freeze/thaw protection. CertainTeed delivers the siding with FiberTect sealant, which penetrates the siding surface

to provide moisture protection while acting as the base coat for painting.

Most recently mentioned in EBN 6:7

Weatherside

GAF Materials Corp.
1361 Alps Rd.
Wayne, NJ 07470

Toll-free: 800-223-1948
Phone: 973-628-3000
Fax: 973-628-3865
www.gaf.com

GAF manufactures Weatherside™ fiber-cement siding available with different textures and dimensions. WeatherSide™ shingles are fire-proof, durable, and resistant

to freeze- thaw conditions — and backed by a 25 year limited warranty.

HardiePlank, HardiePanel, and HardieShingle

James Hardie Building Products, Inc.
26300 La Alameda, Ste. 250
Mission Viejo, CA 92691

Toll-free: 888-542-7343
Phone: 949-348-1800
Fax: 949-367-1294
www.jameshardie.com

HardiePlank™ lap siding is 12' long and is available in widths ranging from 6-1/4" (5" exposure) to 12" (10-3/4" exposure). Textures include Smooth, Select Cedarmill, Colonial Smooth, Colonial Roughsawn, Beaded Smooth, and Beaded Cedarmill. Straight-Edge Shingle Plank™ emulates the look of shingles in an embossed lap-siding product; it comes in 12' lengths and is 8-1/4" wide with a 7" exposure. Hardiepanel™ vertical siding is available in 4' x 8', 4' x 9', and 4' x 10' sheets in Smooth, Stucco, or Sierra textures with vertical grooves at 8" spacings. HardiePlank and HardiePanel carry 50-year limited warranties. Available accessories include HardieSoffit™ and HardieTrim™. HardieShingle™ offers the look of cedar shingles in a fiber-cement siding, is available in a variety of styles and profiles, and comes with a 30-year limited warranty.

Most recently mentioned in EBN 2:3 & 6:7

MaxiTile Fiber-Cement Siding

MaxiTile, Inc.
849 E. Sandhill Ave.
Carson, CA 90746

Toll-free: 800-338-8453
Phone: 310-217-0316
Fax: 310-515-6851
www.maxitile.com

MaxiPlank and MaxiPanel siding products are available in several surface textures and patterns. MaxiPlank is produced in 12' lengths and widths from 6-1/4" to 12". MaxiPanel measures 4' x 8', 4' x 9', and 4' x 10'.

Nichiha Fiber-Cement Rainscreen Siding

Nichiha USA, Inc.
5855 Oakbrook Pkwy.
Norcross, GA 30093

Toll-free: 866-424-4421
Phone: 770-805-9466
Fax: 770-805-9467
www.nichiha.com

Nichiha offers a line of panelized fiber-cement siding installed with special clips that hold the panels away from the sheathing to provide a rainscreen exterior to control water intrusion and increase the durability of the entire wall system. The panels are ship-lapped on four sides and have the appearance of bricks, shakes, or stone. (A lap siding is also available.) Most panels come in 6', 8', or 10' sections, in heights ranging from approximately 8" to 18" and thicknesses ranging from 1/2" to 1". Depending on the product, the manufacturer offers a 30-year or 50-year transferable warranty.

07 52 00
Modified Bituminous Membrane Roofing

Conventional built-up roofing (BUR) is made from multiple layers of asphalt-impregnated felt alternated with layers of hot-mopped bitumen. Material use is relatively high, and considerable waste is generated during reroofing—both from the BUR and from the foam insulation, which is typically ripped off and land-filled at the same time. Recycled-content modified bituminous products can reduce overall environmental impacts. Modified bitumen roofing cap sheets come in rolls, may be cold-installed with low-VOC adhesives, and can offer cool roof performance. (See feature article EBN Vol. 7, No. 10.)

07 00 00
Thermal & Moisture Protection

MM6125-EV

American Hydrotech, Inc.
303 E. Ohio St., Ste. 2700
Chicago, IL 60611

Toll-free: 800-877-6125
Phone: 312-337-4998
Fax: 312-661-0731
www.hydrotechusa.com

MM6125-EV is a roofing membrane with a recycled content consisting of reclaimed rubber and recycled oil. This membrane is most often used in an insulated roof membrane assembly (IRMA).

Derbigum DerbiBrite

Performance Roof Systems, Inc.
4800 Blue Pkwy.
Kansas City, MO 64130

Toll-free: 800-727-9872
Phone: 816-921-0221
Fax: 816-921-5007
www.derbigum.com

Available in the European marketplace since 1996, DerbiBrite® is a polymer-modified bitumen roofing cap sheet with polyester and fiberglass reinforcement. An integral bright white acrylic surface meets Energy Star® reflectivity and Cool Roof Rating Council emissivity requirements. According to the manufacturer, recoating is not needed to maintain cool roof performance (though an annual pressure-washing is). The product is installed without kettles or melting chemicals using relatively low-VOC (185 g/l) Permastic® Cold Process Adhesive, available in reusable tanks and drums. The system offers Class A fire ratings over combustible and noncombustible roof decks.

07 54 00
Thermoplastic Membrane Roofing

Single-ply roofing membranes, typically used on large commercial buildings, are also occasionally used on homes and light-commercial buildings for low-slope roof areas and beneath upper-floor walk-out decks. They can be ballasted, mechanically fastened, or fully adhered. Thermoplastic membranes can be heat-welded at seams, minimizing use of solvent-based adhesives. PVC has long been the most common thermoplastic membrane material. For roof membranes, PVC requires plasticizers for flexibility; these chemicals, which may

dissipate over time and cause brittleness, are a major cause of membrane failure. PVC is targeted by some environmental groups for its chlorine content and the risk of dioxin production in the event of an unintentional fire or during improperly controlled incineration. Phthalate plasticizers, commonly used with PVC, also may mimic natural hormones in humans and other animals, causing health problems. Concerns about the environmental and health impacts and performance characteristics of PVC have led to the development of thermoplastic olefin (TPO) membranes. Polyolefins are a class of polymers that includes polyethylene and polypropylene. These materials obtain their flexibility through the copolymers rather than plasticizers; however, without the addition of fire retardants, some do not pass necessary fire tests for unballasted applications. (See feature article EBN Vol. 7, No. 10.)

UltraPly TPO

Firestone Building Products Company
310 E. 96th St.
Indianapolis, IN 46240

Toll-free: 800-428-4442
Phone: 317-575-7000
Fax: 317-575-7100
www.firestonebpco.com

Firestone's UltraPly TPO is a heat-weldable, solar-reflective roofing material that meets fire codes without chlorine or other halogenated fire-retardants. This prevents the release of hydrochloric acid (HCl), dioxins, or related compounds in the event of fire.

Most recently mentioned in EBN 8:5

Mule-Hide White TPO Roofing   New

Mule-Hide Products Co., Inc.
1195 Prince Hall Dr.
P.O. Box 1057
Beloit, WI 53512

Toll-free: 800-786-1492
Phone: 608-365-3111
Fax: 608-365-7852
www.mulehide.com

Mule-Hide white TPO roofing is flexible, heat-weldable roll roofing available in .045", .060", and 0.80" thicknesses for fully adhered or mechanically attached new or reroof installations. This product is free of chlorine, other halogenated compounds, or plasticizers. It is available in 8' and 10' widths, and may also be used as a flexible membrane flashing. The initial solar reflec-

tance of this white TPO is 0.87, falling to 0.83 (clean) after three years; its thermal emittance is 0.95. For fully adhered installations, look for a low-VOC adhesive.

Stevens EP

Stevens Roofing Systems
9 Sullivan Rd.
Holyoke, MA 01040

Toll-free: 800-621-7663
Phone: 413-533-8100
Fax: 413-522-1070
www.stevensroofing.com

Stevens Roofing Systems is one of the world's largest TPO producers. The Stevens EP family of nonhalogenated TPO membranes uses hydrated mineral salts as a fire retardant. Stevens EP membranes are available in nominal 45-, 60-, and 80-mil thickness, and in standard 76.5"-wide rolls. No solvents or adhesives are required, and no known toxins are released if the product is incinerated. The material is available in many colors and can be installed using several attachment methods. White Stevens EP is highly reflective, reducing energy loads and avoiding contributions to the urban heat island effect. It also meets the EPA Energy Star Roof Products guidelines.

07 55 63
Green Roof Systems

Green roof systems for low-slope roofs protect the roof membrane, reduce stormwater flows, and help green the built environment through rooftop plantings. Green roofs, which are more common in Europe, can detain over 50% of rainwater from a typical storm: stormwater detention reduces the loads placed on storm sewers, making it a particularly attractive system in urban areas that have combined sewer overflow (CSO) events during heavy rains. Multilayered green roof systems are thicker than conventional roofs, and additional structural support is typically required. A green roof includes drainage, geotextile, soil, and vegetation layers; sedums or a thick sod of native grasses interspersed with wildflowers can be a wonderful architectural element which helps to reduce building heat gain and the urban heat island effect. Plantings also absorb CO_2. (See feature articles EBN Vol. 7, No. 10 & Vol. 10, No. 11.)

Garden Roof Assembly

American Hydrotech, Inc.
303 E. Ohio St., Ste. 2700
Chicago, IL 60611

Toll-free: 800-877-6125
Phone: 312-337-4998
Fax: 312-661-0731
www.hydrotechusa.com

American Hydrotech's Garden Roof® Assembly combines the MM 6125®-EV waterproofing membrane (minimum 25% recycled content), a root barrier, water drainage/retention devices engineered specifically for landscaped roofs, and optional rigid foam insulation. The assembly is lightweight and able to accommodate a wide variety of vegetation and soil depths.

Most recently mentioned in EBN 7:10 & 10:11

AMERGREEN Roof Garden System

American Wick Drain Corporation
1209 Airport Rd.
Monroe, NC 28110

Toll-free: 800-242-9425
Phone: 704-238-9200
Fax: 704-296-0690
www.americanwick.com

The Amergreen™ Roof Garden System consists of a needle-punched, nonwoven polypropylene geotextile filter fabric with an optional copper hydroxide root-barrier coating, a polystyrene "drain core" with water-storing cones that also provides airflow, and another polypropylene geotextile separation layer. Their 50RS system has a 7/16"-deep drain core, while the 100RS has a 1" core. American Wick Drain also manufactures products appropriate for reducing hydrostatic pressure on earth-sheltered homes.

Green Roof-Roofscape

Barrett Company
33 Stonehouse Rd.
Millington, NJ 07946

Toll-free: 800-647-0100
Phone: 908-647-0100
Fax: 908-647-0278
www.barrettroofs.com

Barrett's Green Roof-Roofscape is comprised of their RAM Tough 250 membrane, a root barrier, insulation, a drainage/aeration/hydration layer, geotextile, soil medium, and vegetation. Systems are either Low or High Profile. Low Profile are considered low-maintenance with planting media 6" thick or less, while High Profile are considered high-maintenance with soil depths in excess

of 6". Soil and plant specifications are to be provided by a landscape architect or horticulturist.

Most recently mentioned in EBN 10:11

EnviroTech Roof System

Building Logics, Inc.
3213 Virginia Beach Blvd.
Virginia Beach, VA 23452

Phone: 757-431-3170
Fax: 757-431-3172
www.buildinglogics.com

Using the Famogreen name, Building Logics, Inc. supplies green roof systems with the German FAMOS APAO modified bitumen membrane and vegetation mats. Specialized versions of the membrane are available with a copper-impregnated spun-polyester root barrier and/or a lightweight hydrogel to retain water. Technical support for the design and specification of soil mixes and plants is available.

Most recently mentioned in EBN 10:11

Green Roof Systems

Carlisle SynTec Incorporated
P.O. Box 7000
Carlisle, PA 17013

Toll-free: 800-479-6832
Phone: 717-245-7000
Fax: 717-245-7143
www.carlisle-syntec.com

Carlisle SynTec, with 8 billion ft^2 of roofing membrane installed over the past four decades, has entered the living roof arena with its Roof Garden Waterproofing Systems. The systems incorporate a variety of waterproofing options and accessories for shallow, medium, and deep assemblies. These systems are warranted for a minimum of 15 years (longer with material upgrades).

ELT Easy Green System

Elevated Landscape Technologies Inc.
245 King George Rd. Ste. 319
Brantford, ON N3R 7N7 Canada

Toll-free: 866-306-7773
Phone: 866-306-7773
Fax: 866-831-3035
www.eltgreenroofs.com

The ELT Easy Green System is a pre-grown green roof system comprised of an interlocking water retention / drainage layer, filter fabric, root reinforcement layer, and vegetation. Shallow (<6") and deep (>6") systems range from 8lbs/sf to more than 25lbs/sf, and are appropriate for residential or commercial installations.

Optigreen Green Roof System

Resource Conservation Technology, Inc.
2633 N. Calvert St.
Baltimore, MD 21218

New

Toll-free: 800-477-7724
Phone: 410-366-1146
Fax: 410-366-1202
www.conservationtechnology.com

Resource Conservation Technology sells a complete green roof system for up to 10,000 sf of roof that includes a sheet EPDM rubber membrane, a plastic drainage substrate, water-retaining lightweight soil, plants, and a rainwater collection system for irrigation in dry weather.

Roofmeadow

Roofscapes, Inc. (SM)
7114 McCallum St.
Philadelphia, PA 19119

Phone: 215-247-8784
Fax: 215-247-4659
www.roofmeadow.com

Roofscapes, Inc.(SM) is a design and consulting firm that specializes in lightweight green roofs. Services offered include design and consulting, installation, construction inspection, and service and maintenance. Roofscapes is affiliated with Optigreen (Optigruen International AG), a German company with over 30 years of green roof experience.

Most recently mentioned in EBN 10:11

SopraNature

Soprema USA, Inc.
310 Quadral Dr.
Wadsworth, OH 44281

Toll-free: 800-356-3521
Phone: 330-334-0066
Fax: 330-334-4289
www.soprema.us

This French green roof system relies on a two-ply SBS modified bitumen membrane that does not require torches, kettles, or hazardous solvents. Installed over the membrane is a drainage composite that retains rainwater for the plantings and includes a built-in root barrier. Several classes of growing medium are available. The Soprema system available in the U.S. can be installed over a concrete deck or on lightweight and sloped decks able to accept the weight. SopraNature has been used on several high-profile projects in Canada and is now available in the U.S.

Most recently mentioned in EBN 10:11

**07 00 00
Thermal &
Moisture
Protection**

Green Shield Green Roof System

The Garland Company, Inc.
 3800 E. 91st St.
Cleveland, OH 44105

Toll-free: 800-321-9336
Phone: 216-641-7500
Fax: 216-641-0633
www.garlandco.com

Garland produces a fairly simple green roof system with a multi-ply SBS-modified bitumen membrane, a plastic drainage layer above the membrane, and a layer of soil media on top of that. At one time Garland was using the FAMOS green roof system (and the company is an investor in FAMOS), but there is no product relationship between the two companies today. Technical support for the design and specification of soil mixes and plants is available.

Most recently mentioned in EBN 10:11

Green Roof Systems

W. P. Hickman
30700 Solon Industrial Pkwy.
Solon, OH 44139

Phone: 440-248-7760
Fax: 440-248-6524
www.wphickman.com

W. P. Hickman supplies a number of green roof systems using liquid-applied materials and modified bitumen sheet goods (Pika Ply GR). Membranes are customized to the needs and requirements of the specific job. Technical support for design and specification of soil mixes and plants is available.

Most recently mentioned in EBN 10:11

GreenGrid Modular Green Roof System

Weston Solutions, Inc.
20 N. Wacker Dr.
Chicago, IL 60606

Phone: 312-424-3319
Fax: 312-424-3330
www.greengridroofs.com

The GreenGrid® Modular Green Roof System was introduced in August 2001 as a modular green roofing system that can be installed over almost any low-slope roof—even older roofs. The system's modular design allows easy access to the underlying roof for repairs or changes without destroying the Green Roof. Modular 2' x 4', 4"- or 8"-deep "pans" made from 100% post-consumer recycled HDPE plastic are sold with drainage, soil media, and plantings. Also available in 2' by 2' modular pans either 2-1/2" or 4" deep and 40" by 40" modular pans 4" deep. Units in other sizes may be available on request.

GreenGrid® is delivered pre-planted and ready to install.

Most recently mentioned in EBN 10:11

---

07 55 64
Green Roof Components

Green roof systems for low-slope roofs protect the roof membrane, reduce stormwater flows, and help green the built environment through rooftop plantings. A green roof includes drainage, geotextile, soil, and vegetation layers. Products listed here can be used to create one or more of the elements of a green roof system. (See feature articles EBN Vol. 7, No. 10 & Vol. 10, No. 11.)

Enkadrain 3000 Series

Colbond Inc.

For full listing, see CSI section 33 46 00 - Foundation and Slab Drainage

GEOdren Roof Garden Units

Geoproducts Corp.
11-110 Jardin Dr.
Concord, ON L4K 4R4 Canada

Toll-free: 877-GEOTUBE
Phone: 905-760-2256
Fax: 905-760-0491
www.geoproductscorp.com

GEOdren, made from recycled polypropylene, is a modular system for creating green roofs. The interlocking trays combine water retention, drainage, and aeration, and are strong enough to withstand the weight of mini-excavators or small forklifts. Rounded feet allow the trays to be placed directly on the roof's waterproof liner without damage. The trays are intended to be filled with pumice or other porous drainage material, then overlaid with geotextile and covered with planting media.

MODI Roof Garden   (New)

Green Innovations, Ltd
81 Snowhill Crest
Toronto, ON M1S 3T4 Canada

Toll-free: 888-725-7524
Phone: 416-725-7524
Fax: 416-283-6273
www.greeninnovations.ca

MODI Roof Garden trays are made from post-consumer recycled HDPP, come in two depths, and are suitable for use over any type of watertight membrane. The system has high compressive strength, allowing the use

of small loaders or mini-excavators during installation or maintenance. The attachment system accommodates changing slopes and curved surfaces, and in conjunction with the optional MODI Paving Grill, can be used on roofs with slopes greater than 15%. The trays may be shaped with a saw or disc grinder.

GreenTech Roof Garden System

GreenTech, Inc.
470 Clubfield Dr.
Roswell, GA 30075

Phone: 804-363-5048
Fax: 770-587-2445
www.greentechitm.com

The GreenTech® Roof Garden System utilizes HDPE plastic containers that are 46" wide x 46" long x a minimum of 8" deep. The modular units, which can be preplanted and readily reconfigured or replaced, have perforated bottoms and folding sides that can be customized for greater soil depths. Channels below the modules displace soil, reducing weight and enhancing drainage and air circulation, while further discouraging root penetration of the waterproofing membrane by air pruning. Foot locator pads are used to provide consistent positioning and interlocking of the trays. The containers may also be used to create drainage planes for athletic fields, playgrounds, and pathways. When filled with sand and other filtration media, they may be incorporated into graywater treatment systems.

Green Roof Blocks

Saint Louis Metalworks Company
11701 New Halls Ferry Rd.
Florissant, MO 63033

Phone: 314-972-8010
Fax: 314-972-8182
www.greenroofblocks.com

Green Roof Blocks are ready-to-install 22-gauge anodized aluminum 2' x 2' planters with 4", 8", or 12" depths that are placed on a rooftop to create a living roof. Saturated unit weights range from 17 to 51 lbs/sf. Live plants and growth media are included. Pads at each corner and in the center of the planters elevate them from the roof surface, allowing drainage and airflow. Green Roof Blocks are made with 15% recycled metal and 50% recycled rubber. The self contained units are portable, facilitating roof work and aesthetic rearrangement.

Ecogrid

Terrafirm Solutions Ltd.

For full listing, see CSI section 32 14 45 - Porous Unit Paving, Plastic

---

07 00 00
Thermal & Moisture Protection

07 55 65
Green Roof Planting Media

Green roof systems for low-slope roofs protect the roof membrane, reduce stormwater flows, and help green the built environment through rooftop plantings. A green roof includes drainage, geotextile, soil, and vegetation layers. Products listed here represent appropriate planting media for green (living) roofs. (See also 07 55 63 - Green Roof Systems, 07 55 64 - Green Roof Components, 07 55 66 - Green Roof Plants.)

Rooftop Planting Media

Midwest Trading - Horticultural Supplies, Inc.
48W805 Illinois Rte. 64
Virgil, IL 60151

Toll-free: 800-546-9522
Phone: 630-365-1990
www.midwest-trading.com

Midwest Trading is a regional supplier of mulch, mixes, and planting media, including media optimized for green roofs. Green roof planting media should have high absorptivity (high total pore space) and low organic content—properties appropriate for green roofs. A partner company, Midwest Groundcovers, has a number of sedums available for green roof applications.

Rooftop Planting Media

Verdir Systems Inc.   **New**
602-1401 W. Broadway
Vancouver, BC V6H 1H6 Canada

Toll-free: 888-837-3470
Phone: 604-681-3303
Fax: 604-852-2775
www.verdirsystems.com

Verdir offers growing media designed specifically for living roofs and living walls incorporating Tephragro™ (a lightweight black pumice) mixed with soil amendments. Tephragro has low density and high porosity; it is dry-screened rather than crushed to retain its natural shape, structure, and integrity.

Rooftop Planting Media

White Premium Organics, Inc.
2560 Foxfield Rd., Ste. 200
St. Charles, IL 60174

Toll-free: 866-586-1563
Phone: 630-377-9966
Fax: 630-377-9934
www.garveyintl.com

White Premium Organics produces growing mixes specially formulated for rooftop applications. The mixes consist of approximately 80% inorganic matter such as expanded slate or calcined clay with sand, and 20% organic matter such as composted bark, rice hulls, or mushroom compost. These materials have the significant bulk density needed for rooftop applications, resist decomposing, provide excellent aeration, and won't clog filtration systems, according to the company. Media is available for extensive (2"-4" soil depth), semi-intensive (4"-6" soil depth), and intensive (6" soil depth and deeper) roof garden systems. White Premium Organics serves most of the Midwestern U.S.

07 55 66
Green Roof Plants

Green roof systems for low-slope roofs protect the roof membrane, reduce stormwater flows, and help green the built environment through rooftop plantings. A green roof includes drainage, geotextile, soil, and vegetation layers. Products listed here represent appropriate planting media for green (living) roofs. Products listed here are sources for appropriate plants for green (living) roofs. (See also 07 55 63 - Green Roof Systems, 07 55 64 - Green Roof Components, 07 55 65 - Green Roof Planting Media.) (See feature article EBN Vol. 10, No. 11.)

Green Roof Plants

Green Roof Plants - Emory Knoll Farms
3410 Ady Rd.
Street, MD 21154

Phone: 410-452-5880
Fax: 410-452-5319
www.greenroofplants.com

Green Roof Plants (Emory Knoll Farms) is the only company in North America known to specialize solely in plants for extensive (low-profile) green roofs. In operation for six generations, the company has shifted production solely to green roof applications. The company's greenhouse is powered by a 3 kW PV system, and solar power also powers water pumping. The company has an organic growing focus and makes maximum use of reclaimed, recycled, recyclable, and natural materials. Much of the nutrients are provided by the farm's 25 llamas. The company propagates hundreds of species of sedum for green roof projects throughout North America. Green Roof Plants also provides horticultural consulting for extensive green roof projects.

Green Roof Plants

Intrinsic Perennial Gardens, Inc.
10702 Seaman Rd.
Hebron, IL 60034

Toll-free: 800-648-2788
Phone: 815-648-2788
Fax: 815-648-2072
www.intrinsicperennialgardens.com

Intrinsic Perennial Gardens offers over 100 varieties of sedum, as well as other hardy perennials appropriate for green roof applications, and primarily serves the Midwest.

Green Roof Plants

MotherPlants
277 Enfield Main Rd.
Ithaca, NY 14850

Phone: 607-256-2482
www.motherplants.net

MotherPlants grows a wide range of species, primarily Sedums, Delosperma, and Sempervivums. Plants are offered as plugs, cuttings, vegetated mats, or planted in modules. Any species not stocked can be acquired and grown to specification.

07 56 00
Fluid-Applied Roofing

Fluid-applied roofing materials can be applied over an existing roof to extend its life and provide reflective characteristics. Products listed here have low-VOC emissions, recycled content, and reflective surfaces to reduce heat gain. (See feature article EBN Vol. 7, No. 10.)

Astec Coatings

Insulating Coatings Corp. (ICC)
103 Main St.
Binghamton, NY 13905

Toll-free: 800-223-8494
Phone: 607-723-1727
Fax: 607-723-1700
www.icc-astec.com

Astec Coatings are water-based ceramic, elastomeric building coatings with superior energy performance. White Astec coatings reflect solar radiation, as does the ceramic radiant barrier within the coating. ICC products are applied with a paint roller or spray equipment.

**07 00 00
Thermal &
Moisture
Protection**

Karnak Roof Coatings

Karnak Corporation
330 Central Ave.
Clark, NJ 07066

Toll-free: 800-526-4236
Phone: 732-388-0300
Fax: 732-388-9422
www.karnakcorp.com

Karnak 501 and 505-M Elasto-Brite water-based, acrylic-polymer coatings for metal, asphalt, and non-APP (atactic polypropylene) built-up roofs can prolong the life of those membranes and lower the building's air conditioning energy needs—as long as Energy Star®-rated white is applied. White, gray, tan, patina green, and terra cotta red are available in 5-gallon pails and 55-gallon drums. These products have a VOC content of 120 g/l. (When primers, sealers, base coats, and other fluid applications are also used, be aware of the VOC contents of those materials as well.)

Metacrylics

Metacrylics
142 N. 27th St.
San Jose, CA 95116

Toll-free: 800-660-6950
Phone: 408-280-7733
Fax: 408-280-6329
www.metacrylics.com

Metacrylics is an elastomeric acrylic and stitchbond polyester roofing system. The water-based, UV-resistant acrylic coating can be applied to a large number of materials, including tar and gravel and corrugated metal, walking decks, exterior walls, and below-grade waterproofing. Available in 65 colors, white is the heat-reflective option for which Metacrylics qualifies as an Energy Star® Certified Roofs product. According to the manufacturer, Metacrylics had one of the highest Cool Roof Rating combination of any product (Solar Reflectance: 87 and Thermal Emittance: 90) and is ICC ES listed. The company offers a 10-year limited warranty that can be reinstated indefinitely with reapplication of the topcoat.

Acryshield Reflective Roof Coatings

National Coatings Corp.
1201 Calle Suerte
Camarillo, CA 93012

Toll-free: 800-423-9557
Phone: 805-388-7112
Fax: 805-388-8140
www.nationalcoatings.com

The Acryshield® line of acrylic elastomeric roof coatings includes several zero-VOC products with high reflectivity (0.83 to 0.86) and high emissivitiy (up to 0.94), including the following coatings: A400, a multi-purpose coating for use over various substrates with special asphalt bleed-blocking; A500 coating for sprayed polyurethane foam and all single ply roofing; A550, a multipurpose coating with extra toughness for foot traffic and physical abuse; and A600, a fast-setting multipurpose coating.

WetSuit & Reflex Roof Coating System

Neptune Coatings Corp.
972 Golden Gate Ter.
Grass Valley, CA 95945

Toll-free: 800-967-7659
Phone: 530-274-1356
Fax: 530-477-4316
www.neptunecoatingscorp.com

WetSuit® is a seamless, spray-applied, waterbased roof coating that can be applied over almost any substrate to any mil thickness in one pass (60-80 mils recommended) with a nearly instant cure. The UV-stable, Class A fire-rated, asphaltic neoprene rubber is a two-part (adjustable ratio), zero-VOC (80% solids, no solvents) coating. It can be applied vertically or overhead without sag. Minimal surface preparation is required. Elongation over 1500%. Accelerated weathering comparable to seven years showed no adverse effects, according to the company. To meet *GreenSpec* standards, WetSuit is recommended to be used in conjunction with the white acrylic latex reflective top coat, Reflex, manufactured by the same company. This system is applied by licensed applicators, but unlike built-up roofing materials, can be applied by workers wearing short pants and tennis shoes.

Roof Guardian

Roof Guardian Technologies, Inc.
347 Hwy. 289
Comfort, TX 78013

Phone: 830-995-5177
Fax: 830-995-5705
www.roofguardiantech.com

Roof Guardian Technologies offers several lightweight, liquid-applied, elastomeric, acrylic polymer coating options for various roof surfaces including metal, smooth built-up, single-ply, and polymer-modified asphalt. VOC contents of the primers and finish coats range from 5 - 55 g/l. Reflectivity of up to 90% is available.

Sealoflex Waterproofing System

Sealoflex, Inc.
2516 Oscar Johnson Dr.
Charleston, SC 29405

Toll-free: 800-770-6466
Phone: 843-554-6466
Fax: 843-554-6458
www.sealoflex.com

The Sealoflex Waterproofing System consists of a highly flexible emulsion saturant, a nonwoven polyester fabric, and a UV-resistant finish coat. Sealoflex coatings are VOC-compliant.

07 71 23
Gutters and Downspouts

Products that are effective at directing rainwater away from foundations increase building durability. (See feature article EBN Vol. 3, No. 5.)

RainTube

GLI Systems, Inc.
215 S. 4th St.
Jacksonville, OR 97530

Toll-free: 866-724-6356
Fax: 541-899-1762
www.raintube.com

RainTube is a roof gutter debris filter-tube made from 100% post-consumer recycled high-density polyethylene (HDPE) plastic. The filter-tube does not significantly inhibit rainwater capture, allowing the capture of rainfall at more than 100 in/hr. The RainTube can be compressed to fit into narrower gutters. Installed, it crowns slightly above the roof surface. Maintenance consists of occasional light brushing or blowing to remove debris. The system may be useful with rainwater harvesting systems to keep leaves and other debris out of collected rainwater. By preventing clogging of gutters, it may also help to improve building durability.

Recycled-Plastic Landscape Products

Master Mark Plastics

For full listing, see CSI section 32 31 23 - Plastic Fences and Gates

Rain Run

Presto Products Company
670 N. Perkins St.
P.O. Box 2399
Appleton, WI 54912

Toll-free: 800-548-3424
Phone: 920-738-1328
Fax: 920-738-1222
www.prestoproducts.com

Rain Run®, made with recycled plastic, is a splashblock for use at the base of gutter downspouts. The splashblock keeps rainwater away from the foundation and allows it to soak into the ground more effectively.

Rainhandler and Doorbrella

Savetime Corporation
2710 North Ave.
Bridgeport, CT 06604

Toll-free: 800-942-3004
Fax: 800-606-2028
www.rainhandler.com

Rainhandler is an aluminum, multilouvered, self-cleaning device designed to replace gutters. The product breaks up heavy sheets of water into smaller drops that are more easily absorbed into the ground, and spreads the water over a greater area to further facilitate absorption. Doorbrella is an accessory designed to channel water over unprotected doorways to Rainhandlers on each side of the door. Rainhandler is available in brown or white baked-on enamel or unfinished aluminum. Doorbrella is available in brown or aluminum. Both products come with a 25-year limited warranty and a one-year, money-back guarantee.

07 72 00
Roof Accessories

Many different accessories are used to install roofing materials and facilitate access to the roof surface after it's installed. Products listed here have high recycled content.

Rolath

Bedford Technology, LLC
2424 Armour Rd.
P.O. Box 609
Worthington, MN 56187

Toll-free: 800-721-9037
Phone: 507-372-5558
Fax: 507-372-5726
www.plasticboards.com

Rolath is a 1-1/4"-wide strapping product made from recycled plastic. Most of the product's content is waste from Bedford Technology's other manufacturing operations, which uses post-consumer recycled HDPE and LDPE. Rolath is most often used to secure roofing felt but is also effective at securing polyethylene film and building wraps.

Most recently mentioned in EBN 4:3

Recycled-Rubber Roofing Underlayment

CETCO
1500 W. Shure Dr.
Arlington Heights, IL 60004

Toll-free: 800-527-9948
Phone: 847-818-7918
Fax: 847-818-7987
www.strongsealroofing.com

StrongSeal™ Recycled Rubberized Products manufactures roofing underlayments from recycled tire rubber with 40% recycled content. Duck's Back (25 mils thick) is the company's nail-down version, and StrongSeal Plus (40 mils) is a peel-and-stick version. These products do not contain asphalt and, according to the manufacturer, can be exposed to the elements for a period of 12 months. StrongSeal is backed by an industry leading material warranty.

B-Line C-Port Rooftop Support Systems

Cooper B-Line, Inc.
509 W. Monroe St.
Highland, IL 62249

Toll-free: 800-851-7415
Phone: 618-654-2184
www.cooperbline.com

Made with 100% post-consumer recycled rubber from car tires, Cooper B-Line offers elevating rooftop support systems for pipes, ducts, conduit, HVAC components, and walkways. They are UV-resistant, nonpenetrating, and also appropriate in underfloor applications such as access flooring. The systems dampen vibration, will not float, and support up to 2,500 lbs/ft^2.

Roof-Guard Pads

Humane Manufacturing LLC
805 Moore St.
P.O. Box 24
Baraboo, WI 53913

Toll-free: 800-369-6263
Phone: 608-356-8336
Fax: 608-356-8338
www.humanemfg.com

Roof-Guard Pads are made from recycled-tire rubber, are interlocking, and come in sizes ranging from 2' x 3' to 4' x 6'. They are available with either a raised button or impressed pattern.

Roof Walkway Pads and Paving Risers

North West Rubber Mats, Ltd.
33850 Industrial Ave.
Abbotsford, BC V2S 7T9 Canada

Toll-free: 800-663-8724
Phone: 604-859-2002
Fax: 604-859-2009
www.northwestrubber.com

North West Rubber's Roof Walkway Pads are made from recycled-tire rubber for use in protecting low-slope membrane roofs. The pads are 3/8", 1/2", or 3/4" thick. Paving Risers, made from 100% recycled-tire-derived styrene butadiene rubber, come in squares (6" x 6" and 3/8" or 5/8" thick) or circles (4" in diameter and 1" thick) that are used to support cement roof pavers above the roof membrane surface.

07 72 20
Roof Ventilation Products

Adequate ventilation of attic spaces helps keep buildings with pitched roofs cooler in the summer and reduces the risks of ice dams in the winter. Some evidence indicates that certain roofing materials experience less thermal stress and last longer on properly ventilated roofs, though this contention is hotly debated. Ridge vents in conjunction with soffit vents create an effective ventilation flow, with air entering at the soffits and exiting at the ridge. The ventilation performance of ridge and soffit vents is superior to either gable-end vents or rooftop ventilators. Insulated roofs require an air channel between the insulation and the roof sheathing. Ventilating underlayment products installed beneath roof shingles and tiles allows the roofing to dry uniformly between rain events—increasing life and minimizing mold growth.

**07 00 00
Thermal &
Moisture
Protection**

Cedar Breather

Benjamin Obdyke Inc.
199 Precision Dr.
Horsham, PA 19044

Toll-free: 800-523-5261
Phone: 215-672-7200
Fax: 215-672-3731
www.benjaminobdyke.com

Cedar Breather® is a fire-resistant underlayment for use with wood shingles or shakes, providing continuous airflow between the solid roof deck and shingles. Cedar Breather's 0.27"-thick, 3-dimensional nylon matrix allows the entire underside of the shingle to dry, eliminating excess moisture, preventing thermal cupping and warping, and reducing potential rotting. Cedar Breather eliminates the need for furring strips and comes with a 50-year warranty.

Most recently mentioned in EBN 10:6

Cobra Ridge Vents

GAF Materials Corp.
1361 Alps Rd.
Wayne, NJ 07470

Toll-free: 800-223-1948
Phone: 973-628-3000
Fax: 973-628-3865
www.gaf.com

GAF's Cobra ridge vents are made from recycled fibers formed into an airy, fibrous mat that, when capped with asphalt shingles, provides a low-profile ridge vent.

07 72 43
Roof Walk Boards

Roof walk boards made from recycled-tire rubber or other post-consumer waste products make good use of waste material in a durable, reusable product. They're typically applied over membrane roofs to prevent damage while maintaining roofing or roof-mounted mechanical equipment. They are very effective for walkways on green roofs. Residential uses also include poolsides and concrete decks. These heavy duty mats come in a variety of sizes and thicknesses.

07 00 00
Thermal & Moisture Protection

Roof Trak II

Duro-Last Roofing, Inc.
525 Morley Dr.
Saginaw, MI 48601

Toll-free: 800-248-0280
Phone: 989-753-6486
Fax: 800-432-9331
www.duro-last.com

Roof Trak II is a 100% recycled-PVC walkway pad for low-slope roofs. This product is made from the trimmings of PVC roof-membrane manufacture. The 1/8"-thick Roof Trak II measures 5' x 5' or 2-1/2' x 5' and is installed by heat-welding to the roof membrane.

Nova Walkway Pads

EcoStar
P.O. Box 7000
Carlisle, PA 17013

Toll-free: 800-211-7170
Fax: 888-780-9870
www.ecostar.carlisle.com

EcoStar produces Nova Walkway Pads from Starloy, a proprietary polymer made from 100% recycled post-industrial rubber and plastic. Nova is nonabsorbent, impact-resistant, nonslip, and interlocks for easy installation in areas such as roofs. EcoStar is a division of Carlisle SynTec, Inc. As with other flooring products made from recycled automobile tires, installation is only recommended in semi-enclosed spaces, well-ventilated indoor spaces, or outdoors.

UltraGard PVC WBP-100 Heavy Duty Walkway Pad

Johns Manville Corporation
P.O. Box 5108
Denver, CO 80217

Toll-free: 800-654-3103
Phone: 303-978-2000
Fax: 303-978-3661
www.jm.com

UltraGard PVC WBP-100 Heavy Duty Walkway Pad is a recycled thermoplastic-content pad for high-traffic areas of low-slope roofs. This product is available in 3'- and 4'-wide rolls.

07 80 00
Fire and Smoke Protection

Fireproofing materials for steel structures don't eliminate the effects of fire, but rather provide a margin of safety for escaping building occupants. The insulative, non-combustion-supporting qualities of fireproofing products protect steel members from extreme heat that can cause structural failure. Traditionally, products containing asbestos and fiberglass have been used for this application. Recycled-content products that are free from IAQ-related concerns provide an environmentally attractive option relative to resource use and the health of building occupants.

Monokote Type MK-6

W. R. Grace & Company
62 Whittemore Ave.
Cambridge, MA 02140

Toll-free: 800-778-2880
Phone: 617-876-1400
Fax: 800-778-2885
www.na.graceconstruction.com

Monokote® Type MK-6® is a fireproofing material with an integral mold inhibitor for steel and concrete structures that is made from gypsum, post-industrial recycled EPS foam, and recycled newsprint. No water is used in its manufacture. MK-6 was used in the green Conde Nast Building at Four Times Square.

07 91 00
Preformed Joint Seals

Quality weatherstripping and gaskets are very important in achieving airtight, low-energy buildings. Specialized gaskets can also be used as a moisture-control strategy, as in the "Airtight Drywall Approach" for light-frame construction.

Weatherstripping and Joint Sealants

illbruck Sealant Systems, inc.
3800 Washington Ave. N
Minneapolis, MN 55412

Toll-free: 800-438-0684
Phone: 612-521-3555
Fax: 612-588-8396
www.illbruck.de/usa/

illbruck Sealant Systems, inc. offers weatherstripping products that can be used alone or together as part of a system. The company's i2112™ platform focuses on window and door installation. Products include: illbruck Vapor Permeable Tape, illbruck Window Flashing Tape, Perennator 2112™ Window & Perimeter Silicone, and illbruck Insulation Tape. illbruck's willseal 600 is a precompressed, self-expanding polyurethane foam joint sealant for joint sizes from 1/8" to 1-1/2" (in rolls) and from 1-3/4" and wider (in sticks). illbruck products are manufactured in Europe.

Weatherstripping and Gaskets

M-D Building Products
4041 N. Santa Fe Ave.
Oklahoma City, OK 73118

Toll-free: 800-654-8454
Phone: 405-528-4411
Fax: 800-557-3568
www.mdteam.com

M-D manufactures a wide range of weatherstripping and weatherization products.

Weatherstripping and Gaskets

Resource Conservation Technology, Inc.
2633 N. Calvert St.
Baltimore, MD 21218

Toll-free: 800-477-7724
Phone: 410-366-1146
Fax: 410-366-1202
www.conservationtechnology.com

Resource Conservation Technology specializes in building gaskets, weatherstripping, and air barriers.

07 92 13
Caulk Joint Sealants

Environmental considerations for caulking materials include durability, potentially hazardous ingredients, and VOC content. (See also 07 92 14 - Foam Joint Sealants.)

Chem-Calk 600 & 2000

Bostik, Inc.
211 Boston St.
Middleton, MA 01949

Toll-free: 800-366-7837
Phone: 978-777-0100
Fax: 978-750-7319
www.bostik-us.com

Chem-Calk 600 is a white, paintable, water based, siliconized acrylic latex caulk for general purpose architectural sealing. It is appropriate for interior and limited exterior applications, has 39 g/l VOC, and is available in tubes and 5-lb buckets. Chem-Calk 2000 is a modified single-component polyurethane caulk that is solvent- and isocyanate-free. This non-silicone, elastomeric sealant is moisture-curable and is appropriate for exterior architectural applications. It has less than 30 g/l VOC, and is available

in tubes and in sausage packs that limit the amount of waste from empty tubes (ten 20-ounce sausage packs generate the same waste as one 10-ounce tube).

Quick Shield VOC-Free Sealant

Geocel Corporation
P.O. Box 398
Elkhart, IN 46515

Toll-free: 800-348-7615
Phone: 574-264-0645
Fax: 800-348-7009
www.geocelusa.com

Quick Shield is a white, one-part, quick-setting, interior/exterior flexible sealant that contains no VOCs. It is resistant to water within 5 minutes and is paintable within 10 minutes. Quick Shield bonds to wood, aluminum, brick, and concrete without a primer. It cleans up with water, is mold- and mildew-resistant, and is rated to last 50 years.

Henkel Consumer Adhesives & Sealants

Henkel Consumer Adhesives
7405 Production Dr.
Mentor, OH 44060

Toll-free: 800-321-3578
Phone: 440-255-8900
Fax: 800-227-6095
www.henkelca.com

The following Polyseamseal products are water-based with VOC levels from 2 g/l to 32 g/l: Acrylic Caulk with Silicone; Outdoor Window, Door & Siding Sealant; Painters Latex Caulk; and All-Purpose Adhesive Caulk and Tub & Tile Adhesive Caulk (both in clear).

The following OSI Pro Series products are water-based and low-VOC: H2U Acrylic Urethane Sealant (<5 g/l VOC), PC-158 Painter's Choice Latex Caulk (24 g/l), SA-167 Siliconized Acrylic Latex Caulk (colors 41 g/l, clear <5 g/l), CS-150 Latex Concrete Crack Sealant (40 g/l), SC-175 Acoustical Sound Sealant (25 g/l), SW-325 Shear & Drywall Adhesive (<3 g/l), QB-350 Latex Multi Purpose Construction Adhesive (22 g/l), SF-550 High Performance Latex Deck & Subfloor Adhesive (<2 g/l), and SF-555 Fiberglass Construction Adhesive (<2 g/l).

The following PL products are water-based and low-VOC: Tub & Shower Surround Adhesive (<3 g/l VOC), Latex FRP Adhesive (<3 g/l), Ceramic Tile Adhesive (15 g/l), Cove Base Adhesive (20 g/l), and Water Based Contact Cement (10 g/l).

Liquid Nails Brand Supercaulk and Painter's Caulk

Macco Adhesives
15885 Sprague Rd.
Strongsville, OH 44136

Toll-free: 800-634-0015
Phone: 440-297-7304
Fax: 440-297-7366
www.liquidnails.com

Liquid Nails® Brand Super Caulk (LC130) is a water-based acrylic latex sealant that has a VOC content of 26.1 g/l. Liquid Nails Brand Painter's Caulk (LC135) is a water-based acrylic latex sealant that has a VOC content of 70 g/l.

Pecora Sealants

Pecora Corporation
165 Wambold Rd.
Harleysville, PA 19438

Toll-free: 800-523-6688
Phone: 215-723-6051
Fax: 215-721-0286
www.pecora.com

AC-20® + Silicone is a one-part, water-based acrylic/silicone sealant with a VOC content of 31 g/l. It is available in 11 standard colors. Pecora 864, 890, and 895 are all one-part silicone sealants with VOC contents of 12 g/l. Urexpan® NR-200 (two-part) and Urexpan NR-201 (one-part) are both polyurethane traffic-grade sealants. Both parts of NR-200 are zero-VOC. Pro-Silsct 1, at less than 15 g/l VOCs, is a one-part hybrid polymer sealant used for sealing perimeters, expansion joints, EIFS, etc.

Phenoseal and Sealant

Phenoseal
2400 Boston St., Ste. 200
Baltimore, MD 21224

Toll-free: 800-543-3840
Fax: 410-675-2100
www.phenoseal.com

Phenoseal is a vinyl acetate homopolymer-based adhesive caulk. (Note that vinyl acetate does not contain chlorine, so is very different from PVC.) This product is often tolerated by the environmentally sensitive. Uncured Phenoseal can be cleaned up with water. Sealant is a water-based acrylic latex window and door sealant.

**07 00 00
Thermal & Moisture Protection**

Tremflex 834 and Tremco Spectrem 1

Tremco, Inc.
3735 Green Rd.
Company City
Beachwood, OH 44122

Toll-free: 800-852-8173
Phone: 216-292-5000
Fax: 216-292-5036
www.tremcosealants.com

Tremflex 834 is a water-based, siliconized acrylic latex sealant with a VOC content of 13.7 g/l. It is mildew-resistant and can be used in bathrooms and kitchens, as well as for general interior and exterior caulking, as a back bedding glazing compound, and as an acoustical sealant. It is paintable and comes in white only.

Tremco Spectrem 1 is a one-part, zero-VOC, moisture-curing silicone joint sealant suitable for high-movement building joint applications such as aluminum curtain walls, precast concrete panels, metal panels, and window perimeters.

07 92 14
Foam Joint Sealants

The challenge of sealing building envelopes against air infiltration is made easier with foam sealants. Look for products with blowing agents that are non-ozone-depleting and have low global-warming potential. Be aware that a label "no CFCs" is not the same as "ozone-safe"; HCFC propellants/blowing agents, while not as bad as CFCs, still deplete ozone. Foam sealants are commonly available in high-expanding and low-expanding formulations; low-expanding foam is the material of choice for sealing window and door rough openings—it performs significantly better than fiberglass and will be less likely than high-expanding foams to swell the openings (which can make opening and closing difficult). Foam sealants are useful in many applications, especially in building renovation. Some products are available only in disposable cans; the use of bulk tanks and reusable dispensing guns can reduce the environmental costs of using these sealants by minimizing waste. (See also 07 92 13 - Caulk Joint Sealants.)

Touch'n Foam

Convenience Products
866 Horan Dr.
Fenton, MO 63026

Toll-free: 800-325-6180
Phone: 636-349-5333
Fax: 636-349-5335
www.convenienceproducts.com

Touch'n Foam is an HCFC-free foam sealant that uses a mixture of propane and isobutane as the blowing agent. It is available in triple-expanding or low-expanding formulations in disposable cans.

Most recently mentioned in EBN 6:9

CF 116

Hilti, Inc.
P.O. Box 21148
Tulsa, OK 74121

Toll-free: 800-879-8000
Phone: 918-252-6000
Fax: 800-879-7000
www.us.hilti.com

CF 116 is a single-component, polyurethane-based foam sealant propelled by HFC-134a, propane, and isobutane blowing agents. This minimally expanding product is dispensed from a can with a reusable gun. According to the company, one can is equivalent to 46 ten-ounce tubes of caulk.

Most recently mentioned in EBN 6:9

Universal Foam Sealant

illbruck Sealant Systems, inc.
3800 Washington Ave. N
Minneapolis, MN 55412

Toll-free: 800-438-0684
Phone: 612-521-3555
Fax: 612-588-8396
www.illbruck.de/usa/

illbruck's Universal Foam Sealant is an HCFC-free, one-component, moisture-cure polyurethane foam for filling, bonding, and sealing. Manufactured in the Netherlands, the product is hydrocarbon-blown and is dispensed from a gun-grade or tube-grade aerosol can. Universal Foam Sealant has a light green color; other colors are available upon request.

PurFil 1G

Todol Products
25 Washington Ave.
P.O. Box 398
Natick, MA 01760

Toll-free: 800-252-3818
Phone: 508-651-3818
Fax: 508-651-0729
www.todol.com

PurFil 1G uses HFC-134a as its propellant and a mix of propane and isobutane as the blowing agent. It is available in disposable cans with application guns.

Most recently mentioned in EBN 6:9

This Space is Available for Your Notes

**07 00 00
Thermal & Moisture Protection**

08 00 00 Openings

PRODUCT LISTINGS

08 01 00
General Information and Operation & Maintenance of Openings

These listings are for industry representation and ratings organizations for doors and windows.

Industry Representation

National Fenestration Rating Council
8484 Georgia Ave., Ste. 320
Silver Spring, MD 20910

Phone: 301-589-1776
Fax: 301-589-3884
www.nfrc.org

The National Fenestration Rating Council (NFRC), a nonprofit research and educational organization, promulgates standards for determining the energy performance of fenestration products and administers a voluntary, uniform rating and labeling system for communicating the energy performance of windows, doors, curtain wall and storefront systems, and skylights. NFRC provides a freely accessible listing of fenestration products and their related energy performance ratings.

The Efficient Windows Collaborative

The Efficient Windows Collaborative
1850 M St., NW
Suite 600
Washington, DC 20036

Phone: 202-530-2254
Fax: 202-331-9588
www.efficientwindows.org

The Efficient Windows Collaborative is actively involved in promoting energy-efficient windows. A nonprofit coalition comprised of industry, government, and other interested groups, their website provides free resources and information.

08 01 10
Operation and Maintenance of Doors and Frames

Innovative products can prolong the life of doors and improve their energy performance.

GenYDoors Resurfacing System

New

GenYDoors Inc.
145 Schoolhouse St., Ste 28
Coquitlam, BC V3K 4X8 Canada

Phone: 604-551-1137
www.genydoors.com

Using a process developed in Finland, GenYDoors resurfaces existing flat-panel interior doors into paneled-door look-alikes—a more environmentally-friendly and cost-effective alternative to purchasing new doors for renovation projects (especially for non-standard sizes) that keeps old doors out of landfills and avoids the environmental debt of making new ones. The door coating and "panel" edges are made with high-impact polystyrene and adhered using a water-based, zero-VOC glue. Three finishes are offered: white, beech, and cherry. The system requires that the existing doors be brought to a GenYDoors shop location.

08 11 00
Metal Doors and Frames

Even though steel conducts heat more readily than wood, steel entry doors that include foam insulation and are installed in wooden frames with quality weatherstripping generally provide better energy performance than wood entry doors. In choosing an insulated entry door, consider the R-value of the insulation, weatherstripping, and glazing materials.

Contours Steel Doors

Jeld-Wen, Inc.
401 Harbor Isles Blvd.
Klamath Falls, OR 97601

Toll-free: 800-535-3936
Phone: 541-882-3451
Fax: 541-884-2231
www.jeld-wen.com

The Contours steel entry door has an EPS foam core and is available with low-e coated insulating glass. By contrast, most insulation used in entry doors is polyurethane, which is made with ozone-depleting HCFCs. The Contours line replaces Jeld-Wen's Energy Saver line.

08 14 00
Wood Doors

Products listed here include doors made from FSC-certified wood or reclaimed wood. As with other wood products, specifying certified-wood doors promotes long-term forest management for the benefit of forest ecosystems, timber resources, and local economies. Reclaimed wood doors, like other reclaimed wood products, don't carry the environmental burdens of recent timber harvesting. Previously harvested woods remilled into wood doors can provide rich colors and beauty generally not available from today's faster-growing timber. From an energy performance perspective, wood entry doors are usually not the best option. Composite entry doors, like steel doors, are available with foam insulation; these doors far outperform traditional solid-wood doors in terms of energy conservation. Composite doors may also be made from recovered and/or recycled materials. (See also 01 62 02 - Distributors/Retailers, Used Building Materials.)

Reclaimed-Wood Products

Albany Woodworks, Inc.

For full listing, see CSI section 06 22 02 - Reclaimed-Wood Millwork

08 00 00
Openings

Certified Wood Doors

Algoma Hardwoods, Inc.
1001 Perry St.
Algoma, WI 54201

Toll-free: 800-678-8910
Phone: 920-487-5221
Fax: 920-487-3636
www.algomahardwoods.com

Algoma Hardwoods manufactures and supplies FSC-certified interior wood doors for residential and commercial custom orders. Lead time for orders of 20 to 30 doors is 10 weeks. The primary species is red oak, with some birch and cherry available as well.

Interior and Exterior Doors

Alternative Timber Structures, Inc.
1054 Rammell Mt. Rd.
Tetonia, ID 83452

Phone: 208-456-2711
Fax: 208-456-2711
www.alternativetimberstructures.com

The Bead & Batten Door specializes in custom-building of doors in unusual sizes and thicknesses from reclaimed and new woods.

Reclaimed-Wood Products

Crossroads Recycled Lumber

For full listing, see CSI section 06 13 02 - Reclaimed-Wood Heavy Timber

Certified Wood Doors

Eggers Industries
1 Eggers Dr.
P.O. Box 88
Two Rivers, WI 54241

Phone: 920-793-1351
Fax: 920-793-2958
www.eggersindustries.com

Eggers Industries manufactures architectural wood doors in flush as well as stile-and-rail styles that are SmartWood-certified according to the standards of the Forest Stewardship Council. The doors are certified by partial-content rules to contain over 70% certified wood. Current certified offerings include nonrated and 20-minute doors, negative or positive pressure. Some products, such as the wood composite doors, contain urea-formaldehyde resins; check with the manufacturer.

Recycled-Content Wood Doors

Executive Door Company
3939 W. Clarendon
Phoenix, AZ 85019

Phone: 602-272-8076
Fax: 602-272-9460
www.executivedoor.com

Executive Door Company manufactures Environmental residential and commercial interior and exterior doors from medium-density fiberboard (MDF). The doors are constructed of 100% recovered and recycled wood fibers with at least 30% post-industrial recycled waste content. Executive Door offers a lifetime warranty against splitting, cracking, or warping.

Reclaimed-Wood Building Products

General Woodcraft, Inc.

For full listing, see CSI section 09 64 02 - Reclaimed-Wood Flooring

Certified Stave Core Doors

Marshfield DoorSystems™
1401 E. 4th St.
P.O. Box 7780
Marshfield, WI 54449

Toll-free: 800-869-3667
Phone: 715-384-2141
www.marshfielddoors.com

Marshfield DoorSystems' Environmental-Class Architectural Wood Doors are FSC-certified stave core doors available for non-rated as well as 20-minute rated applications with either neutral- or positive-pressure fire labels. The composite products in this door do not contain any added urea-formaldehyde. Doors are available with a wide range of veneer options, Styled™ faces, medium-density overlay (MDO), or plastic laminate. Also available is the Enviroclad™ UV factory finish, which uses water-based stains and ultraviolet-cured topcoats, and releases no VOCs. Glue used in the stave core contains 1-5% formaldehyde, but, according to the manufacturer, the doors are encapsulated and will not release any formaldehyde.

Reclaimed-Wood Carriage Doors

Real Carriage Door Company **New**
13417 82nd Ave. NW
Gig Harbor, WA 98329

Phone: 253-238-6908
Fax: 253-238-6231
www.realcarriagedoors.com

The "Green Line" of doors from Real Carriage Door includes garage or entry doors made from reclaimed wood. Reclaimed-wood doors are made from re-milled aged warehouse beams.

Reclaimed-Wood Building Products

Vintage Log and Lumber, Inc.

For full listing, see CSI section 06 13 02 - Reclaimed-Wood Heavy Timber

Certified Wood Doors

VT Industries, Inc.
1000 Industrial Park
Box 490
Holstein, IA 51025

Toll-free: 800-827-1615
Phone: 712-368-4381
Fax: 712-368-4111
www.vtindustries.com

VT Industries offers a line of architectural wood doors certified by SmartWood according to the standards of the Forest Stewardship Council.

08 16 00
Composite Doors

Products listed here are made with agfiber cores.

Wheatcore Doors and Cabinets

Humabuilt Healthy Building Systems
2305-C Ashland St. #511
Ashland, OR 97520

Phone: 541-488-0931
Fax: 541-488-0932
www.humabuilt.com

Humabuilt Wheatcore Doors are available in a wide variety of styles, sizes, wood-veneer species, and paint-grade finishes. The core is made from chopped wheat straw bound with waterproof, nonformaldehyle, MDI binder. These doors contain 85% rapidly renewable resource by volume. Lag-bolt construction at the door edges strengthens the styles and rails. Ultra-low-VOC water-based adhesives are used for joining components and veneers. The competitively priced doors have a lifetime warranty to the original owner and a five-year commercial warranty. Humabuilt Wheatcore production cabinets are available in a wide variety of styles, sizes, and wood-veneer species. These production cabinets are KCMA certified.

Most recently mentioned in EBN 13:12

08 00 00
Openings

Agrifiber Core Architectural Doors

VT Industries, Inc.
1000 Industrial Park
Box 490
Holstein, IA 51025

Toll-free: 800-827-1615
Phone: 712-368-4381
Fax: 712-368-4111
www.vtindustries.com

VT Industries manufactures architectural wood doors with agrifiber particleboard cores. The core material is manufactured from rapidly renewable materials such as wheat straw, soybean straw, and sunflower hulls, with formaldehyde-free binders. Agrifiber-core doors are available in a variety of sizes and finishes, with FSC certified veneer available by special order. The doors can be manufactured as non-fire-rated, or to meet Category-A 20-minute positive pressure fire ratings, with 45-minute and 60-minute fire ratings also available in limited sizes.

08 36 00
Panel Doors

The energy performance of overhead garage doors is less crucial than for entry doors leading to conditioned spaces. In fact, the prevalence of vehicle emissions and other VOCs in garages may necessitate ventilation instead of airtightness. Material choices are a higher priority environmental consideration for overhead doors. Look for recycled content.

CladPanel Garage Door Inserts

Ankmar, LLC
4600 Kansas Avenue
Kansas City, KS 66106

Phone: 913-621-7000
Fax: 913-621-7171
www.ankmar.com

CladPanel™ (formerly Cladwood®) Garage Door Inserts are made from a phenol-formaldehyde-bonded particleboard core with resin-impregnated recycled-paper overlays. According to the manufacturer, the fiber in this product is 100% post-consumer, post-industrial recovered and recycled content, as certified by Scientific Certification Systems.

08 44 00
Curtain Wall and Glazed Assemblies

With metal-framed curtain wall systems, look for products that offer superior thermal performance, which is a function of both the glazing system and the effectiveness of the thermal break in the frame. Other features to consider include the use of recycled material and the ability to incorporate photovoltaic cells for power generation.

Formawall and Versawall

Centria Architectural Systems
1005 Beaver Grade Rd.
Moon Township, PA 15108

Toll-free: 800-759-7474
www.centria.com

Centria produces insulated composite wall and roof panel systems for commercial buildings that can be used in either new or retrofit applications. The panels consist of ozone-safe polyisocyanurate insulation between steel skins. Two-inch thick panels offer R-13 insulation, and three-inch panels offer R-17 (averaged across the wall). The panels include an integral rainscreen and air barrier for weathertight envelopes in cooling, heating, or mixed climates. These products are Cradle-to-Cradle certified by MBDC. The company offers a variety of colors, finishes, and panel sizes with a 20-year warranty on the finish.

Most recently mentioned in EBN 16:2

1600 PowerWall and 1600 PowerShade

Kawneer Company, Inc., an Alcoa Company
555 Guthridge Ct.
Norcross, GA 30092

Phone: 770-449-5555
Fax: 770-734-1560
www.kawneer.com

1600 PowerWall® and 1600 PowerShade®, formerly PowerSlope®, integrated photovoltaic curtain wall systems combine the 1600 Wall System® with photovoltaic cells. These polycrystalline or amorphous silicon solar electric modules convert light energy from the sun into electricity without using fossil fuels. Fully tested, they can be incorporated into vertical and slope glazed applications. PowerWall and PowerShade can be finished with Interpon® D2000 Advance Powder Coatings, which meet AAMA 1604 requirements.

Most recently mentioned in EBN 10:3

OKASOLAR and OKALUX Insulating Glass Panels

Schott North America, Inc.
555 Taxter Rd.
Elmsford, NY 10523

Phone: 914-831-2200
Fax: 914-831-2346
www.us.schott.com

Okasolar® glazing panels are custom-made insulated glass units with built-in fixed louvers that reflect sunlight upward towards the ceiling. The louvers have a specular reflective coating, and their width and angle is customized for each project's location and requirements for solar transmittance, light transmittance, and views. The panels can be specified for vertical or sloped application. Okalux® light-diffusing glass panels have hollow capillary fibers hermetically sealed between sheets of laminated float glass, offering stronger performance characteristics than ordinary insulated glass. Optimized for inclined roofs and overhead glazings. Schott Corporation's Technical Glass Division is the exclusive North American distributor of Okasolar, which is manufactured in Germany by Okalux Kapillarglas Gmbh.

Superwindow

Viracon
800 Park Dr.
Owatonna, MN 55060

Toll-free: 800-533-2080
Phone: 507-451-9555
Fax: 507-444-3555
www.viracon.com

Viracon's Superwindow insulating glazing for curtain wall applications has two Solarscreen coatings. A reflective coating is applied to the #2 surface, and a low-e coating is applied to the #3 surface. Superwindow glazing has an emissivity of 0.04.

Visionwall Window and Curtain Wall Systems

Visionwall Corporation
17915-118 Ave.
Edmonton, AB T5S 1L6 Canada

Toll-free: 800-400-8633
Phone: 780-451-4000
Fax: 780-451-4745
www.visionwall.com

Visionwall offers factory-assembled high-performance, energy-efficient window, skylight, and curtain wall systems, custom-designed and optimized for climate, orientation, and internal loads of commercial buildings. Visionwall glazing includes one or two suspended films in conjunction with wide air spaces, low-e coatings, and thermally broken frames. Visionwall curtain wall systems have R-values of 3 to 7.

Most recently mentioned in EBN 6:7

08 00 00
Openings

08 45 00
Translucent Wall and Roof Assemblies

Commercial, institutional, and industrial buildings are the primary applications for large translucent wall and roof panels. Some products are available with excellent energy performance while providing daylight into interior spaces. Polycarbonates are omitted from GreenSpec due to concerns about BPA (bisphenol-A), a chemical precursor in the manufacture of polycarbonates. BPA is a bioaccumulating chemical that is a potential endocrine-disrupter. (See also 08 61 00 - Roof Windows.)

Kalwall

Kalwall Corp.
1111 Candia Rd.
P.O. Box 237
Manchester, NH 03105

Toll-free: 800-258-9777
Phone: 603-627-3861
Fax: 603-627-7905
www.kalwall.com

Kalwall is a fiberglass glazing material bonded to a structural grid core. The standard 2-3/4"-thick panels are available in a thermally broken design yielding U-values as low as 0.10 (R-10). The material has a weight of less than 3 lbs/ft². Other panel options include translucent fiberglass insulation (offering a range of shading coefficients) and curved panels. Kalwall is also available with a silica aerogel—Nanogel™—fill that provides higher insulating value (R-20) and greater sunlight transmissivity (10%, 15%, or 20%). The company engineers and prefabricates skylight and curtain wall systems. This rugged material's translucent qualities provide diffuse daylighting without sacrificing energy performance.

Most recently mentioned in EBN 11:12 & 12:3

08 52 00
Wood Windows

As with other building products made from wood, the source of that wood should be an important consideration. Currently, only a very few manufacturers use FSC-certified wood as a standard frame material, though more use it in certain components or as a special-order option. (Certification to Forest Stewardship Council—FSC—standards involves third-party evaluation and monitoring of sustainable forestry practices.) Energy performance is the primary green consideration of windows, and new developments in window technology enable today's products to far outperform those of a few decades ago. Among the improvements are multiple glazing layers, low-conductivity gas fills, better seals on insulated glazing units, heat-reflective (low-emissivity) coatings, advanced weather-stripping, and new frame systems. Low-emissivity coatings which allow short-wavelength solar radiation (sunlight) to pass through but reflect long-wavelength radiation (heat) back into the conditioned space are now standard options from all major window manufacturers. Further improvement in energy performance is achieved with triple-glazing and multiple low-e coatings; sometimes an additional glazing layer is provided as a suspended polyester film. To qualify for GreenSpec, wood windows must achieve an NFRC-certified unit U-factor of 0.25 or lower and must not only be available, but actively marketed. The U-factor threshold is higher (less stringent) for fiberglass, certified-wood, or recycled-content frame materials—and more stringent (lower U-factors) for vinyl because of environmental concerns with PVC.

Certified Wood Windows

J. S. Benson Woodworking & Design, LLC
118 Birge St.
Brattleboro, VT 05301

Toll-free: 800-339-3515
Phone: 802-254-3515
Fax: 802-254-4874
www.jsbensonwoodworking.com

J. S. Benson Woodworking & Design is a manufacturer of high-end, custom, true-divided-lite windows both for the renovation and new construction market. Products are available in FSC-certified mahogany. The company offers dual-sealed insulated units using clear annealed glass. Energy features include low-e coatings, argon-fill, and warm-edge insulated glass spacers.

High-Performance Wood Windows

Jeld-Wen Windows & Doors, Willmar Collection
550 Munroe Ave.
Winnipeg, MB R2K 4H3 Canada

Toll-free: 888-945-5627
Phone: 204-668-8230
Fax: 204-663-1072
www.willmar.ca

Willmar Windows, part of the Jeld-Wen family, manufactures wood windows with 8 glazing options. Included in Willmar's selection are a number of dual-pane and triple-pane glazing options available with Solar Gain and Solar Shield low-e coatings featuring warm-edge Intercept spacers, and with low-conductivity gas-fill. In addition to solid wood, Willmar Windows are available in metal-clad and copper-clad models. The company also makes 100% vinyl windows.

Heat Smart

Loewen Windows
77 Hwy. #52 W
Steinbach, MB R5G 1B2 Canada

Toll-free: 800-563-9367
Phone: 204-326-6446
Fax: 800-563-9361
www.loewen.com

Loewen Window's Heat Smart glazing is available in three versions: double-glazed with low-e coatings and argon gas-fill; triple-glazed with one low-e coating and one argon-filled cavity; and triple-glazed with two low-e coatings and two argon-filled cavities. All products are NFRC-rated. Loewen Windows is a founding member of the DOE Efficient Window Collaborative and is an Energy Star® window partner. Loewen windows incorporate some FSC-certified wood.

Most recently mentioned in EBN 5:2

High-Performance Wood Windows

Marvin Windows and Doors
401 States Ave.
P.O. Box 100
Warroad, MN 56763

Toll-free: 888-537-7828
Phone: 218-386-1430
Fax: 218-386-4027
www.marvin.com

Marvin offers a High-R glazing option with its wood windows that includes triple glazing with two low-E coatings and argon gas-fill. U-factors as low as 0.18 for Marvin wood windows are found in the NFRC Certified Products Directory, with many products having U-factors below 0.25.

08 00 00
Openings

High-Performance Windows

Milgard Manufacturing, Inc.

For full listing, see CSI section 08 54 00 - Composite Windows

High-Performance Wood & Vinyl Windows

Paramount Windows, Inc.
105 Panet Rd.
Winnipeg, MB R2J 0S1 Canada

Toll-free: 800-519-0508
Phone: 204-233-4966
Fax: 204-231-1043
www.paramountwindows.com

Paramount Windows, founded in 1948, has been promoting highly energy-efficient windows for decades. The company introduced insulated-glass windows in 1957 and triple-glazed windows (Canada's first) in 1962. The company primarily produces wood and aluminum-clad wood windows but also offers vinyl windows—mostly for the replacement market. Several glazing options are available: EnerPlus 4 is triple-glazed with one low-e coating, argon gas-fill in one of the interpane spaces, and two energy-saving spacers. EnerPlus 6 is triple-glazed with two low-e coatings, and argon gas-fill in both interpane spaces. The lowest NFRC U-factor ratings are 0.22. The company's wood supplier recently gained FSC certification, so FSC-certified wood windows can be special-ordered for larger jobs.

Pella Designer Series

Pella Corporation
102 Main St.
Pella, IA 50219

Toll-free: 800-847-3552
Phone: 641-621-1000
Fax: 641-621-6070
www.pella.com

Pella's Designer Series® wood windows and doors are made from ponderosa pine, eastern white pine, sugar pine, and some white fir. They are available with an interior hinged panel of glass and with an exterior panel of either single-pane or double-pane argon-filled, low-emissivity glazing. The exterior is clad with recycled aluminum finished with a baked-on EnduraClad™ coating. These windows are made with 21% post-industrial recycled content, per the manufacturer. A number of Pella windows have unit U-factors at or below 0.25.

Most recently mentioned in EBN 5:2

High-Performance Wood Windows

Weather Shield Manufacturing, Inc.
1 Weathershield Plz.
P.O. Box 309
Medford, WI 54451

Toll-free: 800-477-6808
Phone: 715-748-2100
Fax: 715-748-0169
www.weathershield.com

Weather Shield offers a wide range of wood window products and glazing options. The highest performing glazing options are Value R6 and Value R10. Value R6 is a triple-glazed, argon-filled panel with two low-e surfaces. Value R10 is similar to Value R6 but contains a krypton/argon gas mix. The foundation of the glazing program is a warm-edge spacer system that is used to enhance thermal performance. Among the lowest unit U-factors found in the NFRC Certified Products Directory are 0.16 for commercial-sized fixed windows and 0.17 for residential-sized. According to the manufacturer, colored and specialty glass may also be specified to meet SHGC, structural, or safety specs.

Most recently mentioned in EBN 5:2

08 53 00
Plastic Windows

Like vinyl, ABS is very low-maintenance. Because there's no chlorine in ABS, there's no risk of dioxin generation during an accidental fire or incineration at the end of the product's life.

Accent High-Performance Vinyl Windows

Accent Windows, Inc.
12300 Pecos St.
Westminster, CO 80234

Toll-free: 888-284-3948
Phone: 303-420-2002
Fax: 303-432-8674
www.accentwindows.com

Accent Windows is a Colorado manufacturer of vinyl replacement windows. The company uses low-e glass coatings (LoElite™) or suspended Heat Mirror™ films, along with argon or argon/krypton gas-fills to achieve some of the highest energy performance of any replacement windows. Unit U-factors are as low as 0.17. All Accent windows are custom-manufactured, so the dimensions will be optimized to the window opening. The company serves the mountain region from Billings, Montana to Albuquerque, New Mexico and also St. Louis, Missouri.

Gilkey High-Performance Vinyl Windows

Gilkey Window Company, Inc.
3625 Hauck Rd.
Cincinnati, OH 45241

Toll-free: 800-878-7771
Phone: 513-769-4527
Fax: 513-769-2567
www.gilkey.com

Gilkey Window manufactures custom vinyl replacement windows for Ohio, Kentucky, and the Upper Midwest. The company offers a wide range of glazing options and actively promotes super-high-performance windows as well as the strategy of using glazings specifically "tuned" to the orientation. Among the glazing options is a "quad" option with both a low-e coating on two glass panes and a suspended Heat Mirror® coating, with krypton gas-fill and warm-edge glass spacers. The NFRC Certified Products Directory lists products with unit U-factors as low as 0.14 (R-7.1). Company sales reps carry Btu meters to explain and demonstrate energy savings potential to prospective customers, and a 20% energy savings guarantee is provided with certain windows.

Gorell High-Performance Vinyl Windows

Gorell Enterprises, Inc. Windows & Doors
1380 Wayne Ave.
Indiana, PA 15701

Toll-free: 800-9-GORELL
Phone: 724-465-1800
Fax: 724-465-1894
www.gorell.com

Gorell was founded as a manufacturer of vinyl windows in 1994. The company offers a number of energy-conserving glazing options for replacement and new-construction applications; many meet the *GreenSpec* criteria for vinyl windows. All Gorell windows feature heavy-duty construction with four-point fusion welding and the PPG Intercept spacer system. Gorell's best-performing glass is Thermal Master III, a triple-glazed unit with two low-e coatings and krypton gas-fill. The highest-performance Gorell products in the NFRC Certified Products Directory have unit U-factors as low as 0.17. More than 92% of Gorell's product line qualifies for the Energy Star label.

UniFrame Maxuus 10

Great Lakes Window, Inc.
P.O. Box 1896
Toledo, OH 43603

Toll-free: 800-666-0000
Fax: 419-666-8324
www.greatlakeswindow.com

08 00 00
Openings

The UniFrame line of vinyl replacement windows from Great Lakes Window includes a Maxuus 10 option in every configuration (double-hung, slider, casement, awning, etc.). The Maxuus 10 option provides triple glazing with two low-e coatings and krypton gas fill, for a whole-unit U-value of 0.19 to 0.21, depending on the configuration. All UniFrame windows are made from unplasticized, impact-resistant polyvinyl chloride (uiPVC) frames with polyurethane foam insulation in the cores.

Kensington High-Performance Vinyl Windows

Kensington Windows, Inc.
1136 Industrial Park Dr.
Vandergrift, PA 15690

Toll-free: 800-444-4972
Phone: 724-845-8133
Fax: 724-845-9151
www.kensingtonwindows.com

Kensington manufactures fairly high-end vinyl replacement windows sold primarily through dealers east of the Rocky Mountains. The company emphasizes energy efficiency and offers dozens of products that exceed the *GreenSpec* criteria for super energy performance. The highest-performance windows have two panes with low-e coatings, plus a suspended Heat Mirror film (for a total of three low-e coatings), krypton gas-fill, and foam-filled vinyl frames.

High-Performance Windows

Milgard Manufacturing, Inc.

For full listing, see CSI section 08 54 00 - Composite Windows

Paradigm High-Performance Vinyl Windows

Paradigm Windows
P.O. Box 10109
Portland, ME 04104

Toll-free: 877-994-6369
Phone: 207-878-9701
Fax: 207-797-6156
www.paradigmwindows.com

Paradigm's premium double-hung and casement windows have unit U-values that meet the *GreenSpec* standard of .20 for vinyl windows. The highest-performing windows have three glazing layers with krypton fill and multiple low-e films. These windows meet American Architectural Manufacturers Association (AAMA) standards for structural performance, and air and water infiltration.

High-Performance Wood & Vinyl Windows

Paramount Windows, Inc.

For full listing, see CSI section 08 52 00 - Wood Windows

Schuco Homecraft High-Performance Vinyl Windows

SCHÜCO, LP
240 Pane Rd.
Newington, CT 06111

Toll-free: 877-472-4826
Phone: 860-666-0505
Fax: 860-666-2359
www.schuco-usa.com

Schuco Homecraft is the U.S. division of a large European manufacturer that has been producing windows for 40 years. The company offers triple-glazed windows with two low-e coatings and krypton gas-fill. They also use a unique thermoplastic edge spacer, which the company claims outperforms conventional metal spacers both in terms of energy performance and durability.

Stanek High-Performance Vinyl Windows

Stanek Vinyl Windows Corp.
4570 Willow Pkwy.
Cuyahoga Heights, OH 44125

Toll-free: 800-962-5512
Phone: 216-341-7700
Fax: 216-641-0784
www.stanekwindows.com

Stanek Windows is predominantly a regional manufacturer of vinyl replacement windows serving the Cleveland, Ohio area, though the company now sells product in some other areas of the East and Midwest. Included in its offerings are a number of remarkably high-energy-performance windows, including System 9 and System 13—the latter are 1-1/8"-thick quad-glazed windows with two Heat Mirror® suspended films, a low-e coating on one of the panes of glass, and krypton gas-fill. NFRC-based unit U-factors as low as 0.17 are listed in the NFRC Certified Products Directory. Styles offered include casement, double-hung, bays, bows, sliders, and patio doors. All products are custom-fabricated using reinforced vinyl extrusions.

Thermal Industries High-Performance Vinyl Windows

Thermal Industries, Inc.
5450 Second Ave.
Pittsburgh, PA 15207

Toll-free: 800-245-1540
www.ThermalIndustries.com

Thermal Industries, a subsidiary of the Atrium Company, is a Pittsburgh-based manufacturer of custom vinyl replacement windows serving many regions of the eastern U.S. The company's highest-performance glass package, Super Peak Performance™ Glass, has three layers of glass, two low-e coatings, krypton gas-fill, and low-conductivity warm-edge spacers between the panes of glass. The NFRC Certified Products Directory lists unit U-factors as low as 0.18.

High-Performance Non-PVC Thermoplastic Windows

Thermal Line Windows, Inc.
3601 30th Ave. NW
P.O. Box 579
Mandan, ND 58554

Toll-free: 800-662-1832
Phone: 701-663-1832
Fax: 701-663-1832
www.tlwindows.com

A regional company (12-state Midwestern region) founded in 1984, Thermal Line produces both vinyl (PVC) windows and windows made from an engineered ABS plastic called Compozit™. This is a thermoplastic material engineered by GE Plastics division under the name Cycolac/Geloy. Performance is similar to PVC, and the material contains no chlorine. The highest-performance Compozit windows are triple-glazed with two low-e coatings and krypton gas-fill; they have NFRC-listed unit U-factors as low as 0.20 for residential-sized windows and 0.19 for commercial.

08 54 00
Composite Windows

Fiberglass has some distinct advantages over wood, vinyl, and metal for window frame and sash construction. As high-quality wood resources become scarce, fiberglass (a composite of polyester resin and glass fibers) is likely to become more common because of its energy performance and durability. Pultruded fiberglass frame members have a hollow profile that's usually insulated with fiberglass or polyurethane foam. Because the conduction through window frames is a significant source of heat loss, insulated fiberglass frames are an attractive option. The coefficient of thermal expansion of fiberglass is low, very similar to that of glass; limited differential expansion and contraction between the sash and glazing materials puts less stress on the glazing's edge seals. Durability of fiberglass as an exterior material

08 00 00
Openings

is also good. Most fiberglass windows have factory-applied, baked-on coatings and can be repainted. To be included in GreenSpec, fiberglass window lines must include products with NFRC unit U-factors of 0.30 or lower.

High-Performance Fiberglass Windows

Accurate Dorwin Company
1535 Seel Ave.
Winnipeg, MB R3T 1C6 Canada

Toll-free: 888-982-4640
Phone: 204-982-8370
Fax: 204-982-8383
www.accuratedorwin.com

Accurate Dorwin's pultruded fiberglass windows are double- or triple-glazed with one or two low-e coatings, extruded silicone spacers, and argon-filled cavities. U-factors for Accurate Dorwin windows range as low as 0.15 (corresponding to an R-value of 6.7).

Most recently mentioned in EBN 6:5 & 10:7

Renewal by Andersen Windows

Andersen Windows
9900 Jamaica Ave. S
Cottage Grove, MN 55016

Toll-free: 877-773-6392
Phone: 651-264-4000
Fax: 651-264-4070
www.renewalbyandersen.com

Andersen's Renewal by Andersen® line of windows features frames and sashes made from Fibrex® material, a post-industrial wood and waste-PVC composite with a coextruded virgin PVC exterior coating. High Performance™ Low-E4™ glass from Cardinal IG is standard in all products. The highest-performance Renewal by Andersen® windows in the NFRC Certified Products Directory have unit U-factors of 0.29 and qualify for *GreenSpec* because of their recycled content.

Most recently mentioned in EBN 5:2 & 5:5

High-Performance Fiberglass Windows

Comfort Line Ltd.
5500 Enterprise Blvd.
Toledo, OH 43612

Toll-free: 800-522-4999
Phone: 419-729-8520
Fax: 419-729-8525
www.comfortlineinc.com

Comfort Line manufactures fiberglass pultruded frame windows with multi-cavity, sealed-frame members. Comfort Line's most advanced glazing option is a triple-glazed, krypton-filled panel with two low-e coatings and warm edge spacers. All Comfort Line windows and doors are qualified by Energy Star® and NFRC.

High-Performance Fiberglass Windows

Duxton Windows & Doors
10 Higgins Ave.
Winnipeg, MB R3B 0A2 Canada

Phone: 204-339-6456
Fax: 204-334-1800
www.duxtonwindows.com

Duxton Windows & Doors manufactures advanced, high-performance windows and doors with pultruded-fiberglass frames. Glazing options include multiple low-e coatings on glass, suspended Heat Mirror films, and a 90:10 mixture of krypton and argon gas-fill. The highest-performance windows easily meet *GreenSpec* criteria for fiberglass windows, though NFRC unit U-factor testing has not been completed. The company lists center-of-glass R-values as high as 7.6.

High-Performance Fiberglass Windows

Fibertec Window & Door Mfg. Ltd.
157 Rivermede Rd., Unit 2
Concord, ON L4K 3M4 Canada

Toll-free: 888-232-4956
Phone: 905-660-7102
Fax: 905-660-6581
www.fibertec.com

Fibertec™ fiberglass windows have foam-insulated frames and can include Heat Mirror™ or low-e coatings, argon gas-fill, and warm-edge spacers. Fibertec's Santoprene™ weather stripping is applied in three locations for more effective sealing against air infiltration.

High-Performance Fiberglass Windows

Inline Fiberglass Ltd.
30 Constellation Ct.
Toronto, ON M9W 1K1 Canada

Phone: 416-679-1171
Fax: 416-679-1150
www.inlinefiberglass.com

Inline Fiberglass, a world leader in pultrusion technology, manufactures fiberglass windows and doors. A number of units meet or exceed the 0.30 U-value threshold for *GreenSpec* with some quadruple-glazed, krypton-filled units rating as low as 0.18.

The company also licenses their pultrusion technology to other manufacturers.

Integrity Fiberglass Windows

Integrity Windows and Doors - Marvin Marketing Office
2020 Silver Bell Rd., Ste. 15
Eagan, MN 55122

Toll-free: 800-328-0268
Phone: 651-452-3039
Fax: 651-452-3074
www.integritywindows.com

Integrity™ windows from Marvin feature exterior frame and sash components made from Ultrex™, a pultruded composite of fiberglass and polyester resin. Solid wood jambs are bonded to the interior of the Ultrex frame, giving the windows a natural-wood appearance. Integrity's glazing options are limited to low-e2 with argon insulating glass, but a few products meet the *GreenSpec* 0.30 U-factor threshold.

Most recently mentioned in EBN 5:2

High-Performance Windows

Milgard Manufacturing, Inc.
965 54th Ave. E
Tacoma, WA 98424

Toll-free: 800-562-8444
Phone: 253-922-6030
Fax: 253-922-3983
www.milgard.com

Milgard is the largest window manufacturer in the West and produces vinyl, thermally broken aluminum, pultruded fiberglass windows, and fiberglass-clad wood windows. All Milgard windows are custom-manufactured, and the company offers a wide range of glazing options, including several that meet the *GreenSpec* energy performance criteria.

High-Performance Fiberglass Windows

Thermotech Fiberglass Fenestration
2121 Thermotech Rd.
Carp, ON K0A 1L0 Canada

Toll-free: 888-930-9445
Phone: 613-839-6158
Fax: 613-839-9066
www.thermotechfiberglass.com

Thermotech's most energy-efficient windows include silicone foam Super Spacers™, triple panes, and low-e glazing (LOF or AFG), resulting in some of the highest-performance windows in North America (many glazing options produce window unit U-factors below 0.20). Thermotech promotes the use of different glazings on different orientations to optimize energy performance. The company

**08 00 00
Openings**

offers up to 4 different IG (insulating glass) options on a whole house or project order. Other features include: 15% post-industrial recycled-content fiberglass frames, near-zero-solvent waterborne paint, offcut-sourced polystyrene insulation, and river-bottom-recovered pine jamb extensions.

Most recently mentioned in EBN 5:2

08 61 00
Roof Windows

Daylighting serves several green purposes. Studies show that natural daylighting can improve the general well-being of building occupants as well as provide such measurable benefits as increased workplace productivity and enhanced school performance. The energy benefit from daylighting generally comes from both savings in electric lighting and cooling-load avoidance. Not all daylighting systems save energy—careful energy modeling can help determine energy benefits in particular applications. As with window and glazing products, the energy performance of skylights and roof windows varies greatly among different products and should be carefully considered. (See also 08 45 00 - Translucent Wall and Roof Assemblies.)

Roof Windows and Skylights

Insula-Dome
83 Horseblock Rd.
Yaphank, NY 11980

Phone: 631-924-7890
Fax: 631-924-7870
www.insula-dome.com

Insul-Dome skylights have double-glazed, low-e, argon-filled glazing. This product was formerly manufactured by Roto-Frank of America.

Roof Windows and Skylights

Velux
450 Old Brickyard Rd
Greenwood, SC 29648

Toll-free: 800-888-3589
Fax: 864-943-2631
www.veluxusa.com

Velux roof windows and skylights are solid-wood framed and come standard with low-e2 coatings and argon gas-fill. Velux products are EPA Energy Star®-approved.

08 62 00
Unit Skylights

Tubular skylights, or light pipes, allow daylight to be transferred from the roof to occupied space below, even when there's a considerable distance involved (such as through an attic). The system is composed of three parts: an acrylic rooftop dome and flashing, a reflective light pipe, and an interior diffuser. With most of these products, the reflective tube can bend around obstructions, or connect nonaligned roof and ceiling penetrations. Some products include other features such as compact-fluorescent lights or ventilation fans. (See also 08 45 00 - Translucent Wall and Roof Assemblies.)

Sun-Dome Tubular Skylights

Daylighting Technologies, Inc.
8352 Garden Rd.
Riviera Beach, FL 33404

Toll-free: 800-596-8414
Phone: 561-840-0095
Fax: 561-840-7606
www.sun-dome.net

Daylighting Technologies produces 10", 13", and 21" tubular skylights with aluminum flashing and high-impact Lexan polycarbonate domes for both residential and commercial applications. The domes are large-missile impact-tested and Dade County hurricane-approved. The adjustable tubes provide up to 97% reflectivity, according to the company. Daylighting Technologies also provides lighting retrofit systems with fluorescent bulbs, electronic dimmable ballasts, and light sensors to provide constant light levels in all applications.

Most recently mentioned in EBN 8:10

HUVCO Skylights

HUVCO, Daylighting Solutions
P.O. Box 3
Rohrersville, MD 21779

Toll-free: 800-832-6116
Phone: 301-432-0678
Fax: 301-432-7185
www.huvco.com

HUVCO's High Performance Daylighting System utilizes a thermally broken, dual-prismatic dome and a highly reflective, insulated light well. Prismatic interior diffusers are available in flat, double-hip, and drop-pan. These systems are available in 4'x4', 2'x4', 2'x2', and custom sizes; the light well can be custom made in lengths up to thirty feet. Their

High Performance Tubular Skylights (HPTS) come in five diameter sizes: 10", 13", 18", 21" and 24", with recommended maximum pipe lengths of up to 20+. The company offers a lifetime guarantee.

Most recently mentioned in EBN 8:10

ODL Tubular Skylights

ODL, Inc.
215 E. Roosevelt Ave.
Zeeland, MI 49464

Toll-free: 866-635-4968
Phone: 616-772-9111
Fax: 616-772-9110
www.odl.com

ODL manufactures tubular skylights in 10" and 14" diameters. The light tube is coated with a highly reflective, atomically bonded, mirror-finish reflective film and comes with a standard prismatic light diffuser at the ceiling to improve light spread. The product is designed for either contractor or DIY installations. ODL offers the option of an electric light kit, which may reduce light output by approximately 2-3% (when the pipe is straight), according to the manufacturer.

Most recently mentioned in EBN 8:10

SunScope Tubular Skylights

Sky-Tech Sky-Lights
11503 - 160 St.
Edmonton, AB T5M 3V9 Canada

Toll-free: 800-449-0644
Phone: 780-438-6770
Fax: 780-702-1599
www.sunscope.com

SunScope tubular skylights are available in 8-1/2" or 13" diameters, as well as a 21" commercial model, in lengths up to 20'. An optional motorized damper can control light levels. Roof units for multiple SunScopes are also available, allowing any combination of up to six 8-1/2" or 13" tubular skylights to be connected to one rectangular skylight unit, reducing the number of roof penetrations. Per the manufacturer, these tubular skylights do not contribute to heat loss in winter or solar heat gain in the summer.

Most recently mentioned in EBN 8:10

Brighten Up and SolaMaster Tubular Skylights

Solatube International, Inc.
2210 Oak Ridge Way
Vista, CA 92081

Toll-free: 888-765-2882
Phone: 760-477-1120
Fax: 760-599-5181
www.solatube.com

Solatube is the world's leading manufacturer of tubular skylights. For residential and smaller commercial applications, the Brighten Up® series is available in 10" and 14" units and features Solatube's patented Spectralight® Infinity tubing material, and two patented technologies to intercept and collect low angle sunlight. The SolaMaster® Series, featuring a 21" unit, is suitable for commercial buildings and larger residential areas and accommodates a wide variety of ceilings. Installing one 21" SolaMaster can displace approximately two traditional light fixtures, each using three FO32T8 fluorescent lamps, according to the manufacturer. Seamless one-piece flashing is available in both the Brighten Up and SolaMaster series. All Solatube skylights are offered with optional light kits, and the 10" Brighten Up unit is available with an optional ventilation fan. A motorized "Daylight Dimmer" butterfly baffle, which is controlled by a wall-mounted switch, is also available for all sizes, adjusting the skylight's output from 100% to approximately 2%.

Most recently mentioned in EBN 8:10 & 9:1

SunPipe Tubular Skylights

Sun Pipe Co., Inc.
P.O. Box 5760
Elgin, IL 60121

Toll-free: 800-844-4786
Phone: 847-888-9222
Fax: 847-888-9444
www.sunpipe.com

Sun Pipe introduced tubular skylights to the U.S. in 1991. The lined, reflective aluminum pipe is offered in 9", 13", and 21" diameter, with the larger product directed toward the commercial market. SunPipe® Tubular Skylights are lined with real silver, which is more reflective than a mirror because there is no glass on top of it, according to the manufacturer. The company's light control damper, the Eclipse, is scheduled for release in late 2006.

Most recently mentioned in EBN 7:8 & 8:10

Sun-Tek Tube

Sun-Tek Manufacturing
10303 General Dr.
Orlando, FL 32824

Toll-free: 800-334-5854
Phone: 407-859-2117
Fax: 407-859-6607
www.sun-tek.com

The Sun-Tek Tube® is a tubular skylight available in 10"-, 14"-, and 21"-diameter sizes. The company also manufactures a curb-mount tube and a multi-tubed skylight, the Spyder, that can illuminate multiple locations with only a single opening in the roof.

Most recently mentioned in EBN 8:10

Tru-Lite Tubular Skylights

Tru-Lite Skylights, Inc.
13695 E. Davies Pl.
Centennial, CO 80112

Toll-free: 800-873-3309
Phone: 303-783-5700
Fax: 303-781-9196
www.tru-lite.com

Tru-Lite Tubular Skylights® are available in 12" and 16" diameters to illuminate up to 500 ft². No structural modifications or roof curbing are needed. The tube can be raised above the roof plane to improve low-angle daylight collection.

Most recently mentioned in EBN 8:10

Tubular Skylight

Tubular Skylight, Inc.
753 Cattleman Rd.
Sarasota, FL 34232

Toll-free: 800-315-8823
Phone: 941-378-8823
Fax: 941-342-8844
www.tubular-skylight.com

Tubular Skylights are available in three sizes: 8", 13", and 21" diameter.

Most recently mentioned in EBN 8:10

Sun Tunnel Tubular Skylights

Velux
450 Old Brickyard Rd.
Greenwood, SC 29648

Toll-free: 800-888-3589
Fax: 864-943-2631
www.veluxusa.com

The Sun Tunnel has a flexible tube (most other tubular skylights offer only elbows to make slight bends). Double diffusion panes produce even light distribution and reduce the likelihood of condensation. The company indicates that thorough testing shows there is no appreciable heat gain or loss with the Sun Tunnel. It is available in 14" and 22" diameters and carries a 7-year warranty. These tubular skylights were formerly manufactured by Sun Tunnel Skylights, Inc.

Most recently mentioned in EBN 8:10

08 62 13
Domed Unit Skylights

There have been a number of innovations in the area of metal-framed skylights. Active skylighting systems rely on reflectors and sun-tracking mechanisms to increase daylight entry; these systems boost daylighting primarily during early-

morning and late-afternoon hours when the sun is low and little direct sunlight typically enters a conventional skylight. Another technology, prismatic skylights, refracts sunlight to boost daylighting performance.

Solar Tracking Skylights

Solar Tracking Skylights, Inc.
350 N. Orleans St., Ste. 950
Chicago, IL 60654

Phone: 312-881-2222
Fax: 312-881-2001
www.solar-track.com

Solar Tracking Skylights are photovoltaic-powered active daylighting systems for low-slope roofs. A dome-protected array of mirrors tracks the sun across the sky to boost daylighting intensity and duration during, especially during early-morning and late-afternoon hours. The mirrors can also provide shade during summer to reduce unwanted heat gain. The self-contained units require no external power.

08 63 00
Metal-Framed Skylights

There have been a number of innovations in the area of metal-framed skylights. Active skylighting systems rely on reflectors and sun-tracking mechanisms to increase daylight entry; these systems boost daylighting primarily during early-morning and late-afternoon hours when the sun is low and little direct sunlight typically enters a conventional skylight. Another technology, prismatic skylights, refracts sunlight to boost daylighting performance. (See also 08 45 00 - Translucent Wall and Roof Assemblies.)

SunPort Skylights

Atlantic Daylighting
145 Main St.
Norwalk, CT 06851

Toll-free: 877-234-2281
Phone: 203-847-6007
Fax: 203-847-1542
www.sunportdaylighting.com

Atlantic Daylighting offers advanced SunPort skylight systems for commercial buildings. The SunPort 1 is a purely passive skylight, either 4' x 4' or 4' x 8', with three layers of glazing for optimal thermal performance: a roof-mounted prismatic acrylic dome, an intermediate acrylic layer, and an interior acrylic prismatic lens (different lenses are available, depending on the ceiling height).

08 00 00
Openings

The skylight has thermally broken aluminum frames with weepage gutters to drain condensate, a highly reflective (>95%) lightwell that can transmit light as much as 14', and insulated walls. The SunPort 2 adds integral lighting from four integrated high-output T-5 fluorescent lamps that provide diffused downlight. Future models will feature integrated photovoltaic panels to power fluorescent or LED lighting. Atlantic Daylighting was created through the acquisition of technology from California-based skylight innovator U.S. Daylighting.

Formawall and Versawall

Centria Architectural Systems

For full listing, see CSI section 08 44 00 - Curtain Wall and Glazed Assemblies

Hybrid Lighting System

Natural Lighting Co., Inc.
6003 N. 53rd Dr.
Glendale, AZ 85301

Phone: 623-463-0901
Fax: 623-463-0902
www.daylighting.com

Natural Lighting manufactures several hybrid units combining daylighting and T5 fluorescent lighting integrated into one fixture with on-board lighting controls. The line includes units designed for open highbay applications as well as finished interior ceilings. Available in 2' x 2', 2' x 4', and 4' x 4' sizes with a large selection of diffusers for specific applications. On-board lighting controls include motion sensors and photo sensors to maximize energy savings. Hybrid lighting can be used with either active or passive daylighting systems.

UTD-SP 2000

Natural Lighting Co., Inc.
6003 N. 53rd Dr.
Glendale, AZ 85301

Phone: 623-463-0901
Fax: 623-463-0902
www.daylighting.com

The UTD-SP 2000 is a photovoltaic-powered active daylighting system for low-slope roofs. The skylight's array of mirrors, protected under an acrylic dome, tracks the sun to significantly boost daylight entry during the early morning and late afternoon hours. The tracking system returns to an eastern orientation during the night. The company also produces passive daylighting products and automated controllers to regulate light levels from commercial skylights.

Most recently mentioned in EBN 8:10

Advanced Daylighting System

So-Luminaire Daylighting System Corp.
701 Palomar Airport Rd., Third Fl.
Carlsbad, CA 92009

Toll-free: 800-676-5276
Phone: 760-931-4759
Fax: 760-931-4760
www.soluminaire.com

So-Luminaire manufactures an active daylighting system for low-slope roofs. An array of angled sun-tracking mirrors directs additional light into the building, particularly during early morning and late afternoon hours. The daily amount of daylighting is increased in intensity and duration, and the mirrors shade the skylight during high-radiant-heat-gain periods in the summer.

Most recently mentioned in EBN 8:10

SunOptics Skylights

SunOptics Skylights
6201 27th St.
Sacramento, CA 95822

Toll-free: 800-289-4700
Phone: 916-395-4700
Fax: 916-395-9204
www.sunoptics.com

SunOptics manufactures prismatic skylights in which tiny prisms are embedded in the skylight glazing to refract visible light into the skylight, while reflecting infrared and UV light to keep it out. SunOptics skylights transmit more visible light than conventional white-acrylic skylights. Available single-, double-, triple-, and quad-glazed, they are designed with thermal breaks in the frames to reduce heat loss and prevent condensation. SunOptics also makes photo-cell-controlled louvers.

Velux Sage Glass Skylights

Velux
450 Old Brickyard Rd.
Greenwood, SC 29648

New

Toll-free: 800-888-3589
Fax: 864-943-2631
www.veluxusa.com

Velux offers skylights with SageGlass®, a dynamically tintable, electrochromic glazing that blocks glare and UV and controls solar heat gain while preserving views. The touch of a button activates an electrical current to switch the glass from clear to tinted state and to maintain a darkened state. A house with SageGlass skylights uses less energy than a single 40-watt light bulb on a daily basis while providing energy savings and heat and glare control. SageGlass technology is available for a range of skylight models and sizes. There is a substantial up-charge for this glazing.

Most recently mentioned in EBN 15:6

Visionwall Window and Curtain Wall Systems

Visionwall Corporation

For full listing, see CSI section 08 44 00 - Curtain Wall and Glazed Assemblies

Lumi-Duct Skydome + Reflective Light Well System

Wasco Products, Inc.
22 Pioneer Ave.
P.O. Box 351
Sanford, ME 04073

Toll-free: 800-388-0293
Fax: 207-490-5270
www.wascoproducts.com

Wasco Lumi-Duct Skydome™ Light Well Systems minimize space conditioning losses while maximizing the benefits of daylighting. The system's light well reflects 89% of the light transmitted through the prismatic diffuser, without loss of color. Appropriate for all types of high ceiling/drop ceiling applications, the system includes a self-flashing, thermally broken, aluminum integral curb, and a double-glazed roof dome skylight that accommodates flat or pitched roofs. Standard or impact-modified acrylic skylight glazing may be specified (*GreenSpec* does not recommend polycarbonate glazing). The light well system fits 2' x 2' or 4' x 4' T-bar ceiling grids; custom sizes and lengths are available up to 8 feet. Standard finishes include anodized and baked enamel. The Lumi-Duct Skydome can also be used in hybrid systems combining natural and artificial light. The skylight mounting system contains PVC components.

08 80 00 Glazing

Specifying glazing is common in commercial building applications and with some residential window products. The high-performance glazings listed here help control heating and cooling loads. Careful selection of glazing for specific applications (orientation, building type, etc.) is critical for optimum energy performance and building comfort.

08 00 00 Openings

Solera Translucent Glazing

Advanced Glazings Ltd.
870 Kings Rd.
P.O. Box 1460, Station A
Sydney, NS B1P 6R7 Canada

Phone: 902-794-2899
Fax: 902-794-1869
www.advancedglazings.com

Solera® is a translucent architectural glazing primarily used to convert glare from clear ("vision") glazing to diffuse light; it also provides increased thermal insulation. Solera consists of two layers of glass separated by 2.5" of clear, acrylic, honeycombed film insulation plus light diffusing veils. There are no internal mullions or fixed modules. Neither low-e coatings nor low-conductivity gas-fill are required to achieve a 0.20 U-factor, but any glass from any manufacturer may be specified. Light transmittance can range from 3% to 73%; shading coefficients from .04 to .75; STC from 44 up; and variable degrees of diffusion are attainable from almost clear to completely diffused.

Most recently mentioned in EBN 10:6

Comfort E2, Comfort Ti, and Solar Glass

AFG Industries, Inc.
1400 Lincoln St.
Kingsport, TN 37660

Toll-free: 800-251-0441
Phone: 423-229-7200
Fax: 423-229-7321
www.afgglass.com

AFG Industries is a leading manufacturer of float glass and solar glass products. AFG manufactures Comfort E2 and Comfort Ti for the residential market and several specialized solar glass products for PV, passive, and active solar applications.

Heat Mirror Glass

Alpen Glass
5400 Spine Rd.
Boulder, CO 80301

Toll-free: 800-882-4466
Phone: 303-530-1150
Fax: 800-321-1753
www.alpeninc.com

Alpen Glass manufactures insulating glass with Heat Mirror™-coated films suspended between two panes of glass filled with argon or krypton gas. Alpen offers high-performance glazings with 99.5% reduction in UV transmission.

LoE2 and LoE3

Cardinal Glass Industries
775 Prairie Center Dr., Ste. 200
Eden Prairie, MN 55344

Toll-free: 800-843-1484
Phone: 952-929-3134
Fax: 952-935-5538
www.cardinalcorp.com

LoE2 is a soft-coat, low-e glazing. When combined with clear glass in a double-pane unit, thermal heat flow is significantly reduced, as is solar heat gain. In applications where passive solar heating is desired, a glazing with a higher solar heat gain coefficient is preferable. LoE3 366 ("Low-e cubed 366") offers a solar heat gain coefficient as low as many tinted low-e glazings while the visible light transmittance is nearly as high as the widely used LoE2 product. Cardinal is the largest manufacturer of coated glass for residential windows in North America. LoE3 glass is used by window and door manufacturers such as Milgard, Weather Shield, Kolbe & Kolbe, and Atrium - sometimes under their own tradenames, such as SunCoatMAX™ and Zo-e-shield™.

Most recently mentioned in EBN 5:4 & 16:1

Formawall and Versawall

Centria Architectural Systems

For full listing, see CSI section 08 44 00 - Curtain Wall and Glazed Assemblie

Photovol Glass

MSK Corporation

For full listing, see CSI section 08 88 26 - Building Integrated Photovoltaic Glazing

Pilkington Energy Advantage

Pilkington NA
811 Madison Ave.
P.O. Box 0799
Toledo, OH 43695

Toll-free: 800-221-0444
Phone: 419-247-3731
Fax: 419-247-3821
www.pilkington.com

Pilkington® Energy Advantage is a hard-coat (pyrolytic), low-e glass with an emissivity of 0.15. In a double-pane unit, a SHGC of 0.7 is achieved. This is an excellent glazing for use in passive solar buildings on southern orientations where solar gain needs to be high.

Most recently mentioned in EBN 5:2 & 8:5

PPG High-Performance and Solar-Control Glazings

PPG Industries, Inc.
Guys Run Rd.
Glass Technology Center
Pittsburgh, PA 15238

Toll-free: 800-377-5267
Fax: 412-826-2299
www.ppgglazing.com

Sungate 500 low-e glass from PPG offers high solar transmission using a hard-coat (pyrolytic) low-e coating, so it is particularly appropriate for passive solar heating applications where high total solar transmission is desirable. Solarban 60, Solarban 70XL, and Solarban 80 glass are products that offer high visible light transmission, yet block more solar radiation. Azuria, Atlantica, Solexia, and Caribia glasses are tinted, spectrally selective glazings with high visible light transmittance and relatively low SHGC. Starphire glass is a particularly clear glass that can be combined with Solarban 60 coatings.

SageGlass Insulated Glass Unit

New

SAGE Electrochromics, Inc.
One Sage Way
Faribault, MN 55021

Phone: 507-331-4848
Fax: 507-333-0145
www.sage-ec.com

SAGE Electrochromics manufactures Sage-Glass®, an electronically tintable exterior glazing that blocks solar heat gain while providing glare control and preserving views. SageGlass incorporates durable thin-film ceramic coatings and uses 0.28 W/ft² to switch the glass from clear to tinted state and 0.1 W/ft² to maintain a darkened state. Used with typical clear glass to fabricate an insulated unit, the tinting reduces the visible transmittance from 62% to 3.5%, while reducing the solar heat gain coefficient (SHGC) from 0.48 to 0.09. SAGE is partnering with window, skylight, and curtainwall manufacturers to produce efficient commercial and residential products that can be used to provide energy savings, control peak electricity demand, and possibly downsize HVAC systems, while improving occupant comfort and control.

Most recently mentioned in EBN 15:6 & 15:12

OKASOLAR and OKALUX Insulating Glass Panels

Schott North America, Inc.

For full listing, see CSI section 08 44 00 - Curtain Wall and Glazed Assemblies

08 00 00
Openings

Superglass Quad with Heat Mirror

Southwall Technologies
3788 Fabian Way
Palo Alto, CA 94303

Toll-free: 800-365-8794
Phone: 650-798-1200
Fax: 650-798-1406
www.southwall.com

Southwall developed and manufactures solar radiation control films, including Heat Mirror® with a range of performance properties. These films are fabricated into insulated-glass units (IGUs) and laminated glass by approximately 30 manufacturers in North America. Southwall's highest-performing Superglass® incorporates two Heat Mirror suspended films and three gas-filled cavities between dual panes of glass. Center-of-glass R-values above R-10 can be achieved with dual Heat Mirror films and low-conductivity gas-fill.

Most recently mentioned in EBN 5:2, 7:2, 7:8

Wausau SageGlass Windows

Wausau Window and Wall Systems
1415 West St.
P.O. Box 1746
Wausau, WI 54402

New

Toll-free: 877-678-2983
Phone: 715-845-2161
Fax: 715-843-4055
www.wausauwindow.com

Wausau offers windows with SageGlass®, an electronically tintable, electrochromic glazing that blocks glare and UV and controls solar heat gain while preserving views. The windows use 0.28 W/ft² to switch from clear to darkened state, and 0.1 W/ft² to maintain that darkened state. (On a daily average, 1,500sf of SageGlass uses less power than a 60W bulb, according to the SageGlass manufacturer). Tinting is controlled locally by the occupant or automatically by the energy management system. Tint windows dynamically save energy, reduce peak electricity demand, and potentially allow downsizing of HVAC systems, while improving occupant comfort and control. SageGlass windows are available by special order for commercial, institutional, and healthcare buildings.

Most recently mentioned in EBN 15:6

08 00 00
Openings

08 87 13
Solar-Control Window Film

Solar-control plastic window films have been used for decades as a retrofit measure to control solar heat-gain through windows. Dye-tinted films attempt to prevent solar gain by absorbing both light and heat, and are better at reducing light levels than heat gain. Spectrally-selective films rely on reflectivity and emissivity rather than absorption, blocking the infrared spectrum responsible for almost half the heat of sunlight while allowing much of the visible light through. Use of these films in commercial applications can result in rapid payback through lowered cooling costs. Always check with the window manufacturer before applying window films, or having them applied professionally; application of films may void the window's warranty.

Scotchtint Plus All Season Films

3M Specified Construction Products Department
3M Center 223-2S-24
St. Paul, MN 55144

Toll-free: 800-480-1704
www.3m.com

Scotchtint™ Plus All Season Films from 3M offer the same solar gain and glare control as their popular Scotchtint Sun Control Window Film line—but with cold-weather heat loss reduction ratings of 23% for silver, and 30% for amber, thanks to a low-e coating that reflects interior heat back to the interior. A ten-year commercial and governmental warranty is offered; residential applications are given a lifetime warranty.

Most recently mentioned in EBN 14:6

V-Kool Window Film

V-KOOL, Inc.
13805 West Rd., Ste. 400
Houston, TX 77041

Toll-free: 800-786-2468
Phone: 713-856-8333
www.v-kool-usa.com

V-Kool® offers virtually colorless, spectrally-selective films that block up to 55% of solar gain while maintaining high optical clarity. Minimal visible light reflection avoids the "mirror" effect. V-Kool holds global distribution rights for the film, which is manufactured by Southwall Technologies. It had previously been marketed by Southwall as XIR, and by V-Kool as Solis. This film has been most widely used in OEM laminated automotive windows overseas, with millions of installations in place. A ten year-commercial warranty is offered, and a lifetime residential warranty.

Most recently mentioned in EBN 14:6

08 88 26
Building Integrated Photovoltaic Glazing

Photovoltaics (PV) enable the direct conversion of sunlight into electricity. Some PV modules are integrated into building components, such as roofing and wall glazings—these are often referred to as building-integrated photovoltaics (BIPV). (See also 26 31 00 - Photovoltaic Collectors.) (See feature article EBN Vol. 10, No. 3.)

Photovol Glass

MSK Corporation
6th Floor Nishishinjuku K Building
3-6-11 Nishishinjuku, Shinjuku Ward
Tokyo 160-0023 Japan

Phone: +81 3-3342-3881
Fax: +81 3-3342-6534
www.msk.ne.jp/english/index.shtml

Photovol Glass is a semitransparent, building-integrated photovoltaic (BIPV) glazing element that allows visible light transmission while generating electricity. The glazing panels are available with 10% light transmittance with nominal 44 watts of power output; 5% transmittance with 50 W output; and 1% transmittance with 55 W output. An edge-mounted electrical connection system conceals all wiring within the framing. The power output is guaranteed to at least 80% of the rated output for 20 years. Photovol Glass is available in standard 10.5 mm-thick (0.41") glass, and 13.5 mm (0.53") reinforced glass. It can be used vertically or horizontally to generate power while reducing glare, UV penetration, and solar heat gain.

Most recently mentioned in EBN 13:11 & 13:12

RWE Schott ASI Solar Glazing

RWE Schott Solar, Inc.
2260 Lava Ridge Ct., Ste. 102
U.S. Sales & Marketing
Roseville, CA 95661

Toll-free: 888-457-6527
Phone: 916-774-3000
Fax: 916-784-9781
www.us.schott.com

RWE Schott offers ASI® solar modules for building-integrated photovoltaic (BIPV) glazing applications. The modules provide limited daylighting (10% for the ASE THRU® modules) while generating electricity (3.9 peak watts per square foot). These panels rely on tandem-junction, amorphous silicon PV technology laminated between heat-strengthened glass. Electrical leads are integrated into the panel edges.

Most recently mentioned in EBN 10:3 & 13:11

09 00 00 Finishes

PRODUCT LISTINGS

09 01 93
Paint Removers

Conventional paint strippers, including those containing methylene chloride, are notoriously hazardous and should be avoided. Less-hazardous alternatives are becoming increasingly available. Products listed here are low-VOC, nontoxic, and/or biodegradable.

Orange Peel

Conspec

For full listing, see CSI section 03 01 00 - Maintenance of Concrete

Peel Away 6 and Peel Away 7

Dumond Chemicals, Inc.
1501 Broadway
New York, NY 10036

Phone: 212-869-6350
Fax: 212-764-5762
www.peelaway.com

Peel Away™ 6 and Peel Away™ 7 are paint removers made from biodegradable materials. They contain nonhazardous dibasic ester solvent rather than methylene chloride or caustic. The products are not water-based and their odors may irritate chemically sensitive individuals. Stronger biodegradable paint-stripping products (with higher VOC levels) are also available from Dumond.

Piranha IV Paint Stripper

Fiberlock Technologies, Inc.
150 Dascomb Rd.
Andover, MA 01810

Toll-free: 800-342-3755
Phone: 978-623-9987
Fax: 978-475-6205
www.fiberlock.com

Piranha® IV paint stripper is a gel formulated specifically to remove lead-based paint that provides an alternative to more toxic, conventional paint strippers. Piranha I does not contain methylene chloride, methanol, toluene, methyl ethyl ketone, or acetone. There are 5 formulations in the Piranha line with varying degrees of toxicity for use on virtually any paint-removal project.

Soy-Gel

Franmar Chemical, Inc.
P.O. Box 5565
Bloomington, IL 61702

Toll-free: 800-538-5069
Phone: 309-452-7526
Fax: 309-827-9308
www.franmar.com

Soy Gel is a soy-based paint remover suitable for stripping urethanes, polyurethanes, and all paints, including lead-based paint. The product contains methylated soybean oil and mild surfactants, N-Methyl-2-Pyrolidone.

SOYsolv Graffiti Remover

SOYsolv
6154 N. CR 33
Tiffin, OH 44883

Toll-free: 800-231-4274
Phone: 419-992-4570
Fax: 419-992-4595
www.soysolv.com

SOYsolv® Graffiti Remover is a water-rinsable, nontoxic, biodegradable paint remover derived from corn and soybeans for removal of such materials as permanent marker, tape residue, decals, ink, and spray and enamel paint.

09 22 00
Supports for Plaster and Gypsum Board

In addition to metal and wood lath for interior and exterior plasters and stuccos, special forming and trim accessories are included here. Foam and plastic trim substrates—water-blown or extruded—should have high recycled content or be made from polymers with low environmental impacts. Products listed here are made with high recycled content, minimal materials use, or have other compelling environmental attributes.

Trim Tech Stucco Trim Substrate

Trimtechnologies LLC
P.O. Box 6168
Santa Maria, CA 93454

Toll-free: 866-487-4695
Phone: 805-348-1907
Fax: 805-348-1908
www.trimtechnologies.com

Trim Tech pre-shaped forms for projecting portland cement stucco trim details (typically around windows and doors, and as belly-bands) are made with wire, recycled paper, and non-toxic ethylene hot-melt glue. This alternative to foam or wood forms provides a substrate that does not twist, warp, swell, or crack. Trim Tech forms are attached on top of the stucco lath, and are available in 3/8 Diamond for 2-coat, or conventional 3-coat. Standard sizes range from 2x4 through 2x12; arches, pot shelves, and special shapes are also available.

09 25 00
Other Plastering

Lime plasters have slightly lower embodied energy than portland-cement-based plasters, and they don't include petroleum-based ingredients, as acrylic plasters do. Integral natural pigments obviate the need for painting. Products listed here include natural lime plasters and wall coatings made from ingredients such as clay, sand, and cellulose.

American Clay Earth Plaster

American Clay Enterprises, LLC
2601 Karsten Ct. SE
Albuquerque, NM 87102

Toll-free: 866-404-1634
Phone: 505-243-5300
Fax: 505-244-9332
www.americanclay.com

American Clay is a 100% natural earth plaster veneer made from clay, aggregates (including 65-75% post-industrial recycled marble dust), nontoxic mineral pigments, and a boric acid mold inhibitor. Designed for interior use, the product can be applied to many substrates (including painted surfaces, though a primer is required). American Clay

09 00 00
Finishes

Earth Plaster is breathable and is not for areas that come into direct contact with water, such as shower stalls (areas subject to splashing can be sealed to resist damage). Available in 12 standard colors; custom colors may be ordered. American Clay Earth Plaster is mixed with water to apply and can be rewet and reworked indefinitely if left unsealed. Produced in New Mexico exclusively with U.S.-sourced materials. No water or heat is used in production, and virtually no waste is generated, according to the company.

Armourcoat Polished Plaster

Armourcoat USA
4629 S 136th St.
Omaha, NE 68137

Toll-free: 888-368-5893
Phone: 402-896-2005
Fax: 402-895-7238
www.armourcoatusa.com

Armourcoat Polished Plaster is a zero-VOC, durable, decorative troweled finish. The marble powders used as the main ingredient are byproducts from the manufacture of marble slabs and tiles. The product is vapor-permeable, making it particularly well-suited to old or historic buildings.

Adobe and Earth Plasters

Clay Mine Adobe, Inc.
For full listing, see CSI section 04 24 00 - Adobe Unit Masonry

Dimensions Plasters

Dimensions Plaster
1967 W. 9th St., Ste. B
Riviera Beach, FL 33404

Toll-free: 877-242-8935
www.dimensionsplaster.com

Dimensions Plaster sells non-toxic, VOC-free, lime plasters and primers from Italy. The plasters come in five finishes, which are made by adding marble dust and talc, clay, sand, and vegetable oils, such as linseed oil, to the lime plaster. Dimensions Plaster also sells 14 mineral pigments for use with the plaster and their lime paints. The limestone is from family-owned quarries in Italy, and profits are returned annually to the communities where they do business. The product is designed for the professional plastering contractor.

Aglaia Natural Finishes

Environmental Building Supplies
For full listing, see CSI section 09 91 23 - Interior Paints

Tierrafino Clay Plaster

Hopper Handcrafted Specialty Finishes
302 S. 30th St.
Phoenix, AZ 85034

Phone: 602-273-1338
Fax: 602-275-5933
www.hopperfinishes.com

Tierrafino® is a 100% natural clay interior finish made from colored sands and clays mined from European quarries. The product contains no pigment or chemical additives. Mother of pearl or straw can be mixed in to add interest. Because Tierrafino sets mechanically and not chemically, it may be reworked over and over again and the surface refreshed by wiping down with a wet sponge and rubbing with a soft brush. Tierrafino is available in several colors, which can be changed after installation by applying fresh Tierrafino powder with a wet sponge. The manufacturer claims the finish is suitable for areas of high humidity, though use should be avoided where it can come in contact with streams of water or excessively wet walls, such as in cellars.

Terramed

Med Imports
1710 N. Leg Ct.
Augusta, GA 30909

Toll-free: 866-363-6334
Phone: 706-733-6120
Fax: 706-733-8120
www.medimports.net

Med Imports is the North American distributor for Terramed, an all-natural interior wall coating made from clay, sand, and cellulose. Terramed is available in 12 colors that are derived from clays from the Mediterranean plate of Europe. The product is shipped dry and mixed with water prior to application.

Tobias Stucco

Tobias Stucco Interior Wall Finish, Inc.
608 Fifth St.
Santa Rosa, CA 95404   **New**

Phone: 707-577-8196
Fax: 707-577-8197
www.tobiasstucco.com

Tobias Stucco is a non-toxic, odor-free, virtually VOC-free, trowelled-on wall finishing product. The limestone-and-sand-based product can be used as an alternative to paint or plaster and applied to most building substrates. Tobias Stucco is available in a variety of colors and can be applied to provide various textures. The product is designed for the professional plastering contractor and is sold in quart, gallon, and 5-gallon containers through a national sales network of building supply distributors, and independent sales reps.

St. Astier Natural Hydraulic Lime

TransMineral USA, Inc.
201 Purrington Rd.
Petaluma, CA 94952

Phone: 707-769-0661
Fax: 707-769-0352
www.limes.us

St. Astier Natural Hydraulic Lime, or NHL, is a 100% natural product that has been in production since 1851. St. Astier NHL Mortar is widely used in the restoration of old buildings. This natural hydraulic lime mortar imported from France allows stone to "breathe" naturally. Used in construction as plaster, stucco, mortar, and paint, its high level of vapor exchange and mineral composition can help reduce the risk of mold development and dry rot. NHL products are highly permeable, elastic, low shrinking, zero VOC, self-healing, and recyclable. Transmineral USA also offers Le Decor Selection, a line of high-end, all-natural interior/exterior limestone finishes which require trained installers and crushed limestone aggregate imported from France instead of the domestically available aggregate used for the St. Astier NHL products.

09 28 00
Backing Boards and Underlayments

Underlayment products for flooring serve several functions and can be made from a variety of materials. Environmentally preferable materials for flooring underlayment include natural cork, strawboard, and recycled-paper-based fiberboard. Using underlayment products beneath wood, tile, resilient flooring, or carpet and carpet cushion provides a level surface and helps insulate floors from sound transmission and, to a limited extent, heat loss. Cork rolls and sheets provide particularly high added resilience to the floor system, with significantly less thickness than fiberboard products or a gypsum-cement poured-in-place slab. Use of a sound-deadening underlayment below a hard-surface floor can reduce the need to further control sound transmission with carpeting or rugs. (See also 06 16 00 - Sheathing.)

BetterBoard Tile Backer

Curb Appeal Materials, LTD
3824 N. Johnsburg Rd.
McHenry, IL 60050

Phone: 815-344-7926
Fax: 815-344-7960
www.vortexcomposites.com

BetterBoard™ is a flexible tile backer board for kitchens and other interior building locations with or without high moisture loads. It's made with 100% recycled materials—nylon carpet waste with some commingled plastic from post-consumer and post-industrial sources. The thermoplastic waterproof sheets can be cut with standard tools, screwed, nailed, and glued; they will not rot, deteriorate, or support mold or insects. According to the manufacturer, no waste is generated in the manufacturing process, and the product is recyclable. BetterBoard is a vapor barrier; has 1/4 the weight of traditional backer board; contains no asbestos, gypsum, fiberglass, formaldehyde, or silica; and it doesn't generate dust when cut.

Most recently mentioned in EBN 6:6

DensArmor Plus and DensShield

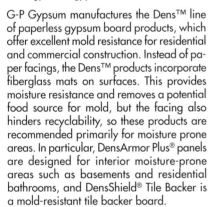

G-P Gypsum Corporation
133 Peachtree St., NE
Atlanta, GA 30303

Toll-free: 800-284-5347
Phone: 404-652-4000
Fax: 404-230-7052
www.gp.com/gypsum

G-P Gypsum manufactures the Dens™ line of paperless gypsum board products, which offer excellent mold resistance for residential and commercial construction. Instead of paper facings, the Dens™ products incorporate fiberglass mats on surfaces. This provides moisture resistance and removes a potential food source for mold, but the facing also hinders recyclability, so these products are recommended primarily for moisture prone areas. In particular, DensArmor Plus® panels are designed for interior moisture-prone areas such as basements and residential bathrooms, and DensShield® Tile Backer is a mold-resistant tile backer board.

Most recently mentioned in EBN 12:7

Ny-Backer

NYCORE
200 Galleria Pkwy., Ste. 2000
Atlanta, GA 30339

Phone: 770-980-0000
www.nycore.com

Nybacker is a flexible tile backer board for interior building locations with or without

high moisture loads. Made with 100% recycled materials (nylon carpet waste with some commingled plastic from post-consumer and post-industrial sources), the thermoplastic waterproof sheets can be cut with standard tools, screwed, nailed, and glued; they will not absorb water, rot, deteriorate, or support mold or insects. According to the manufacturer, no waste is generated in the manufacturing process. Nybacker is one-quarter the weight of cement backer boards; serves as a vapor barrier; contains no asbestos, gypsum, fiberglass, formaldehyde, or silica; and does not generate dust when cut. It is available in 3x5, 4x4, and 4x8 panels; special orders for large projects are accepted.

Most recently mentioned in EBN 14:12

Fiberock Brand Aqua Tough Panels

USG Corporation
125 S. Franklin St.
Chicago, IL 60606

Toll-free: 800-874-4968
Phone: 312-606-4000
Fax: 312-606-4476
www.usg.com

Fiberock Interior panels and Sheathing with Aqua Tough are an FGD (flue-gas desulfurization) gypsum and cellulose formulation suitable for a wide range of applications. Interior panels can be used in wet and dry areas as a tile backer board or as a standard drywall panel when mold resistance is required. Fiberock AR and VHI are products that offer an exceptional level of abuse resistance. Fiberock panels have been certified by Scientific Certification Systems (SCS) to contain 95% recycled material, 85% of which is post-industrial recycled gypsum and 10% recycled paper fiber.

Most recently mentioned in EBN 2:3, 7:1, 9:2, 9:11, 12:7, 14:4

Fiberock Brand Aqua Tough Underlayment / Tile Backerboard

USG Corporation
125 S. Franklin St.
Chicago, IL 60606

Toll-free: 800-874-4968
Phone: 312-606-4000
Fax: 312-606-4476
www.usg.com

Fiberock Underlayment and Tile Backerboard with Aqua Tough Technology are an FGD gypsum and cellulose formulation suitable for a wide range of applications in both wet and dry areas. Fiberock underlayment is a suitable substrate for ceramic tile and composite flooring, while Fiberock Tile Backerboard is specifically for floor and

wall applications under ceramic tile (including shower applications). These panels are indentation-resistant and use no adhesives, solvents, or resins; and they have been certified by Scientific Certification Systems (SCS) to contain 95% recycled material, 85% of which is post-industrial recycled gypsum and 10% recycled paper fiber.

Most recently mentioned in EBN 9:2

09 29 00
Gypsum Board

Gypsum board, or drywall, is typically made with 100% recycled, unbleached paper facings that are bonded without adhesives onto a gypsum core. Though mined virgin gypsum is still widely used in gypsum board production, recycled and synthetic gypsum comprise an increasing portion of product manufacturing. Recycled gypsum board is derived from in-plant scrap and some clean construction waste; advances in recycling technology allow separation of the paper from the core so that each may be recycled separately. Synthetic, or flue-gas, gypsum is a waste product obtained from stack scrubbers that remove sulfur from coal-fired power plant emissions. (In these scrubbers, calcium carbonate is converted to calcium sulfate, or gypsum.) Synthetic gypsum may replace up to 100% of the natural gypsum in drywall. Reducing waste is an important consideration in green building projects; 54"-wide gypsum board may allow more efficient wall coverage in rooms with 9' ceilings. Be aware that paper facings may provide a medium for mold growth in conditions of high humidity and low air circulation; some drywall is made with integral cellulose or fiberglass fibers instead of paper facing to eliminate mold risk. These products, however, are less recyclable. Products listed here are manufactured by companies with at least one U.S. plant operating or planned that uses 100% synthetic gypsum. Additionally, some products listed here are designed to eliminate mold risk. (See feature article EBN Vol. 9, No. 11.)

DensArmor Plus and DensShield

G-P Gypsum Corporation

For full listing, see CSI section 09 28 00 - Backing Boards and Underlayments

G-P Gypsum Board

G-P Gypsum Corporation
133 Peachtree St., NE
Atlanta, GA 30303

Toll-free: 800-284-5347
Phone: 404-652-4000
Fax: 404-230-7052
www.gp.com/gypsum

G-P Gypsum operates 18 manufacturing plants for gypsum board. The Wheatfield, Indiana and Tacoma, Washington plants use synthetic gypsum, while the remaining plants use varying amounts of recycled gypboard.

Gold Bond Gypsum Wallboard

National Gypsum Company
2001 Rexford Rd.
Charlotte, NC 28211

Toll-free: 800-628-4662
Phone: 704-365-7300
Fax: 800-329-6421
www.national-gypsum.com

National Gypsum manufactures Gold Bond® gypsum wallboard with synthetic gypsum in some plants.

Most recently mentioned in EBN 2:3 & 14:4

QuietRock

Quiet Solution, Inc.
1250 Elko Dr.
Sunnyvale, CA 94089

Toll-free: 800-797-8159
www.quietsolution.com

QuietRock™ sound-control drywall for walls and ceilings is made with a thin layer of steel embedded in viscoelastic polymer and sandwiched between sheets of gypsum drywall. It provides impressive sound transmission reduction, installs quickly, and results in very little increase in wall thickness, compared with other sound-control options. QuietRock is available in thicknesses ranging from 5/8" to 1-7/16".

Most recently mentioned in EBN 14:3

Temple-Inland Gypsum

Temple-Inland Forest Products
303 S. Temple Dr.
P.O. Drawer N
Diboll, TX 75941

Toll-free: 800-231-6060
Phone: 936-829-5511
Fax: 800-426-7382
www.templeinland.com

Temple-Inland produces over 60% of its wallboard using synthetic gypsum derived from flue-gas desulphurization. All wallboard coming from their Tennessee and Arkansas plants has an SCS-certified recycled content of 99% with the exception of sheathing and moisture-resistant wallboard, which is certified to contain 95% recycled content. Wallboard can be specified from these plants and comes with endtapes designating production source.

Fiberock Brand Aqua Tough Panels

USG Corporation

For full listing, see CSI section 09 28 00 - Backing Boards and Underlayments

Sheetrock Brand Gypsum Panels

USG Corporation
125 S. Franklin St.
Chicago, IL 60606

Toll-free: 800-874-4968
Phone: 312-606-4000
Fax: 312-606-4476
www.usg.com

Sheetrock® Brand Gypsum Panels are USG's brand of standard drywall products. USG uses flue-gas desulfurization (FGD) gypsum, an industrial waste product derived from pollution-control equipment at coal-fired power plants, in its standard drywall products—over 3 million tons of it in 2004, more than any other wallboard supplier. However, this content changes from plant to plant and even day to day at any one plant due to availability. The recycled content of USG boards nationwide for 2004 was over 37% by weight, according to the company; over 32% was recaptured gypsum. All USG wallboard uses 100% post-consumer recycled paper. USG has seven plants that make panels with over 97% recycled content, and an additional seven plants use a blend of natural gypsum and FGD gypsum.

Most recently mentioned in EBN 2:3 & 14:4

09 29 13
Gypsum Board Accessories

Using drywall clips at corners and partition-wall intersections allows a reduction in steel or wood studs, saving resources and reducing costs. Used at corners, drywall clips allow slight movement of drywall panels to accommodate expansion and contraction of framing members, minimizing cracking and call-backs. In addition, drywall clips and stops do not take up space that insulation could occupy in wall cavities where interior partitions meet exterior walls. Products listed here are accessories for gypsum board construction that have various environmental features or benefits in use such as drywall clips or "stops."

PowerSand and QuikSand Sanding Blocks

Earthstone International
101 S. Coit Rd., Ste. 36-319
Richardson, TX 75080

Toll-free: 888-994-6327
Fax: 972-509-5755
www.goearthstone.com

Earthstone PowerSand, made with limestone and 90% post-consumer recycled glass, are self-sharpening, pumice-like blocks or discs that attach to palm-sized power sanders or electric drills (with mount adapters). QuikSand is a hand-held, wet-or-dry version of the product made with limestone and 96% post-consumer recycled glass. In addition to smoothing wood, they can be used to remove finishes from most substrates without the need for stripping chemicals. The PowerSand blocks produce less airborne dust than sandpaper, and the porous material won't clog or rip. One block is the equivalent of several sheets of sandpaper, so fewer change-outs are required.

Prest-on Cornerbacks

Prest-on Company
312 Lookout Pt.
Hot Springs, AR 71913

Toll-free: 800-323-1813
Phone: 501-767-3855
Fax: 501-767-5173
www.prest-on.com

Prest-on's steel Cornerbacks are "pressed" onto the drywall and nailed or screwed to the structural member. This product is not designed for floating corners.

Simpson Drywall Stop (DS)

Simpson Strong-Tie Connectors
5956 W. Las Positas Blvd.
P.O. Box 10789
Pleasanton, CA 94588

Toll-free: 800-999-5099
Phone: 925-560-9000
Fax: 925-833-1496
www.strongtie.com

The Simpson Drywall Stop (DS) is a galvanized steel product that installs with nails.

Most recently mentioned in EBN 3:1

No-Nail and Stud Claw

Stud Claw USA
5370 Chestnut Ridge Rd.
Orchard Park, NY 14127

Phone: 716-662-7877
Fax: 716-662-4430
www.studclaw.com

No-Nail™ is a sheet metal drywall clip that creates floating corners. It friction-fits to one sheet of drywall and grips the adjoining sheet with its own spurs. This clip can accommodate non-right-angle applications such as cathedral ceilings. The Stud Claw is a metal wire clip that grips two-by wood framing with spurs and also facilitates floating corners. Two sizes are available: GC-15 (1-1/2") for single top plates and studs, and GC-30 (3") for double plates.

The Nailer

The Millennium Group, Inc.
2300 W. Eisenhower Blvd.
Loveland, CO 80537

Toll-free: 800-280-2304
Phone: 970-663-1200
Fax: 970-292-1024
www.thenailer.com

The Nailer® is a 100% recycled-content, high-density polyethylene (HDPE) plastic drywall stop or backer. The Nailer installs with flat-head nails or staples and the standard component "Tec" screw for steel studs. Drywall may be screwed or glued to The Nailer or may simply be floated behind the adjacent drywall sheet. The Nailer allows for full-size friction fit insulation in wall cavities and can reduce cracking due to truss uplift.

Most recently mentioned in EBN 3:1

DC1 Drywall Clip

USP Structural Connectors
14305 Southcross Dr., Ste. 200
Burnsville, MN 55306

Toll-free: 800-328-5934
Fax: 952-898-8683
www.uspconnectors.com

The DC1 Drywall Clip is a galvanized steel clip that is installed with nails.

Most recently mentioned in EBN 3:1

ButtHanger and EZ-Backer

Wilco Tools, Inc.
1122 Siddonsburg Rd.
Mechanicsburg, PA 17055

Toll-free: 888-292-1002
Phone: 717-766-4594
Fax: 717-795-9160
www.butthanger.com

The ButtHanger, a simple device made from wood strapping and metal cross pieces, eliminates the single most problematic aspect of interior finish work—the drywall butt joint. By enabling the laying out and hanging of board finish ends to space rather than to framing, the Butthanger bends the butt ends inward about 1/8". This changes a labor-intensive and difficult 3'-wide mud joint into a quick and easy 1'-wide one while both reducing cut-off waste and joint compound used for butt joints. EZ-Backer is an all-steel commercial version of the ButtHanger.

Most recently mentioned in EBN 10:11

09 29 14
Gypsum Board Taping and Finishing

Products listed here are accessories for gypsum board taping and finishing that have various environmental features or benefits in use such as low-VOC joint compounds.

Murco M100 Joint Compound

Murco Wall Products
2032 N. Commerce
Fort Worth, TX 76106

Toll-free: 800-446-7124
Phone: 817-626-1987
Fax: 817-626-0821
www.murcowall.com

Murco Wall Products manufactures a powdered all-purpose joint cement and texture compound formulated with inert fillers and natural binders only. It does not contain any preservatives or slow-releasing compounds and is zero-VOC. M100 mixes easily with tap water.

Most recently mentioned in EBN 9:11

09 30 13
Ceramic Tiling

Tile is an inherently low-toxic, waterproof, durable finish material for flooring, walls, and other applications. While tile is somewhat energy-intensive to manufacture, the materials involved are readily available and mined with fairly low impact. Products listed here contain post-consumer or post-industrial recycled content.

GeoStone EcoCycle

Crossville Porcelain Stone
P.O. Box 1168
Crossville, TN 38557

Phone: 931-484-2110
www.crossvilleinc.com

Crossville Porcelain Stone offers a line of ceramic tile called GeoStone EcoCycle made from 50-100% in-house manufacturing scrap generated during the manufacturing process of standard-color porcelain tiles. This manufacturing scrap, which would otherwise be landfilled, is not recycled content as defined by the EPA. The scrap also includes a small percentage of dust from the air and water filtration systems. The tiles measure 12" x 12" with matching 4" x 12" bullnose trim. Available in five colors, GeoStone EcoCycle is recommended for interior floors and walls as well as exterior walls.

Debris Series Ceramic Tile and Pavers

Fireclay Tile
495 W. Julian St.
San Jose, CA 95110

Phone: 408-275-1182
www.fireclaytile.com

Fireclay Tile manufactures the Debris Series of handmade tile using post-industrial and post-consumer recycled material. Fire Clay's terra cotta body is made from 25% recycled granite dust, 19% broken window panes, and 8.5 % recycled brown and green glass bottles. The company's white clay body contains 47.5% recycled broken window panes and clear glass bottles. The terra cotta tile can be unglazed or glazed. The tiles made with the white clay body have transparent glazes. The glazes do not contain lead.

Eco-Tile

Quarry Tile Company
6328 E. Utah Ave.
Spokane, WA 99212

Phone: 509-536-2812
Fax: 509-536-4072
www.quarrytile.com

Eco-Tile™ is a commercial-grade, glazed ceramic tile made with approximately 70% recycled solid waste as defined by the EPA's CPG program. This waste content is made up of post-consumer recycled glass (about 25%), post-industrial grinding paste from the computer industry, and post-industrial mining waste from the sand and gravel industry (post-industrial content about 45%). The company also utilizes reprocessed glaze waste from their other manufacturing operations. Glaze from overspray, body scrap, and process waste is recycled in a closed-loop,

09 00 00
Finishes

zero-discharge, water reclamation system. Eco-Tile may contain up to 10% by weight of this material. All the recycled content in Eco-Tile comes from within a 10- to 350-mile radius of the plant and replaces virgin materials from as far away as 2,300 miles. Currently produced in over 50 colors and 5 sizes, Eco-Tile must be special-ordered (minimum 300 ft²).

Terra Classic and Terra Traffic

Terra Green Ceramics
1650 Progress Dr.
Richmond, IN 47374

Phone: 765-935-4760
Fax: 765-935-3971
www.terragreenceramics.com

Terra Green Ceramic Tiles are made with 55% post-industrial recycled glass. Terra Classic and Terra Traffic (slip-resistant) are each available in 17 colors, several sizes, and with a wide range of accessories.

Most recently mentioned in EBN 3:3, 6:1, 6:5

09 30 24
Recycled-Glass Tiling

Tile is an inherently low-toxic, durable finish material for flooring, walls, and other applications. Products listed here are specialty tiles produced from recycled glass.

Architectural Accents

Aurora Glass
2345 W. Broadway
Eugene, OR 97402

Toll-free: 888-291-9311
Phone: 541-681-3260
Fax: 541-681-8755
www.auroraglass.org

Aurora Glass Architectural Accents include glass tiles, rosette blocks, sconces, and drawer pulls made from 100% recycled glass. Aurora Glass is a program of St. Vincent de Paul of Lane County, Inc. The glass foundry's profits support homeless and low-income people through emergency services, housing, jobs, training, and other charitable endeavors.

Blazestone

Bedrock Industries
1401 W. Garfield St.
Seattle, WA 98119

Toll-free: 877-283-7625
Phone: 206-283-7625
Fax: 206-283-0497
www.bedrockindustries.com

Blazestone® tiles are made from 100% recycled glass, most of which is post-consumer content. They come in 2" x 2", 2" x 4", 4" x 4", 5" x 5", 5" x 10", and 4" hex sizes, as well as mosaic pieces. Color varies with the recycled glass materials used. Bedrock also makes architectural accents and non-architectural accessories from recycled glass. Three of the 28 colors offered are made exclusively from 100% post-industrial waste. For the others, the manufacturer has certified the following recycled-content levels (by weight): total recovered material 100% typical, 100% guaranteed; post-consumer material 50% typical, 50% guaranteed.

Recycled-Glass Tiles

Hot Glass
1224 East Georgia
Vancouver, BC V6A 2B1 Canada

Phone: 604-886-0202

Hot Glass hand-makes sand-cast, 2" x 2" tiles from 100% post-consumer recycled wine bottles. Colors include green, three shades of blue, clear, and several others.

Oceanside Glass Tiles

Oceanside Glasstile Co.
2293 Cosmos Ct.
Carlsbad, CA 92011

Toll-free: 877-648-8222
Phone: 760-929-4000
Fax: 760-929-5860
www.glasstile.com

Oceanside produces four styles of tile hand-cast from 85% post-consumer recycled glass. They are semi-transparent, have an iridescent surface, and are available in a range of colors. Tessera is available in 29 colors and 4 sizes. Casa California includes larger-format tiles with a full line of decoratives. Minerali is a specialty tile with wide color variation and a textured surface. Haiku features opal glass with Asian motifs.

Recycled-Glass Tiles

Sandhill Industries
6898 S. Supply Rd., Ste. 100
Boise, ID 83716

Phone: 208-345-6508
Fax: 208-345-4424
www.sandhillind.com

Sandhill Industries manufactures wall and floor tile from 100% post-industrial plate glass. The company's manufacturing process can produce both glossy and matte finishes, and results in no wastewater or air emissions. Tiles come in a standard variety of square, bar, and triangle sizes, as well as rail pieces and film-mounted mosaic patterns. A wide assortment of colors, shapes, and textures can be produced by special order.

UltraGlas

UltraGlas, Inc.
9200 Gazette Ave.
Chatsworth, CA 91311

Toll-free: 800-777-2332
Phone: 818-772-7744
Fax: 818-772-8231
www.ultraglas.com

UltraGlas® is sculpted/embossed, molded architectural glass with 15-30% recycled-glass (cullet) content. A variety of decorative textures, designs, and patterns are available with varying levels of translucency. If so specified, UltraGlas can be made from 100% recycled glass, subject to its availability.

09 30 26
Plastic Flooring

Recycled plastic flooring products are relatively inexpensive, often interlocking, floor tiles that are particularly appropriate in wet areas. Though not always durable enough for heavy traffic areas, plastic flooring is suitable for outdoor showers and certain other utilitarian spaces where easy maintenance and some resilience are required. Textures and open-weave construction also lend slip-resistance to some products. Some offer adhesive-free installation. Products listed here have a recycled content value (equal to post-consumer plus 1/2 pre-consumer) of at least 40%, with many products using 100% post-consumer and/or post-industrial recycled plastic.

Power-Bloc

C&A, a Tandus Company
311 Smith Industrial Blvd.
P.O. Box 1447
Dalton, GA 30722

Toll-free: 800-248-2878
Phone: 706-259-9711
Fax: 706-259-2179
www.tandus.com

Power-Bloc® is industrial flooring made from 100% recycled materials, including reclaimed vinyl-backed carpet, polyethylene, and in-plant scrap. Blocks are 4" x 6" and 1", 2", and 3" thick. This product is used in industrial buildings in place of creosote-treated woodblock flooring.

Most recently mentioned in EBN 6:6

Plastic Flooring Tiles

Curb Appeal Materials, LTD
3824 N. Johnsburg Rd.
McHenry, IL 60050

Phone: 815-344-7926
Fax: 815-344-7960
www.vortexcomposites.com

Free Style interlocking floor tiles are made with 92% recycled materials nylon carpet waste with some commingled plastic from post-consumer and post-industrial sources. These slip-resistant tiles are available in wood-grain and stone patterns, and carry a 10-year warranty. SelecTile interlocking floor tiles are made of post-industrial recycled PVC. These slip-resistant tiles are available in static-dissipative or conductive versions for electrostatic discharge (ESD) protection in applications with sensitive electronics. They are available in smooth, coin, and diamond surfaces in seven colors. SelecTile ESD is available in black only. Both lines of these tiles can be placed directly over existing floors (including glued carpets); no adhesive is needed.

PlasTEAK Recycled-Plastic Tiles

PlasTEAK
3563 Copley Rd.
P.O. Box 4290
Akron, OH 44321

Toll-free: 800-320-1841
Phone: 330-668-2587
Fax: 330-666-0844
www.plasteak.com

PlasTEAK tiles are made with 100% post-consumer recycled HDPE in a paraffin base—they become more slip-resistant when wet. Locking Tiles are open-weave, 12" x 12" x 3/4", UV-stabilized, interlocking tiles;

transitional edge ramps are available. Patio Pads are solid-surface 24" x 24" x 1-1/2" pavers with a decorative appearance. The made-for-function, solid-surface Pro Pads tiles come in two-inch-thick sizes ranging from 24" x 24" to 36" x 48".

ArobiTile and ShowerTile

RB Rubber Products, Inc.
904 N.E. Tenth Ave.
McMinnville, OR 97128

Toll-free: 800-525-5530
Phone: 503-472-4691
Fax: 503-434-4455
www.rbrubber.com

ArobiTile and ShowerTile are made from 90% post-consumer and 10% pre-consumer recycled PVC plastic in a choice of 9 colors. ArobiTile is a solid product with "goose bumps" for traction, while ShowerTile has an open-weave pattern to allow drainage.

Patio Tiles

New

Renew Resources Ltd.
81 Mack Ave.
Toronto, ON M1L 1M5 Canada

Toll-free: 800-439-5028
Phone: 416-335-4040
Fax: 416-335-4039
www.renewresources.com

Renew Resources offers recycled-plastic tiles made of 100% pre-consumer HDPE, available in grey, taupe, redwood, and cedar. Primarily used over solid surfaces such as rooftops, patios, and balconies, the tiles may also be laid directly on the ground for temporary or permanent yard patios. Available in two sizes: 23" x 23" and 17" x 17".

SelecTiles

SelecTech, Inc.
33 Wales Ave., Unit F
Avon, MA 02322

Phone: 508-583-3200
Fax: 508-583-3260
www.selectechinc.com

SelecTiles™ are heavy-duty, recycled-PVC interlocking floor tiles measuring 24" x 24" and weighing 6 lbs. each. The tiles, which are resistant to most solvents and chemicals, come in a variety of colors including black, gray, blue, red, yellow, green, and brown, as well as custom colors, and can be ordered with different surface finishes. Only Black is made from 100% recycled materials. Other colors are 10% minimum recycled materials.

Turtle Tiles

Turtle Plastics
7450-A Industrial Pkwy.
Lorain, OH 44053

Toll-free: 800-437-1603
Phone: 440-282-8008
Fax: 440-282-8822
www.turtleplastics.com

Turtle Tiles are open-weave floor tiles made from 50% post-consumer recycled PVC plastic. The interlocking tiles are 3/4" x 12" x 12" and come in 17 solid colors.

Flexisurf

Yemm & Hart Ltd.
1417 Madison 308
Marquand, MO 63655

Phone: 573-783-5434
Fax: 573-783-7544
www.yemmhart.com

Flexisurf is a tough, resilient flooring product made from 100% recycled commingled post-industrial PVC and polyester plastic such as from swimming pool cover, industrial roofing membrane, and auto-upholstery trimmings. Treated with Vinyzene® fungicide to resist mold and bacterial growth, Flexisurf is available in sheets or in square-cut or interlocking tiles in a variety of colors and textures. Flexisurf is self-healing, and seams can be welded chemically or by heat to produce watertight joints. Indoor use requires sealing and a properly ventilated space to mitigate IAQ concerns.

09 30 29
Metal Tiling

Products listed here are made from recycled metals and are available for countertops, tables, backsplashes, and walls.

Cast Aluminum Products

Eleek, Inc.

For full listing, see CSI section 26 51 14 - Interior Luminaires

09 00 00
Finishes

09 30 53
Tiling Adhesive

Adhesives can be a major source of indoor air quality problems, often more so than the products they adhere. Water-based adhesives have lower VOC emissions than solvent-based products. Tile adhesives, like many other adhesives, can have high VOC levels. VOCs contribute to poor indoor air quality (IAQ), and are a major component of smog. Products listed here have low VOC levels. (See also 09 60 13 - Flooring Adhesives.)

Safecoat 3 in 1 Adhesive

American Formulating & Manufacturing (AFM)
3251 Third Ave.
San Diego, CA 92103

Toll-free: 800-239-0321
Phone: 619-239-0321
Fax: 619-239-0565
www.afmsafecoat.com

Safecoat 3 in 1 Adhesive is designed for hard composition—ceramic, vinyl, parquet, formica, and slate—floor and counter tiles. It is a water-based alternative to solvent-based adhesives and has significantly lower VOC content of 44 g/l (82 g/l less water).

EcoTimber HealthyBond Adhesive

EcoTimber

For full listing, see CSI section 09 60 13 - Flooring Adhesives

Envirotec Floor Covering Adhesives

W. F. Taylor Company

For full listing, see CSI section 09 60 13 - Flooring Adhesives

09 31 00
Thin-Set Tiling

Like tile adhesives, thin-set mortars can have high VOC levels. VOCs contribute to poor indoor air quality (IAQ), and are a major component of smog. Products listed here have low or zero-VOC levels.

D-5 Premium and D-40 Duraflex Thin-Set Mortar

Bostik, Inc.
211 Boston St.
Middleton, MA 01949

Toll-free: 800-366-7837
Phone: 978-777-0100
Fax: 978-750-7319
www.bostik-us.com

D-5 Premium Thin-Set Mortar (formerly D-505+) and D-40™ Duraflex™ are zero-VOC, thin-set tile mortars.

09 51 00
Acoustical Ceilings

Acoustical ceiling materials vary depending on the specific performance criteria desired (e.g., durability, light reflectance, sound absorption, washability, design flexibility, fire resistance). Most common in commercial suspended ceilings are wet-pressed mineral-fiber tiles and panels, typically made from a mixture of waste paper, mineral fiber (which may include slag, a waste product from steel-making), cornstarch, and various other mineral-based components. A number of these products have high recycled content; some, however, may contain low levels of formaldehyde. Fiberglass ceiling panels are also available with recycled content, though the percentage is typically lower than with mineral-fiber products. Most fiberglass ceiling panel products use a phenol-formaldehyde binder. Though far more common in Europe, wood-fiber-based ceiling panel products are also available in the U.S.—these are free of mineral fibers and formaldehyde but are typically more expensive, and they contain no recycled content. Metal ceiling products may or may not include a backing of fiberglass. Products for use in food service facilities, hospitals, or other areas with high sanitary standards have a PVC covering or scrubbable paint finish. Poorly controlled burning of PVC (polyvinyl chloride) may release dioxins and furans. Residential acoustical ceiling panels are not available in as many materials or styles as commercial products.

Armstrong Ceiling Recycling Program

Armstrong Ceiling Systems
2500 Columbia Ave.
P.O. Box 3001
Lancaster, PA 17604

Toll-free: 888-234-5464 (then Option 3)
Phone: 717-397-0611
www.armstrong.com/environmental

The Armstrong Ceilings Reclamation Program is a one-of-its-kind, closed-loop program that diverts used ceilings from landfills to Armstrong plants where they are recycled into new ceilings.

Most recently mentioned in EBN 7:10 & 9:10

Mineral Fiber and Glass Based Drop-in Ceiling Tile

Armstrong World Industries, Inc.
2500 Columbia Ave.
P.O. Box 3001
Lancaster, PA 17604

Toll-free: 877-276-7876
Phone: 717-397-0611
www.armstrong.com

Armstrong Ceiling Systems offer a complete line of acoustical ceiling products that include both post-consumer and post-industrial waste, as well as abundant natural materials, including recycled newspaper, mineral wool, perlite, and cornstarch. Armstrong Ceilings offers products that contain up to 82% recycled content. Through its ceiling recycling program, old ceiling tiles are recycled and made into new ones.

Most recently mentioned in EBN 8:11

Celotex, Gyptone, Interior Pro, and Capaul

BPB America Inc.
5301 West Cypress St., Ste. 300
Tampa, FL 33607

Toll-free: 866-427-2872
Phone: 813-286-3900
Fax: 813-286-3990
www.bpb-na.com

Celotex®, Gyptone®, Interior Pro®, and Capaul® are among BPB's complete lines of acoustical ceiling products. BPB acoustical ceilings have up to 88% total recycled content, of which 0 to 22% is post-consumer material, and 0 to 82% is pre-consumer. Recycled content varies with product type. Manufacturing facilities are located in L'Anse, MI, Meridian, MS, and Plymouth, WI.

EuroStone

Chicago Metallic
4849 S. Austin Ave.
Chicago, IL 60638

Toll-free: 800-323-7164
Phone: 708-563-4600
Fax: 800-222-3744
www.chicagometallic.com

EuroStone is a lightweight (1.6 lbs/ft²) acoustical ceiling panel made from volcanic perlite, clay, and an inorganic binder. The recyclable, inorganic panels will not support mold, bacteria, or fungus, are impervious to water, and are recyclable. EuroStone panels are available in seven designs with 8 earth-tone™ colors. They measure 7/8" x 24" x 24" and fit either 15/16" or narrow 9/16" T-bar suspension grids. EuroStone has ASTM E84 flame-spread and smoke development ratings of 0, and a limited lifetime warranty program.

Most recently mentioned in EBN 6:1

Sonopan and Securpan

Louiseville Specialty Products
161 Saint Paul
Louiseville, QC J5V 2G9 Canada

Toll-free: 800-561-4279
Phone: 819-228-2789
Fax: 819-228-2845
www.materiauxspecl.com

Sonopan sound insulation panels are made from recycled wood fiber impregnated with a paraffin wax binder. Panels are perforated to improve acoustical performance. Securpan is a similar product that is fire-retardant.

Tectum Interior Products

Tectum, Inc.
P.O. Box 3002
Newark, OH 43058

Toll-free: 888-977-9691
Phone: 740-345-9691
Fax: 740-349-9305
www.tectum.com

Tectum panels are high-impact, wood-fiber, acoustical wall and ceiling products available in a wide range of sizes. Panels are available with a noise reduction coefficient of up to 1.0 and light reflection of up to 70%. Tectum panels are made from strands of aspen wood fibers blended with an inorganic, hydraulic, cementitious mix of magnesium oxide, sodium silicate, and magnesium sulfate. They are noncombustible, lightweight, paintable, and formaldehyde-free.

Most recently mentioned in EBN 7:4 & 8:1

Acoustical Ceiling Panels and Tiles

USG Corporation
125 S. Franklin St.
Chicago, IL 60606

Toll-free: 800-874-4968
Phone: 312-606-4000
Fax: 312-606-4476
www.usg.com

USG Interiors manufacturers a range of ceiling products, including acoustical panels that have a high recycled content (up to 78%). Many are made from slag wool (a post-industrial by-product of the steel industry), cornstarch, waste newspaper, and clay. These panels have low VOC emissions, meeting CHPS (Collaborative for High Performance Schools) guidelines. Eight product lines are classified as formaldehyde-free and exceed standards set by the California Office of Environmental Health Hazard Assessment. Other product lines are classified as low-formaldehyde. USG also has a mineral wool ceiling panel recycling program in which old panels are turned into new construction products.

Most recently mentioned in EBN 16:1

09 54 00
Specialty Ceilings

Metal ceiling tiles or panels are often made from aluminum, due to its low weight. These may include recycled content and are always recyclable. Metal ceiling panels are also durable and offer at least as much design flexibility as their fiber-based counterparts. Panels may be painted or unpainted, and they may include a backing of fiberglass to improve acoustical performance.

Aluminum Ceiling Systems

Hunter Douglas Architectural Products
5015 Oakbrook Pkwy., Ste. 100
Norcross, GA 30093

Toll-free: 800-366-4327
Phone: 770-806-9557
Fax: 770-806-0214
www.hunterdouglasceilings.com

Hunter Douglas Aluminum Ceiling Systems are made with high levels of recycled aluminum (the manufacturer estimates over 70%) and come in five styles in a complete range of colors, finishes, and patterns.

Gage Ceilings and Gage Wall Surfacing

The Gage Corp., International
803 S. Black River St.
Sparta, WI 54656

Toll-free: 800-786-4243
Phone: 608-269-7447
Fax: 608-269-7622
www.gageceilings.com

Gage ceiling and wall products are made from aluminum with 50% recycled content. These lightweight panels are available in a large selection of designs.

09 60 13
Flooring Adhesives

Flooring adhesives can be a major source of indoor air quality problems, often more so than the flooring products they adhere. Water-based adhesives have lower VOC emissions than solvent-based products. While some products are sold as multipurpose, others are specific to a particular application or product (linoleum, for example, requires special adhesives due to its linseed oil content). If a flooring manufacturer recommends a specific low- or zero-VOC, water-based product for use with its material, then use it; otherwise consider a product known to minimize indoor air pollution and check with the flooring product manufacturer to find out whether that product can be used with their flooring material. Some air quality management districts restrict the manufacture, sale, and installation of flooring adhesives that exceed a VOC content of 150 grams per liter. Products listed here are low or zero-VOC, water-based and solvent free, or made from natural materials.

BioShield Cork Adhesive #16

BioShield Paint Company
3215 Rufina Street
Santa Fe, NM 87507

Toll-free: 800-621-2591
Phone: 505-438-3448
Fax: 505-438-0199
www.bioshieldpaint.com

BioShield Cork Adhesive #16 is a water-based, solvent-free adhesive specially designed for cork flooring.

09 00 00
Finishes

09 00 00
Finishes

Safe-Set Adhesives

Chicago Adhesive Products Co.
1105 S. Frontenac St.
Aurora, IL 60504

Toll-free: 800-621-0220
Phone: 630-679-9100
Fax: 800-942-9876
www.chapco-adhesive.com

Safe-Set products are solvent-free, zero-VOC, nonflammable, nontoxic floor covering adhesives.

EcoTimber HealthyBond Adhesive

EcoTimber
1611 4th St.
San Rafael, CA 94901

Toll-free: 888-801-0855
Phone: 415-258-8454
Fax: 415-258-8455
www.ecotimber.com

EcoTimber offers a low-odor, solvent-free, virtually VOC-free (7 g/l), 100% solids urethane adhesive for wood and bamboo flooring for residential and commercial use. Adheres to hardwood, bamboo, cork, plywood, concrete, vinyl, particleboard, and terrazzo. Not recommended for True Teak. Water-proof, flexible, freeze-thaw stable, and strong enough to glue down solid wood planks. It is packaged in 4-gallon containers that provide approximately 240 ft^2 of coverage.

EcoTimber HealthyBond Adhesive

New

EcoTimber
1611 4th St.
San Rafael, CA 94901

Toll-free: 888-801-0855
Phone: 415-258-8454
Fax: 415-258-8455
www.ecotimber.com

HealthyBond Adhesive from EcoTimber is used for installation of wood and bamboo flooring. The product's resin-based formula adheres to hardwood, bamboo, cork, plywood, concrete, vinyl, particleboard, and terrazzo, and EcoTimber claims it is strong enough for use with plank flooring. Healthy-Bond Adhesive is isocynate-free, urethane-free, solvent-free, has low VOC content (7g/l), and is Greenguard Indoor Air Quality Certified as a low-emitting product.

#965 Flooring and Tread Adhesive

Johnsonite
16910 Munn Rd.
Chagrin Falls, OH 44023

Toll-free: 800-899-8916
Phone: 440-543-8916
Fax: 440-543-8920
www.johnsonite.com

Johnsonite's #965 is a high-strength, solvent-free, water-based, acrylic latex adhesive. It was formulated for rubber sheet flooring as well as rubber and vinyl stair treads and nosings on porous and nonporous surfaces.

Most recently mentioned in EBN 15:2

380 Natural All-Purpose Floor Adhesive

Sinan Co. Environmental Products
P.O. Box 857
Davis, CA 95616

Phone: 530-753-3104
Fax: 270-675-7423
www.sinanco.com

Sinan 380 Natural All-Purpose Adhesive is a water-based product made with organic binders for use with cork, wood, linoleum, and carpeting. Sinan products are made from all-natural, primarily plant-based materials, all of which are listed on the packaging.

Envirotec Floor Covering Adhesives

W. F. Taylor Company
11545 Pacific Ave.
Fontana, CA 92337

Toll-free: 800-397-4583
Phone: 909-360-6677
Fax: 909-360-1177
www.wftaylor.com

Envirotec is W. F. Taylor Company's line of nontoxic, solvent-free, low-VOC adhesive products. These products include multipurpose flooring adhesives, carpet adhesives, and cove base adhesives.

Most recently mentioned in EBN 3:6

09 60 14
Flooring Underlayment

Underlayment for wood, bamboo, composite, and other floorings may be made from a variety of recycled, natural, and/or synthetic materials. As with the flooring itself, care should be taken not to expose the cushion to moisture—including long-term moisture from concrete slabs—to minimize the potential for microbial growth. Flexible-foam padding frequently contains brominated flame retardants (BFRs) which have been identified as a growing health and environmental concern.

AcoustiCORK

Amorim Industrial Solutions
26112 110th St.
P.O. Box 25
Trevor, WI 53179

Toll-free: 800-255-2675
Phone: 262-862-2311
Fax: 262-862-2500
www.acousticorkusa.com

AcoustiCORK sheets and rolls are made with cork granules and a polyurethane-based binder. They may be used under a variety of flooring types, such as ceramic tile, natural stone tiles, and hardwood flooring, although an additional board underlayment is advised for use with vinyl sheet and vinyl composition tile. The AcoustiCORK AC 55 Plus product, made with cork sheets and a coconut fiber core, offers higher levels of acoustical performance.

Most recently mentioned in EBN 5:1

QuietWalk

New

MP Global Products LLC
2500 Old Hadar Rd.
PO Box 2283
Norfolk, NE 68702-2283

Toll-free: 888-379-9695
Phone: 402-379-9695
Fax: 402-379-9737
www.mpglobalproducts.com

Quiet Walk™ underlayment for laminate flooring is designed to smooth out subfloor imperfections and provide ambient and impact sound control. It is manufactured from minimum 80% post-industrial recycled synthetic fibers and polyethylene film bound with an inert hot-melt adhesive. Quiet Walk has passed the ASTM E1333 offgas test with no detected level of formaldehyde. The product has an attached vapor barrier and is 1/8" thick, providing an insulation value of R-0.5 (R-4 per inch). Quiet Walk is marketed as an upgrade to poly foam with a cost less than 1/2 that of cork or rubber. Quiet Walk is available in 100 and 360 square-foot rolls and distributed in both Canada and the US.

09 00 00
Finishes

Cork Underlayment

Natural Cork, Inc.
1710 N. Leg Ct.
Augusta, GA 30909

Toll-free: 800-404-2675
Phone: 706-733-6120
Fax: 706-733-8120
www.naturalcork.com

Natural Cork sound control underlayment comes in 5/64", 1/8", or 1/4" thicknesses in 4' x 50' rolls or 1/4" and 1/2" thicknesses in 2' x 3' sheets.

Whisper Wool Acoustic Underlay

Nature's Acoustics
80 Old East Rd.
Chatsworth, GA 30705

Phone: 706-422-8660
Fax: 706-422-8661
www.naturesacoustics.com

Whisper Wool offers carpet padding as well as acoustic underlayment for laminate, engineered, and hardwood floors made from 100% sheep wool. The underlayment has a clear polypropylene moisture barrier laminate to help prevent mold, fungus, and bacteria growth. Both products feature Sanitized® antimicrobial treatment. The 1/8-inch-thick underlayment comes in 3-foot-wide, 33.5-foot-long rolls (covering 100 ft²). The 1/2"-thick, high-density carpet padding weighs 38 ounces per sq. yard, and comes in 6.5-foot-wide rolls.

Nova Underlayment

Nova Distinctive Floors
1710 E. Sepulveda Blvd.
Carson, CA 90745

Toll-free: 866-576-2458
Fax: 310-830-9589
www.novafloorings.com

Nova Cork rolled cork underlayment can be used under a wide variety of floorcoverings and has a 20-year residential warranty; 10-year commercial. It's available as 6 mm-thick 4' x 50" rolls (200 ft² per roll), 6 mm-thick 2' x 3' sheets (300 ft² per carton), and 12 mm-thick 2' x 3' sheets (150 ft² per carton). NovaCork is manufactured in Switzerland.

09 62 23
Bamboo Flooring

Most bamboo for flooring comes from the Hunan province of China. It's not a food source for pandas, which generally inhabit higher-elevation forests. Despite the long-distance transport of the product to the United States, the durability, hardness, and short regeneration time of bamboo provide justification for using it for flooring instead of conventionally harvested wood. Bamboo is typically processed without preservatives or with benign boric acid, but more toxic preservatives are occasionally used when unprocessed poles are exported. Most bamboo flooring is glued together with urea-formaldehyde binders, which is the primary negative aspect. As the popularity and availability of bamboo increases, so does the need for uniform and credible certification of green attributes. Ideally there would be verification of: (1) low ambient VOC emissions using chamber testing (certified to meet Floorscore or Greenguard), (2) limited use of pesticides and preservatives, (3) growing practices (certified to FSC standards), and (4) manufacturing conditions. GreenSpec listings will be updated to reflect such information as it becomes available. Products listed here are made with binders and adhesives that have ultra-low formaldehyde concentrations (<=0.02 ppm), or have formaldehyde emissions of 0.05ppm or lower using the ASTM E-1333 test for Europe's E1 standard or another roughly equivalent standard (because testing protocols are different, standards are not truly comparable). (See feature article EBN Vol. 15, No. 3.)*

Bamboo Hardwoods Flooring

Bamboo Hardwoods, Inc.
510 S. Industrial Way
Seattle, WA 98108

Toll-free: 800-783-0557
Phone: 206-264-2414
Fax: 206-264-9365
www.bamboohardwoods.com

Bamboo Hardwoods, a U.S. company with a factory in Vietnam, sells both unfinished and prefinished flooring. The unfinished product is vertically laminated, and the prefinished product includes a rubber-tree-wood inner core. These flooring products are manufactured with a melamine adhesive and a boric acid insecticide. The rubberwood used is harvested from over-mature trees on rubber plantations that are out of production. Bamboo Hardwoods also reports that their engineered floor now uses a much harder bamboo (measuring 2048 on the Janka Ball Hardness Test)—the hardest bamboo ever discovered, according to the company.

Most recently mentioned in EBN 6:10 & 15:3

Bamboo Mountain

Bamboo Mountain, Inc.
110 Pacific Ave. #357
San Francisco, CA 94111

Toll-free: 877-700-1772
Phone: 415-839-7271
Fax: 415-449-6623
www.bamboomountain.com

Bamboo Mountain™, founded in 1997, offers very-low-VOC bamboo flooring in seamless 3' strip, 6' long strip, and 6' plank flooring, along with a trim line that includes heater vent covers, stair treads & riser, and baseboards. All flooring is made with the mid-stalk of Moso bamboo that is harvested on a 6-year cycle, using formaldehyde-free glues in an ISO 9002-certified factory. Bamboo Mountain provides a 25-year warranty.

Most recently mentioned in EBN 15:3

Avanti Bamboo Flooring

Central Bamboo Flooring Inc.
2501 Channing Ave.
San Jose, CA 95131

Phone: 408-943-8599
Fax: 408-943-8048
www.centralfloors.com

Central Bamboo Flooring is the sole importer and distributor of Avanti Brand bamboo flooring and molding. The 3-5/8" x 5/8" tongue-and-groove flooring is available unfinished or pre-finished with water-based, non-off-gassing finishes. Avanti offers a variety of patterns, colors, and finishes.

GreenFloors Bamboo Flooring

GreenFloors
3170 Draper Dr.
Fairfax, VA 22031

Phone: 703-352-8300
Fax: 703-691-3935
www.greenfloors.com

GreenFloors Premium bamboo flooring uses formaldehyde-free glues. A wide variety of lengths, widths, colors and styles (solid, engineered, hand scraped, and stained) are available, including glueless, click-together, floating systems. Veneers and panels are also offered. GreenFloors offers a lifetime structural warranty, and a 25-year finish warranty.

Most recently mentioned in EBN 15:3

09 00 00
Finishes

GreenWood Bamboo Flooring

GreenWood Products Company
33049 Calle Aviador, Unit A
San Juan Capistrano, CA 92675

Toll-free: 866-593-4454
Phone: 949-369-2733
Fax: 949-369-2739
www.greenwoodflooring.com

GreenWood Products Company offers horizontally and vertically laminated bamboo flooring in natural or carbonized colors with a 7-coat aluminum oxide urethane finish. Both styles are 5/8" thick and measure 3-5/8" x 72". The horizontal style is also offered in a 6"-wide version. Formaldehyde emissions are a very low 0.0127 ppm.

Most recently mentioned in EBN 15:3

JMX Bamboo Molding and Flooring

New

JMX International Corporation
2123 Porter Lake Dr., Unit H
Sarasota, FL 34240

Toll-free: 866-272-6773
Phone: 941-377-5112
Fax: 941-554-2133
www.jmxbamboo.com

JMX International imports pre-finished bamboo products including flooring and molding in a wide variety of sizes and styles.

Silkroad Bamboo Flooring

K&M Bamboo Products, Inc.
300 Esna Park Dr., Unit 26
Markham, ON L3R 1H3 Canada

Phone: 905-946-8128
Fax: 905-946-8126
www.silkroadflooring.com

K&M Bamboo Products Inc. offers Silkroad™ horizontally or vertically laminated bamboo flooring in natural or carbonized colors, 3-5/8" wide x 5/8" or 1/2" thick, and 36" or 72" long. Also offered are a carbonized composite lamination (3-5/8" wide x 1/2" thick x 36" long) and an amber horizontally-laminated plank (3-5/8" wide x 5/8" thick x 36" long). Accessories include bull-nosing, baseboards, reducers, T-moldings, quarter-rounds, and stair treads. Finish options are 100% UV-cured urethane and aluminum oxide. Silkroad bamboo has a total VOC emission of .017 mg/m^2/hr and is the first—and currently the only—flooring product to be certified by the Canadian government's Environmental Choice Program (EcoLogo). K&M also offers bamboo plywood and veneer, as well as cork and FSC-certified maple flooring.

Most recently mentioned in EBN 6:10, 7:2, 15:3

Mill Valley Bamboo Flooring

Mill Valley Bamboo Flooring and Building Products, Inc.
14 E. Sir Francis Drake Blvd.
Larkspur, CA 94939

Toll-free: 877-392-2626
Phone: 415-925-1188
Fax: 415-925-6088
www.mvbamboo.com

Mill Valley Bamboo designs and imports bamboo products from their own factories in China, using only 5-6 year old, fully matured bamboo and non-offgassing, formaldehyde-free, water-based glues and finishes. The exceptionally hard flooring comes in six assorted lengths per box, and can be shipped directly to the site. Custom specifications are available. The company offers 66 styles.

Most recently mentioned in EBN 15:3

MOSO Bamboo Building Products

MOSO International NA, Ltd.
2220 40th Ave. E
Seattle, WA 98112

Toll-free: 800-617-2324
Fax: 800-290-7427
www.moso.com

MOSO offers bamboo flooring, veneer, and paneling. Flooring is available as strip or plank, flat- or vertical-pressed, and pre- or unfinished in natural or caramel hues. Prefinished flooring is coated with five coats of UV-cured polyurethane acrylic—the second coat applied has aluminum oxide added for improved wear resistance. Veneer and paneling are available in thicknesses from 1/42" to 1"; sheet sizes are to specification up to dimensions of 5' x 8'. Laminations are bonded with urea-formaldehyde; however, the manufacturer claims that the product exceeds stringent European standards for formaldehyde emissions. All MOSO products are manufactured in P.R. China.

Most recently mentioned in EBN 15:3

Plyboo Bamboo Flooring

Smith & Fong Company
375 Oyster Point Blvd. #3
S. San Francisco, CA 94080

Toll-free: 866-835-9859
Fax: 650-872-1185
www.plyboo.com

Plyboo® Bamboo Flooring comes either flat or vertical-grained in a natural or amber color. Unfinished or prefinished with aluminum oxide, all flooring measures 5/8" x 3-3/4" x 75" and comes 23.4 ft^2 per box. Plyboo is laminated with a low- or no-VOC adhesive, with formaldehyde emissions testing for the

entire product line at 0.3ppm or below. The company also offers a comprehensive range of trim moldings in stairnosing, threshold, reducer, and baseshoe profiles, and baseboard prefinished in amber or natural color.

Most recently mentioned in EBN 6:10 & 15:3

Teragren Bamboo Flooring, Panels, and Veneer

Teragren
12715 Miller Rd. NE, Ste. 301
Bainbridge Island, WA 98110

Toll-free: 800-929-6333
Phone: 206-842-9477
Fax: 206-842-9456
www.teragren.com

Teragren (formerly TimberGrass) manufactures solid strip bamboo flooring in tongue-and-groove or locking system, prefinished or site-finished. All flooring products are available in vertical or flat (horizontal) grains and natural or caramelized standard colors as well as stained cherry, walnut, charcoal and espresso colors. Coatings are water-based and solvent-free. The company uses the MOSO specie of bamboo which is harvested at maturity at 6 years. Teragren also manufactures coordinating stair parts, flooring accessories and vents, panels and veneer for cabinetry, furniture, interior paneling, countertops, and other interior applications as a direct replacement for wood sheet goods. (Note that while the adhesive used to manufacture the panels and veneer exceeds E1 standards, it is not food grade; if the surface is to be used for food preparation, a food grade sealer is recommended.)

Wellmade Bamboo Flooring

Wellmade
P.O. Box 2704
Wilsonville, OR 97070

Phone: 503-582-0848
Fax: 503-582-8402
www.bamboofloorings.com

Wellmade's bamboo flooring is available 3/8", 1/2", 5/8", and 3/4" thick by 3-5/8" or 3-4/5" wide, and 36", 37-4/5", or 72-3/4" in length. Planks are T&G on all sides, available in natural or carbonized colors, and come prefinished with three coats of UV-cured acrylic or an aluminum oxide lacquer. Also available are wide and narrow molding, stair nosing, stair tread, and base molding in natural or carbonized colors. Be sure to ask for flooring with an ultra-low formaldehyde glue such as DYNO adhesives, since Wellmade makes bamboo flooring with different glues.

Most recently mentioned in EBN 15:3

09 62 29
Cork Flooring

Cork is a natural flooring material that's been used for more than a century. Obtained from the outer bark of the cork oak (Quercus suber), it can be harvested sustainably without killing the tree. The cork regenerates in about 10 years. Grown in Portugal, Algeria, Spain, Morocco, France, Italy, and Tunisia, all cork flooring products available in the U.S. are imported. There's almost no material waste from the manufacturing process, but agglomerating the cork requires binders to hold the ground granules together. Urea-formaldehyde binders should be avoided in favor of urea-melamine, phenol-formaldehyde, polyurethane, or all-natural protein binders. Cork flooring is typically available in a variety of shades in tile form, and in some cases is sandwiched with other flooring materials. It's durable, sound-absorbing, and naturally moisture-, rot-, and mold-resistant. Cork is typically finished with a polyurethane or wax coating, which is periodically reapplied. While cork is naturally fire-resistant, wax finishes reduce this quality. Cork-PVC laminate tiles or cork tiles with a PVC wear layer are not listed in GreenSpec.

Wicanders Natural Cork

Amorim Flooring North America, Inc.
7513 Connelley Dr., Ste. M - Front
Hanover, MD 21076

Toll-free: 800-828-2675
Phone: 410-553-6062
Fax: 410-553-6123
www.wicanders.com

Wicanders Series 100 is a PVC-free floating natural cork flooring system. The tiles are made with a phenolic resin binder and measure 900 x 295 x 10.5 mm (35.4" x 11.6" x 0.4"; they are available in 5 collections with a total of 108 designs. Series 200 is a glue-down version, available in 600 x 300 mm (23.6" x 11.8") and 600 x 600 mm (23.6"-square) tiles, 6 mm (1/4") thick, in more than 100 designs.

Dodge Cork Tile

Dodge-Regupol, Inc.
715 Fountain Ave.
Lancaster, PA 17601

Toll-free: 866-883-7780
Phone: 717-295-3400
Fax: 717-295-3414
www.regupol.com

Dodge™ Cork's 12" x 12" tiles are 3/16" or 5/16" thick and available in three finishes (unfinished, waxed, and polyurethane satin).

Most recently mentioned in EBN 5:1

Expanko Cork Tiles

Expanko Cork Co.
3135 Lower Valley Road
Parkesburg, PA 19365

Toll-free: 800-345-6202
Phone: 610-436-8300
Fax: 610-593-3027
www.expanko.com

Expanko cork tiles are 12" or 24" square and come in 3/16" and 5/16" thicknesses. They are available in 17 different face patterns either unfinished or finished with a polyurethane or wax coating.

Globus Cork Flooring

Globus Cork
741 E. 136th St.
Bronx, NY 10454

Phone: 718-742-7264
Fax: 718-742-7265
www.corkfloor.com

Globus Cork Flooring is available in a wide range of sizes and shapes (including triangles, hexagons, and baseboard tiles) and comes in more than 40 colors. All pigments, finishes, and adhesives are water-based and solvent-free. The cork granules are agglomerated with a polyurethane binder. The tiles come with a latex adhesive on their underside and are installed using a second adhesive on the subfloor. Finished with three coats of water-based varnish, the company suggests that a commercial-grade finish coat be applied in the field by the installer.

Cork Mosaic Floor Tile

Habitus
166 E. 108th St.
New York, NY 10029

Phone: 212-426-5500
Fax: 212-426-5200
www.habitusnyc.com

These floor tiles are made with circular plugs recycled from the cork-stopper industry, sliced into nominal 1/4" thick, 1" chips, fixed to a 12" x 24" paper-net backing and 1-3/8" chips, fixed to a 24" x 24" paper-net backing. Sheets are glued to the substrate, then grouted. Due to the larger joint size of the 1-3/8' chips, the manufacturer recommends utilizing a sanded grout product. Sealing is required with polyurethane or wax. This product is available unfinished, pre-varnished (water-based), or custom colored (minimum quantities required). According to the manufacturer, the product is durable and suitable for wet areas.

ProntoKorQ Floor and Wall Panel

Habitus
166 E. 108th St.
New York, NY 10029

Phone: 212-426-5500
Fax: 212-426-5200
www.habitusnyc.com

ProntoKorQ is a tongue-and-groove floating cork flooring or fixed wall panel that comes in 3/8" x 12" x 36" planks. Cork floor tiles measure 3/16" x 12" x 12". Both products are available in over 40 manufactured patterns and unfinished or prefinished with a water-based varnish. Over 100 custom colors are available.

Most recently mentioned in EBN 5:1

Cork Floating Floor and Parquet Tile

Natural Cork, Inc.
1710 N. Leg Ct.
Augusta, GA 30909

Toll-free: 800-404-2675
Phone: 706-733-6120
Fax: 706-733-8120
www.naturalcork.com

Natural Cork Floating Floor™ is a tongue-and-groove cork plank product measuring 1/2" x 11-13/16" x 35-11/16" and is available prefinished with an acrylic coating. The Floating Floor is constructed with a cork surface layer, exterior grade fiberboard core featuring CLIC installation, and cork underlayment. Parquet Tile measures 3/16" x 12" x 12" and is prefinished with an acrylic coating. Parquet Tile can also be purchased unfinished in 3/16" x 12" x 24".

Nova Cork

Nova Distinctive Floors
1710 E. Sepulveda Blvd.
Carson, CA 90745

Toll-free: 866-576-2458
Fax: 310-830-9589
www.novafloorings.com

Nova Cork™ Floating Floor cork flooring, available in 28 designer patterns, is FSC- and SCS-certified. The 7/16" x 12" x 36" planks snap together with a glueless "Klick" system. They consist of 3 layers—a high-density cork wear layer with a water-based polyurethane finish; a high-density tongue-and-groove fiberboard layer made with recycled fibers; and a low-density cork base layer. This product has a 20-year residential warranty; 10-year commercial. Nova Distinctive Floors is the exclusive North American distributor/importer of Nova Cork, which is manufactured in Switzerland.

WE Cork Flooring

WE Cork
16 Kingston Rd., Unit 6
Exeter, NH 03833

Toll-free: 800-666-2675
Phone: 603-778-8558
Fax: 603-778-7052
www.wecork.com

WE Cork Classic Collection cork flooring comes in tiles and planks measuring 12" x 12" x 3/16" and 4" x 36" x 3/16", respectively. The flooring is available in light, medium, dark, or leopard shades and either unfinished, waxed, or in varnished matte. The company also manufactures a line of floating floors, which do not require gluing, and two lines of sound-control underlayment for flooring, WECU Soundless™ and WECU Soundless +™.

09 63 00
Masonry Flooring

Brick and stone, particularly if locally produced or salvaged, can provide an extremely long-lasting, low-maintenance, visually interesting floor with low environmental costs. These materials create an unyielding surface that may be hard on joints and feet, however; and uneven floors may collect dirt and debris in low spots and prove difficult or even dangerous for some to traverse. Products listed here are from salvaged materials.

Salvaged Brick

Gavin Historical Bricks

For full listing, see CSI section 32 14 16 - Brick Unit Paving

Thin-Sliced Salvaged Chicago Brick

New

Vintage Brick Salvage LLC.
1303 Harrison Ave.
Rockford, IL 61104

Toll-free: 800-846-8243
Phone: 847-714-3652
Fax: 815-226-1360
www.bricksalvage.com

Vintage Brick Salvage sells 1/2" and 3/4" thick antique brick that has been thin-sliced from antique common brick for use as flooring, paving, and veneer tile on walls. The brick installs like tile, using thin-set adhesive over a sub floor or backerboard, and can be sealed with polyurethane or a water-based terra cotta sealer. Some split-brick pieces may show saw marks or be flecked with iron deposits. Vintage Brick also sells full-size salvaged bricks and cobblestone pavers.

09 64 01
FSC-Certified Wood Flooring

Certified wood products are verified by a third party as originating from well-managed forests. GreenSpec recognizes the Forest Stewardship Council (FSC) standards as currently the most rigorous and also the only certification system with established chain-of-custody certification to ensure that products used were derived from certified forests. The availability of domestic hardwood from third-party FSC-certified forests makes flooring a great application for certified wood. Products listed here are made of certified wood. However some companies listed here sell both certified and noncertified wood products, or products that have been certified according to different, less stringent environmental standards. To make certain that you get environmentally responsible wood products, be sure to specify your interest in FSC-certified wood. (See also 06 05 70 - Wood Products Certification and Information.)

Certified Wood Flooring

A. E. Sampson & Son, Inc.
171 Camden Rd.
Warren, ME 04864

Toll-free: 800-769-6196
Phone: 207-273-4000
Fax: 207-273-4006
www.aesampsonandson.com

A. E. Sampson & Son offers FSC-certified wood flooring in many species, including Eastern White Pine, birch, maple, oak, and ash. Call with specifications.

Most recently mentioned in EBN 3:6

AltruWood Certified Wood Products

AltruWood, Inc.
P.O. Box 3341
Portland, OR 97208

Toll-free: 877-372-9663
Fax: 302-348-5799
www.altruwood.com

AltruWood, chain-of-custody certified by SGS, only sells and distributes FSC-certified new domestic (including oak, pine, cherry and Douglas Fir) and tropical wood (including Jatoba, Ipe, and Massaranduba). Sourced and shipped from multiple locations, transportation costs and impacts are minimized. A custom cutting service allows the specification of exact sizes and dimensions, minimizing waste. AltruWood also sells reclaimed lumber.

Certified Wood Products

Cascadia Forest Goods, LLC

For full listing, see CSI section 06 11 01 - FSC-Certified Wood Framing Lumber

SmartChoice Wood Products

Certified Forest Products, LLC.

For full listing, see CSI section 06 11 01 - FSC-Certified Wood Framing Lumber

Certified Wood Sports Floors

Connor Sports Flooring Corporation
545 E. Algonquin Rd., Ste. L
Arlington Heights, IL 60005

Toll-free: 800-283-9522
Phone: 847-290-9020
Fax: 847-290-9034
www.connorfloor.com

Connor FSC-certified wood sports floors are made from certified maple in a full range of engineered flooring systems for indoor athletic applications.

FSC-Certified Wood Products

Dwight Lewis Lumber / Lewis Lumber Products
30 S. Main St.
P.O. Box 356
Picture Rocks, PA 17762

Toll-free: 800-233-8450
Phone: 570-584-4460
Fax: 570-584-4466
www.lewislp.com

Dwight Lewis Lumber sells FSC-certified moldings, flooring, paneling, and hardwoods, subject to availability. Certified species are cherry, hard and soft maple, and red oak.

Endura Wood Products

Endura Wood Products, Ltd.

For full listing, see CSI section 01 62 03 - Distributors/Retailers, FSC-Certified Wood

F.D. Sterritt Certified-Wood Building Products

F.D. Sterritt Lumber Co.

For full listing, see CSI section 06 22 01 - FSC-Certifed Millwork

Georgian Bay Wetwood

Georgian Bay Wetwood Inc.

For full listing, see CSI section 06 40 26 - Wood Veneer

Certified Cherry Flooring

Green River Lumber
29 Locust Hill Rd.
P.O. Box 329
Great Barrington, MA 01230

Phone: 413-528-9000
Fax: 413-528-2379
www.greenriverlumber.com

Green River Certified Cherry Flooring is a solid hardwood flooring milled from well-managed, FSC-certified forests in Pennsylvania. The cherry hardwood flooring is 25/32" thick and comes in 2-1/4", 3", 4", and 5" widths (actual face width).

Most recently mentioned in EBN 3:6

Harmonized Tropical Wood

Harmonized Wood Products

For full listing, see CSI section 06 11 01 - FSC-Certified Wood Framing Lumber

Hoboken Floors

Hoboken Floors
70 Demarest Dr.
Wayne, NJ 07470

Toll-free: 800-222-1068
Phone: 973-694-2888
Fax: 973-694-6885
www.hobokenfloors.com

Hoboken Floors is a large distributor of flooring products that can provide unfinished and prefinished wood flooring from three different FSC-certified Canadian sources. They also distribute multi-ply, laminated flooring products made from certified ash, hackberry, maple, and oak.

Sonic Floor Laminate Flooring **New**

Kronopol Marketing
44 Woodbine Downs Blvd.
Rexdale, ON M9W 5R2 Canada

Toll-free: 888-276-6648
Phone: 416-675-1048
Fax: 416-675-3772
www.kronopol.com

European manufacturer Kronopol has entered the U.S. market with Sonic Floor™, an FSC-certified laminate flooring with an integral underpad of felt and rubber that reduces impact noise transmission. The glueless, snap-together, floating floor requires no underlayment, and has very low VOC and formaldehyde emissions. The plank-style flooring comes in 54" lengths for faster installation and fewer visible joints. Sonic Floor for residential and light commercial installations has a 30-year warranty against fading, staining, wear, and "topographical moisture." Sonic Floor Plus Embossed for medium commercial use carries a lifetime limited warranty. Swiss-owned, Poland-based Kronopol is among the world's largest manufacturers of laminate flooring, and is one of only a few manufacturers to have FSC certification for its entire range of products.

Certified Hardwood Building Products

Maine Woods Company, LLC

For full listing, see CSI section 06 11 01 - FSC-Certified Wood Framing Lumber

Certified Lumber, Flooring, Wainscoting, and Veneer

McDowell Lumber Company, Inc.
Rte. 46 S
P.O. Box 148
Crosby, PA 16724

Phone: 814-887-2717
Fax: 814-887-2214
www.mcdowelllumber.com

McDowell Lumber deals in FSC-certified lumber, flooring, wainscoting, and veneer in over 15 species including red oak, cherry, hard and soft maple, ash, and a variety of other hardwoods harvested in Pennsylvania.

Certified Parquet Flooring

Parquet By Dian
16601 S. Main St.
Gardena, CA 90248

Phone: 310-527-3779
Fax: 310-527-4322
www.parquet.com

Parquet By Dian (PBD) received its chain-of-custody SmartWood Certification in September 2001. This square-edged flooring results in a much longer life than traditional tongue-and-groove (T&G) flooring, which can be sanded down only as far as the tongue. In addition, the manufacturer claims they can produce 2 ft² of parquet from 1 board foot of lumber, whereas manufacturers of T&G can only produce 1 ft² of 3/4" strip flooring. The 7/16"-thick pieces of FSC-certified wood are preassembled into "tile" sections held together by adhesive sheets of plastic and then installed with polyurethane adhesive. Sealing the perimeter and applying a surface finish results in an installation that is essentially waterproof, according to the manufacturer. PBD flooring can be installed immediately (no acclimation time is required), and the product is available in a large variety of patterns and a number of wood species.

Certified Wood Flooring

Plaza Hardwood, Inc.
219 W. Manhattan Ave.
Santa Fe, NM 87501

Toll-free: 800-662-6306
Phone: 505-992-3260
Fax: 505-992-8766
www.plzfloor.com

Plaza Hardwood offers FSC-certified maple, birch, cherry, ash, red oak, and white oak flooring.

Certified-Wood Products

Randall Custom Lumber, Ltd.

For full listing, see CSI section 06 11 01 - FSC-Certified Wood Framing Lumber

Certified Oak Flooring

Smith Flooring
P.O. Box 99
Mountain View, MO 65548

Phone: 417-934-2291
www.smithflooring.com

09 00 00
Finishes

A portion of Smith Flooring's output consists of FSC-certified oak flooring, available through a national network of distributors. Most is red oak; a small amount of white oak is sometimes available. This flooring meets all NOFMA (Wood Flooring Manufacturers Association) specifications. The solid oak strips are 3/4" thick, available in 2-1/4", 3-1/4" or 1-1/2" faces; all pallets conform to NOFMA standards for average length. Shorts are also available.

Certified Wood Flooring

Tembec, Inc., Huntsville Division
80 Old North Rd.
P.O. Box 5616
Huntsville, ON P1H 2J4 Canada

Toll-free: 800-461-5386
Phone: 705-789-2371
Fax: 705-789-8566
www.muskokaflooring.com

Tembec's Muskoka wood flooring is produced (on a special-order basis) from FSC-certified maple harvested from lands that the company manages.

Most recently mentioned in EBN 12:5

Certified Teak Flooring

Unique American Teak
6154C 15th St. E
Bradenton, FL 34203

Phone: 941-758-0365
www.uniqueamericanteak.com

Unique American Teak is a direct importer of FSC-certified teak that manufactures and sells pre-finished, natural, and stained solid teak flooring. A three-layer laminate made with a urethane adhesive is also offered. Tongue-and-groove planks are available in 3 ¼" and 4 ¾" widths and sold in a set of random lengths from 12" to 48"; 2 ¼" strips are available by special order.

Most recently mentioned in EBN 15:10

Certified Wood Building Products

West Wind Hardwood, Inc.
P.O. Box 2205
Sidney, BC V8L 3S8 Canada

Toll-free: 800-667-2275
Phone: 250-656-0848
Fax: 250-656-9663
www.westwindhardwood.com

Family-owned and -operated West Wind Hardwood offers locally harvested, FSC-certified custom Douglas fir lumber, timbers,

and flooring in clear and vertical grain. Other species, such as hemlock, pine, red oak, birch, and maple may be available, depending on supply. The company also offers SmartWood Rediscovered salvaged woods on request and availability. The dimensions and appearances of salvaged and recycled woods may vary due to the nature of the materials. The company specializes in Douglas fir, and is recognized for custom wood products for less usual applications.

Certified Wood Flooring

Whitethorn Construction
545 Shelter Cove Rd.
P.O. Box 400
Whitethorn, CA 95589

Phone: 707-986-7412
Fax: 707-986-7413
www.whitethornconstruction.com

Whitethorn specializes in FSC-certified tan oak flooring, available in varied earth-tones in widths ranging from 2-1/4" to 4-1/4".

Windfall Lumber and Milling

Windfall Lumber and Milling

For full listing, see CSI section 01 62 03 - Distributors/Retailers, FSC-Certified Wood

Wood Floor Resource Group Flooring

Wood Floor Resource Group, LLC
122 Kissel Rd.
Burlington, NJ 08016

Toll-free: 888-964-6832
Phone: 856-764-2501
Fax: 856-764-2503
www.woodfloorrg.com

The Wood Floor Resource Group (WFRG) supplies a comprehensive range of environmentally friendly wood flooring products including FSC-certified wood, salvaged or reclaimed wood, rapidly renewable non-wood materials, and low- or zero-formaldehyde products. The Eco Products Selector on their website allows users to select products based on relevance to LEED Credit or specific environmental attributes, width, color, solid or engineered construction, and whether the product is finished or unfinished. WFRG also provides LEED assistance and other support to customers. WFRG acts as an expert resource to the architectural community and works through major flooring distributors. They also sell flooring directly for personal use by professionals using their services.

09 64 02
Reclaimed-Wood Flooring

As the demands on forest resources have increased, nonforest sources of wood have grown in importance. Reclaimed-wood flooring is made from timbers salvaged from old buildings, bridges, or other timber structures. It may also be manufactured from logs salvaged from river bottoms, or from trees being removed in urban and suburban areas.

As with other resources, the supply of reclaimed wood is limited. Efficient and appropriate use of reclaimed wood is important for its long-term availability. White pine, longleaf yellow pine, cypress, oak, walnut, and chestnut reclaimed-wood flooring may be available from Eastern and Midwestern suppliers. Western suppliers commonly stock Douglas fir. Plan your needs with plenty of lead time, as availability and pricing fluctuate widely. (See feature article EBN Vol. 9, No. 5.)

Reclaimed-Wood Lumber and Products

A Reclaimed Lumber Co.

For full listing, see CSI section 06 22 02 - Reclaimed-Wood Millwork

Reclaimed-Wood Flooring and Millwork

Aged Woods / Yesteryear Floorworks Company

For full listing, see CSI section 06 22 02 - Reclaimed-Wood Millwork

Reclaimed-Wood Products

Albany Woodworks, Inc.

For full listing, see CSI section 06 22 02 - Reclaimed-Wood Millwork

AltruWood Reclaimed-Wood Products

AltruWood, Inc.
P.O. Box 3341
Portland, OR 97208

Toll-free: 877-372-9663
Fax: 302-348-5799
www.altruwood.com

132

AltruWood sells a variety of reclaimed-wood species and products, mostly salvaged from old buildings, barns, factories, warehouses and rivers in the U.S.—principally including domestic pine varieties, Douglas fir, oak, cedar, redwood, chestnut, cypress, and cherry. Products include flooring, timbers, siding, paneling, millwork, and lumber. The company will work with clients to locate recycled lumber from their region. A custom cutting service allows the specification of exact sizes and dimensions, minimizing waste. AltruWood also sells new domestic and tropical FSC-certified wood.

Reclaimed-Wood Flooring

Antique Speciality Flooring
169 Paridon St.
Springfield, MA 01118

Toll-free: 888-SAVEWOOD
Phone: 413-782-3900
Fax: 413-783-9866
www.antiquespecialtyflooring.com

Antique Speciality Flooring offers reclaimed, random-width wood flooring in tongue-and-groove planks of chestnut, oak, heart pine, white pine, and hemlock.

Antique Woods & Colonial Restorations

Antique Woods & Colonial Restorations, Inc.
121 Quarry Rd.
Gouverneur, NY 13642

Toll-free: 888-261-4284
Phone: 610-913-0674
Fax: 610-913-0674
www.vintagewoods.com

Antique Woods & Colonial Restorations, Inc. (formerly Vintage Barns, Woods & Restorations) sells reclaimed and remilled wood products including flooring, siding, millwork, and whole barn frames.

Appalachian Woods

Appalachian Woods, LLC
1240 Cold Springs Rd.
Stuarts Draft, VA 24477

Toll-free: 800-333-7610
Phone: 540-337-1801
Fax: 540-337-1030
www.appalachianwoods.com

Appalachian Woods reclaims and remills timber for a variety of custom millwork applications. Lumber is generally sold rough, but can be provided S4S and S2S. Lumber, flooring, and furniture is available in a variety of species including American chestnut, heart pine, and oak. Appalachian Woods has been a family-run business since 1976.

Reclaimed-Wood Products

Architectural Timber and Millwork

For full listing, see CSI section 06 13 02 - Reclaimed-Wood Heavy Timber

Barnstormers Reclaimed Hand-Hewn Beams

Barnstormers
166 Malden Tpke.
Saugerties, NY 12477

Phone: 845-661-7989
www.barnstormersflooring.com

Barnstormers sells antique hand-hewn beams from disassembled barns. Species include oak, chestnut, hemlock, and other hardwoods. The company also remills tongue-and-groove barnwood hardwood flooring and siding out of this reclaimed wood, using a technique called "skip planing" to mill the boards while leaving some of the original milling marks for aesthetic purposes.

Reclaimed-Wood Materials

Black's Farmwood, Inc.
P.O. Box 2836
San Rafael, CA 94912

Toll-free: 877-321-WOOD
Phone: 415-454-8312
Fax: 415-454-8393
www.blacksfarmwood.com

Black's Farmwood sells reclaimed wood products from deconstructed buildings and river bottoms. Products are available in a variety of species and include salvaged timbers and beams, remilled flooring, and barn siding. The company has a showroom in San Rafael, CA and uses two mills, one in Kentucky and another in New York.

Reclaimed-Wood Materials

BT Timberworks

For full listing, see CSI section 06 13 02 - Reclaimed-Wood Heavy Timber

Used Building Materials

Caldwells

For full listing, see CSI section 01 62 02 - Distributors/Retailers, Used Building Materials

Reclaimed-Wood Flooring

Carlisle Restoration Lumber
1676 Rte. 9
Stoddard, NH 03464

Toll-free: 800-595-9663
Phone: 603-446-3937
Fax: 603-446-3540
www.wideplankflooring.com

Carlisle Restoration specializes in large-dimension antique flooring, available in heart pine, chestnut, and oak. The "Antique Wood" line provides recycled wood planks.

Reclaimed-Wood Products

Centre Mills Antique Floors
P.O. Box 16
Aspers, PA 17304

Phone: 717-677-9698
Fax: 717-334-6223
www.centremillsantiquefloors.com

Centre Mills Antique Floors salvages, remills, and sells several species and types of wood products, many hand-hewn. Species include chestnut, oak, white pine, and fir. Centre Mills uses the old gristmill, built in 1841, in Centre Mills, Pennsylvania as their storage facility.

Reclaimed-Wood Products

Chestnut Specialists, Inc.
P.O. Box 304
Plymouth, CT 06782

Phone: 860-283-4209
www.chestnutspec.com

Chestnut Specialists dismantles buildings and remills reclaimed timbers for resale in a variety of products, including siding and flooring. Rough timber, planks, and beams in their original milled or hand-hewn condition are also available.

Wood Materials from Urban Trees

CitiLog
370 Pittstown Rd.
P.O. Box 685
Pittstown, NJ 08867

Toll-free: 877-248-9564
Phone: 908-735-8871
Fax: 908-735-6893
www.citilogs.com

CitiLog™, also known as D. Stubby Warmbold, is SmartWood-certified for the harvesting of trees in urban areas of New Jersey and Pennsylvania. Wood is sent by rail to Amish craftsmen in central Pennsylvania who take extra care to turn the lesser graded wood into higher quality products such as flooring, lumber, custom architectural millwork, furniture, and kitchen cabinets. Where appropriate, wood is now harvested using horses.

Reclaimed-Wood Building Products

Conklin's Authentic Antique Barnwood

For full listing, see CSI section 06 13 02 - Reclaimed-Wood Heavy Timber

Craftmark Reclaimed Wood

Craftmark Reclaimed Wood, Inc.

For full listing, see CSI section 01 62 03 - Distributors/Retailers, FSC-Certified Wood

Reclaimed-Wood Products

Crossroads Recycled Lumber

For full listing, see CSI section 06 13 02 - Reclaimed-Wood Heavy Timber

D. Litchfield Reclaimed Wood

D. Litchfield & Co. Ltd.

For full listing, see CSI section 06 11 02 - Reclaimed-Wood Framing Lumber

Reclaimed-Wood Products

Duluth Timber Co.

For full listing, see CSI section 06 13 02 - Reclaimed-Wood Heavy Timber

Reclaimed-Wood Flooring

Early New England Restorations
32 Taugwonk Rd Unit A12
Stonington, CT 06359

Phone: 860-599-4393
Fax: 860-535-1628
www.werestoreoldhomes.com

Early New England Restorations, formerly Horse Drawn Pine, remills pine plank flooring.

Reclaimed-Wood Building Products

Endura Wood Products, Ltd.
1303 S.E. 6th Ave.
Portland, OR 97214

Phone: 503-233-7090
Fax: 503-233-7091
www.endurawood.com

Endura Wood Products currently has access to over 3.5 million board feet of Douglas fir that is being reclaimed from the old Portland Dry Dock #2. Also available is a limited supply of Douglas fir with a distinct red hue that has been reclaimed from maraschino cherry vats.

Reclaimed-Wood Building Products

General Woodcraft, Inc.
531 Broad St.
New London, CT 06320

Phone: 860-444-9663
Fax: 860-444-0517
www.generalwoodcraftinc.com

General Woodcraft provides wood flooring and other products milled from beams and timbers salvaged from barns and factories built a century ago—often from old-growth timber. Species (as available) include pine, chestnut, and oak.

Georgian Bay Wetwood

Georgian Bay Wetwood Inc.

For full listing, see CSI section 06 40 26 - Wood Veneer

River-Reclaimed Wood Products

Goodwin Heart Pine Company
106 S.W. 109th Pl.
Micanopy, FL 32667

Toll-free: 800-336-3118
Phone: 352-466-0339
Fax: 352-466-0608
www.heartpine.com

Goodwin manufactures antique wood flooring, millwork, stair parts, paneling, and siding made from antique heart pine and heart cypress logs—200 years old or older—recovered from Southern river bottoms. Flooring, siding, and paneling is kiln-dried, graded, and precision-milled. Decorative wood moldings are architecturally drawn and are designed to classic proportions. Stair parts include solid or laminated treads, and a full range of balusters, newels, and rails. Reclaimed timbers from old buildings are also available.

Reclaimed-Wood Flooring

Green Mountain Woodworks
P.O. Box 1433
Phoenix, OR 97535

Toll-free: 866-888-7478
Phone: 541-535-5880
Fax: 541-535-5331
www.greenmountainwoodworks.com

Green Mountain Woodworks offers a full line of unique hardwood flooring, emphasizing environmentally responsible, antique reclaimed, and Northwest woods. Green Mountain Woodworks clearly defines the "EcoStatus" of each wood, including FSC-certified, those from ecosystem restoration projects, reclaimed/recycled woods, and woods rescued from low value or waste streams (fire wood and pulp/chip).

Most recently mentioned in EBN 9:4

Heartwood Reclaimed-Wood Flooring

Heartwood Industries
3658 State Road 1414
Hartford, KY 42347

Phone: 270-298-0084
Fax: 270-298-7755
www.whiskeywood.com

Heartwood is an international distributor of dimension lumber and timbers salvaged from warehouses and whiskey distilleries. They specialize in flooring but also offer custom millwork and moldings in longleaf yellow pine, oak, chestnut, and cypress.

Reclaimed-Wood Building Products

J. Hoffman Lumber Co.

For full listing, see CSI section 06 13 02 - Reclaimed-Wood Heavy Timber

Reclaimed-Wood Millwork

J. L. Powell & Co., Inc.
723 Pine Log Rd.
Whiteville, NC 28472

Toll-free: 800-227-2007
Phone: 910-642-8989
Fax: 910-642-3164
www.plankfloors.com

J. L. Powell & Co. specializes in custom architectural millwork, including stair parts and flooring, produced from reclaimed antique heart pine.

Reclaimed and Urban-Harvested Millwork

Jackel Enterprises
347 Locust St.
Watsonville, CA 95076

Toll-free: 800-711-9663
Phone: 831-768-3880
Fax: 831-768-3883
www.jackelenterprises.com

Jackel Enterprises processes urban and suburban forestry—the low-impact removal of city-owned and back-yard trees, ranch maintenance, and the like. Species include redwood, Douglas fir, Monterey cypress, black acacia, and California black walnut. Jackel also processes forest floor salvage from private parties, primarily old growth redwood, as well as milling recycled hardwoods and softwoods, including Douglas fir, redwood, western red cedar, heart pine, bald cypress, walnut, oak, and hickory.

Logs End Reclaimed-Wood Building Products

New

Logs End Inc.
1520 Triole St.
Ottawa, ON K1B3S9 Canada

Phone: 613-738-7851
Fax: 613-738-0647
www.logsend.com

Logs End, Inc., retrieves sinker logs in Canada's Upper Ottawa Valley area and processes them into lumber and timber, wide-plank flooring, paneling, siding, and trim in standard and custom dimensions. Old-growth, clear pine is typically recovered, though birch, red and white oak, and hard and soft maple are also available. Certificates of authenticity for educational purposes are issued by the company. Logs End lumber and timbers carry Smartwood "Rediscovered" certification.

Reclaimed-Wood Building Products

Longleaf Lumber
115 Fawcett St.
Cambridge, MA 02138

Toll-free: 866-653-3566
Phone: 617-871-6611
Fax: 617-871-6615
www.longleaflumber.com

Longleaf Lumber, founded in 1997, remills antique timbers into millwork and flooring at the company's sawmill in southern Maine. Longleaf specializes in heart pine, but other salvaged woods such as chestnut, red and white oak, eastern white pine, and maple are also available from buildings dismantled in various locations around the New England region. Longleaf also sells unmilled reclaimed timbers and reclaimed barn siding. In addition to the sawmill, the company operates a retail store at their Cambridge, MA location.

M. Fine Lumber Company

M. Fine Lumber Company

For full listing, see CSI section 06 11 02 - Reclaimed-Wood Framing Lumber

Reclaimed-Wood Building Products

Mayse Woodworking Co.
319 Richardson Rd.
Lansdale, PA 19446

Toll-free: 888-566-4532
Phone: 215-822-8307
Fax: 215-822-8307

Mayse Woodworking offers reclaimed heart pine millwork including flooring, trim, moldings, stair treads, and risers in three styles: American Country, Signature, and Federal. The products are remanufactured from recycled heart pine beams.

Michael Evenson Natural Resources

Michael Evenson Natural Resources

For full listing, see CSI section 06 13 02 - Reclaimed-Wood Heavy Timber

Reclaimed-Wood Building Products

Mountain Lumber
6812 Spring Hill Rd.
P.O. Box 289
Ruckersville, VA 22968

Toll-free: 800-445-2671
Phone: 434-985-3646
Fax: 434-985-4105
www.mountainlumber.com

Mountain Lumber reclaims timbers from buildings slated for demolition and ships them to their mill in Virginia for remilling into wide-plank flooring, beams, rough-sawn cabinet lumber, and an extensive range of architectural millwork including stair parts and moldings. Species include heart pine, oak, American chestnut, maple, and elm.

Old Wood Flooring

New

Old Wood Workshop, LLC.
193 Hampton Rd.
Pomfret Center, CT 06259

Phone: 860-655-5259
Fax: 860-974-3622
www.oldwoodworkshop.com

The Old Wood Workshop offers salvaged and remilled antique flooring as well as salvaged building materials including beams, boards, and joists. Old Wood Workshop also offers custom harvest tables made from reclaimed wood, and architectural antiques such as iron hardware, doors, and fireplace mantles. Remilled chestnut flooring is priced by width. Salvaged flooring in the online inventory is available in limited-size batches only.

Pinocchio's

Pinocchio's

For full listing, see CSI section 06 13 02 - Reclaimed-Wood Heavy Timber

Reclaimed-Wood Building Products

Pioneer Millworks
1180 Commercial Dr.
Farmington, NY 14425

Toll-free: 800-951-9663
Phone: 585-924-9970
Fax: 585-924-9962
www.pioneermillworks.com

Pioneer Millworks remills salvaged wood into flooring and a number of molding profiles, in addition to timbers, cabinetry, stair parts, doors, and trusses. The primary species is longleaf yellow pine; others that are often available include redwood, bald cypress, chestnut, white oak, Douglas fir, and white pine.

Re-Tech Wood Products

Re-Tech Wood Products

For full listing, see CSI section 06 13 02 - Reclaimed-Wood Heavy Timber

Resource Woodworks

Resource Woodworks, Inc.

For full listing, see CSI section 06 13 02 - Reclaimed-Wood Heavy Timber

Durapalm Palm Flooring

Smith & Fong Company
375 Oyster Point Blvd. #3
S. San Francisco, CA 94080

Toll-free: 866-835-9859
Fax: 650-872-1185
www.plyboo.com

Smith & Fong's Durapalm® flooring is made from plantation-grown coconut palm trees that no longer produce coconuts. The 5/8" x 3" tongue-and-groove planks come in 2' to 4' lengths and range from dark to medium-red mahogany in color. They contain no added urea-formaldehyde or VOCs and are available unfinished or prefinished with an 8-coat ceramic/urethane UV-cured finish. Smith & Fong reports that they use only the darker, harder palm for a durable surface (1450 PSI Janka Ball Test, ASTM D1037). Reducer, baseboard, quarter round, and stairnosing and threshold molding are available.

09 00 00 Finishes

09 00 00
Finishes

Reclaimed-Wood Building Products

Solid Wood Products
3756 Pineridge Dr.
Lac Le Jeune, BC V1S 1Y8 Canada

Phone: 250-320-0936
Fax: 250-374-9602
www.solidwoodpro.com

Solid Wood Products manufactures building and finish products primarily wide-plank flooring from reclaimed Douglas fir. The one-inch flooring is available in 6" to 14" widths. Also offered are trim, wainscot, panels, and stair parts; timber-frame components including beams, braces, purlins, and rafters; as well as custom furniture.

Reclaimed-Wood Flooring

Sylvan Brandt
651 E. Main St.
Lititz, PA 17543

Phone: 717-626-4520
Fax: 717-626-5867
www.sylvanbrandt.com

Sylvan Brandt reclaimed-wood flooring is made from resawn beams and barn siding. Tongue-and-groove planks of oak, heart pine, white pine, and hemlock are available.

Reclaimed-Wood Building Products

TerraMai
1104 Firenze St.
P.O. Box 696
McCloud, CA 96057

Toll-free: 800-220-9062
Phone: 530-964-2740
Fax: 530-964-2745
www.terramai.com

TerraMai produces several grades of flooring, ranging from clear tongue-and-groove to rough-cut plank, from reclaimed lumber and tropical hardwoods. All flooring is available in "Character" (with evidence of previous use) and "Select" (clear) grades. Douglas fir, ponderosa pine, and southern yellow pine are among their most popular species. TerraMai also mills various architectural woodwork products from their 700,000-board-foot inventory of reclaimed woods. All of TerraMai's varied products are from reclaimed wood.

Reclaimed-Wood Flooring

The Woods Company, Inc.
985 Superior Ave.
Chambersburg, PA 17201

Toll-free: 888-548-7609
Phone: 717-263-6524
Fax: 717-263-9346
www.thewoodscompany.com

The Woods Co. specializes in wide-plank flooring and custom interior millwork made from wood reclaimed from demolished buildings.

Reclaimed-Wood Flooring and Millwork

Treasured Timbers, Inc.
173 Hunter Lake Rd.
Upper Golden Grove, NB E2S 3B4 Canada

Phone: 506-849-8016
Fax: 506-849-3089
www.treasuredtimbers.com

Treasured Timbers, Inc. specializes in hardwood plank flooring and millwork made from sinker logs salvaged from the Saint John River.

Trestlewood

Trestlewood
292 N. 2000 W, Ste. A
Lindon, UT 84042

Toll-free: 877-375-2779
Phone: 801-443-4002
Fax: 801-443-4007
www.trestlewood.com

Trestlewood deals exclusively in reclaimed wood. Their wood comes from the Lucin Cutoff railroad trestle, which crosses the Great Salt Lake, and other salvage projects. Trestlewood products include flooring, millwork, timbers, decking, and siding. Available species include Douglas fir, redwood, southern yellow pine, longleaf yellow pine, oak, and other hardwoods.

Urban Hardwoods

Urban Hardwoods
4755 C. Colorado Ave. S
Seattle, WA 98134

Phone: 206-766-8199
Fax: 206-766-7997
www.urbanhardwoods.com

Urban Hardwoods salvages urban trees from within a 50-mile radius of the company and mills them into custom, made-to-order furniture, flooring, and other millwork. Urban Hardwoods continually designs products to make use of manufacturing "fall-down." Remaining waste material is given away or sold as firewood, or is used for heating their facility. The company ships 99% of its products blanket-wrapped; all blankets are reused. Products will be accepted back at the end of their useful life to be refurbished or recycled in the manufacture of new products. The company is SmartWood-certified under the "Rediscovered Wood" category.

Reclaimed-Wood Flooring

Vintage Lumber Co.
1 Council Dr.
P.O. Box 485
Woodsboro, MD 21798

Toll-free: 800-499-7859
Fax: 301-845-6475
www.vintagelumber.com

Since 1973, Vintage Lumber has been reusing historic old wood obtained from dismantled derelict barns to produce reclaimed, antique solid-wood flooring. "The Vintage Collection" uses old beams and boards, ranging in age from 50 to 200 years, which are milled into Vintage and Vintage/Distressed plank flooring. Vintage Lumber mills the lower grades of native Appalachian hardwoods into rustic/character flooring in "The American Country Collection." Both collections are milled in random widths and end-matched in 2' to 10' lengths.

Reclaimed-Wood Building Products

Vintage Material Supply Co.
730 Shady Ln.
Austin, TX 78702

Phone: 512-386-6404
Fax: 512-386-6417
www.vintagematerialsupply.com

Vintage Material Supply Co. offers salvaged wood flooring available "as is" with edges cleaned, as well as new flooring milled from wood recovered from such sources as demolished buildings, ranch recovery, urban logging, and river bottoms. Primary species include old-growth longleaf pine, Tidewater cypress, mesquite, and walnut.

Reclaimed-Wood Building Products

Vintage Timberworks

For full listing, see CSI section 06 13 02 - Reclaimed-Wood Heavy Timber

Reclaimed-Wood Building Products

West Wind Hardwood, Inc.
P.O. Box 2205
Sidney, BC V8L 3S8 Canada

Toll-free: 800-667-2275
Phone: 250-656-0848
Fax: 250-656-9663
www.westwindhardwood.com

Family-owned and -operated West Wind Hardwood offers SmartWood Rediscovered salvaged woods for flooring, planks, lumber, timber, and other applications. The dimensions and appearances of salvaged and recycled woods may vary due to the nature of the materials. The company also offers locally harvested, FSC-certified custom Douglas fir flooring in clear and vertical grain. Other species, such as hemlock, pine, red oak, birch, and maple may be available, depending on supply. The company specializes in Douglas fir, and is recognized for custom wood products for less usual applications.

Reclaimed-Wood Building Products

What It's Worth, Inc.
P.O. Box 162135
Austin, TX 78716

Phone: 512-328-8837
Fax: 512-328-8837
www.wiwpine.com

What Its Worth can provide reclaimed longleaf yellow pine and Douglas fir to custom specs. Their milled product is 100% heartwood, and the wood's harvesting usually predates 1925.

09 64 14
Suppressed Wood Flooring

Suppressed wood comes from trees growing in the understory of mature forests—usually where forestry practices have prevented fires, so natural thinning and succession hasn't occurred. It is now generally recognized that overly dense forests increase fire hazard and leave trees vulnerable to insect infestation and disease. These small, slow-growing trees were once regarded as waste, suitable only for fuel and firewood. Attributes of these trees include close grain, fine texture, and small tight knots. This can provide a raw material for joinery, flooring, and panels.

Alpine Grade Douglas Fir Flooring

Green Mountain Woodworks
P.O. Box 1433
Phoenix, OR 97535

Toll-free: 866-888-7478
Phone: 541-535-5880
Fax: 541-535-5331
www.greenmountainwoodworks.com

Green Mountain Woodworks produces this Douglas fir flooring from trees thinned out of overly dense forests in southwest Oregon. Green Mountain Woodworks is associated with the Healthy Forests Healthy Communities Partnership, which works with communities in National Forests to develop locally owned small businesses that make products from the wood recovered during forest restoration. (Timber from National Forests is not eligible for FSC certification.)

Most recently mentioned in EBN 9:4

09 64 19
Wood Composition Flooring

Most wood composition products are made with urea-formaldehyde (UF) binders that can offgas significant concentrations of formaldehyde gas—an indoor air quality concern and a human carcinogen. Wood composition products can also be made with a non-formaldehyde-emitting methyl diisocyanate (MDI) binder, a polyurethane, which does not offgas formaldehyde. Unlike the FSC 100% label, wood products with the FSC mixed label may contain "company controlled" wood sources and recycled material as well as FSC certified forests. Company controlled sources exclude illegally harvested timber, among other requirements. (Certification to Forest Stewardship Council—FSC—standards involves third-party evaluation and monitoring of sustainable forestry practices.) Products listed here use FSC certified wood and MDI binders.

Subflor Advance Plus and Subflor Supreme

Supra Floors, Inc.
44 Woodbine Downs Blvd.
Rexdale, ON M9W 5R2 Canada

Toll-free: 866-782-3567
Phone: 416-675-1048
Fax: 416-675-3772
www.subflor.com

Subflor Advance Plus and Subflor Supreme floating floors are made with water-resistant FSC-certified OSB using an MDI binder. An integral HDPE bottom layer has 5/16" corrugations to allow moisture drainage and some airflow. Though designed for installation over concrete slabs, their sound-attenuating properties provide an appropriate flooring system for many applications. These interlocking tongue-and-groove products require no nails or glue. Subflor Advance Plus® has an unfinished OSB surface and comes in 2' x 2' panels; the 7/8" height preserves headroom. Subflor Supreme comes in 7-3/4" x 54-1/16" planks, finished with a color-saturated varnish.

09 00 00
Finishes

09 65 16
Resilient Sheet Flooring

Natural linoleum is a durable, low-maintenance flooring made from linseed oil, pine rosin, sawdust, cork dust, limestone, natural pigments, and a jute backing—all minimally processed and commonly available materials. Linoleum does not contain significant petroleum-based products or chlorinated chemicals, as does vinyl (PVC) flooring—which is often mistakenly referred to as "linoleum." The ongoing oxidation of linoleic acid in the flooring leads to offgassing of volatile organic compounds (VOCs) that taper off over time, but some argue that linoleum's VOCs, as compared to petroleum-derived VOCs, are a lesser health threat. Recycled-tire rubber provides a highly durable, resilient, slip-resistant, anti-fatigue surface suitable for a variety of flooring requirements. Rubber granules from ground tires may be vulcanized (reformed under high heat using a sulfur additive), or agglomerated with a synthetic binding matrix, such as polyurethane. The rubber and its binders or additives, however, may be significant sources of indoor air pollutants, including VOCs and heavy metals; actual emissions vary widely from product to product. Thus, rubber flooring isn't recommended for most indoor spaces unless there is evidence of low emissions. Indoor/outdoor spaces, such as entrances and skating rinks, or commercial/industrial areas with high ventilation rates, are potentially excellent applications for these recycled-content products. (See feature article EBN Vol. 7, No. 9.)

09 00 00
Finishes

Stratica

Amtico International Inc.
6480 Roswell Rd.
Atlanta, GA 30328

Toll-free: 800-404-0102
Phone: 404-267-1900
Fax: 404-267-1901
www.stratica.com

Stratica is a chlorine-free, low-VOC, durable alternative to vinyl or VCT flooring. It is flexible yet free of plasticizers, which are used in sheet vinyl flooring. Stratica manufacture meets ISO 14001 standards for environmental management. Stratica is lightweight, flexible, and extremely durable. It is made with a base layer of mineral-filled copolymer and a DuPont Surlyn® wear layer and is sold primarily in 13" x 13" tiles. Stratica is available in a wide range of solid colors and patterns including marble, granite, stone, various woods, and terrazzo.

Most recently mentioned in EBN 7:10

DLW Linoleum

Armstrong World Industries, Inc.
2500 Columbia Ave.
P.O. Box 3001
Lancaster, PA 17604

Toll-free: 877-276-7876
Phone: 717-397-0611
www.armstrong.com

DLW linoleum is made in Germany and comes in a wide variety of colors and styles in both sheet and tile. Tile is available by special order only. Marmorette is available in 2, 2.5 and 3.2 mm thicknesses. Colorette and Uni Walton are available in 2.5 and 3.2 mm thicknesses, and Linorette is 2.5 mm thick. Linodur is a heavy-duty 4 mm product. In 1998, Armstrong World Industries, the largest manufacturer of vinyl flooring (and out of the linoleum industry since the 1970s) purchased DLW, reentering this product field.

Most recently mentioned in EBN 7:9 & 8:1

Marmoleum and Artoleum

Forbo Linoleum, Inc.
2 Maplewood Dr., Humboldt Industrial Park
P.O. Box 667
Hazleton, PA 18201

Toll-free: 800-842-7839
Phone: 570-459-0771
Fax: 570-450-0258
www.forboflooringNA.com

Forbo, the largest producer of linoleum in the world, operates a sophisticated production facility that helps it meet criteria for the Netherlands Environmental Quality Mark and the Nordic Swan Label. The product also received the Sequoia Award from the U.S. Association of Woodworking and Furnishing Suppliers (AWFS) in recognition of the company's commitment to environmental innovation. A large range of colors and styles is available, including custom-designed borders. Marmoleum® and Artoleum® are available in sheet form. Marmoleum Dual is also available as a 20" x 20" or 13" x 13" tile mounted on a polyester backing to improve dimensional stability. The optional, water-based Topshield finish provides a significant reduction of initial maintenance and chemicals, lowers ongoing cleaning costs, and improves long-term appearance.

Most recently mentioned in EBN 6:1, 7:9, 12:5, 13:2, 13:4, 13:10

noraplan Commercial Flooring

Freudenberg Building Systems, Inc.
94 Glenn St.
Lawrence, MA 01843

Toll-free: 800-332-6672
Phone: 978-689-0530
Fax: 978-975-0110
www.norarubber.com

noraplan® resilient floorcovering is made from natural and synthetic rubber, mineral fillers, and color pigments. Unlike alternative products such as VCT and sheet vinyl, this durable, low-maintenance floorcovering requires no maintenance coatings. noraplan contains no PVC, plasticizers, or halogens. In June 2004, noraplan was the first rubber flooring to be awarded Greenguard Indoor Air Quality Certification from the Greenguard Environmental Institute. Available in rolls or tiles in a wide range of solid and multicolors, noraplan can be inlaid and combined in mixed installations of different styles and colors. Seams can be either hot- or cold-welded. The product comes with a 5-year wear warranty. Freudenberg Building Systems is ISO 9002 and ISO 14001 certified.

ECOsurfaces Commercial Flooring

Gerbert Limited
119 South Tree Dr.
P.O. Box 4944
Lancaster, PA 17604

Toll-free: 877-326-7873
Phone: 717-299-5035
Fax: 717-394-1937
www.ecosurfaces.com

ECOsurfaces® 100% recycled-rubber flooring, available in 54 standard color blends as well as custom blends, is appropriate for a variety of commercial indoor and outdoor applications. One of the world's largest users of scrap tire rubber, Dodge-Regupol uses 45 million pounds of scrap tires annually, as well as post-industrial EPDM color material from Europe. Available in both tiles and rolls. As with other flooring products made from recycled automobile tires, installation is only recommended in semi-enclosed spaces, well-ventilated indoor spaces, or outdoors.

Prontolino

Habitus
166 E. 108th St.
New York, NY 10029

Phone: 212-426-5500
Fax: 212-426-5200
www.habitusnyc.com

Prontolino is a linoleum-cork hybrid flooring product. It comes in 3/8" x 12" x 36" tongue-and-groove planks of natural linoleum laminated onto a thick cork backing. The linoleum surface is available in 9 colors.

Mondo Commercial Flooring

Mondo America Inc.
2655 Francis Hughes
Laval, QC H7L 3S8 Canada

Toll-free: 800-361-3747
Phone: 450-967-5800
Fax: 450-663-7927
www.mondousa.com

Mondo produces commercial flooring made from natural and synthetic rubber, mineral fillers, and color pigments. Unlike products such as VCT and sheet vinyl, these durable, easy-to-clean floorcoverings require no maintenance coatings. The products contain no PVC, solvents, halogens, plasticizers, or heavy metals and are available in tiles or rolls. Made in a variety of styles and colors suitable for a wide range of applications, Mondo Commercial Flooring is nonporous, heat weldable, and fungus-resistant (ASTM G-21-90). The products are also compliant with California Indoor Air Quality Requirement section 01350.

Nova Linoleum

Nova Distinctive Floors
1710 E. Sepulveda Blvd.
Carson, CA 90745

Toll-free: 866-576-2458
Fax: 310-830-9589
www.novafloorings.com

Nova Linoleum™comes in 7/16" x 12" x 36" planks or 7/16" x 12" x 12" tiles, and is available in 9 colors. The planks and tiles consist of 3 layers: a 5/64" linoleum wear layer; a high-density fiberboard core; and a 5/64" cork composition layer. This floating floor system snaps together with a glueless "Klick" system. Nova Linoleum is manufactured in Switzerland and includes a 20-year residential warranty; 10-year commercial.

Commercial Rubber Flooring

RB Rubber Products, Inc.
904 N.E. Tenth Ave.
McMinnville, OR 97128

Toll-free: 800-525-5530
Phone: 503-472-4691
Fax: 503-434-4455
www.rbrubber.com

RB Commercial Flooring is made from recycled-tire rubber with a synthetic binder. One side has an anti-skid surface; the other side is smooth. The flooring is available as mats in 3/4", 1/2", and 3/8" thicknesses. Rolls are 4' wide and available in thicknesses from 2 mm to 1/2" and lengths of 25', 50', and 75'. Optional flecks of colored EPDM, totaling 10%, 15%, or 20% of the material, are also available in a choice of 5 standard and several premium colors. As with other flooring products made from recycled automobile tires, installation is only recommended in semi-enclosed spaces, well-ventilated indoor spaces, or outdoors.

Tarkett Linoleum

Tarkett Commercial
2728 Summer St.
Huston, TX 77007

Toll-free: 800-877-8453
Phone: 713-344-2733
Fax: 713-344-2770
www.tarkett.com

Tarkett linoleum is available in five lines: Veneto, Toscano, Linosport, and Etrusco. Tarkett linoleum comes in a wide variety of colors, including unique earth-toned patterns. It is available in sheet form in 2, 2.5, 3.2, and 4 mm thicknesses and tile form (20" by 20" tiles). Tarkett offers Veneto Acoustic as a special order, with the linoleum pre-bonded to a cork underlay. Manufactured in Italy, Tarkett linoleum is available in the U.S. through Tarkett Commercial, formerly Azrock, a division of Domco Tarkett, Inc.

Most recently mentioned in EBN 7:9 & 15:2

09 65 19
Resilient Tile Flooring

Natural linoleum is a durable, low-maintenance flooring made from linseed oil, pine rosin, sawdust, cork dust, limestone, natural pigments, and a jute backing—all minimally processed and commonly available materials. Linoleum does not contain significant petroleum-based products or chlorinated chemicals, as does vinyl (PVC) flooring—which is often mistakenly referred to as "linoleum." The ongoing oxidation of linoleic acid in the flooring leads to offgassing of volatile organic compounds (VOCs) that taper off over time, but some argue that linoleum's VOCs, as compared to petroleum-derived VOCs, are a lesser health threat. Recycled-tire rubber provides a highly durable, resilient, slip-resistant, anti-fatigue surface suitable for a variety of flooring requirements. Rubber granules from ground tires may be vulcanized (reformed under high heat using a sulfur additive), or agglomerated with a synthetic binding matrix, such as polyurethane. The rubber and its binders or additives, however, may be significant sources of indoor air pollutants, including VOCs and heavy metals; actual emissions vary widely from product to product. Thus, rubber flooring isn't recommended for most indoor spaces unless there is evidence of low emissions. Indoor/outdoor spaces, such as entrances and skating rinks, or commercial/industrial areas with high ventilation rates, are potentially excellent applications for these recycled-content products.

Stonescape Polymer Composition Tile

American Biltrite Canada, Ltd.
440-B Britannia Rd. E
Mississauga, ON L4Z 1X9 Canada

Toll-free: 800-479-0190
Phone: 905-507-2400
Fax: 905-507-2388
www.american-biltrite.com

Stonescape™, from American Biltrite Canada, is a PVC-free alternative to vinyl composition tile (VCT). This resilient flooring tile is made from limestone and ethylene acrylic polymers. It is free of all halogens and plasticizers, and emits no volatile organic compounds (VOCs). It is also much harder than most VCT (2,000 psi vs. up to 300 psi) and should require far less regular surface treatment (stripping and waxing) than VCT,

according to the manufacturer. Introduced in 2005, Stonescape has little track record to date, though an initial year-long test installation has apparently been very successful. This product is also marketed by Mohawk as StoneWalk™.

Most recently mentioned in EBN 14:12

CushionWalk Pavers

Dinoflex Manufacturing, Ltd.
P.O. Box 3309
Salmon Arm, BC V1E 4S1 Canada

Toll-free: 877-713-1899
Phone: 252-832-7780
Fax: 800-305-2109
www.dinoflex.com

Cushion Walk® Pavers are made from 91% recycled-tire rubber and are designed primarily for covering patios, rooftop decks, and walkways. Paving tiles are available in terra-cotta red, forest green, stone beige, teak brown, and midnight black.

noraplan Commercial Flooring

Freudenberg Building Systems, Inc.

For full listing, see CSI section 09 65 16 - Resilient Sheet Flooring

ECOsurfaces Commercial Flooring

Gerbert Limited

For full listing, see CSI section 09 65 16 - Resilient Sheet Flooring

StoneWalk Polymer Composition Tile

Mohawk
500 TownPark Ln., Ste. 400
Kennesaw, GA 30144

Toll-free: 800-554-6637
www.mohawkgroup.com

StoneWalk™, from Mohawk, is a PVC-free alternative to vinyl composition tile (VCT). This resilient flooring tile is made from limestone and ethylene acrylic polymers. It is free of all halogens and plasticizers, and emits no volatile organic compounds (VOCs). It is also much harder than most VCT (2,000 psi vs. up to 300 psi) and should require far less regular surface treatment (stripping and waxing) than VCT, according to the manufacturer. Introduced in 2005, StoneWalk has little track record to date, though an initial year-long test installation has apparently been very successful. This product is also marketed by American Biltrite Canada, Ltd. as Stonescape™.

Most recently mentioned in EBN 14:12

09 00 00
Finishes

09 00 00
Finishes

SuperFlexx Paver Tiles, Sports Floor, and SureStep

U.S. Rubber Recycling, Inc.

For full listing, see CSI section 09 65 66 - Resilient Athletic Flooring

Tire Veneer

Yemm & Hart Ltd.

For full listing, see CSI section 09 65 66 - Resilient Athletic Flooring

---

09 65 66
Resilient Athletic Flooring

Recycled-tire rubber is an appropriate material for athletic flooring because it is highly durable, resilient, slip-resistant, and water-resistant. Many products also resist damage from ice skates, cleats, and golf spikes. The rubber and its binders and other additives, however, may be significant sources of indoor air pollutants. We do not widely recommend rubber flooring for indoor spaces, though the high rate of ventilation in athletic spaces mitigates this concern. Products may have color integrated into the rubber as flecks or binding matrix, or applied as a thick wear layer. Athletic flooring may come in rolls, mats, or other shapes and may be interlocking, square-cut, or tapered. Interlocking floor systems have the advantage of minimizing, if not eliminating, the need for flooring adhesives, which themselves often pose a serious indoor air quality concern. (See also 32 18 23 - Athletic Surfacing.)

EcoScore

Burke Industries, Endura Products Division
2250 S. 10th St.
San Jose, CA 95112

Toll-free: 800-447-8442
Fax: 800-832-5398
www.endura-flooring.com

Endura EcoScore multifunctional athletic rubber flooring for commercial interiors is made with a 1/4" performance layer of 100% post-consumer recycled rubber with a 1/8" wear layer of virgin rubber (for 67% total recycled content). The 24" x 24" x 3/8" tiles are available in interlocking loose-lay tiles for adhesive-free installation, or in square-edge tiles for glue-down. They come in a variety of solid colors or speckled patterns; color-matching is available. Maintain with neutral pH detergent using a deck brush or automatic scrubber; waxing, top-coating, and stripping is not recommended. EcoScore has a 10-year wear warranty. As with other flooring products made from recycled automobile tires, installation is only recommended in semi-enclosed spaces, well-ventilated indoor spaces, or outdoors.

EVERLAST Performance Flooring

Dodge-Regupol, Inc.
715 Fountain Ave.
Lancaster, PA 17601

Toll-free: 866-883-7780
Phone: 717-295-3400
Fax: 717-295-3414
www.regupol.com

Everlast™ Performance Flooring is 100% recycled-rubber fitness flooring available in nineteen color blends, as well as in custom colors and cuts. One of the world's largest users of scrap tire rubber, Dodge-Regupol uses 45 million pounds of scrap tires annually, as well as post-industrial EPDM color material from Europe. Available in both tiles and rolls. As with other flooring products made from recycled automobile tires, installation is only recommended in semi-enclosed spaces, well-ventilated indoor spaces, or outdoors.

EVERLAST UltraTile

Dodge-Regupol, Inc.
715 Fountain Ave.
Lancaster, PA 17601

Toll-free: 866-883-7780
Phone: 717-295-3400
Fax: 717-295-3414
www.regupol.com

Everlast UltraTile is made from recycled-tire rubber with a polyurethane binder. Its elevated pedestal underside allows wiring to be routed beneath the surface. Tiles can be easily moved and replaced. No glue is necessary. The 1"-thick, 24" x 24" pavers have a disc tread pattern on the bottom and a smooth, tile, or brick pattern on the top surface. Choose from 12 standard colors. Step tiles, stair nosings, and edge pieces are also available. As with other flooring products made from recycled automobile tires, installation is only recommended in semi-enclosed spaces, well-ventilated indoor spaces, or outdoors.

PlayGuard

Dodge-Regupol, Inc.
715 Fountain Ave.
Lancaster, PA 17601

Toll-free: 866-883-7780
Phone: 717-295-3400
Fax: 717-295-3414
www.regupol.com

PlayGuard, a resilient shock-absorbing tile system made from ground-up used tire treads, has a firm surface that is suitable for wheelchairs and mobility aids. PlayGuard 24" x 24" rubber pavers come in a variety of colors for indoor and outdoor use in playgrounds and recreation rooms. They may also be used as ballast on low-slope roof systems. PlayGuard offers perimeter access ramps, molded 45- and 90-degree corners, and half tiles to complete the system. PlayGuard products meet ASTM and CPSC standards, are ADA compliant and IPEMA certified. As with other flooring products made from recycled automobile tires, installation is only recommended in semi-enclosed spaces, well-ventilated indoor spaces, or outdoors.

Guardian Super Sport and Loktuff

Humane Manufacturing LLC
805 Moore St.
P.O. Box 24
Baraboo, WI 53913

Toll-free: 800-369-6263
Phone: 608-356-8336
Fax: 608-356-8338
www.humanemfg.com

Guardian Super Sport and Loktuff are made from recycled-tire rubber. Guardian Super Sport comes in 4' x 6' straight-edge mats in 3/8", 1/2", and 3/4" thicknesses. Loktuff comes in 4' x 4' mats with interlocking edges in 3/8" and 1/2" thicknesses. Both are also available in 4 standard colors with 15% color flecks, which reduces the total recycled content to 80%. The colored product is not available in 3/4" thickness. The manufacturer has certified the following recycled-content levels of basic black (by weight): total recovered material 93% typical, 93% guaranteed; post-consumer material 93% typical, 93% guaranteed. As with other flooring products made from recycled automobile tires, installation is only recommended in semi-enclosed spaces, well-ventilated indoor spaces, or outdoors.

Replay

Johnsonite
16910 Munn Rd.
Chagrin Falls, OH 44023

Toll-free: 800-899-8916
Phone: 440-543-8916
Fax: 440-543-8920
www.johnsonite.com

Replay™ sports and multi-functional flooring from Johnsonite is made from 85% post-consumer truck tires. The interlocking tile option requires no adhesive. Replay is available in 14 colors as 3/8" (9.5mm) thick 24" x 24" square-edge tiles, or 25" x 25" interlocking tiles; 48" wide rolls are 1/4" (6.35mm) thick. Other thicknesses are available by special order. As with other flooring products made from recycled automobile tires, installation is only recommended in semi-enclosed spaces, well-ventilated indoor spaces, or outdoors.

Most recently mentioned in EBN 15:2

Ergo Mattas

Mat Factory, Inc.
760 W. 16th St., Bldg. E
Costa Mesa, CA 92627

Toll-free: 800-628-7626
Phone: 949-645-3122
Fax: 949-645-0966
www.matfactoryinc.com

Ergo Mattas is a flexible matting made from a composite of recycled-tire rubber and recycled PVC plastic intended for anti-fatigue and wet floor applications. The product is available in three styles: Softfoot Original, Aqua Tred, and Cushion Tred. Available in 7 colors with matching edge ramps, Ergo Mattas has an open-weave pattern and comes in 10" x 20" tiles that interlock to form runners that can be easily rolled up. As with other flooring products made from recycled automobile tires, installation is only recommended in semi-enclosed spaces, well-ventilated indoor spaces, or outdoors.

SportFloor

North West Rubber Mats, Ltd.
33850 Industrial Ave.
Abbotsford, BC V2S 7T9 Canada

Toll-free: 800-663-8724
Phone: 604-859-2002
Fax: 604-859-2009
www.northwestrubber.com

Sport Floor® mats are made from recycled-tire rubber with a synthetic binder. Mats come in various sizes, thicknesses, and colors. As with other flooring products made from recycled automobile tires, installation is only recommended in semi-enclosed spaces, well-ventilated indoor spaces, or outdoors.

Roppe Recreational Flooring

Roppe Corp.
1602 N. Union St.
Fostoria, OH 44830

Toll-free: 800-537-9527
Phone: 419-435-8546
Fax: 419-435-1056
www.roppe.com

Roppe Recreational Flooring is made from recycled-rubber flooring and tire products. The 20"-square interlocking tiles are 3/8" thick. Edging and corner tiles are also available. As with other flooring products made

from recycled automobile tires, installation is only recommended in semi-enclosed spaces, well-ventilated indoor spaces, or outdoors.

Tuflex

Tuflex Rubber Products, Inc.
4521 W. Crest Ave.
Tampa, FL 33614

Toll-free: 800-543-0390
Phone: 813-870-0390
Fax: 813-875-2312
www.tuflex.com

Tuflex is 100% recycled-rubber flooring designed for heavy traffic commercial areas. It is extremely durable, intended for applications such as stadiums, ice arenas, and gyms and is available in a variety of colors. As with other flooring products made from recycled automobile tires, installation is only recommended in semi-enclosed spaces, well-ventilated indoor spaces, or outdoors.

SuperFlexx Paver Tiles, Sports Floor, and SureStep

U.S. Rubber Recycling, Inc.
2225 Via Cerro, Unit B
Riverside, CA 92509

Toll-free: 888-473-8453
Phone: 951-342-0177
Fax: 951-342-0197
www.usrubber.com

SuperFlexx Paver Tiles and Sports Floor are 24" x 24" tiles made from high-density, urethane-bonded primary crumb rubber buffings. The Paver Tiles are available in red, green, or black, and are suitable for indoor/outdoor usage, especially in wet areas. Sports Floor is black tiles decorated with EPDM granules of red, green, blue, or off-white (consisting of 15% of the material's content). SureStep Traffic Tire Tile is made from recycled truck and bus tire linings; this durable flooring is available in 12" x 12" and 12" wide x 25' long rolls. As with other flooring products made from recycled automobile tires, installation is only recommended in semi-enclosed spaces, well-ventilated indoor spaces, or outdoors.

Tire Veneer

Yemm & Hart Ltd.
1417 Madison 308
Marquand, MO 63655

Phone: 573-783-5434
Fax: 573-783-7544
www.yemmhart.com

Tire Veneer polymer-bonded recycled-tire rubber flooring comes in 18"- and 36"-square tiles or 48"-wide rolls. It is available in solid black or with up to 50% EPDM flecks in a choice of 14 colors (though this

will reduce the recycled content). As with other flooring products made from recycled automobile tires, installation is only recommended in semi-enclosed spaces, well-ventilated indoor spaces, or outdoors.

---

09 66 03
Terrazzo Flooring Aggregate

Some terrazzo products include recycled content aggregate material. Be aware that different binders are used in terrazzo products, not all of which are environmentally attractive. The products listed here are recycled glass aggregate for use in terrazzo. (See also 09 66 16 - Terrazzo Floor Tile.)

Recycled Glass Aggregates and Powders

American Specialty Glass, Inc.
829 N. 400 W.
North Salt Lake, UT 84054

Phone: 801-294-4222
Fax: 801-294-3135
www.americanspecialtyglass.com

American Specialty Glass, Inc., provides recycled-glass aggregate in a range of sizes and colors for terrazzo floors, pavers, and countertops. Sources include post-consumer bottle glass and post-industrial float glass cullet. Glass sand, a substitute for silica sand, is also available, as are powder fines that can be used as concrete coloring agents, providing a different effect than pigments. Polished or unpolished landscaping nuggets in a range of sizes are offered as well.

Recycled Glass for Terrazzo

Heritage Glass, Inc.
130 W. 700 S, Bldg. E
Smithfield, UT 84335

Phone: 435-563-5585
Fax: 435-563-5583
www.heritageglass.net

Heritage Glass offers recycled-glass aggregate in a range of colors and sizes for terrazzo flooring and countertop applications. Sources include post-industrial float glass cullet and post-consumer bottle glass. Heritage also provides 1/2" to 2" recycled-glass aggregate with dulled edges for landscaping applications.

09 00 00
Finishes

09 00 00
Finishes

09 66 16
Terrazzo Floor Tile

Some terrazzo products include recycled content aggregate material. Be aware that different binders are used in terrazzo products, not all of which are environmentally attractive. The products listed here contain recycled aggregate.

Bio-Glass

Coverings Etc, Inc.
7610 N.E. 4th Ct.
Miami, FL 33138

Phone: 305-757-6000
Fax: 305-757-6100
www.coveringsetc.com

Bio-Glass™ solid surfacing for countertops, walls, floors, and other applications is made from 100% recycled glass, heated and agglomerated under pressure. There are no binders, colorants, fillers, or other admixtures. Depending on color, the product is either pre- or post-consumer, or a blend. The translucent, nonporous material is available as 110-inch by 49-inch slabs, about 3/4 inches thick with a lightly textured, slip-resistant surface; smooth-surfaced slabs are also available, approximately 4 inches thick. The product is currently available in white and light green, with blue, brown, and dark green to follow.

IceStone

IceStone, LLC
For full listing, see CSI section 12 36 00 - Countertops

QuartzStone

Quartzitec
15 Turner Ct.
Sussex, NB E4E 2S1 Canada

Toll-free: 877-255-9600
Phone: 506-433-9600
Fax: 506-433-9610
www.quartzitec.com

QuartzStone tiles are manufactured from quartz fragments bound with white portland cement rather than polyester resin. The tiles measure 11.8" x 11.8" and 15.7" x 15.7" and are available in 3 series with 40 colors. Unit pavers are also available in 8 colors. Both products can be color-customized.

Recycled-Glass "Terrazzo" Tile

Wausau Tile, Inc.
9001 Business Hwy. 51
Rothschild, WI 54474

Toll-free: 800-388-8728
Phone: 715-359-3121
Fax: 715-355-4627
www.wausautile.com

Wausau Tile, one of the largest terrazzo manufacturers in the world, produces a line of terrazzo-like tile from recycled glass (approximately 33% recycled glass by weight) using technology developed by the Civil Engineering Dept. of Columbia University. According to the company, the patented chemical additives result in a much stronger and more water-resistant product than traditional terrazzo.

Most recently mentioned in EBN 10:9

09 67 00
Fluid-Applied Flooring

A range of different materials can be applied as a fluid to make flooring. Look for recycled content. (See also 09 65 00 - Resilient Flooring.)

Dura Rubber Floor

Northern Industries, Inc.
429 Tiogue Ave.
Coventry, RI 02816

Toll-free: 800-346-5543
Phone: 401-821-2121
Fax: 401-821-9335
www.northerncoatings.com

Dura Rubber Floor is a seamless indoor/outdoor surfacing made from recycled tire rubber mixed with a waterborne epoxy binder. One pound covers 2 to 6 ft² when poured to a minimum thickness of 1/16". Applications include ramps and anti-slip surfaces. Tire rubber is reclaimed from local tire retreaders. As with other flooring products made from recycled automobile tires, installation is recommended in semi-enclosed spaces, well-ventilated indoor spaces, or outdoors.

09 68 13
Tile Carpeting

Carpet tile is an environmentally preferable alternative to carpeting because damaged or stained carpet tiles can be replaced individually without having

to replace carpeting on an entire floor. Though primarily used in commercial buildings, carpet tile is beginning to appear for residential applications as well. Products listed here contain recycled content or have other environmental attributes such as low VOC emissions, or certification as a climate-neutral product. (See feature articles EBN Vol. 3, No. 6 & Vol. 6, No. 6.)

BPS Carpet Tile with GlasBac RE

Bentley Prince Street
14641 E. Don Julian Rd.
City of Industry, CA 91746

Toll-free: 800-423-4709
www.bentleyprincestreet.com

Bentley Prince Street (BPS), sister company to Interface Flooring Systems, offers a number of recycled-content options. Kings RoadRC and New StratfordRC commercial carpeting, available in tile or broadloom, is made with 100% post-industrial 6,6 nylon yarn recovered from automotive-part scrap waste. Additionally, BPS offers 18 carpet tile products that use GlasBac® RE backing, made with 36-42% post-consumer and post-industrial recycled PVC. All BPS carpet tile products can be specified with GlasBac RE for a minimal upcharge. A portion of the electricity used to manufacture Bentley Prince Street products comes from solar-generated power. All BPS products are certified as "Environmentally Preferable Products" by Scientific Certification Systems.

Most recently mentioned in EBN 15:1

ER3® RS® Modular Tile

C&A, a Tandus Company
311 Smith Industrial Blvd.
P.O. Box 1447
Dalton, GA 30722

Toll-free: 800-248-2878
Phone: 706-259-9711
Fax: 706-259-2179
www.tandus.com

ER3® RS® Modular Tile is a dense, high-performance commercial carpet with low-pile nylon fiber and a 100% post-consumer recycled-content backing made from the PVC carpet backing and nylon fibers of used carpet and carpet tile. The recycled-content backing gives the carpet a total of 30-52% recycled content by weight. The precoat to which the backing adheres is made from virgin PVC. A peel-and-stick system is used to install the carpet tiles using factory-applied, low-VOC adhesive. The Powerbond ER3 products have a long service life. The RS system eliminates wet adhesives so indoor air quality is minimally affected.

Most recently mentioned in EBN 6:6, 8:1, 13:8

i2 Cool Carpet Tile

Interface Flooring Systems, Inc.
2859 Paces Ferry Rd., Ste. 2000
Atlanta, GA 30339

Toll-free: 866-281-3567
Phone: 770-437-6800
www.interfaceinc.com

The i2™ collection consists of more than 100 designs based on the principles of biomimicry and divided into three design categories. i2 Monolithic designs such as Entropy® allow for nondirectional installation. The i2 Patterns and i2 Linear collections allow for quarter-turn, ashlar, brick or monolithic installation. Examples of these two categories include the Pictorials™ Collection, Sewn Up™ and Chenille Warp™. The Cool Carpet designation is standard on i2 products and available as an option on other Interface products. As a "Cool Carpet™" product, all greenhouse gases emitted during the life cycle of i2 are offset or balanced, as certified by the Climate Neutral Network.

Most recently mentioned in EBN 12:10 & 13:3

Interface Carpet Tile with GlasBac RE

Interface Flooring Systems, Inc.
2859 Paces Ferry Rd., Ste. 2000
Atlanta, GA 30339

Toll-free: 866-281-3567
Phone: 770-437-6800
www.interfaceinc.com

All Interface® Flooring Systems products with GlasBac® RE recycled PVC contain at least 39% total recycled content (minimum 19% post-consumer). The Florentine™ Collection, Interference™, Shantung™ and Transformation™ all come standard with GlasBac RE and Ultron® Renew nylon 6,6 by Solutia™. The Florentine Collection contains at least 50% total recycled content, 19% of which is post-consumer material. Interference, Shantung and Tansformation contain at least 47% total recycled content and 19% post-consumer material. Gist™ and Method™ all contain at least 47% recycled content when specified with GlasBac RE. Interface Flooring Systems is a division of Interface, Inc., which maintains a website, www.interfacesustainability.com, outlining in detail the many steps Interface is taking to become a truly sustainable company.

Interface FLOR Terra with Ingeo PLA Fiber

Interface Flooring Systems, Inc.
2859 Paces Ferry Rd., Ste. 2000
Atlanta, GA 30339

Toll-free: 866-281-3567
Phone: 770-437-6800
www.interfaceinc.com

The Terra line in Interface's FLOR collection of residential carpet tile products is the first floorcovering to use Ingeo® PLA (polylactic acid) fibers. Cargill Dow's Ingeo is a form of polyester derived from corn. The face fiber in this line is made with one third of Ingeo, while the other twenty lines in this collection use more conventional fibers. The FLOR collection uses PVC backings.

Most recently mentioned in EBN 12:6

TacTiles   New

Interface Flooring Systems, Inc.
2859 Paces Ferry Rd., Ste. 2000
Atlanta, GA 30339

Toll-free: 866-281-3567
Phone: 770-437-6800
www.interfaceinc.com

TacTiles™ are three-inch, self-adhesive, PET squares for "floating floor" commercial carpet tile installations designed for use with products that have InterfaceFLOR's GlasBac® backing. They allow fast, easy installation on top of almost any hard surface by adhering the carpet tiles together underneath each intersecting corner. The adhesive prevents horizontal movement of the carpet tiles, yet allows easy removal of individual tiles or sections as needed. When the flooring is eventually reclaimed, the TacTiles can be recycled along with the carpet.

Earth Square

Milliken Carpet
201 Lukken Industrial Dr. W
P.O. Box 2956
LaGrange, GA 30240

Toll-free: 800-528-8453
Phone: 706-880-5344
Fax: 706-880-5906
www.millikencarpet.com

Earth Square™ from Milliken Carpet, a division of Milliken & Company, provides a patented process for carpet renewal. The three-step, closed-loop recovery process supercleans, retextures, and updates designs on used modular carpet for commercial customers at substantial savings versus the cost of new carpet tiles, while adding product life cycles. Earth Square carpet carries a 10-year fiber-wear warranty and a 1-year latent-defects warranty.

Most recently mentioned in EBN 6:6 & 7:8

Carpet Tile with EcoSolution Q and EcoWorx

Shaw Contract Group
P.O. Drawer 2128
Dalton, GA 30722

Toll-free: 800-257-7429
Phone: 877-502-7429
Fax: 706-879-4537
www.shawcontractgroup.com

EcoSolution Q™ is a durable, solution-dyed nylon fiber from the world's largest carpet manufacturer. This fiber contains a minimum of 25% post-industrial and post-consumer recycled material. Ecoworx™ carpet backing contains 40 percent recycled content, some post-industrial fly ash, is recyclable, an alternative to PVC (no chlorine or phthalates), and has low VOC emissions. Product lines made with these technologies include A Walk in the Garden designed by William McDonough, and Green with Envy. Shaw promises to take back any of its used carpet, from any place in the continental U.S., at no cost to the end user.

Most recently mentioned in EBN 13:8 & 15:3

09 68 16
Sheet Carpeting

Carpeting is almost ubiquitous in our homes, schools, and office buildings. Almost two billion square yards of carpeting are sold each year, nearly all of it made from petrochemicals. Carpet is a good absorber of sound and impact, yielding a surface associated with comfort. Its absorbent nature, however, also makes it a good medium for holding moisture and harboring dirt, mold, and dust mites. This, along with potential off-gassing from the carpet and its adhesive, has led to indoor air quality concerns. Carpet companies are each taking different approaches to improving the environmental profile of their products. (See also 09 68 13 - Tile Carpeting.) (See feature articles EBN Vol. 3, No. 6 & Vol. 6, No. 6.)

BPS High Recycled-Content Broadloom

Bentley Prince Street
14641 E. Don Julian Rd.
City of Industry, CA 91746

Toll-free: 800-423-4709
www.bentleyprincestreet.com

09 00 00
Finishes

Bentley Prince Street, sister company to Interface Flooring Systems, offers recycled-content options. Kings RoadRC commercial carpeting, available in broadloom or tile, is made with 100% post-industrial 6,6 nylon yarn recovered from automotive-part scrap waste. A number of their lines utilize high post-industrial recycled-content nylon 6,6 face fiber - either DuPont Antron Legacy® cf nylon or Ultron® Color cf nylon 6,6 by Solutia. Prestige PlusRC, a backing option, includes a cushion-backing component made from 100% post-consumer recycled content. A portion of the electricity used to manufacture Bentley Prince Street products comes from solar-generated power. All Bentley Prince Street products are certified as "Environmentally Preferable Products" by Scientific Certification Systems.

Most recently mentioned in EBN 15:1

Wool and Cotton Carpet

Carousel Carpets
3315 Superior Ln.
Bowie, MD 20715

Phone: 301-262-2650
Fax: 301-262-2651
www.carouselcarpets.com

Carousel produces carpets made from wool, linen, and cotton fibers, with a poly backing. They also make custom carpets and rugs.

Nature's Carpet

Colin Campbell & Sons, Ltd.
1428 W. 7th Ave.
Vancouver, BC V6H 1C1 Canada

Toll-free: 800-667-5001
Phone: 604-734-2758
Fax: 604-734-1512
www.naturescarpet.com

Nature's Carpet, made from 100% New Zealand raw wool, is completely free of chemical residues from all stages of the process—from the washing and spinning of the wool through manufacture of the finished carpet. The line currently consists of six loop-pile carpets in natural wool hues, two loop-pile ribbed products, and one cut-pile carpet with vegetable-dyed colors. The backing is made from jute and strengthened with unbleached cotton. Nature's Carpet uses no moth treatment, uses natural latex rather than synthetic, and has negligible VOC ratings. The carpet has been used extensively for people with chemical sensitivities.

Natural Design Collection and Natural Textures Collection

Design Materials, Inc.
241 S. 55th St.
Kansas City, KS 66106

Toll-free: 800-654-6451
Phone: 913-342-9796
Fax: 913-342-9826
www.dmikc.com

These carpet collections from Design Materials are made exclusively from natural fibers. Products in the Natural Design Collection are manufactured from sisal, coir, and reed, while those in the Natural Textures Collection are made from sisal, wool, and jute. These carpets come in 13'2"-wide broadloom rolls in a variety of colors, patterns, and weaves.

Most recently mentioned in EBN 13:2

Bio-Floor Collection

Earth Weave Carpet Mills, Inc.
P.O. Box 6120
Dalton, GA 30722

Phone: 706-278-8200
Fax: 706-278-8201
www.earthweave.com

Earth Weave Carpet Mills produces wall-to-wall carpeting and area rugs from 100% biodegradable, all natural materials such as wool, hemp, jute, and natural rubber. Their Bio-Floor line of wool carpeting is nonwoven and uses a 100% biodegradable adhesive to bond the wool to a hemp-cotton primary backing and then a secondary backing of jute fibers. No chemical treatments are used, and color variation is achieved through the selection of naturally pigmented wool.

J & J Invision and Commercial

J & J / Invision
P.O. Box 1287
Dalton, GA 30722

Toll-free: 800-241-4586
Fax: 800-628-4329
www.jj-invision.com

All J & J Commercial carpet produced from Encore® SD Ultima fiber—representing over 60% of the company's over 50 available styles—contains at least 25% recycled nylon 6 yarn and is eligible for J & J's carpet reclamation program. Encore SD Ultima fiber is made with nylon chips from BASF and is solution-dyed for minimal water waste. Note that some products contain both nylon 6 and nylon 6,6, which may hamper future recyclability.

Recycled-Content Residential Carpet

Mohawk Industries, Inc.
160 S. Industrial Blvd.
Calhoun, GA 30703

Phone: 800-622-6227
Fax: 706-602-0278
www.mohawkind.com

Residential polyester Mohawk carpets have 100% recycled-content face fiber from recovery of soda-bottle PET.

Six-Foot Carpet with EcoTek 6 Backing

Shaw Contract Group
PO Drawer 2128
Dalton, GA 30722

Toll-free: 800-257-7429
Phone: 877-502-7429
Fax: 706-879-4537
www.shawcontractgroup.com

The EcoTek 6 backing is Shaw's 6-foot carpet system made with the same PVC-free technology as the EcoWorx backing for carpet tile, but in a lighter weight. The product is made with EcoSolution Q™, a durable, solution-dyed nylon fiber containing a minimum of 25% post-industrial and post-consumer recycled material.

Most recently mentioned in EBN 15:3

Natural Fiber Floor Coverings

Sisal Rugs Direct
P.O. Box 313
Excelsior, MN 55331

Toll-free: 888-613-1335
Phone: 952-448-9602
Fax: 952-448-9603
www.sisalrugs.com

Sisal Rugs Direct markets broadloom and area rugs of sisal, sisal/wool blend, seagrass, and mountain grass imported from Brazil, China, and Africa with natural latex-rubber backings.

09 68 19
Carpet Cushion

Carpet cushions may be made from a variety of recycled, natural, and/or synthetic materials. Natural materials include jute fibers and animal hair; synthetic materials include nylon and polypropylene waste from carpet manufacturing, recycled-tire rubber, and rebond polyurethane (reprocessed from virgin prime flexible polyurethane products). As with carpet itself, care should be taken not to expose the cushion to moisture—including long-term moisture from concrete slabs—to minimize the potential for microbial growth. Flexible-foam carpet padding frequently contains brominated flame retardants (BFRs) which have been identified as a growing health and environmental concern. Carpet cushion is used primarily in residential applications. (See also 06 16 29 - Acoustical Underlayment.) (See feature articles EBN Vol. 6, No. 6 & Vol. 13, No. 6.)

AcoustiCORK

Amorim Industrial Solutions

For full listing, see CSI section 09 60 14 - Flooring Underlayment

UnderFleece

Appleseed Wool Corp.
55 Bell St.
Plymouth, OH 44865

Toll-free: 800-881-9665
Phone: 419-687-9665
Fax: 419-687-8272
www.appleseedwoolcorp.com

UnderFleece™ carpet cushion is made from 100% wool felt needled to a woven jute scrim and contains no glues, dyes, mothproofing, or other chemical treatments.

ethos Carpet-Cushion Backing

C&A, a Tandus Company
311 Smith Industrial Blvd.
P.O. Box 1447
Dalton, GA 30722

Toll-free: 800-248-2878
Phone: 706-259-9711
Fax: 706-259-2179
www.tandus.com

The non-PVC Ethos™ carpet-cushion backing from C&A Floorcovering, Inc., is made from non-chlorinated polyvinyl butyral (PVB) safety-glass film collected when auto windows and other safety-glass panes are recycled. Ground recycled glass is added as filler, along with a small amount of aluminum trihydrate as a flame retardant. This backing is available for all of C&A's carpet products at no added cost, but it must be specified.

Most recently mentioned in EBN 13:8 & 13:12

Carpet Padding

Earth Weave Carpet Mills, Inc.
P.O. Box 6120
Dalton, GA 30722

Phone: 706-278-8200
Fax: 706-278-8201
www.earthweave.com

Earth Weave Carpet Mills offers a natural rubber rug gripper padding and a 100% natural untreated wool padding (made from 80% post-industrial waste).

EcoSoft Carpet Cushion

Invista Commercial Flooring
175 TownPark Dr. NW
Kennesaw, GA 30144

Toll-free: 800-438-7668
Phone: 770-420-7791
Fax: 770-420-7900
www.antron.invista.com

EcoSoft carpet cushion is 100% recycled fibers with half the recycled content coming from reclaimed commercial carpet.

Hartex Carpet Cushions

Leggett & Platt, Inc.
400 Davidson St.
Nashville, TN 37213

Toll-free: 800-888-4136
Phone: 615-734-1600
Fax: 615-251-8915
www.leggett.com

Hartex carpet cushions are made with recycled nylon fiber from carpet manufacturing bonded to a polypropylene interliner. Hartex cushions come in 24-oz. (5/16"), 32-oz. (3/8"), and 40-oz. (7/16") weights and are sold primarily for commercial and hotel applications.

PL and DublBac Series Carpet Cushion

Leggett & Platt, Inc. - Fairmont Division
2245 W. Pershing Rd.
Chicago, IL 60609

Toll-free: 800-621-6907
Phone: 773-376-1300
Fax: 773-376-3037
www.leggett.com

PL and DublBac Series carpet cushion is made from bonded 100% recycled polyurethane foam from post-industrial and post-consumer sources.

Cork Underlayment

Natural Cork, Inc.

For full listing, see CSI section 09 60 14 - Flooring Underlayment

Whisper Wool Acoustic Underlay

Nature's Acoustics

For full listing, see CSI section 09 60 14 - Flooring Underlayment

Nova Underlayment

Nova Distinctive Floors

For full listing, see CSI section 09 60 14 - Flooring Underlayment

Reliance Carpet Cushion

Reliance Carpet Cushion Division
15902 S. Main St.
Gardena, CA 90248

Toll-free: 800-522-5252
Phone: 323-321-2300
Fax: 310-323-4018

Imperial Carpet Cushion products are made from recycled textile waste fibers. Rather than using a chemical bonding agent, as do most other manufacturers, Reliance uses heat as a bonding agent in the Imperial Cushion products. Inter-Loc, Embassy, Marathon, Ambassador, and the Environmental Performance Collection of products, including Natural Wonder, Performa Bond, Berber Tradition and Broadloom Delight synthetic fiber carpet cushions, are manufactured with 100% post-consumer carpet fiber content. The manufacturer has certified the following recycled-content levels (by weight): total recovered material 100% typical, 100% guaranteed; post-consumer material 0% typical.

Rug-Hold 100% Natural

Rug-Hold - Division of Leggett and Platt, Inc.
5070 Phillip Lee Dr.
Atlanta, GA 30336

Toll-free: 800-451-4653
Phone: 404-691-9500
Fax: 800-284-6538
www.rughold.com

Rug-Hold® 100% Natural rug underlayment is made of jute fiber coated with natural rubber. All Rug-Hold products use natural rubber.

09 00 00
Finishes

09 00 00
Finishes

Endurance II Carpet Pad

Shaw Contract Group
P.O. Drawer 2128
Dalton, GA 30722

Toll-free: 800-257-7429
Phone: 877-502-7429
Fax: 706-879-4537
www.shawcontractgroup.com

Endurance II™ carpet pad is made from 100% post-industrial recycled fiber from carpet manufacturing, needle-punched to a synthetic interliner. It is available in 20- to 40-oz. weights.

Most recently mentioned in EBN 15:3

---

09 69 00
Access Flooring

Access flooring greatly simplifies renovation or reconfiguration of office spaces, dramatically reducing "churn" costs. In addition to providing a plenum for electrical and communications cabling, access flooring with appropriate height can be used for underfloor air delivery (UFAD)—an economically and environmentally attractive combination of floor and air duct. Compared to conventional ceiling-located air-supplies, displacement ventilation from access flooring systems more effectively diffuses conditioned air into the occupied space to displace stale air, which leaves via ceiling-mounted return ducts. More effective air distribution leads to other efficiencies as well: air handlers can be downsized, and conditioned air does not have to be chilled as much to provide the same levels of comfort. Often, ceiling height can also be increased, improving daylighting potential. (See feature article EBN Vol. 7, No. 1.)

Access Flooring Systems

aspmaxcess
880 Equestrian Ct.
Oakville, ON L6L 6L7 Canada

Phone: 905-847-0138
Fax: 905-847-0141
www.aspmaxcess.com

aspmaxcess (formerly asp and Maxcess Technologies), owned by Japanese raised floor manufacturer Hitachi, produces a full line of access flooring systems and components. 85% to 99% of the raw materials used in their WCG-Series wood-core access floor panels are derived from post-industrial recycled content (and these panels are also available with formaldehyde-free resins). Refurbished systems are available.

Most recently mentioned in EBN 7:1

Access Flooring Salvage and Refurbishing

Camino Modular Systems, Inc.
89 Carlingview Dr.
Toronto, ON M9W 5E4 Canada

Toll-free: 800-370-0226
Phone: 416-675-2400
Fax: 416-675-2424
www.camino-access-floors.com

Camino Modular Systems salvages and refurbishes access flooring systems. Refurbished systems sell for 10-20% less than the price of new systems. The company also has a U.S. location in Elk Grove Village (Chicago), Illinois.

Most recently mentioned in EBN 5:5 & 7:1

Low-Profile Access Flooring

Free Axez USA
420 Keim Blvd.
Burlington, NJ 08016

Toll-free: 888-747-8515
Phone: 609-747-8400
Fax: 609-747-8600
www.freeaxez.com

Free Axez USA offers low-profile access flooring systems for wire and cable management (but not for underfloor air supply). The modular, snap-together, 16-gauge, zinc-plated steel system is available in 2.75" or 1.6" profiles. Base units have 34 welded support legs to provide exceptional load-bearing capacity without "bounce," which also offers a compensatory quality for some unevenness in the subfloor. Defined cable channels offer improved wire management with less tangling. This product can significantly reduce churn costs and downtime, and is particularly appropriate in applications where ceiling heights restrict the use of combined access-floor/air-plenum systems. Wood-finished systems are available.

Most recently mentioned in EBN 7:1

Haworth Access Flooring

Haworth, Inc.   **New**
One Haworth Center
Holland, MI 49423

Phone: 616-393-3000
Fax: 616-393-1570
www.haworth.com

Haworth manufactures access flooring systems and components. Its TecCrete and Nexus systems are low-emitting, achieving SCS Indoor Advantage Gold certification. TecCrete is a concrete and steel flooring system for wiring and air distribution that can be used without additional finish flooring. Nexus, made of steel wrapped MDF panels and steel supports, is a low-profile (2.5" high) system for wiring that may allow specification of non-plenum rated cable. The Haworth access flooring product line was purchased from Interface Flooring in 2003 and has been further developed.

Most recently mentioned in EBN 12:12 & 13:1

Access Flooring Salvage and Refurbishing

Irvine Access Floors, Inc.
9425 Washington Blvd., Ste. Y-W
Laurel, MD 20723

Phone: 301-617-9333
Fax: 301-617-9907
www.irvineaccessfloors.com

Irvine Access Floors salvages and refurbishes access flooring systems.

Most recently mentioned in EBN 7:1

Access Flooring Systems

Tate Access Floors
7510 Montevideo Rd.
Jessup, MD 20794

Toll-free: 800-231-7788
Phone: 410-799-4200
Fax: 410-799-4207
www.tateaccessfloors.com

Tate is the largest U.S. manufacturer of access flooring systems. The company offers a full line of access floor support systems, flooring panels, and floor coverings. Tate, York, and CII have teamed up to provide an integrated access flooring system that efficiently delivers conditioned air and provides a flexible framework for electrical and communications cabling. This is known as the Building Technology Platform™.

Most recently mentioned in EBN 7:1

Floor Diffusers

Titus
990 Security Row
Richardson, TX 75081

Phone: 972-699-1030
Fax: 972-918-8880
www.titus-hvac.com

Titus, a leading name in ceiling air diffusers for commercial buildings, offers a full line of floor diffusers for access floor systems that are used for conditioned air delivery.

Most recently mentioned in EBN 7:1

09 69 26
Carpet Recycling

Vast quantities of used carpet end up in landfills each year—more than 1.7 million tons, according to recent estimates. Carpet accounts for approximately 1% of all municipal solid waste by weight, and roughly 2% by volume. Programs to recycle carpet waste are, thus, extremely important. Recycling was made easier by the content labeling program instituted in 1996. Some collected carpet is now, or soon will be, recycled into new carpet. Other uses include plastic products for automobile interiors and engine parts, industrial flooring, and parking stops. (See feature article EBN Vol. 6, No. 6.)

C&A Carpet Buy Back Program

C&A, a Tandus Company
311 Smith Industrial Blvd.
P.O. Box 1447
Dalton, GA 30722

Toll-free: 800-248-2878
Phone: 706-259-9711
Fax: 706-259-2179
www.tandus.com

The C&A Carpet Buy Back Program accepts old vinyl-backed carpet and recycles that carpet into new floorcovering. A sample of the old carpet must be sent to C&A for testing to ensure that it is a type that can be recycled. Then the carpet is shipped to the company—which generally costs less than landfill disposal. C&A guarantees that 100% of the collected carpet is recycled into new floorcovering.

6ix Again

Honeywell Nylon
475 Reed Rd. NW
Dalton Carpet Center
Dalton, GA 30720

Toll-free: 800-839-3233
Phone: 706-259-1200
Fax: 706-259-1283
www.zeftronnylon.com

The 6ix Again™ carpet recycling program recovers used nylon 6 face fibers from qualifying commercial carpets for remanufacturing into new nylon yarns or other nylon products. All recovered face fiber is guaranteed not to be landfilled or incinerated. Honeywell acquired the 6ix Again program from BASF when the company sold its worldwide engineering-plastics business

in 2003 to BASF in exchange, in part, for BASF's worldwide nylon-fiber business.

Most recently mentioned in EBN 3:6, 6:6, 12:6, 12:9

ReEntry Carpet Reclamation Program

Interface Americas Corporate Services Group
2859 Paces Ferry Rd., Ste. 2000
Atlanta, GA 30339

Phone: 770-437-6800
Fax: 706-883-6198
www.interfaceinc.com

The Interface ReEntry® program has diverted more than 4.1 million yards (32 million lbs.) of carpet from the solid waste stream since 1994. Some carpet in good shape is cleaned and donated to charity. Vinyl-backed carpets provide feedstock for the company's GlasBac® RE high-recycled-content carpet backing. Carpet that cannot be recycled or "repurposed" is incinerated in a waste-to-energy plant. Carpet "diversion" cost is significantly reduced when using the Interface ReEntry Program, according to the company. Restrictions apply.

Most recently mentioned in EBN 12:6

Invista Reclamation Program

Invista Commercial Flooring
175 TownPark Dr. NW
Kennesaw, GA 30144

Toll-free: 800-438-7668
Phone: 770-420-7791
Fax: 770-420-7900
www.antron.invista.com

The Invista Reclamation(SM) Program offers a unique service for reclaiming and recycling used commercial carpets. Invista collects commercial carpets throughout North America at specific collection locations. Carpets are shipped to a central processing facility where they are sorted according to face fiber and backing type. Reclaimed carpet materials are used in automobile parts and various padding and soundproofing products.

Most recently mentioned in EBN 3:6, 6:6, 7:10

Tarkett Reuse Initiative

Tarkett Commercial
2728 Summer St.
Huston, TX 77007

Toll-free: 800-877-8453
Phone: 713-344-2733
Fax: 713-344-2770
www.tarkett.com

Tarkett's ReUse™ Reclamation Program allows customers to recycle non-installed jobsite waste and samples. Clean, non-installed Tarkett flooring waste is packaged in bags provided by Tarkett and mailed to Alabama or Texas for recycling. Samples are packed in a self-addressed box and postage is prepaid for carry boards and architectural folders. 100% of the returned materials are recycled, and installation waste from heterogeneous sheet, composition tile, luxury tile, and homogeneous sheet and tile, are recycled into new flooring.

09 72 00
Wall Coverings

Textile and vinyl wall coverings are commonly used in commercial buildings for sound control and durability. Paper and vinyl "wallpaper" is widely used in homes. Avoiding vinyl (PVC) products is environmentally desirable for several reasons: interior finishes containing PVC can be a significant source of VOCs (tests have shown that VOC levels do drop off dramatically within weeks after installation); during disposal at the end of the wall covering's useful life, toxins (including dioxin) may be released if the material is incinerated improperly; combustion of PVC during accidental building fires can produce both dioxin and hydrochloric acid; phthalate plasticizers in many vinyl products, including wall coverings, are also increasingly being identified as health concerns, particularly due to their ability to mimic natural hormones; finally, most vinyl wall coverings have very low moisture permeability, and there is potential for mold growth if moisture is trapped behind these wall coverings. Using low-VOC adhesives is another important step in establishing good indoor air quality. Products listed here are synthetic and natural-fiber alternatives to PVC-based wall coverings. (See also 09 72 03 - Wall Covering Adhesives.) (See feature article EBN Vol. 10, No. 7.)

Rauhsaser

Better Wall System
P.O. Box 567
Kenora, ON P9N 3X5 Canada

Toll-free: 800-461-2130
Phone: 807-548-2130
Fax: 807-548-1812

Rauhsaser (Rough Fiber), a thick wallpaper designed to be painted, is made from recycled paper with a wood chip texture. Five patterns are available. This product was previously sold in the U.S. under the name CoverAge.

Most recently mentioned in EBN 1:1 & 4:2

Xorel Wall Covering

Carnegie
110 N. Centre Ave.
Rockville Centre, NY 11570

Toll-free: 800-727-6770
Phone: 516-678-6770
Fax: 516-678-6848
www.carnegiefabrics.com

Xorel® is a woven polyethylene alternative to paint and vinyl. Xorel fabric is inherently stain-resistant, flame-retardant, colorfast, and water-repellent. Although Xorel is a petrochemical product, it is very durable and has extremely low VOCs, thus avoiding the IAQ- and fire-related problems associated with PVC. Xorel is also used as a fabric for workstation panels and upholstering furniture.

Most recently mentioned in EBN 9:2 & 10:7

Duraprene Wallcovering

Designtex
200 Varick St.
New York, NY 10014

Toll-free: 800-221-1540
Phone: 212-886-8161
Fax: 212-886-8149
www.dtex.com

Duraprene wallcoverings, formerly offered by Blumenthal, Inc., are made from a wood pulp mixed with latex and sealed with a water-based polyurethane coating, providing a scrubbable, durable surface without environmental or IAQ concerns. Recycled office paper and salvage from carton manufacturing are used in the product. Colors used in the eleven current patterns are absorbed by the paper so they do not lift off with cleaning—as do some vinyl wall coverings.

Innvironments Collection

Innovations in Wallcoverings, Inc.
150 Varick St.
New York, NY 10013

Toll-free: 800-227-8053
Phone: 212-807-6300
Fax: 212-807-1944
www.innovationsusa.com

The Innvironments® Collection is comprised of breathable, Class A fire-rated wall coverings manufactured from materials such as sisal, cellulose, honeysuckle vines, and cork using water soluble inks that contain no heavy metals. The Allegory® Series, which has a Type II wall covering rating, is made from 50% wood fiber and 50% spun-woven polyester. Because Allegory is permeable, it avoids IAQ problems associated with non-permeable wall coverings associated with PVC-based products.

Most recently mentioned in EBN 9:1, 9:2, 9:7

G405 and G406 Sanparrel Wallcovering

InPro Corporation
P.O. Box 406
Muskego, WI 53150

Toll-free: 800-222-5556
Phone: 262-679-5521
Fax: 888-715-8407
www.inprocorp.com

G405 and G406 Sanparrel Wallcovering in the EnviroGT line from InPro are rigid, non-PVC wallcovering sheets extruded from polyester-based PETg—glycol-modified polyethylene terephthalate. The 4x8 sheets carry a Class A fire rating without the use of brominated or halogenated flame retardants; they also do not contain phthalate plasticizers or bisphenol A, and incineration will not generate dioxins or furans. The product is made from virgin polymers, and provides chemical, stain, and impact resistance. InPro's conventional Sanparrel line is made from PVC; included here is just the EnviroGT Sanparrel line.

Surface IQ

Len-Tex Corporation
18 Len-Tex Ln.
N. Walpole, NH 03609

Phone: 603-445-2342
Fax: 603-445-5001
www.lentexcorp.com

Surface IQ looks like a high-end vinyl wallcovering, but it is made from polyethylene and is free of heavy metals, halogens, formaldehyde, and plasticizers. Surface IQ passes the California Section 1350 VOC emission test, and uses a non-arsenate antimicrobial additive, a non-halogen natural clay fire retardancy additive, and heavy-metal and chlorine free water-based inks. Textured polyethylene film is adhered to a standard cellulose-and-polyester backing, so the product is installed with a standard vinyl wallcovering adhesive. Surface IQ is available in a variety of styles and of colors.

Natural Textiles

MDC Wallcoverings
1200 Aurthur Ave.
Elk Grove, IL 60007

Toll-free: 800-621-4006
Phone: 847-437-4017
www.mdcwall.com

Natural Textiles from MDC Wallcoverings, formerly Muraspec N.A., includes environmentally responsible wall coverings made from such materials as linen and mulberry fibers, flax, silk, recycled paper, and water-based vegetable dyes.

180 Walls

Milliken & Company
900 Milliken Rd
Spartanburg, SC 29306

Toll-free: 888-487-8499
Phone: 864-503-1629
www.180walls.com

180 Walls™ from Milliken is a highly permeable, woven wallcovering for commercial applications made from 100% pre-consumer recycled polyester. It has a self-adhesive backing that eliminates the need for paste. This product has achieved a Silver rating in McDonough Braungart Design Chemistry's Cradle-to-Cradle program, and is certified to meet the Greenguard Children and Schools standard. (It was the first Greenguard-certified wallcovering to be tested with its adhesive.) 180 Walls is less expensive than most fabric wallcoverings.

Most recently mentioned in EBN 16:1

EnVision

NaturDecor & Supply LLC
1020 N.W. 6th St., Ste. H
Deerfield Beach, FL 33442

Toll-free: 888-401-6002
Phone: 954-427-2242
Fax: 954-429-8208
www.naturdecor.com

The EnVision® collection of Type I and Type II commercial wallcovering are made from a nonwoven polyester-cellulose blend. These breathable wallcoverings have a protective scrubbable finish and are designed expressly as an alternative to vinyl wallcovering. EnVision is produced with water-based inks, and is Class A fire rated. Type I is available in 3 designs and 8 coordinating colors; Type II in 6 designs and 8 coordinating colors. Both types are available in a 54"-wide contract size.

The South Seas Collection

Newcastle Fabrics Corp.
80 Wythe Ave.
Brooklyn, NY 11211

Toll-free: 800-404-5560
Phone: 718-782-5560
Fax: 718-782-7367
www.newcastlefabrics.com

The South Seas Collection is a series of wall coverings made from hand-woven natural fibers in a wide variety of patterns.

DuraWeave

Roos International Ltd. Inc.
1020 N.W. 6th St., Ste. H
Deerfield Beach, FL 33442

Toll-free: 800-888-2776
Phone: 954-429-3883
Fax: 954-429-8208
www.roosintl.com

DuraWeave™ Wallcovering is a woven glass textile wall covering. Designed to be painted, DuraWeave is available in a large variety of textures and patterns and is washable (when painted), nontoxic, nonflammable, and repairable. DuraWeave allows walls to breathe and is particularly resistant to mold and mildew in high-moisture areas. DuraWeave can be applied to nearly all wall surfaces, providing additional reinforcement and bridging minor imperfections and cracks.

Moment

Roos International Ltd. Inc.
1020 N.W. 6th St., Ste. H
Deerfield Beach, FL 33442

Toll-free: 800-888-2776
Phone: 954-429-3883
Fax: 954-429-8208
www.roosintl.com

Moment is a sturdy (Type I) nonwoven, breathable wall covering designed expressly as an alternative to vinyl wall covering. A protective finish resists grease and stains while providing a scrubbable surface. Moment contains 38% cellulose fiber, 37% polyester, and 25% acrylic polymers; is entirely free of PVC and chlorine; and may be fully recycled. Moment is available in a range of 40 colors and carries a Class A fire rating.

Texturglas

Roos International Ltd. Inc.
1020 N.W. 6th St., Ste. H
Deerfield Beach, FL 33442

Toll-free: 800-888-2776
Phone: 954-429-3883
Fax: 954-429-8208
www.roosintl.com

Texturglas is a woven glass textile wall covering that is durable, flame-retardant, washable (when painted), and repairable. Texturglas allows walls to breath and is suitable for high-moisture areas to reduce the risk of mold and mildew. This product can be applied to nearly all wall surfaces providing additional reinforcement and bridging minor imperfections and cracks. Available in a large variety of patterns and textures, Texturglas can be painted approximately 8 times without losing its texture and provides an estimated service life of over 30 years.

09 72 03
Wall Covering Adhesives

A large quantity of adhesive is required for wall coverings, especially when highly porous materials such as sisal are installed. Testing a small area of the covering with the chosen adhesive is recommended to determine whether offgassing or unpleasant odors will be a problem; this is especially important if any building occupants suffer from chemical sensitivity. Products listed here are low-VOC adhesives.

389 Natural Wallpaper Adhesive

Sinan Co. Environmental Products
P.O. Box 857
Davis, CA 95616

Phone: 530-753-3104
Fax: 270-675-7423
www.sinanco.com

Sinan 389 Natural Wallpaper Adhesive is sold in powder form to be mixed with water. It is suitable for up to medium-weight paper-based wall coverings. Sinan products are made from all-natural, primarily plant-based materials, all of which are listed on the packaging.

09 72 13
Cork Wall Coverings

Long used as a wall covering, cork is available in sheets or tiles of various thicknesses. It's tackable, self-healing, durable, sound absorbing, and naturally resistant to moisture, rot, mold, and fire. Obtained from the outer bark of the cork oak (Quercus suber), cork can be harvested sustainably without killing the tree. (See also 09 72 00 - Wall Coverings & 10 11 23 - Tackboards.)

Cork Fabric Wall Covering

Habitus
166 E. 108th St.
New York, NY 10029

Phone: 212-426-5500
Fax: 212-426-5200
www.habitusnyc.com

Cork Fabric wall covering or upholstery is made from a thin layer of cork laminated onto a 50% cotton, 50% polyester backing. It is available in a roll width of 57". Cork Fabric is available in a variety of styles. Custom production is an option.

Natural Cork Wall Tile

Natural Cork, Inc.
1710 North Leg Ct.
Augusta, GA 30909

Toll-free: 800-404-2675
Phone: 706-733-6120
Fax: 706-733-8120
www.naturalcork.com

Natural Cork Wall Tile is 1/8" thick, 12" high x 24" wide, features a peel-and-stick application, and comes prefinished with a wax coating in 6 patterns.

09 72 19
Textile Wall Coverings

Because large amounts of adhesive may be needed for some special wall coverings, low-VOC adhesives are a high priority. Products listed here include unusual wall covering products with recycled content or made of natural materials. (See also 09 72 03 - Wall Covering Adhesives.)

No-Flame Sisal Wallcovering

Design Materials, Inc.
241 S. 55th St.
Kansas City, KS 66106

Toll-free: 800-654-6451
Phone: 913-342-9796
Fax: 913-342-9826
www.dmikc.com

No-Flame Sisal Wallcovering is manufactured in Merida, Mexico. A natural fiber obtained from the Agave plant (Agave sisalana), sisal can be woven into durable, resilient, sound-absorbing, and tackable fabrics and textiles of various thicknesses. Its hydroscopic property helps modify a room's humidity without conducting static electricity. It can be directly applied to concrete masonry walls and other surfaces with a trowel-on

09 00 00
Finishes

adhesive. The sisal fiber for this product is treated with borax for fire retardance, dyed, spun into yarn, and woven into sheets with a boucle weave construction. The end-product is available in 12 colors. Design Materials also offers a zero-VOC adhesive.

Most recently mentioned in EBN 6:6

Plaster in a Roll and Faster Plaster Underliner

Flexi-Wall Systems
208 Carolina Dr.
P.O. Box 89
Liberty, SC 29657

Toll-free: 800-843-5394
Phone: 864-843-3104
Fax: 864-843-9318
www.flexiwall.com

Plaster in a Roll™ is a 35-mil-thick jute fabric wall covering impregnated with gypsum plaster and a factory-applied clear coating. It comes in 48"-wide rolls and can be applied to any rigid wall or ceiling surface. It is available in two textures: Classics, available in 16 colors; and Images, available in 10 colors. Flexi-Wall Adhesive #500, used to adhere the product to the surface, also crystallizes the gypsum. Faster Plaster™ Underliner is a similar 50-mil wall liner designed to be adhered to concrete or masonry as a substrate for painting, plastering, or application of a finish wall covering.

09 81 16
Acoustic Blanket Insulation

Noise, both from indoor and outside sources, adds to stress and discomfort. A wide range of products are available to help absorb noise and prevent it from spreading. Products listed here are designed to provide acoustical isolation in addition to any thermal insulation properties they may have. If these products are also listed under thermal insulation, they must meet GreenSpec's criteria for that type of thermal insulation. (See also 09 81 29 - Sprayed Acoustic Insulation.)

The Insulator

Bonded Logic, Inc.
411 E. Ray Rd.
Chandler, AZ 85225

Phone: 480-812-9114
Fax: 480-812-9633
www.bondedlogic.com

The Insulator™ Thermal-Acoustic Insulation is a 3/8"-thick thermal and acoustic insulation made from post-industrial denim and cotton fiber and faced on either one or both sides with an aluminum barrier (also available in a two- or three-ply version). The product is formaldehyde-free and comes in 4' x 6' or 4' x 75' rolls (in 3/8" thickness only). The Insulator is thermally bonded using a synthetic fiber binder and is treated with a boric acid antimicrobial agent. It is Class A fire-rated, and no protective clothing or gear is necessary for installation. The 3/8" pad has a noise reduction coefficient of 0.45 and an R-value of 1.47.

Most recently mentioned in EBN 13:3

Formaldehyde-Free Insulation Batts

Johns Manville Corporation

For full listing, see CSI section 07 21 16 - Blanket Insulation

09 81 29
Sprayed Acoustic Insulation

Noise, both from indoor and outside sources, adds to stress and discomfort. A wide range of products are available to help absorb noise and prevent it from spreading. Products listed here are designed to provide acoustical isolation in addition to any thermal insulation properties they may have. If these products are also listed under thermal insulation, they must meet GreenSpec's criteria for that type of thermal insulation. (See also 09 81 16 - Acoustic Blanket Insulation.) (See feature article EBN Vol. 2, No. 5.)

Thermal-Pruf, Dendamix, and Sound-Pruf

American Sprayed Fibers, Inc.

For full listing, see CSI section 07 21 29 - Sprayed Insulation

Cellulose Insulation

Can-Cell Industries, Inc.

For full listing, see CSI section 07 21 23 - Loose-Fill Insulation

K-13 and SonaSpray "fc" Insulation

International Cellulose Corporation

For full listing, see CSI section 07 21 29 - Sprayed Insulation

09 83 13
Acoustical Wall Coating

Noise, both from indoor and outside sources, adds to stress and discomfort. A wide range of products are available to help absorb noise and prevent it from spreading.

These wall finishes provide acoustic dampening and may be panelized or trowel-applied products. Products listed here contain recycled content and non-urea formaldehyde binders.

BASWAphon Acoustic Insulation

Sound Solutions Services, LLC
3900 Ben Hur Ave., Ste. 10
Willoughby, OH 44094

Phone: 440-951-6022
www.baswaphonusa.com/

The BASWAphon seamless finish system has acoustic dampening properties and the appearance of plaster or painted drywall. The system, which may be applied to walls or ceilings - including curves, vaults, and domes - is comprised of 5 components: a 32 mm-thick mineral wool supporting panel (74% post-consumer recycled glass and phenol-formaldehyde binder), a factory-applied precoating, and a trowel-applied gap filler containing glass-foam spheres (75% post-consumer recycled glass and vinyl acetate-copolymer binders), and trowel-applied base and top coats (95% recycled marble dust with a vinyl-acetate copolymer binders and acrylic-copolymer binder, respectively). The supporting panels are glued to the substrate with USG Durabond® adhesive. BASWAphon comes in thicknesses of 40 mm and 68 mm and can be colored with integral pigments. The materials for the system are manufactured in Switzerland.

09 91 03
Recycled Paints

Some recycled paints are commingled paints from partially used containers, often collected under municipal waste programs. These are sometimes referred to as consolidated or reusable paint and are typically sold as primers because the color is variable. Other recycled paints are collected and reprocessed or remanufactured to achieve higher quality and consistency. The two resulting products are generally very different. The better recycled paint brands have sophisticated testing and quality control. (See feature articles EBN Vol. 8, No. 1 & Vol. 8, No. 2.)

Amazon Select Recycled Paint

Amazon Environmental, Inc.
6688 Doolittle Ave.
Riverside, CA 92503

Phone: 951-588-0206
Fax: 951-588-0379
www.amazonpaint.com

Amazon Select Recycled Paint is available in whipped white, ivory white, concrete gray, tawny beige, and chocolate brown. Custom colors are available upon request. Recover Brand recycled paint is sold exclusively through Dunn-Edwards Paint Co. in California, Colorado, Nevada, Texas, Arizona, and New Mexico. Amazon Select is sold directly through the manufacturer in all markets.

Most recently mentioned in EBN 10:2

E-Coat Recycled Latex Paint

Kelly-Moore Paint Co.
5101 Raley Blvd.
Sacramento, CA 95838

Toll-free: 800-874-4436
Phone: 916-921-0165
Fax: 916-921-0184
www.kellymoore.com

E-Coat is an interior/exterior line of paint made from recycled latex paint. Typically available in a flat finish, semi-gloss is also available by special order. Seven standard colors are available, as well as a wide range of custom colors.

Most recently mentioned in EBN 8:2

Local Color Recycled Latex Paint

The Environmental Depot
1021 Redmond Rd.
Williston, VT 05495

Phone: 802-872-8100
Fax: 802-878-5787
www.cswd.net

Local Color recycled latex paint is made from 100% recycled, filtered latex paint that has been sorted by color and reblended. The cost is less than half the price of new paint, and quality satisfaction is guaranteed. Local Color interior and exterior paints are available for purchase at the Vermont Environmental Depot in a variety of colors including off-white, tan, green, gray, and blue. All paint is eggshell finish.

VRI Remanufactured Latex Paint

Visions Recycling, Inc.
4481 Kilzer Ave.
McClellan, CA 95652

Toll-free: 800-770-7664
Phone: 916-564-9121
Fax: 916-568-1485
www.visionsrecycling.com

Visions Recycling, Inc. (VRI) produces recycled latex paint from post-consumer (contractor overstock and city and county paint collection sites) and secondary recycled sources (mistints and overstock from factory and store-level distributors). Minimum post-consumer/secondary recycled content is 50%. The paint is checked for quality, sorted, and reblended with virgin materials and additives to produce a high-resin paint that the company claims is comparable in quality to major brands of virgin, one-coat latex paints for roughly one-third the cost. The paints are available for interior and exterior applications, and they come in flat, eggshell, and semi-gloss in twelve stock colors (custom colors are available upon request). VRI also manufactures a low VOC recycled paint made from zero VOC slurry and recycled content. The average VOC content is 17.25 grams/litre.

09 91 13
Exterior Painting

Paints for exterior surfaces may be listed here for a number of reasons, including minimal offgassing and superior durability. Included are mineral silicate paints that chemically react with mineral surfaces (stucco, plaster, concrete, etc.)

in a process called petrification to form a highly durable finish. Mineral silicate paints can also be used indoors. Some listings may exceed 50 grams of VOC per liter; this threshold is anticipated to be adjusted down in future editions of GreenSpec. (See also 02 80 00 - Facility Remediation.)

09 00 00
Finishes

Safecoat Exterior Satin Enamel

American Formulating & Manufacturing (AFM)
3251 Third Ave.
San Diego, CA 92103

Toll-free: 800-239-0321
Phone: 619-239-0321
Fax: 619-239-0565
www.afmsafecoat.com

Safecoat Exterior Satin Enamel contains no ammonia, formaldehyde, ethylene glycol, mildewcides, or fungicides. This premium exterior paint has a VOC content of 17 g/l (42 g/l less water), virtually no odor during application and none when dry, and a satin sheen. It is suitable for use on wood, stucco, aluminum, vinyl, and fully-cured concrete.

Most recently mentioned in EBN 8:2

Best Duracryl Exterior Paint

Best Paint, Inc.
1728 Fourth Ave. S
Seattle, WA 98134

Phone: 206-783-9938
Fax: 206-783-5017
www.bestpaintco.com

Best Paint's Duracryl Exterior Paint is a 100% acrylic resin formula, which contains a low-toxic zinc compound for mold and mildew protection. Best Paint's water-based formula contains less than 50 g/l VOC (less water) and is manufactured for interior and exterior applications with a semi-gloss or eggshell finish. Duracryl Exterior Primer is also available. Suitable for wood, stucco, masonry, primed metal, and other typical surfaces.

Keim Mineral Silicate Paint

Cohalan Company, Inc.
102 Savannah Road
Lewes, DE 19958

Phone: 302-684-3299
Fax: 302-684-5974
www.keimmineralsystems.com

Keim Mineral Systems invented mineral silicate paints in Bavaria (Germany) in 1878, and Keim paints are widely used around the world today. The binder is potassium silicate dissolved in water (also known

09 00 00
Finishes

as "waterglass"). This is combined with inorganic fillers and natural earth oxide to produce an inorganic "liquid stone" finish through a process of petrification. Durability in excess of 100 years has been reported, according to Keim. Used on plaster, concrete, and other mineral surfaces; not suitable for wood, metal, or any flexible surface. Available in both exterior and interior products, with 370 standard colors and over 38,000 recorded custom colors available. Keim mineral silicate paints are solvent-free, odorless, nontoxic, vapor-permeable, naturally resistant to fungi and algae, noncombustible, light-reflective, resistant to acid rain, and extremely durable. Keim Mineral Systems carries ISO 14001 certification.

Most recently mentioned in EBN 12:10

Eco-House Mineral Silicate Paint

Eco-House, Inc.
P.O. Box 220, Stn. A
Fredericton, NB E3B 4Y9 Canada

Toll-free: 877-326-46873
Phone: 506-366-3529
Fax: 506-366-3577
www.eco-house.com

Eco-House, Inc. was the first manufacturer to produce mineral silicate paints in North America. The binder is potassium silicate dissolved in water (also known as "waterglass"), which petrifies when it chemically reacts with lime. Used on plaster, concrete, and other mineral surfaces, this product is not suitable for wood, metal, or any flexible surface. According to Eco-House, silicate paints are solvent-free, completely odorless after 1-2 days, made from widely available materials (water, quartz sand, potash, lime, and silicate minerals), naturally antimicrobial (not requiring fungicides), noncombustible at any temperature, and extremely durable.

Most recently mentioned in EBN 12:10

EverKote 300

Edison Coatings, Inc.
3 Northwest Dr.
Plainville, CT 06062

Toll-free: 800-697-8055
Phone: 860-747-2220
Fax: 860-747-2280
www.edisoncoatings.com

EverKote 300 is a waterborne, inorganic mineral-silicate coating made with a potassium silicate binder, sometimes known as "waterglass," that forms a chemical bond (petrifies) with suitable substrates. It is appropriate for application on calcareous stone (such as limestone or marble), masonry, concrete, cement plaster, ceramics, as well as on iron and other metals. EverKote 300 is

extremely durable, nonflammable, UV-resistant, breathable, and naturally antimicrobial. It is available in two grades: low-viscosity, semi-transparent Penetral; and medium-viscosity, opaque Patinar. EverKote 300 comes in a flat (matte) finish in 900 standard colors; custom color matching is also available.

Most recently mentioned in EBN 12:10

ZVOC Coatings

Fuhr Industrial

For full listing, see CSI section 09 93 23 - Interior Staining and Finishing

Ecological Interior/Exterior Paint

Innovative Formulations Corporation
1810 S. Sixth Ave.
Tucson, AZ 85713

Toll-free: 800-346-7265
Phone: 520-628-1553
Fax: 520-628-1580
www.innovativeformulations.com

Ecological Paint is a line of professional-quality, odor-free, interior/exterior, zero-VOC, hypo-allergenic, water-based acrylic urethanes containing no known hazardous, toxic, or carcinogenic materials. Available with or without a mold inhibitor in semi-gloss, high-gloss, eggshell, satin, and flat. Clay paint and "direct-to-metal" paint are also available.

Rodda Zero-VOC Paint

Rodda Paint

For full listing, see CSI section 09 91 23 - Interior Paints

Silacote Mineral Silicate Paint

Silacote USA LLC
5310 Windward Way
New Port Richey, FL 34652

Toll-free: 800-766-3157
Phone: 419-326-0106
Fax: 419-326-3010
www.silacote.com

Silacote Mineral Silicate Paint is made from natural inorganic compounds such as quartz, other minerals, and mineral colorants with a potassium silicate binder. It is suitable for coating inorganic substrates such as concrete, lime plaster, marble, natural stone, brick, and new gypsum wallboard. For interior and exterior applications, Silacote is breathable, nontoxic, noncombustible, zero-VOC (including colorants), and will not support mold growth. This water-based product chemically bonds (petrifies) with the substrate, producing a coating with a life expectancy of 25 to 30+ years, according

to the manufacturer. Silacote forms a microcrystalline structure that reflects light and heat. Fully tintable, with a large number of colors available; colors not affected by UV or acid rain.

Most recently mentioned in EBN 12:10

09 91 23
Interior Paints

A primary consideration for most interior paints is their potential impact on occupant health. To this end, very-low-VOC or zero-VOC paints are generally preferred, though some chemically sensitive people find that even these can be difficult to tolerate. Note that liquid carriers (including water and exempt VOCs) are usually excluded when stating VOC levels, which are expressed as grams of VOC per liter of VOC-plus-paint-solids. Most zero-VOC paints still use colorant systems that contain VOCs, so custom-coloring will increase emissions. Some paints are made from minimally processed plants and minerals; while these products may contain relatively high levels of VOCs, they may not be as troublesome as the compounds released from petrochemical-based paints. Products listed here contain less than 50 grams of VOCs per liter and may include other environmental features. (See also 02 80 00 - Facility Remediation.) (See feature articles EBN Vol. 8, No. 1 & Vol. 8, No. 2.)

Safecoat Interior Paints

American Formulating & Manufacturing (AFM)
3251 Third Ave.
San Diego, CA 92103

Toll-free: 800-239-0321
Phone: 619-239-0321
Fax: 619-239-0565
www.afmsafecoat.com

Safecoat Zero-VOC interior paints in flat, eggshell, and semi-gloss have little odor when wet and none when dry. None of these paints contains formaldehyde, ammonia, crystalline silica, or ethylene glycol, and they are tinted using zero-VOC colorants. Safecoat Enamels are low-VOC, do not contain extenders, heavy-metal drying agents, formaldehyde, acetone, or heavy-duty preservatives. They are available in a variety of finishes and can be tinted to virtually any color. Safecoat paints have long been used by people with chemical sensitivities.

Most recently mentioned in EBN 8:2

Pristine Eco-Spec

Benjamin Moore & Co.
101 Paragon Dr.
Montvale, NJ 07645

Toll-free: 800-344-0400
Phone: 201-573-9600
Fax: 201-573-6673
www.benjaminmoore.com

Pristine® Eco-Spec® is a zero-VOC 100% acrylic latex interior paint available in primer/sealer, flat, eggshell, and semi-gloss. The product line is for the professional contractor market.

Most recently mentioned in EBN 4:1, 4:6, 5:3, 8:2, 12:10, 13:2

Best Paints

Best Paint, Inc.
1728 Fourth Ave. S
Seattle, WA 98134

Phone: 206-783-9938
Fax: 206-783-5017
www.bestpaintco.com

Best Paint's Interior and Breathe-EZ products are Zero VOC, with no biocide and low to no odor. They are available in flat, satin, eggshell, and semi-gloss in a wide range of colors.

Most recently mentioned in EBN 8:2

BioShield Interior Paint

BioShield Paint Company
3215 Rufina Street
Santa Fe, NM 87507

Toll-free: 800-621-2591
Phone: 505-438-3448
Fax: 505-438-0199
www.bioshieldpaint.com

The BioShield product line, available online and through the BioShield Paint Catalog,

includes paints, stains, thinners and waxes made from naturally-derived raw materials including citrus peel extracts, essential oils, seed oils, tree resins, inert mineral fillers, tree and bee waxes, lead-free dryers and natural pigments. Thinners are derived from low-toxic, non-petroleum-based ingredients.

Most recently mentioned in EBN 8:2

Enviro-Safe Paint

Chem-Safe Products Company
P.O. Box 33023
San Antonio, TX 78265

Phone: 210-657-5321
www.ecowise.com

Enviro-Safe zero-VOC paints are available in flat, satin, and semi-gloss for interior use, and satin for exterior use. The product line uses a grapefruit-derived low-toxic preservative, so shelf life is guaranteed for only one year.

Most recently mentioned in EBN 8:2

Air-Care Odorless Paints

Coronado Paint Company
308 Old County Rd.
Edgewater, FL 32132

Toll-free: 800-883-4193
Phone: 386-428-6461
Fax: 386-427-7130
www.coronadopaint.com

The Air-Care line consists of Odorless Acrylic Primer, Odorless Acrylic Flat, Odorless Acrylic Eggshell, and Low Odor Acrylic Semi-Gloss. All these formulations are zero-VOC, though colorants add some VOCs.

Most recently mentioned in EBN 8:2

Genesis Odor-Free

Duron Paints & Wallcoverings
10406 Tucker St.
Beltsville, MD 20705

Toll-free: 800-723-8766
Fax: 301-595-3919
www.duron.com

Genesis Odor-Free interior acrylic latex paint has a calculated zero-VOC content and is available in flat, low-lustre, and semi-gloss.

Most recently mentioned in EBN 8:2

Aglaia Natural Finishes

Environmental Building Supplies
819 S.E. Taylor St.
Portland, OR 97214

Phone: 503-222-3881
Fax: 503-222-3756
www.ecohaus.com

Aglaia Natural Finishes are biodegradable, plant- and mineral-based products free of petrochemicals and artificial resins. Available in Germany since the late 1960s and now being imported into North America, a variety of interior paints, stains, plasters, and texture coats are also offered. Note than some Aglaia products may have relatively high VOC levels (from plant-based materials), though others have zero VOC content.

Eurolux Waterborne Paints and Varnishes

Fine Paints of Europe
P.O. Box 419
Woodstock, VT 05091

Toll-free: 800-332-1556
Phone: 802-457-2468
Fax: 802-457-3984
www.finepaintsofeurope.com

Eurolux waterborne varnishes and acrylic paints are made in Holland. The varnishes have less than 60 g/l VOCs, and the paints less than 30 g/l. These are durable, high-quality coatings at a premium price.

EnviroKote Interior Low Odor Paint

Frazee Paint
6625 Miramar Rd.
San Diego, CA 92121

Toll-free: 800-477-9991
Phone: 858-626-3600
Fax: 858-452-3568
www.frazeepaint.com

EnviroKote paint is a very-low-VOC acrylic latex available in flat, eggshell, and semi-gloss formulations. White and medium-tint base paints are available.

Most recently mentioned in EBN 8:2

ZVOC Coatings

Fuhr Industrial

For full listing, see CSI section 09 93 23 - Interior Staining and Finishing

HealthyHues Paint New

HealthyHome.com
2894 22nd Ave. N
Saint Petersburg, FL 33713

Toll-free: 800-583-9523
Phone: 727-322-1058
www.healthyhome.com

HealthyHome sells HealthyHues, a line of zero-VOC latex interior paint available in primer, flat, eggshell, and semigloss. HealthyHome is the sole distributor for this paint, which is manufactured for them by Southern Diversified Products of Mississippi (which also makes American Pride paints).

09 00 00
Finishes

Devoe Wonder Pure, Dulux LifeMaster, Prep & Prime

ICI Paints
15885 W. Sprague Road
Strongsville, OH 44136

Toll-free: 800-984-5444
Phone: 216-344-8000
Fax: 216-344-8900
www.iciduluxpaints.com

The Wonder-Pure line of Devoe Paint, manufactured by Glidden, is zero-VOC. The line includes primer, interior flat, eggshell, and semi-gloss. They are available only through independent Glidden dealers. LifeMaster interior latex paints have zero-VOC content and are available in flat, eggshell, and semi-gloss finishes. Prep & Prime Odor-Less Primer Sealer is a zero-VOC tintable primer and sealer for interior use. Prep & Prime Vapor Barrier Interior Primer/Sealer is a latex primer-sealer formulated to reduce the permeability of wall surfaces. It is low-VOC (85 g/l) and tintable; it may also be topcoated with latex or alkyd paints of any finish. This product has a perm rating of 0.6 when applied at a coverage rate of 400 ft²/gal to smooth surfaces, which compares favorably with the performance of a 2-mil-thick sheet of medium-density polyethylene.

Most recently mentioned in EBN 8:2

Kelly-Moore Enviro-Cote

Kelly-Moore Paint Co.
5101 Raley Blvd.
Sacramento, CA 95838

Toll-free: 800-874-4436
Phone: 916-921-0165
Fax: 916-921-0184
www.kellymoore.com

Kelly-Moore Enviro-Cote acrylic satin enamel paint is zero-VOC, their Acry-prime has a maximum VOC content of 15 g/l, semi-gloss enamel has a maximum VOC content of 6 g/l, and flat finish paints have VOC contents of less than 13 g/l.

Most recently mentioned in EBN 8:2

Everfresh Paint

Mercury Paint Corporation
4808 Farragut Rd.
Brooklyn, NY 11203

Toll-free: 800-858-8787
Phone: 718-469-8787
Fax: 718-941-8133
www.mercurypaintcorp.com

Mercury Paint's Everfresh zero-VOC 100% acrylic latex interior paint is available in primer (5900), flat (6900), eggshell (9150), and semi-gloss (8900). Everfresh paint is free of lead, mercury and chromate compounds. Colorants may contain VOCs.

Murco LE-1000 and GF-1000

Murco Wall Products
2032 N. Commerce
Fort Worth, TX 76106

Toll-free: 800-446-7124
Phone: 817-626-1987
Fax: 817-626-0821
www.murcowall.com

Murco paints are water-based, low-VOC, latex products for interior use, popular with chemically sensitive individuals. Available in flat (GF-1000) and high-gloss (LE-1000).

Most recently mentioned in EBN 8:2

Milk Paint

Old Fashioned Milk Paint Co.
436 Main St.
P.O. Box 222
Groton, MA 01450

Toll-free: 866-350-6455
Phone: 978-448-6336
Fax: 978-448-2754
www.milkpaint.com

Milk Paint is a powdered paint made from casein (milk protein) mixed with lime, clay, and earth pigments. Water is added to make a pint, quart, or gallon size. It is available in 20 historical colors, which can be blended or tinted. Milk Paint is marketed primarily as a paint for wood furniture or other porous surfaces such as bare masonry; however, different additives and clear sealers can be used to enhance durability and adhesion to nonporous surfaces. Although Milk Paint contains a natural mildewcide, the use of a clear sealer over the paint in damp areas such as bathrooms is recommended to prevent waterspotting and for washability.

Most recently mentioned in EBN 8:2

Zero-VOC Premium Interior Line

New

Olympic Paint and Stain
PPG Architectural Finishes, Inc.
PPG World Headquarters, One PPG Place
Pittsburgh, PA 15272

Toll-free: 800-441-9695
Phone: 412-434-3131
www.ppg.com

Olympic's zero-VOC Premium Interior Paint, made by PPG Architectural Finishes, is available at Lowes Hardware Centers and includes four standard sheens and two specialty interior paints. 1,224 standard colors are available as well as custom colors to match other paints. The paint is Green Seal certified, meeting Green Seal's GS-11 standard for coatings.

Pure Performance

PPG Architectural Finishes
One PPG Pl.
Pittsburgh, PA 15272

Toll-free: 800-441-9695
Phone: 412-434-3131
Fax: 412-434-3744
www.ppgaf.com

PPG Architectural Finishes sells Pure Performance zero-VOC interior latex paint under its Pittsburgh Paints brand. A full range of sheens can be tinted to any Pittsburgh Paints color (tints contribute a minimal amount of VOCs—2 g/l maximum). Pure Performance, which replaced the company's second-to-the-top Wallhide line, is the first paint certified under the Green Seal standard and meets the special "Class A" rating reserved for zero-VOC paints. PPG claims that the Pure Performance line, made with vinyl acetate ethylene resin, is the first to offer zero-VOC with no compromise on durability and at a price similar to that of conventional paints.

Most recently mentioned in EBN 11:5 & 11:12

Kurfees Fresh Air

Progress Paint Manufacturing Co., Inc.
201 E. Market St.
P.O. Box 33188
Louisville, KY 40202

Toll-free: 800-626-6407
Phone: 502-587-8685
Fax: 502-587-2440
www.progresspaint.com

Kurfees Fresh Air interior paint has a calculated maximum VOC content of 24 g/l and is available in flat, eggshell, and satin finishes or as primer.

Most recently mentioned in EBN 8:2

Rodda Zero-VOC Paint

Rodda Paint
6107 N. Marine Dr.
Portland, OR 97203

Toll-free: 800-452-2315
Phone: 503-737-6033
www.roddapaint.com

Rodda Paint's Horizon line includes 42 different products in various finishes for interior, exterior, and priming applications. The interior products are nominally zero-VOC, with less than one gram of VOCs per liter. The Horizon line also includes the first exterior paint that meets Green Seal's GS-11 standard for coatings. Rodda is a founding member of the Oregon Natural Step Network, a statewide group of businesses working towards environmental sustainability.

Most recently mentioned in EBN 12:5

Sico Ecosource Paints

Sico, Inc.
2505 de la Metropole
Longueuil, QC J4G 1E5 Canada

Toll-free: 800-463-7426
www.sico.ca

Ecosource is a new line of odor-free, zero-VOC paints from Sico, the largest paint manufacturer in Canada. The 100% acrylic latex paint is available in a range of finishes in 1,680 colors, and is certified by Green Seal®. Sico paints are primarily distributed in Canada.

Natural Paints

Sinan Co. Environmental Products
P.O. Box 857
Davis, CA 95616

Phone: 530-753-3104
Fax: 270-675-7423
www.sinanco.com

Sinan natural interior paint products include primers, a professional wall paint (satin only), and a milk paint in powder form. Manufactured in white, they can be tinted using a concentrate available in 8 earth-tone colors. Sinan products are made from all-natural, primarily plant-based materials, all of which are listed on the packaging.

Most recently mentioned in EBN 8:2

American Pride High Performance, Low VOC

Southern Diversified Products, LLC
2714 Hardy St.
Hattiesburg, MS 39401

Phone: 601-264-0442
www.americanpridepaint.com

Southern Diversified Products is manufacturing a line of interior latex paints called "American Pride" that is based on technology by polymer science researchers at the University of Southern Mississippi. American Pride has a VOC content of 0-5 g/l and virtually no smell, allowing interior painting without evacuating a building or providing additional ventilation. The paint is the second to be certified under the paint standard by the independent nonprofit Green Seal and, according to the organization, performs well compared to other high-end interior latex paints, while being priced competitively with them. American Pride's flat white has a scrub rating of 2,500 strokes (ASTM D2486-89), while its eggshell white withstood 3,100 strokes. The paints are currently for sale at independent dealers throughout the United States.

Most recently mentioned in EBN 12:2 & 12:4

Gold Label Premium Enviro Paints

Spectra-tone Paint Company
1595 E. San Bernardino Ave.
San Bernardino, CA 92408

Toll-free: 800-272-4687
Phone: 909-478-3485
Fax: 909-478-3499
www.spectra-tone.com

Gold Label Premium Enviro Paints for interior use are VOC-free and come in flat (#410), low-lustre enamel (#8800), and semi-gloss (#9900). The product line is made with a terpolymer resin that may not be as durable as acrylic latex resins.

Most recently mentioned in EBN 8:2

The Real Milk Paint Co.

The Real Milk Paint Co.
11 West Pumping Station Rd.
Quakertown, PA 18951

Toll-free: 800-339-9748
Phone: 215-538-3886
Fax: 215-538-5435
www.realmilkpaint.com

The Real Milk Paint Company's Real Milk Paint is derived from purified milk protein, lime, natural fillers, and nontoxic lead-free pigments. Real Milk Paint comes ready to be mixed with water for a desired consistency from thin wash to thick paint. Once mixed with water, the paint will remain usable from 2 to 4 weeks. Real Milk Paint is virtually odorless during application and drying, and contains no VOCs.

Harmony Coating System

The Sherwin-Williams Company Stores Group
101 Prospect Ave. NW
Cleveland, OH 44115

Toll-free: 800-524-5979
Phone: 216-566-2000
Fax: 440-826-1989
www.sherwin-williams.com

Harmony Interior Latex Flat, Eg-Shel, Semi-Gloss, and Primer provide a durable, low-odor, anti-microbial, interior paint system formulated without silica. These products can be used, without typical odor complaints, in occupied areas because of the very low odor during application and drying. The Harmony line contains zero-VOCs.

Yolo Colorhouse Paint

New

YOLO Colorhouse LTD
1001 S.E. Water Ave., Ste. 140
Portland, OR 97214

Phone: 503-493-8275
www.yolocolorhouse.com

YOLO Colorhouse is a collection of Green-Seal-certified, zero-VOC, latex interior paint, available in primer, flat, satin, and semigloss. 40 colors are offered, with poster-sized swatches available for purchase.

09 00 00
Finishes

09 93 13
Exterior Staining and Finishing

VOC emissions are the primary concern with exterior stains and finishes. Products listed here have low VOC levels, are derived from natural oils, or are biodegradable. (See also 09 91 13 - Exterior Painting.)

Safecoat DuroStain

American Formulating & Manufacturing (AFM)
3251 Third Ave.
San Diego, CA 92103

Toll-free: 800-239-0321
Phone: 619-239-0321
Fax: 619-239-0565
www.afmsafecoat.com

Safecoat® DuroStain is a premium fast-curing, flat-finish, semi-transparent interior/exterior wood stain. It contains no aniline dyes, gilsonite, asphalt, aromatic solvents, or formaldehyde, and has a VOC content of 100 g/l (349 g/l less water).

BioShield Exterior Stains and Finishes

BioShield Paint Company
3215 Rufina Street
Santa Fe, NM 87507

Toll-free: 800-621-2591
Phone: 505-438-3448
Fax: 505-438-0199
www.bioshieldpaint.com

The BioShield product line, available online and through the BioShield Paint Catalog, includes paints, stains, thinners and waxes made from naturally-derived raw materials including citrus peel extracts, essential oils, seed oils, tree resins, inert mineral fillers, tree and bee waxes, lead-free dryers and natural pigments. Thinners are derived from low-toxic, non-petroleum-based ingredients.

09 00 00
Finishes

Broda Pro-Tek-Tor

Broda Coatings Ltd.
#102 - 876 Cordova DVSN
Vancouver, BC V6A 3R3 Canada

Toll-free: 888-311-5339
Phone: 604-254-3325
Fax: 604-215-2278
www.cbrproducts.com

Broda Pro-Tek-Tor Natural Oil Wood Finish is an oil-based, waterborne, non-film-forming, penetrating wood finish. This product needs only soap and water cleanup and is available in clear, transparent, semi-transparent, and semi-solid formulations. Mold and mildew resistance is provided by liquid microbiocides with low acute oral toxicity.

Envirolast XT

E3 Coatings, Inc.

For full listing, see CSI section 09 93 23 - Interior Staining and Finishing

ZVOC Coatings

Fuhr Industrial

For full listing, see CSI section 09 93 23 - Interior Staining and Finishing

GCP 1000

Genesis Coatings, Inc.
2780 La Mirada Dr., Ste. A
Vista, CA 92081

Toll-free: 800-533-4273
Phone: 760-599-6011
Fax: 760-599-6015
www.genesiscoatings.com

GCP 1000 coating is an odorless, water-based, zero-VOC, two-part aliphatic polyurethane designed to be a high-performance general maintenance coating that is resistant to scuff marks and other unwanted markings. Genesis Coatings has also developed nontoxic, biodegradable graffiti removers: Graffiti Gold Remover, Graffiti Eaze Away, and Graffiti Terminator.

SoySeal

Natural Soy, LLC

For full listing, see CSI section 07 19 00 - Water Repellents

9400 and 9400W Impregnant

Palmer Industries, Inc.

For full listing, see CSI section 07 19 00 - Water Repellents

SOYsolv Soy Seal

SOYsolv

For full listing, see CSI section 07 19 00 - Water Repellents

Timber Pro UV Wood Finishes

Timber-Pro UV
2232 E. Burnside
Portland, OR 97214

Toll-free: 888-888-6095
Phone: 503-232-1705
Fax: 503-235-8794
www.timberprocoatings.com

Timber Pro UV wood finishes are waterborne, plant-based oil/acrylic blend finishes. These non-petroleum products contain less than 251 g/l of VOCs. Timber Pro UV transparent, semi-transparent, and semi solid finishes are for use on cedar, redwood, cypress, pine, fir and all products made from softwoods such as log homes, wood siding, decks, fences, and shakes and shingles.

Zar Exterior Polyurethane

United Gilsonite Laboratories (UGL)
P.O. Box 70
Scranton, PA 18501

Toll-free: 800-272-3235
Phone: 570-344-1202
Fax: 570-969-7634
www.ugl.com

Zar Exterior Water-Based Polyurethane is an amber-colored protective finish for exterior wood surfaces as well as fiberglass and metal entry doors. The product contains ultraviolet-radiation inhibitors to provide additional protection from UV rays.

Weather-Bos Finishes

Weather-Bos International
316 California Ave., Ste. 1082
Reno, NV 89509

Toll-free: 800-664-3978
Fax: 530-272-8098
www.weatherbos.com

Weather-Bos transparent finishes are made from natural, nontoxic vegetable oils and resins as well as other natural ingredients. These finishes are low-odor, water-reducible, nonflammable, and free of harmful fungicides. The small amount of pigment in some formulas provides UV protection. The Boss™ is the company's original all-purpose wood finish; Deck Boss™ protects and weatherproofs wood decks; and Log Boss™ is for use on log homes.

09 93 23
Interior Staining and Finishing

In recent years, polyurethane and other clear interior finishes have dramatically decreased the amount of volatile organic compounds (VOCs) that they offgas. Waterborne polyurethanes are becoming common alternatives to conventional solvent-based products. Low-VOC stains are also becoming available. Products listed here have low VOC levels, are derived from natural materials, are biodegradable, or have exceptional durability.

Safecoat Clear Finishes

American Formulating & Manufacturing (AFM)
3251 Third Ave.
San Diego, CA 92103

Toll-free: 800-239-0321
Phone: 619-239-0321
Fax: 619-239-0565
www.afmsafecoat.com

Hard Seal is a clear finish for highly porous surfaces including bare wood, cabinetry, vinyl or porous tile, or previously painted surfaces; it forms a tight membrane to reduce offgassing from walls, ceilings, and floors. Hard Seal is formaldehyde-free, nonflammable, low-odor, and has a VOC content below 72 g/l (less water). It is not for use on surfaces subject to standing water, heavy moisture, or unsealed particleboard. Acrylacq is a clear, water-based replacement for solvent-based lacquers that creates a hard, high-gloss or satin finish over wood, galvanized or properly primed metal, or plastics. AcriGlaze is a clear, odorless, mildew-resistant mixing medium and finish for faux finishing, sealing pigmented plaster, or restoring old finishes.

Safecoat Safe Seal and SafeChoice Carpet Seal

American Formulating & Manufacturing (AFM)
3251 Third Ave.
San Diego, CA 92103

Toll-free: 800-239-0321
Phone: 619-239-0321
Fax: 619-239-0565
www.afmsafecoat.com

Safe Seal is a clear sealer designed to limit offgassing from particleboard and other manufactured wood products containing formaldehyde. It lends water repellency and serves as the base coat for adhesives and finishes on porous surfaces, including wood and concrete products. SafeChoice® Carpet Seal is designed to help prevent the offgassing from synthetic carpet backing and adhesives. Applied directly after shampooing carpet, Carpet Seal cures into a clear membrane. According to the company, Carpet Seal is odorless and remains effective for up to a year, depending on traffic and cleaning frequency. It cannot be applied to wool carpet.

BioShield Interior Stains and Finishes

BioShield Paint Company
3215 Rufina Street
Santa Fe, NM 87507

Toll-free: 800-621-2591
Phone: 505-438-3448
Fax: 505-438-0199
www.bioshieldpaint.com

The BioShield product line, available online and through the BioShield Paint Catalog,

includes paints, stains, thinners and waxes made from naturally-derived raw materials including citrus peel extracts, essential oils, seed oils, tree resins, inert mineral fillers, tree and bee waxes, lead-free dryers and natural pigments. Thinners are derived from low-toxic, non-petroleum-based ingredients.

Envirolast XT

New

E3 Coatings, Inc.
813 Harbor Blvd. #163
Sacramento, CA 95691

Phone: 916-669-8498
www.envirolast.com

Envirolast XT™ is a zero-VOC, waterborne oil/alkyd emulsion sealer for interior and exterior wood surfaces. It provides a transparent, semi-transparent, or semi-solid pigmented finish, and may be applied over most existing wood finishes.

Aglaia Natural Finishes

Environmental Building Supplies

For full listing, see CSI section 09 91 23 - Interior Paints

OSMO Hardwax Oil

Environmental Home Center
4121 1st Ave. S
Seattle, WA 98134

Toll-free: 800-281-9785
Phone: 206-682-7332
Fax: 206-682-8275
www.environmentalhomecenter.com

OSMO Hardwax Oil, formerly known as OS Hardwax Oil, is a penetrating floor finish made from natural vegetable oils and waxes, and contains no biocides or preservatives. Because OSMO is very high in solids, it can be applied in only two coats and is very durable. The finish may also be spot-repaired.

Eurolux Waterborne Paints and Varnishes

Fine Paints of Europe

For full listing, see CSI section 09 91 23 - Interior Paints

ZVOC Coatings

Fuhr Industrial
6780 Exchange
Mansfield, TX 76063

Toll-free: 800-558-7437
Phone: 817-225-0083
Fax: 682-518-9600
www.fuhrinternational.com

Fuhr International's ZVOC line of zero-VOC coatings includes stains, sealers, and primers. ZVOC water-based stain is an acrylic wood stain for interior and exterior use suitable for a wide variety of applications, including kitchen cabinets, decks, and windows and doors. High Solids Clear Coat and Wax Seal & Finish water-based acrylic products for interior and exterior wood substrates were designed for the kitchen cabinet industry and exceed KCMA finish-coat testing requirements with proper application. Sanding Sealer is a water-based acrylic sanding sealer designed as a companion product for the ZVOC line. ZVOC White Primer and Topcoat are water-based acrylic wood coatings suitable for interior and exterior use. The Primer is acceptable as a "primed only" finish for use on wood products that will receive a finish coat of some type to be determined at a later date. The Topcoat is compatible with a wide variety of primers.

Land Ark Wood Finishes

Land Ark Wood Finishes
213 Townes Rd.
N. Augusta, SC 29860

Phone: 803-279-4116
Fax: 803-278-6996
www.universalweb.com/wood/index.html

Land Ark wood finishes are formulated for use on timber frames as well as both exterior and interior finish applications. These finishes—including tung oil, linseed oil, beeswax, D-limonene (cold-pressed from orange peels), and resin (from pine trees)—have no chemical additives, petroleum products, or heavy-metal driers and are completely biodegradable.

Penofin

Performance Coatings, Inc.
360 Lake Mendocino Dr.
P.O. Box 1569
Ukiah, CA 95482

Toll-free: 800-736-6346
Phone: 707-462-3023
Fax: 707-462-6139
www.penofin.com

Penofin is a low-VOC, semi-transparent, penetrating oil finish. The main ingredient is Brazilian rosewood oil—made from the harvested nut of this tree, not the wood. Performance Coatings reduced the VOC levels of Penofin in advance of the 2002 standard of 250 g/l adopted in California, and the product also meets all National AQ standards.

Sinan 160 Series Natural Stain

Sinan Co. Environmental Products
P.O. Box 857
Davis, CA 95616

Phone: 530-753-3104
Fax: 270-675-7423
www.sinanco.com

Sinan products are made from all-natural, primarily plant-based materials, all of which are listed on the packaging. Sinan 160 Series Natural Stain is available in 12 earth-tone colors and can be thinned using purified water.

Sutherland Welles Low-Toxic Wood Finishes

Sutherland Welles Ltd.
P.O. Box 180
North Hyde Park, VT 05665

Toll-free: 800-322-1245
Phone: 802-635-2700
Fax: 802-635-2722
www.tungoilfinish.com

09 00 00
Finishes

09 00 00
Finishes

Sutherland Welles Low-Toxic Wood Finishes are polymerized tung oils with natural Di-Citrusol™ solvent and reduced chemical driers. The products are botanicals, free of petroleum distillates, and are available in various lustres and as a sealer. Performance and coverage of the low-toxic products are comparable to those features of conventional lines, according to the company. Millie's All Purpose Penetrating Wood Oil is formulated with polymerized tung oil, Di-Citrusol™ and beeswax; no chemical driers are added. All the botanical products are formulated from 99.4% tree-derived raw materials that also contribute to ozone renewing. The Di-Citrusol™ is formulated using oil extracted from discarded citrus peels used by the juice industry.

Pure Tung Oil

The Real Milk Paint Co.
11 West Pumping Station Rd.
Quakertown, PA 18951

Toll-free: 800-339-9748
Phone: 215-538-3886
Fax: 215-538-5435
www.realmilkpaint.com

The Real Milk Paint Company's 100% Pure Tung Oil contains no petroleum distillates or other additives and has a light, nutty odor. Tung oil, which comes from the seed of the tung tree, is a suitable treatment for wood and stone, forming a tough, flexible, water- and alkali-resistant coating. Pure Tung Oil produces a nontoxic finish that is suitable for food preparation surfaces. Other applications include children's toys and furniture, wooden instruments, and wood paneling and molding. A light coating on metal surfaces acts as an effective rust inhibitor.

Tried & True Wood Finishes

Tried & True Wood Finishes
14 Prospect St.
Trumansburg, NY 14886

Phone: 607-387-9280
Fax: 607-387-5264
www.triedandtruewoodfinish.com

Tried & True™ Wood Finishes are made from polymerized linseed oil through a proprietary heat treatment process. Original Wood Finish includes beeswax. Varnish Oil includes varnish resin (hardened tree sap). All are nontoxic with zero VOCs and no heavy-metal driers. The ingredients are derived from renewable agricultural resources. By contrast, conventional "boiled" linseed oil finishes typically include toxic, heavy-metal drying agents. Tried & True finishes are appropriate for a wide range of applications from interior millwork to fine furniture. Application labor costs are similar to those for conventional products. The Danish Oil

Finish may also be used as a rammed-earth floor finish, while the Varnish Oil may be used as a concrete countertop sealant as well as a sealer for terra cotta and thrown-tile products.

Most recently mentioned in EBN 3:5 & 8:11

Aqua ZAR

United Gilsonite Laboratories (UGL)
P.O. Box 70
Scranton, PA 18501

Toll-free: 800-272-3235
Phone: 570-344-1202
Fax: 570-969-7634
www.ugl.com

Aqua ZAR® Water-Based Polyurethane is a low-odor, nonyellowing, clear interior wood finish available in gloss and satin. According to the manufacturer, Aqua Zar's fast-drying, low-odor formula resists most household chemicals and abrasions.

Most recently mentioned in EBN 2:3

09 94 00
Decorative Finishing

Decorative finishes are typically high-grade, multicolored and/or textured coatings for interior and exterior applications. Textures and colors are achieved by proprietary mixtures of pigments, oils, and inorganic fillers. Such products offer a durable and environmentally preferable alternative to common vinyl wall coverings, which offgas plasticizers and pose heightened health risks during a fire or end-of-life incineration. Products listed here are waterborne and have relatively low-VOC content.

Ferroxton-W, Crafton, and Crafton Plus

Bollen International, Inc.
9218 Viscount Row
Dallas, TX 75247

Toll-free: 800-248-4808
Phone: 214-631-9300
Fax: 214-631-9302
www.bolleninternational.com

Ferroxton-W is a water-based metallic coating with a foundry-like texture for exterior or interior spray-on applications over metal, brick, concrete, sheetrock, or plaster. It has a VOC content of less than 60 g/l. Crafton and Crafton Plus are odorless, multicolor, water-based emulsion interior paints designed to provide a soft, fabric-like texture and can be applied to any substrate.

Aglaia Natural Finishes

Environmental Building Supplies

For full listing, see CSI section 09 91 23 - Interior Paints

Duroplex, Duroplex EXT, and Fresco

Triarch Industries, Inc.
1 Energy Way
W. Warwick, RI 02893

Toll-free: 800-537-6111
Phone: 401-822-4100
Fax: 401-822-2984
www.triarchinc.com

Duroplex® is a textured acrylic latex interior coating that the manufacturer claims is 80% as hard as mild steel. It has a VOC content of 103 g/l. Duroplex comes in 80 standard colors and several dozen textures, plus custom color and texture options. Duroplex EXT is the exterior version of Duroplex and can be applied to concrete and masonry surfaces. Fresco® is a high-solids, high-performance acrylic latex coating that forms a vapor-permeable membrane over interior or exterior concrete, masonry, stucco, or EIFS surfaces. It has a VOC content of 103 g/l and is available in single colors and a multicolored speckle.

Polomyx, Lluminations, Metal, and Kinesis by Zolatone

Zolatone Interior Finishes
400 Charter Way
N. Billerica, MA 01862

Toll-free: 800-965-2866
Phone: 978-663-0050
Fax: 978-667-1980
www.zolatone.com

Polomyx (All-Acrylic), Lluminations™, Metal™, Kinesis™ and Airless™ by Zolatone® are spray-applied, water-based specialty paints for commercial interiors. A wide variety of colors and visual textures are available. All finishes are low VOC (60 to 100 g/l), permeable, and contain anti-microbial agents to prevent the growth of mold and mildew on the paint surface. A variety of water based primers (70 to 200 g/l of VOC) are also available. These coating systems are Class A Fire rated. Polomyx, Lluminations, Metal and Airless are durable, cleanable and spot-repairable finishes, with ASTM D 2486 scrub ratings of 5,130, 3,000, 3,000 and 3,180 respectively. Zolatone finishes may be used in place of paint or vinyl wall-covering. The Kinesis system is a decorative application and is not recommended for areas subject to high abuse; it requires application by a certified applicator.

09 96 14
Mold-Resistant Coatings

Mold can compromise both human health and the integrity of building materials. It is generally preferable to design and maintain structures in a way that prevents moisture accumulation, and thereby control and mold growth. However surface-applied mold-resistant coatings are increasingly available, and there are certain applications, such as in bathrooms, where such coatings are appropriate. Care must be taken to ensure that surface applied coatings will not introduce different indoor air quality or environmental problems.

American MoldGuard

American MoldGuard, Inc.
30200 Rancho Viejo Rd., Ste. G
San Juan Capistrano, CA 92675

Toll-free: 877-665-3482
Phone: 949-240-5144
Fax: 949-240-6144
www.americanmoldguard.com

American MoldGuard offers a mold-inhibiting treatment program for new construction utilizing a proprietary, non-volatizing, non-migrating antimicrobial silicon polymer—a highly permeable, water-stabilized organosilane that inhibits the growth of mold, mildew, algae, and bacteria without the use of heavy metals or other conventional toxins. Certified applicators treat surfaces during three phases of construction: the first application occurs prior to drywall installation and treats all interior structural surfaces; a second application occurs after drywall is installed and prior to painting; the third application happens after all interior surfaces have been finished. The company provides a 10-year prevention warranty against mold infestation.

Concrobium Mold Control

Siamons International   **New**
36 Meteor Dr.
Toronto, ON M9W 1A4 Canada

Toll-free: 866-811-4148
Phone: 416-213-0219
www.concrobium.com

Concrobium Mold Control is a surface-applied product that, when dry, produces a thin polymeric film that surrounds and encapsulates microbes, inhibiting mold growth. Concrobium Mold Control is odorless and colorless, contains no bleach, ammonia, acids or volatile organic compounds

(VOCs), and can be applied by hand-spray, paintbrush, roller, immersion, or airless sprayer. Larger areas can be professionally treated using a cold fogging machine. The product is EPA-registered as a Fungistat and Mildewstat.

09 96 34
Low-Emissivity Paint

When they face a heat source, radiant barriers work by reflecting heat. When faced away from a heat source, radiant barriers function primarily by virtue of their low emissivity. This means that the surface does not radiate heat well. A radiant-barrier surface on roof sheathing, for example, heats up from the sunlight striking the roof, but that heat energy is not readily emitted into the attic space—so that attic remains cooler. This is why the radiant barrier seems to "reflect" heat back out of the building. An air space is required on at least one side of a radiant barrier in order for it to function as designed. Radiant barriers in attics are most beneficial in reducing cooling loads; their effectiveness in reducing heating loads is more limited. When comparing low-emissivity aluminized paints,, look for the lowest emissivity (which corresponds to the highest reflectivity), and low VOC levels. Do not rely on "effective" or "equivalent" R-values, which are only relevant in certain climates or under certain conditions. (See also 06 16 13 - Insulating Sheathing.)

Radiance Paints

BASF Corporation
889 Valley Park Dr.
Shakopee, MN 55379

Toll-free: 800-433-9517
Fax: 800-496-6067
www.corporate.basf.com

The Radiance™ e-0.25 AB-C attic barrier contains tiny metallic particles that impart low-e characteristics to painted surfaces. Energy savings from the paint in most situations will be fairly low, except when the ceilings are very poorly insulated. VOC content is 418 g/l with 0.25 emissivity. Radiance paints were formerly produced by Degussa Building Systems acquired by BASF in March of 2006.

E-Barrier Coating

The Sherwin-Williams Company Stores Group
101 Prospect Ave. NW
Cleveland, OH 44115

Toll-free: 800-524-5979
Phone: 216-566-2000
Fax: 440-826-1989
www.sherwin-williams.com

E-Barrier reflective coating for commercial or residential attic decking contains microscopic metal particles to create a low-e surface. Its emissivity when applied over wood is 0.32, and is 0.29 when applied over metal. The VOC content is under 300 g/L —below the 500 g/l limit for metallic pigmented coatings under California Rule 1113. It can be applied with brush, roller, or sprayer. A 2" minimum air space between E-Barrier and the next substrate is required for maximum effectiveness, according to the manufacturer. Energy savings will vary depending upon building materials, home location, and conditions.

09 97 13
Steel Coatings

Paints, rust inhibitors, and other coatings for steel have traditionally been lead-based and/or very high in VOCs. A few environmentally preferable products exist.

MetalCoat Acrylic Metal Primer

American Formulating & Manufacturing (AFM)
3251 Third Ave.
San Diego, CA 92103

Toll-free: 800-239-0321
Phone: 619-239-0321
Fax: 619-239-0565
www.afmsafecoat.com

MetalCoat Acrylic Metal Primer is a thermoplastic emulsion primer fortified with rust-inhibiting pigments. It is designed for use on steel, aluminum, and galvanized metal but is not recommended for copper. The product contains no hazardous chemicals and has a low-VOC content of 44 g/l (88 less water).

09 00 00
Finishes

CCI 921, CCI 921 High Build, and CCI Flex Cote

Corrosion Control Industries
P.O. Box 4717
Johnson City, TN 37602

Toll-free: 877-661-7878
Phone: 423-926-2423
Fax: 423-926-6556
www.neutrarustinc.com

Corrosion Control Industries, formerly Neutra Rust, markets three products designed to convert rusted surfaces. CCI 921 (formerly 661) converts ferric hydroxide (rust) to ferrous oxide and combines with ferrous oxide to form a black organic fersoferric complex. CCI 921 High Build (formerly Neutra Rust HB) has triple the solids content for deeply pitted surfaces. CCI Flex Cote (formerly Neutra Rust TL) is a more flexible coating that is shock-resistant. Minimal surface preparation is needed to use these products, avoiding the environmental and monetary costs of sandblasting. They can be topcoated with common paint or left unprotected. VOC levels are fairly low.

09 97 23
Concrete and Masonry Coatings

Federal VOC-content limits include 350 grams per liter for concrete-curing compounds and 700 grams per liter for concrete curing and sealing compounds. A range of products, particularly waterborne ones, are available that fall well below these federal limits. (See also 07 13 00 - Sheet Waterproofing, 07 14 00 - Fluid-Applied Waterproofing, 07 16 00 - Cementitious and Reactive Waterproofing, 07 19 00 - Water Repellents, 03 05 16 - Waterproofing Admixtures.)

Aquafin-IC Crystalline Waterproofing

Aquafin, Inc.

For full listing, see CSI section 07 16 00 - Cementitious and Reactive Waterproofing

Industraseal

US Mix Products Company
112 S. Santa Fe Dr.
Denver, CO 80223

Toll-free: 800-397-9903
Phone: 303-778-7227
Fax: 303-722-8426
www.usmix.com

Industraseal is a sodium-silicate-based coating for concrete surfaces that creates a clear, water-resistant seal, while allowing vapor to migrate through it. Industraseal is water-based, with zero VOCs. It hardens and densifies the concrete, improving the abrasion and chemical resistance of the surface. It is available in 5-gallon or 55-gallon containers, with a coverage of about 200 – 250 square feet per gallon. Industraseal is part of the US SPEC line of concrete products from US Mix Co.

Xypex Concentrate

Xypex Chemical Corporation

For full listing, see CSI section 07 16 00 - Cementitious and Reactive Waterproofing

This Space is Available for Your Notes

10 00 00 Specialties

PRODUCT LISTINGS

10 11 23
Tackboards

Cork is the traditional, natural solution for vertical tackable surfaces, and it remains an excellent green option. Cork is obtained from the outer bark of the cork oak tree (Quercus suber). After harvesting, the bark regenerates and can be harvested again in about 10 years. The substrate for some tackboards is made from recycled paper and paraffin. Products listed here are made with natural cork. (See also 09 72 13 - Cork Wall Coverings.)

Dodge Cork Rolls and Sheets

Dodge-Regupol, Inc.
715 Fountain Ave.
Lancaster, PA 17601

Toll-free: 1-866-883-7780
Phone: 717-295-3400
Fax: 717-295-3414
www.regupol.com

Dodge Cork comes in 36" x 36" and 28" x 50" sheets and 36", 42" or 48"-wide rolls. Roll thickness available from 1/32" to 1/4". Sheet thickness available from 1/32" to 1"

Bulletin Board

Forbo Linoleum, Inc.
2 Maplewood Dr., Humboldt Industrial Park
P.O. Box 667
Hazleton, PA 18201

Toll-free: 800-842-7839
Phone: 570-459-0771
Fax: 570-450-0258
www.forboflooringNA.com

Bulletin Board is a colored, 1/4"-thick, granulated linoleum-cork composite product sold in full-size sheets for use as tack panels, or as a decorative finish for furniture, doors, or moveable partitions. Bulletin Board is durable, washable, low-glare, and will not warp or crumble. It is available in 12 solid colors.

10 14 00
Signage

Outdoor or indoor signs are an excellent application for recycled materials. Besides identification or directional signage, there can be significant value in signs that interpret green building features—explaining how a composting toilet works, for example, or providing instructions for operable window use. Products listed here are made with a high percentage of recycled content, are energy-conserving (if powered), or have other compelling attributes. (See also 27 42 19 - Public Information Systems.) (See feature articles EBN Vol. 5, No. 1 & Vol. 12, No. 3.)

3form Varia & 100 Percent

3form

For full listing, see CSI section 10 22 23 - Portable Partitions, Screens, and Panels

LED-Illuminated Signage

Carmanah Technologies Corporation
Building 4, 203 Harbour Rd.
Victoria, BC V9A 3S2 Canada

Toll-free: 877-722-8877
Phone: 250-380-0052
Fax: 250-380-0062
www.carmanah.com

Carmanah offers interior and exterior signage that is edge-illuminated by LEDs for such applications as wayfinding, residential address, street name, and traffic control. Carmanah's LED Sign Group has more than 50,000 LED edge-lit sign installations worldwide. The company also offers solar LED hazard lighting and photovoltaic equipment.

Custom Signage

Eagle One Site Furnishings
1340 N. Jefferson St.
Anaheim, CA 92807

Toll-free: 800-448-4409
Phone: 714-983-0050
Fax: 714-203-8444
www.eagleoneproducts.com

Eagle One Site Furnishings offers monument, directional, informational, and identification signage made with 100% recycled HDPE plastic or laminated HDPE up to 40% recycled content.

Earthwater Storm Drain Stencils

Earthwater Stencils, Ltd.
98 Clinic Ave., Ste. B
P.O. Box 1850
Hayfork, CA 96040

Phone: 530-628-5334
Fax: 530-628-4212
earthwater.org

Earthwater® Stencils produces stencils for use in labeling storm drains with messages about protecting the environment—for example: "Dump No Waste: Drains to Stream" with the image of a fish. Stencils can be customized for local waters. Such signs have been important in increasing public awareness about stormwater runoff. The reusable stencils are made from polyester plastic mill ends; the company is looking into sourcing recycled plastic. The company recommends a latex spray paint specially made for roadway use that is low-VOC and compliant with California standards.

Enviropoly Signs

Envirosigns
2417 Cleveland Ave. NW
Canton, OH 44709

Toll-free: 888-492-5377
Phone: 330-236-4713
Fax: 330-456-6999
www.envirosigns.com

Enviropoly standard model signs are a combination of co-extruded thermoplastics with contrasting color cores and 100% recycled-plastic sign posts. Lettering and logos are CNC routed through the face color into the contrasting core color. In addition to 41 standard models, an unlimited number of custom designs are available.

Non-Petroleum Plastic Signage

Gemini Incorporated
103 Mensing Way
Cannon Falls, MN 55009

Phone: 800-538-8377
www.signletters.com

Gemini Incorporated makes vacuum-formed and injection-molded dimensional signage letters and logos from cellulose acetate butyrate, a non-petroleum resin derived from cellulose. The manufacturer indicates that the material is exceptionally UV-stable and temperature-hardy, colorfast, and chemical-resistant. A lifetime guarantee is included.

Recycled-Plastic Site Amenities

Great Lakes Specialty Products

For full listing, see CSI section 12 93 43 - Site Seating and Tables, Plastic

Niagara Fiberboard

Niagara Fiberboard, Inc. (NFI)
P.O. Box 520
Lockport, NY 14095

Phone: 716-434-8881
Fax: 716-434-8884
www.niagarafiberboard.com

Made from recycled paper, Niagara Fiberboard is a laminated paperboard used for signage, displays, and packaging. It is available in panels up to 8' wide and 32' long.

PlasTEAK Traffic Control Devices

PlasTEAK

For full listing, see CSI section 32 17 13 - Parking Bumpers (Car Stops)

Recycled-Plastic Site Amenities

The Plastic Lumber Company, Inc.

For full listing, see CSI section 12 93 43 - Site Seating and Tables, Plastic

Origins Signage

Yemm & Hart Ltd.
1417 Madison 308
Marquand, MO 63655

Phone: 573-783-5434
Fax: 573-783-7544
www.yemmhart.com

Origins signage can be as simple as cut-out letters and shapes from various thicknesses of Yemm and Hart's standard Origins 100% post-consumer recycled material, or it can be made with laminated colors that are routed through to reveal an interior color. Origins can be specifically made with UV inhibitors for longer life outdoors.

10 21 00
Compartments and Cubicles

Toilet compartments should be cleanable, moisture-resistant, and not conducive to mold growth. Recycled plastic (typically HDPE) is an excellent material for toilet compartments; other lightweight, durable materials may also be appropriate. Products listed here have a high level of recycled content.

3form Varia & 100 Percent

3form

For full listing, see CSI section 10 22 23 - Portable Partitions, Screens, and Panels

PaperStone Certified

KlipTech Composites

For full listing, see CSI section 12 36 00 - Countertops

Origins

Yemm & Hart Ltd.

For full listing, see CSI section 06 64 00 - Plastic Paneling

10 22 23
Portable Partitions, Screens, and Panels

Moveable partition systems allow spaces to be easily reconfigured, thus reducing cost and environmental impact. Products listed here have recycled content, certified wood, low-VOC content, and other green attributes.

3form Varia & 100 Percent

3form
2300 S. 2300 W, Ste. B
Salt Lake City, UT 84119

Toll-free: 800-726-0126
Phone: 801-649-2500
Fax: 801-649-2699
www.3-form.com

3form manufactures recycled-content plastic panels for interior design applications such as movable office partitions, work surfaces, and trim. Their 40% pre-consumer Ecoresin is the base for the transparent and translucent Varia panels that come in a wide variety of colors, patterns, and textures, including the kami line showcasing natural materials. The Varia line is certified by Scientific Certification Systems for its recycled content and by the Greenguard Environmental Institute for low indoor emissions. The 100 Percent line is made with color-sorted 100% post-consumer HDPE flakes that are heat and pressure fused without added binders. 3form is seeking certification for 100 Percent by Scientific Certification Systems for its recycled content and by the Greenguard Environmental Institute for low indoor emissions. 100 Percent can be used for a variety of applications and is 3form's toughest material.

Most recently mentioned in EBN 15:10 & 15:12

IrisWall

Environmental Wall Systems, Ltd
31100 Solon Rd.
Solon, OH 44139

Toll-free: 800-528-0903
Phone: 440-542-6600
Fax: 440-542-9840
www.ewswalls.com

The IrisWall® moveable wall system is made with recycled-content aluminum frames, a 95% recycled-content panel face, and a recycled-content glass panel option. Water-based coatings and adhesives are used with the system, and powder-coat finishes are used on exposed aluminum components (an anodizing option is also available). The company has also replaced the use of traditional rotary-spun fiberglass insulation with IrisFiber®, a nonrespirable, long-filament fiberglass insulation, and offers Interface fabric options, data/communication raceways, and a 12-year warranty. IrisWall is manufactured in Ohio.

Bulletin Board

Forbo Linoleum, Inc.

For full listing, see CSI section 10 11 23 - Tackboards

LifeSPACE

SMED International
10 Smed Ln. SE
Calgary, AB T2C 4T5 Canada

Toll-free: 800-661-9163
Phone: 403-203-6000
Fax: 403-203-6001
www.smednet.com

SMED International produces LifeSpace™, a movable wall system for offices that eliminates the construction and demolition waste and the disruption of the internal environment common to traditional renovations. The LifeSpace system is designed to utilize Nexus™ access flooring (but will work with any flooring system) and compact fluorescent lighting. All wooden components in LifeSpace are available from FSC-certified forests upon special request.

10 26 00
Wall and Door Protection

Wall and corner guards, particularly in heavily-trafficked commercial buildings, increase the life of wall coverings, reducing repairs and cleaning that require the use of paints and chemicals. Products listed here are made with recycled content or FSC-certified woods, and avoid the use of PVC.

Acrovyn Wall and Corner Guards

Construction Specialties, Inc.; Wall Protection Division
6696 Rte. 405 Hwy.
Muncy, PA 17756

Toll-free: 800-233-8493
Phone: 570-546-5941
Fax: 570-546-5169
www.c-sgroup.com

C/S Group pioneered PVC wall protection 40 years ago, and are now offering hundreds of profiles manufactured from PVC-free Acrovyn 3000, FSC certified wood, bamboo, and wood/metal combinations. Acrovyn 3000 is a proprietary plastic formulation (based on polycarbonate chemistry) that contains no brominated or halogenated flame retardants (yet achieves a UL Class 1 fire rating), no phthalate plasticizers, and no dioxin or furan formers. All wood products are available with FSC-certified wood or bamboo, and finished with low-VOC, waterborne stains and finishes. Aluminum components contain 80% recycled content (30% post-consumer); stainless steel components contain 86% recycled content (56% post-consumer).

Most recently mentioned in EBN 14:1

EnviroGT Handrail, Wall and Corner Guards

InPro Corporation
P.O. Box 406
Muskego, WI 53150

Toll-free: 800-222-5556
Phone: 262-679-5521
Fax: 888-715-8407
www.inprocorp.com

InPro Corporation's EnviroGT handrails are made from FSC-certified ash with a snap-on protective cover made from 100% post-industrial recycled HDPE. Model G4100 has exposed ash on the underside of the handrail; Model G4000 has no exposed wood. Both models are available with either molded ABS plastic mounting brackets or stainless steel brackets that have 90% recycled content, according to the company.

10 28 13
Toilet Accessories

Use of electric hand dryers generally carries significantly lower environmental burdens than use of paper towels. Products listed here are energy-efficient, fast, and convenient.

XLerator Electric Hand Dryer

Excel Dryer, Inc.
357 Chestnut St.
P.O. Box 365
East Longmeadow, MA 01028

Toll-free: 800-255-9235
Phone: 413-525-4531
Fax: 413-525-2853
www.exceldryer.com

By using a powerful blast of air to blow off water droplets, the XLerator electric hand dryer uses about one-third as much energy and one-third as much time to dry hands (10-15 seconds) as conventional electric hand dryers. The XLerator also draws 1,500 watts instead of the usual 2,200, making it easier to install in older buildings and contributing to its energy efficiency. The editors of Environmental Building News estimate that the energy used by the XLerator is significantly less than the energy required to manufacture a typical paper towel. XLerator is available in all voltages; 110/120V, 208V, 220-240V, and 277V. A kit is available for recessing the unit in compliance with ADA.

Most recently mentioned in EBN 11:1, 11:12, 15:2, 15:4

Mitsubishi Jet Towel Electric Hand Dryer

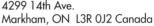

Mitsubishi Electric Sales Canada Inc.
4299 14th Ave.
Markham, ON L3R 0J2 Canada

Phone: 905-475-7728
Fax: 905-475-5231
www.mitsubishielectric.ca

The touch-free Jet Towel electric hand dryer's strong air current (nearly 300 feet per second) removes water from the both sides of the hands in five to six seconds, according to the manufacturer. Users insert their hands to start the cycle, then slowly withdraw them, which turns off the fans. Water blown off the hands is collected in the unit's drain tank, keeping the floor dry. A timer automatically halts operation after 30 seconds to prevent misuse or abuse. The manufacturer provides explanatory stickers with simple instructions for first-time users. The total energy input per cycle is reputed to be 0.65kw. The noise level is 65 dB, considerably lower than some other electric hand dryers.

Most recently mentioned in EBN 15:4

Mitsubishi Jet Towel Electric Hand Dryer

PACARC, LLC
2101 N. 34th St., Ste. 130
Seattle, WA 98103

Toll-free: 877-651-8820
Phone: 206-547-4591
www.mitsubishijettowel.com

The touch-free Jet Towel electric hand dryer's strong air current (nearly 300 feet per second) removes water from both sides of the hands in five to six seconds, according to the manufacturer. Users insert their hands to start the cycle, then slowly withdraw them, which turns off the fans. Water blown off the hands is collected in the unit's drain tank, keeping the floor dry. A timer automatically halts operation after 30 seconds to prevent misuse or abuse. The manufacturer provides explanatory stickers with simple instructions for first-time users. The total energy input per cycle is reputed to be 0.65kw. The noise level is 65 dB, considerably lower than some other electric hand dryers.

Most recently mentioned in EBN 15:4

10 00 00
Specialties

Sloan XLerator Electric Hand Dryer

Sloan Valve Company
10500 Seymour Ave.
Franklin Park, IL 60131

Toll-free: 800-982-5839
Phone: 847-671-4300
Fax: 800-447-8329
www.sloanvalve.com

Built for Sloan by Excel Dryer, Inc., the 1,500-watt XLerator® provides a 10-15 second drying cycle that begins with a 16,000 LFM air blast (78-80 dB) and ends with a 135° F warm air stream, reducing energy use by up to 2/3 over conventional hand dryers. The sensor-activated dryer has a 35-second lockout.

Most recently mentioned in EBN 11:1, 11:12, 15:2, 15:4

AirMax Electric Hand Dryer

World Dryer Corporation
5700 McDermott Dr.
Berkeley, IL 60163

Toll-free: 800-323-0701
Phone: 708-449-6950
Fax: 708-449-6958
www.worlddryer.com

Launched in 2005, the AirMax electric hand dryer from World Dryer Corporation (a division of Carrier) has a 15-second drying cycle that draws less than 0.01 kilowatt-hours per cycle (~90 kJ). The large orifice provides 275 CFM at the nozzle (155 CFM one inch from the nozzle; 5,600 linear feet per minute). Operation is quieter than many electric hand dryers. ADA kits are available. Motor brush replacement is required approximately once every two years.

Most recently mentioned in EBN 15:4

Zurn AirMax Electric Hand Dryer

Zurn Plumbing Products Group
5900 Elwin Buchanan Dr.
Sanford, NC 27330

Toll-free: 800-997-3876
Phone: 919-775-2255
Fax: 919-775-3541
www.zurn.com

Zurn® markets the World Dryer AirMax electric hand dryer as model Z6704. Zurn claims a 15-second drying time with the high-velocity heated air flow (275 cfm). The sensor-activated, stainless steel, hand dryer is the quietest in this product class, according to the manufacturer, and it offers a 90-95% cost savings compared with paper towels.

Most recently mentioned in EBN 15:1 & 15:4

10 28 19
Tub and Shower Doors

Products listed here have high recycled content and other environmental attributes.

UltraGlas

UltraGlas, Inc.

For full listing, see CSI section 09 30 24 - Recycled-Glass Tiling

10 56 00
Storage Assemblies

Products listed here have recycled content, low-VOC coatings, or other green features.

Dura-Shelf, Dunnage Rack, and Modular-Kart

Structural Plastics Corp.
3401 Chief Dr.
Holly, MI 48442

Toll-free: 800-523-6899
Phone: 810-953-9400
Fax: 810-953-9440
www.spcindustrial.com

Structural Plastics specializes in recycled HDPE plastic products for commercial and industrial shelving and storage. Dura-Shelf™ and Dunnage Rack™ are bulk-storage and display-shelving systems. Modular-Kart™ is a similar product with wheels in the form of a multilevel mobile cart.

10 71 13
Exterior Sun Control Devices

Products that can be used to selectively block out solar gain, including those that support vegetation along walls, can provide important energy conservation benefits while improving light quality for the occupants. (See also 12 26 13 - Light Shelves.)

ASCA Sun Control Devices

ASCA Inc.
P.O. Box 1140
Portsmouth, NH 03802

Phone: 603-433-6700
Fax: 603-433-3349
www.asca-design.com

ASCA Inc. designs and manufactures custom aluminum architectural sun control and natural daylighting systems, lightshelves, reflective panels, and climate control facades and canopies. Cantilevered, suspended, and radiused products, as well as adjustable systems with computer-automated or manual controls, are available. Products are manufactured from aluminum with a wide range of finishes, including anodized, power-coated, and baked enamel.

Facadescape SS Trellis System

Carl Stahl DécorCable, LLC
660 W. Randolph St.
Chicago, IL 60661

Toll-free: 800-444-6271
Phone: 312-474-1100
Fax: 312-474-1789
www.decorcable.com

Facadescape SS is a system of stainless steel cables and hardware that can be custom-designed from the company's extensive catalog of parts to screen and shade a building façade, roof area, patio, or other indoor or outdoor space. Thoughtful plant selection may be important for success of the system. In addition to the numerous environmental benefits of encouraging the growth of vegetation and that of energy savings from shading, Facadescape can also play an important role in making the most of growing area in small-space and rooftop applications. Carl Stahl Decorcable is part of the Germany-based Carl Stahl Group.

C/S Sun Control Products

Construction Specialties, Inc.; Sun Control Division
49 Meeker Ave.
Cranford, NJ 07016

Toll-free: 800-631-7379
Phone: 908-272-5200
Fax: 908-272-5844
www.c-sgroup.com

C/S Sun Control products include a wide range of cantilevered, suspended, vertical, and horizontal sunshades, as well as skylight shutters. C/S Lightshelves, manufactured for interior installation, are designed to distribute daylight more deeply into the interior of a commercial building; the top surface is highly reflective and typically hinged to rotate downward for periodic cleaning. Lightshelves can be integrated with exterior sunshades to further control heat and glare. All C/S products are custom-manufactured from standardized extruded aluminum profiles with a wide range of finish options, and are available in both fixed and operable versions. These aluminum products are recyclable, but the recycled content is generally fairly low.

Colt Shadometal Solar Shading Systems

Exterior Technologies, Inc.
200 Bridge St.
P.O. Box 9543
Pittsburgh, PA 15223

Toll-free: 800-500-8083
Phone: 412-781-0991
Fax: 412-781-9303
www.extech-voegele.com

Colt International, Ltd., of the United Kingdom, manufacturers a full line of exterior fixed and controllable solar shading systems. Solar C is a line of fixed louver systems. Solarfin is a line of controllable fin systems that can be installed in horizontal or vertical configurations. The company's Sunfax software can be used to optimize both fixed and controllable sun-shade systems on different building facades. For the controllable fins, the company offers a number of automated control systems, including a passive thermo-hydraulic system that operates with differential temperatures from the sun, and advanced Soltronic microprocessor-based control systems. Colt solar shading systems are distributed in the U.S. by Exterior Technologies, Inc.

Greenscreen Trellising System

Greenscreen
1743 S. La Cienega Blvd.
Los Angeles, CA 90035

Toll-free: 800-450-3494
Phone: 310-837-0526
Fax: 310-837-0523
www.greenscreen.com

Greenscreen™ is a three-dimensional, welded-wire trellis system that can be installed freestanding or wall-mounted. The basic trellis module is 4' wide, 2" or 3" thick, and 6', 8', 10', or 12' long. Custom-sized panels can be ordered in 2" increments. Greenscreen is available in a wrinkled matte finish of green or black, as well as a glossy finish of green, black, silver, or white. Various accessories, such as planter straps, edge trim, and specialty shapes, are also available. Thoughtful plant selection may be important for success of the system. In addition to the numerous environmental benefits

of encouraging the growth of vegetation and that of energy savings from shading, Greenscreens can also play an important role in making the most of growing area in small-space and rooftop applications.

Jakob INOX Line

Jakob, Inc.
955 NW 17th Ave., Unit B
Delray Beach, FL 33445

Toll-free: 866-215-1421
Phone: 561-330-6502
Fax: 561-330-6508
www.jakob-usa.com

Jakob offers a system of stainless steel cables and hardware that can be used to screen and shade a building façade, roof area, patio, or other indoor or outdoor space. Jakob's Green Solutions catalog provides detailed information on system design, plant selection, upkeep, and maintenance. In addition to the numerous environmental benefits of encouraging the growth of vegetation and that of energy savings from shading, a green trellis system can also play an important role in making the most of growing area in small-space and rooftop applications. Jakob, Inc. is the North American distributor for the Swiss manufacturer, Jakob AG.

Sun Control Devices

Nysan Solar Control
1, 115 - 28 St. SE
Calgary, AB T2A 5K4 Canada

Phone: 403-204-8675
Fax: 403-204-8676
www.hunterdouglascontract.com

Nysan Solar Control, formerly Arc Structures, Inc., offers customizable solar control systems in a range of designs and colors to control solar heat gain and daylighting, including lightshelves - horizontal window elements that shade perimeter areas from too much sun while reflecting more light deeper into the room, creating more uniform natural light distribution. Exterior and interior systems are available. Some components may be retractable or otherwise adjustable, controlled via sensors, timers, or switches. Most components are made with aluminum containing an unspecified percentage of recycled content. Some parts may be coated with PVC.

Ruskin Sunshades

Ruskin Company
3900 Dr. Greaves Rd.
Kansas City, MO 64030

Phone: 816-761-7476
Fax: 816-765-8955
www.ruskin.com

Constructed of extruded and/or formed aluminum components, Ruskin Sunshades are available in a wide variety of configurations and blade styles—including airfoil, louver, tube, and eggcrate. Unlimited overall sizes are possible by joining modules together; custom designs are available. Field assembly and supporting structure are not provided by the manufacturer. All models are available with a variety of Kynar or anodized finishes.

10 00 00
Specialties

10 81 00
Pest Control Devices

Termite control in buildings has traditionally been accomplished with pesticides—in the past with chlordane and heptachlor, and more recently with chlorpyrifos. With all of these pesticides no longer in use because of health and environmental concerns, there's tremendous interest in alternatives. Products listed here include totally nontoxic termite barrier systems as well as less toxic, or more precisely targeted, chemical treatments. Termite barriers and full-control bait systems are generally quite expensive. (See feature article EBN Vol. 9, No. 9.)

Basaltic Termite Barrier

Ameron Hawaii
2344 Pahounui Dr.
P.O. Box 29968
Honolulu, HI 96820

Phone: 808-832-9200
Fax: 808-832-9470
www.ameronhawaii.com

Basaltic Termite Barrier is a regionally available product made from basaltic aggregates (a coarse sand) on the Hawaiian Islands. These aggregates, when graded to a specific size, shape, and weight, form an effective, nontoxic barrier to standard subterranean and Formosan termite entry. The aggregates are too large and heavy for termites to move and the spaces between too small to move through.

Most recently mentioned in EBN 3:2

Roach and Ant Baits

Blue Diamond, LLC
P.O. Box 953
Rogersville, TN 37857

Phone: 423-585-6312
Fax: 888-268-2929
www.bluediamonddistribution.com

Blue Diamond offers a number of dustless roach and ant baits in paste or gel formulations for residential, commercial, and industrial applications. The manufacturer claims that insects cannot build up resistance to the boric acid in these products, while they can with many chemical insecticides. The baits are spot-applied, odorless, noncombustible, and effective for a year after application. These products work outdoors, but must be protected from rain. The roach baits are not available in all U.S. states.

Sentricon Termite Colony Elimination System

Dow AgroSciences, LLC
9330 Zionsville Rd.
Indianapolis, IN 46268

Toll-free: 800-352-6776
www.sentricon.com

The Sentricon® Termite Colony Elimination System eliminates termites with a highly targeted noviflumuron-based bait. This bait is considered to be highly targeted because worker termites carry it back to the colony to feed others. The chemical affects chitin formation in termites. In a management-intensive approach that limits environmental impact, the noviflumuron pesticide is employed only when regularly inspected bait stations reveal termite activity. The Sentricon System is offered as part of an ongoing service contract.

Most recently mentioned in EBN 9:9

Exterra

Ensystex, Inc.
P.O. Box 2587
Fayetteville, NC 28302

Toll-free: 888-398-3772
Fax: 888-368-4749
www.exterra.com

The Exterra® Termite Interception and Baiting System is similar to the Sentricon System, using a chitin synthesis-inhibitor called diflubenzuron. A unique feature of Exterra's bait station, the Labyrinth, is the ability to install pesticide in the bait core without disturbing termites feeding on the bait box perimeter.

Most recently mentioned in EBN 9:9

Termimesh System

Termimesh, LLC
9519 N IH 35
Austin, TX 78753

Phone: 512-997-0066
Fax: 512-837-9671
www.termimesh.com

The Termimesh™ System is a termite barrier from Australia made from a tight-weave stainless steel mesh. Proper installation of Termimesh may avoid the repeated application of pesticides. Currently this system is available only in a few Southern states.

Most recently mentioned in EBN 9:9

This Space is Available for Your Notes

11 00 00 Equipment

PRODUCT LISTINGS

11 13 13
Loading Dock Bumpers

Dock bumpers are an excellent application for recycled-tire rubber.

Dock Bumpers

Durable Corp.
75 N. Pleasant St.
Norwalk, OH 44857

Toll-free: 877-938-7225
Phone: 419-668-8138
Fax: 800-537-6287
www.durablecorp.com

Durable's Dock Bumpers are made from re-cycled tires. The new Dura-Soft dock bumper has a unique loop design for high-impact absorption.

Dock Bumpers and Marine Fenders

Schuyler Rubber Co., Inc.

For full listing, see CSI section 35 50 00 - Marine Construction and Equipment

Wearwell Dock Bumpers

Tennessee Mat Co.
1414 Fourth Ave. S
Nashville, TN 37210

Toll-free: 800-264-3030
Phone: 615-254-8381
Fax: 800-874-4551
www.wearwell.com

Wearwell Laminated Dock Bumpers, made from rubber-impregnated, durable fabric strips, are available in several sizes or may be customized to accommodate special installation requirements. They can easily be attached to new buildings or may be retrofitted for existing docks.

11 31 14
Residential Refrigerators and Freezers

The energy efficiency of refrigerators has improved dramatically in the last several decades. National standards have helped reduce the energy use of refrigerators to less than one-third that of pre-1973 models; and in the short amount of time since 2001, the energy use of conventional refrigerators has dropped by 40%. Developments in re-frigerator design, including increased insulation, tighter door seals, and more efficient compressors, are continuing that trend. Different options and freezer com-partment configurations affect energy use. A side-by-side refrigerator-freezer with such amenities as through-the-door ice service and automatic defrost may use nearly 40% more energy than a top-freezer, manual-defrost, basic model. Products listed here must exceed the fed-eral minimum standard by at least 20% in the full-sized and apartment-sized category. Compact refrigerators—less than 7.75 cubic feet of volume, and less than 36" tall—must exceed the minimum federal standard by 30% or more. Also listed here are super-efficient refrig-erators that are usually sold for use in off-grid houses; these generally haven't qualified for Energy Star because the companies are too small to be required to submit to testing.

Absocold Compact Refrigerators

Absocold Corporation
P.O. Box 1545
Richmond, IN 47375

Toll-free: 800-843-3714
Fax: 765-935-3450
www.absocold.com

Absocold offers one compact refrigerator that qualifies for *GreenSpec* as of April, 2007. Model ARD298C*10R/L, with a top freezer, exceeds federal standards by 31%. It has partial defrost, an adjusted volume (freezer volume x 1.5 + refrigerator volume) of 3.34 cubic feet and projected annual

electric consumption of 290 kWh. (Note that even though compact refrigerators may be much better than federal standards, they can still use more than two-thirds as much energy as a top-efficiency full-size refrigerator with nearly four times the interior volume.)

Amana Refrigerators

Amana
403 W. 4th St. N
Maytag Customer Service
Newton, IA 50208

Toll-free: 800-843-0304
www.amana.com

Amana offers three side-by-side models pro-jected to use 580 kWh/year: 20% less en-ergy than federal standards for models of the type, just reaching the *GreenSpec* threshold. These models (ASD2626HE*, ASD2627KE*, and ASD2628HE*) are automatic defrost and include through-the-door ice, and are among the largest residential refrigerators listed in *GreenSpec*, with an adjusted volume (freezer volume x 1.5 + refrigerator volume) of 31.76 cubic feet. The bottom-freezer, ice-dispensing model AFD2535DE* is 26% better than the minimum federal standard, estimated to use 505 kWh per year for its 29.4 cubic feet of adjusted volume. Other bottom-freezer models paradoxically use less energy, but are only 20% - 21% above the federal minimum standard - due to the machinations of considering features like through-the-door ice dispensing. Always compare energy-use data on the yellow En-ergyGuide labels. These other models num-bers include ABB1922FE*, ABB2522FE*, ABL1922FE*, ABL2522FE*, ABR1922FE*, ABR2522FE*, ABB2222FE*, ABL2222FE*, and ABR2222FE*.

Avanti Apartment-Sized Refrigerators

Avanti Products
10880 N.W. 30th St.
Miami, FL 33172

Toll-free: 800-323-5029
Phone: 305-592-7830
Fax: 305-591-3629
www.avantiproducts.com

Avanti offers three apartment-sized refrig-erator models that meet *GreenSpec*'s require-ments. Models BCA902W and RM901W are single-door, refrigerator-only configurations. The former has automatic defrost, a volume of 8.87 cubic feet, and uses 32% less energy than federal standards, at 247 kWh/year. The second model listed is a manual-defrost unit with a volume of 8.7 cubic feet; it uses 29% less energy than federal standards, at 230 kWh/year. (Note that the unit that uses less energy is actually rated as less in excess of federal standards, which don't use a single formula in establishing energy thresholds for refrigerators. Adjustments are made for features and size—which is confusing at best and misleading at worst. When in doubt, read the EnergyGuide label, which presents energy consumption in a neutral way.) Avanti also offers model 1201W-1: a single-door refrigerator/freezer with manual defrost. The volume is 11 cubic feet; the adjusted volume (freezer volume x 1.5 + refrigerator volume) is 11.69 cubic feet. Estimated annual energy use is 277 kWh.

Frigidaire Refrigerators

Electrolux Home Products
P.O. Box 212378
Martinez, GA 30917

Toll-free: 800-374-4432
Phone: 706-651-1751
Fax: 706-651-7116
www.frigidaire.com

Frigidaire, an Electrolux company, has two *GreenSpec*-qualifying refrigerator-freezers as of December, 2005. Models FRT21KR7E* and FRT21FR7E* exceed federal standards by 28%. They have top freezer compartments, auto defrost, and through-the-door ice service. Estimated annual electric use is 432 kWh. Volume is 20.6 cubic feet.

Conserv

Equator Corporation
2801 W. Sam Houston Pkwy. N
Equator Plz.
Houston, TX 77080

Toll-free: 800-935-1955
Phone: 713-464-3422
Fax: 713-464-2151
www.equatoronline.com

Conserv™ is a specialized very-low-energy-usage refrigerator designed for homes with or without connection to the utility grid. A Danish product formerly marketed as Vest-frost™, the manual-defrost Conserv is built with all recyclable parts, CFC-free foam and refrigerant, and separate compressors for the refrigerator and freezer.

Most recently mentioned in EBN 7:8

GE Refrigerators

GE Appliances
9500 Williamsburg Office Plz.
General Electric Answer Center
Louisville, KY 40222

Toll-free: 800-626-2000
www.geappliances.com

General Electric produces 20 models that just achieve *GreenSpec*'s criteria by exceeding federal energy standards by 20%. They are all automatic-defrost, bottom-freezer units, none with through-the-door ice; volumes are all either approximately 19.5 or 22.25 cubic feet. Projected energy use for models with volumes of 19.5 ft^3 is 453 kWh/year; for those with 22.5 ft^3, 464 kWh/year. 19.5-foot models include GBS20KBR**, PDS20MBR, PDS20MCR, PDS20SBR, PDS20SCR, GB*20******, GBS20HBS**, GDL20KCS**, GDS20KBS**, GDS20KCS**, GDS20SBS**, GDS20SCS**, and SDL20KCS**; 22.25-foot models include GBS22HBR**, GBS22HCR**, PDS22MBR, PDS22MCR, PDS22SBR, PDS22SCR, and GBS22KBR**.

Monogram Refrigerators

GE Appliances
9500 Williamsburg Office Plz.
General Electric Answer Center
Louisville, KY 40222

Toll-free: 800-626-2000
www.geappliances.com

Monogram, a brand of GE, offers three side-by-side units for the built-in market that meet the *GreenSpec* threshold. Models ZIS360NR and ZISS360NRS both have a volume of 21.62 cubic feet, are automatic defrost, have through-the-door ice service, and a projected energy use of 547 kWh/year; they exceed minimum federal standards by 20%. Bottom-freezer model ZICP360S, an ice-dispensing auto-defrost, is 27% better than the federal minimum standard: 485 kWh/year with an adjusted volume of 24.37 cubic feet.

Jenn-Air Refrigerators

Jenn-Air
403 W. 4th St. N.
Newton, IA 50208

Toll-free: 800-688-1100
Phone: 641-792-7000
Fax: 641-787-8264
www.jennair.com

Jenn-Air, a Maytag brand, offers eight models that meet *GreenSpec*'s requirements (as of April, 2007). These models are all in side-by-side configuration, have automatic defrost, and just meet the *GreenSpec* threshold by exceeding federal energy standards by

20%. Projected energy use ranges from 510 to 580 kWh/year. Models JCB2280HE*, JCB2282HT*, and JCB2285HES have 21.47 cubic feet of volume, no ice dispenser, and the lowest estimated energy use of the models in this listing. Models JSD2690HE*, JSD2695KE*, JSD2695KG*, and JSD2697KE* have 25.6 cubic feet, through-the-door ice, and 580 kWh/year estimated electric use. Models JCD2290HE* is 21.57 cubic feet, has through-the-door ice, and is rated at 537 kWh/year.

KitchenAid Refrigerators

KitchenAid
701 Main St.
P.O. Box 218
St. Joseph, MI 49085

Toll-free: 800-422-1230
www.kitchenaid.com

KitchenAid, a Whirlpool brand, offers four side-by-side, automatic defrost models with through-the-door ice that exceed federal energy standards for refrigerators of this class with the same options by 20%. These models each have volumes of 23.05 cubic feet, and are projected to use 557 kWh/year. The model numbers are KSBP23IN**0*, KSBS23IN**0*, KSCS23FS**0*, and KSCS23IN**0*. Six auto-defrost bottom-freezers are also available - 20.46 cubic feet, 453 kWh per year - models KBLC36FT*0*, KBLO36FT*0*, KBLS36FT*0*, KBRO36FT*0*, KBRS36FT*0*, and KRBC36FT*0*.

LG Refrigerators

LG Appliances
1000 Sylvan Ave.
Englewood Cliffs, NJ 07632

Toll-free: 800-243-0000
www.lgappliances.com

LG Electronics model LSC2696#** is an automatic defrost, side-by-side refrigerator-freezer with through-the-door ice. It has a volume of 25.51 cubic feet, and is projected to use 565 kWh/year, exceeding by 22% the federal standard for refrigerators of this size with the same features. Model LRD*20731** is an auto-defrost bottom-freezer without ice service; it has a volumes of 19.74 cubic feet, is projected to use 440 kWh/year, 23% better than the federal standard for refrigerators of this size with the same features. Similar model LFX25970** has 24.7 cubic feet of volume and uses 515 kWh/year, yet is rated as 25% better than the federal minimum standard - because it has a larger adjusted volume and an ice-dispensing feature, which changes the efficiency formula. Always compare the projected energy usage on the yellow EnergyGuide labels.

Maytag Refrigerators

Maytag Appliances
403 W. Fourth St. N
P.O. Box 39
Newton, IA 50208

Toll-free: 888-462-9824
Phone: 641-792-7000
Fax: 641-787-8376
www.maytag.com

Maytag manufactures nine side-by-side, automatic defrost refrigerator models with ice dispensing that each exceed the federal standards for similar refrigerators by 20%. Models MCB2256HE*, MCD2257HE*, and MCD2257KE* each have about 21.5 cubic feet of volume, using between 510 - 537 kWh/year. Models MSD2656KE*, MSD2656KG*, MSD2657HE*, MSD2659KE*, MSD2660KE*, and MSD2660KG* each have a volume of 25.6 and a 727 kWh/year estimate. Thirteen bottom-freezer models (MBF1956KE*, MBF2556KE*, MBL1956KE*, MBL2556KE*, MBR1956KE*, MBR2556KE*, MB2216PUA*, MBF2255KE*, MBF2256KE*, MBL2255KE*, MBL2256KE*, MBR2255KE*, and MBR2256KE*) have volumes ranging from 18.5 - 25 cubic feet, using between 560 - 595 kWh/year.

Microfridge Compact Refrigerators

MicroFridge
10 Walpole Park S
Walpole, MA 02081

Toll-free: 800-994-0165
Phone: 508-660-9200
www.microfridge.com

Microfridge® offers several compact units. Model MHRA-4E is a single-door, 4-cubic-foot-capacity, auto-defrost refrigerator-freezer projected to use 241 kWh/year. Models MF-3XPNTPS, MF-3XPNTP, MF-3XNTP, MF-3XNTPS, and MFR-3** all have identical attributes: 2.9 cubic feet capacity in a top-freezer configuration, 31% better than federal standards for units of this size and type—estimated to use 290 kWh/year. (Note that although these refrigerators are up to 31% better than federal standards, they still use about two-thirds as much energy as a top-efficiency full-size refrigerator with nearly four times the interior volume.)

Kenmore Refrigerators

Sears
3333 Beverly Rd.
Hoffman Estates, IL 60179

Toll-free: 800-349-4358
www.sears.com

Sears offers a whopping 29 full-size models under the Kenmore brand that qualify for *GreenSpec* (as of December, 2005)—18 in top-freezer configuration, and 11 side-by-side. All are 20-21% better than federal standards, with the exception of one side-by, which is 23%, and two 28% top-freezers. All have automatic defrost; the side-by-side models have ice service, while all but two of the top-freezers don't (and in part because of that have lower annual electric use projections). The lowest energy use numbers (387 kWh/year) are for models 7490*40* and 7491*40*, top-freezers with 18.79 cubic feet; the highest energy use numbers (581 kWh/year) are for models 5460*30*, 5656*40*, and 5657*40*, side-by-sides with over 25.5 cubic feet. (It's revealing to note that the models exceeding federal standards by 28%—7682*40* and 7683*40*—are the smallest top-freezers included in this listing; but they have through-the-door ice dispensers, and are projected to use 569 kWh/year. The federal standards include multiple adjustments for features and size—which is confusing at best and misleading at worst. When in doubt, read the EnergyGuide label, which presents energy consumption data in a neutral way.) A list of all qualifying Kenmore models as of December, 2005: 7491*40*, 7490*40*, 7499*40*, 7592*40*, 7390*30*, 7498*40*, 7594*40*, 7398*30*, 6398*30*, 7393*30*, 6397*30*, 7397*30*, 7682*40*, 7683*40*, 7420*40*, 7421*40*, 7428*40*, 7429*40*, 4432*40*, 5420*30*, 5637*40*, 5636*40*, 5520*40*, 5521*40*, 5561*40*, 5560*40*, 5656*40*, 5657*40*, and 5460*30*. Most of these models are manufactured for Sears by Whirlpool.

Summit Compact Refrigerators

Summit Appliance Division - Felix Storch, Inc.
770 Garrison Ave.
Bronx, NY 10474

Phone: 718-893-3900
Fax: 718-842-3093
www.summitappliance.com

Summit Appliances offers its compact two-door, top-freezer model CP-35*. With a volume of 3.34 cubic feet and a projected energy use of 290 kWh/year, it exceeds the federal standard for refrigerators of its type by 31%. The refrigerator compartment is auto-defrost; the freezer is manual. (Note that although this refrigerator is 31% better than federal standards, it still uses about two-thirds as much energy as a top-efficiency full-size refrigerator with nearly four times the interior volume.)

Sun Frost Refrigerators

Sun Frost
P.O. Box 1101
Arcata, CA 95518

Phone: 707-822-9095
Fax: 707-822-6213
www.sunfrost.com

Sun Frost produces refrigerators and freezers with extremely low energy use. Model R-19 is an auto-defrost, passive (fanless), single-door, refrigerator-only model. It has a total volume of 16.14 cubic feet and a projected energy use of 204 kWh/year—exceeding the federal standard by 53%. Models RF-12 and RF-16 have a two-door, top-freezer configuration with volumes of 10.12 and 14.31 cubic feet, respectively. Projected electric use for these fanless units is 171 kWh/year for the RF-12 (51% better than the federal standard), and 254 kWh/year (36% better) for the RF-16. Both have auto-defrost refrigerators and manual-defrost freezers. All models are available in 12- and 24-volt DC, and 110- and 220-volt AC. They are particularly suitable for homes not connected to the utility grid.

Most recently mentioned in EBN 8:1 & 13:2

SunDanzer

SunDanzer
11135 Dyer Ste. C
El Paso, TX 79934

Phone: 915-821-0042
Fax: 775-201-0236
www.sundanzer.com

SunDanzer produces small, DC-powered refrigerators and freezers with extremely low energy use. All SunDanzer freezers and refrigerators have 11" (4.3 cm) of polyurethane insulation, an aluminum interior, a galvanized steel exterior, a patented low-frost system, and a drain hole at the bottom for easy cleaning. The brushless, thermostatically controlled DC compressor runs on either 12 or 24 volts and operates with ozone-safe HFC-134a refrigerant. In most climates, a single 75-watt photovoltaic module will generate enough power to run a freezer. The chest style refrigerators and freezers are available in 165 liter (5.8 cubic feet) and 225 liter (8 cubic feet) capacities. The units are custom-manufactured for SunDanzer by Electrolux at a factory in Hungary and are particularly suitable for homes not connected to the utility grid.

Most recently mentioned in EBN 15:10

11 00 00
Equipment

Whirlpool Refrigerators

Whirlpool Corporation
2000 N. Hwy. M-63
Benton Harbor, MI 49022

Toll-free: 800-253-1301
www.whirlpool.com

Whirlpool models GC3SHE*N*0*, GC3PHE*N*0*, and EC3JHA*R*0* are side-by-side refrigerator-freezers with through-the-door ice dispensers and automatic defrost. They have a capacity of 23.07 cubic feet, with a projected energy use of 557 kWh/year. Model ED2GTG*N*0* is slightly smaller unit (21.8 cubic feet) with similar attributes. Projected energy use is 572 kWh/year. These units all exceed federal standards for similar models by 20%. Whirlpool also makes a number of other *GreenSpec*-approved units sold under Kenmore and KitchenAid labels.

11 00 00
Equipment

11 31 16
Residential Dishwashers

Most of the energy consumed by dishwashers is used to heat the water; therefore, water-efficient dishwashers are also energy-efficient. As with other home appliances, national energy standards have catalyzed the development of more efficient dishwashers. As a measure of efficiency, the Energy Factor (EF) describes energy performance under carefully defined conditions, and provides a basis of comparison among different models. The national energy standard requires all regular size dishwashers to have an energy factor of at least 0.46. The Energy Star program qualifies dishwashers exceeding that standard by at least 25% (EF of 0.58). Products listed here must exceed the national minimum energy standard by at least 60%, with an EF of 0.74 or higher. (See feature article EBN Vol. 6, No. 8.)

Asko Dishwashers

AM Appliance Group - Asko
P.O. Box 851805
Richardson, TX 75085

Toll-free: 800-898-1879
Phone: 972-644-8595
Fax: 972-234-2709
www.askousa.com

Swedish manufacturer Asko offers 15 dishwasher models in their D3000 line that are among the most energy-efficient available, with energy factors as high as 1.11—which is 141% better than minimum federal energy standards. As of March 2007, Asko model numbers (followed parenthetically by kWh/year, EF, and %-better than federal minimum standard) meeting *GreenSpec* standards include: D3232 (278, 0.77, 67.00%); D3112 and D3121 (278, 0.78, 70.00%); D3122, D3331, and D3432 (242, 0.89, 93.00%); D3251FI, D3251HD, D3251XLFI, D3251XLHD, D3252, and D3451 (231, 0.93, 102.00%); D3531XLFI, D3531XLHD, and D3731 (194, 1.11, 141.00%). Features may vary between models, and affect overall electric use.

Eurotech Dishwashers

AM Appliance Group - Eurotech
P.O. Box 851805
Richardson, TX 75085

Toll-free: 800-898-1879
Phone: 972-644-8595
www.eurotechappliances.com

Eurotech, a division of Texas-based AM Appliance Group, manufactures four *GreenSpec*-qualifying models. All are 61% better than the minimum federal energy standards for dishwashers, with a .74 EF. As of March 2007, Eurotech model numbers meeting *GreenSpec* standards include: EDW242C, EDW254E, EDW274E, and EDW294. Features vary between models, and may affect overall electric use.

Ariston Dishwashers

Ariston Appliances US
3027 E. Sunset, Ste. 101
Ultra 8 International
Las Vegas, NV 89120

Toll-free: 888-426-0845
www.aristonappliances.us

Six dishwasher models in the Elegance and Premier lines from Italian manufacturer Ariston exceed U.S. federal minimum energy standards by 74%—all have an EF of 0.8 and are rated at 270 kWh per year. Features may vary by model and affect overall energy use. As of March 2007, Ariston model numbers meeting *GreenSpec* standards include: LI640, LI670, LI700, L63, LL64, AND LL65.

Bosch Dishwashers   **New**

BSH Home Appliances Corp.
5551 McFadden Ave.
Huntington Beach, CA 92649

Toll-free: 800-944-2904
Phone: 714-901-6600
Fax: 714-901-5360
www.boschappliances.com

Bosch offers 17 dishwasher models with energy factors of 0.74, which is 61% better than the Energy Star standard. They are rated at 290 kWh/year. As of March 2007, model numbers meeting *GreenSpec* standards include: SHE58C02UC, SHE58C05UC, SHE58C06UC, SHE66C02UC, SHE66C05UC, SHE66C06UC, SHE99C05UC, SHV56C03UC, SHV57C03UC, SHV99A13UC, SHX56C02UC, SHX56C05UC, SHX56C06UC, SHX57C02UC, SHX57C05UC, SHX57C06UC, and SHX99A15UC. Features such as soil sensing may vary between models, and affect overall electric use.

Danby Designer Dishwashers

Danby Products Inc.
P.O. Box 669
Findlay, OH 45839

Toll-free: 800-26-DANBY
Phone: 419-425-8627
Fax: 419-425-8629
www.danby.com

Canadian company Danby offers built-in model DDW1802W, and portable version DDW1805W. Both have an energy factor of 0.77, which is 67% better than the minimum federal energy standard for dishwashers. Low water consumption settings offer 3.8-gallon washes. Features may affect overall energy use. Manufactured in China.

Fisher & Paykel / DCS Dishwashers

Fisher & Paykel
5900 Skylab Rd.
Huntington Beach, CA 92647

Toll-free: 888-936-7872
Fax: 949-790-8913
www.usa.fisherpaykel.com

Fisher & Paykel's DishDrawer (model DD603-USA), made in New Zealand, is a double-drawer dishwasher with an energy factor of 0.72, rated at 189 kWh/year, 97% better than the Energy Star threshold. DCS, recently acquired by Fisher & Paykel, offers model DD124, which has the same statistics. Dishwashers may have features such as soil sensing that can affect overall electric use.

Gaggenau Dishwashers   **New**

Gaggenau USA / Canada
780 Dedham St.
Canton, MA 02021

Toll-free: 800-828-9165
Fax: 714-901-5360
www.gaggenau.com

Gaggenau, a Bosch luxury brand, offers four models with 0.74 EF (61% higher than the Energy Star baseline), rated at 290 kWh/year. As of March 2007, model numbers include DF241760, DF290760, DF291760, and DI291730. Note that dishwashers may have features such as soil sensing that can affect overall electric use.

GE Dishwashers

GE Appliances
9500 Williamsburg Office Plz.
General Electric Answer Center
Louisville, KY 40222

Toll-free: 800-626-2000
www.geappliances.com

As of March 2007, GE has one dishwasher that meets GreenSpec's standard. Their model GSM18**J in the Monogram line is rated at 282 kWh operating electricity per year; with an EF of 0.76, it's 65% better than the minimum Energy Star standard for dishwashers. Optional features may affect overall energy use.

KitchenAid Dishwashers

New

KitchenAid
701 Main St.
P.O. Box 218
St. Joseph, MI 49085

Toll-free: 800-422-1230
www.kitchenaid.com

KitchenAid's compact, single-drawer dishwasher model KUDD01S in their Architect line exceeds Energy Star's minimum threshold by 97%, with an Enegy Factor (EF) of 1.22 and an estimated annual energy use of 189 kWh. As of March 2007, this is the only KitchenAid dishwasher meeting GreenSpec's standard. Certain features, such as soil-sensing, may affect overall energy use.

LG Dishwashers

New

LG Appliances
1000 Sylvan Ave.
Englewood Cliffs, NJ 07632

Toll-free: 800-243-0000
www.lgappliances.com

LG Electronics standard-sized dishwasher model LDF881#** has an Energy Factor (EF) of 0.75, which is 63% better than the Energy Star baseline. It is projected to used 285 kWh of electricity per year. As of March 2007, this is the only LG dishwasher meeting Green-Spec's standard. Certain features, such as soil-sensing, may affect overall energy use.

Kenmore Dishwashers

Sears
3333 Beverly Rd.
Hoffman Estates, IL 60179

Toll-free: 800-349-4358
www.sears.com

Sears offers a Kenmore compact dishwasher in the Elite line (model 1332*) that exceeds the Energy Star minimum standard by 110%, with an EF of 1.30 and an estimated energy use of 174 kWh/year. As of March 2007, only Asko has more efficient dishwashers listed in GreenSpec. Kenmore dishwashers are made in the U.S.A. by Electrolux. Certain features such as soil-sensing may affect overall energy use.

Siemens Dishwashers

New

Siemens Home Appliances
5551 McFadden Ave.
Huntington Beach, CA 92649

Toll-free: 888-474-3636
Phone: 714-901-6600
Fax: 714-901-5360
www.siemens-home.com

In its hiDefinition line, Siemens offers dishwasher models SL33A00-2UC, -5UC, and -6UC; and SL34A01-2UC, -5UC, and -6UC. These dishwashers have an Energy Factor (EF) of 0.79 and an estimated annual energy use of 270 kWh, exceeding the Energy Star minimum by 72%. Certain dishwasher features, such as soil-sensing, may affect overall energy use.

Thermador Dishwashers

New

Thermador
5551 McFadden Ave.
Huntington Beach, CA 92649

Toll-free: 800-656-9226
www.thermador.com

Thermador dishwasher models DWHD64C*, DWHD94B-F, -P, and -S have an energy factor of 0.74, which is 61% better than the Energy Star minimum, and are projected to use 290 kWh/year. Certain features, such as soil sensing, may affect overall electric use. Thermador dishwashers are manufactured in the U.S.

Viking Dishwashers

Viking Range Corporation
111 Front St.
Greenwood, MS 38930

Toll-free: 888-845-464
Phone: 662-455-1200
www.vikingrange.com

Viking dishwasher models DFUD042 and DFUD142 each have an energy factor of 0.92, which is 100% better than the minimum Energy Star standard for dishwashers. Certain features may affect overall energy use. Made in the U.S.

11 31 23
Residential Laundry Appliances

Manufacturers have made tremendous strides in increasing the energy efficiency of clothes washers in recent years. This has been aided by U.S. Department of Energy (DOE) minimum efficiency standards, the federal Energy Star program, and efforts of the Consortium for Energy Efficiency (CEE). Energy Star standards require a minimum Modified Energy Factor (MEF) of 1.72 and a maximum Water Factor (WF) of 8.0. The higher the MEF, the more efficient the washer is in the entire laundry cycle (including drying; the MEF factors in Remaining Moisture Content—RMC—to predict dryer energy use). The WF is a measure of the number of gallons of water used per cubic foot of laundry. A significant amount of the energy used for clothes washing is for heating the water—so clothes washers that use less water are usually more energy efficient. Some manufacturers also offer condensing dryers; these do not require exterior venting, and they release all generated heat inside the building (an advantage in the winter but a disadvantage in the summer). The primary problem with single units that both wash and dry laundry in a common drum is that the volume required for drying a load of laundry is larger than the volume required for washing—so when one drum has to serve both needs, the wash volume is reduced. Condensing dryers can also increase water consumption by running cold water through condensation coils. Products listed here have a minimum MEF of 1.85, and a maximum WF of 5.0.

Ariston Clothes Washers & Washer-Dryers

Ariston Appliances US
3027 E. Sunset, Ste. 101
Ultra 8 International
Las Vegas, NV 89120

Toll-free: 888-426-0845
www.aristonappliances.us

As of March 2007, Italian manufacturer Ariston offers a clothes washer (model AW120) and a washer-dryer (model AWD120) that exceed minimum federal standards by 52%. These models both have an MEF of 1.92 and a WF of 5. These 1.92 cubic-foot appliances are projected to use 143 kWh and 3763 gallons of water per year.

11 00 00
Equipment

Bosch Clothes Washers

BSH Home Appliances Corp.
5551 McFadden Ave.
Huntington Beach, CA 92649

Toll-free: 800-944-2904
Phone: 714-901-6600
Fax: 714-901-5360
www.boschappliances.com

Bosch offers ten large-capacity (3.31 cubic feet), horizontal-axis clothes washers that qualify for *GreenSpec* as of March, 2007. These models exceed federal standards by 69% to 93%, with MEF ratings of 2.13 to 2.43, and WF ratings of 4.1 to 4.7. Annual water use, based on standard assumptions, ranges from 5268 to 6150 gallons of water per year, and annual electricity use ranges from 146 to 182 kWh. Models numbers (and MEF numbers) include: WFMC2100UC (2.13), WFMC6400UC (2.2), WFMC1001UC (2.24), WFMC4300UC (2.31), WFMC3301UC (2.4), WFMC330SUC (2.4), WFMC4301UC (2.4), WFMC2201UC (2.43), WFMC6401UC (2.43), WFMC640SUC (2.43). Features may vary between models, and some features may affect overall energy use.

Most recently mentioned in EBN 7:9

11 00 00
Equipment

Inline Exhaust Duct Fans

Continental Fan Manufacturing

For full listing, see CSI section 23 34 00 - HVAC Fans

Equator Clothes Washers

Equator Corporation
2801 W. Sam Houston Pkwy. N
Equator Plz.
Houston, TX 77080

Toll-free: 800-935-1955
Phone: 713-464-3422
Fax: 713-464-2151
www.equatoronline.com

Two residential laundry products from Equator Corporation qualified for *GreenSpec* as of March, 2007. Models EZ 3612 CEE (combination washer and ventless dryer) and EZ 1612 V are 1.92 cubic foot capacity machines that exceed federal standards by 52% and 62% respectively, with MEFs of 1.92 and 2.04, and WFs of 5 and 4.9. Estimated annual water and electrical use is 3763 gallons for the 3612, 3650 gallons for the 1612; and 143 or 135 kWh respectively. These appliances are made in Italy.

Dryer-Ell

New

In-O-Vate Technologies, Inc.
810 Saturn St., Ste. 21
Jupiter, FL 33477

Toll-free: 888-443-7937
Phone: 561-743-8696
Fax: 561-745-9723
www.dryerbox.com

The Dryer-Ell™ dryer-duct elbow is a 4"-diameter, large-radius elbow with a smooth interior that is designed to reduce friction in dryer venting systems. The elbow reduces the need for a booster fan and increases the allowable duct length by about five feet, compared with standard elbows (based on ASHRAE methodology for calculating friction loss).

The Dryerbox

In-O-Vate Technologies, Inc.
810 Saturn St., Ste. 21
Jupiter, FL 33477

Toll-free: 888-443-7937
Phone: 561-743-8696
Fax: 561-745-9723
www.dryerbox.com

The Dryerbox™ is a 21"-high aluminized steel box designed to be installed in the wall behind a dryer to eliminate bends in the flex transition hose. According to the manufacturer, this reduces lint build-up and the attendant risk of fire. The company also claims it shortens the necessary drying time to save the typical household $6 per year (based on testing carried out by the company). Because the dryer can then be installed right up against the wall, about 1 ft of living space is gained, and the elimination of a 90-degree bend gives the HVAC contractor a 5' credit in duct run length. The company's website contains a wealth of information on dryer venting.

Kitchen Aid Clothes Washers

KitchenAid
701 Main St.
P.O. Box 218
St. Joseph, MI 49085

Toll-free: 800-422-1230
www.kitchenaid.com

As of March 2007, Kitchen Aid offers two high-end, 3.3-cubic-foot clothes washers meeting *GreenSpec* the threshold. Model KHWV01R* exceeds energy Star standards by 66%, offering an MEF of 2.09, a WF of 4.2, estimated annual water use of 5485 gallons, and estimated annual electric use of 214 kWh. Models KHWS01P#** and KHWS02R*+ exceed Energy Star by 47%, with 1.85 MEF, 4.3 WF, using an estimated 5524 gallons and 311 kWh per year.

Use of certain features may affect overall energy use.

LG Clothes Washers

LG Appliances
1000 Sylvan Ave.
Englewood Cliffs, NJ 07632

Toll-free: 800-243-0000
www.lgappliances.com

LG Appliances offers 23 models qualifying for *GreenSpec* as of March 2007—among them the most efficient clothes washers to date, exceeding federal standards by up to 97%. (Siemens and Whirlpool have a couple slightly more efficient models.) The most efficient model is WM268#H**, the 3.47 CF "SteamWasher," with a 2.48 MEF, 3.5 WF, and estimated annual electric and water use of 171 kWh and 4690 gallons. Compare the yellow EnergyGuide labels on other LG models using this one as a benchmark. These appliances are manufactured in Korea. Use of certain features on clothes washers may affect their overall water and energy consumption.

Maytag Clothes Washers

Maytag Appliances
403 W. Fourth St. N
P.O. Box 39
Newton, IA 50208

Toll-free: 888-462-9824
Phone: 641-792-7000
Fax: 641-787-8376
www.maytag.com

Maytag's Neptune line includes two *Green-Spec*-qualifying models in their Epic line as of March 2007: MFW9700S#** and MFW9600S*+. Respectively, they exceed federal standards by 68% and 55%. MEFs are 2.12 and 1.95; WFs are 4.4 and 4.5; estimated annual kWh, 212 and 218; estimated annual water use, 5649 and 5855 gallons. These machines are manufactured by Maytag in the U.S. Certain features may affect overall water and energy use.

Most recently mentioned in EBN 6:4, 6:9, 7:2, 7:4, 7:9

Miele Clothes Washers

Miele, Inc.
9 Independence Way
Princeton, NJ 08540

Toll-free: 800-843-7231
Phone: 609-419-9898
Fax: 609-419-4298
www.mieleusa.com

Miele offers seven German-made clothes washers that qualify for *GreenSpec* as of March 2007. Two 3.07 CF models (W4800 and W4840) exceed federal minimum thresholds by 90%, with 2.4 MEF and 4.2 WF; 186 kWh and 5091 gallons of water estimated use annually. 2.08 CF models W1203, W1213, and W1215 are rated at 2.04 MEF, 4.4 WF, 127 kWh and 3547 gallons per year... 62% better than the federal minimum. The small 1.73 CF models W1113 and W1119 exceed federal standards by 67%, with 2.11 MEF, 4.5 WF, using an estimated 113 kWh and 3045 gallons of water annually. Certain features may be included that, when used, may affect overall energy and water use.

Most recently mentioned in EBN 6:4, 7:9, 8:1

Samsung Clothes Washers

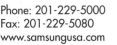

Samsung Electronics
105 Challenger Rd.
Ridgefield Park, NJ 07660

Phone: 201-229-5000
Fax: 201-229-5080
www.samsungusa.com

Samsung offers six clothes washers that meet *GreenSpec*'s criteria. All have 3.29 cubic feet of capacity, and a 3.9 WF. Annual electric use estimates run between 210 - 220 kWh per year, with MEFs of either 2.01 or 2.06, depending on model. They exceed federal minimum standards by 60% and 63%. Model numbers are WF206***, WF306BHW, WF306LAW, WF316***, WF326LAS, and WF326LAW.

Kenmore Clothes Washers

Sears
3333 Beverly Rd.
Hoffman Estates, IL 60179

Toll-free: 800-349-4358
www.sears.com

With 31 models qualifying for *GreenSpec* as of March 2007, the Kenmore brand—manufactured for Sears by Electrolux and Whirlpool—impresses. The most efficient models overall include the 3.29 CF 4708#60** and 4709#60**, which exceed Energy Star standards by 89%: a 2.38 MEF, and 4.1 WF, estimated to use 173 kWh and 5288 gallons of water per year. Compare other Kenmore models to these using the yellow EnergyGuide label.

Siemens Clothes Washer

Siemens Home Appliances
5551 McFadden Ave.
Huntington Beach, CA 92649

Toll-free: 888-474-3636
Phone: 714-901-6600
Fax: 714-901-5360
www.siemens-home.com

Siemens Home Appliances offers three 3.31-cubic-foot models that qualify for *GreenSpec*. WFXD8400UC is estimated to use 178 kWh and 5,839 gallons of water per year, with a 2.2 MEF and 4.5 WF, making it 75% better than the federal minimum standard. WFXD840AUC is estimated to use 176 kWh and 5,268 gallons of water per year, with a 2.43 MEF and 4.1 WF, making it 93% better than the federal minimum standard. WFXD5201UC is estimated to use 182 kWh and 5,514 gallons of water per year, with a 2.57 MEF and 4.3 WF, making it 104% better than the federal minimum standard.

Splendide Clothes Washer-Dryers

Splendide
15650 S.E. 102nd Ave.
P.O. Box 427
Clackamas, OR 97015

Toll-free: 800-356-0766
Fax: 503-656-8829
www.splendide.com

Splendide offers models WDC6200CEE and WD2100, washer-dryer combos that exceed federal standards by 52%. Each has a capacity of 1.92 cubic feet and a WF of 5 and 4.9 respectively, with 1.92 MEF. Estimated annual water use is about 3700 gallons, with a corresponding annual electric use of 143 kWh. Certain features may affect overall energy use. The 6200 has an integral ventless dryer; the 2100's dryer is vented.

Whirlpool Clothes Washers

Whirlpool Corporation
2000 N. Hwy. M-63
Benton Harbor, MI 49022

Toll-free: 800-253-1301
www.whirlpool.com

Whirlpool offers a dozen models that qualify for *GreenSpec* as of April, 2007. All offer 3 cubic feet capacity (give or take .30 cubic feet), have MEF numbers around 2 and WF numbers between 4 and 5; annual water and electric use is estimated to be 5300 – 5900 gallons and 170 – 285 kWh. They range between 57% and 113% better than federal standards; the most efficient models are WFW9400T*#**, WFW9600T*#**, and WFW9200T*#**. Certain features may affect overall water and energy use. These washers are made in Europe by Whirlpool.

Most recently mentioned in EBN 7:9 & 10:11

11 41 00
Food Storage Equipment

Products listed here include innovative commercial refrigeration equipment (e.g., for walk-in coolers) that save energy by using outside air, or optimizing performance on other ways.

Freeaire Refrigeration System and Cool Breeze Outside Air Package

R. H. Travers Company
200 Burnt Mountain Rd.
Warren, VT 05674

Toll-free: 877-305-3733
Phone: 802-496-5205
Fax: 802-496-5205
www.freeaire.com

The Basic Freeaire® Refrigeration System utilizes an electronic controller to optimize energy-efficiency and to extend the service life of commercial walk-in coolers and other refrigeration equipment in any climate by running all the equipment—condensing fans, compressors, evaporator fans, and glass door "heaters"—only as much as is needed. For example, evaporator fans, which are usually running constantly, might operate 50-75% less. For refrigeration equipment in cold climates, the Cool Breeze™ Outside Air Package uses cool outdoor air to supplement mechanical cooling or even replace it entirely during winter months. This offers dramatic energy savings and can extend the service life of equipment. Worksheets are available to calculate potential energy savings, which can be significant—often times providing a payback period of less than two years, according to the company.

11 53 13
Laboratory Fume Hoods

Air-flow through fume hoods is a primary driver of energy use in laboratories, and a significant energy load in classrooms and other buildings with fume safety cabinets. Energy is used both to move the large amounts of ventilation air, and to condition the replacement air. Conventional fume hoods with constant air-flow exhaust systems draw about the same amount of air regardless of whether the hood is open or closed. Variable air volume systems can be designed to draw significantly less air when the sash is closed. Advanced fume

hoods offer many features to provide safe containment while reducing airflow, and/or to reduce the size and duration of sash openings.

Pioneer Laboratory Fume Hoods

Fisher Hamilton, LLC
1316 18th St.
Two Rivers, WI 54241

Phone: 920-793-1121
Fax: 920-793-3084
www.fisherhamilton.com

Pioneer Fume Hoods feature automated and warning systems designed to keep the sash at a working opening height of no more than 18". When the sash is opened above this height for set-up, a special laminar airflow is directed downwards across the opening to ensure that the operator's breathing zone is not contaminated. This safety system allows the Pioneer to meet safety standards with face velocities as low as 50 ft/min.

Bi-Stable Vortex Fume Hood

Flow Safe, Inc.
30 Broad St.
Denville, NJ 07834

Toll-free: 888-356-9723
www.flowsafe.net

The Bi-Stable Vortex Fume Safety Cabinet offers a number of features that ensure safety while optimizing energy efficiency. These include aerodynamic design of the cabinet, an articulating baffle at the back of the cabinet that adjusts to optimize airflow, a variable airflow control system that adjusts the baffle dynamically based on actual flow conditions in the cabinet, various foils to streamline air entry and reduce turbulence, and a combination horizontal and vertical sash for maximum access with a limited-size opening.

Protector XStream Laboratory Hoods

Labconco Corporation
8811 Prospect Ave.
Kansas City, MO 64132

Toll-free: 800-821-5525
Phone: 816-333-8811
Fax: 816-363-0130
www.labconco.com

The Protector XStream fume hoods were designed using computational fluid dynamics to provide safe operation with face velocities as low as 60 ft/min, for an anticipated 40% energy savings.

11 68 13
Playground Equipment

Products listed here are made from recycled plastic, high-recycled-content metal, or Forest Stewardship Council-certified wood.

Playfield Equipment

Children's Playstructures, Inc.
9892 Titan Park Cir., Unit 1
Littleton, CO 80125

Toll-free: 800-874-9943
Phone: 303-791-7626
Fax: 303-791-3314
www.childrensplaystructures.com

Children's Playstructures custom-designs, constructs, and installs playground structures for schools and parks made primarily from 100% recycled HDPE plastic lumber produced by U.S. Plastic Lumber Co./Eaglebrook. Children's Playstructures services the Colorado and Wyoming area.

Playground Equipment

Landscape Structures Inc.
601 7th St. S
P.O. Box 198
Delano, MN 55328

Toll-free: 888-438-6574
Phone: 763-972-3391
Fax: 763-972-3185
www.playlsi.com

Landscape Structures manufactures a wide range of playground equipment from various recycled materials. Most notably, wire tunnels and barriers, vertical ladders, roller-slide rollers, rubber floor tiles, and plastic benches, decks, and walls are made from either pre-consumer or post-consumer recycled materials. Landscape Structures is ISO 14001-certified.

Recreation Equipment

Playworld Systems
1000 Buffalo Rd.
Lewisburg, PA 17837

Toll-free: 800-233-8404
Phone: 570-522-9800
Fax: 570-522-3030
www.playworldsystems.com

Playworld Systems manufactures recreation equipment with powder-coated recycled aluminum and steel in all products, and some recycled plastic in certain components. Products are packaged in 85% post-consumer recycled-paper cardboard with biodegradable, nonstyrofoam packing material. Products include PlayDesigns, Playworld, Climbing Boulders, Woodward Ramps and Rails, and LifeTrail.

RCI Playground Equipment

Recreation Creations, Inc.
215 W. Mechanic St.
Hillsdale, MI 49242

Toll-free: 800-766-9458
Phone: 517-439-1591
Fax: 517-439-1878
www.rec-creations.com

RCI Playground Equipment is made with several recycled-content materials. Most notably, PlasTech™ posts and decking contain 96% post-consumer recycled HDPE plastic. Steel, aluminum, and plastic panel materials also have recycled content. RCI makes a wide range of equipment for schools and playgrounds.

Safeplay Playground Equipment

Safeplay Systems
4452 Winifred Dr.
Marietta, GA 30066

Toll-free: 800-260-7218
Phone: 770-591-7000
Fax: 770-926-4194
www.safeplaysystems.com

Safeplay playground equipment and amenities are made with EcoPlay®, a recycled-HDPE extruded lumber containing a minimum of 95% post-consumer content and covered by a 50-year warranty. Structural posts are 6x6; decking is 2x6 planks with 4x4 support members. Coloring is integral for a maintenance-free finish. Metal components are powder-coated galvanized steel and are covered by a ten-year warranty. Products include age-appropriate play equipment (for infants and toddlers, preschool, and school age), and amenities like swing sets, picnic tables, trash can containers, and benches.

Recycled-Plastic Site Amenities

The Plastic Lumber Company, Inc.

For full listing, see CSI section 12 93 43 - Site Seating and Tables, Plastic

11 00 00
Equipment

11 82 00
Recycling and Solid Waste Handling Equipment

Enabling commercial and public building and campus occupants to be good environmental stewards is important. Systems that make it easy to recycle wastes should be provided in offices, institutions, parks, and other public spaces. Many of the products described here are themselves made from recycled waste materials.

Recycling Receptacles

Busch Systems International Inc.
343 Saunders Rd.
Barrie, ON L4N 9A8 Canada

Toll-free: 800-565-9931
Phone: 705-722-0806
Fax: 705-722-8972
www.buschsystems.com

Busch Systems International provides recycling container solutions to industries, municipal governments, and educational systems. They produce dozens of styles of curbside, deskside, and centralized recycling containers, as well as carts and composters. Most products contain a minimum of 25% post-consumer recycled material. They also offer novelties to promote recycling and composting.

Feeny Lidded Waste and Recycle and Rotary Recycling Center

Knape & Vogt Manufacturing Company
2700 Oak Industrial Dr. NE
Grand Rapids, MI 49505

Toll-free: 800-253-1561
Phone: 616-459-3311
Fax: 616-459-7620
www.knapeandvogt.com

Knape & Vogt offers two products for residential recyclable collection. The Feeny Lidded Waste and Recycle is intended for base cabinet applications; it has up to 3 bins and rolls out. The Feeny Rotary Corner Recycling Center has 3 bins and works like a lazy susan.

Most recently mentioned in EBN 1:3

Curbside or Work-Area Recycling Bins

Microphor
452 E. Hill Rd.
Willits, CA 95490

Toll-free: 800-358-8280
Phone: 707-459-5563
Fax: 707-459-6617
www.microphor.com

Microphor recycling bins, made from plastic, are designed for curbside or office-paper recycling. These stackable bins have large handles and measure 12-1/4" x 12-1/2" x 20-1/2". Standard colors are white, navy blue, blue, red, green, and yellow.

Recycling Equipment

Recy-CAL Supply Co.
42597 De Portola Rd.
Temecula, CA 92592

Toll-free: 800-927-3873
Phone: 951-302-7585
Fax: 951-302-7530
www.recy-cal.com

Recy-CAL Supply is a distributor of recycling containers, waste receptacles, and mobile collection containers. Many styles and sizes of products from more than 30 manufacturers are available to fit various needs, budgets, and decors.

PV-powered Compacting Waste Receptacle

Seahorse Power Company

For full listing, see CSI section 12 93 23 - Trash, Litter, and Recycling Receptors

Recycling Collection Containers

The Fibrex Group, Inc.
4164 Pruden Blvd. - Bldg 2
Suffolk, VA 23434

Toll-free: 800-346-4458
Phone: 757-487-5744
Fax: 800-444-8380
www.fibrexgroup.com

The Fibrex Group supplies recycling and trash receptacles in many styles and sizes including containers for used motor oil collection and bins for curbside recycling collection. Many of these products are made from recycled-content plastics.

Roll Out Carts

Toter, Inc.
841 Meacham Rd.
P.O. Box 5338
Statesville, NC 28677

Toll-free: 800-424-0422
Phone: 704-872-8171
Fax: 704-878-0734
www.toter.com

Toter is the largest U.S. manufacturer of plastic rollout carts for automated collection of residential solid waste and recyclables. Toter also supplies commercial, industrial, and institutional containers with matching mechanical lifter systems ranging in size from 21 gal. to 2 yd3.

Recycling and Waste Bins

United Receptacle

For full listing, see CSI section 12 93 23 - Trash, Litter, and Recycling Receptors

Hi-Rise Recycling System

Wilkinson Hi-Rise, LLC.
2821 Evans Ave.
Hollywood, FL 33020

Toll-free: 800-231-3888
Phone: 954-342-4400
Fax: 626-633-0740
www.wilkinsonhirise.com

The Hi-Rise Recycling System is a patented source-separation recycling system for multistory buildings. The primary application is apartment buildings. The system includes 6 turntable-mounted bins that receive recyclables from a building's trash chute. The basement-located unit is controlled by electronic keypads in each apartment.

Most recently mentioned in EBN 2:5 & 6:3

11 00 00
Equipment

This Space is Available for Your Notes

11 00 00
Equipment

12 00 00 Furnishings

PRODUCT LISTINGS

12 05 14
Natural Fiber Fabrics

Natural fibers such as cotton, linen, ramie, wool, silk, jute, and hemp are traditional fabric materials. Unlike their polymer-based replacements, natural fibers require little energy to process and are biodegradable—but they may have other environmental impacts. Cotton is typically grown with significant chemical fertilizer and pesticide use, although the availability of organically grown cotton is increasing. Silk and wool, both animal products, are obtained primarily from overseas sources; both are prone to moth attack and microbial growth, so are often treated with chemicals. Hemp and jute, also primarily from overseas sources, are relatively resistant to pests, both as plants and after manufacture into fabrics. Natural dyes are sometimes used with these fabrics, but synthetic dyes are more commonly employed for greater color retention. Natural-fiber fabrics may be used as furniture upholstery, workstation fabrics, draperies, etc.

Climatex Lifecycle by Carnegie

Carnegie
110 N. Centre Ave.
Rockville Centre, NY 11570

Toll-free: 800-727-6770
Phone: 516-678-6770
Fax: 516-678-6848
www.carnegiefabrics.com

Climatex® Lifecycle™ is a natural-fiber fabric made from wool and ramie for upholstery applications. Carnegie has been licensed by Designtex, the fabric's developer, to utilize the Designtex manufacturing processes in developing its own patterns, colors, and styles. (See The Designtex Group listing this section for more information.)

Cotton Plus

Cotton Plus, Inc.
822 Baldridge St.
O'Donnell, TX 79351

Phone: 806-428-3345
Fax: 888-439-6647
www.organiccottonplus.com

Cotton Plus fabrics are made from organically grown cotton fiber, woven into chambray, twill, canvas, and flannel. In addition to natural-color cotton fabrics, some fabrics are dyed using low-impact processing.

Climatex Lifecycle by Designtex

Designtex
200 Varick St.
New York, NY 10014

Toll-free: 800-221-1540
Phone: 212-886-8161
Fax: 212-886-8149
www.dtex.com

Award-winning Climatex® Lifecycle™ is a line of natural-fiber textiles. The fibers are a blend of wool and organically grown ramie—totally compostable biological nutrients, designed to turn back into soil at the end of their useful life. Every dye chemical has been proven nontoxic. The water flowing out of the plant at the end of the manufacturing process is safe to drink, and all waste trimmings are pressed into felt, which is sold to farmers for use as mulch. Since introducing the first collection of Climatex Lifecycle fabrics, designed by William McDonough, Designtex has embraced the concept of "leadership not ownership" by making the construction available to the entire textile industry.

Most recently mentioned in EBN 4:6

LIFE Textiles

INSTYLE Contract Textiles USA
735 Grand View Ave.
San Francisco, CA 94114

Phone: 415-515-9851
Fax: 415-401-0015
www.instylecontracttextiles.com

LIFE (Low Impact For the Environment) Textiles®, developed by INSTYLE and Woolmark Americas for use in commercial interiors, are renewably-sourced, biodegradable contract textiles made from either third-party certified organic wool or "eco wool" (tested in its raw state for negligible pesticide residue). The non-mutagenic dyes don't contain heavy metals, and no flame retardants or anti-static treatments are applied. INSTYLE is an Australian company with domestic offices in San Francisco, Los Angeles, and Denver; product is manufactured in Australia or New Zealand.

Mantero ReSilk

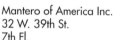

Mantero of America Inc.
32 W. 39th St.
7th Fl.
New York, NY 10018

Phone: 212- 575-7050
www.mantero.com

Mantero produces a felt upholstery fabric made from 50% pre-consumer recycled silk and 50% wool. The felt is naturally flame retardant, recyclable, and manufactured in a water-based process without chemical additives or toxic byproducts. Mantero's primary business is manufacturing silk for top fashion brands.

Mod Green Pod

New

Mod Green Pod
46 Waltham St., Ste. 101
Boston, MA 02118

Phone: 617-670-2000
Fax: 610-602-2765
www.modgreenpod.com

Mod Green Pod produces 100% organic cotton upholstery fabrics that are silk-screen printed by hand with water-based paints and without chemical finishing agents. Fabrics are sold by the yard to the trade.

Foxfibre Colorganic Fabric

Vreseis Ltd.
P.O. Box 69
Guinda, CA 95637

Phone: 530-796-3007
Fax: 530-796-3007
www.vreseis.com

Vreseis manufactures upholstery fabrics from Foxfibre® Colorganic® organic cotton, which has been selectively bred and grown to produce cotton in shades of green, brown, and natural off-white. The brown color is naturally flame-retardant, though additional chemicals have to be added to meet most commercial standards.

12 05 15
Synthetic Fiber Fabrics

Many conventional synthetic fabrics are made from virgin polymers using toxic catalysts or additives and are not designed to be recycled. Because of their durability, PVC or PVC-coated fabrics have traditionally dominated the market for products such as awnings, truck covers, gym mats, and banner materials. Polyester fabrics are often specified in commercial settings for panel and workstation applications because of their inherent fire-resistant qualities and relatively low cost. Products listed here are made from recycled synthetic material, bio-based polymers, or are designed for recycling and were manufactured without toxic additives.

12 00 00
Furnishings

INSIGHT PLA Terratex Fabrics

Carnegie
110 N. Centre Ave.
Rockville Centre, NY 11570

Toll-free: 800-727-6770
Phone: 516-678-6770
Fax: 516-678-6848
www.carnegiefabrics.com

Carnegie offers the INSIGHT™ line of Terratex® fabric made from polylactic acid (PLA). This biobased, biodegradable fabric is manufactured by Interface Fabrics Group using Ingeo™ fiber produced from corn by NatureWorks LLC (previously Cargill-Dow). Insight fabric is primarily used as a workstation panel fabric.

Most recently mentioned in EBN 14:12

Eco Intelligent Polyester Contract Fabric by Designtex

Designtex
200 Varick St.
New York, NY 10014

Toll-free: 800-221-1540
Phone: 212-886-8161
Fax: 212-886-8149
www.dtex.com

Sea Breeze, Lagoon, and Closed Loop Eco Intelligent™ polyester are contract fabrics for commercial interiors made with antimony-free polyester (titanium dioxide is used as the catalyst for polymerization). The fabric requires no chemical backing during application, which would inhibit recycling. In addition, all chemicals and dyes used in its manufacture have been screened for toxicity and ecological impact according to a protocol from McDonough Braungart Design Chemistry (MBDC), so the fabric qualifies as a "level 4" (out of 5) in MBDC's protocol, and is considered a "technical nutrient" that can be recycled indefinitely. Sea Breeze is a panel fabric; Lagoon and Closed Loop are seating fabrics. These fabrics are manufactured for Designtex by Victor Innovatex.

Most recently mentioned in EBN 12:6 & 14:7

Greentex

Fabinno
6083 Valencia St.
Corona, CA 92880

Phone: 909-773 -0232
www.fabinno.com

Unlike traditional coated fabrics with chemically different fibers and coatings, the Greentex™ line of 100% recyclable, coated polypropylene fabrics can easily be recycled into the same or different products, though the infrastructure for doing so is not currently in place. These fabrics are about 30% lighter than traditional coated alternatives and don't require the use of solvents in their manufacture. Greentex fabrics can be used in applications where PVC or PVC-coated fabrics have traditionally dominated the market, such as awnings, truck covers, gym mats, and banner materials. Fabinno, formerly Korean Tarpaulin Inc., is a South Korea-based manufacturer of industrial fabrics.

Petals by Clickeze and New Leaf by Clickeze

New

InPro Corporation
P.O. Box 406
Muskego, WI 53150

Toll-free: 800-222-5556
Phone: 262-679-5521
Fax: 888-715-8407
www.inprocorp.com

Clickeze, a division of InPro Corporation, offers cubicle privacy curtains through the Enso Collection by Momentum Textiles. Two products in the collection, Petals by Clickeze, and New Leaf by Clickeze, are polyester textiles using Victor Innovatex's Eco Intelligent fabric. The Eco Intelligent fabric is certified Cradle to Cradle Gold by McDonough Braungart Design Chemistry (MBDC), meaning that materials designated by MBDC as hazardous, including fire retardants, and antimony, are not used. The fabric is also designed to be recyclable. The product is designed for healthcare industry, with designs inspired by nature that are intended to produce a calming effect on occupants. The Clickeze system includes an aluminum track containing 70% post-industrial recycled content.

Terratex Fabrics

Interface Fabrics
437 Fifth Ave., 9th Fl.
New York, NY 10016

Phone: 212-684-2380
Fax: 212-684-2522
www.terratex.com

Terratex® fabrics are made from one of the following: 100% recycled material, fully compostable natural fiber, or biobased polylactic acid (PLA) polymer. Each product in the Terratex line is made from a single type of fiber without backcoating so that it can be recycled or composted at the end of its useful life. Most Terratex fabrics are used in commercial furniture and workstations.

Most recently mentioned in EBN 11:9 & 14:12

Eco Intelligent Polyester Contract Fabric

Victor Innovatex, Inc.
2805 90th St.
Saint-Georges, QC G6A 1K1 Canada

Phone: 418-227-9897
Fax: 418-227-9899
www.victor-innovatex.com

Eco Intelligent™ polyester is a contract fabric for commercial interiors made with antimony-free polyester (titanium dioxide is used as the catalyst for polymerization instead of antimony). The fabric requires no chemical backing during application, which would inhibit recycling. In addition, all chemicals and dyes used to produce the fabric have been screened for toxicity and ecological impact according to a protocol from McDonough Braungart Design Chemistry (MBDC), so the fabric qualifies as a "level 4" (out of 5) in MBDC's protocol, and is considered a "technical nutrient" that can be recycled indefinitely. Eco Intelligent polyester is available to furniture manufacturers and, through contract fabric distributors, to interior designers.

Most recently mentioned in EBN 12:6 & 14:7

12 24 00
Window Shades

Window shades, blinds, and other treatments can control daylight penetration and significantly reduce heat loss or heat gain through windows. In commercial buildings, engineered window shading installations can be part of an integrated design strategy addressing glare, heat gain, and solar penetration. In residential buildings, insulating win-

dow blinds and quilts may be appropriate retrofits for older, leaky windows, when window replacement can't be justified. In new construction or when replacement can be justified, installing high-performance windows is usually a better option than investing in energy-conserving blinds or shades.

Warm Windows

Cozy Curtains
4295 Duncan Dr.
Missoula, MT 59802

Toll-free: 800-342-9955
Fax: 406-721-1595
www.cozycurtains.com

Warm Windows® is a custom-made insulating Roman-shade system which folds above the window when not in use. The shades are made up of 4 layers: High Density Dacron Holofil II®, a polyethylene moisture vapor barrier, metalized Mylar®, and the customer's choice of fabric. The company reports an R-value of 7.69 for installations over single-pane and 8.69 over double-pane windows. Shades attach to a board over the window frame with Velcro® and are pulled up and down with a cord. Magnetic strips around the frame and concealed within the shade provide a magnetically tight seal. Cozy Curtains also offers individual components for sale for do-it-yourselfers.

Draper PVC-Free Interior Shade Screening

New

Draper, Inc.
411 S. Pearl St.
Spiceland, IN 47358

Phone: 765-987-7999
Fax: 866-637-5611
www.draperinc.com

Draper offers PVC-free mesh and blackout shades made of fiberglass, acrylic-coated fiberglass, or cotton/poly blend from Hexcel, Rockland Industries, and 3G Mermet. These fabrics are thinner and lighter than PVC fabrics, requiring smaller tubes and hardware. Some of these fabrics have recycled content and are halogen-free.

Earthshade Natural Fiber Window Treatments

Earthshade Natural Window Fashions
P.O. Box 1003
Great Barrington, MA 01230

Toll-free: 866-528-5443
www.earthshade.com

Made from mostly wildcrafted grasses and reeds grown without the use of fertilizers or pesticides, Earthshade custom window treatments are handwoven in Mexico and assembled in Texas. The materials are handharvested, sundried, and if treated at all, bathed in hydrogen peroxide to meet import regulations. Glues are water-based, and the only finishes are a water-based stain on one pattern (others are baked to achieve their color) and an optional water-based flame retardant for commercial spaces. Nylon cords are used to operate the shades though the company is currently testing hemp as a replacement. Earthshade natural window treatments are available in 10 operating styles and come with the industry standard lifetime limited warranty making them suitable for both contract and residential applications.

Handwoven Collection

Hartmann & Forbes
P.O. Box 1149
Tualatin, OR 97062

Toll-free: 888-582-8780
Phone: 503-692-9313
Fax: 503-692-9315
www.hfshades.com

Hartmann & Forbes produces handwoven window coverings made from natural materials, such as reeds, grasses, bamboos, and cotton string. The PapyrusWeave™ line includes woven roman shades, draperies, rollershades, and a panelscreen that operates on a track. There is no glue used in the weave; non-chlorine polyvinyl acetate (PVA) glue is used in assembly of the finished product. Hartmann&Forbes also has a Take-Back Initiative™ to collect and recycle used shades.

Shades & Blinds

Hunter Douglas Window Covering
1 Duette Way
Broomfield, CO 80020

Toll-free: 800-789-0331
Phone: 303-466-1848
Fax: 303-876-3374
www.hunterdouglas.com

The Duette® Honeycomb shades from Hunter Douglas offer significantly better energy performance than standard shades because of their unique accordion-fold design. When lowered, the fabric opens up providing pockets of trapped air. The opaque Duette shades include a reflective layer to boost energy performance.

EcoVeil PVC-Free Interior Shade Screening

MechoShade Systems, Inc.
42-03 35th St.
Long Island City, NY 11101

Phone: 718-729-2020
Fax: 718-729-2941
www.mechoshade.com

EcoVeil™ is an interior shade-screen product line for commercial buildings made from a thermoplastic olefin (TPO) yarn called EarthTex™, developed by the Twitchell™ Corporation. EarthTex is an infinitely recyclable "technical nutrient," and MechoShade encourages customers to return EcoVeil screens to the company when they're no longer wanted. This is the first solar shade screen to earn an approval rating from Mc-Donough Braungart Design Chemistry, LLC (MBDC). These shades are washable and antimicrobial, resist UV degradation, and are about a third lighter than conventional shade cloth. The fabric currently comes in eight colors, with an openness factor of 5%. (Weaves ranging from 1% to 12% are expected to be introduced in 2005). MechoShade offers several manual and automated systems for raising and lowering the shades, including the motorized WhisperTrack™ series.

Most recently mentioned in EBN 13:10, 13:12, 16:2

12 00 00
Furnishings

SolarTrac Daylighting Manager System

MechoShade Systems, Inc.
42-03 35th St.
Long Island City, NY 11101

Phone: 718-729-2020
Fax: 718-729-2941
www.mechoshade.com

The whole-building AAC SolarTrac™ WindowManagement™ Daylighting Manager System automatically adjusts shade positions incrementally to maximize views and daylighting using a PC-based program. It will interface with most automated building management systems. The system accounts for "clear", "cloudy," or "bright-overcast" conditions; it also factors in the sun's angle of incidence, solar heat gain (in Btu or W/M^2), allowable solar penetration, and brightness and glare control. The primary market is commercial, though the manufacturer is entering the consumer-residential market with a simpler version of the AAC Solar Tracking System. MechoShade also manufactures EcoVeil, a "cradle-to-cradle" sustainable, ecologically sound shade cloth.

Most recently mentioned in EBN 13:10

GreenScreen PVC-Free Interior Shade Screening

Nysan Shading Systems, Ltd.
#1 115 28th St., S.E.
Calgary, AB T2A 5K4 Canada

Phone: 403-204-8675
Fax: 403-204-8676
www.nysan.com

GreenScreen®, an interior shade-screen product line for commercial buildings, uses a prestretched polyester yarn impregnated with an acrylic-based material, rather than the industry-standard PVC. The fabrics come in openness factors from 3% to 25% and a range of styles and colors. In addition to the standard coating, an exterior aluminized coating is available that increases solar reflectivity up to 97%. Nysan offers multiple systems for raising and lowering the shades, including their fully automated Matrix™ system that can be programmed to track the angle of the sun and automatically adjust shades in different areas of a building as the sun moves across the sky.

Most recently mentioned in EBN 12:12, 13:3, 13:10

Sailshade Window Coverings

Sailshade/Cloth Construction
P.O. Box 3935
Westport, MA 02790

Phone: 508-677-3160
Fax: 636-438-3536
www.sailshadeyourhome.com

Sailshade® multilayer window coverings are estimated by the manufacturer to provide R-8 insulating values in combination with a double-glazed window. When not in use, they fold compactly in a "self-creating valance" to maximize solar gain. The standard face fabric is minimally processed 100% cotton twill (washed, but no chemical finishes); 100% hemp linen is an available option, or customer's own material may be supplied. The blackout lining is non-PVC (Roc-lon), and an interior layer of Reflectix® insulation is standard.

Window Quilt

The Warm Company
954 E. Union St.
Seattle, WA 98122

Phone: 206-320-9276
Fax: 206-320-0974
www.warmcompany.com

Window Quilt is an insulating blind for windows. Blinds roll up at the top of the window, and the edges fit into a track, making the blind fairly airtight. The product makes the most sense for older windows; with new construction or when windows are being replaced, investing in super-high-performance windows generally makes more sense. The Warm Company finalized the acquisition of Window Quilt®, a Vermont company, in early 2006.

12 25 00
Window Treatment Operating Hardware

Products listed here have recycled content or specialized features that save energy or achieve other environmental benefits.

Drapery Rods

Antique Drapery Rod Co., Inc.
140 Glass St.
Dallas, TX 75207

Phone: 214-653-1733
Fax: 214-653-1776
www.antiquedraperyrod.com

Antique Drapery Rod Co. manufactures drapery rods from 100% recycled steel produced at an energy-efficient mini-mill. Other steel products contain minimum 65% post-consumer recycled content. Aluminum products are made from 100% post-consumer content. The company uses recycled wood for their drapery rods, brackets, and rings, as well as offering rods and rings made from bamboo. Wood stains are water-based and low-VOC. The bamboo "tortoise shell" finish is produced using only fire, earth, and water. Antique Drapery Rod minimizes packaging material and uses shipping materials with high recycled content.

Window Treatment Hardware

S&L Designs
P.O. Box 222325
Dallas, TX 75222

Toll-free: 800-788-0358
Phone: 214-742-6417
Fax: 214-748-2136
www.s-ldesigns.com

S&L Designs manufactures decorative window treatment hardware, including rods, finials, and tiebacks. Most products are handcrafted from recycled-content metals; items made from aluminum have 100% recycled content. The company donates part of its profits to environmental causes.

12 26 13
Light Shelves

Light shelves can be installed on the inside or outside of fenestrations to reduce brightness near the window while bouncing light deeper into the space. Exterior light shelves also serve as shading devices, preventing solar gain from entering the building. (See also 10 71 13 - Exterior Sun Control Devices.)

C/S Sun Control Products

Construction Specialties, Inc.; Sun Control Division

For full listing, see CSI section 10 71 13 - Exterior Sun Control Devices

LightLouver

LightLouver, LLC
2540 Frontier Ave., Ste. 100
Boulder, CO 80301

Phone: 303-444-8773
Fax: 303-444-4304
www.lightlouver.com

The LightLouver™ Daylighting System consists of an aluminum framed set of highly reflective fixed louvers that redirect light from any incoming angle onto the ceiling plane. Under typical conditions, for each foot (300 mm) of unit height, daylight will be reflected about 14 feet (4 m) into a room. The units are installed, like lightshelves, on daylight glazing high on a wall, redirecting about 76% of direct overhead sunlight and 54% of available light under overcast conditions. The units can be fabricated in any height from 14" (360 mm) to 48" (1,200 mm) and in any width up to 68" (1,700 mm). For larger glazed areas, multiple units can be combined. They cost anywhere from $30 to $45 per ft^2 ($300–$450/m^2), depending on the size and configuration.

Most recently mentioned in EBN 16:2

Sun Control Devices

Nysan Solar Control

For full listing, see CSI section 10 71 13 - Exterior Sun Control Devices

12 35 00
Specialty Casework

Environmental features to look for with specialty casework, such as laboratory casework, include FSC-certified or salvaged wood, recovered-fiber wood products, agrifiber panels, low-formaldehyde wood products, and low-VOC finishes. (Certification to Forest Stewardship Council—FSC—standards involves third-party evaluation and monitoring of sustainable forestry practices.) (See also 12 32 13 - Manufactured Wood-Veneer-Faced Casework, 12 35 30 - Residential Casework, 12 35 53 - Laboratory Casework, 06 05 70 - Wood Products Certification and Information.)

Green Leaf Series

Cabinet King, Inc.

For full listing, see CSI section 12 35 30 - Residential Casework

Fisher Hamilton Casework

Fisher Hamilton, LLC
1316 18th St.
Two Rivers, WI 54241

Phone: 920-793-1121
Fax: 920-793-3084
www.fisherhamilton.com

Fisher Hamilton wood laboratory furniture uses sustainably harvested wood; low-VOC adhesives; and chemically resistant, water-based finishes exclusively. Fisher Hamilton has FSC chain-of-custody certification.

Greenline

Forefront Designs
1075 Shelley St.
Springfield, OR 97477

Toll-free: 888-245-0075
Phone: 541-747-4884
Fax: 541-747-4840
www.forefrontdesigns.com

Greenline builds cabinets, casework, and countertops using wheatboard structural cores, FSC-certified veneers, high pressure plastic laminates, and various ISO 14001-certified materials. Casework is formaldehyde- and solvent-free and is suitable for laboratories, hospitals, schools, assisted living centers, and other commercial projects. Environmental interior design and consultation are available.

LSI Environments Agrifiber Casework

LSI Corporation of America, Inc.
2100 Xenium Ln.
Minneapolis, MN 55441

Phone: 763-559-4664
Fax: 763-559-4395
www.lsi-casework.com

Since June 2003, LSI Corporation of America's entire casework production has been manufactured with agrifiber-based particleboard. Referred to as LSI Environments™, the line has a particleboard core, high-pressure laminate or plastic surfacing, and PVC edge banding. The core material is PrimeBoard® Premium Blend—referred to as LSI EnvironmentCore™—a composite agrifiber panel comprised of chopped wheat straw and sunflower hulls. The sunflower hulls provide some performance advantages, including improved screw-holding ability, and less "barnyard aroma." The panels are produced with formaldehyde-free polyurethane binders. LSI is also introducing a new panel coating alternative to high-pressure-laminate or plastic veneers that the company calls "LSI Naturally™." In addition, LSI is switching its edge banding from PVC—the industry standard—to ABS.

Most recently mentioned in EBN 12:12 & 15:11

FSC-Certified Cabinetry

Silver Walker Studios
P.O. Box 70667
Richmond, CA 94807

Phone: 510-215-1266
www.silverwalker.com

Silver Walker Studios provides custom-designed cabinetry in a variety of styles and finishes using only FSC-certified wood. The products use only low-VOC glues and finishes and are free of added formaldehyde.

Architectural Furniture

The Valley City Manufacturing Company Ltd.
64 Hatt St.
Dundas, ON L9H 2G3

Phone: 905-628-2253
Fax: 905-628-4470
www.valleycity.com

Valley City Manufacturing Company, chain-of-custody certified according to FSC standards, custom-manufactures architectural furniture for houses of worship, courthouses, laboratories, and other facilities. Specialty furniture offered includes library tables, study carrels, computer workstations, and trading desks. All of the company's distribution is manufacturer-direct.

12 35 30
Residential Casework

Environmental features to look for with residential casework include FSC-certified or salvaged wood, recovered-fiber wood products, agrifiber panels, low-formaldehyde wood products, and low-VOC finishes. (Certification to Forest Stewardship Council—FSC—standards involves third-party evaluation and monitoring of sustainable forestry practices.) (See also 12 32 13 - Manufactured Wood-Veneer-Faced Casework & 12 36 19 - Wood Countertops.)

Reclaimed-Wood Building Products

Aged Woods / Yesteryear Floorworks Company

For full listing, see CSI section 06 22 02 - Reclaimed-Wood Millwork

Green Leaf Series

Cabinet King, Inc.
2444 Lakeside Ave.
Cleveland, OH 44114

Toll-free: 877-422-2463
Phone: 216-522-0022
Fax: 216-522-0023
www.cabinetking.com

Cabinet King's Green Leaf series uses Prime-Board® agrifiber particleboard (made from agricultural residue fibers and a formaldehyde-free binder) for sides, tops, bottoms, backs, shelving, and drawer bottoms, and FSC-certified wood for frames and drawers (sides and backs). Finishes are either Safecoat® Acrylacq or PrimeBoard's all-paper-based melamine. Forbo Marmoleum® will also soon be available as a countertop option. Adhesives are water-based. Cabinet King is also a dealer for cabinets made by other companies, as well as a line of green building products including PrimeBoard, Marmoleum, Safecoat finishes, Titebond® solvent-free construction adhesive, and Bonded Logic recycled-cotton insulation.

Furniture and Kitchen Cabinetry from Urban Trees

CitiLog
370 Pittstown Rd.
P.O. Box 685
Pittstown, NJ 08867

Toll-free: 877-248-9564
Phone: 908-735-8871
Fax: 908-735-6893
www.citilogs.com

12 00 00
Furnishings

CitiLog™, also known as D. Stubby Warmbold, is SmartWood-certified for the harvesting of trees in urban areas of New Jersey and Pennsylvania. Wood is sent by rail to Amish craftsmen in central Pennsylvania who take extra care to turn the lesser graded wood into higher quality products such as flooring, lumber, custom architectural millwork, furniture, and kitchen cabinets. Where appropriate, wood is now harvested using horses.

Wheatboard Cabinets

CitiLog
370 Pittstown Rd.
P.O. Box 685
Pittstown, NJ 08867

Toll-free: 877-248-9564
Phone: 908-735-8871
Fax: 908-735-6893
www.citilogs.com

CitiLog™ offers cabinets made with formaldehyde-free wheatboard cores veneered in North American hardwoods or South American tropical woods, both FSC-certified. Wheatboard is similar to MDF and wood particleboard but is made with wheat stems left over after grain harvesting. These cabinets can be custom-manufactured to meet particular specifications. CitiLog also offers wheatboard millwork and doors.

Wheatcore Doors and Cabinets

Humabuilt Healthy Building Systems
For full listing, see CSI section 08 16 00 - Composite Doors

Neil Kelly Naturals Collection

Neil Kelly Cabinets
2636 N.W. 26th Ave. Ste. 200
Portland, OR 97210

Phone: 503-335-9207
Fax: 503-282-7932
www.neilkellycabinets.com

The Neil Kelly "Naturals Collection" is an award-winning cabinet line that features formaldehyde-free wheatboard case material, low-VOC finishes, and optional FSC-certified lumber doors/drawers. Unlimited customization and virtually any desired upgrade are available.

Most recently mentioned in EBN 7:8

Schiffini Eco Panel Cabinets

Schiffini USA Sales   **New**
175 Sunset Hill Rd.
New Canaan, CT 06840

Phone: 203-966-3234
Fax: 203-972-3124
www.schiffini.it

Designer-kitchen manufacturer Schiffini is a member of the Consorzio Pannello Ecologico, a group of companies employing panels made from FSC-certified, 100% post-consumer recycled wood. The reclaimed wood travels primarily by rail from a network of 30 European collection centers to the manufacturing facility in Italy. Formaldehyde emissions from the UF resin achieve European class E1 (releasing =0.13 mg/m3 air). Schiffini uses these panels for most of their wall-mount and base cabinets; the panels are mechanically fastened, without glue. Many of Schiffini's designs use facing components made from virgin aluminum, which has high embodied energy; those lines are not specified here.

FSC-Certified Cabinetry

Silver Walker Studios
For full listing, see CSI section 12 35 00 - Specialty Casework

12 36 00
Countertops

Countertops have particular performance demands because of their high use and exposure to water, especially at the seams of sink cutouts and backsplashes. A variety of suitable countertop products with environmental advantages are available. Ceramic tile or natural linoleum surfaces also offer green countertop options. Products listed here have a recycled content value (equal to postconsumer plus 1/2 pre-consumer) of at least 20% or are made of FSC-certified wood or rapidly renewable materials. Forest Stewardship Council (FSC) certification involves third-party evaluation and monitoring of sustainable forestry practices. (See also 09 65 16 - Resilient Sheet Flooring, 09 66 16 - Terrazzo Floor Tile, 06 05 70 - Wood Products Certification and Information.)

3form Varia & 100 Percent

3form
For full listing, see CSI section 10 22 23 - Portable Partitions, Screens, and Panels

Shetkastone

All Paper Recycling, Inc.
435 W. Industrial St.
P.O. Box 38
Le Center, MN 56057

Phone: 507-357-4177
Fax: 507-357-2373
www.shetkastone.com

All Paper Recycling manufactures tables and countertops using a patented process and 100% recycled paper. The material, called Shetkastone, can be recycled over and over again through the same process. This process uses no binders or adhesives, just pre-consumer and post-consumer waste paper, including items such as wax paper and phone books. The material has a Class A fire rating without the addition of chemicals and a 400-pound screw test.

Avonite Surfaces Recycled Collection

Aristech Acrylics LLC   **New**
7350 Empire Dr.
Florence, KY 41042

Toll-free: 800-354-9858
Phone: 859-283-1501
Fax: 859-283-7378
www.avonitesurfaces.com

Avonite produces a recycled collection which is made from 40% SCS-certified post-industrial scrap (equal to a recycled content value of 20%), as well as virgin polyester and Aluminium Trihydrate (ATH), which acts as both filler and fire retardant. The recycled material is reclaimed solid surface material from their other product lines. The collection includes 6 patterns and is sold in ½" thick, 36" x 120" sheets. The Kaleidoscope and Cozumel are Class 3 fire rated, while the other four patterns are Class 1 fire rated.

Reclaimed-Wood Products

Centre Mills Antique Floors
For full listing, see CSI section 09 64 02 - Reclaimed-Wood Flooring

Vetrazzo

Counter Production
710 Bancroft Way
Berkeley, CA 94710

Toll-free: 866-809-4898
Phone: 510-843-6916
Fax: 510-843-6948
www.counterproduction.com

Vetrazzo countertops have mixed colors of recycled-glass chips embedded in a masonry binder for a terrazzo-like look. Vetrazzo is available in a wide variety of colors and in thicknesses up to 1-1/4".

Most recently mentioned in EBN 10:9

Bio-Glass

Coverings Etc, Inc.

For full listing, see CSI section 09 66 16 - Terrazzo Floor Tile

Reclaimed-Wood Products

Duluth Timber Co.

For full listing, see CSI section 06 13 02 - Reclaimed-Wood Heavy Timber

Endura Wood Products

Endura Wood Products, Ltd.

For full listing, see CSI section 01 62 03 - Distributors/Retailers, FSC-Certified Wood

Greenline

Forefront Designs

For full listing, see CSI section 12 35 00 - Specialty Casework

Reclaimed-Wood Building Products

General Woodcraft, Inc.

For full listing, see CSI section 09 64 02 - Reclaimed-Wood Flooring

IceStone

IceStone, LLC
63 Flushing Ave., Unit 283, Bldg. 12
Brooklyn Navy Yard
Brooklyn, NY 11025

Phone: 718-624-4900
Fax: 718-624-4002
www.icestone.biz

IceStone is a terrazzo-like material made from a minimum of 75% recycled glass, 17-18% type-3 white portland cement, and small quantities of proprietary ingredients. Although IceStone would not divulge the process they use to avoid the alkali-silica reaction (ASR) that typically affects concrete with glass aggregate, they claim it does not involve the use of epoxy, which is sometimes used for this purpose. IceStone is produced in standard 52.5 x 8' slabs that can be made into large-format tiles, 1-1/4" thick. A 2"-thick product is also available. The slabs are shipped to local stone-finishing companies for cutting, routing, sandblasting, and polishing. IceStone is available in 20 standard colors, based largely on the color of the re-

cycled glass used in the product. The cement matrix can also be pigmented, providing a wide range of color options.

Most recently mentioned in EBN 12:12

PaperStone Certified

KlipTech Composites
2999 John Stevens Way
Hoquiam, WA 98550

Phone: 360-538-9815
Fax: 360-538-1510
www.paperstoneproducts.com

PaperStone Certified is made with 100% FSC-certified, post-consumer recycled paper. The proprietary water-based resin system uses non-petroleum phenols, including cashew nut shell liquid derivatives. The finished product works easily with a triple-chip, carbide-tipped saw blade and carbide-tipped router bits. It has no detectable free formaldehyde, is Class A fire-rated, heat-resistant to 350 degrees, and stain-resistant. PaperStone comes in 30" and 60" widths, lengths of 8', 10', & 12', with thicknesses ranging from 1/4" - 2". The product is available in a variety of colors. The regular PaperStone product line is made with 50% post-consumer recycled content, versus 100% for PaperStone Certified.

Most recently mentioned in EBN 15:4

Teragren Bamboo Flooring, Panels, and Veneer

Teragren

For full listing, see CSI section 09 62 23 - Bamboo Flooring

Squak Mountain Stone Composite Countertops

Tiger Mountain Innovations, Inc.
14221 N.E. 190th St., Ste. 150
Woodinville, WA 98072

Phone: 425-486-3417
www.tmi-online.com

Squak Mountain Stone™ is a precast, relatively lightweight (14 lbs/sf), paper and cement-based composite with the appearance of natural stone. It is made with post-consumer recycled paper (2.5% by weight), pre-consumer crushed glass and fly ash (49%), and has no steel reinforcement. The cement content is similar to cast concrete. This product is available in five standard colors and several standard sizes including 12" x 12", 30" x 48", and 18" x 72". Factory-sealed with a two-part, water-based sealer, Squak Mountain Stone is appropriate for countertops, tabletops, tiling, and other architectural and decorative applications. Non-pH-neutral cleaning products, cutting,

and abrasion may leave marks and damage the sealer. Liquids such as coffee, wine, or oils left on this product for extended periods may cause staining. Hot objects may cause surface darkening, cause micro-cracking, and damage the sealer. Periodic sealer reapplication may be necessary.

Urban Hardwoods

Urban Hardwoods

For full listing, see CSI section 09 64 02 - Reclaimed-Wood Flooring

EQcountertops

VT Industries, Inc.
1000 Industrial Park
Box 490
Holstein, IA 51025

Toll-free: 800-827-1615
Phone: 712-368-4381
Fax: 712-368-4111
www.vtindustries.com

VT Industries manufactures EQcountertops with SkyBlend™ cores made from 100% pre-consumer recycled wood-fiber with a phenol-formaldehyde binder. The countertops use water based biodegradable zero-VOC adhesives, and Greenguard certified laminates.

12 45 00
Bedroom Furnishings

Products listed here are produced from recycled materials, from organic cotton, or without chlorine bleaches and other hazardous chemicals.

Mattresses, Bedding, Upholstered Furniture

Furnature
86 Coolidge Ave.
Watertown, MA 02472

Toll-free: 800-326-4895
Phone: 617-926-0111
Fax: 617-924-5432
www.furnature.com

Furnature's upholstered furniture, mattresses, and bedding are made with chemical-free organic cotton fabrics. The company provides a kit for chemically sensitive customers that includes samples of all materials used in the furniture so that customers can test for sensitivity. In some cases, substitutions can be made for objectionable materials. Pillows, as well as fabrics made from organic fibers, are also available.

Cotton Futons

Futon Man
5280 N.W. Hwy. 99 W
Corvallis, OR 97330

Phone: 541-753-6395
Fax: 541-753-4483
www.fatfuton.com

Natural Life Furnishings manufactures futons with untreated cotton and wool with a poly layer made from recycled plastic. Futon mattresses can be made from organic cotton on request.

Wellspring Futon Mattresses and Covers

Rising Star...Stellar Home Furnishings
35 N.W. Bond St.
Bend, OR 97701

Toll-free: 800-828-6711
Phone: 541-382-4221
Fax: 541-383-5925
www.risingstarfurniture.com

Wellspring Futon Mattresses are made with 100%-recycled PET fiber batt, and cases are made from 100% organic cotton or a 50/50 cotton/polyester blend.

Natural Fiber Bedding and Mattresses

Vivètique
11911 Clark St.
Arcadia, CA 91006

Toll-free: 800-365-6563
Fax: 626-357-3248
www.vivetique.com

Vivètique natural-fiber mattresses are available in three types: standard cotton, organic cotton, hemp, and an organic cotton/wool blend. Organic cotton mattresses are made without the use of fire-retardant chemicals and, therefore, require a doctor's prescription showing chemical sensitivity to purchase. The organic cotton/wool blend mattress contains naturally fire-resistant wool. Organic cotton and wool pillows and wool mattress covers and comforters are also available.

---

12 48 13
Entrance Floor Mats and Frames

Dust and dirt can be carried into buildings on people's footwear, contributing to IAQ problems and reducing the life of interior floor finishes. Inclement weather increases the risk of personal injury due to slips and falls on wet floors. One way to treat both of these problems is to install comprehensive systems for removing dirt at the entrance to buildings. Properly maintained protective entryways also help reduce the use of hazardous cleaning goods. While very sophisticated entryway track-off systems are commonly installed in commercial buildings, simpler track-off systems also make sense for homes—as does a recommendation that homeowners and guests remove their outdoor shoes when they enter a home. (See feature article EBN Vol. 10, No. 10.)

EnvIRONtread

Arden Architectural Specialties, Inc.
151 5th Ave. NW, Ste. J
St. Paul, MN 55112

Toll-free: 800-521-1826
Phone: 651-631-1607
Fax: 651-631-0251
www.ardenarch.com

EnvIRONtread® II floor mats and grates provide highly durable entrance flooring made with recycled truck and aircraft tire treads alternating with recycled aluminum divider bars.

Most recently mentioned in EBN 10:10

C/S Pedisystems

Construction Specialties, Inc., Entrance Flooring Division
6696 Rte. 405 Hwy.
Muncy, PA 17756

Toll-free: 800-233-8493
Phone: 570-546-5941
Fax: 570-546-5169
www.c-sgroup.com

C/S Pedisystems offers a wide range of commercial entryway track-off floor products and systems including Pedimat®, TreadLine®, DuroMat®, PediTred®, Pedigrid®, and Grid-Line™. Aluminum components contain a minimum of 70-90% recycled content (roughly 33% post-consumer, 33% post-industrial). Powder coat finishes are available. Some products include PVC components; in some cases, PVC-free options are available. The C/S mat and grid carpet insert material has passed the air quality test of the Carpet and Rug Institute. Poured abrasive insert material has been GreenGuard certified.

Flex-Tuft

Flexco
1401 E. Sixth St.
P.O. Box 553
Tuscumbia, AL 35674

Toll-free: 800-633-3151
Phone: 256-383-7474
Fax: 800-346-9075
www.flexcofloors.com

Flex-Tuft® is a durable, anti-slip flooring made from recycled truck and bus tires. It has high sound-absorption characteristics and is suitable for damp, wet, and high-traffic areas, both indoor and outdoor. The brushed-nylon, tufted surface is available in tweed, delft-and-gray, cranberry-and-gray, and spruce-and-gray. Flex-Tuft is 3/8" thick; tiles are 12" x 12", and rolls are 12" x 30'. As with other flooring products made from recycled automobile tires, installation is only recommended in semi-enclosed spaces, well-ventilated indoor spaces, or outdoors.

Floor Keeper

Johnsonite
16910 Munn Rd.
Chagrin Falls, OH 44023

Toll-free: 800-899-8916
Phone: 440-543-8916
Fax: 440-543-8920
www.johnsonite.com

Floor Keeper™ from Johnsonite is an entrance track-off system made with recycled rubber and non-fading, nylon-fiber carpeting. The system can be cleaned in place; the mat does not need to be lifted to remove dirt and liquids. The surface mounted option is ½" thick, in black or gray, composed of a .375"-thick mat with 5/16"-high by 1"-wide carpet strips in an alternating rib pattern across a 19-5/8" width. The recess mounted option is 3/4" thick, composed of a ½" mat thickness with 5/16"-high by 1"-wide carpet strips in an alternating rib pattern across a 19-5/8" width. An aluminum matwell frame is required for the recessed option. Floor Keeper is available in nine colors.

Most recently mentioned in EBN 15:2

Terra-Turf

Johnsonite
16910 Munn Rd.
Chagrin Falls, OH 44023

Toll-free: 800-899-8916
Phone: 440-543-8916
Fax: 440-543-8920
www.johnsonite.com

Terra-Turf® from Johnsonite, made with recycled aircraft and truck tires, is a non-skid flooring particularly appropriate for ramps and entrances. It comes in 12" x 12" tiles or

12 00 00
Furnishings

12" x 25' coiled lengths, 3/8" thick. Available in black or brown, Terra-Turf comes with a 5-year warranty. As with other flooring products made from recycled automobile tires, installation is only recommended in semi-enclosed spaces, well-ventilated indoor spaces, or outdoors.

Most recently mentioned in EBN 15:2

Ruffian and Ruffian Ridge

Mannington Commercial
1844 U.S. Hwy. 41 S.E.
P.O. Box 12881
Calhoun, GA 30701

Toll-free: 800-241-2262
Phone: 706-629-7301
Fax: 706-625-6210
www.mannington.com

Mannington Commercial's Ruffian entryway track-off is a two-step system. Ruffian Ridge is a molded bi-level scraper tile with a network of reservoir channels to catch and hold water, soil, and debris from arriving occupants. Then the brush-like surface of Ruffian cleans and dries footwear, trapping and storing oil and finer dirt particles until cleaning. Ruffian and Ruffian Ridge are 18" x 18" modular nylon-polypropylene blend carpet tiles; Ruffian has a vinyl backing, while Ruffian Ridge has a neoprene rubber backing. Both are available in six colors. These products contain no recycled content.

Safetrack Recycled-Aluminum Foot Grilles

Mats, Inc.
37 Shuman Ave.
P.O. Box 839
Stoughton, MA 02072

Toll-free: 800-628-7462
Phone: 781-344-1536
Fax: 781-344-1537
www.matsinc.com

Safetrack is part of the Mats, Inc. Recycled Aluminum Foot Grille group. The "open waffle" design of the SafeTrack foot grille provides an intense scraping action for all types of footwear. SafeTrack also provides a 1"-deep recess to trap and accumulate debris. Foot Grilles allow removed soil to fall below the surface of the floor, thus eliminating the possibility of the debris tracking onto the interior floor covering. Construction is dimensionally stable with mechanical fasteners and is constructed of a min. 50% post consumer aluminum.

First Appearances

Milliken Carpet
201 Lukken Industrial Dr. W
P.O. Box 2956
LaGrange, GA 30240

Toll-free: 800-528-8453
Phone: 706-880-5344
Fax: 706-880-5906
www.millikencarpet.com

Milliken's First Appearances™ is a three-part "track-off" entryway system designed to capture soil and moisture tracked into a building. EZScrub™ is placed outside, typically in a protected space. This is then followed with BrushOff™, located inside the doorway or between double sets of doors. Lastly, CleanSweep™ can be installed in the lobby to capture any remaining dirt. A total length of 30' is recommended for most commercial and institutional buildings. First Appearances does not contain any PVC components.

Most recently mentioned in EBN 10:10

Fluff Cord

R. C. Musson Rubber Co.
1320 Archwood Ave.
P.O. Box 7038
Akron, OH 44306

Toll-free: 800-321-2381
Phone: 330-773-7651
Fax: 330-773-3254
www.mussonrubber.com

Made from recycled-tire rubber, Fluff Cord is a 12" x 12" floor-covering tile with a mesh backing. As with other flooring products made from recycled automobile tires, installation is only recommended in semi-enclosed spaces, well-ventilated indoor spaces, or outdoors.

12 48 44 Rubber Floor Mats

Floor mats made from recycled-tire rubber are durable, resilient, and slip-resistant. These products are often specified for their anti-fatigue benefits. Floor mats may be square-cut or tapered, with a choice of smooth or textured surfaces. These predominantly black products may have color integrated into the rubber as flecks, as the binding matrix, or as a thick wear layer. Custom logo options are also often available. The recycled-tire rubber and its binders or additives, however, may be significant sources of indoor air pollutants and are recommended only for indoor-outdoor or well-ventilated spaces. (See also 12 48 13 - Entrance Floor Mats and Frames.)

Eco-Link

Ashland Rubber Mats Co., Inc.
1221 Elm St.
P.O. Box 267
Ashland, OH 44805

Toll-free: 800-289-1476
Phone: 419-289-7614
Fax: 419-281-7356

Made from recycled truck tires, Eco-Link is a 1/2"-thick tire-link mat available in plain tire link or with a carpet-like finish, two styles in sizes from 13" x 23" to 24" x 36". Custom sizes are also available. As with other flooring products made from recycled automobile tires, installation is recommended in semi-enclosed spaces, well-ventilated indoor spaces, or outdoors.

Dinomat

Dinoflex Manufacturing, Ltd.
P.O. Box 3309
Salmon Arm, BC V1E 4S1 Canada

Toll-free: 877-713-1899
Phone: 252-832-7780
Fax: 800-305-2109
www.dinoflex.com

Dinomat® measures 4' x 6' and is made from 100% revulcanized recycled-tire rubber. Available in black only, Dinomat is a tough, abrasion-resistant flooring, typically used in such areas as free-weight rooms and ice hockey players' boxes.

Dura-Rug 400 and Dura-Tile II

Durable Corp.
75 N. Pleasant St.
Norwalk, OH 44857

Toll-free: 877-938-7225
Phone: 419-668-8138
Fax: 800-537-6287
www.durablecorp.com

Dura-Rug 400 is an open-weave mat made from strips of recycled tires. Dura-Rug has a chenille surface and is available with yellow or black nosings. Dura-Tile II is an entrance mat for heavy traffic areas and comes in 12"x12" tile or 12" strips up to 25' long. As with other flooring products made from recycled automobile tires, installation is recommended in semi-enclosed spaces, well-ventilated indoor spaces, or outdoors.

12 00 00
Furnishings

Dura Rug

R. C. Musson Rubber Co.
1320 Archwood Ave.
P.O. Box 7038
Akron, OH 44306

Toll-free: 800-321-2381
Phone: 330-773-7651
Fax: 330-773-3254
www.mussonrubber.com

Dura Rug is a recycled fluffed tire-link mat available in sizes from 2' x 3' up to 6' x 12'. As with other flooring products made from recycled automobile tires, installation is recommended in semi-enclosed spaces, well-ventilated indoor spaces, or outdoors.

Most recently mentioned in EBN 3:3

Rubber Mats

RB Rubber Products, Inc.
904 N.E. Tenth Ave.
McMinnville, OR 97128

Toll-free: 800-525-5530
Phone: 503-472-4691
Fax: 503-434-4455
www.rbrubber.com

RB Rubber mat products are made from recycled-tire rubber mixed with a synthetic binder. RB Rubber's 1/2"- and 3/4"-thick anti-fatigue/industrial matting has a raised anti-skid surface on one side and a smooth surface on the other. RB Tenderfoot Stall Mats are also available using the same polymer-bonded technology. As with other flooring products made from recycled automobile tires, installation is recommended in semi-enclosed spaces, well-ventilated indoor spaces, or outdoors.

Stall Mats

Recycled Technology, Inc.
19475 S.W. Teton Ave.
Tualatin, OR 97062

Toll-free: 800-455-6287
Phone: 503-691-5845
Fax: 503-692-9503
www.recycledtech.com

Recycled Technology's products are all made from recycled-tire rubber with a polyurethane binder. Redi-Mat and Stall Mats are 3/4" thick and come in 4' x 6' sizes and several textures. As with other flooring products made from recycled automobile tires, installation is recommended in semi-enclosed spaces, well-ventilated indoor spaces, or outdoors.

Wearwell Mats

Tennessee Mat Co.
1414 Fourth Ave. S
Nashville, TN 37210

Toll-free: 800-264-3030
Phone: 615-254-8381
Fax: 800-874-4551
www.wearwell.com

Tennessee Mat Company manufactures several products that contain over 80% recycled material. Enviromat (No. 405) is an 3/8"-thick indoor-outdoor anti-fatigue mat made from recycled-tire buffings with a polyurethane binder. It has a particularly high compressive strength. Heavy-Duty Rubber Tire Matting (No. 406), also 3/8" thick, is made from recycled-rubber reinforced with nylon cording and woven on galvanized wire. As with other flooring products made from recycled automobile tires, installation is recommended in semi-enclosed spaces, well-ventilated indoor spaces, or outdoors.

12 48 45
Plastic Floor Mats

Products listed here include high recycled content.

Add-A-Level and Poly-Riser Plastic Flooring

Structural Plastics Corp.
3401 Chief Dr.
Holly, MI 48442

Toll-free: 800-523-6899
Phone: 810-953-9400
Fax: 810-953-9440
www.spcindustrial.com

Add-A-Level is a molded plastic grid mat system designed to raise employees off wet, slippery floors and resist oils, grease, and chemical corrosion. Units are designed to be stackable to create an ergonomic working height. Poly-Riser is a plastic flooring product for similar purposes that is designed to be clipped together to fit any flooring configuration. Both products are made from recycled HDPE plastic.

Comfort Deck

Tennessee Mat Co.
1414 Fourth Ave. S
Nashville, TN 37210

Toll-free: 800-264-3030
Phone: 615-254-8381
Fax: 800-874-4551
www.wearwell.com

Comfort Deck is a porous anti-fatigue mat made from 100% recycled PVC. It is 7/8" thick and comes in 12"-square tiles. A similar product is available with a gritty surface. An absorbent, disposable underlayment made from 100% post-industrial recycled textiles (principally cotton) for use under porous floor matting products is also available.

12 48 46
Natural Fiber Floor Mats

These mats are made from durable natural fibers in a variety of styles and weaves. Common natural fibers for matting include sisal (often used in wall coverings), jute (used to make rope and burlap bags), and coir (from coconut husks). Natural-fiber mats generally don't have backings or chemical treatments. They're durable but may shed broken fibers, requiring periodic sweeping or vacuuming of the surrounding floor area.

Plain Herringbone-Weave Cocoa Matting

Allied Mat & Matting, Inc.
52-08 Grand Ave.
Maspeth, NY 11378

Toll-free: 800-452-5588
Phone: 718-381-9824
Fax: 718-894-4998
www.alliedmat.com

Plain Herringbone-Weave Cocoa Matting is made from coir fiber and comes in rolls that are 18", 27", 36", 45", 54", 63" or 72" wide and approximately 3/8" thick.

12 50 01
FSC-Certified Wood Furniture

Products listed here are produced using wood certified under standards established by the Forest Stewardship Council (FSC). Certification to FSC standards involves third-party evaluation and monitoring of sustainable forestry practices. SmartWood and Scientific Certification Services are the primary FSC-accredited third-party certifying organizations in North America. (See also 06 05 70 - Wood Products Certification and Information.)

Certified Wood Furniture

Beeken Parsons
1611 Harbor Rd.
Shelburne Farms
Shelburne, VT 05482

Phone: 802-985-2913
Fax: 802-985-8123
www.beekenparsons.com

Beeken Parsons offers Vermont Forest Furniture, a line of FSC-certified forest furniture handcrafted out of character wood incorporating knots, grain textures, and colors that reflect the life of the tree and "tell the story of the forest." Character Wood often comes from trees that are relegated to such low-value uses as firewood and paper pulp. Increasing the value of these trees will help to offset the costs of responsible forest stewardship. Beeken Parsons has been designing and building custom furniture for more than 20 years. Its shop is located at historic Shelburne Farms in Shelburne, Vermont.

Certified Hardwood Furniture

Berkeley Mills
2830 Seventh St.
Berkeley, CA 94710

Phone: 510-549-2854
Fax: 510-548-0865
www.berkeleymills.com

Berkeley Mills is a manufacturer of high-end custom and limited-production furniture available in FSC-certified hardwoods including cherry and maple. Distribution is nationwide though primarily on the West Coast.

Certified Hardwood Furniture

Cotswold Furniture Makers
904 Sawyer Rd.
Whiting, VT 05778

Phone: 802-623-8400
Fax: 802-623-8501
www.cotswoldfurniture.com

Cotswold Furniture Makers offers handcrafted home and office furniture. Pieces are typically made from American black cherry from FSC-certified sources. Other hardwoods—such as oak, maple, and walnut—may be offered but may not be available FSC-certified.

Environmental Language Furniture

New

Environmental Language
Four 2 Five Park Barrington Dr.
Barrington, IL 60010

Phone: 847-382-9285
Fax: 847-382-9311
www.el-furniture.com

Environmental Language offers high-end home furniture made with locally reclaimed wood, rapidly renewable materials, and wood which can be specified as FSC for a 10% upcharge. Upholstered products are made with natural latex, organic cotton, wool, and jute with 100% organic materials also specified for a 10% upcharge. El furniture uses non-toxic low-VOC finishes and adhesives. El collections include tables, chairs, stools, sofas, sleepers, desks, nightstands and dressers.

Modular Furniture

IKEA, North American Service Office
496 W. Germantown Pike
Plymouth Meeting, PA 19462

Phone: 610-834-0180
Fax: 610-834-0439
www.ikea.com

Swedish-based IKEA has taken a number of steps to reduce the environmental impact of its modular, build-it-yourself furniture products. An FSC member, IKEA's long term goal is to have all wood used in its products certified by the Forest Stewardship Council (FSC) or an equivalent program. Currently all high-value tropical wood species must originate from forests certified by the FSC. PVC has been eliminated in all products except the isolating plastic of electric cables, and the company is looking to find an alternative for this as well. Bromine fire-retardants have been eliminated entirely. IKEA uses water-based and UV-cured coatings, powder coatings for metal components, and white and hot-melt glues. A line of air-filled seating products is available as well.

Certified Wood Furniture

Island Pond Woodproducts Inc.
306 Meadow St.
P.O. Box 236
Island Pond, VT 05846

Phone: 802-723-6611
Fax: 802-723-6622
www.islandpondwoodproducts.com

Founded by displaced workers after a multinational furniture manufacturer shut its doors on a local plant, employee-owned Island Pond Woodproducts produces handcrafted residential, business, and institutional furniture from locally harvested FSC-certified lumber or sustainably harvested lumber.

Low Toxicity Furniture

Karp Woodworks
136 Fountain St.
Ashland, MA 01721

Phone: 508-881-7000
Fax: 508-881-7084
www.karpwoodworks.com

Karp Woodworks specializes in building custom furniture for chemically sensitive people. Low-VOC finishes are used, as well as organic cotton and special batting for upholstered designs.

Knoll Certified Wood Furniture

Knoll, Inc.
1235 Water Street
East Greenville, PA 18041

Toll-free: 800-343-5665
Phone: 215-679-7991
Fax: 215-679-1385
www.knoll.com

All of Knoll®, Inc.'s standard furniture lines are now available with FSC-certified wood. Using FSC's percentage-based claims rules, the company can label products as certified as long as 70% of the wood in the overall job is certified. Knoll currently has no products for which FSC-certified wood is used by default, due to difficulties in procuring the quantity of wood required.

Most recently mentioned in EBN 12:3

Certified Wood Furniture

South Cone Trading Company
19038 S. Vermont Ave.
Gardena, CA 90248

Toll-free: 800-466-7282
Phone: 310-538-5797
Fax: 310-538-2406
www.southcone.com

South Cone Trading Company is an FSC-certified furniture manufacturer with factories in Lima, Peru (FSC-certified) and Santa Fe, Argentina (FSC certification in progress). According to the manufacturer, about 30% of their production is certified, but they expect to have 90% certified by the end of 2005. The company offers a variety of home furnishings sold nationwide through approximately 300 independently owned retail stores and also sells to hotels and

12 00 00 Furnishings

resorts on a contract basis. South Cone is the founder of PaTS (Partnerships and Technology for Sustainability), a nonprofit organization pursuing sustainable development in the Peruvian rainforest through the implementation of market-driven forms of forest conservation.

Certified Wood Furniture

The Joinery
4804 S.E. Woodstock Blvd.
Portland, OR 97206

Toll-free: 800-259-6762
Phone: 503-788-8547
Fax: 503-788-4608
www.thejoinery.com

The Joinery hand-crafts a wide variety of home and office furniture with lines reflecting Mission, Shaker, Asian, and French styles. FSC-certified hardwood, mostly cherry, is used in 75% of their work. Custom orders are commonly filled. The Joinery guarantees its furniture for life.

12 00 00
Furnishings

Architectural Furniture

The Valley City Manufacturing Company Ltd.

For full listing, see CSI section 12 35 00 - Specialty Casework

Certified Cherry Furniture

Thos. Moser Cabinetmakers
72 Wright's Lndg.
Auburn, ME 04211

Toll-free: 800-708-9045
Phone: 207-784-3332
Fax: 207-784-6973
www.thosmoser.com

Thos. Moser Cabinetmakers offers FSC-certified cherry, upon request if available, for large-volume, contracted furniture. Their products are backed by a 5-year guarantee.

Certified Wood Furniture

Wiggers Custom Furniture
173 Reach Industrial Park Rd.
Port Perry, ON L9L 1B2 Canada

Phone: 905-985-1128
Fax: 905-985-0889
www.wiggersfurniture.com

Wiggers Custom Furniture manufactures individually crafted casegoods, desks, tables, consoles, and wall hung consoles made from FSC-certified woods. Wiggers Custom Furniture is one of the first custom furniture makers in the world to become FSC-certified.

12 50 02
Reclaimed-Wood Furniture

Products listed here have significant wood content that was reclaimed or salvaged from other uses (barns and buildings slated for demolition, for example). Some of these products use salvaged wood sources that have been certified through the SmartWood Rediscovered Wood Program. (See feature article EBN Vol. 9, No. 5.)

Antique Woods & Colonial Restorations

Antique Woods & Colonial Restorations, Inc.

For full listing, see CSI section 09 64 02 - Reclaimed-Wood Flooring

Appalachian Woods

Appalachian Woods, LLC

For full listing, see CSI section 09 64 02 - Reclaimed-Wood Flooring

Barnstormers Reclaimed Hand-Hewn Beams

Barnstormers

For full listing, see CSI section 09 64 02 - Reclaimed-Wood Flooring

Furniture and Kitchen Cabinetry from Urban Trees

CitiLog

For full listing, see CSI section 12 35 30 - Residential Casework

Salvaged-Wood Furniture

Clayoquot Crafts   **New**
1336 Chesterman Beach Rd.
Tofino, BC V0R 2Z0 Canada

Toll-free: 877-522-3327
Phone: 250-725-3990
www.clayoquotcrafts.com

Clayoquot Crafts hand-builds furniture suitable for outdoor or indoor use from Western Red Cedar or Alder locally salvaged from discards remaining after logging operations. Clayoquot Crafts is located in Tofino, British Columbia, Canada.

Millennium Oak

Ecologic, Inc.
921 Sherwood Dr.
Lake Bluff, IL 60044

Toll-free: 800-899-8004
Phone: 847-234-5855
Fax: 847-234-5845
www.ecoinc.com

Ecologic's Millennium Oak furnishings are made from recycled, plantation-grown hardwood with an oak color. The product line includes beds and lofts, desks, dressers, nightstands, and bookcases.

Reclaimed-Wood Building Products

Endura Wood Products, Ltd.

For full listing, see CSI section 09 64 02 - Reclaimed-Wood Flooring

River-Reclaimed Wood Products

Goodwin Heart Pine Company

For full listing, see CSI section 09 64 02 - Reclaimed-Wood Flooring

Reclaimed-Wood Building Products

Solid Wood Products

For full listing, see CSI section 09 64 02 - Reclaimed-Wood Flooring

Wooden Duck Reclaimed Furniture   **New**

The Wooden Duck
2919 Seventh St.
Berkeley, CA 94710

Toll-free: 866-848-3575
Phone: 510-848-3575
Fax: 510-848-3512
www.thewoodenduck.com

The Wooden Duck offers furniture, including custom work, made with reclaimed California Douglas fir or imported reclaimed teak. Their product lines are sold to the wholesale market and through their retail store, which also features the work of local craftspeople working exclusively with reclaimed wood.

Urban Hardwoods

Urban Hardwoods

For full listing, see CSI section 09 64 02 - Reclaimed-Wood Flooring

Reclaimed-Wood Building Products

Vintage Log and Lumber, Inc.

For full listing, see CSI section 06 13 02 - Reclaimed-Wood Heavy Timber

Reclaimed-Wood Building Products

Vintage Material Supply Co.

For full listing, see CSI section 09 64 02 - Reclaimed-Wood Flooring

12 50 03
Recycled-Content Furniture

Conventional furniture may offgas formaldehyde and VOCs, and is often very resource-intensive to produce. A number of innovative furniture products have been introduced in recent years made with both high recycled content and low emitting materials. Products listed here have high recycled content, and are produced from materials that will not compromise indoor air quality.

Shetkastone

All Paper Recycling, Inc.

For full listing, see CSI section 12 36 00 - Countertops

Danko Chairs & Benches

Danko Design Initiative
839 McKinzie St.
York, PA 17403

Phone: 717-309-3731
Fax: 717-848-5858
www.peterdanko.com

Danko offers recycled-content furniture, most of which incorporates frames of structural ply-bent veneers (which provide higher yields of usable wood from a log than does solid lumber). Veneer laminations are made with water-based adhesives. Recycled materials, including post-industrial automotive seat belt material, are used for seat suspension and padding. As of March, 2006, the company is migrating to FSC certified wood veneer, and indicates that all their products will be free of added formaldehyde, isocyanates, and brominated flame retardants.

ECO+Plus

Ecologic, Inc.
921 Sherwood Dr.
Lake Bluff, IL 60044

Toll-free: 800-899-8004
Phone: 847-234-5855
Fax: 847-234-5845
www.ecoinc.com

Ecologic designs and manufactures furniture of recycled HDPE. Founded in 1992 to manufacture better college dormitory furniture, the company also makes products for other markets, including federal and municipal office buildings and fire stations. Eco+Plus is an attractive line of desks, bookcases, lofts, beds and bunks, dressers, nightstands, and wardrobes. Products generally do not require tools for assembly.

Olive Designs Contract Furniture

Olive Designs
230 South Rd.
High Point, NC 27262

Phone: 336-841-2180
www.olivedesigns.net

Olive Designs uses a high percentage of organic and recycled material in its contemporary contract seating and tables, including recycled textiles; hemp textiles; wheat-straw board; recycled and salvaged glass; regrind nylon; and rebond foam (which may contain PBDE flame retardants). Waterborne adhesives are used in the upholstery process; wood components are laminated with formaldehyde-free glue and have waterborne or hybrid acrylic/urethane water finishes; metal frames have powder-coat or nickel-plate finishes. All products are made with more than 50% recycled content (some approach nearly 100%), and have little or no VOC emissions. The manufacturer donates a percentage of profits from each order to the Karen Beasley Sea Turtle Rescue and Rehab Hospital.

Pulp Furniture

Poesis Design
P.O. Box 246
Norfolk, CT 06058

Phone: 860-542-5152
www.poesisdesign.com

The Pulp Armchair (31" x 31" x 26", cube-shaped with upholstered cushions) is made of recycled newspaper blended with water and wax, and is designed with maple or walnut trim. FSC-certified wood may be specified. Pulp end tables, coffee tables, beds, bureaus, and file cabinets are also available.

Salvaged-Metal-Parts Furnishings

Resource Revival, Inc.
P.O. Box 440
Mosier, OR 97040

Toll-free: 800-866-8823
Phone: 503-282-1449
Fax: 800-736-0984
www.resourcerevival.com

Resource Revival crafts furniture, door and window grates, and other items from discarded bicycle and automotive parts and other recycled materials. Additional products include clocks, desk accessories, picture frames, promotional items and corporate gifts, trophies and awards. All items are handmade. The manufacturer has certified the following recycled-content levels (by weight): total recovered material 90% typical, 90% guaranteed; post-consumer material 90% typical, 90% guaranteed.

12 51 00
Office Furniture

12 00 00
Furnishings

Conventional office furniture may offgas formaldehyde and VOCs, and is often very resource-intensive to produce. Where feasible, re-using or refurbishing existing furniture or selling it for re-use can save both financial and environmental resources, Products listed here are re-manufactured or refurbished, produced from materials that will not compromise indoor air quality, or carry particularly low life-cycle environmental burdens.

Refurbished Office Furniture

Conklin Office Furniture
56 Canal St.
Holyoke, MA 01040

Toll-free: 800-817-1187
Phone: 413-315-6777
Fax: 413-315-6454
www.conklinoffice.com

Conklin Office Furniture has been offering salvaged office furniture since 1981. Panel systems and furniture are sold "as is" (when available) as well as refurbished. The company's main location is in Holyoke, Massachusetts with branch offices in New York City and Philadelphia.

Recycled/Remanufactured Office Furniture

Creative Office Systems, Inc. (COS)
2470 Estand Way
Pleasant Hill, CA 94523

Toll-free: 800-400-7787
Phone: 925-686-6355
Fax: 925-686-8469
www.creativeoffice.com

Creative Office Systems specializes in the recycling and remanufacturing of UL-listed Herman Miller and Haworth systems furniture and other products.

Most recently mentioned in EBN 11:9

Refurbished Office Furniture

Davies Office Refurbishing, Inc.
38 Loudonville Rd., Entrance A
Retail Outlet
Albany, NY 12204

Toll-free: 888-773-3872
Phone: 518-449-2040
Fax: 518-449-4036
www.daviesoffice.com

Davies Office Refurbishing offers "as is" salvaged and refurbished office furniture from all major office furniture manufacturers. The company also offers rentals, a trade-in and banking program, powder coat finishes, and recycled content fabric options.

Ecowork Furniture

Ecowork LLC
P.O. Box 210
30 Cascade Mall N
Bonneville, WA 98639

Phone: 509-427-4100
www.ecowork.com

Ecowork is a line of freestanding office furniture using low-VOC paints, finishes, and adhesives and made from 95% recycled or rapidly renewable materials, including post-consumer automobile tires, cardboard, wastepaper (Homasote™), and Greenboard MDF from FSC-certified pine or ag waste. Ecowork's flexible system of modular pieces are shipped flat and user-assembled to form acoustic partitions, workstations, bookshelves, tables, and printer stands. Ecowork also provides workstation-integrated accessories for managing power and data cables.

Most recently mentioned in EBN 9:9, 10:3, 10:4, 10:11

Refurbished and Remanufactured Office Furniture

Mansers Office Interiors
185 Paularino Ave., Ste. A
Costa Mesa, CA 92626

Toll-free: 800-473-3393
Phone: 714-754-1696
Fax: 714-754-1697
www.mansers.com

Mansers Office Interiors refurbishes Haworth and Steelcase system furniture, workstations, desks, chairs, and files. Mansers also refurbishes and/or remanufactures Herman Miller office furniture.

Remanufactured Office Furniture

Open Plan Systems, Inc.
14140 N. Washington Hwy.
P.O. Box 1810
Ashland, VA 23005

Toll-free: 800-728-0781
Phone: 804-228-5600
Fax: 804-228-5656
www.openplan.com

Open Plan Systems (OPS) is an independent remanufacturer of Herman Miller workstations. The structural components of workstations are repainted using low-VOC powder coating processes, and new finishes are applied. 100% recycled fabrics are offered as an option.

Refurbished Office Furniture

R.A.C.E.
1000 N.W. First Ave., Ste. 28
Boca Raton, FL 33432

Toll-free: 888-893-7223
Phone: 561-347-7666
Fax: 561-347-8648
www.raceinc.org

R.A.C.E. refurbishes Herman Miller office furniture and partitioning systems.

Remanufactured Office Furniture

RBF Interiors
5055 Natural Bridge Ave.
St. Loius, MO 63115

Phone: 314-383-7003
Fax: 314-383-5791
www.rbfstl.com

In business since 1984, RBF Interiors remanufactures Steelcase, Herman Miller, and Haworth office furniture. RBF uses powder-coat finishes on most high-wear parts and offers a 100% recycled-content fabric option. The company has retail locations in Cincinnati, Ohio, and St. Louis, Missouri; its manufacturing facility is in St. Louis.

Sonrisa Refurbished Office Furniture

Sonrisa Furniture
7609 Beverly Blvd.
Los Angeles, CA 90036

Toll-free: 800-668-1020
Phone: 323-935-8438
Fax: 323-935-7338
www.sonrisafurniture.com

Sonrisa sells refurbished vintage American steel furniture, including office and institutional products, ranging from chairs and desks to lamps and lockers. Old paint is removed from the furniture, and a clear sealer is used in the refinishing process.

Office Furniture

Steelcase, Inc.
901 44th St. SE
Grand Rapids, MI 49508

Toll-free: 800-333-9939
Phone: 616-247-2710
www.steelcase.com

Steelcase has adopted a broad range of corporate environmental principles that have contributed to more efficient materials usage and reductions in VOC and other emissions. The company conducts extensive IAQ testing of all products. The Answer® line of panel-based workstation components has achieved a Silver rating from the MBDC Cradle to Cradle™ certification program.

Most recently mentioned in EBN 4:3, 4:4, 14:9, 16:1, 16:2

Verde Business Furniture

Verde Interior Products
P.O. Box 1507
Goldenrod (Orlando), FL 32792

Phone: 407-673-7474
Fax: 407-679-1567
www.verdeproducts.com

Verde Interior Products manufactures a line of standard and custom-made business furniture relying on high recycled-content, low- or no-VOC, and biobased materials. The core material for many of the offerings consists of 100% recycled-content SONOBoard3D made by Sonoco, a lightweight, high-strength material with no added binders. Other materials used are recycled-denim acoustical insulation; nontoxic, low-VOC paints and finishes; and Climatex® Lifecycle™ or industrial hemp fabrics. Worktop surfaces can be finished with a choice of linoleum or plastic laminate. Some of the products are adjustable for height and other dimensions and can be reconfigured to suit many different situations. No PVC is used in any of Verde's products.

12 52 00
Seating

Seating is made from a wide variety of materials, and may be both resource-intensive to produce and contribute to poor indoor air quality. Seating products listed here have features such as being made from recycled materials or certified wood; having "green" upholstery; safety from an indoor-air-quality standpoint; design-for-disassembly and refurbishment or recycling; and avoiding materials with high environmental burdens (brominated flame retardants, plasticizers, PVC, etc.).

Zody Chair

Haworth, Inc.
One Haworth Center
Holland, MI 49423

Phone: 616-393-3000
Fax: 616-393-1570
www.haworth.com

The Zody™ chair from Haworth was created to conform with the MBDC protocol. It features a patented asymmetrical lumbar support that allows for separate adjustments to each side of the back, and sophisticated arm-rest adjustments. Haworth claims that the chair contains up to 50% recycled content (depending on options). The factory in which it is manufactured is wind-energy powered and ISO 14001 certified.

Most recently mentioned in EBN 14:7, 15:2, 16:2

Mirra and Celle Office Chairs

Herman Miller, Inc.
855 E. Main Ave.
P.O. Box 302
Zeeland, MI 49464

Toll-free: 888-443-4357
Phone: 616-654-3000
Fax: 616-654-3632
www.hermanmiller.com

The Mirra chair was designed by Studio 7.5 Berlin in cooperation with McDonough Braungart Design Chemistry in accordance with MBDC's ecological design protocol. It has a minimum number of components, most of which are readily recycled and made from relatively benign materials, including polypropylene (the back), and nylon 6 (the base). Each part is labeled for future processing. At its release in June 2003, color options for Mirra include 2 finishes, 10 seat colors, and 8 back colors. The Celle chair has a seat and back made of a pliable polymer molded into cells and loops that provide varying amounts of flex throughout the seat and back. Celle contains 33% recycled content, is 99% recyclable, and can be disassembled using common hand tools in five minutes, according to the company. It is fully adjustable, with a wide range of options, including the same Latitude upholstery that is available on Mirra chairs. Celle chair is manufactured using green electricity.

Most recently mentioned in EBN 12:6 & 16:2

Life Chair and Chadwick Chair

Knoll, Inc.
1235 Water Street
East Greenville, PA 18041

Toll-free: 800-343-5665
Phone: 215-679-7991
Fax: 215-679-1385
www.knoll.com

Knoll's ergonomic, Greenguard-certified Life chairs have a total post-consumer and post-industrial recycled content of 52% to 64% (depending on the model) and are 70-80% readily recyclable. 100% recycled-content fabric may be specified. The burnished aluminum structure is coating-free; other coatings and adhesives used contain almost no VOCs. Life chairs are PVC-free, and most plastic parts have molded labels to facilitate eventual recycling. Knoll offers a 10-year warranty on these chairs. Knolls Chadwick chair was designed in accordance with the company's own Environmental Design Guide. Like many of the others, it has a mesh back and seat, which allow for air circulation to enhance comfort while avoiding the difficulties of procuring foam without brominated flame retardants. Chadwick is also designed for disassembly, and Knoll claims an overall recycled content rate of 41%.

Jersey Seating

Steelcase, Inc.
901 44th St. SE
Grand Rapids, MI 49508

Toll-free: 800-333-9939
Phone: 616-247-2710
www.steelcase.com

Steelcase's Jersey Seating line is PVC-, chrome-, and adhesive-free, uses water-blown cushioning foams, powder-coated metal finishes, and is Greenguard™-certified for low VOC emissions. The steel components contain 30% recycled content; the fabric is 100% recycled; and the company indicates that the product is 99.8% recyclable. Available as a four-leg frame or as an office chair, with or without arms, on casters or gliders.

Think Chair

Steelcase, Inc.
901 44th St. SE
Grand Rapids, MI 49508

Toll-free: 800-333-9939
Phone: 616-247-2710
www.steelcase.com

Steelcase's Think chair contains no PVC, solvents, brominated flame retardants, benzene, chrome, lead, mercury, or adhesives, and is Greenguard™-certified for low VOC emissions. Complete life-cycle analysis for several environmental categories was performed and verified by independent third-party institutes as part of the design phase. The highly adjustable ergonomic chair is comprised of up to 47% recycled material and is 99% recyclable. The chair can easily be disassembled for recycling with common hand tools.

Most recently mentioned in EBN 13:8 & 15:1

Picto Office Chairs

Vecta
1800 S. Great Southwest Pkwy.
Grand Prairie, TX 75051

Toll-free: 800-333-9939
Phone: 972-641-2860
Fax: 972-660-1746
www.vecta.com

The Picto line of office chairs from Wilkhahn (distributed in North America by Vecta, a division of Steelcase) uses materials that were selected for minimal environmental impact. The chairs have a perforated polypropylene back and polypropylene seat shell. Optional armrests are available in laminated beech wood or polypropylene. Picto chairs are also designed for ease of disassembly and recycling. The line includes both swivel chairs and stationary cantilevered chairs.

12 59 00
Systems Furniture

Modular, flexible, integrated interior architecture for office partitions and cubicles that incorporate such features as access flooring, walls, wiring and cabling, and lighting, can decrease building and remodeling time significantly. When the access flooring doubles as ducting,

12 00 00
Furnishings

use of these systems can contribute to improved air handling and reduced energy use. Products listed here contain recycled or rapidly-renewable materials, certified wood, and/or have low emissions.

Recycled- and Biobased-Content Office Furniture

Baltix Furniture, Inc.
2160 Daniels St.
Long Lake, MN 55356

Phone: 763-210-0155
Fax: 763-210-0152
www.baltix.com

Baltix commercial furniture is made with materials such as sunflower seed hulls, wheat straw, recycled wood fiber, and recycled plastics and paper - with no added formaldehyde, and no toxic binders or finishes. The competitively-priced stock and custom workstations, tables, seating, and accessories (including bookshelves, files, cabinets, and partitions) are available in low VOC clear coat, and a wide range of Marmoleum® (linoleum) colors. Frames are constructed of anodized aluminum (with a minimum of 75% pre-consumer recycled content), or 30% recycled content steel with an available VOC-free powder-coat option. Baltix will assist in proper reuse or recycling of their products at the end of their useful life.

Evolve Office Systems

Global Contract Furniture
1350 Flint Rd.
Downsview, ON M3J 2J7 Canada

Phone: 416-661-3660
Fax: 416-736-6685
www.globalcontract.com

The Evolve line of office furnishings from Global Contract includes modular wall systems, desks, and work surfaces. The wall panels contain a honeycomb core made with 75% recycled Kraft paper, insulated on both sides with Roxul® acoustical mineral board made from slag. Work surface substrates are made with Woodstalk™ agrifiber cores. Fabric offerings include product made from 100% recycled plastics. Wood and polypropylene for molded elements of the system are sourced as wastes from other Global divisions. Only water-based adhesives are used. The Evolve line is GreenGuard certified for low emissions.

Most recently mentioned in EBN 14:12

Pathways Architectural Solutions

Steelcase, Inc.
901 44th St. SE
Grand Rapids, MI 49508

Toll-free: 800-333-9939
Phone: 616-247-2710
www.steelcase.com

Pathways Architectural Solutions from Steelcase integrates flexible architectural walls, modular power, zone cabling, access floors, and managed lighting. The access flooring is available in heights from 3" to 24". In floor heights above 8", the access flooring can be used for HVAC ducting, which can reduce energy costs. The modular zone cabling consists of pre-engineered, snap-together, multi-circuit components for complete distribution systems. The moveable wall systems are available in solid or glass; vertical slots accommodate installation of work surfaces, storage components, panels, and lighting. In addition to reducing construction and reconfiguration schedules, all elements of the system are Greenguard™-certified—some wood option exceptions may apply—and can be disassembled and recycled at the end of their useful life. Steelcase uses no brominated flame retardants in the Pathways suite of products. Small amounts of PVC are used on the Work Surfaces, Post and Beam, and Pathways Privacy Wall components.

Systems Furniture

New

Watson Furniture Group
26246 Twelve Trees Ln. NW
Poulsbo, WA 98370

Toll-free: 800-426-1202
Phone: 360-394-1300
Fax: 360-394-1322
www.watsonfurniture.com

The Watson Desking line includes adaptable, ergonomic desks, tables, storage, and partition components. The Activewerks line of adjustable workstations is offered with a coordinated line of tables, pedestals, files, and bookcases. The Synergy line is designed for communications hubs. Components include 100% recycled polyester fabrics, polyester powder-coated steel, laminate surfaces made with 30 – 40% recycled paper content (with a phenolic resin binder), waterbased adhesives, and wood substrates made with 100% pre-consumer recycled wood. Rapidly renewable, FSC-certified, and formaldehyde-free substrates may be specified. Typical desks and storage components contain more than 60% pre-consumer recycled material, according to the manufacturer. Some trim components contain PVC.

Most recently mentioned in EBN 15:3

12 93 13
Bicycle Racks

Embracing the needs of more sustainable forms of transportation is a key component of a green building design. Bicycle usage needs include racks for locking bicycles, enclosed storage lockers, and shower facilities in workplaces. Products listed here are considered green by virtue of their use, however some products also include recycled content. (See feature article EBN Vol. 5, No. 1.)

Recycled-Plastic Products

American Recycled Plastic, Inc.

For full listing, see CSI section 12 93 43 - Site Seating and Tables, Plastic

Cycle-Safe

Cycle-Safe, Inc.
4630 Ada Dr., Ste. B
Ada, MI 49301

Toll-free: 888-950-6531
Phone: 616-954-9977
Fax: 616-954-0290
www.cycle-safe.com

The Cycle-Safe® Wallrack™ is a space-efficient, vertical bike hanger system for campus, transit stations, and workplaces. Front tires and frames can be secured with common D-locks. Cycle-Safe's PROPark® bicycle lockers are closed molded from fiberglass-reinforced polyester. (Unlike the open molding process used by many other manufacturers, closed molding prevents VOCs from being released into the atmosphere.) An interior partition is made from OSB. Each 4' 2" high by 6' 5" deep by 3' 2" wide module holds two bicycles. A variety of configurations are available, with the longest continuous locker model having 12 units to hold 24 bicycles.

Earthcare Series

Litchfield Industries

For full listing, see CSI section 12 93 43 - Site Seating and Tables, Plastic

Site Amenities

Recycled Plastic Man, Inc.

For full listing, see CSI section 12 93 43 - Site Seating and Tables, Plastic

Mini-Mum and Little Parker Bike Racks

Rutland Industries
123 Park St.
Rutland, VT 05702

Phone: 802-775-7638
Fax: 802-775-9746
www.rutlandindustries.com

Rutland Industries manufactures two bike rack systems made from steel with powder-coat finishes. The Mini-Mum™ vertical bike hangers are designed to be anchored to a wall and are available with an optional vinyl-coated security cable. When installed using a "w" configuration, bikes can be stored as close as 1' apart. Little Parker™ can be placed against a wall or anchored to concrete for freestanding function; it holds one bicycle per bollard-like rack in a secure upright position. Optional connector bars are available for multiple installation. Formerly offered by Bike Track, Inc., these products are made in Vermont by the non-profit Rutland Industries and can be shipped compactly via UPS.

Dura-Locker

Trilary, Inc.
2700 Laura Ln.
Middleton, WI 53562

Toll-free: 800-448-7931
Phone: 608-831-9040
Fax: 608-831-7623
www.madrax.com

Dura-Locker™ bicycle enclosures provide secure storage for bicycles.

12 93 23
Trash, Litter, and Recycling Receptors

Enabling homeowners and commercial building occupants to be good environmental stewards is important. Systems that make it easy to recycle wastes should be provided in houses, apartment buildings, offices, and institutions. Recycled plastic receptacles are most commonly made from either HDPE or commingled plastics. Recycled commingled plastics may have slightly inconsistent properties, but this is a lower-grade waste material that is generally more of a disposal problem. Products listed here contain recycled content.

Recycled-Plastic Products

American Recycled Plastic, Inc.

For full listing, see CSI section 12 93 43 - Site Seating and Tables, Plastic

Barco Recycled-Content Products

Barco Products

For full listing, see CSI section 12 93 43 - Site Seating and Tables, Plastic

Bedford Technology Recycled-Plastic Products

Bedford Technology, LLC

For full listing, see CSI section 06 53 13 - Solid Plastic Decking

Site Furnishings

Doty & Sons Concrete Products, Inc.
1275 E. State St.
Sycamore, IL 60178

Toll-free: 800-233-3907
Fax: 815-895-8035
www.dotyconcrete.com

Doty & Sons Concrete Products uses recycled HDPE plastic in its precast concrete site amenities, including benches and table sets, recycling and waste receptacles.

Recycled-Plastic Site Amenities

DuMor, Inc.

For full listing, see CSI section 12 93 43 - Site Seating and Tables, Plastic

Recycled-Plastic Site Furnishings

Durable Plastic Design, LLC.

For full listing, see CSI section 12 93 43 - Site Seating and Tables, Plastic

Benches, Picnic Tables, and Recycling Receptacles

Eagle One Site Furnishings

For full listing, see CSI section 12 93 43 - Site Seating and Tables, Plastic

Eco Outdoor Series

Ecologic, Inc.

For full listing, see CSI section 12 93 43 - Site Seating and Tables, Plastic

Conservancy Series - Benches, Picnic Tables, and Recycling Receptacles

Florida Playground and Steel Co.
For full listing, see CSI section 12 93 43 - Site Seating and Tables, Plastic

Recycled-Plastic Site Amenities

Great Lakes Specialty Products

For full listing, see CSI section 12 93 43 - Site Seating and Tables, Plastic

Site Furnishings and Materials

Inteq Corp.

For full listing, see CSI section 12 93 43 - Site Seating and Tables, Plastic

12 00 00
Furnishings

Benches, Picnic Tables, Waste Receptacles, and Planters

Kay Park Recreation Corp.

For full listing, see CSI section 12 93 43 - Site Seating and Tables, Plastic

Benches, Picnic Tables, and Trash Receptacles

Landscape Forms, Inc.

For full listing, see CSI section 12 93 43 - Site Seating and Tables, Plastic

Earthcare Series

Litchfield Industries

For full listing, see CSI section 12 93 43 - Site Seating and Tables, Plastic

Recycled-Plastic Recycling Stations

Midpoint International, Inc.
35 Furbacher Ln., Unit 1
Aurora, ON L4G 6W3 Canada

Toll-free: 888-646-4246
Phone: 905-726-9658
Fax: 888-547-5411
www.midpoint-int.com

Midpoint International's Recycled Recyclers are a series of containers made from 100% recycled content. Molded components are comprised of mixed plastics and wood flour; lumber components are an extruded mix of post-consumer and post-industrial #2 plastic—at least 90% HDPE.

Pilot Rock Site Furnishings

R. J. Thomas Manufacturing Co., Inc.
For full listing, see CSI section 12 93 43
- Site Seating and Tables, Plastic

Site Amenities

Recycled Plastic Man, Inc.

For full listing, see CSI section 12 93 43
- Site Seating and Tables, Plastic

PV-powered Compacting Waste Receptacle

Seahorse Power Company
50 Brook Rd.
Needham, MA 02494

Toll-free: 888-820-0300
Phone: 617-901-3454
Fax: 781-444-6004
www.seahorsepower.com

The rugged BigBelly compacting trash/recycling receptacle saves energy in more than one way. Deposits are compacted up to 90% of the original size with 2,000 lbs of force, reducing the frequency of pick-ups; and the unit signals wirelessly for pick-up when it's full, reducing vehicle emissions to pick up trash that isn't there. And it does these things using solar power. The cordless, movable, and vandal-resistant unit eliminates unsightly and potentially hazardous overflowing bins. Animals, bugs, and bees can't enter the machine, which has a pull-down door similar to a mailbox. A thick plexiglass cover protects the PV panel; and the heavy-gauge steel exterior has powder-coat finish appropriate for icy and marine environments. The internal sealed battery should be replaced and recycled every four years.

12 00 00
Furnishings

Recycled-Plastic Site Furnishings

Taylors Recycled Plastic Products Inc.

For full listing, see CSI section 12 93 43
- Site Seating and Tables, Plastic

Recycled-Plastic Site Amenities

The Plastic Lumber Company, Inc.

For full listing, see CSI section 12 93 43
- Site Seating and Tables, Plastic

Recycle Design Site Furnishings

Trimax Building Products, Inc.

For full listing, see CSI section 12 93 43
- Site Seating and Tables, Plastic

Recycling and Waste Bins

United Receptacle
P.O. Box 870
Pottsville, PA 17901

Toll-free: 800-233-0314
Phone: 570-622-7715
Fax: 570-622-3817
www.unitedrecept.com

United Receptacle offers a variety of receptacles for recycling and waste collection. All steel products have at least 30% recycled content. Aluminum products contain up to 70% recycled content. Perma-wood™ slats are 100% recycled polyethylene. Uni-Koat® powder-coated finish contains no VOCs, and overspray is 98% reusable.

2nd Site Systems

Victor Stanley, Inc.

For full listing, see CSI section 12 93 43
- Site Seating and Tables, Plastic

Recycling Containers and Waste Receptacles

Vital Visions Corp.
9663 Hwy. 20 W
Freeport, FL 32439

Toll-free: 800-324-1318
Phone: 850-835-2121
Fax: 850-835-4768
www.vvmfg.com

Vital Visions manufactures a variety of receptacles for recyclables, including used oil. V-Barrels, Cycle-Go-Round, and V-Squared are made from 95% post-consumer recycled HDPE lumber materials. Other products are made from fiberglass. The company is researching the use of recycled beverage glass cullet in their fiberglass products. Vital Visions products are designed for use in parks, outdoor areas, and apartment buildings.

Clusters

Windsor Barrel Works
P.O. Box 47
Kempton, PA 19529

Toll-free: 800-527-7848
Fax: 610-756-6389
www.windsorbarrel.com

Windsor Barrel Works specializes in outdoor recycling receptacles made with 100% recycled plastic and appropriate signage. The Clusters product includes 2 to 4 bins surrounding a central pole.

Recycled-Plastic Site Furnishings

Wishbone Industries Ltd.

For full listing, see CSI section 12 93 43
- Site Seating and Tables, Plastic

12 93 33
Outdoor Planters

Recycled plastic site furnishings are most commonly made from either HDPE or commingled plastics. Recycled commingled plastics may have slightly inconsistent properties, but this is a lower-grade waste material that is generally more of a disposal problem. Wood planters and furnishings can be made from salvaged materials or certified wood. Forest Stewardship Council (FSC) certification involves third-party evaluation and monitoring of sustainable forestry practices and chain-of-custody certification to ensure that labeled products were derived from FSC-certified forests. Products listed here contain recycled content or are made from salvaged materials or FSC-certified wood.

Recycled-Plastic Products

American Recycled Plastic, Inc.

For full listing, see CSI section 12 93 43
- Site Seating and Tables, Plastic

Barco Recycled-Content Products

Barco Products

For full listing, see CSI section 12 93 43
- Site Seating and Tables, Plastic

Recycled-Plastic Products

BJM Industries, Inc.

For full listing, see CSI section 12 93 43
- Site Seating and Tables, Plastic

BetterBarrel and EcoPlanter

Curb Appeal Materials, LTD
3824 N Johnsburg Rd.
McHenry, IL 60050

Phone: 815-344 7926
Fax: 815-344 7960
www.vortexcomposites.com

BetterBarrel™ and EcoPlanter™ are made with 100% commingled plastics, minimum 30% post-consumer. BetterBarrel is a thick-walled, lightweight planter with a whiskey-barrel appearance, and has a 20-year warranty. EcoPlanters are terra-cotta look-alikes with a 50-year warranty.

Recycled-Plastic Site Amenities

DuMor, Inc.

For full listing, see CSI section 12 93 43 - Site Seating and Tables, Plastic

Recycled-Plastic Site Furnishings

Durable Plastic Design, LLC.

For full listing, see CSI section 12 93 43 - Site Seating and Tables, Plastic

Perennial Park Outdoor Furniture

Engineered Plastic Systems

For full listing, see CSI section 12 93 43 - Site Seating and Tables, Plastic

Recycled-Plastic Site Amenities

Great Lakes Specialty Products

For full listing, see CSI section 12 93 43 - Site Seating and Tables, Plastic

Site Furnishings and Materials

Inteq Corp.

For full listing, see CSI section 12 93 43 - Site Seating and Tables, Plastic

Benches, Picnic Tables, Waste Receptacles, and Planters

Kay Park Recreation Corp.

For full listing, see CSI section 12 93 43 - Site Seating and Tables, Plastic

PlasTEAK Site Furnishings

PlasTEAK

For full listing, see CSI section 12 93 43 - Site Seating and Tables, Plastic

Recycled-Plastic Site Furnishings

Taylors Recycled Plastic Products Inc.

For full listing, see CSI section 12 93 43 - Site Seating and Tables, Plastic

Recycled-Plastic Site Amenities

The Plastic Lumber Company, Inc.

For full listing, see CSI section 12 93 43 - Site Seating and Tables, Plastic

Recycled-Plastic Site Furnishings

Wishbone Industries Ltd.

For full listing, see CSI section 12 93 43 - Site Seating and Tables, Plastic

12 93 43
Site Seating and Tables, Plastic

Recycled plastic is a durable material for outdoor furniture. Recycled plastic site furnishings are most commonly made from either HDPE or commingled plastics. Recycled commingled plastics may have slightly inconsistent properties, but this is a lower-grade waste material that is generally more of a disposal problem. Products listed here contain recycled content. (See also 11 68 13 - Playground Equipment & 12 93 13 - Bicycle Racks.)

Recycled-Plastic Products

American Recreational Products
1535 Locust Ave.
Bohemia, NY 11716

Toll-free: 800-663-4096
Phone: 631-244-0011
Fax: 631-750-2624
www.americanrecreational.com

American Recreational Products offers benches, picnic tables, landscape ties, wheel stops, speed bumps, and marine docks made from 100% recycled commingled plastics. Products are typically made from 50% post-consumer plastic and 50% post-industrial plastic.

Recycled-Plastic Products

American Recycled Plastic, Inc.
1500 Main St.
Palm Bay, FL 32905

Toll-free: 866-674-1525
Phone: 321-674-1525
Fax: 321-674-2365
www.itsrecycled.com

American Recycled Plastic manufactures a range of products from recycled HDPE, including lumber and timbers, car stops, speed bumps and humps, and vehicle barriers. They also offer a wide variety of recycled-HDPE site furnishings, including benches, outdoor tables, waste receptacles, mailboxes, planters, custom wildlife structures, and bicycle racks.

Barco Recycled-Content Products

Barco Products
11 N. Batavia Ave.
Batavia, IL 60510

Toll-free: 800-338-2697
Phone: 630-879-0084
Fax: 630-879-8687
www.barcoproducts.com

Barco Products offers site furnishings, landscape timbers, and traffic devices made with recycled content, including dozens of styles of picnic tables and park benches made with recycled commingled HDPE and LDPE averaging 40% post-consumer, as well as planters and waste receptacles made from recycled HDPE (90 to 100% post-consumer). Landscape Timbers are made from 100% recycled commingled HDPE and LDPE, sized as railroad ties with premolded holes for rebar reinforcement and interlocking edges for stacking stability. Each timber weighs 42 lbs, about half that of most plastic landscape timbers. 100% recycled tire rubber speed bumps and 100% recycled plastic speed bumps are offered, and colored wheel stops made of 95% recycled commingled HDPE and LDPE. Gray wheel stops contain 85% recycled PVC. Bollards are made from 96% recycled commingled LDPE and HDPE (50 to 80% post-industrial).

Bedford Technology Recycled-Plastic Products

Bedford Technology, LLC

For full listing, see CSI section 06 53 13 - Solid Plastic Decking

12 00 00 Furnishings

Recycled-Plastic Products

BJM Industries, Inc.
12478 U.S. Route 422
Kittanning, PA 16201

Toll-free: 800-683-3810
Phone: 724-548-2440
Fax: 724-548-4928
www.bjmindustries.com

BJM Industries manufactures site furnishings, such as picnic tables, park and garden benches, and planters, from Millennium Lumber - a combination of 100% post-consumer recycled HDPE and post-industrial recycled cellulose (from diaper factory trimmings).

Benches, Picnic Tables, and Planters

Cascades Re-Plast, Inc.
1350 chemin Quatre Saisons
Bon Conseil, QC J0C 1A0 Canada

Toll-free: 888-313-2440
Phone: 888-313-2440
Fax: 819-336-2442
www.cascadesreplast.com

Cascades Re-Plast manufactures an assortment of recycled-plastic outdoor furniture and accessories in brown, beige, green, gray, and black. Re-Plast plastic wood contains mixed polymers including HDPE, polypropylene, polystyrene, and PET from post-consumer sources.

Site Furnishings

Doty & Sons Concrete Products, Inc.
1275 E. State St.
Sycamore, IL 60178

Toll-free: 800-233-3907
Fax: 815-895-8035
www.dotyconcrete.com

Doty & Sons Concrete Products uses recycled HDPE plastic in its precast concrete site amenities, including benches and table sets, recycling and waste receptacles.

Recycled-Plastic Site Amenities

DuMor, Inc.
P.O. Box 142
Mifflintown, PA 17059

Toll-free: 800-598-4018
Phone: 717-436-2106
Fax: 717-436-9839
www.dumor.com

DuMor offers a wide array of site amenities made from recycled HDPE plastic lumber. Products include benches, picnic tables, planters, and waste receptacles.

Recycled-Plastic Site Furnishings

Durable Plastic Design, LLC.
17725 N.E. 65th St., A-100
Redmond, WA 98052

Phone: 425-883-2570
Fax: 425-885-0628
www.orcaboard.com

Durable Plastic Design offers park benches, picnic tables, waste bin surrounds, dock & deck boxes, planter boxes, raised-bed garden kits, and Adirondack chairs made from Orcaboard™, a 100% post-consumer recycled HDPE plastic lumber. Framing members are steel.

Benches, Picnic Tables, and Recycling Receptacles

Eagle One Site Furnishings
1340 N. Jefferson St.
Anaheim, CA 92807

Toll-free: 800-448-4409
Phone: 714-983-0050
Fax: 714-203-8444
www.eagleoneproducts.com

EagleOne Site Furnishings offers site amenities, including benches, picnic tables, and recycling receptacles, made from recycled HDPE plastic.

Eco Outdoor Series

Ecologic, Inc.
921 Sherwood Dr.
Lake Bluff, IL 60044

Toll-free: 800-899-8004
Phone: 847-234-5855
Fax: 847-234-5845
www.ecoinc.com

Ecologic is a large producer of furniture based on recycled HDPE plastic. They have an extensive range of outdoor furniture suitable for residential and public spaces, ranging from individual Adirondack chairs and ottomans to tables, benches, trash receptacles (designed to take standard Rubbermaid inserts), and fan trellises. Some of these products contain recycled steel to add stiffness. The entire line is manufactured with 97.5% recycled content. UV protection is integral to the plastic in each component.

Perennial Park Outdoor Furniture

Engineered Plastic Systems
740 Industrial Dr., Ste. B
Cary, IL 60013

Phone: 847-462-9001
Fax: 847-462-9002
www.epsplasticlumber.com

Environmental Plastic Systems manufactures Perennial Park outdoor furniture and accessories from 100% recycled HDPE (typically 100% post-consumer content). Products include benches and picnic tables, planter benches, and serving tables. Kid-sized and handicapped-accessible tables, as well as custom orders, are also available. Colors currently include white, gray, redwood, forest green, black, cedar, and tan. All EPS plastic products come with a 50-year limited warranty.

Re-Bench

Falcon Products, Inc.
5303 East Morris Blvd.
Morristown, TN 37813-1028

Toll-free: 800-873-3252
Fax: 423-318-7301
www.falconproducts.com

The Re-Bench is a park bench with recycled plastic slats fastened to recycled cast iron supports. The Re-Bench is available in three colors: cedar, weathered redwood, and white. Seat height is 18", depth is 17" and overall height is 34-5/8".

Conservancy Series - Benches, Picnic Tables, and Recycling Receptacles

Florida Playground and Steel Co.
4701 S. 50th St.
Tampa, FL 33619

Toll-free: 800-444-2655
Phone: 813-247-2812
Fax: 813-247-1068
www.fla-playground.com

Conservancy Series benches, picnic tables, and recycling receptacles are made from recycled plastic/wood composite materials and steel.

Recycled-Plastic Site Amenities

Great Lakes Specialty Products
206 Enterprise Rd.
Delafield, WI 53018

Toll-free: 800-505-7926
Phone: 262-646-9470
Fax: 800-962-3455
www.greatlakesspecialty.com

Great Lakes Specialty Products manufactures a wide variety of high-recycled-content site furnishings including waste/recycling receptacles, planters, benches and chairs, picnic tables, podiums, wait-staff stations, barrier posts, and message centers made with Everlasting Lumber - 95% recycled #2 HDPE from consumer and industrial sources, impregnated with UV inhibitors and nonmetallic colorants. A foamless manufacturing process is claimed to enhance the material's usable life. Fasteners are marine-grade or solid stainless steel. Some products also use Ironwood and teak from FSC-certified suppliers, though Great Lakes Specialty Products is not chain-of-custody certified.

Site Furnishings and Materials

Inteq Corp.
35800 Glen Dr.
Eastlake, OH 44095

Phone: 440-953-0550
Fax: 440-953-0564
www.4-inteqcorp.com

Inteq's benches and picnic tables are made from recycled HDPE plastic. Tables are either standard 6' or 8' length or hexagonal. Benches come in a variety of styles and can be custom designed. Inteq's waste receptacles and planters contain recycled HDPE plastic and are available in many styles including custom production. All are offered in a variety of colors. Recycled content is up to 100% (minimum 20% post-consumer). Inteq nonstructural landscape timbers are available in multiple colors up to 12' in length in standard sizes of 4x4, 4x6, and 6x6. Decking and railing material is also made from recycled HDPE plastic and is available in multiple colors.

Benches, Picnic Tables, Waste Receptacles, and Planters

Kay Park Recreation Corp.
1301 Pine St.
P.O. Box 477
Janesville, IA 50647

Toll-free: 800-553-2476
Fax: 319-987-2900
www.kaypark.com

Kay Park Recreation manufactures picnic tables, benches, waste receptacles, and planters containing 96% post-consumer recycled commingled plastics.

Benches, Picnic Tables, and Trash Receptacles

Landscape Forms, Inc.
431 Lawndale Ave.
Kalamazoo, MI 49048

Toll-free: 800-430-6209
Fax: 269-381-3455
www.landscapeforms.com

Landscape Forms offers site furnishings made with PolySite plastic timbers which contain 90% post-consumer recycled HDPE. Steel and aluminum components contain 65 to 100% recycled content (generally 60% post-

consumer and 40% post-industrial). Also offered is FSC-certified wood for selected designs upon request (may incur upcharge and extended lead time).

Earthcare Series

Litchfield Industries
4 Industrial Dr.
Litchfield, MI 49252

Toll-free: 800-542-5282
Phone: 517-542-2988
Fax: 517-542-3939
www.litchfieldindustries.com

The Earthcare Series of site furnishings is made from 100% post-consumer recycled plastic. The Series includes picnic tables, benches, and trash receptacles.

PlasTEAK Site Furnishings

PlasTEAK
3563 Copley Rd.
P.O. Box 4290
Akron, OH 44321

Toll-free: 800-320-1841
Phone: 330-668-2587
Fax: 330-666-0844
www.plasteak.com

PlasTEAK offers a wide range of tables, chairs, planters, and benches made with 100% post-consumer recycled HDPE and steel structural elements.

Recycled-Plastic Site Furnishings

Plastic Lumber Yard, LLC
220 Washington St.
Norristown, PA 19401

Phone: 610-277-3900
Fax: 610-277-3970
www.plasticlumberyard.com

Plastic Lumber Yard, LLC manufactures a wide range of outdoor site furnishings from 100% recycled plastic. Products include picnic tables and benches, chairs (Adirondack and others), "gliders" and porch swings, as well as hexagonal, rectangular, and wheelchair-accessible tables.

Picnic Tables and Benches

Plastic Recycling of Iowa Falls, Inc.
10252 Hwy. 65
Iowa Falls, IA 50126

Toll-free: 800-338-1438
Phone: 641-648-5073
Fax: 641-648-5074
www.hammersplastic.com

Plastic Recycling of Iowa Falls, formerly Hammer's Plastic Recycling, manufactures

several park benches and picnic tables, including ADA-compliant products, of commingled recycled HDPE, LDPE, LLDPE, and other miscellaneous plastics.

Benches and Picnic Tables

Polly Products, LLC
12 N. Charlotte St.
Mulliken, MI 48861

Toll-free: 877-609-2243
Phone: 517-649-2243
Fax: 517-649-2284
www.recycletechproducts.com

RecycleTech Products manufactures park benches and picnic tables from recycled HDPE.

Poly-Wood

Poly-Wood Inc.
1001 W. Brooklyn St.
Syracuse, IN 46567

Toll-free: 877-457-3284
Phone: 574-457-3284
Fax: 574-457-4723
www.polywoodinc.com

Poly-Wood manufactures outdoor residential furniture from 98% recycled HDPE plastic.

Pilot Rock Site Furnishings

R. J. Thomas Manufacturing Co., Inc.
P.O. Box 946
Cherokee, IA 51012

Toll-free: 800-762-5002
Phone: 712-225-5115
Fax: 712-225-5796
www.pilotrock.com

Pilot Rock Site Furnishings are made from recycled HDPE and LDPE plastic. The Pilot Rock line includes benches, picnic tables, waste receptacles, and car stops.

Site Amenities

Recycled Plastic Man, Inc.
P.O. Box 609
Placida, FL 33946

Toll-free: 800-253-7742
Phone: 941-698-1060
Fax: 941-698-1038
www.recycledplasticman.com

Recycled Plastic Man manufactures a wide variety of recycled plastic site amenities from both HDPE and commingled resins. Products include benches, picnic tables, and waste receptacles. Bike racks made with recycled plastic and galvanized pipes are available in single or double style in 6' and 8' sections with a limited lifetime warranty.

12 00 00
Furnishings

Recycled-Plastic Site Furnishings

Taylors Recycled Plastic Products Inc.
581 Hwy. 28
Bailieboro, ON K0L 1B0 Canada

Phone: 705-939-6072
Fax: 705-939-6256
www.taylorsplastic.com

Taylors Recycled Plastic Products, Inc. offers a wide range of outdoor tables, chairs, benches, receptacle coverings, and planters in an array of styles colors. All are made primarily from post-consumer recycled plastic.

Recycled-Plastic Site Amenities

The Plastic Lumber Company, Inc.
115 W. Bartges St.
Akron, OH 44311

Toll-free: 800-886-8990
Phone: 330-762-8989
Fax: 330-762-1613
www.plasticlumber.com

The Plastic Lumber Company offers site furnishings, playground equipment, and signage made with recycled plastic. Commercial-grade benches, picnic tables, and waste receptacles/recycling centers are available in a variety of color combinations and are made with 97% post-consumer recycled content. Signage products have a post-industrial recycled content level up to 40% depending on color selection. (The Digital DeSigns line of signs does not contain recycled material.)

Recycle Design Site Furnishings

Trimax Building Products, Inc.
2600 W. Roosevelt Rd.
Chicago, IL 60608

Toll-free: 866-987-4629
www.trimaxbp.com

The award-winning Recycle Design site furnishings are made with Durawood PE plastic lumber that contains 90% post-consumer recycled HDPE by weight, and steel or aluminum structural components. The Recycle Design line includes benches, picnic tables, and waste receptacles.

Most recently mentioned in EBN 13:9 & 15:2

2nd Site Systems

Victor Stanley, Inc.
P.O. Drawer 330
Dunkirk, MD 20754

Toll-free: 800-368-2573
Phone: 301-855-8300
Fax: 410-257-7579
www.victorstanley.com

2nd Site Systems utilizes a patented slat design of 100% recycled plastic lumber reinforced with recycled steel bar. Products include park benches, picnic tables, and trash receptacles.

Recycled-Plastic Site Furnishings

Wishbone Industries Ltd.
Unit 2-27250 58th Crescent
Langley, BC V4W 3W7 Canada

New

Toll-free: 866-626-0476
Phone: 604-626-0476
Fax: 604-626-0496
www.wishboneltd.com

Wishbone Industries manufactures site furnishings, including benches, picnic tables, trash receptacles, planters, and bike racks from 100% pre- and post-consumer recycled plastic. They use plastic lumber from manufacturers Cascades, Polyboard, and Xpotential.

12 93 44
Site Seating and Tables, Wood

Forest Stewardship Council (FSC) certification involves third-party evaluation and monitoring of sustainable forestry practices and chain-of-custody certification to ensure that labeled products were derived from FSC-certified forests. Products listed here are FSC-certified or made from salvaged materials.

Certified Wood Outdoor Furniture

Landscape Forms, Inc.
431 Lawndale Ave.
Kalamazoo, MI 49048

Toll-free: 800-430-6209
Fax: 269-381-3455
www.landscapeforms.com

Landscape Forms offers site furnishings made with FSC-certified ipe, hard maple, and red oak. Steel and aluminum components contain 65 to 100% recycled content (generally 60% post-consumer and 40% post-industrial).

Certified Ipe Outdoor Furniture

Modern Outdoor
15952 Strathern St.
Van Nuys, CA 91406

Phone: 818-785-0171
Fax: 818-785-0168
www.modernoutdoor.com

Modern Outdoor offers domestically produced, high-style outdoor furniture made from Brazilian ipe hardwood. Due to difficulties in sourcing FSC-certified ipe, the manufacturer may use wood certified under the less-stringent ITTO (International Tropical Timber Organization) or IBAMA (Brazilian Institute of Environment and Renewable Resources) programs. Specify FSC-certified (Forest Stewardship Council) wood. The furniture uses electro-polished stainless steel frames. Stainless steel contains little or no recycled content and is not recyclable, but it is very long-lasting.

Certified Teak Outdoor Furniture

TTD, Inc. / Skagerak Denmark
P.O. Box 964
Williston, VT 05495

Toll-free: 866-490-2448
Phone: 802-878-1489
Fax: 802-879-2590
www.ttd-inc.com

TTD, Inc. is the North American distributor for Skagerak Denmark teak furniture. Three of the company's lines of park and garden furniture—Drachmann, Vitas Bering, and Selandia, a line of folding chairs and tables—have products available for an upcharge in FSC-certified teak. Skagerak Denmark is ISO 14001-certified.

12 93 45
Site Seating and Tables, Other

Products listed here embody creative reuse, or use non-standard recycled content to make durable alternatives to wood or plastic outdoor furnishings.

Ski and Snowboard Furniture

Reeski, Inc.
P.O. Box 781
Aspen, CO 81612

Toll-free: 800-826-5447
Phone: 970-948-3491
Fax: 970-704-0866
www.reeski.com

Reeski manufactures chairs, benches, coat racks, and more from used skis and snowboards. Reeski offers many durable and creative designs; custom orders are welcome. Furniture often includes 100% recycled plastic lumber. Uncertified redwood is used for some items.

13 00 00 Special Construction

PRODUCT LISTINGS

13 20 00
Special Purpose Rooms

Special purpose rooms include clean rooms and other strictly maintained environments. Products listed here incorporate highly efficient conditioning, ventilation, and other equipment.

The EGC GreenRoom

Environmental Growth Chambers
510 E. Washington St.
Chagrin Falls, OH 44022

Toll-free: 800-321-6854
Fax: 440-247-8710
www.egc.com

The EGC GreenRoom—an environmental room for industries such as food service, scientific research, medical, educational, government, and military—meets rapid temperature recovery specifications efficiently using integrated controls and non-ozone depleting R404 refrigerant systems that reduce energy use by 25-40%. Temperature and humidity uniformity are guaranteed with 100% redundant systems.

This Space is Available for Your Notes

13 00 00
Special Construction

This Space is Available for Your Notes

13 00 00
Special
Construction

14 00 00 Conveying Equipment

PRODUCT LISTINGS

14 20 00
Elevators

Elevators are a promising area for realizing energy savings; they can account for 4-10% of a building's electric energy load. Additionally, elevator shafts are often poorly sealed, or even vented at the top. Larger commercial buildings with minimal or nonexistent heating loads may benefit from such ventilation, but low- and mid-rise buildings will benefit from more energy-conscious elevator engineering. (See also 14 28 01 - Biodegradable Hydraulic Elevator Oils.) (See feature article EBN Vol. 13, No. 8.)

Talon Drive System Elevator

Fujitec North America, Inc.
401 Fujitec Dr.
Lebanon, OH 45036

Phone: 513-932-8000
Fax: 513-933-5504
www.fujitecamerica.com

Fujitec's Talon™ Drive System, introduced in 2004, uses an innovative belt system to transfer power directly to the elevator hoistropes. Talon uses a highly efficient and compact AC gearless permanent magnet motor that can be mounted in the hoistway, eliminating the need for a machine room. It has a passenger capacity of up to 4,500 lbs., and travels up to 190', serving up to 24 stops, at speeds of up to 350 fpm.

Most recently mentioned in EBN 13:8

Monospace and EcoSpace Elevators

KONE Inc.
One KONE Ct.
Moline, IL 61265

Toll-free: 800-956-5663
Phone: 309-764-6771
Fax: 309-743-5469
www.kone.com

KONEs EcoSystem Monospace elevator, first introduced in North America in 1998, revolutionized the low- and mid-rise elevator market with its efficient permanent magnet A/C gearless motors and machine-room-less configuration, which saves space and simplifies installation. It can provide up to 230' of travel and 36 stops at speeds of up to 800 fpm, with a maximum passenger capacity of 4,500 lbs. The energy usage of an Eco-System elevator is typically one-half that of a traditional traction elevator and one-third that of a hydraulic elevator and it offers a smoother ride. The KONE EcoSpace elevator, introduced in 2004, brings the efficiency, environmental benefits, and space savings of the MonoSpace elevator into a smaller, less expensive package for 2- to 10-stop applications. It has a passenger capacity of up to 5,000 lbs., and travels up to 83' at speeds of up to 150 fpm. The EcoSpaces EcoDisc motor mounts in the hoistway, eliminating the need for a machine room.

Most recently mentioned in EBN 7:6, 8:7, 13:8

Gen2 Elevator System

Otis Elevator Company
10 Farm Springs
Farmington, CT 06032

Phone: 860-676-5400
Fax: 860-676-6973
www.otis.com

The Gen2™ is a gearless, lubrication-free elevator system for low- to mid-rise buildings. Equipped with a regenerative drive, the Gen2 is up to 75% more efficient than conventional geared systems, according to the manufacturer. Its machine is one-quarter the size of conventional systems and does not require a machine room. It can provide up to 300' of travel and 30 stops at speeds of up to 400 fpm. It has a maximum passenger capacity of 4,000 lbs. Instead of conventional steel ropes, the Gen2 uses 1/10"-thick belts comprised of woven steel strands encased in polyurethane to lift the elevator car. The belts wrap around a 4" diameter sheave. The machine-room-less design simplifies installation and offers flexible control space placement. Otis is a subsidiary of United Technologies.

Most recently mentioned in EBN 13:8

400A Traction Elevator System

Schindler Elevator Corporation
20 Whippany Rd.
Morristown, NJ 07962

Phone: 973-397-6500
Fax: 973 397-3619
www.us.schindler.com

Shindler's 400A uses a variable-frequency, AC gearless drive with a compact, permanent magnet motor to provide energy efficiency and space savings over conventional geared traction elevators and hydraulic elevators. The small motor mounts in the hoistway, so no machine room is needed. It comes with passenger capacities of up to 3,500 lbs., can travel up to 200' at speeds of up to 350 fpm, and can serve up to 20 stops.

Most recently mentioned in EBN 13:8

14 28 01
Biodegradable Hydraulic Elevator Oils

Leaking hydraulic oil, like all spilled oil, poses environmental risks in the form of soil and water contamination. Cleanup of hydraulic-oil-contaminated soils is a difficult and costly task that is best avoided by practicing routine elevator maintenance and/or using plant-based hydraulic oil. In general, it's best to install more efficient, non-hydraulic elevators, but for servicing an existing elevator, or in situations in which a hydraulic elevator is the only option, using a biodegradable fluid is advisable. Products listed here are biobased, biodegradable hydraulic oils.

Industrial Hydraulic Oil

Environmental Lubricants Manufacturing, Inc.
1307 Badger Ave.
Plainfield, IA 50666

Phone: 319-276-4801
Fax: 319-276-4803
www.elmusa.com

ELM's Biotechbased™ industrial hydraulic oil is recommended for most hydraulic systems, including elevators. It protects against wear, has a high flash point, and is virtually biodegradable. ELM manufactures a range of lubricants, greases, and fluids from natural vegetable and seed oils.

**14 00 00
Conveying
Equipment**

Greenplus Hydraulic Fluid ES

Greenland Corporation
7016-30 St. SE
Calgary, AB T2C 1N9 Canada

Toll-free: 800-598-7636
Phone: 403-720-7049
Fax: 403-720-4951
www.greenpluslubes.com

Greenland Corporation manufactures the Greenplus line of biodegradable, vegetable oil-based lubricants suitable for a wide variety of lubricating applications. Customized products are also available, as well as technical support for the proper product choice and ongoing support. Greenplus Hydraulic Fluid ES can be used for a number of hydraulic applications including hydraulic elevators. The manufacturer claims that vegetable oil-based lubricants operate at a lower temperature than petroleum-based products, have high natural viscosity and stability, and can improve the performance levels of machinery and increase equipment life.

Hydro Safe Hydraulic Oil

Hydro Safe Oil Division, Inc.
13626 Pearwood Dr.
DeWitt, MI 48820

Toll-free: 800-500-5058
Fax: 517-336-9213
www.hydrosafe.com

Hydro Safe™ is a family of biodegradable, nontoxic, high-oleic-acid, rapeseed-oil-based hydraulic fluids. These ISO- and ASTM-graded products are suitable for hydraulic marine applications, heavy and light industrial and construction hydraulic equipment, hydraulic elevators, and timber harvesting equipment. These hydraulic fluids are particularly well suited to applications where conventional petroleum-based products could contaminate groundwater. 90% of Hydro Safe biodegrades within 120 days, 60% converts to CO_2 in 28 days. Hydro Safe meets the reporting requirements of relevant sections of the SuperFund and EPA legislation.

EnviroLogic 132E and 168L

Terresolve Technologies
35585 Curtis Blvd.
Eastlake, OH 44095

Phone: 440-951-8633
Fax: 440-951-4341
www.terresolve.com

Terresolve recommends its vegetable-based EnviroLogic 132E (ISO 32 grade) and EnviroLogic 168L (ISO 68 grade) hydraulic fluids for use in elevators. Both oils are biodegradable and nonhazardous. Both are based on natural ester technology and intended for use in general-purpose hydraulic systems as direct replacements for petroleum-based hydraulic fluids. Terresolve offers a full range of biobased ISO 32, 46, and 48 hydraulic fluids.

14 45 00
Vehicle Lifts

Vehicle lifts can be used to create very efficient parking services that require less space and reduce vehicle emissions.

AutoMotion Parking System

AutoMotion, Inc.
411 Hempstead Turnpike,
Ste. 200
West Hempstead, NY 11552

New

Phone: 516-565-5600
Fax: 516-908-4411
www.automotionparking.com

The AutoMotion Parking System creates a fully automated parking garage. Drivers park their cars at a door, swipe their credit cards, and the system, using conventional elevator components and a pivoting mechanism, transfers cars onto a lift that conveys them into an available slot. The system can double the capacity of indoor parking garages, according to the company, and it reduces energy consumption and health risks of operating cars in enclosed spaces.

Most recently mentioned in EBN 16:4

This Space is Available for Your Notes

14 00 00
Conveying Equipment

22 00 00 Plumbing

PRODUCT LISTINGS

22 07 00
Plumbing Insulation

Mineral wool insulation is made from either molten slag—a waste product of steel production—or igneous rock, such as basalt or diabase. Some products contain a mix of slag and rock. Mineral wool can be blown in as loose-fill, used in batts, spray-applied with a binding adhesive, or formed into rigid board stock. Typical R-values are 2.8 to 3.7 per inch. Mineral wool has a higher density than fiberglass, so it has better sound-blocking properties. It's also more fire-resistant than fiberglass. Rigid boardstock mineral wool insulation is a superb foundation insulation and drainage material, because it is extremely hydrophobic.

Mineral Wool Pipe and Tank Insulation

Roxul Inc.
551 Harrop Dr.
Milton, ON L9T 3H3 Canada

Toll-free: 800-265-6878
Phone: 905-878-8474
Fax: 905-878-8077
www.roxul.com

Roxul offers formed mineral wool products for thermal insulation and fireproofing for pipes and tanks. Roxul's mineral wool—made from approximately equal amounts of natural basalt rock and recycled slag (with 1%-6% urea extended phenolic formaldehyde binder)—is vapor-permeable, water-repellant, and non-combustible. The dimensionally stable, chemically inert material doesn't degrade or support mold, and is made with CFC- and HCFC-free processes. R-values per inch range from 4 to 4.3. Roxul also offers faced and unfaced rigid and semi-rigid rock wool boards and batts.

Most recently mentioned in EBN 4:6 & 5:6

22 11 16
Domestic Water Piping

The three major materials currently used in supply piping in North America are copper, chlorinated polyvinyl chloride (CPVC), and cross-linked polyethylene (XLPE or, more commonly, PEX). CPVC has toxic manufacturing intermediaries, requires the use of hazardous solvents for welding the joints, and can generate highly toxic dioxins in the case of accidental fire or improper incineration. Copper's environmentally intensive extraction and manufacturing process make it an even worse performer in terms of life-cycle environmental and human health impacts, according to recent studies. In contrast, XLPE and Polypropylene (PP) are 'clean' hydrocarbons, provided harmful additives are not used for application-specific properties. Products listed here are made of nonhalogenated plastics that contain no heavy metals or brominated flame retardants.

Fusiotherm Piping

Aquatherm Piping Systems, LLC
Box 110
Romeo, MI 48065

Phone: 248-830-7037
www.aquatherm-usa.com

Fusiotherm® piping from Aquatherm Piping Systems is an exceptionally strong, non-PVC piping for pressurized applications such as potable water distribution and hydronic heating. The polypropylene pieces are heat-joined in the field with an electric fusing tool to create truly monolithic plumbing systems without the use of solvents or glues. Fusiotherm is available in a wide range of diameters from 16 mm to 160 mm (0.63" to 6.29") in three wall-thickness ratios (SDR classifications); over 400 fittings are available. Introduced in the U.S. in 2003, the product has been used in Europe for three decades with great success. Fusiotherm® piping was awarded ESR 1613 listing by the International Code Council in September 2005.

Most recently mentioned in EBN 13:9 & 14:11

22 13 00
Sanitary Sewerage, Facilities

Conventional on-site wastewater treatment systems—septic tanks and leach fields—typically deliver the nutrients in the wastewater (nitrogen and phosphorous) directly into the groundwater. Various alternative wastewater treatment systems provide some nutrient removal. Some plastic-matrix products incorporate recycled content. This section includes products that are appropriate for homes and small facilities. (See feature article EBN Vol. 3, No. 2.)

Puraflo

Bord na Mona Environmental Products U.S., Inc.
P.O. Box 77457
Greensboro, NC 27417

Toll-free: 800-787-2356
Fax: 336-547-8559
www.bnm-us.com

Puraflo® is a biofiltration wastewater system using fibrous peat to treat septic tank effluent. The peat media filters wastewater and provides a substrate for microorganisms that naturally purify wastewater. Puraflo systems may be used for residential and small commercial applications.

Solar Aquatics

Ecological Engineering Associates
508 Boston Post Rd.
P.O. Box 415
Weston, MA 02493-0003

Toll-free: 866-326-7462
Phone: 978-369-9440
Fax: 978-369-2484
www.ecological-engineering.com

Ecological Engineering designs and maintains wastewater treatment facilities that accept sewage as a food source for a complex, greenhouse-contained ecosystem including bacteria, algae, plants, snails, and fish.

Most recently mentioned in EBN 4:5 & 5:4

22 00 00
Plumbing

In-Drain System

Eljen Corporation
125A McKee St.
East Hartford, CT 06108

Toll-free: 800-444-1359
Phone: 860-610-0426
Fax: 860-610-0427
www.eljen.com

The Eljen In-Drain System uses recycled-content cuspated plastic sheets in conjunction with Bio-Matt™ fabric, instead of aggregate, to create an effective leach field. The Bio-Matt fabric is suspended between the plastic sheets, adding a second bio-mat to the one at the sand/In-Drain interface. According to the manufacturer, this system is 3 to 10 times more durable than a conventional leach field.

Natural Wastewater Treatment

John Todd Ecological Design, Inc.
P.O. Box 497
Woods Hole, MA 02543

Phone: 508-548-2545
www.toddecological.com

John Todd is the father of ecologically engineered wastewater treatment systems that produce high-quality effluent. His company, John Todd Ecological Design, Inc., provides clients with environmentally responsible solutions for wastewater and stormwater treatment, aquatic environment management, and biosolids conversion. Wastewater systems can be designed to handle a wide range of flows from residential and commercial-buiding sewage flows to specialized waste streams from industrial manufacturing processes.

Most recently mentioned in EBN 3:2, 5:4, 8:6, 11:7

Living Machine Systems

Living Designs Group, LLC
125 La Posta Rd.
Taos, NM 87571

Phone: 505-751-9481
Fax: 505-751-9483
www.livingmachines.com

Living Machine® systems are a family of engineered biological wastewater treatment systems that produce high-quality effluent. They can be designed to handle a wide range of flows from domestic and commercial waste streams, and certain manufacturing processes.

Most recently mentioned in EBN 3:2, 5:4, 11:7, 11:11

AdvanTex Wastewater Treatment Systems

Orenco Systems, Inc.
814 Airway Ave.
Sutherlin, OR 97479

Toll-free: 800-348-9843
Phone: 541-459-4449
Fax: 541-459-2884
www.orenco.com

AdvanTex® onsite wastewater treatment systems are particularly appropriate for small lots, poor soils, and environmentally sensitive sites. The standard AX20 system accommodates a single-family dwelling; the AX100 model is for multifamily use, resorts, parks, schools, etc. Wastes recirculate five times through a textile filtration media "pod" before discharging into a drain field in small, continuous amounts. Some jurisdictions allow a reduction in drain field area with the system. The pump typically runs 30 to 60 minutes per day, using about 150 kWh per year—about $1.25-$2.50 per month in electric costs, based on $.08 per kWh. Installation includes computerized, Internet-based monitoring which allows remote diagnosis and settings adjustment. A service contract is required as a condition of the warranty.

Sand Filter Wastewater Treatment

Orenco Systems, Inc.
814 Airway Ave.
Sutherlin, OR 97479

Toll-free: 800-348-9843
Phone: 541-459-4449
Fax: 541-459-2884
www.orenco.com

Orenco Systems is a leading designer and supplier of sand filter secondary wastewater treatment systems, which are appropriate for environmentally sensitive areas or poor soils. Sand filters are typically positioned between a septic tank and a downsized leach field or drip irrigation dispersal. Sand filters consist of a contained area of sand (typically 440 square feet) that is periodically dosed with effluent. The sand filter environment promotes the growth of aerobic bacteria that lower the biochemical oxygen demand (BOD) and total suspended solids (TSS), reduce fecal coliform and pathogens, convert ammonia into nitrate, and reduce total nitrogen by 30 to 50%. Associated leach fields can often be up to 50% smaller, although such downsizing is not accepted by all states.

Most recently mentioned in EBN 3:2

Waterloo Biofilter

Waterloo Biofilter Systems Inc.
143 Dennis St.
P.O. Box 400
Rockwood, ON N0B 2K0 Canada

Phone: 519-856-0757
Fax: 519-856-0759
www.waterloo-biofilter.com

The scalable Waterloo Biofilter® system uses an absorbent synthetic material in its aerobic, single-pass, biological wastewater treatment system. Microbial action in the filter medium is enhanced by the large available surface area and flow characteristics that allow a high loading rate in a small area—typically 10 times greater than sand filters or soils. The Biofilter, which is installed downstream of a conventional septic tank, typically removes 90-95% biochemical oxygen demand (BOD), 85-98% total suspended solids (TSS), 20-50% total nitrogen (TN),and 90-99% coliform bacteria. Depending on applicable codes, it may be possible to discharge treated effluent into a short shallow trench rather than an extensive leach field. The system is suitable for cold weather and seasonal operation.

22 13 16
Sanitary Waste and Vent Piping

Most sanitary drain waste and vent (DWV) piping used today is made from PVC or ABS plastic. Both of these have toxic manufacturing intermediaries and require the use of hazardous solvents for welding the joints. PVC can also generate highly toxic dioxins in the case of accidental fire or improper incineration. Cast iron, the traditional DWV pipe material, has high recycled content, but the scrap metal is melted primarily with coke, and the toxic and carcinogenic emissions from coke manufacture makes cast iron worse than available plastic alternatives on a life-cycle basis. Vitrified clay pipe can be used in buildings as drain pipe but is more commonly used for larger-diameter sewage applications (where it competes with concrete and PVC); although heavy and labor-intensive, vitrified clay is the most durable waste and sewage piping material. Finally, there are some polyolefin (polyethylene and polypropylene) plastic pipes that can be used for drainage and venting. If plastic piping products are being chosen, look for recycled content. Products listed here now include vitrified clay pipe, but lower-impact plastic DWV piping will be listed if and when it becomes available.

Vitrified Clay Pipe

Building Products Company
4850 W. Buckeye Rd.
Phoenix, AZ 85043

Phone: 602-269-8314
Fax: 602-269-7433
www.mcpind.com

Building Products Company is a manufacturer of vitrified clay pipe for waste line and sewage piping.

Vitrified Clay Pipe

Can-Clay Corporation
402 Washington St.
P.O. Box 158
Cannelton, IN 47520

Toll-free: 800-282-2529
Phone: 812-547-3461
Fax: 812-547-6514
www.canclay.com

Can-Clay is a manufacturer of vitrified clay pipe for open-trench waste line and sewage applications.

Vitrified Clay Pipe

Gladding, McBean & Co.
P.O. Box 97
Lincoln, CA 95648

Toll-free: 800-776-1133
Phone: 916-645-3341
Fax: 916-645-9538
www.gladdingmcbean.com

Gladding McBean is a manufacturer of vitrified clay pipe for waste line and sewage piping.

Vitrified Clay Pipe

Mission Clay Products
P.O. Box 549
Corona, CA 92878

Toll-free: 800-795-6067
Phone: 951-277-4600
Fax: 951-273-2708
www.missionclay.com

Mission Clay Products is a manufacturer of vitrified clay pipe for waste line and sewage piping. Diameters range from 4" to 40". The company has plants located in California, Kansas, and Texas.

Industry Representation

National Clay Pipe Institute
P.O. Box 759
Lake Geneva, WI 53147

Phone: 262-248-9094
Fax: 262-248-1564
www.ncpi.org

The National Clay Pipe Institute represents the manufacturers of vitrified clay waste and sewer pipe. Clay pipe is the environmentally preferable, highly durable, corrosion-resistant alternative to PVC sewer pipe.

Most recently mentioned in EBN 3:1 & 3:2

Vitrified Clay Pipe

Superior Clay Corp.
P.O. Box 352
Uhrichsville, OH 44683

Toll-free: 800-848-6166
Phone: 740-922-4122
Fax: 740-922-6626
www.superiorclay.com

Superior Clay is a manufacturer of vitrified clay pipe, with available diameters ranging from 3" to 30".

Vitrified Clay Pipe

The Logan Clay Products Co.
P.O. Box 698
Logan, OH 43138

Toll-free: 800-848-2141
Phone: 740-385-2184
Fax: 740-385-9336
www.loganclaypipe.com

The Logan Clay Products Co. is a manufacturer of vitrified clay pipe for waste line and sewage piping.

22 14 00
Facility Storm Drainage

Siphonic roof drain systems are particularly appropriate for large, low buildings such as office complexes, transportation centers, malls, factories, and warehouses. During rainfall events, siphonic roof drain installations employ full-bore flow to the sewer network or other outlet—unlike conventional roof drain systems that require a high volume of air in the pipes. As a result, fewer and smaller pipes are needed for siphonic systems; and they are capable of long, slopeless, vertical runs, mitigating the excavation typically needed to accommodate conventional roof drainage. These

systems must be designed and sized appropriately. Rainfall events below the design threshold may result in vibration and noise, which can be a potential consideration. These systems are common in many countries, but have only recently been introduced in the U.S.

HydroMax Siphonic Roof Drainage System

Hydromax North America
One Gateway Center, Ste. 2600
Newark, NJ 07102

Phone: 973-645-9488
Fax: 973-622-3423
www.hydromax.com

The HydroMax™ siphonic roof drain system reduces material use by 40 – 50% by providing approximately ten times the carrying capacity of a traditional atmospheric-pressure drain system. Steady-state hydraulic pressure allows long, slopeless vertical runs anywhere below the roof deck, reducing excavation needs. Pipework is typically polyethylene (recyclable) or cast iron (typically made of recycled materials). These systems are not yet written into ICC building codes; local approval is required in the meantime. Documentation and design support, including the proprietary HydroTechnic™ analytic design software, is available.

22 16 00
Greywater Systems

Graywater is defined either as all wastewater other than that from toilets, or as wastewater from baths, showers, lavatories, and clothes washers (not including kitchen sinks and dishwashers). In some states, codes allow graywater to be collected and used for below-ground landscape irrigation. Products listed here are used in graywater systems. (See feature articles EBN Vol. 3, No. 2 & Vol. 4, No. 2.)

BioGreen

BioGreen System (Pacific) Ltd.
#4 11443 Kingston St.
Maple Ridge, BC V2X OY6 Canada

Phone: 604-460-0203
Fax: 604-460-0263
www.biogreensystems.com

BioGreen is a biological wastewater treatment system for use in rural and suburban areas and recreational facilities without a central sewage system.

22 00 00
Plumbing

Envirosink

Bismart Distributors, Inc.
2790 McKenzie Ave.
Surrey, BC V4A 3H4 Canada

Toll-free: 888-663-4950
Phone: 604-596-5894
Fax: 604-542-8510
www.envirosink.com

The Envirosink® is a secondary kitchen sink that drains to an approved graywater system instead of a sewage or septic system. Collected graywater can then be used for landscape irrigation.

Brac Systems

 **New**

Brac Systems
3571 Ashby
Ville St-Laurent
Montreal, QC H4R 2K3 Canada

Toll-free: 866-494-2722
Phone: 514-856-2722
Fax: 514-856-2723
www.bracsystems.com

The Brac System filters water from showers, bathing, and laundry, and reuses it for toilet flushing or irrigation. According to the manufacturer, the system operates seamlessly with the existing plumbing, and will reduce a household's water usage by one-third. The W-200 has a 53-gallon tank and is sized for homes with 5 or fewer people. The W-325 holds 86 gallons for households of 6 or more. Larger systems can be custom-designed. The filter requires manual cleaning every two or three weeks; the tank requires draining and cleanout two or three times per year. The manufacturer recommends using a chlorinated toilet-cleaning tablet every other month; *GreenSpec* recommends exploring alternatives to chlorine-based sanitizers. These systems carry a two-year guarantee.

Graywater Treatment Systems

Clivus Multrum, Inc.
15 Union St.
Lawrence, MA 01840

Toll-free: 800-425-4887
Phone: 978-725-5591
Fax: 978-557-9658
www.clivusmultrum.com

Clivus Multrum custom-designs graywater irrigation systems for commercial and residential applications.

Most recently mentioned in EBN 3:3, 4:2, 4:5

Recirculating Wastewater Garden

Ecological Engineering Group, Inc.
50 Beharell St.
Concord, MA 01742

Toll-free: 866-432-6364
Phone: 978-369-9440
Fax: 978-369-2484
www.ecological-engineering.com

Ecological Engineering Group, Inc. is an engineering design and consulting firm specializing in alternative on-site wastewater treatment systems including graywater systems such as Recirculating Wastewater Garden.

ReWater System

ReWater Systems, Inc.
P.O. Box 210171
Chula Vista, CA 91921

Phone: 619-421-9121
Fax: 619-421-9121
www.rewater.com

The ReWater® System is a graywater irrigation system comprised of two primary sections. A self-cleaning filter captures and pressurizes the water, which is then released through either a surface or subsurface drip irrigation network, depending on your state code. An electronic controller operates all 156 filtration and irrigation functions with 21 stations capable of being programmed for fresh water or drip of recycled water, with four independent irrigation programs. The electronic controller adds supplemental fresh water to recycling stations when required by the programs.

Most recently mentioned in EBN 4:2

Aqus System

New

Watersaver Technologies LLC
13400 U.S. Highway 42, Ste. 214
Prospect, KY 40059

Toll-free: 502-741-1859
Phone: 502-550-1506
Fax: 502-228-1858
www.watersavertech.com

The Aqus System from Watersaver Technologies captures graywater from a bathroom sink in a 5.5-gallon reservoir that is housed inside the vanity. The device filters the water and controls bacteria with disinfection tablets, and pumps it to the toilet tank, where it replaces the use of fresh, potable water. The system works with toilet tanks of any size, but it will not work with pressurized toilet tank systems. Watersaver estimates that installation will take 1–2 hours, and will save 10–20 gallons of water a day in

a two-person household. The product was introduced in 2006, following testing that began in 2004.

Z-MOD Packaged Plants for Wastewater Treatment

Zenon Environmental Inc.
3239 Dundas St. W
Oakville, ON L6M 4B2 Canada

Phone: 905-465-3030
Fax: 905-465-3050
www.zenon.com

The Z-MOD on-site wastewater treatment system for graywater and blackwater combines membrane technology with biological processes and disinfection to produce colorless and odorless water that can be reused in applications such as toilet flush water, laundry, cooling towers, and green roof irrigation. Capable of handling virtually any flow, the Z-MOD system is appropriate for industrial, commercial, or residential wastewater treatment applications.

22 32 00
Domestic Water Filtration Equipment

Products included here are used to purify water. Such systems can help to ensure high-quality drinking water. Some are also key components of rainwater harvesting systems.

ECO-Nomad

Architectural & Community Planning Inc.
For full listing, see CSI section 23 56 16 - Packaged Solar Heating Equipment

SunRay-30 and SunRay-1000

Safe Water Systems
1600 Kapiolani Blvd, Ste. 721
Honolulu, HI 96814

Phone: 808-949-3123
Fax: 808-949-3103
www.safewatersystems.com

The SunRay-30 and SunRay-1000 can provide inexpensive microbial water purification without electricity, pumps, chemicals, or boiling. The SunRay-30 is comprised of a black, double-walled HDPE collector covered by two layers of transparent acrylic glazing. Up to 3.5 gal. of untreated water is poured into the unit and placed in the sun; when pasteurization is complete, an indicator will

22 00 00
Plumbing

change color. The SunRay-1000 is designed to purify approximately 260 gal. of water a day in sunny climates, utilizes a flat plate collector, a high-efficiency heat exchanger, and a fail-safe thermal control valve. On cloudy days, or at night, an optional backup burner can use any form of combustible fuel. Neither unit can be used in freezing temperatures.

Most recently mentioned in EBN 15:4

SolAqua Water Distillation

SolAqua
P.O. Box 4976
El Paso, TX 79914

New

Phone: 915-383-1485
www.solaqua.com

SolAqua sells passive-solar water distillation systems that provide purified distilled water without electricity, pumps, chemicals, or boiling. Products include the Rainmaker 550, which produces a maximum of 1.5 gallons of distilled water per day, do-it-yourself installation plans and kits, and community-size solar distiller arrays. SolAqua also provides consulting and installation for large systems.

Most recently mentioned in EBN 15:4

Solar Turtle

Solar Turtle, Inc.

For full listing, see CSI section 26 31 00 - Photovoltaic Collectors

UV Water Disinfection Systems

Sunlight Systems
4-D Pearl Ct.
Allendale, NJ 07401

Phone: 201-934-7772
Fax: 201-934-6886
www.sunlightsystems.com

Sunlight Systems designs, manufactures, and markets ultraviolet (UV) water disinfection systems for residential, commercial, and industrial use and also supplies replacement parts and service. UV purification is suitable for disinfecting water that is microbially contaminated. In certain situations, it may be necessary to pretreat water with another filtration system to remove impurities which can interfere with UV light transmission.

22 34 00
Fuel-Fired Domestic Water Heaters

The most efficient domestic water heaters include electronic-ignition gas-fired on-demand models, direct-contact commercial water heaters, heat-pump water heaters, and advanced combination space- and water-heating systems. (All electric resistance water heaters have the inefficiencies and fuel-source pollution concerns inherent to electric power generation.) Some water heaters—especially electronic-ignition on-demand water heaters—can also be used as boilers for heating, particularly in very-low-energy buildings. Other factors to consider include indoor air quality (in terms of combustion gases) and the ozone-depletion impacts associated with refrigerants for heat pumps and blowing agents for storage tank insulation. On-demand water heaters have no standby losses or storage tank insulation concerns, and some models have sealed combustion and no pilot lights. Gas-fired condensing storage-tank type water heaters have fuel efficiencies greater than 90% and use a variety of types of insulation. Heat-pump water heaters have tremendous efficiencies, but these are still very uncommon. In combined or integrated systems, efficiencies are boosted by uniting space heating and/or cooling into a single system that includes water heating. In almost every type of high-efficiency water heater there are issues of rate-of-use, climate, and maintenance that require consideration to make the appropriate selection for optimal results. (See also 23 52 00 - Heating Boilers, 23 56 13 - Heating Solar Flat-Plate Collectors, 23 56 15 - Heating Solar Vacuum-Tube Collectors.) (See feature article EBN Vol. 11, No. 10.)

Cyclone Commercial Gas-fired Water Heaters

A. O. Smith Water Products Co.
500 Tennessee Waltz Pkwy.
Ashland City, TN 37015

New

Toll-free: 800-527-1953
Fax: 615-792-2163
www.aosmithwaterheaters.com

Cyclone commercial water heaters feature down-fired burners with sealed, submerged combustion chambers and helical heat exchanger coils for hot fuel gasses; these features result in 94% and 99% efficiencies. The 99% efficient BTH-300 and BTH-400 models have double the heat exchanger length of the lower-efficiency models. Six models are available with three capacities (60,100,130 gallons) and a range of recovery times. The largest unit's maximum input is 400,000 Btu/hr. Units can be ganged to serve high-demand applications. Cyclone units are available in a variety of venting configurations, including options that minimize installation space requirements. Units can use either natural gas or propane for fuel.

KC 1000 Gas-fired Commercial Water Heating System

AERCO International, Inc.
159 Paris Ave.
Northvale, NJ 07647

Phone: 201-768-2400
Fax: 201-768-7789
www.aerco.com

Model GWW is a 1 M-Btu condensing, modulating water heater with efficiencies ranging from 93% to 99+%. Sealed combustion installation is an option. 20:1 modulation of the burner permits matching to load for energy savings. The system may be optionally equipped with a low NOx, SCAQM-certified burner (<30 ppm).

Polaris Heating Systems

American Water Heater Company
500 Princeton Rd.
Johnson City, TN 37601

Toll-free: 800-937-1037
Phone: 423-283-8000
Fax: 800-581-7224
www.americanwaterheater.com

Polaris Heating Systems are high-efficiency, combination water and residential space-heating products. The gas-fired unit has a submerged stainless steel flue that transfers combustion energy to the water with 95+% efficiency. Polaris heaters are available in 34-, 50-, and 100-gal. sizes with outputs of 100,000 to 199,000 Btu/hr and energy factors of 0.86.

22 00 00
Plumbing

Heat-Pump Water Heater

Applied Energy Recovery Systems
6670A Corners Industrial Ct.
Norcross, GA 30092

Phone: 770-734-9696
Fax: 770-453-9323
www.aers.com

Applied Energy Recovery Systems manufactures a series of commercial heat-pump water heaters, one with small enough capacity for residential use. All models utilize R-134a and R-22 as refrigerants instead of the ozone-depleting HCFC-22.

FloDirect Direct Fired Water Heater

Armstrong International, Inc.
816 Maple St.
Three Rivers, MI 49093

Phone: 269-273-1415
Fax: 269-278-6555
www.armstrong-intl.com

Previously manufactured by Direct Fire Technical, the Armstrong FloDirect™ Direct Fired Water Heater (formerly the DFT Hot Water Generator) for commercial and industrial applications can produce up to 600 gpm with a 145 degrees F temperature rise (peak temperature 185 degrees F). Its efficiency nears 100% because of the recovery of heat lost in combustion exhaust. Applications include facilities such as hospitals, hotels, and laundries as well as industrial process heat and other applications where large volumes of hot water are consumed.

Bosch ProTankless Water Heaters

Bosch Water Heating
340 Mad River Park
Waitsfield, VT 05673

Toll-free: 866-330-2725
Phone: 802-496-4436
Fax: 802-496-6924
www.protankless.com

The Bosch ProTankless line of gas-fired, tankless water heaters offer efficiencies up to 87%. The ProTankless 635ES and 635ESO water heaters supply two hot water outlets simultaneously at a combined rate of 6 gpm. The heaters can also be fueled by either natural gas or propane, and have an electronic ignition, digital temperature control, an energy factor of 0.85, and a 15-year warranty. Model ES contains a sealed-combustion unit for indoor installation that can be vented horizontally or vertically. Model ESO has built in freeze protection to 5°F for exterior installation.

Broad Absorption Chiller/ Heater

Broad USA, Inc.

For full listing, see CSI section 23 64 00 - Packaged Water Chillers

Indirect Water Heater Tanks

Buderus
50 Wentworth Ave.
Londonderry, NH 03053

Toll-free: 800-283-3787
Phone: 603-552-1100
Fax: 603-584-1681
www.buderus.net

The TBS-Isocal, S, ST, L, and LT domestic hot water tanks allow water heating by a gas- or oil-fired boiler. Unlike most domestic indirect water heater tanks, the Buderus uses non-ozone-depleting rigid foam. Because the unit is made in Germany, there are environmental impacts of shipping to consider.

HPA Heat Pump Water Heaters

Colmac Coil Manufacturing, Inc.
370 N. Lincoln St.
P.O. Box 571
Colville, WA 99114

Toll-free: 800-845-6778
Phone: 509-684-2595
Fax: 509-684-8331
www.colmaccoil.com

Colmac's HPA Series are commercial heat-pump water heaters for applications such as laundry and restaurant facilities. They utilize heat content of outdoor air in warm climates and heat content of indoor air in northern climates. All Colmac units use a non-ozone-depleting HFC refrigerant.

System 2000

Energy Kinetics

For full listing, see CSI section 23 52 00 - Heating Boilers

GWH150 Water Heater

GlowCore A.C. Inc.
4007 Platinum Way
Dallas, TX 75237

Toll-free: 800-676-4546
Fax: 214-467-4613
www.glowcoreac.com

GlowCore's model GWH150 sealed-combustion water heater has a thermal efficiency rating of 94%. It has an electronic ignition, a first-hour rating of 22.1 gallons, and a low-NOx output of 7.4 ppm.

Direct Contact Gas-Fired Water Heater

Kemco Systems
11500 47th St. N
Clearwater, FL 33762

Toll-free: 800-633-7055
Phone: 727-573-2323
Fax: 727-573-2346
www.kemcosystems.com

By capturing the heat content of incoming combustion air and combustion byproducts, KEMCO direct-contact water heaters achieve ratings up to and over 100% efficiency. Used in commercial applications in which several hundred gallons per minute delivery are required, KEMCO can deliver up to 540 gpm at a 180 degrees F rise.

Demand Water Heaters

Low Energy
4975 E. 41st Ave.
Denver, CO 80216

Toll-free: 800-873-3507
Phone: 303-781-9437
Fax: 303-781-3608
www.tanklesswaterheaters.com

Low Energy Systems is a specialized distributor of Paloma, Infinion, and Takagi demand gas hot water heaters, the latter of which offers *GreenSpec*-approved models. Homeowner-friendly maintenance kits, and solar thermal systems and components, are also available.

Most recently mentioned in EBN 7:4

Baxi Niagara Tankless Water Heater

Marathon International
1815 Sismet Rd.
Mississauga, ON L4W 1P9 Canada

Phone: 905-602-5360
www.wallhungboilers.com

New

Marathon International is the North American distributor for the Baxi line of boilers and water heating products from Britain. The Niagara tankless water heater is a zero-clearance, direct-venting, gas-fired unit with sealed combustion and electronic ignition. The rated heat output is 95,540 Btu/hr (75 degree F rise at 3 gpm), and the rated efficiency is 85.5.

Noritz Tankless Water Heaters

Noritz America Corp.
25172 Arctic Ocean Dr., Ste. 102
Lake Forest, CA 92630

Toll-free: 866-766-7489
Phone: 949-420-0409
Fax: 949-420-0414
www.noritzamerica.com

Noritz, the world's largest manufacturer of gas-fired, tankless, on demand water heaters, offers a full line of electronic-ignition, wall-hung models for residential and commercial applications. Models range in output from 194,000 Btu/hour up to 380,000 Btu/hour, with options for ganging multiple units for large commercial applications. Minimum output ranges from 21,000 to 25,000 Btu/hour; efficiencies are 80-85%. Direct-vent, sealed-combustion configurations are recommended for most applications (specify DV models). Residential products carry a 10-year warranty on the heat exchanger and 3-year warranty on all other parts; commercial products carry a 3-year warranty on all parts, including heat exchanger.

Most recently mentioned in EBN 11:10

Raypak Advanced Design Boilers

Raypak Corporate Office
For full listing, see CSI section 23 52 00 - Heating Boilers

AdvantagePlus

Rheem Manufacturing Company
101 Bell Rd.
Montgomery, AL 36117

Toll-free: 800-432-8373
Phone: 334-260-1500
www.rheem.com

The AdvantagePlus commercial water heater is a gas-fired, sealed-combustion model with a thermal efficiency of 95%. The storage tank is insulated with 2" of polyurethane foam (the blowing agent could not be identified).

Rheem Pronto! Tankless Gas Water Heaters

Rheem Manufacturing Company
101 Bell Rd.
Montgomery, AL 36117

Toll-free: 800-432-8373
Phone: 334-260-1500
www.rheem.com

The Rheem Pronto!™ series Tankless Water Heaters for natural or LP gas feature electronic ignition, power venting, low NOx emissions, electric freeze protection, and an exclusive oxygen-depletion-sensor safety device and overheat limiter. Model 4.2 has an input rating from 31,500 to 118,000 Btu/hr, delivering 4.2 gallons per minute with a 45-degree temperature rise at a 0.81 energy factor. Model 7.4 has an input rating of 19,000 to 199,900 Btu/hr and delivers 7.4 gallons at a 45-degree temperature rise with an 0.82 energy factor.

Most recently mentioned in EBN 14:2

Rinnai Continuum and Integrity Tankless Water Heaters

Rinnai
103 International Dr.
Peachtree City, GA 30269

Toll-free: 800-621-9419
Phone: 678-829-1700
Fax: 678-364-8643
www.rinnai.us

The Rinnai Continuum 2532FFU is a forced-combustion, tankless water heater with electronic ignition and the combustion unit installed outside. The heater can deliver 180,000 Btu/hr. Highly sophisticated freeze protection is provided, allowing installation in freezing climates. The Integrity REU 2532WC is a direct-vent version of the Continuum designed for installation inside the building.

Most recently mentioned in EBN 9:2 & 14:2

Water and Gas Safety Valve

Taco, Inc.
1160 Cranston St.
Cranston, RI 02920

Phone: 401-942-8000
Fax: 401-942-2360
www.taco-hvac.com

WAGS is a leak-detection and shut-off valve for domestic water heaters. This mechanical valve sits in a drip pan under the water heater. If leaking water accumulates to a level of 3/4", a water-soluble fiber element dissolves, releasing a piston that closes the flow of water to the tank and, in gas-fired heaters, breaking a fuse to shut off the gas supply. The system has the potential to provide savings from eliminating water leakage as well as any resulting mold growth or damage. Once activated in a leak, the valve must be replaced.

Flash and Mobius Tankless Water Heaters

Takagi Industrial Co. USA, Inc.
5 Whatney
Irvine, CA 92618

Toll-free: 888-882-5244
Phone: 949-770-7171
Fax: 949-770-3171
www.takagi-usa.com

Takagi's Flash T-H1, T-K2, T-KD20, and T-KJr. tankless gas water heaters are suited for residential and commercial applications and have no pilot, so standby losses are negligible. They do use electricity for a power burner and power vent. The Mobius T-M1 is a tankless, pilotless, computer-controlled gas water heater. Up to 20 units can be operated by a single control module, and several control modules can be linked together, making the Mobius practical for offices, hotels, hospitals, and other large facilities. The T-K1S pilotless, demand water heater is designed for single-use residential or commercial applications.

Most recently mentioned in EBN 11:10 & 13:2

Multi-Fuel and Wood Boilers

Tarm USA, Inc.

For full listing, see CSI section 23 52 00 - Heating Boilers

Oil Miser Water Heaters

Toyotomi U.S.A., Inc.
604 Federal Rd.
Brookfield, CT 06804

Phone: 203-775-1909
Fax: 203-775-6330
www.toyotomiusa.com

The only oil-fired, sealed-combustion, on-demand water heating systems in North America, Oil Miser Water Heater models OM-148 and BS-36UFF from Toyotomi have efficiency ratings of 88%. Both models provide up to 148,000 Btu/hr—the OM-148 consuming fuel at a rate of 1.05 gal/hr, and the BS-36UFF at 1.1 gal/hr. An external fuel tank is required (No. 1 or No. 2 fuel oil for the OM-148; ASTM No. 1-K Grade Kerosene or No. 1 Fuel Oil for BS-36UFF). The units require 120-volt AC power for ignition loads of 110 watts (no pilot light) and 98 watts while operating. Units may be direct- or chimney-vented and offer overheat protection, ignition safety, and no-water shutoff.

22 00 00
Plumbing

AquaMaster Q100

Vebteck Research

For full listing, see CSI section 23 52 00 - Heating Boilers

Vitodens 200 Wall-Mounted Boiler

Viessman Manufacturing Co. (U.S.) Inc.

For full listing, see CSI section 23 52 00 - Heating Boilers

22 35 00
Domestic Water Heat Exchangers

In the building industry, "domestic" water includes all potable water, whether in a residence or any kind of commercial building. A number of different opportunities exist to use waste heat for heating water. With refrigeration and air-conditioning equipment, waste heat is typically captured through desuperheating. Desuperheaters are most common in commercial settings, but equipment is available for residential use as well. To be cost-effective, a significant cooling load must support desuperheating operation—in homes, this means those in southern climates, and in commercial buildings this applies to businesses such as supermarkets that have large, year-round cooling and refrigeration loads. Waste heat from fuel-fired boilers can also be recovered for water heating. The heat content of wastewater can be recovered as well, using several different heat exchange technologies; the greater the surface area of contact between the two fluids, the more efficiently heat recovery can be achieved (but this must be balanced against the risk of blockage). Wastewater heat recovery systems are available for both commercial and residential applications. (See feature article EBN Vol. 11, No. 10.)

22 00 00
Plumbing

AC Series - Heat Recovery

Doucette Industries, Inc.
20 Leigh Drive
York, PA 17402

Toll-free: 800-445-7511
Phone: 717-845-8746
Fax: 717-845-2864
www.doucetteindustries.com

Doucette's desuperheaters use waste heat from commercial refrigeration and air conditioning systems to safely preheat water up to 140 degrees F for domestic and commercial uses, saving energy for water heating and improving the system's efficiency. They are available for systems sized from 5 to 200 tons.

HRP - Heat Recovery Option

FHP Manufacturing
601 N.W. 65th Ct.
Ft. Lauderdale, FL 33309

Phone: 954-776-5471
Fax: 954-776-5529
www.fhp-mfg.com

Florida Heat Pump makes a Heat Recovery Option or desuperheater that uses a heat exchanger to capture the waste heat from air conditioning units. The captured heat is then used for domestic water heating. System capacities are appropriate for both residential and commercial applications. Installation is appropriate where air conditioning loads are significant.

GFX Wastewater Heat Reclaimer

Fuel Cell Components & Integrators, Inc.
400 Oser Ave., Ste. 1950
Hauppauge, NY 11788

Toll-free: 888-871-9679
Phone: 631-234-8700
Fax: 631-234-0279
www.gfxtechnology.com

The GFX (gravity film exchange) drainline heat recovery device is a section of 2", 3" or 4" copper wastewater drainpipe wrapped by a coil of 1/2" copper supply line. Fresh water coming in through the supply line is warmed by the film of warm water descending the inner surface of the waste pipe. The GFX is available in various lengths and configurations for residential, institutional, and industrial uses. When hot water is being drawn, energy savings are obtained, and the heating capacity of water heaters extended.

Stack Economizer

Kemco Systems
11500 47th St. N
Clearwater, FL 33762

Toll-free: 800-633-7055
Phone: 727-573-2323
Fax: 727-573-2346
www.kemcosystems.com

The Kemco Systems Stack Economizer captures flue gas heat from the combustion exhaust of commercial boilers. The heat content is used for hot water needs within the commercial facility. The manufacturer claims nearly 100% fuel efficiency of the boiler using the Stack Economizer.

Wastewater Heat Recovery System

Kemco Systems
11500 47th St. N
Clearwater, FL 33762

Toll-free: 800-633-7055
Phone: 727-573-2323
Fax: 727-573-2346
www.kemcosystems.com

KEMCO's commercial-scale Heat Recovery System preheats incoming fresh water. Because this system does not require prefiltering of wastewater, the electric consumption of filtration is eliminated. Recovery of up to 60% of the original energy expended is possible.

Power-Pipe Drainwater Heat Recovery

RenewABILITY Energy Inc.
60 Baffin Place, Unit 2
Waterloo, ON N2V 1Z7 Canada

Toll-free: 877-606-5559
Phone: 519-885-0283
Fax: 519-885-4475
www.power-pipe.biz

The Power-Pipe™ installs in a vertical plumbing drain stack, recovering heat energy from draining water to warm an incoming cold water supply. As liquid drains, it clings to the inner surface of the copper pipe due to surface tension; part of the draining water's thermal energy is transferred to incoming water line (squared copper for maximum contact area) coiled around the stack. The heat transfer is most effective with equal drain and incoming flow volumes. Multiple units may be used in parallel for large flows. The energy savings potential can be significant, particularly in commercial or institutional applications with showers, laundry, dishwashing, boiler blowdown, etc. The Power Pipe can also be effective in residential applications, and is approved for potable water.

Heat Recovery System

Therma-Stor LLC
P.O. Box 8050
Madison, WI 53708

Toll-free: 800-533-7533
Phone: 608-222-5301
Fax: 608-222-1447
www.thermastor.com

Therma-Stor's Heat Recovery System is a type of desuperheater in which the waste heat from an air-cooled compressor is run through a heat exchanger to boost the temperature of domestic hot water. The system is designed for commercial applications such as hotels, restaurants, and supermarkets with large cooling and water-heating needs.

22 41 13
Residential Toilets

Since 1992, federal law has mandated that nearly all new toilets use no more than 1.6 gallons per flush (gpf)– the exception being commercial blow-out toilets, which are still allowed to use 3.5 gallons in some states. As toilet flushing is the largest single use of water in most residential and commercial buildings (accounting for up to 40% of residential use), water savings from toilet replacement is very significant. In addition to improvements to the traditional gravity system, pressure- and vacuum-assisted flushing systems have been developed that offer superior performance, albeit with the addition of some noise. Dual-flush toilets have been available for years overseas and are now making inroads in the U.S. These save additional water by making two flushes available: one for solid wastes and a lower-volume flush for liquids and paper. Products listed here must meet the minimum standards of the Uniform North American Requirements (UNAR) for toilets, which includes elements of the Maximum Performance (MaP) flush-quality testing protocol and Los Angeles Supplementary Purchase Specification (SPS), which discourages the use of toilets that might be adjusted to use significantly more water. Products listed here use at least 20% less than the federal minimum of 1.6 gallons (6 liters) per flush– that is, 1.28 gallons (4.8 liters) or less. The toilet must also evacuate at least 250 grams of solid waste per flush, as tested under the Maximum Performance (MaP) protocol. Toilets that are included without MaP testing are extremely low-water use or have other unique green features. For dual-flush toilets, we factor water savings by averaging the high and low volume flush levels. Other factors considered in GreenSpec evaluations include bowl washing effectiveness and water surface area. (See also 22 42 13 - Commercial Toilets.) (See feature articles EBN Vol. 6, No. 8 & Vol. 13, No. 1.)

American Standard FloWise Toilet

American Standard
One Centennial Plaza
P.O. Box 6820
Piscataway, NJ 08855

Toll-free: 800-442-1902
Phone: 732-980-3000
Fax: 732-980-3335
www.americanstandard-us.com

The FloWise™ toilet, introduced in 2005 by American Standard, uses advanced design to achieve very good flush performance with just 1.28 gallons—20% savings compared with a standard 1.6 gpf toilet. The toilet relies on the Champion flush technology, which uses a 3" flush valve and a 2-3/8" trapway to achieve a high-velocity, forceful flush. On the MaP tests, the FloWise is rated at 550 grams—more than twice the minimum acceptable rating of 250 grams.

Metzi 0.6 gpf Toilet

Bogo Global
3525 Ellicott Mills Dr., Ste. A
Ellicott City, MD 21043

Phone: 410-465-1841
www.bogoglobal.com

The Metzi toilet uses 0.6 gallons per flush. The patented South Korean technology uses a straight pipe with an odor prevention trap instead of a siphoning system. The performance of the Metzi toilet has not been tested by the MaP (Maximum Performance) protocol, but is included for its very low water consumption.

Turbo Capizzi

Capizzi
413 Interamerica Blvd.
WH1, PMB-006-225
Laredo, TX 78045

Toll-free: 866-250-8833
www.capizzi.com

The Turbo Capizzi high-efficiency toilet, which has an 8" x 9.5" water surface area, uses less than one gallon per flush. A fully glazed 2-1/8" (2" ballpass) trapway and Flushmate IV pressure-assist siphon-jet flush provide reliable performance. The low-profile, low-profile ADA, and high-profile models performed well under MaP testing, evacuating 400 - 500 grams with measured flush volumes between 3.1 and 3.7 liters— about 130 grams per liter, give or take a few grams. The Turbo Capizzi high-profile model meets LA SPS non-tamperng specifications. These toilets have limited lifetime warranties; the Sloan Flushmate flush mechanism has a five-year warranty.

Caroma Caravelle and Reflections Dual-Flush Toilets

Caroma USA, Inc.
2650 N.E. Aurora Dr.
Hillsboro, OR 97124

Toll-free: 800-605-4218
Phone: 503-681-2720
Fax: 503-681-2150
www.caromausa.com

Caroma USA, the North American subsidiary of Australian Caroma International Pty Ltd, offers a variety of two-button, dual-flush 1.6/0.8 gpf toilets. All units feature full 4" trapways. When MaP-tested at the high-volume flush, the Caravelle 270 and One-Piece each removed 500 grams, while the Caravelle 305 and Reflections 270 each removed 650 grams—resulting in grams-per-liter flushes between 90 and 110. The best results came from the Caravelle 270 ADA, which evacuated 800 grams, for a grams-per-liter rating of 133.

Most recently mentioned in EBN 13:2

Ifo Cera Dual-Flush Toilets

DEA Bathroom Machineries
495 Main St.
Murphys, CA 95247

Toll-free: 800-255-4426
Phone: 209-728-2031
Fax: 209-728-2320
www.deabath.com

Ifo toilets have a 50-year track record in Sweden, and theirs were among the first water-conserving toilets to gain acceptance in the American market. Their dual-flush Cera line offers users the choice of a 1.6-gallon full flush, or a 0.8-gallon half-volume flush. Note that Ifo toilets are constructed to European plumbing conventions and require a 4" rough-in rather than 12" or 14", or accommodation for rear-outlet. Retrofitting existing plumbing may not be feasible; refer to rough-in diagrams before ordering. The flush performance of these toilets has not been tested by the MaP (Maximum Performance) protocol; these toilets are included for their water-saving attribute.

Happy D Dual-Flush Toilets

Duravit USA, Inc.
1750 Breckinridge Pkwy., Ste. 500
Duluth, GA 30096

Toll-free: 888-387-2848
Phone: 770-931-3575
Fax: 770-931-8454
www.duravit.com

22 00 00
Plumbing

The Happy D dual-flush, gravity-type designer toilet from Duravit is available in floor-mounted and wall-mounted models. Both models removed 600 grams of solids under the MaP testing protocol. The average full-flush volume for the floor-mount model was 1.45 gallons; the wall-mount model averaged 1.51 gallons. Both averaged 0.8 gallon reduced flushes. These toilets meet LADWP SPS requirements. All Duravit wall-mounted toilets are dual-flush.

Gerber Ultra Flush 1.1-Gallon & Dual Flush Toilets

Gerber Plumbing Fixtures LLC
2500 Internationale Pkwy.
Woodridge , IL 60517

Phone: 630-754-0183
www.gerberonline.com

Gerber's Ultra Flush line of pressure-assist toilets includes dual-flush and 1.1-gallon models that returned impressive performances in third-party MaP testing. All used about 3.5 liters of measured flush volume (at high flush, in the case of dual-flush models); the dual-flush models evacuated 1000 grams (at high-flush—about 290 grams per liter), while the 1.1-gallon models evacuated 800 grams (about 230 grams per liter). Rear-discharge models of both are available. These toilets, which use pressure-assist technology by WDI International, do not meet LA SPS non-tampering requirements.

Most recently mentioned in EBN 13:1

Cimarron Comfort Height 1.28 GPF Toilet

Kohler Co.
444 Highland Dr.
Kohler, WI 53044

Toll-free: 800-456-4537
Phone: 920-457-4441
Fax: 920-457-6952
www.kohler.com

22 00 00
Plumbing

The Cimarron Comfort Height high-efficiency toilet (HET) with Class Five EcoSmart™ flush technology uses 1.28 gallons per flush. This gravity-flush toilet features a flapperless flush tower, and meets the requirement for programs offering rebates on HETs.

Highline 1.1-Gallon Toilet

Kohler Co.
444 Highland Dr.
Kohler, WI 53044

Toll-free: 800-456-4537
Phone: 920-457-4441
Fax: 920-457-6952
www.kohler.com

The Highline™ Pressure Lite 1.1-gpf toilet is a redesign of Kohler's older Highline toilets. The new Highline 1.1 uses the Sloan FlushMate IV flushing system, which was recognized by BuildingGreen as one of our 2004 Top-10 Green Building Products. By using a smaller pressure vessel, Kohler was able to design a smaller, more streamlined tank than is possible with 1.6-gpf (6.0-lpf) pressure-assist toilets. Kohler used advanced "noise-mapping and frequency analysis technology" to make this toilet among the quietest pressure-assist toilets on the market. This toilet removed 1,000 grams of solids per flush under third-party MaP testing.

Most recently mentioned in EBN 15:2

Sterling Rockton and Karston Dual-Flush Toilets

Kohler Co.
444 Highland Dr.
Kohler, WI 53044

Toll-free: 800-456-4537
Phone: 920-457-4441
Fax: 920-457-6952
www.kohler.com

The Rockton™ and Karston™ are dual-flush, flapperless, gravity-fed toilets from Sterling (a Kohler brand), offering users the choice of a 1.6 gal. or 0.8 gal. flush. The two-button flush actuator is integrated into the tank lid. The flush performance of the Karston has not been tested by the MaP (Maximum Performance) protocol; the Rockton evacuated 325 grams with an averaged water volume of 4.5 liters—flushing 72 grams per liter. The Karston is included for its water-saving attribute. These toilets are on the Los Angeles Department of Water and Power's SPS-Certified Ultra-Low-Flush Toilet list.

Most recently mentioned in EBN 13:6

Mancesa Cyclone 4

Mancesa (Division of Mansfield Plumbing Products, LLC)
150 First St.
P.O. Box 620
Perrysville, OH 44864

Toll-free: 877-850-3060
Phone: 419-938-5211
Fax: 419-938-6234
www.mancesa.com

The 1.1-gallon-per-flush Cyclone 4, from Colombian manufacturer Mancesa (a Mansfield brand), uses Sloan's Flushmate IV® pressure-assist flushing system. In MaP testing, it evacuated 650 grams with a measured flush of 3.6 liters—removing over 180 grams per liter of flush water. This toilet has a 2" trapway and an 8.5" x 10.25" water surface area.

Most recently mentioned in EBN 13:1

Mansfield EcoQuantum and QuantumOne Toilets

Mansfield Plumbing Products, LLC
150 First St.
P.O. Box 620
Perrysville, OH 44864

Toll-free: 877-850-3060
Phone: 419-938-5211
Fax: 800-984-7802
www.mansfieldplumbing.com

The pressure-assisted, dual-flush EcoQuantum line from Mansfield provides either a 1.6-gallon or 1.1-gallon flush, depending on whether the flush lever is pushed up or pressed down. Under MaP testing using the 1-gallon flush setting, models evacuated between 825 and 925 grams with measured flush volumes of 3.4 liters—grams-per-liter removal of 250 to 270. These toilets use the EcoFlush™ Dual Flushing Technology system. The QuantumOne one-gallon per flush line uses Flushmate IV™ pressure-assist technology; with a measured flush volume of 3.1 liters, models yielded grams-per-flush levels of 170 to 217 (525 to 675 grams).

Pressure-Assist Low-Flush Toilets

Microphor
452 E. Hill Rd.
Willits, CA 95490

Toll-free: 800-358-8280
Phone: 707-459-5563
Fax: 707-459-6617
www.microphor.com

Microphor produces pressure-assisted toilets, including the Microflush® toilets that use 0.5 gpf. Compressed air is used to assist flushing. Noise may be a concern. Microflush is also available in a 12-volt DC version. The flush performance of these toilets has not been tested by the MaP (Maximum Performance) protocol; these toilets are included in *GreenSpec* for their water-saving attribute.

Most recently mentioned in EBN 6:8

Peerless Pottery-The Predator

Peerless Pottery
P.O. Box 145
Rockport, IN 47635

Toll-free: 800-457-5785
Fax: 812-649-6429
www.peerlesspottery.com

Manufactured by Capizzi, Peerless Pottery offers two models (ADA and low-profile) in the Predator line that meet *GreenSpec* standards. Both use Sloan's FlushMate® technology to achieve 1.1-gallon flushes. In MaP testing, the ADA model evacuated 500 grams with a measured flush volume of 3.7 liters (135 grams per liter). The low-profile model evacuated 400 grams with 3.1 liters (129 grams per liter). These toilets do not meet LA SPS non-tampering requirements.

SaniFlo Macerating Toilets

SFA Saniflo, Inc.
1 - 685 Speedvale Ave. W
Guelph, ON N1K 1E6 Canada

New

Phone: 519-824-1134
Fax: 519-824-1143
www.saniflo.com

The Sanicompact 1.1-gallon-per-flush macerating toilet uses a 1" diameter discharge pipe, and can be installed in tight spaces as well as below-grade. A switch activates the flush sequence that fills and washes the toilet bowl with water, pumps the effluent to the macerator, and then pumps the discharge away. Effluent can be pumped a maximum of 9 feet vertically, or 100 feet horizontally. Saniflow offers a number of other macerating toilet and plumbing systems as well.

FlushMate IV

Sloan Valve Company

For full listing, see CSI section 22 42 43 - Flushometers

Eclipse Mariner II Pressure-Assist Toilets

St. Thomas Creations
9393 Waples St., Ste 120
San Diego, CA 92121

Phone: 858-812-2550
Fax: 858-812-2555
www.stthomascreations.com

The 1.0 gpf Eclipse Mariner II ™ pressure-assist toilet uses Sloan's Flushmate IV operating system. A supply line with a minimum water pressure of 25 psi is required. Two models were tested using the MaP (Maximum Performance) protocol in May 2004: both had a 5.9-liter flush volume; the elongated rim model removed 500 grams of solids for a grams-per-liter rating of 85, while the round-front model evacuated 465 grams for a rating of 79.

TOTO Aquia Dual-Flush Toilet

TOTO USA, Inc.
1155 Southern Rd.
Morrow, GA 30260

Phone: 770-282-8686
Fax: 770-282-8697
www.totousa.com

The Aquia™ dual-flush toilet, introduced to the North American market in 2005, uses 1.6 gallons at the full flush and 0.9 gallons at the low flush. The company estimates that a typical family of four will save approximately 7,000 gallons of water per year over a standard 1.6 gallon-per-flush toilet. Unlike other TOTO gravity-flush toilets, this is a wash-down design, which like other TOTO toilets is highly clog-free. The toilet successfully removed 800 grams of test media at full flush, based on standardized MaP testing. The toilet is offered in six colors.

Most recently mentioned in EBN 14:11 & 14:12

VitrA Dual Flush Toilet

VitrA USA
305 Shawnee North Dr., Ste. 600
Suwanee, GA 30024

Phone: 770-904-6830
Fax: 770-904-6830
www.vitra-usa.com

European manufacturer VitrA offers two floor-mounted, dual-flush toilets that use 1.6 gallons at full flush and 0.8 gallons at low flush. The round front dual-flush model removed 475 grams of solids at full flush under third-party MaP testing. The elongated dual flush model, removed 800 grams of solids at full flush.

Vortens Tulip, Rhodas, Tornado, and Vienna

Vortens U.S. Office
1498 Brookpark Dr.
Mansfield, OH 44906

Toll-free: 800-471-5129
Fax: 419-756-3905
www.vortens.com

The Tulip and Rhodas dual-flush toilets from Mexican manufacturer Sanitarios Lamosa S.A. de C.V. offer 1.0 or 1.6 gallon flushes. The flush performances were MaP-tested as having evacuated 400 and 550 grams respectively, with measured flush volumes of 5.5 and 6 liters. With high- and low-flush volumes averaged, the grams-per-liter removal was 80 and 110. In the same test, the Tornado pressure-assisted 1.1-gallon-flush toilet used a measured flush volume of 4 liters to evacuate 700 grams—175 grams per liter. The performance of Vortens' Vienna dual flush toilet has not been tested by the MaP (Maximum Performance) protocol, but is included for its water-saving attribute.

Zurn EcoVantage Dual-Flush Toilet

Zurn Plumbing Products Group
5900 Elwin Buchanan Dr.
Sanford, NC 27330

Toll-free: 800-997-3876
Phone: 919-775-2255
Fax: 919-775-3541
www.zurn.com

The Zurn® EcoVantage™ dual-flush toilet uses a pressure tank that flushes with either 1.6 or 1.1 gallons. This two-piece toilet, elongated-bowl toilet is manufactured for Zurn by WDI. Air is compressed in a sealed tank during the refill; when flushed, a high-velocity, forceful flush is produced. The EcoVantage features a 2-1/8" fully glazed trapway, siphon-jet flush action, a "large" water surface area, and "ultra-quiet" flush action, according to the manufacturer. Available in both standard height and ADA-compliant height (17"). This toilet evacuated 1,000 grams with a *Green-Spec*-adusted water use of 1.35 gallons per average flush in MaP testing.

Most recently mentioned in EBN 15:1

---

22 41 14
Composting Toilet Systems

Composting toilets convert human waste into nutrient-rich fertilizer for non-food plants, rather than mixing the waste with potable water and flushing it down the drain. The advantages of composting toilets include dramatic reductions in water use, reduced groundwater pollution or sewage-treatment impacts, and a recycling of nutrients. Some composting chambers can be used with microflush toilets, though most are nonflush. Proper sizing is critical for effective composting; a model with undersized capacity won't function appropriately. If composting toilets are used, graywater treatment and disposal still need to be addressed. (See also 22 42 14 - Commercial Composting Toilet Systems.) (See feature article EBN Vol. 3, No. 2.)

22 00 00
Plumbing

Phoenix Composting Toilet

Advanced Composting Systems
195 Meadows Rd.
Whitefish, MT 59937

Toll-free: 888-862-3854
Phone: 406-862-3854
Fax: 406-862-3855
www.compostingtoilet.com

Phoenix Composting Toilet systems are used in residential and public-facility applications such as parks and recreation areas. They have mixing tines for aerating the compost and a system for recycling leachate. The only electrical load is a 12-volt DC, 5-watt exhaust fan.

Most recently mentioned in EBN 7:6 & 7:8

ExcelAerator

Bio-Sun Systems, Inc.

For full listing, see CSI section 22 42 14 - Commercial Composting Toilet Systems

Clivus Multrum Composting Toilet Systems

Clivus Multrum, Inc.
15 Union St.
Lawrence, MA 01840

Toll-free: 800-425-4887
Phone: 978-725-5591
Fax: 978-557-9658
www.clivusmultrum.com

Clivus Multrum popularized the composting toilet in the U.S. and is still one of the most widely recognized manufacturers. The company offers a range of composting toilets for various applications, from small residences to large public facilities. All include a composting chamber below one or more toilet fixtures. In addition to non-water-using models, Clivus offers a foam flush fixture that uses a soap solution and 3 oz. of water for flushing. Electricity is required for ventilation and moistening systems. Design, installation, and maintenance services are available.

Most recently mentioned in EBN 3:2, 3:3, 4:5, 7:9

Ecotech Carousel

Ecotech
50 Beharell St.
Concord, MA 01742

Phone: 978-369-3951
Fax: 978-369-2484
www.ecological-engineering.com

The EcoTech Carousel is a "batch" composting toilet that processes waste faster and more completely without raking. Available from Gaiam Real Goods.

Equaris Biomatter Resequencing Converter

Equaris Corporation
15711 Upper 34th St. S
P.O. Box 6
Afton, MN 55001

Phone: 651-337-0261
Fax: 651-337-0265
www.equaris.com

Equaris Corporation, formerly AlasCan, Inc., manufactures a composting toilet system that operates as part of a system of integrated technologies to separate toilet and organic kitchen wastes from the wastewater stream at the source. Solid waste is deposited into the Equaris Biomatter Resequencing Converter (BMRC), where 90-95% of the toilet and organic wastes are biologically converted into odorless carbon dioxide and water vapor; the remaining 5-10% can be used safely as a soil amendment. The toilets used with this system require one cup of water or less per flush. Graywater is treated aerobically in the Equaris Greywater Treatment System utilizing a small continuously operating 67-watt linear air compressor to filter and remove most pollutants. This system eliminates septic tanks and reduces leachfields or mounds by 40-90%, according to the manufacturer. The water can then be diverted through the Equaris Water Recycling System to produce potable water using reverse osmosis, ozone and UV treatment, and physical filtration.

Most recently mentioned in EBN 3:2

Nepon Foam Flush Toilet

Nepon-USA **New**
P.O. Box 127
North Andover, MA 01845

Toll-free: 866-396-3766
Phone: 978-794-4810
Fax: 978-794-9444
www.neponusa.com

The Nepon foam-flush toilet for ultra-low-flush or composting toilet applications uses a biodegradable soap solution and 3 ounces of water for each flush. An electric air pump aerates the soap, generating a foam of soap bubbles. The foaming action provides lubrication, prevents splashing and streaking, and keeps the toilet bowl clean. This toilet design relies on a physical trapway, as the flushing system does not accommodate the internal water-trap found in conventional toilets. Nepon offers a flush-accumulator system to allow this toilet to be used with conventional plumbing in retrofit applications.

Envirolet

Sancor Industries Ltd.
140-30 Milner Ave.
Scarborough, ON M1S 3R3 Canada

Toll-free: 800-387-5126
Phone: 416-299-4818
Fax: 416-299-3124
www.envirolet.com

Sancor™ Envirolets are small composting toilets, some self-contained and others with a separate composting chamber below. Available in non-water-using and low-water models in non-electric, 12-volt DC, and 120-volt AC. Envirolet™ has been sold worldwide since 1977.

Sun-Mar Composting Toilet

Sun-Mar Corp.
5370 S. Service Rd.
Burlington, ON L7L 5L1 Canada

Toll-free: 888-341-0782
Phone: 905-332-1314
Fax: 905-332-1315
www.sun-mar.com

Sun-Mar offers over 20 different models of composting toilets, some self-contained and others with a separate composting chamber below. In general, composting toilets with separate compost chambers have proven more reliable. Any composting toilet must be correctly sized and installed, and appropriately maintained, in order to function properly.

Most recently mentioned in EBN 3:2

22 41 15
Residential Urinals

Products listed here are low-water-use urinals for residential use. (See also 22 42 15 - Commercial Urinals.) (See feature article EBN Vol. 6, No. 8.)

Mister Miser Urinal **New**

Mister Miser Urinal
1800 W. Roscoe, Ste. 325
Chicago, IL 60657

Phone: 773-975-8170
www.mistermiser.net

Designed primarily for residential use, the 10-ounce (1-1/4 cup) flush Mister Miser urinal—made of ABS with a porcelain-like coating—installs at any height between 2x4 studs. A hinged cover folds down for use; the silent flush activates when the lid is closed, providing adequate surface wash and enough liquid to evacuate the built-in

22 00 00
Plumbing

P-trap. The manufacturer offers a 5-year warranty. Made in Chicago. This product returned to the market in 2006, after being unavailable for a number of years.

Most recently mentioned in EBN 6:8 & 15:8

22 41 16
Residential Lavatories and Sinks

Products listed here contain recycled content or can contribute to innovative wastewater treatment practices, such as graywater separation. (See also 22 42 16 - Commercial Lavatories and Sinks.)

Envirosink

Bismart Distributors, Inc.

For full listing, see CSI section 22 16 00 - Graywater Systems

Cast Aluminum Products

Eleek, Inc.

For full listing, see CSI section 26 51 14 - Interior Luminaires

22 41 39
Residential Faucets and Controls

Many conservation efforts — in industrial, commercial, and residential settings — are making significant improvements in water-use efficiency. These advances are also reducing our wastewater treatment burden and expense. Products listed here dispense water efficiently or improve controllability of the water supply. (See also 22 42 39 - Commercial Faucets and Controls.) (See feature article EBN Vol. 6, No. 8.)

Metlund Hot Water D'MAND System

ACT, Inc. Metlund Systems
3176 Pullman St., Ste. 119
Costa Mesa, CA 92626

Toll-free: 800-638-5863
Phone: 714-668-1200
Fax: 714-668-1927
www.gothotwater.com

Metlund Hot Water D'mand System is an electronically controlled valve and pumping system that rapidly distributes hot water from the water heater to fixtures in a home or commercial building. This system can operate either with a return line or by the existing cold-water line. The Metlund System pumps cold tapwater back to the water heater and delivers hot water instead, saving otherwise wasted water and shortening the wait for hot water. Because it circulates the water only on demand, this system avoids the energy penalties of continuously circulating systems. The Metlund System can also be activated by either a low-voltage remote button or a motion sensor.

Most recently mentioned in EBN 4:2 & 11:10

Bricor Elite Series Showerheads

Bricor Southwest

For full listing, see CSI section 22 42 39 - Commercial Faucets and Controls

The Chilipepper Appliance

Chilipepper Systems
4623 Hasting Pl.
Lake Oswego, OR 97035

Toll-free: 800-914-9887
Phone: 209-401-8888
Fax: 503-699-6998
www.chilipepperapp.com

The Chilipepper Appliance is an on-demand water circulation device that speeds the availability of hot water at the tap. This energy- and money-saving appliance is easily mounted at the most remote tap. The 115-volt pump moves cold water out of the hot-water line and back to the water heater via the cold-water line. The Chilipepper is activated by either a wireless remote or a wired controller.

Water-Efficient Showerheads **New**

Delta Faucet Company
55 East 111th St.
P.O. Box 40980
Indianapolis, IN 46280

Toll-free: 800-345-3358
Phone: 317-848-1812
Fax: 317-848-0713
www.deltafaucet.com

Delta Faucet Company offers water-efficient showerheads with H2Okinetic Technology™ that use only 1.6 gallons per minute yet deliver a satisfying shower. The showerhead provides 36% water savings over standard 2.5 gpm showerheads; this saves both water and energy (for heating water). The showerhead produces water droplets that are fairly large,

resulting in good heat retention and body wetting. Most low-flow showerheads either create very small droplets or aerate the water.

Most recently mentioned in EBN 15:5 & 15:12

ETL Low-Flow Showerheads

Energy Technology Laboratories
2351 Tenaya Dr.
Modesto, CA 95354

Toll-free: 800-344-3242
Phone: 209-529-3546
Fax: 209-529-3554
www.etlproducts.com

The Oxygenics® line of showerheads, made with DuPont Delrin® 500P acetal resin, employs a venturi air-induction design using a single, centered orifice — rather than a lot of small holes in the face of the showerhead — and stationary fins to break the spray into pulsating droplets. Showerheads in the Oxygenics line are rated to use from 1.5 to 2.5 gpm and are optimized for different water pressures. The products achieve remarkably satisfying shower force and are guaranteed for life never to clog.

Most recently mentioned in EBN 6:8 & 11:10

Water-Efficient Showerheads **New**

Kohler Co.
444 Highland Dr.
Kohler, WI 53044

Toll-free: 800-456-4537
Phone: 920-457-4441
Fax: 920-457-6952
www.kohler.com

MasterShower™ Eco showerheads and handshowers from Kohler use 2 gallons per minute, offering a 20% water savings compared with conventional 2.5 gpm showerheads. These products feature three-position spray patterns. The standard MasterShower line uses 2.5 gpm.

Water-Conserving Fixtures

Niagara Conservation Corp.
45 Horsehill Rd.
Cedar Knolls, NJ 07927

Toll-free: 800-831-8383
Phone: 973-829-0800
Fax: 973-829-1400
www.niagaraconservation.com

Niagara Conservation Corporation offers water- and energy-conserving products including showerheads, toilets, toilet retrofit kits, faucet aerators, light bulbs, and weatherization products. They also produce a patented tamperproof, flapperless, 1.6-gal. toilet suitable for both 10" and 12" rough-ins.

Most recently mentioned in EBN 6:8 & 8:3

22 00 00
Plumbing

Pedalworks and Footworks

Pedal Valves, Inc.
13625 River Rd.
Luling, LA 70070

Toll-free: 800-431-3668
Phone: 985-785-9997
Fax: 985-785-0082
www.pedalvalve.com

Footworks and Pedalworks are unique, single-pedal faucet controllers. The Footworks product is for commercial applications and bolts into the floor beneath the sink; the residential Pedalworks controller is installed in the base of a kitchen cabinet or bathroom vanity. The conventional hand controls are used to set the temperature balance between hot and cold water, and the foot pedal is used to turn the flow on and off. A lock-on button allows the water to be left running when necessary. Water savings are significant but difficult to quantify. In applications such as hospitals (when water is often left running while surgeons scrub their hands and arms) and commercial kitchens, water savings can be dramatic. The products also help with hygiene and productivity.

Most recently mentioned in EBN 8:6

Foot-Operated Sink Valve

Step-Flow, Inc.

For full listing, see CSI section 22 42 39 - Commercial Faucets and Controls

Foot-Pedal Faucet Controls

T&S Brass and Bronze Works, Inc.

For full listing, see CSI section 22 42 39 - Commercial Faucets and Controls

Taco Hot Water D'MAND System

Taco, Inc.
1160 Cranston St.
Cranston, RI 02920

Phone: 401-942-8000
Fax: 401-942-2360
www.taco-hvac.com

The Taco D'MAND® System is an electronically activated water-pumping system that quickly delivers hot water to a fixture while returning water that has been sitting in the hot-water pipes back to the hot-water tank. The pump may be activated on demand by pushing a button near the fixture or by remote control. The system switches off when hot water reaches the temperature sensor on the pump at the fixture. Aside from quicker hot water delivery, benefits include energy savings and the elimination of water waste while waiting for hot water. In retrofit ap-

plications, the cold-water line serves as the return line; in new construction, a third plumbing line is usually installed.

Most recently mentioned in EBN 12:5

Tapmaster

Tapmaster Incorporated
20175 Township Rd. 262
Calgary, AB T3P 1A3 Canada

Toll-free: 800-791-8117
Phone: 403-275-5554
Fax: 403-275-5928
www.tapmaster.ca

Tapmaster is a foot- or knee-activated switch that controls the flow to a faucet. The conventional hand controls are used to set the temperature balance and flow volume between hot and cold water, and the foot switch is used to turn the flow on and off. A lock-on button allows the water to be left running when necessary. Water savings are significant but difficult to quantify, as they depend on user habits. Tapmaster is widely used in dental offices for hygienic reasons, as well as homes. Easy installation with no electronics or wires, pressure tank, bulky mechanical devices, or ongoing maintenance.

Zurn AquaSpec Foot Pedal Valves

Zurn Plumbing Products Group

For full listing, see CSI section 22 42 39 - Commercial Faucets and Controls

Zurn AquaSpec Low-Flow Showerheads

Zurn Plumbing Products Group

For full listing, see CSI section 22 42 39 - Commercial Faucets and Controls

22 42 13
Commercial Toilets

Since 1992, federal law has mandated that nearly all new toilets use no more than 1.6 gallons per flush (gpf)– the exception being commercial blow-out toilets, which are still allowed to use 3.5 gallons in some states. As toilet flushing is the largest single use of water in most residential and commercial buildings, water savings from toilet replacement is very significant. In addition to improvements to the traditional gravity system, pressure- and vacuum-assisted flushing systems have been developed that offer superior performance, albeit with the

addition of some noise. Dual-flush toilets have been available for years overseas and are now making inroads in the U.S. These save additional water by making two flushes available: one for solid wastes and a lower-volume flush for liquids and paper. Products listed here must meet the minimum standards of the Uniform North American Requirements (UNAR) for toilets, which includes elements of the Maximum Performance (MaP) flush-quality testing protocol and Los Angeles Supplementary Purchase Specification (SPS), which discourages the use of toilets that might be adjusted to use significantly more water. Products listed here use at least 20% less than the federal minimum of 1.6 gallons (6 liters) per flush– that is, 1.28 gallons (4.8 liters) or less. The toilet must also evacuate at least 250 grams of solid waste per flush, as tested under the Maximum Performance (MaP) protocol. Toilets that are included without MaP testing are extremely low-water use or have other unique green features. For dual-flush toilets, we factor water savings by averaging the high and low volume flush levels. Other factors considered in GreenSpec evaluations include bowl washing effectiveness and water surface area. (See also 22 41 13 - Residential Toilets.) (See feature articles EBN Vol. 6, No. 8 & Vol. 13, No. 1.)

EVAC Vacuum Toilet Systems

Evac - Sanitec Group
1702 Hutchins Rd.
Rockford, IL 61115

Toll-free: 800-438-3822
Phone: 815-654-8300
Fax: 815-654-8306
www.evac.com

EVAC makes commercial and institutional vacuum toilet systems, including stainless steel fixtures for correctional facilities. EVAC vacuum toilets use 3 pints of water per flush, saving 2 million gallons of water annually in a 250-bed facility. The flush performance of these toilets has not been tested by the MaP (Maximum Performance) protocol; these toilets are included in *GreenSpec* for their water-saving attribute.

Most recently mentioned in EBN 13:1

FlushMate IV

Sloan Valve Company

For full listing, see CSI section 22 42 43 - Flushometers

22 00 00
Plumbing

AquaSaver

The Fuller Group, Inc.
3461 Summerford Ct.
Marietta, GA 30062

Phone: 770-565-8539
Fax: 770-565-4197

AquaSaver is a small, inexpensive, adjustable, water-saving device for gravity-flush, tanked toilets. The product is a plastic manifold that clips over the toilet's overflow pipe. It saves 15-25% of water per flush without impeding the flushing ability of the toilet. It does this by diverting some of the excess refill water that typically overfills the toilet bowl, keeping it in the toilet tank. It saves more water in older, less-efficient toilets. Sales are primarily in bulk to large institutions or water-conservation contractors.

Most recently mentioned in EBN 8:3

VitrA Commercial 1.0 GPF Toilet

New

VitrA USA
305 Shawnee North Dr., Ste. 600
Suwanee, GA 30024

Phone: 770-904-6830
Fax: 770-904-6830
www.vitra-usa.com

The VitrA commercial 1.0-gallon-per-flush toilet uses the Sloan FlushMate IV® pressure-assist flushing system to remove 800 grams of solids per flush (about 230 grams per liter) under third-party MaP testing. This toilet has an elongated bowl and can be installed to be ADA-compliant (17" high) with use of the recommended seat.

Most recently mentioned in EBN 15:6

VitrA Dual Flush Toilet

VitrA USA

For full listing, see CSI section 22 41 13 - Residential Toilets

Zurn EcoVantage 1.1 GPF Toilet

Zurn Plumbing Products Group
5900 Elwin Buchanan Dr.
Sanford, NC 27330

Toll-free: 800-997-3876
Phone: 919-775-2255
Fax: 919-775-3541
www.zurn.com

The Zurn® EcoVantage™ 1.1 gpf toilet uses pressure-assist technology by WDI International to achieve good flush performance using just 1.1 gallons. The EcoVantage two-piece toilet, manufactured for Zurn by WDI, compresses air in a sealed tank during the refill; when flushed, a high-velocity, forceful flush is produced. The EcoVantage features a 2-1/8" fully glazed trapway, siphon-jet flush action, a "large" water surface area, and "ultra-quiet" flush action, according to the manufacturer. Available only with an elongated bowl in both standard height and ADA-compliant height (17"). In MaP testing, the toilet achieved a remarkable 800-gram rating.

Most recently mentioned in EBN 15:1

22 42 14
Commercial Composting Toilet Systems

Composting toilets convert human waste into nutrient-rich fertilizer for non-food plants, rather than mixing the waste with potable water and flushing it down the drain. The advantages of composting toilets include dramatic reductions in water use, reduced groundwater pollution or sewage-treatment impacts, and a recycling of nutrients. Some composting chambers can be used with microflush toilets, though most are nonflush. Proper sizing is critical for effective composting; a model with undersized capacity won't function appropriately. If composting toilets are used, graywater treatment and disposal still need to be addressed. (See also 22 41 14 - Composting Toilet Systems.) (See feature article EBN Vol. 3, No. 2.)

Phoenix Composting Toilet

Advanced Composting Systems

For full listing, see CSI section 22 41 14 - Composting Toilet Systems

ExcelAerator

Bio-Sun Systems, Inc.
7088 Rte. 549
Millerton, PA 16936

Toll-free: 800-847-8840
Phone: 570-537-2200
Fax: 570-537-6200
www.bio-sun.com

Bio-Sun composting toilet systems can serve multiple toilets. The ExcelAerator™ system extracts by-product gasses from the composting chamber and also injects air directly into the waste piles for accelerated decomposition. A vent extraction device is incorporated which simultaneously removes byproduct gases.

Clivus Multrum Composting Toilet Systems

Clivus Multrum, Inc.

For full listing, see CSI section 22 41 14 - Composting Toilet Systems

Equaris Biomatter Resequencing Converter

Equaris Corporation

For full listing, see CSI section 22 41 14 - Composting Toilet Systems

22 42 15
Commercial Urinals

Compared with the federal-standard 1.0 gallon per flush, a single non-water-using urinal can save over 10,000 gallons of water per year (depending on the number of males in the building); when older 3 gpf urinals are replaced, the savings can be as great as 50,000 gallons per year. Products listed here include low-water-use flush valves, low-water-use urinals, and next-generation non-water-using urinals that use a lighter-than-urine fluid to provide the "trap" that keeps odors out of the restroom. (See also 22 41 15 - Residential Urinals.) (See feature article EBN Vol. 6, No. 8.)

Automatic Flush Valve

AMT Corporation

For full listing, see CSI section 22 42 43 - Flushometers

Dry Non-Water-Using Urinal

Duravit USA, Inc.
1750 Breckinridge Pkwy., Ste. 500
Duluth, GA 30096

Toll-free: 888-387-2848
Phone: 770-931-3575
Fax: 770-931-8454
www.duravit.com

22 00 00
Plumbing

Duravit, USA, a subsidiary of the German company Duravit AG, Ltd., offers a stylish German-made, all-porcelain non-water-using urinal. Introduced in 2002, the Dry urinal relies on a lighter-than-urine fluid (Dry Blue, comprised of hexyldecanol and perfume) that serves as the trap. This sealing liquid is replaced monthly or after about 5,000 uses, whichever comes first. During this servicing, the urinal drain must also be flushed out for one to two minutes with a hose, according to the manufacturer, but there are no other components that have to be replaced. One quart of the Dry Blue fluid is added at the time of servicing.

Most recently mentioned in EBN 11:12, 12:2, 13:11

Falcon Waterfree Urinal

Falcon Waterfree Technologies LLC
751 Kenmoor SE, Ste. F
Grand Rapids, MI 49546

Toll-free: 866-275-3718
Phone: 616-954-3570
Fax: 616-954-3579
www.falconwaterfree.com

Falcon Waterfree urinals offer a water- and maintenance-saving alternative to conventional urinals. No water supply or valves are needed—only a standard drain line. The product uses an ABS plastic cartridge with biodegradable sealing liquid to trap sediment and odors. Replacement of the cartridge is required approximately three to four times per year. There is no need to replenish sealant between cartridge changes. Falcon Waterfree urinals are ADA compliant and available in four porcelain models.

Most recently mentioned in EBN 11:2, 11:5, 11:7, 13:2, 13:11

Kohler Non-Water-Using Urinals

New

Kohler Co.
444 Highland Dr.
Kohler, WI 53044

Toll-free: 800-456-4537
Phone: 920-457-4441
Fax: 920-457-6952
www.kohler.com

Kohler offers two models of vitreous china, waterless urinals. The Steward and the Steward S both feature a conical bowl that prevents splash, and a non-cartridge, fully glazed vitreous trapway that uses a proprietary, biodegradable, vegetable-based sealing liquid. The Steward model easily replaces existing urinals in retrofit applications and can also be used in new construction; the much smaller Steward S is only appropriate for new installations.

Most recently mentioned in EBN 15:5

22 00 00
Plumbing

Sloan Waterfree Urinal

Sloan Valve Company
10500 Seymour Ave.
Franklin Park, IL 60131

Toll-free: 800-982-5839
Phone: 847-671-4300
Fax: 800-447-8329
www.sloanvalve.com

Sloan Waterfree urinals offer a water- and maintenance-saving alternative to conventional urinals. No water supply or valves are needed—only a standard drain line. The product uses an ABS plastic cartridge and a biodegradable sealing liquid to trap sediment and odors. Replacement of trap and sealing liquid is required approximately every 7,000 uses. Sloan Waterfree urinals are available in porcelain (in white and custom colors) and in acrylic or fiberglass (in faux finishes, white, and custom colors).

Most recently mentioned in EBN 13:7 & 13:11

"Fuzzy Logic" Sensor Urinal Flush Valve

TOTO USA, Inc.
1155 Southern Rd.
Morrow, GA 30260

Phone: 770-282-8686
Fax: 770-282-8697
www.totousa.com

TOTO's TEU1DNCR-12 infrared sensor-activated urinal flush valve uses a "fuzzy logic"-controlled microprocessor to sense high frequency of usage and adjust consumption as much as 50% (minimum 30%) during high use periods. At 28 psi, the valve uses 0.5-1.0 gpf and will perform well with supply pressures ranging from 15 psi to 100 psi. When not in use, it flushes once every 24 hours for trap seal protection. The unit features a solid bronze piston valve and a self-cleaning debris screen. Four AA alkaline batteries are included, with a 2-year life based on 4,000 cycles per month.

Waterless No-Flush Urinal

Waterless Co. LLC
1050 Joshua Way
Vista, CA 92081

Toll-free: 800-244-6364
Phone: 760-727-7723
Fax: 760-727-7775
www.waterless.com

The Waterless No-Flush™ Urinal is a water-saving alternative to standard urinals. The product's EcoTrap® contains Blue Seal®, a proprietary, lighter-than-water mix of biodegradable oils and alcohol that seals the trap. Periodic replenishment of Blue Seal and replacement of the plastic EcoTrap is necessary. The urinal is plumbed to a standard 2" noncopper drain line. No water supply or valves are needed. Made from fiberglass-reinforced polyester and available in white or custom colors.

Most recently mentioned in EBN 7:2, 11:2, 11:5, 11:7, 13:2, 13:11, 14:11

ZeroFlush Non-Water-Using Urinals

ZeroFlush, Inc.
3008-3016 Lions Ct.
Kissimmee, FL 34744

Toll-free: 888-785-9376
Phone: 407-935-1180
Fax: 407-935-1103
www.zeroflush.com

ZeroFlush® offers nonflushing urinals in two vitreous china styles, as well as a stainless steel model. No water supply is needed—only a standard drain line. According to the manufacturer, the units average 15,000 uses before routine maintenance is required—which consists of flushing and rinsing the waste trap and replacing the nontoxic, biodegradable, lighter-than-urine, sanitary sealing fluid. The drain design eliminates cartridge traps; a plastic drain tube insert may be either replaced (using a simple puller key for touch-free handling), or rinsed and re-used during routine maintenance.

Most recently mentioned in EBN 14:6

Zurn EcoVantage 1/8th Gallon Flush Urinal

New

Zurn Plumbing Products Group
5900 Elwin Buchanan Dr.
Sanford, NC 27330

Toll-free: 800-997-3876
Phone: 919-775-2255
Fax: 919-775-3541
www.zurn.com

The Zurn® Commercial Brass Z5798 EcoVantage is a wall-hung, vitreous china, ultra-low flow urinal that uses an automatic sensor flushometer valve and internal flow regulator to deliver a consistent 1/8th gallon (0.5 liters) per flush at constant flow independent of line pressures. The urinal was redesigned from the ground up to function with such a low-volume flush; it meets the same ASME A112.19.2 performance criteria as standard 1.0 gpf urinals. The valve is operated by an infrared proximity sensor powered by 4 AA batteries (which the company claims will last for 200,000 flushes) with a vandal resistant chrome plated metal housing and a reversible cover for right or left hand supplies. The urinal meets ADA requirements when mounted appropriately.

Most recently mentioned in EBN 15:11

Zurn Half-Gallon Urinal Flush Valves

Zurn Plumbing Products Group

For full listing, see CSI section 22 42 43 - Flushometers

Zurn Z5795 Non-Water-Using Urinal

Zurn Plumbing Products Group
5900 Elwin Buchanan Dr.
Sanford, NC 27330

Toll-free: 800-997-3876
Phone: 919-775-2255
Fax: 919-775-3541
www.zurn.com

The Zurn® Z5795 is a wall-hung, vitreous china, non-water-using urinal. As with other such urinals, it relies on a soy-based sealant, GreenSeal, which has a lower specific gravity than urine, to provide the sanitary trap. Unlike most non-water-using urinals, the Zurn Z5795 does not use a throwaway cartridge; the trapway is integral with the urinal. A small amount of sealant is added every two months, according to the manufacturer, and twice a year the cap is removed and the trapway flushed with water to remove detritus and deposits. The urinal has a 14" extended rim, providing handicap compliance when installed at the proper ADA height.

Most recently mentioned in EBN 15:1

22 42 39
Commercial Faucets and Controls

Many conservation efforts—in industrial, commercial, and residential settings—are making significant improvements in water-use efficiency. These advances are also reducing our wastewater treatment burden and expense. Products listed here dispense water efficiently or improve controllability of the water supply. (See also 22 41 39 - Residential Faucets and Controls.) (See feature article EBN Vol. 6, No. 8.)

Metlund Hot Water D'MAND System

ACT, Inc. Metlund Systems

For full listing, see CSI section 22 41 39 - Residential Faucets and Controls

ndite PV-powered Lavatories

Bradley Corporation
W142 N9101 Fountain Boulevard
Menomonee Falls, WI 53051

Toll-free: 800-272-3539
Fax: 262-251-5817
www.bradleycorp.com

Bradley's ndite™ technology employs photovoltaic (PV) cells permanently embedded in the top of the sprayhead of their Express SS and MG lavatory systems to power the solenoid valve and adaptive infrared sensors for water activation. The PV panels are protected with clear Terreon® polyester resin for vandal resistance. No electrical connection is needed, making this a good option for parks and other applications where AC power is not available. A minimum of 400 lux (37 fc) of natural or artificial light is required for an average 50 cycles per hour; 800 lux will accommodate 180 cycles per hour. A power-saving mode will allow the unit to work for up to five days by functioning only when lights are turned on. This system is most appropriate for well-lit applications, but inappropriate for installations with light levels below 400 lux.

Bricor Elite Series Showerheads

Bricor Southwest
1345 Industrial Dr., Ste. A
New Braunfels, TX 78130

Phone: 830-624-7228
Fax: 830-624-7208
www.bricor.com

Bricor Elite Series showerheads have a small hole on the side of the throat that generates a vacuum, pulling air into the showerhead. This aerates the water, boosting the pressure. According to the company, this venturi-induction technology increases the shower intensity by 1.75 times over other conventional low-flow systems. There are seven 1.5 gpm models to choose from. Other flow rates are possible with custom orders. For multilevel buildings, the company can provide custom-manufactured showerheads for each floor to provide consistent flow throughout the building.

Most recently mentioned in EBN 12:7

Omni Products

Chronomite Laboratories, Inc.
1420 W. 240th St.
Harbor City, CA 90710

Toll-free: 800-447-4962
Phone: 310-534-2300
Fax: 310-530-1381
www.chronomite.com

Chronomite Labs/Omni Products makes several faucet flow regulators that reduce water use by over 27%. Omni products use laminar water flow to create the look and feel of a far higher flow rate (these are not faucet aerators; the water looks like a solid stream).

Most recently mentioned in EBN 6:8

Touch & Flow

DEA Bathroom Machineries
495 Main St.
Murphys, CA 95247

Toll-free: 800-255-4426
Phone: 209-728-2031
Fax: 209-728-2320
www.deabath.com

The Touch & Flow faucet controller is an omnidirectional valve installed at the outlet of a sink faucet. A clapper hangs from the spigot; water runs when the valve is toggled. The flow is adjustable by maintenance personnel down to a minimum of 1/3 gpm.

ETL Low-Flow Showerheads

Energy Technology Laboratories

For full listing, see CSI section 22 41 39 - Residential Faucets and Controls

Foot- and Knee-Operated Faucet Controls

Fisher Manufacturing Company
1900 "O" St.
Tulare, CA 93274

Phone: 800-421-6162
Fax: 800-832-8238
www.fisher-mfg.com

Fisher Manufacturing offers double- and single-pedal, wall- and floor-mounted, foot-operated water faucet controls as well as unusual single- and double-valve versions of nonstirrup knee "pedals." These controllers are made for commercial applications. Each valve may be installed to facilitate hot, cold, or tempered water. (For tempered water, conventional hand controls can be used to set the temperature balance and flow rate, and the pedal used to turn the flow on and off.) Hands-free operation saves water and encourages sanitary sink conditions. Water savings are significant but difficult to quantify.

Foot- and Knee-Operated Faucet Controls

Kohler Co.
444 Highland Dr.
Kohler, WI 53044

Toll-free: 800-456-4537
Phone: 920-457-4441
Fax: 920-457-6952
www.kohler.com

Kohler offers double-pedal, wall- and floor-mounted, foot-operated water faucet controls for commercial and residential applications. Each pedal may be set up to control hot, cold, or tempered water. (For tempered water,

22 00 00
Plumbing

conventional hand controls can be used to set temperature balance and flow rate, and the pedal used to turn the flow on and off.) Knee stirrup controls with similar functions are also available, as are single-pedal, temperature-moderated controls for use in showers. Water savings are significant but difficult to quantify.

Pedalworks and Footworks

Pedal Valves, Inc.

For full listing, see CSI section 22 41 39 - Residential Faucets and Controls

Optima Solis Solar-Powered Faucet

Sloan Valve Company
10500 Seymour Ave.
Franklin Park, IL 60131

Toll-free: 800-982-5839
Phone: 847-671-4300
Fax: 800-447-8329
www.sloanvalve.com

Sloan Valve Company's Optima Solis™ hands-free faucet has a small PV cell embedded in its top that utilizes either fluorescent or natural lighting to power an optical sensor. This feature increases the life of the lithium battery (which powers the water valve and provides back-up power for the sensor) as much as fivefold—to 10 years or more.

Most recently mentioned in EBN 13:7

Foot-Operated Sink Valve

Step-Flow, Inc.
2361 Campus Dr. #99
Irvine, CA 92612

Toll-free: 888-783-7356
Fax: 949-851-1740
www.stepflow.com

Step Flow is a retrofit (or OEM) foot-operated valve system, which converts any sink from hand operation to foot operation. This foot-pedal faucet control uses a sheathed flex cable for the pedal-to-valve controller so that no plumbing extends to the foot pedal. "Hands free" usage of sinks results in a sanitary application and conserves water.

Foot-Pedal Faucet Controls

T&S Brass and Bronze Works, Inc.
2 Saddleback Cv.
P.O. Box 1088
Travelers Rest, SC 29690

Toll-free: 800-476-4103
Phone: 864-834-4102
Fax: 800-868-0084
www.tsbrass.com

T&S Brass manufactures double- and single-pedal, wall- and floor-mounted, foot-operated water faucet controls. Each pedal may be set up to control hot, cold, or tempered water. (For tempered water, conventional hand controls can be used to set the temperature balance and flow volume, and the pedal used to turn the flow on and off.) Hands-free operation saves water and encourages sanitary sink conditions. Water savings are significant but difficult to quantify.

Tapmaster

Tapmaster Incorporated

For full listing, see CSI section 22 41 39 - Residential Faucets and Controls

Foot- and Knee-Operated Faucet Controls

The Chicago Faucet Company
2100 S. Clearwater Dr.
Des Plaines, IL 60018

Phone: 847-803-5000
Fax: 847-803-5454
www.chicagofaucets.com

Chicago Faucets manufactures double- and single-pedal, wall- and floor-mounted, foot-operated water faucet controls for commercial applications. Each pedal may be installed to control hot, cold, or tempered water. (For tempered water, conventional hand controls can be used to set the temperature and flow rate, and the pedal used to turn the flow on and off.) A knee-actuated stirrup control is also available. Hands-free operation saves water and encourages sanitary sink conditions. Water savings are significant but difficult to quantify.

EcoPower Sensor-Activated Controls

TOTO USA, Inc.
1155 Southern Rd.
Morrow, GA 30260

Phone: 770-282-8686
Fax: 770-282-8697
www.totousa.com

TOTO's sensor-activated EcoPower flush valves and faucets are self-powered by a miniature hydroelectric generator - no electrical hookup is required. The rechargeable manganese dioxide lithium battery is optimized for 10 uses per day but will retain its charge with five. At 150 cycles per month, the batteries are expected to last 9 years; at 300 cycles, 16 years; at 4000, 19 years. The flush valve is equipped with TOTO's Smart Sensor System, which adapts to use

patterns to optimize water use and performance; this standard-size valve works with water pressures from 15 psi to 125 psi and has a three-year warranty. The EcoPower faucet uses 0.5 gallons per minute during a maximum cycle of 10 seconds, well below the federal standard. With an average use cycle of approximately five seconds, this faucet consumes 0.04 gallons of water per use, 83% less than the LEED baseline (or 67% less if used for the maximum 10 seconds).

Most recently mentioned in EBN 12:1 & 13:7

Zurn AquaSpec Foot Pedal Valves

Zurn Plumbing Products Group
5900 Elwin Buchanan Dr.
Sanford, NC 27330

Toll-free: 800-997-3876
Phone: 919-775-2255
Fax: 919-775-3541
www.zurn.com

Zurn® both single-pedal and double-pedal AquaSpec® foot pedal valves that provide hands-free faucet operation (model numbers Z85100 and Z85500 respectively). A wall-mounted knee-control product (Z85700) and several specialized faucet controls are also available. In commercial kitchens, hospitals, and homes foot- and knee-control valves for faucets can save water for allowing users to save water by faucets on and off easily without altering the temperature mix.

Most recently mentioned in EBN 15:1

Zurn AquaSpec Low-Flow Showerheads

Zurn Plumbing Products Group
5900 Elwin Buchanan Dr.
Sanford, NC 27330

Toll-free: 800-997-3876
Phone: 919-775-2255
Fax: 919-775-3541
www.zurn.com

Zurn® offers a variety of AquaSpec® showerheads (produced for the company by other manufacturers) that use less than the federally mandated maximum of 2.5 gallons per minute. The Z7000-S3-EWS is a 1.5 gpm, chrome-finish showerhead with brass ball joint connector and volume control with integral tamper-resistant flow control. The AquaSpec Z7300-SS-HW-MT-EWS is a 2.0 gpm handwall shower unit with metal hose and tamper-resistant water-conserving handset.

Most recently mentioned in EBN 15:1

22 00 00
Plumbing

22 42 43
Flushometers

As toilet flushing is the largest single use of water in most residential and commercial buildings (accounting for up to 40% of residential use), water savings from replacement and retrofit is very significant. Products listed here include retrofit dual-flush flushometers and low-water-use flush valves for toilets and urinals. (See feature articles EBN Vol. 6, No. 8 & Vol. 13, No. 1.)

Automatic Flush Valve

AMT Corporation
6409 Independence Ave.
Woodland Hills, CA 91367

Toll-free: 800-874-7822
Phone: 818-883-2682
Fax: 818-883-2620
www.amtcorporation.com

The AEF-801 Dualflush® by AMT Corporation is not a dual-flush valve that provides users with two different flush volumes (the usual meaning of the term "dual-flush"); it is a retrofit automatic flush valve for Sloan® or Zurn® manual diaphragms that offers manual flushing as a back-up. (The unit can be flushed manually even when the four AA batteries are drained; thus, the misleading product name.) This flush valve is included in GreenSpec for its water-saving settings and options; it can be set to flush with 0.5 gallons or less or, with urinals, flush after every other use.

The Controllable Flush

Athena
17175 S.W. TV Hwy.
Aloha, OR 97006

Toll-free: 888-426-7383
Phone: 503-356-1233
Fax: 503-292-5284
www.watersavingdevice.com

The Controllable Flush is a simple, dual-mode flushing device designed to convert most front-flushing standard toilets into low-flush toilets. The Controllable Flush provides the option of the toilet's standard flush or a reduced 1.5-gal. flush, depending on whether the handle is operated in an upward or downward direction. No tools are necessary for installation.

Dual-Flush Flushometer Valve

Sloan Valve Company
10500 Seymour Ave.
Franklin Park, IL 60131

Toll-free: 800-982-5839
Phone: 847-671-4300
Fax: 800-447-8329
www.sloanvalve.com

Sloan Valve Company's Uppercut™ flushometer for commercial toilets has a dual-flush handle for liquid or solid wastes. Pull the handle up to flush liquid wastes (and paper) with a water-saving 1.1 gallon flush, or down to flush solid wastes with a 1.6 gallon standard flush. Installation procedures and plumbing are standard. The Uppercut's anti-microbial handle is a distinctive green color, and ships with two explanatory etched metal plaques to place near the toilet. Sloan also offers an Uppercut dual-flush handle retrofit kit that can be fitted onto the company's Royal®, Regal®, Crown® II, and other similar-style manual flushometer valves, providing a water-saving flush volume of 30% of the existing valve's standard flush volume. The Uppercut is not appropriate for installation on urinals.

Most recently mentioned in EBN 14:9 & 14:12

FlushMate IV

Sloan Valve Company
10500 Seymour Ave.
Franklin Park, IL 60131

Toll-free: 800-982-5839
Phone: 847-671-4300
Fax: 800-447-8329
www.sloanvalve.com

The FlushMate IV pressure-assisted toilet flushing mechanism is a water-conserving (1.0 gpf) flush mechanism produced by the Sloan Valve Company. The FlushMate IV uses an airtight flushometer vessel inside the toilet tank (a tank-within-a-tank configuration). The inner tank is pressurized by the incoming clean water after the toilet is flushed—as it refills, air becomes compressed at the top of the tank. The next time the toilet is used, this pressure provides a high-velocity flush that very effectively evacuates wastes and prevents clogging.

Most recently mentioned in EBN 13:12 & 15:2

Zurn Dual-Flush Flushometer Valve

Zurn Plumbing Products Group
5900 Elwin Buchanan Dr.
Sanford, NC 27330

Toll-free: 800-997-3876
Phone: 919-775-2255
Fax: 919-775-3541
www.zurn.com

The Zurn® dual-flush flushometer handle turns a conventional flushometer for commercial, water-pressure-operated toilets into dual-flush toilets, with the water-saving flush reducing water use by about 30%. Pushing down flushes the toilet at full volume, while pulling up on the handle reduces the flush volume by 30%—for use with liquid wastes and paper. If installed on a modern 1.6 gpf toilet, the water-saving flush uses 1.1 gallons. The company provides a wall sticker that explains the flush handle operation.

Most recently mentioned in EBN 15:1

Zurn Half-Gallon Urinal Flush Valves

Zurn Plumbing Products Group
5900 Elwin Buchanan Dr.
Sanford, NC 27330

Toll-free: 800-997-3876
Phone: 919-775-2255
Fax: 919-775-3541
www.zurn.com

Zurn® offers sensor-activated urinal flush valves that use 0.5 gpf (model numbers ZER6003 and ZER6003AV) as well as retrofit urinal diaphragm kits for standard urinal flush valves that cut flush volume in half. The diaphragm kits are available for both AquaFlush and AquaVantage urinals. According to the manufacturer, most urinals designed to flush with 1.0 gallon will flush adequately with 0.5 gallons.

Most recently mentioned in EBN 15:1

22 51 00
Swimming Pool Plumbing Systems

22 00 00
Plumbing

Products listed here include specialized systems to use solar thermal energy for pool water heating. (See also 23 56 13 - Heating Solar Flat-Plate Collectors.)

Solar Pool Heating Systems

Aquatherm Industries, Inc.
1940 Rutgers University Blvd.
Lakewood, NJ 08701

Toll-free: 800-535-6307
Phone: 732-905-9002
Fax: 732-905-9899
www.warmwater.com

Aquatherm produces unglazed polypropylene collectors designed for pool heating. These are used with existing conventional filtration systems to circulate pool water through the collectors then back into the pool. Most systems utilize an automatic temperature control. The swimming pool serves as the heat-storage reservoir.

Most recently mentioned in EBN 8:7

Solar Pool Heating Systems

Fafco, Inc.
435 Otterson Dr.
Chico, CA 95928

Toll-free: 800-994-7652
Phone: 530-332-2100
Fax: 530-332-2109
www.fafco.com

Fafco is the oldest manufacturer of solar water-heating equipment in the U.S.—since 1969. The company manufactures a line of pool-heating systems.

Most recently mentioned in EBN 8:7

Heliocol Solar Pool-Heating Systems

Heliocol
13620 49th St. N
Clearwater, FL 33762

Phone: 727-572-6655
Fax: 727 572 7922
www.heliocol.com

Heliocol manufactures unglazed polypropylene, solar pool-heating systems.

Most recently mentioned in EBN 8:7

Solar Collectors

Radco Products, Inc.

For full listing, see CSI section 23 56 13 - Heating Solar Flat-Plate Collectors

Solar Collectors

Sealed Air Corp. - Solar Pool Heating
200 Riverfront Boulevard
Elmwood Park, NJ 07407

Toll-free: 201-791-7600
Phone: 510-887-8090
Fax: 510-783-6817
www.sealedair.com

Sealed Air Corporation is primarily in the packaging business but also produces a line of flat-plate solar collectors for pool heating.

Most recently mentioned in EBN 8:7

This Space is Available for Your Notes

22 00 00
Plumbing

23 00 00 Heating, Ventilating, & Air Conditioning

PRODUCT LISTINGS

23 05 93
Testing, Adjusting, and Balancing for HVAC

Blower doors and duct pressurization systems are invaluable diagnostic tools for air-sealing buildings and ducts and for measuring the airtightness of buildings. Other instruments listed here can provide information on electricity usage.

Infiltec Blower Door

Infiltec Radon Control Supply
108 S. Delphine Ave.
P.O. Box 1125
Waynesboro, VA 22980

Toll-free: 888-349-7236
Phone: 540-943-2776
Fax: 540-932-3025
www.infiltec.com

Infiltec Radon Control Supply manufactures and distributes blower doors, micro-manometers, and duct leakage testers.

Minneapolis Blower Door and Duct Blaster

The Energy Conservatory
2801 21st Ave. S, Ste. 160
Minneapolis, MN 55407

Phone: 612-827-1117
Fax: 612-827-1051
www.energyconservatory.com

The Minneapolis Blower Door and Duct Blaster® are products that test for air leakage in building envelopes and forced-air mechanical systems, respectively. Various available gauges measure air pressure losses relative to the fan's speed and convert those figures into an air leakage value. Tectite software in conjunction with Minneapolis Blower Door provides enhanced data-handling capabilities.

TrueFlow Air Handler Flow Meter

The Energy Conservatory
2801 21st Ave. S, Ste. 160
Minneapolis, MN 55407

Phone: 612-827-1117
Fax: 612-827-1051
www.energyconservatory.com

The TrueFlow® Air Handler Flow Meter temporarily replaces the filter in a residential air handler system during the airflow measurement procedure. Filter location directly adjacent to the air handler will result in measurement of the total air handler flow. Remote placement of the filter at a single central return will measure airflow through the central return. The TrueFlow Meter will fit most standard-size filter slots and provides direct ft^3 per minute values in 2-3 minutes without extensive calculations. For airflow handlers rated from 1 to 5 tons.

23 07 00
HVAC Insulation

Air-supply and return ducts can be a medium for mold growth or (with insulated ducts) a source of fiber-shedding, both of which can pose significant indoor air quality concerns. Products listed here allow easy duct cleaning, or protect against mold growth or fiber-shedding. Also included are specialized insulation products for piping and other mechanical equipment. For hydronic heating pipes that experience high temperature (over 150 degrees F), inexpensive foam-plastic pipe insulation sleeves may not be adequate; high-temperature pipe insulation is required.

Armaflex Low VOC Spray Contact Adhesive

New

Armacell LLC.
7600 Oakwood Street Extension
Mebane, NC 27302

Phone: 919-304-3846
Fax: 919-304-3720
www.armacell.com

Armacell's Armaflex 520 BLV is a hexane-free, toluene-free, low-VOC spray contact adhesive for use with HVAC sheet and roll insulation. It is designed for use with their Armaflex insulation, but can be used on other light elastomeric products. The adhesive has no chlorinated solvents, no ozone-depleting compounds, and complies with SCAQMD Rule 1168, with a VOC content of 59 g/l. The adhesive is sold in a 27lb aerosol canister which covers approximately 1000 sf of surface area.

ToughGard

CertainTeed Corporation

For full listing, see CSI section 23 31 00 - HVAC Ducts and Casings

Knauf Air-Handling Insulation Products

Knauf Insulation
One Knauf Dr.
Shelbyville, IN 46176

Toll-free: 800-825-4434
Phone: 317-398-4434
Fax: 317-398-3675
www.knaufusa.com

Knauf air-handling insulation products, including duct wrap, duct board, duct liner, and plenum liner contribute minimal levels of formaldehyde and other pollutants to the indoor environment. Duct wrap rolls are available with a variety of facings, including PSK (polypropylene-scrim-kraft); duct liner rolls have an airstream surface mat facing of tightly bonded fiberglass. Duct board is available with a nonwoven mat face; the rigid plenum liner has a polymer overspray on the airstream side.

Cotton Insulating Duct Wrap

Payless Insulation, Inc.
1331 Seamist Dr.
Houston, TX 77008

Phone: 713-868-1021
Fax: 713-868-7014
www.superiorairducts.com

Superior R8 Cotton Duct Wrap™ is an insulating HVAC duct wrap for commercial or residential applications. It is made with 85% post-industrial fibers (2.2 lbs/ft^3 density, borax-treated cotton) bonded to a metallized mylar jacket and is resistant to fungus, bacteria, fire, and moisture.

**23 00 00
HVAC**

Standard available size is 2" thick x 25' long x 5' wide. The cotton fiber is supplied by Bonded Logic, Inc.

Foamglas Pipe and Equipment Insulation

Pittsburgh Corning Corporation (PCC)
800 Presque Isle Dr.
Pittsburgh, PA 15239

Toll-free: 800-359-8433
Fax: 724-325-9704
www.foamglasinsulation.com

Foamglas® cellular glass insulation from Pittsburgh Corning Corporation is appropriate in a wide range of applications, including pipes, equipment, tanks and vessels of nearly any temperature. The product is 100% glass, made with sand (41%), feldspar (22%), limestone (17%), soda (17%), and trace minerals (3%). Production is free of HCFCs. It is noncombustible, resists corrosion in any environment, is dimensionally stable, has a high compressive strength, and provides operating temperatures ranging from -450 to +900 degrees F (-270 to +480 degrees C). Blocks of Foamglas are laminated with proprietary methods by the manufacturer into billets fabricated to the desired shape and size, or bonded in segments to a flexible facing. The manufacturer supplies several types of adhesives and sealants (some with high-VOC content), reinforcing mesh, and jackets for use with Foamglas. This product is also available as sheet insulation for roofs and other flat applications.

Canvas Mechanical Insulation Jackets

Robson Thermal Manufacturing Ltd.
15048 Victoria Ave.
White Rock, BC V4B 1G3 Canada

Toll-free: 888-976-2766
Phone: 604-538-6681
Fax: 604-538-6692
www.RobsonThermal.com

Robson Thermal Manufacturing makes canvas finishing jackets, coatings, and adhesives for mechanical systems and insulations. Fire-rated and non-fire-rated 6 oz. and 3 oz. canvas jackets for mechanical system insulation and pipe fittings are available, as well as many other mechanical system products, including adhesives and sealants for insulation, ducts and plenums; anti-fungal duct liner repair coating (prevents having to replace damaged fiberboard ducts); anti-condensation paint; liquid insulation coating for hot pipe fittings; elastomeric pipe insulation bevel finish (an alternative to PVC or metal); anti-fungal lagging; FRP panel adhesive and anti-rodent paint for electrical cables. Per the manufacturer, all products are nontoxic and don't contain

brominated flame retardants. Robson also develops specialty chemical-based products that reduce maintenance and operating costs for airports.

23 07 14
Mastic Removers

Products listed here include low-VOC, nontoxic, and biodegradable mastic removers.

BEANedoo Mastic Remover

Franmar Chemical, Inc.
P.O. Box 5565
Bloomington, IL 61702

Toll-free: 800-538-5069
Phone: 309-452-7526
Fax: 309-827-9308
www.franmar.com

FranMar's BEANedoo® Mastic Remover is made from soybeans to remove ceramic tile mastic, asbestos mastic, and carpet mastic. BEANedoo Mastic Remover has no odor, is nontoxic, noncaustic, 100% biodegradable, and rinses with water.

23 09 00
Instrumentation and Control for HVAC

Good HVAC instrumentation and control systems are important for maintaining high levels of comfort as well as energy savings.

Aprilaire Ventilation Control System

Aprilaire
1015 E. Washington Ave.
P.O. Box 1467
Madison, WI 53701

Toll-free: 800-334-6011
Phone: 608-257-8801
Fax: 608-257-4357
www.aprilaire.com

The Aprilaire Ventilation Control System works in conjunction with an included Aprilaire motorized damper as part of a home's heating/cooling system. The controller monitors interior humidity and outdoor air temperature; user-adjustable controls react to this information, allowing homeowners to manage the quantity and quality of fresh air being brought into the home. Setpoints for high and low outdoor temperature and

high indoor humidity override the system to prevent increased heating, cooling, and dehumidification loads; and the system will ventilate only during a heating cycle when outdoor temperatures are below 20 degrees F.

Electronic Control Valves and Damper Actuators

Belimo Aircontrols (USA), Inc.
For full listing, see CSI section 23 33 13 - Dampers

HK2000 Fresh Air / Economizer

EWC Controls, Inc.
385 Hwy. 33
Englishtown, NJ 07726

Toll-free: 800-446-3110
Fax: 732-446-5362
www.ewccontrols.com

The Ultra-Zone HK2000 Fresh Air and Economizer panel from EWC helps minimize HVAC loads while maintaining indoor comfort levels and providing controlled air changes. EWC makes a wide range of HVAC zone controls for commercial and residential applications with multi-stage, dual-fuel, and heat pump compatibility. The company also provides a range of dampers, pressure regulators, registers, diffusers, and thermostats. Avoid thermostats containing mercury switches.

Programmable Thermostats

Honeywell Home & Building Controls
P.O. Box 524
Minneapolis, MN 55440

Toll-free: 800-328-5111
Phone: 612-951-1000
Fax: 763-954-5138
yourhome.honeywell.com

Honeywell produces a wide range of programmable thermostats, including a line of microprocessor-controlled electronic thermostats for heating and/or cooling. This series allows for programmed temperature setbacks and for gradual temperature recovery. Several models are available for replacement and new installation applications.

Most recently mentioned in EBN 3:4

Hunter Set & $ave

Hunter Fan Co.
2500 Frisco Ave.
Memphis, TN 38114

Toll-free: 800-448-6837
Phone: 901-743-1360
Fax: 901-248-2376
www.hunterfan.com

23 00 00
HVAC

Hunter Fan manufactures a full line of programmable digital and mechanical thermostats.

Invisible Service Technician

Invisible Service Technicians, LLC
502 TechneCenter Dr., Ste. B
Milford, OH 45150

Phone: 513-248-0900
Fax: 513-248-2470
www.istmonitor.com

The Invisible Service Technician (IST) is a data acquisition and monitoring system for residential and light-commercial HVAC&R applications. It monitors heating, cooling, and refrigeration equipment using a system of electronic sensors and the HVAC&R unit's control board, transmitting any problems to a central monitoring facility. Measured data includes various temperatures, pressure differentials, control signals, and any on-board fault-detection processes in the native HVAC&R control system. The IST is powered by the 24-volt power circuit of the HVAC&R system and requires a (non-dedicated) working phone line to transmit performance data. This system can reduce the increased energy use and environmental impacts caused by poorly functioning equipment.

Personal Environments System

Johnson Controls, Inc.
5757 N. Green Bay Ave.
P.O. Box 591
Milwaukee, WI 53209

Toll-free: 800-972-8040
Phone: 414-524-1200
Fax: 800-356-1191
www.johnsoncontrols.com

The Personal Environmental Module (PEM) provides building occupants with individual workstation climate control capability. PEM modules are located at each workstation, and they include occupancy sensors to shut systems down for optimum energy savings. The Personal Environments® System is especially compatible with access floor systems. Johnson Controls announced in August 2005 that it would acquire York International Corporation, a leading manufacturer of heating and cooling equipment.

Most recently mentioned in EBN 7:1 & 13:7

PaceController

PaceControls LLC
40 W. Evergreen Ave.
Philadelphia, PA 19118

Phone: 267-286-0337
Fax: 215-248-2381
www.pacecontrols.com

The PaceController can be installed in existing control lines on a wide range of HVAC and refrigeration equipment. It establishes optimal run-time intervals for compressors and burner units, maintaining full performance, while "pacing" the equipment's consumption of electricity or fuel. The controller can be set to adjust run-time intervals based on local conditions. According to the manufacturer, energy cost savings can be 20% or more with a typical payback of 1 to 3 years. PaceControllers come with a 5-year warranty, and the manufacturer has partnered with lending institutions to provide 100% financing.

DynaFuser

Titus

For full listing, see CSI section 23 33 13 - Dampers

23 23 23
Refrigerants

Products listed here are non-ozone-depleting refrigerants. (See also 23 60 00 - Central Cooling Equipment & 23 64 00 - Packaged Water Chillers.)

SP34E Refrigerant

Solpower Corporation
307 E. 22nd St.
San Pedro, CA 90731

Toll-free: 888-289-8866
Phone: 818-865-9176

Fax: 818-706-3772
www.solpower.com

SP34E is a new refrigerant that has zero ODP and is a near drop-in refrigerant for R-12. SP34E has a GWP (global warming potential) of 0.24-0.29 and is also compatible with R-134a systems. Check with equipment manufacturer before installing refrigerant.

23 31 00
HVAC Ducts and Casings

Air-supply and return ducts can be a medium for mold growth or (with insulated ducts) a source of fiber-shedding, both of which can pose significant indoor air quality concerns. Products listed here allow easy duct cleaning, or protect against mold growth or fiber-shedding.

ToughGard

CertainTeed Corporation
750 E. Swedesford Rd.
P.O. Box 860
Valley Forge, PA 19482

Toll-free: 800-233-8990
Phone: 610-341-7000
Fax: 610-341-7777
www.certainteed.com

CertainTeed's ToughGard™ fiberglass duct board is a ducting material with integral insulation. At 75 degrees F, the company claims an R-value of 4.3 for 1" board, 6.5 for 1-1/2" board, and 8.7 for 2" board. To prevent fiber shedding, ToughGard has both a nonwoven composite interior facing of textile fiberglass and polypropylene, and a reinforced foil-laminate exterior facing. The material's ship-lap design helps minimize air leakage at joints. This product carries the Greenguard certification for low emissions.

Most recently mentioned in EBN 4:2 & 12:10

DuctSox Fabric Air Dispersion Products

DuctSox Corp.
4343 Chavenelle Rd.
Dubuque, IA 52002

Toll-free: 866-563-7729
Phone: 563-589-2777 ext. 6055
Fax: 563-589-2754
www.ductsox.com

DuctSox fabric air dispersion products are a lightweight, less resource-intensive, and often less expensive alternative to conventional metal ductwork. DuctSox offers 3 models, 7 fabrics, and a variety of suspension systems to deliver heated, cooled, refrigerated, and/or make-up air through linear vents, orifices, and/or breathable fabrics. The fabrics, most of which are machine washable, vary from impervious to porous and are zippered together to form ducts of 8" to 80" in diameter. DuctSox products are manufactured in Dubuque, Iowa.

FabricAir Air Distribution Devices

FabricAir, Inc.
211 E. Ontario St.
18th Floor
Chicago, IL 60611

Phone: 502-493-2210
Fax: 502-493-4002
www.fabricair.com

FabricAir product offerings are divided into two main categories. The first, with low surface velocity, is used primarily for comfort applications. These can be either a fabric diffuser alone (for cooling applications

23 00 00
HVAC

primarily) or contain integral air diffuse slots (mainly for heating/cooling). The second category is for industrial applications where long throws and higher terminal velocities are needed. This product is normally manufactured from impervious, fire-retardant fabric. FabricAir air distribution devices can be unzipped and removed for cleaning in a standard washing machine.

Flow/Con

FOF Incorporated
1505 Racine St.
P.O. Box 904
Delavan, WI 53115

Phone: 262-728-2686
Fax: 262-728-5999
www.fabricairducts.com

Flow/Con fabric air ducts, a lower-cost alternative to sheetmetal ductwork and registers, are made with impermeable or permeable fabrics (coated woven polyester, polyethylene, fiberglass, or cotton) and are particularly efficient at distributing, mixing, and displacing air over large areas. Airjet ports are custom-positioned along the pressurized fabric diffuser plenum to meet distribution and mixing requirements. Flow/Con diffuser systems typically have snap hooks attached for installation on steel cable. Each system is custom engineered to meet specific needs. Some fabrics have a vinyl (PVC) laminate; inquire of the manufacturer.

Dryer-Ell

In-O-Vate Technologies, Inc.
For full listing, see CSI section 11 31 23 - Residential Laundry Appliances

SuperDuct

Johns Manville Corporation
P.O. Box 5108
Denver, CO 80217

Toll-free: 800-654-3103
Phone: 303-978-2000
Fax: 303-978-3661
www.jm.com

SuperDuct™ is constructed from glass fibers bonded with a thermosetting resin and faced with a durable, fire-resistant Foil-Scrim-Kraft facing. The interior surface is coated with Permacote®, a proprietary, thermosetting acrylic polymer. The SuperDuct coating protects against the incursion of dust and minimizes the potential for microbiological growth in the media. The Permacote coating is formulated with an immobilized, EPA-registered protective agent so it will not support the growth of fungus or bacteria. Part of the SuperDuct Air Duct System, this duct board meets or exceeds all UL 181 requirements.
Most recently mentioned in EBN 4:2

Textile-Based Ventilation Ducts

KE Fibertec North America
1212 Churchville Rd., Ste. 301
Bel Air, MD 21014-3482

Toll-free: 877-229-0695
Phone: 410-588-5693
Fax: 410-588-5695
www.kefibertec.com

KE Fibertec textile ducts function like conventional steel ductwork with air outlets but also provide final filtration as conditioned air passes through the duct's walls. The ducts are uninsulated and must be run through conditioned space. This product is readily disconnected from its installation hardware and unzipped into appropriate lengths for washing in standard clothes washers. Comfort is enhanced due to lower room air velocities from the nonpoint release of air, as opposed to point-source metal duct grills. The textile material should be more resource-efficient than conventional duct material. Available in 5 standard and 1,600 optional colors.
Most recently mentioned in EBN 9:2

Cotton-Insulated Semi-Flex Ducts

Payless Insulation, Inc.
1331 Seamist Dr.
Houston, TX 77008

Phone: 713-868-1021
Fax: 713-868-7014
www.superiorairducts.com

Superior Air Ducts™ R8 Cotton Insulated Semi Flex Ducts are integrally insulated round ducts made with 85% post-industrial recycled cotton fibers. The jacket is reflective metallized mylar; the inner core is made with clear mylar sheets encapsulating a steel wire helix. As with most flexible ducts, the inner surface is not smooth, so more fan energy will be needed than with a smooth-surfaced duct. Designed for low to medium operating pressures, these ducts are resistant to mold and bacteria, are Class A fire-rated, and have a 10-year warranty. The 2.2 lb/ft^3 cotton walls are indicated by the manufacturer to be 2" thick, for an R-value of 8. These ducts are available in 12.5' and 25' sections in a dozen different diameters ranging from 2" to 20". The cotton fiber is supplied by Bonded Logic, Inc.

23 33 13
Dampers

Quality dampers and other air duct accessories are a crucial part of most large HVAC systems.

Electronic Control Valves and Damper Actuators

Belimo Aircontrols (USA), Inc.
43 Old Ridgebury Rd.
Danbury, CT 06810

Toll-free: 800-543-9038
www.belimo.us

Belimo manufactures several models of electronic control valves as well as spring-return and non-spring-return actuators for HVAC installations. Their precision, reliability, and durability result in energy savings and improved indoor air quality.

DynaFuser

Titus
990 Security Row
Richardson, TX 75081

Phone: 972-699-1030
Fax: 972-918-8880
www.titus-hvac.com

The Titus DynaFuser provides an automatic, thermal switch that changes air diffusion patterns when an air distribution system switches between heating and cooling. Using a metal alloy actuator, the DynaFuser switches between horizontal airflow for cooling and vertical airflow for heating automatically and without an external power source. The snap-action changeover prevents energy waste during transitions, while reducing maintenace needs. The DynaFuser, which is made of steel with aluminum parts, operates between 60°F and 80°F (16°C to 27°C), and has been tested for a minimum of 10,000 cycles. Standard configuration is a 10-inch plenum height.

23 00 00
HVAC

23 33 54
Duct Mastic

Duct leakage is a major problem with forced-air heating or air-conditioning systems. When ducts are run outside of the conditioned space, heating and cooling efficiencies may be cut in half due to leakage. Tightly sealed ducting is extremely important in ensuring high energy efficiency of forced-air HVAC equipment. Experts strongly recommend duct mastics—not duct tape—for sealing ducts.

Duct Sealants

Hardcast, Inc.
900 Hensley Ln.
P.O. Box 1239
Wylie, TX 75098

Toll-free: 800-527-7092
Phone: 888-229-0199
Fax: 972-442-0076
www.hardcast.com

Hardcast manufactures a line of VOC-free and water-based duct sealants.

UNI-MASTIC 181 Duct Sealer

McGill Airseal Corporation
2400 Fairwood Ave.
Columbus, OH 43207

Toll-free: 800-624-5535
Phone: 614-443-5520
Fax: 614-542-2620
www.mcgillairseal.com

Uni-Mastic™ 181 duct sealer is a water-based product that is designed to remain flexible over time in applications including sheet-metal, flexible, and fiberglass duct. It is UL181 listed and contains antimicrobial agents that remain effective after curing.

Duct Mastics

RCD Corporation
2850 Dillard Rd.
Eustis, FL 32726

Toll-free: 800-854-7494
Phone: 352-589-0099
Fax: 352-589-0863
www.rcdmastics.com

RCD Corporation is a leading manufacturer of elastomeric, water-based adhesives, sealants, and duct mastics.

23 34 00
HVAC Fans

Fans for air circulation, air distribution, and exhaust and key components of most mechanical systems, and major users of energy. For optimal efficiency fans should be properly sized and controlled with efficient motors and drives. In residences, unless there's a central ventilation system, kitchen and bathroom spot-ventilators may be the only mechanical ventilation system in a house. To increase the likelihood that fans will be used, they should be quiet. To be included in GreenSpec, bathroom ventilators must have sone ratings no higher than 1.5. ("Sone" is a measure of loudness; one sone is about as loud as a common residential refrigerator.) Quiet kitchen range-hood fans are much more difficult to find; often the best option is to use a remote, in-line fan. Ceiling fans are designed to mix air in a room and provide airflow for enhanced comfort—they do not provide fresh air.

Multi-Port Exhaust System

American Aldes Ventilation Corp.
4537 Northgate Ct.
Sarasota, FL 34234

Toll-free: 800-255-7749
Phone: 941-351-3441
Fax: 941-351-3442
www.americanaldes.com

American Aldes produces a line of multiport, whole-building exhaust systems. Their "octopus" system draws exhaust air from multiple locations using flexible ducting.

Thermal Equalizers   New

Avedon Engineering, Inc.
811 S. Sherman St.
Longmont, CO 80501

Phone: 303-772-2633
Fax: 303-772-8276
www.airius.us

Airius Thermal Equalizers reduce heating and cooling energy needs through air destratification in rooms with 10- to 60-foot ceilings. The turbines "drill" air down in a column, keeping floor and ceiling temperatures within three degrees of each other in conditioned spaces. Power consumption for the different models ranges from 14 to 110 watts, with the most common using 35 watts. Product selection is based on ceiling height and area coverage. Larger models feature highly efficient electronically commutated motors (ECM).

Big Ass High-Volume/ Low-Speed Fans

Big Ass Fans
2425 Merchant St.
Lexington, KY 40511

Toll-free: 877-244-3267
Phone: 859-233-1271
Fax: 859-233-0139
www.bigassfans.com

Big Ass Fans improve air circulation and worker comfort year round, particularly in high-ceilinged industrial and commercial buildings. The fans range from 6' to 24' in diameter and move up to 337,000 cfm of air over up to 20,000 ft² with very little noise and relatively low energy usage.

Inline Exhaust Duct Fans

Continental Fan Manufacturing
203 Eggert Rd.
Buffalo, NY 14215

Toll-free: 800-779-4021
Phone: 716-842-0670
Fax: 716-842-0611
www.continentalfan.com

Continental Fan Manufacturing's AXC inline centrifugal duct fans for residential, commercial, and industrial applications offer quiet, efficient operation with high exhaust capacities, and are particularly appropriate where long vent runs are required. These fans use backward-curved impellers and infinitely variable RPM motors to meet versatile air-moving needs. With the fan and motor above the plane of the ceiling, operating noise is significantly dampened. Pressure, fan speed, dehumidistat, and timer controls are available, as well as backdraft dampers. For dryer venting applications—such as in apartment complexes—the pressure switch is preferable to using a timer in terms of energy conservation.

F. R. Series Fans

Fantech
1712 Northgate Blvd.
Sarasota, FL 34234

Toll-free: 800-747-1762
Fax: 800-487-9915
www.fantech.net

Fantech's in-line duct fans are often specified where minimizing noise is a high priority. These in-line fans range in size from 122 cfm to 649 cfm, 4" to 10" duct diameter, with energy consumption from 19 W to 241 W. Smaller products are generally used for residential applications; larger for commercial. Fantech's F.R. Series fans carry a 5-year warranty.

23 00 00
HVAC

Gossamer Wind Ceiling Fans

King of Fans, Inc.
1951 N.W. 22nd St.
Ft. Lauderdale, FL 33311

Toll-free: 800-330-3267
Phone: 954-484-7500
Fax: 954-484-7602
www.king-of-fans.com

King of Fans is now manufacturing the energy-efficient Gossamer Wind Ceiling Fans for Home Depot's Hampton Bay label. Tests have shown that the production models are 40-50% more energy-efficient than conventional fans.

Most recently mentioned in EBN 10:3

Ventilation and Airflow Equipment

Tamarack Technologies, Inc.
320 Main St.
P.O. Box 963
Buzzards Bay, MA 02532

Toll-free: 800-222-5932
Phone: 508-759-4660
Fax: 508-759-6001
www.tamtech.com

Tamarack Technologies produces specialized ventilators and ventilation controllers. Among its innovative products are the sophisticated whole-house ventilators (HV 1000 and HV 1600-Gold). These fans have motorized, insulated covers that seal the exhaust opening tightly when the units are not in operation.

Most recently mentioned in EBN 5:5 & 6:9

Quiet-Vent

Therma-Stor LLC
P.O. Box 8050
Madison, WI 53708

Toll-free: 800-533-7533
Phone: 608-222-5301
Fax: 608-222-1447
www.thermastor.com

Quiet-Vent is a multiport, central exhaust ventilation system designed to quietly, effectively, and automatically ventilate airtight homes.

23 00 00
HVAC

23 34 19
Powered Attic Exhaust Fans

Attic fans are used for whole-house exhaust and airflow or for heat removal from attics. In certain climates, attic fans

can be used very effectively for night-flush cooling—in which household air is replaced with cooler air during the nighttime hours. (See feature article EBN Vol. 10, No. 6.)

SolarCool Attic Vent

Air Vent, Inc.
4117 Pinnacle Point Dr., Ste. 400
Dallas, TX 75211

Phone: 800-247-8368
Fax: 800-635-7006
www.airvent.com

The SolarCool roof- or gable-mounted attic vent from Air Vent, Inc., is a low-profile, galvanized steel dome with a high-efficiency 24-volt DC motor powered by a small solar panel. The photovoltaic panel is mounted either on an adjustable bracket directly on the vent dome or up to 10 feet away, allowing it to be positioned for optimal solar exposure. No auxiliary electricity is required. It ventilates up to 800 cfm for attics up to 1,200 ft^2, and comes with a 5-year limited warranty.

Fan-Attic

NuLight Solutions
1350 Dell Ave,. Ste. 202
Campbell, CA 95008

Toll-free: 877-326-2884
Phone: 408-369-7447
Fax: 408-254-7910
www.fan-attic.com

The Fan-Attic™, (formerly available from Sun Tunnel Skylights and SteelTile Distributing), is a PV-powered roof ventilator fan that can move up to 800 cfm. This product is used instead of (or in addition to) ridge or gable vents. This solar-powered fan works hardest when ventilation is needed most and saves on installation costs because electrical wiring is not necessary.

Active Ventilation System

SolarAttic, Inc.
15548 95th Cir. NE
Elk River, MN 55330

Phone: 763-441-3440
Fax: 763-441-7174
www.solarattic.com

SolarAttic produces an electronic attic temperature switch for attic ventilation in all seasons. This product is used to automate ventilation equipment; it is compatible with existing fans or can be a part of a SolarAttic system.

Cyclone Solar Fan

Solar Dynamics, Inc.
212 Gateway Dr.
Ottumwa, IA 52501

Toll-free: 800-775-2134
Phone: 817-676-6192
Fax: 641-683-3031
www.solardynamicsinc.com

The Cyclone solar powered attic fan is powered by a 20-watt photovoltaic panel and moves up to 1275 cfm of air. Its compact, low-profile design allows it to be used to reduce extreme heat build-up and condensation in a variety of locations. The fan is available with self flash, curb mount, and gable mount flashing for pitched or flat roof applications. The 'Remote' systems separate the panel from the fan for more flexible installation, and the turbine retrofit solar fan is designed to fit the base assembly of any 12" turbine fan.

Solar Star Attic Fan

Solatube International, Inc.
2210 Oak Ridge Way
Vista, CA 92081

Toll-free: 888-765-2882
Phone: 760-477-1120
Fax: 760-599-5181
www.solatube.com

The Solar Star® is a PV-powered attic fan available with flashing for pitched or flat roof applications. The Solar Star utilizes an integral photovoltaic panel to move up to 800 cfm of air depending upon current solar conditions. Its compact, low-profile design allows it to be used to reduce extreme heat build-up and condensation in a variety of locations.

23 34 20
Bathroom Ventilators

Exhaust fans are an important component of today's tightly sealed buildings. Unless there's a central ventilation system, kitchen and bathroom spot-ventilators may be the only mechanical ventilation system in a house. To increase the likelihood that fans will be used, they should be quiet. Products listed here have sone ratings no higher than 1.5. ("Sone" is a measure of loudness; one sone is about as loud as a common residential refrigerator.) (See feature article EBN Vol. 10, No. 6.)

Broan-Nutone Fans

Broan-NuTone LLC
926 W. State St.
P.O. Box 140
Hartford, WI 53027

Toll-free: 800-558-1711
Phone: 262-673-4340
Fax: 262-673-8638
www.broan.com

Broan-NuTone produces a number of quiet bathroom fans for residential and commercial applications. The Ultra Silent™ series of residential bathroom fans operate at 0.3-1.4 sones depending on size (50-150 CFM). The Ultra Quiet Humidity Sensing Fan operates at 0.9 sones (110 CFM), and detects rapid rises in humidity for automated start with an adjustable auto shut-off time. LoSone Select Ventilators are quiet continuous-operation commercial ventilators, with the 100/150 CFM model rated at 0.9 Sones.

Most recently mentioned in EBN 5:5

Vent-Axia LoWatt

Coast Products, Inc.
954 Elliott Ave. W
Seattle, WA 98119

Toll-free: 800-735-7026
Phone: 206-285-5120
Fax: 206-285-5123
www.coastproducts.com

The Vent-Axia LoWatt through-the-wall exhaust fan has an electric opening shutter with positive closure. Its motor's service life is reported to be 5 times longer than that of conventional motors, and the fan delivers an incredible 10.8 watts/cfm.

Ultra-QuieTTest

NuTone, Inc.
4820 Red Bank Rd.
Cincinnati, OH 45227

Toll-free: 888-336-6151
Phone: 513-527-5100
Fax: 513-527-5177
www.nutone.com

NuTone produces the Ultra-QuieTTest® line of bathroom fans.

Most recently mentioned in EBN 5:5

Panasonic Exhaust Fans

Panasonic Consumer Electronics Building Department
Panazip 4A-6
One Panasonic Way
Secaucus, NJ 07094

Toll-free: 866-292-7292
Fax: 847-468-4359
www.panasonic.com

Panasonic, the first company to introduce a truly quiet bathroom fan, remains an industry leader with a full line of very quiet high-efficiency ceiling, wall, and inline exhaust fans. The WhisperGreen™ series use an improved DC motor and are 70 - 400% more energy efficient than minimum Energy Star® standards. Automated variable speed controls, CFM optimization, and motion sensors enhance performance for spot or whole-house ventilation systems.

Most recently mentioned in EBN 5:5 & 6:2

23 36 00
Air Terminal Units

Large office buildings often use dozens or hundreds of fan-powered terminals in their HVAC system. These terminals may contain integral resistance-heating coils, which can use significant amounts of energy; hot-water or steam heating coils should generally be preferred. Units should be thermally insulated, and consideration should be given to the potential for condensation when chilled air is being delivered. In some applications, sound generation can be a significant evaluation criterion; rigid construction or stiffeners can reduce vibration noise. If included, filtration media should be accessible and washable.

Therma-Fuser VAV Modules

Acutherm
1766 Sabre St.
Hayward, CA 94545

Toll-free: 800-544-1840
Phone: 510-785-0510
Fax: 510-785-2517
www.acutherm.com

Each Acutherm Therma-Fuser module provides an independent zone of variable air volume (VAV) control, including thermostat, modulating damper, and diffuser.

T3SQ Thermally Powered VAV Diffusers

Titus
990 Security Row
Richardson, TX 75081

Phone: 972-699-1030
Fax: 972-918-8880
www.titus-hvac.com

The T3SQ is an occupant-controllable, thermally powered, variable-volume ceiling diffuser that can provide cost-effective, individual comfort control. It maintains the local temperature by varying the volume of air delivered, which is controlled by a thermally-responsive wax-filled element in the diffuser. No input energy, sensors, or wall-mounted thermostats are needed. The T3SQ is available in cooling-only and heating/cooling configurations.

Titus ECM Motor Fan-Powered Terminals

Titus
990 Security Row
Richardson, TX 75081

Phone: 972-699-1030
Fax: 972-918-8880
www.titus-hvac.com

High-efficiency, brushless DC electronically commutated motors (ECM) with microprocessor based controllers can significantly outperform standard permanent split capacitor (PSC) motors. Titus offers variable-volume, fan-powered terminals with ECM motors that offer 70% minimum efficiency across the entire operating range (300 – 1200 rpm), and 80% efficiency above 400 rpm. The field-adjustable microprocessor controllers ensure consistent airflow despite downstream static pressure changes. The company claims payback in as little as two years, depending on local electric rates, fan settings, operating schedule, and unit sizes.

23 37 00
Air Outlets and Inlets

These listings include passive air inlets and outlets used in HVAC systems, as well as fresh-air make-up inlets that replace air removed by exhaust-only ventilation systems. (See feature articles EBN Vol. 3, No. 3 & Vol. 10, No. 6.)

Speedi-Boot

Lance-Larkin
2700 N.W. Front Ave.
Portland, OR 97210

Toll-free: 866-268-5953
Phone: 360-636-4321
www.speediboot.com

The Speedi-Boot™ boot hanger for air-supply ducts is a mounting system that allows air supply boots (the termination that connects a round duct to a rectangular grill opening) to be tightly sealed to a ceiling, wall, or subfloor. This product also helps keep dust and debris out of the duct system during construction. It comes with protective cardboard covers that are easily removed after construction is completed. The adjustable hanger installs between joists, trusses,

23 00 00
HVAC

or studs. A foam gasket provides a tight seal to the drywall or subfloor, reducing air leakage. The Speedi-Boot is available in 15 sizes, is designed for both residential and commercial construction, and works with wood or steel framing.

Most recently mentioned in EBN 13:12

Fresh 80 and Reton 80 Passive Air Inlets

Therma-Stor LLC
P.O. Box 8050
Madison, WI 53708

Toll-free: 800-533-7533
Phone: 608-222-5301
Fax: 608-222-1447
www.thermastor.com

Fresh 80 and Reton 80 through-the-wall passive air inlets supply controlled trickle ventilation for tight buildings. A single unit is designed to supply fresh air for up to 270 ft² of floor area. Both are available in a larger "100" version, supplying more fresh air for a given indoor-outdoor pressure difference.

Most recently mentioned in EBN 2:2

Trickle Ventilators

Titon Inc.
P.O. Box 241
Granger, IN 46530

Phone: 574-271-9699
Fax: 574-271-9771
www.titon.com

Titon produces a range of trickle ventilators designed to suit a variety of window applications, including retrofits. Tests indicate that IAQ is improved with little negative effect on energy costs. The moving air also helps to reduce condensation mold.

Diffusers

Trox USA, Inc.
926 Curie Dr.
Alpharetta, GA 30005

Phone: 770-569-1433
Fax: 770-569-1435
www.troxtechnik.com

Trox is a leading German manufacturer of floor diffusers for access floor systems that are used as conditioned air supply plenums.

Most recently mentioned in EBN 7:1

23 38 00
Ventilation Hoods

Kitchen exhaust hoods in commercial settings typically run at 100% capacity, even during times when nothing is being cooked. In addition to wasting significant amounts of energy directly, these fans also are evacuating conditioned air, compounding the energy penalty. Exhaust hoods can account for up to two-thirds of the HVAC load of a restaurant, and nearly one-third of the total power consumption. Look for more energy-efficient motors and sensor-equipped controls, which reduce fan speed as conditions permit, saving energy and improving the work environment. With residential applications, look for quieter fans that are more likely to be used by homeowners.

Pioneer Laboratory Fume Hoods

Fisher Hamilton, LLC

For full listing, see CSI section 11 53 13 - Laboratory Fume Hoods

Bi-Stable Vortex Fume Hood

Flow Safe, Inc.

For full listing, see CSI section 11 53 13 - Laboratory Fume Hoods

Protector XStream Laboratory Hoods

Labconco Corporation

For full listing, see CSI section 11 53 13 - Laboratory Fume Hoods

Intelli-Hood Kitchen Ventilation Controls

Melink Corporation
5140 River Valley Rd.
Milford, OH 45150

Toll-free: 513-965-7350
Phone: 513-965-7300
www.melinkcorp.com

Melink's Intelli-Hood® is an aftermarket control system utilizing sensors and a microprocessor to reduce the hood and make-up air fan speeds during idle periods to save fan energy and to reduce the removal of conditioned air. The manufacturer claims efficiency increases of up to 50%, with typical annual operating savings of $1,500 to $3,000 per hood. The hood and make-up

fans should ideally use variable-speed ECPM (electronically commutated, permanent-magnet) motors for the greatest fan energy savings. The system can also monitor the exhaust air temperature, sounding an alarm or deactivating the cooking appliances if the temperature approaches the activation point of the hood's fire extinguisher. Additionally, CO_2 levels can be monitored in nearby areas; if levels exceed a certain threshold, the exhaust and make-up air quantities can be increased to 100%.

23 40 00
HVAC Air Cleaning Devices

Air filtration is an important part of HVAC design. Quality products should have high filtration efficiency over a range of particle sizes, be energy-efficient (low pressure drop across filters), and durable. Measures of filtration defined by ASHRAE standards include arrestance efficiency, dust-spot efficiency, and Minimum Efficiency Reporting Value (MERV) ratings. High-efficiency particulate air (HEPA) filters are designed to capture extremely fine particulates but require increased duct pressure, which may necessitate an oversized mechanical system. Some lower-efficiency filters use recycled materials or are washable. (See feature articles EBN Vol. 5, No. 3, Vol. 10, No. 6, Vol. 12, No. 10.)

High-Efficiency Air Filters

AAF International
10300 Ormsby Park Pl., Ste. 600
Lousiville, KY 90223

Toll-free: 888-223-2003
Fax: 502-637-0321
www.aafintl.com

The VariCel V (MERV 15) high capacity mini-pleat V-bank filter from AAF International replaces MERV 14 filters with minimal increase in resistance, up to 750 FPM. Their DriPak 2000 non-supported pocket filters are available in MERV 14 and 15. These UL Class 1 synthetic-media filters are available in a wide range of sizes.

Most recently mentioned in EBN 12:10

Airguard Air Filters

Airguard, Inc.
3807 Bishop Ln.
Louisville, KY 40218

Toll-free: 800-999-3458
Phone: 502-969-2304
Fax: 502-961-0930
www.airguard.com

23 00 00
HVAC

Airguard produces a wide range of air filtration products, including rigid-cell filters with MERV 13 and higher ratings and HEPA filters. The company's Permalast® latex-coated natural-fiber (hog's hair) media and foam media, both with arrestance values of 60-70% (MERV 1-2), can be washed for repeated use but are only suitable for filtering the coarsest particulates. StreamLine™ filters, with arrestance values of 85-95% (MERV 5-6), are produced primarily from post-consumer recycled polyester fiber. Variflow filters, including the Compact Series, which rely on ultrafine fiberglass and wet-laid paper filtration, are available with dust-spot efficiencies of 60-95% (MERV 11-14).

Most recently mentioned in EBN 12:10

High-Efficiency Air Filters

Camfil USA, Inc.
One North Corporate Dr.
Riverdale, NJ 07457

Toll-free: 866-422-6345
Phone: 973-616-7300
Fax: 973-616-7771
www.camfilfarr.com

Camfil Farr offers a variety of types, sizes, and styles of air filters rated up to MERV 14 including pleated, mini-pleat, and V-bank filters, UL Class 1 and 2, and carbon filters offering 95% odor removal efficiency with a low pressure drop. Packaged prefilters, roll media, and specialty filters are also available.

Most recently mentioned in EBN 12:10

C.A.S.T. Air Scrubbers

CAST Inc.
7443 S. Marion St.
Centennial, CO 80161

Phone: 303-797-3556
Fax: 303-797-0247
www.airscrubbers.com

Cyclonic Air Scrubbing Technology, Inc. manufactures air pollution control units (PCUs) with contaminant removal rates for grease, smoke, odors, and VOCs of 90% - 98.7%. The PCUs use low-pressure-drop Airguard HEPA filters (approximately MERV 18), carbon cell filters, and a catalyst medium. Replacement frequency for filters and catalyst depends on pollutant concentrations. Two models are available in a variety of sizes. The Maxium is a rooftop unit designed for heavy grease and high VOC concentrations. The 'Low Boy' model is designed for lighter oils and works in above-ceiling and sidewall exhaust discharge situations. The Low Boy optional air recirculation system for 80% recirculated air applications reduces A/C, makeup air, and exhaust fan loads, and can reduce conditioning costs by 30%, according to the manufacturer.

Filtera Air Filters

Filtera
12999 Murphy Rd., Ste I-1
Stafford, TX 77477

Toll-free: 888-933-0100
Phone: 281-933-1100
Fax: 281-933-1159
www.filtera.com

Filtera offers mini-pleat air filters with efficiencies up to MERV 14 in 2- and 4-inch frames; these filters are available in UL Class 1 and 2. High-velocity, 12"-deep mini-pleat V-cell filters are also offered. The polypropylene media in these pleated filters doesn't support mold or bacteria, and doesn't corrode or degrade in humid conditions. Custom sizes are available. UL Class 2 HEPA glass-fiber gasketed filters—including high-temperature, high capacity, and turbine style—are also available in wood or metal frames.

Most recently mentioned in EBN 12:10

Viledon Air Filters from Freudenberg

Freudenberg Nonwovens L.P.
2975 Pembroke Rd.
Filtrations Division
Hopkinsville, KY 42240

Toll-free: 800-542-2804
Phone: 270-886-9251
Fax: 270-886-5878
www.viledon-filter.com

Freudenberg Nonwovens L.P. produces some of the most advanced air filtration products available in the Viledon product line. A wide range of filters is available, including high-efficiency products (MERV 13 and higher). Viledon filters provide immediate high filtration efficiency (some other filters reach rated efficiency only after a period of operation), minimal static pressure drop (thus good energy performance), and excellent durability. Freudenberg is one of the world's leading manufacturers of filtration equipment; the company's Hopkinsville, Kentucky plant has achieved ISO 14001 certification for environmental performance.

Most recently mentioned in EBN 12:10

High-Efficiency Air Filters

Glasfloss Industries
400 South Hall St.
P.O. Box 150469
Dallas, TX 75315

Phone: 214-741-7056
Fax: 800-435-8377
www.glasfloss.com

Glasfloss offers a variety of types and sizes of air filters rated up to MERV 14, including

UL Class 1 and 2 filters. Z-Pak pleated filters have plastic or fiberglass media in 6" and 12" depths for mixed- and high-velocity systems; the pleated fiberglass-media Magna line, also in 6" and 12" depths, has turbine, high-temperature, and HEPA options; the mini-pleated Puracell fiberglass line offers up to MERV 14 in a 4" depth, as well as a 12" V-pack filter model; and bag filters are available in plastic media (Excel line) and fiberglass (PuraPak line).

Most recently mentioned in EBN 12:10

HEPA Filtration Systems

Pure Air Systems
1325 Church St.
Clayton, IN 46118

Toll-free: 800-869-8025
Phone: 317-539-4097
Fax: 317-539-4959
www.pureairsystems.com

Pure Air Systems offers HEPA filtration systems for commercial and industrial applications. The products are attached to forced-air heating/cooling system ducts, or are self-containing.

Most recently mentioned in EBN 12:10

StrionAir System

StrionAir, Inc.
410 S. Arthur Ave.
Louisville, CO 80027

Toll-free: 866-840-5872
Phone: 303-664-1140
Fax: 303-664-1210
www.strionair.com

The StrionAir System offers high-efficiency filtration with very low pressure drop by combining ionization, electrostatics, and media filtration. A control module, powered by 120V AC, operates up to sixteen system modules and can be connected to a building automation system. Each system module consumes approximately 10 watts of power. The Disposable Filter Element (which includes the downstream electrode) generally needs to be replaced at the same frequency as standard air filters. Prefiltering is typically not needed. At 500 feet per minute, the powered system rates MERV 15; at 400 fpm, MERV 16.

Most recently mentioned in EBN 12:10

High-Efficiency Air Filters

Tri-Dim Filter Corp.
93 Industrial Dr.
Louisa, VA 23093

Toll-free: 800-458-9835
Phone: 540-967-2600
Fax: 540-967-2835
www.tridim.com

23 00 00
HVAC

Tri-dim offers air filters from MERV 5 to MERV 20 and HEPA/ULPA in a range of types, sizes, and depths, including pleated, mini-pleat, V-cell, rigid box, and bag in fiberglass and synthetic media. Packaged prefilters, roll media, and bulk pads are also available.

Most recently mentioned in EBN 12:10

Photox Air Purification Systems

Zentox Corporation
310-G Ed Wright Ln.
Newport News, VA 23606

Phone: 757-369-9870
Fax: 757-369-9871
www.zentox.com

The Photox™ is a stand-alone air purification system that removes VOCs and microorganisms (including bacteria, virus, and mold spores; urine and fecal odors; carbon monoxide and hydrogen sulfide; cooking odors and musty air; cleaning solvents, paint odors, and formaldehyde) from indoor air through photocatalytic oxidation. The system does not generate or make use of ozone. Photox 500 is for rooms up to 40' x 50', moving up to 500 cfm with an 180W draw. Photox 100 is for rooms up to 20' x 20', moving 50 to 100 cfm with a 25W draw. Annual replacement of the 32-watt fluorescent UV lamps and air filters is required.

23 40 13
Air Quality Monitoring and Assessment

Alerting building occupants about toxins or contaminants is important in many situations. With some toxins, an immediate warning is needed; with others, long-term exposure is the concern. (See also 31 21 13 - Radon Mitigation.)

IAQ Test Kit

Aerotech Laboratories, Inc.
1501 W. Knudsen Dr.
Phoenix, AZ 85027

Toll-free: 800-651-4802
Phone: 623-780-4800
Fax: 623-780-7695
www.aerotechlabs.com

Aerotech provides a wide array of sampling devices for measuring IAQ, including Zefon Air-O-Cell Cassettes for gathering mold and bioaerosol samples. Samples are returned to Aerotech for analysis. Aerotech also supplies and rents equipment for gathering specimens.

IAQ Test Kits

Air Quality Sciences, Inc.
1337 Capital Cir.
Marietta, GA 30067

Toll-free: 800-789-0419
Phone: 770-933-0638
Fax: 770-933-0641
www.aqs.com

Air Quality Sciences produces a variety of IAQ test kits to screen for molds and other allergens, as well as VOCs and formaldehyde. These self-administered kits are simple to use and fairly economical. Results are analyzed by AQS, including comparisons to existing standards, and delivered in an easy-to-read report.

Most recently mentioned in EBN 8:6

Optima Portable IEQ Monitoring System

Aircuity, Inc.
39 Chapel St.
Newton, MA 02458

Phone: 617-641-8800
Fax: 617-969-3233
www.aircuity.com

Optima™ is an automated, portable system for sampling and analyzing air for contaminants. The Optima can be used both indoors and outdoors for monitoring atmospheric conditions (temperature, relative humidity, and carbon dioxide) and contaminants, including particulates (large and fine), total volatile organic compounds (TVOCs), carbon monoxide, ozone, radon, and mold (the latter by mailing sampling cartridges to Aircuity-affiliated laboratories). Collected data is analyzed with the integrated, Internet-based Knowledge Center™ at Aircuity and reported through the Aircuity Advisor™, which uses artificial intelligence technology to extract and interpret results.

AIRxpert 7000

AIRxpert Systems, Inc.
1 John Wilson Ln.
Lexington, MA 02421

Phone: 781-862-4739
Fax: 781-860-0188
www.airxpert.com

The AIRxpert 7000 is an air monitoring system that helps building managers diagnose ventilation system performance with respect to IAQ. The unit continuously measures carbon dioxide (CO_2) at up to 48 locations to assess outside air delivery to occupied areas, while simultaneously providing carbon monoxide (CO) and absolute humidity (dewpoint) data for health and comfort purposes. The system can also help to minimize energy costs associated with conditioning outside air by continuously exporting CO_2 data to the building automation system (BAS), which uses that data to modulate outside air dampers as occupancy fluctuates.

Most recently mentioned in EBN 11:12

Air Ion Counter

AlphaLab, Inc.
1280 S. 300 W
Salt Lake City, UT 84101

Toll-free: 800-658-7030
Phone: 801-487-9492
Fax: 801-487-3877
www.trifield.com

AlphaLab's handheld, battery-operated Air Ion Counter detects natural and artificial ions, including radon gas.

23 51 00
Breechings, Chimneys, and Stacks

Products listed here help prevent the escape of combustion gases into conditioned space.

FasNSeal Direct Vent System

ProTech Systems, Inc.
400 S. Pearl St.
Albany, NY 12202

Toll-free: 800-766-3473
Phone: 518-463-7284
Fax: 518-463-5271
www.protechinfo.com

FasNSeal, made from AL29-4C® (a super-ferritic stainless steel designed to resist chloride ion pitting, crevice corrosion and stress corrosion cracking), is a direct vent system for category II, III, and IV heating equipment. FasNSeal combines a built-in gasket and locking band designed for high efficiency gas heaters where cool flue gases are vented under pressure. Installation involves sliding the FasNSeal units together and tightening the clamps. FasNSeal requires no silicone, eliminating cure time so the appliance can be started immediately. Every vent length and component can be taken apart and reassembled without destroying the integrity of the system.

23 00 00
HVAC

23 52 00
Heating Boilers

Boilers heat water in hydronic heating systems; the heat may be distributed through baseboard radiators (convectors), panel radiators, or radiant-floor piping, or transferred to an air distribution system via a fan coil in a central air handler or in air terminal units. These listings include the highest-efficiency oil- or gas-fired boilers and products, as well as biomass-fired alternatives. (Well-designed biomass-fueled boilers have very high burning efficiencies which reduce particulate emissions to less than half of the levels of the best wood stoves.) Some water heaters—especially electronic-ignition on-demand water heaters—can also be used as boilers for heating, particularly in very-low-energy buildings. Condensing boilers are listed separately in this directory. (See also 22 34 00 - Fuel-Fired Domestic Water Heaters.)

Burkay Legend 2000 Gas Boilers

A. O. Smith Water Products Co.
500 Tennessee Waltz Pkwy.
Ashland City, TN 37015

Toll-free: 800-527-1953
Fax: 615-792-2163
www.aosmithwaterheaters.com

The Burkay Legend 2000® line of commercial boilers has an integrated baffle design to enhance thermal efficiency for ratings up to 90%. The units offer sealed combustion and can use either natural gas or propane for fuel. The Legend 2000 boilers' small footprint at 23" x 32" enables them to fit through standard 30" doorways. A variety of venting options and three sizes are available with maximum inputs of 500,000; 750,000; and 1,000,000 Btu/hr.

Benchmark Gas-Fired Hot Water Boiler System

AERCO International, Inc.
159 Paris Ave.
Northvale, NJ 07647

Phone: 201-768-2400
Fax: 201-768-7789
www.aerco.com

Aerco's Benchmark (BMK) Gas-Fired Hot Water Boiler System is a commercial boiler for any closed-loop hydronic system. The condensing units utilize 20:1 modulation to increase their efficiency as load decreases to achieve seasonal efficiencies as high as 95%. These natural gas fueled units measure 79" H x 55" D x 28" W with zero side-wall clearance and can be used alone or in tandem. A large variety of venting options are possible; sealed combustion is optional. Maximum output is 1,720,000 to 1,840,000 Btu/hr. Dual fuel (gas and propane) and IRI gas train options are available. The unit may also be equipped with a Low NOx burner package (<30ppm).

Polaris Heating Systems

American Water Heater Company

For full listing, see CSI section 22 34 00 - Fuel-Fired Domestic Water Heaters

Broad Absorption Chiller/ Heater

Broad USA, Inc.

For full listing, see CSI section 23 64 00 - Packaged Water Chillers

G115 Sealed-Combustion Oil Boilers

Buderus
50 Wentworth Ave.
Londonderry, NH 03053

Toll-free: 800-283-3787
Phone: 603-552-1100
Fax: 603-584-1681
www.buderus.net

The smallest three models in this German hydronic boiler line are among the only true sealed-combustion, oil-fired residential boilers on the market. They are noted for their quiet operation and 86% combustion efficiency. A sophisticated "Logamatic" optional control module allows boiler water temperature control based on outside temperature (outdoor reset), plus priority control for indirect water heating. Buderus also makes indirect water heater tanks.

MPO Oil-Fired Boiler

Burnham Corporation
P.O. Box 3079
Lancaster, PA 17604

Toll-free: 877-567-4328
Phone: 717-397-4701
Fax: 717-293-5827
www.burnham.com

The MPO™ oil-fired, noncondensing, hydronic boiler is available in four sizes with GPH burner capacities ranging from 0.6 to 1.65, and and DOE Heating Capacities (MBH) from 74 to 203. All four models have an 87% AFUE, and are available in natural draft or direct vent. These boilers can be used for residential or light commercial applications, or installed in tandem for larger applications.

Wood Boilers

Chiptec
48 Helen Ave.
S. Burlington, VT 05403

Toll-free: 800-244-4146
Phone: 802-658-0956
Fax: 802-660-8904
www.chiptec.com

Chiptec wood energy gasifiers and boilers generate process steam and/or heat for industrial energy users such as lumber mills and kilns, or for multifamily buildings, schools, and large building complexes. Chiptec gasifiers burn mill residue, shavings, and sawdust as well as other clean biomass fuels fed via an automated auger. Chiptec provides entire systems, including gasifiers, boilers, fuel automation handling equipment, and controls.

Dryair Hydronic Construction Heater

New

Dryair Inc.
1095 N. Main St.
Bowling Green, OH 43402

Toll-free: 866-354-8546
Phone: 419-354-8546
Fax: 419-354-9706
www.dryair.us

The Dryair System uses a portable central heating plant and a low-pressure hydronic circulation system with remote heat exchangers to provide temporary, thermostatically-controlled heat for construction areas. The heat plant (individual models are fueled by propane or natural gas, or diesel / light oil) is located outdoors; no fumes, water vapor, or other combustion by-products are added to the conditioned space. Eliminating the supplemental ventilation required for conventional construction heat sources can reduce heating fuel use by half. Two sizes of fan/coil powered heat exchangers (120v) deliver an average of 80,000 or 200,000 Btu/h. Hose-type line heat exchangers transfer heat by conduction and radiation for ground thaw, frost prevention, and curing applications. These systems may also provide total structure dryout in disaster or accident mitigation situations.

23 00 00
HVAC

System 2000

Energy Kinetics
51 Molasses Hill Rd.
Lebanon, NJ 08833

Toll-free: 800-323-2066
Fax: 800-735-2068
www.energykinetics.com

System 2000, for residential and light commercial applications, has an AFUE rating of 87% and steady state efficiency of 99%. This integrated system provides multi-zone control of warm air, radiant heat, hydronic baseboard, and domestic hot water, as well as heating capabilities for pools or spas. It uses oil or natural gas or propane.

Fulton PulsePak Hydronic Boiler

Fulton Boiler Works, Inc.
3981 Port St.
Box 257
Pulaski, NY 13142

Phone: 315-298-5121
Fax: 315-298-6390
www.fulton.com

Fulton PulsePak commercial boilers have thermal efficiencies of up to 98% when coupled with modulation. Their standard efficiency is approximately 84-90%. Fulton models PHW-1400 and PHW-2000 are supplied with modulation as standard equipment. The small footprint of the Fulton PulsePak Boilers allows installation in multiple buildings or in isolated areas of large plants. Fulton boilers are equipped to use natural gas or propane for fuel. Maximum output ranges from 300,000 to 2,000,000 Btu/hr.

Intelli-Fin Boilers

Lochinvar Corporation
300 Maddox Simpson Pkwy.
Lebanon, TN 37090

Phone: 615-889-8900
Fax: 615-547-1004
www.lochinvar.com

Lochinvar Corporation's line of Intelli-Fin gas-fired water boilers uses a variable frequency drive to adjust the balance of gas and air supply to the boiler in order to enhance thermal efficiency up to 97%. Intelli-Fin boilers do not require high-pressured gas service, and a range of venting options is available. Multiple units can be sequenced to enhance efficiency as well. The Intelli-Fin boilers have a narrow footprint and are less than 80" high, making them highly adaptable for retrofit projects. Maximum output ranges from 1,410,000 to 1,890,000 Btu/hr.

Industrial Biomass Combustion System

Messersmith Manufacturing, Inc.
2612 F Rd.
Bark River, MI 49807

Phone: 906-466-9010
Fax: 906-466-2843
www.burnchips.com

The Industrial Biomass Combustion System is comprised of a large fuel storage bin, a series of augers, and a conveyer belt feeding fuel into an integral boiler. The system is also available for use with an existing boiler or furnace. A control panel varies fuel and air supply to control heat output, and maintains a pilot when there is little or no heat load. Btu outputs of the various industrial-scale units range from about 500,000 to 20,000,000 Btu/hr.

HeatManager Heating Boiler Economizer

R. W. Beckett Corporation
P.O. Box 1289
Elyria, OH 44036

Toll-free: 800-645-2876
Phone: 440-327-1060
Fax: 440-327-1064
www.beckettcorp.com

R. W. Beckett guarantees that its HeatManager Model 7512 will reduce oil, natural gas, or propane consumption by at least 10% in most residential boiler heating systems (sized up to 300,000 Btu, and if the boiler temperature regularly exceeds 150 degrees F during the heating season). The economizing microprocessor works with the existing boiler controls, adjusting firing patterns and boiler water temperature according to system load. Cycling may be reduced by 30%. This aftermarket product is optimally used in multi-zoned systems and also works with domestic hot water systems.

Raypak Advanced Design Boilers

Raypak Corporate Office
2151 Eastman Ave.
Oxnard, CA 93030

Phone: 805-278-5300
Fax: 805-278-5468
www.raypak.com

Raypak Advanced Design Boilers are commercial, fan-assisted boilers for domestic hot water and heating applications. When used with a condensing heat exchanger (CHX), they attain up to 97% thermal efficiency, using natural gas or propane for fuel. The four models in this boiler line are designed to

contain condensation in a corrosion-resistant secondary heat exchanger. Maximum output ranges from 420,000 to 1,470,000 Btu/hr (with a CHX).

Multi-Fuel and Wood Boilers

Tarm USA, Inc.
5 Main St.
P.O. Box 285
Lyme, NH 03768

Toll-free: 800-782-9927
Phone: 603-795-2214
Fax: 603-795-4740
www.woodboilers.com

The HS-Tarm Excel 2000 Boiler is a multi-fuel boiler and domestic water heater that operates at over 80% efficiency on wood and 85% on oil. It has fully automatic controls to maintain the wood fire and the oil or gas backup that will automatically turn on the oil or gas burner when the wood fire dies down. The Excel 2000 burns very cleanly and generates very little ash for clean up.

The HS-Tarm Solo Plus-MKII boiler and domestic hot-water heater uses substantially less wood than conventional boilers and outdoor water stoves and also has a very clean burn. Three sizes are available with outputs from 100,000 to 198,000 Btu/hr.

Multi-Pulse Boilers

The Hydrotherm Corp.
260 N. Elm St.
Westfield, MA 01085

Phone: 413-564-5515
Fax: 413-568-9613
www.hydrotherm.com

The Multi-Pulse sealed-combustion gas boiler is available in three sizes. Seasonal efficiency is 90% (AFUE). Units may be joined in modules and linked to heat exchangers for even greater efficiencies.

AquaMaster Q100 New

Vebteck Research
30 Riviera Dr.
Markham, ON L3R 5M1 Canada

Phone: 905-479-4048
Fax: 905-479-9413
www.ekocomfort.com

The AquaMaster Q100 is a joint development effort from Vebteck Research, Nutech Energy Systems, and Fleetline Products that offers integrated high-efficiency space heating (forced air or hydronic), domestic water heating, and continuous whole-house, heat-recovery ventilation (HRV) under a single, unified control system. The small system—it has a 4' x 2' footprint—includes a high-efficiency, low-mass, low-water-volume

23 00 00
HVAC

boiler (natural gas, propane, or fuel oil); a single, multi-speed, ECM blower; and an aluminum HRV core. The AquaMaster is a product of the eKOCOMFORT® consortium, a partnership of Canadian manufacturers and governmental agencies developing efficient, gas-fired, module-based units integrating space heating, ventilation, and domestic hot water.

Vitodens 200 Wall-Mounted Boiler

Viessman Manufacturing Co. (U.S.) Inc.
45 Access Rd.
Warwick, RI 02886

New

Toll-free: 800-288-0667
Phone: 401-732-0667
Fax: 401-732-0590
www.viessmann-us.com

Vitodens 200 is a wall-mounted, gas-fired, condensing boiler with efficiencies of up to 94.2% AFUE. This small, quiet, low-emission, zero-clearance, sealed-combustion unit can be installed in a living space. The five models have a maximum input ranging from 91,000 to 230,000 Btu/hr. The smaller WB2-24 and -32 models have a variable-speed pump for low electrical consumption and precise heating, and the WB2 6-24C has a plate-type heat exchanger to supply domestic hot water in addition to space heating. Up to four of the larger WB2-44 and -60 models can be ganged together for light-commercial applications.

23 52 16
Condensing Boilers

Condensing boilers capture and cool the combustion gases that are normally vented. Water condenses from those combustion byproducts, which releases additional heat and raises the overall efficiency of the system.

Q95M-200 Modulating Condensing Boiler

Dunkirk
85 Middle Rd.
Dunkirk, NY 14048

New

Phone: 877-386-5475
Fax: 716-366-1209
www.dunkirk.com

Dunkirk's Q95M-200 gas-fired, modulating, condensing boiler has an AFUE of 95%. Rather than cycling on and off, the sealed-combustion boiler modulates from 80,000 to 200,000 BTUs/hour to meet real-time load requirements.

Quantum Series Boilers

ECR International, Inc.
2201 Dwyer Ave.
Utica, NY 13501

Phone: 315-797-1310
Fax: 315-797-3762
www.ecrinternational.com

The Q95-200M condensing, gas-fired, residential hot water boiler features a cast aluminum heat exchanger and an AFUE of 95%. Via a second heat exchanger, hot flue gases heat condensate which is used to saturate and heat combustion air so that 90+% efficiencies can be obtained at return water temperatures up to 160 degrees F. The system is most efficient (up to 98%), however, with lower temperature water returns such as with radiant systems. The boiler offers sealed combustion and direct venting. PVC exhaust piping requires 0" clearance to combustible construction. The other unit in the series, the Quantum 90 (AFUE 90%), is similar but does not use condensate to heat and saturate combustion air. According to the manufacturer, both units substantially reduce CO and NOx emissions (acid rain and smog components)—to less than 10 ppm for the Q95-200M and 30 ppm for the Quantum 90.

Gasmaster Condensing Boilers

Gasmaster Industries Incorporated
#8 - 15050 54A Ave.
Surrey, BC V3S 5X7 Canada

Phone: 604-574-9874
Fax: 604-574-9572
www.gasmaster-ind.com

Gasmaster commercial gas-fired condensing boilers use a unique and patented throttle mechanism capable of maintaining water temperature within 1 degree F of the desired value. This digitally regulated mechanism almost eliminates the on/off cycles of the boiler and water heater, thus increasing the thermal efficiency of the system. Thermal efficiency ratings for Gasmaster models range from 97 to 99.8%. Maximum output ranges from 200,000 to 8,000,000 Btu/hr.

Baxi Luna Condensing Boilers

Marathon International
1815 Sismet Rd.
Mississauga, ON L4W 1P9 Canada

New

Phone: 905-602-5360
www.wallhungboilers.com

Marathon International is the North American distributor for the Baxi line of boilers and water heating products from Britain. The Luna wall-hung, condensing boiler is a gas-fired, sealed-combustion, direct-venting boiler for home heating applications. (One model in the line will also supply domestic hot water.) Btu/hr deliveries range from as low as 32,804 to as high as 221,789, with efficiencies up to 97%. Multiple boilers can be ganged together to share a common venting system while increasing Btu output for commercial applications. Circuitry-based anti-freeze protection comes standard.

FCX Oil-Fired Condensing Boiler

Monitor Products, Inc.
P.O. Box 3408
Princeton, NJ 08543

Toll-free: 800-524-1102
Phone: 732-329-0900
Fax: 732-329-0904
www.monitorproducts.com

The FCX is a small, oil-fired condensing boiler measuring 33-1/2" H x 23" W x 24-1/2" D with a Btu output of 76,100 and an application efficiency of 95%. The unit (which produces heat and domestic hot water) contains a primary, noncondensing heat exchanger coupled to a stainless steel condensing secondary heat exchanger. The FCX is approved as a sealed combustion device and can be fitted to take combustion air from the outside via a concentric vent.

MZ Boiler

Monitor Products, Inc.
P.O. Box 3408
Princeton, NJ 08543

Toll-free: 800-524-1102
Phone: 732-329-0900
Fax: 732-329-0904
www.monitorproducts.com

Monitor is the U.S. distributor for the fully condensing gas-fired MZ Boiler. All three models are wall-mounted and perform with up to 97.7% efficiency (minimum of 90%, according to the company). The units offer spark ignition, sealed combustion, and zero clearance, and use only 108 watts of electricity to operate. The MZ25S (the only unit of the three to provide both heat and domestic hot water) and the MZ25C have 94,000 Btu/hr input. The MZ40C has 142,500 Btu/hr input in two 71,000 Btu stages (high/low fire). These hydronic heat sources meet German "Blue Angel" environmental standards.

23 00 00
HVAC

Vitocrossal Gas-Fired Condensing Boilers

Viessman Manufacturing Co. (U.S.) Inc.
45 Access Rd.
Warwick, RI 02886

Toll-free: 800-288-0667
Phone: 401-732-0667
Fax: 401-732-0590
www.viessmann-us.com

Viessman offers the Vitocrossal (previously the Vertomat) line of commercial, natural gas-fired, condensing water boilers, which are easy to use in retrofitting projects. The lightweight boiler shells are of narrow construction, and larger models are sectional. Vertomat boilers use corrosion-resistant Inox-Crossal heat-exchanging stainless steel surfaces. Thermal efficiency is up to 96.2%. Output ranges from 614,000 to 3,233,000 Btu/hr.

Vitodens 200 Wall-Mounted Boiler

Viessman Manufacturing Co. (U.S.) Inc.

For full listing, see CSI section 23 52 00 - Heating Boilers

23 54 00
Furnaces

Furnaces heat air that is then distributed through ducting and warm-air registers. Products listed here are among the highest-efficiency, sealed-combustion furnaces.

Amana AMV9 Gas Furnace

Amana Heating and Air Conditioning
1810 Wilson Pkwy.
Fayetteville, TN 37334

Phone: 800-647-2982
Fax: 931-438-2279
www.amana-hac.com

Amana's AMV9 two-stage, variable-speed gas furnace has an efficiency of up to 96% AFUE. Heating capacity ranges from 30,800 to 109,000 Btu/hr. These furnaces are available in a variety of airflow configurations. Amana offers a lifetime warranty on the heat exchanger and recuperative coil, and five years on the balance of the system.

Plus 90 High-Efficiency Furnaces

Bryant Heating & Cooling Systems
7310 W. Morris St.
Indianapolis, IN 46231

Toll-free: 800-428-4326
Phone: 317-243-0851
Fax: 315-428-4326
www.bryant.com

Bryant's Plus 90i (also known as the 355AAV) series of gas furnaces has AFUEs ranging from to 95.0 to 96.6%. Heating capacities from its two-stage gas valve range from 25,000/38,000 Btu/hr for the smallest model to 73,000/112,000 for the largest. These furnaces have variable-speed fans and advanced humidity-control technology, and are available in upflow, downflow, or horizontal airflow configurations. The Plus 90 (or 350AAV) line is 95.5% efficient, with multi-speed blowers (rather than variable speed) and a single-stage valve. Its output ranges from 38,000 to 139,000 Btu/hr.

Infinity Series

Carrier Corp.
Carrier Parkway
P.O. Box 4808
Syracuse, NY 13221

Toll-free: 800-227-7437
Phone: 315-432-6000
Fax: 315-432-6620
www.carrier.com

Carrier's Infinity™ gas furnaces feature a smart microprocessor control center and variable-speed motors that minimize electrical usage. Sealed combustion protects indoor air quality and reduces noise. Models in this series range in heating capacity from 40,000 to 154,000 Btu per hour. The 58MVB, with an efficiency of up to 96.6% AFUE, is Carrier's most efficient gas furnace. It has a variable-speed fan, 4-way multipoise, and advanced humidity-removal capabilities.

UltraMAX III

ECR International, Inc.
2201 Dwyer Ave.
Utica, NY 13501

Phone: 315-797-1310
Fax: 315-797-3762
www.ecrinternational.com

Olsen's UltraMAX III high-efficiency furnaces are available in heating capacities ranging from 47,000 to 95,000 Btu/hr. The GTH 85 and GTH 100 models have efficiencies of up to 95% AFUE. GTH 50 and GTH 70 have efficiencies of up to 94% AFUE.

Encore NC 1450

New

Vermont Castings
1000 E. Market St.
Huntington, IN 46750

Toll-free: 800-227-8683
Fax: 219-356-9672
www.vermontcastings.com

The Encore NC 1450 is a cast-iron, non-catalytic wood stove with emissions of 0.7 grams per hour (gph), which is lower than most catalytic wood stoves and pellet stoves. The 40,000 Btu/hour (max.) stove uses Vermont Casting's EVERBURN combustion technology. It is the lowest-emitting wood stove that has been certified by the U.S. Environmental Protection Agency (EPA), and it handily meets the strict Washington State emission limit of 4.5 gph for non-catalytic wood stoves. (For catalytic stoves, the limit is 2.5 gph.) A slightly larger Defiant NC 1610 has emissions nearly as low and produces up to 60,000 Btu/hour.

Diamond 90 and Diamond 95 ULTRA

York International Corp.
5005 York Dr.
Unitary Products Group
Norman, OK 73069

Toll-free: 877-874-7378
Phone: 405-364-4040
Fax: 405-419-6545
www.yorkupg.com

The Diamond 90 gas-fired, sealed-combustion furnace has an efficiency of up to 94.3% AFUE. This condensing-type furnace is suitable for commercial and residential installation. The Diamond 90 has a primary and secondary heat exchanger to maximize efficiency. The Diamond 95 Ultra comes with a variable-speed fan.

23 56 13
Heating Solar Flat-Plate Collectors

These listings include flat-plate solar collectors used for water and space heating. Building-integrated transpired collectors are also included here.

23 00 00
HVAC

Solar Thermal Flat Plate Collectors

Alternate Energy Technologies
1057 N. Ellis Rd., Unit 4
Jacksonville, FL 32254

Toll-free: 800-874-2190
Phone: 904-781-8305
Fax: 904-781-1911
www.aetsolar.com

Alternate Energy Technologies is a manufacturer of copper-tube, flat-plate collectors with a nontoxic collector coating.

Most recently mentioned in EBN 8:7

Solar Pool Heating Systems

Aquatherm Industries, Inc.

For full listing, see CSI section 22 51 00 - Swimming Pool Plumbing Systems

InSpire Transpired Solar Collector

ATAS International, Inc.
6612 Snowdrift Rd.
Allentown, PA 18106

Toll-free: 800-468-1441
Phone: 610-395-8445
Fax: 610-395-9342
www.atas.com

InSpire™ Transpired Solar Collectors utilize metal wall panels to preheat fresh ventilation air. Perforated aluminum panels in colors with high solar absorption are mounted away from the outer wall of the building. The solar-preheated air at the surface is drawn into the wall cavity by ventilation fans that direct the air into the building through conventional HVAC systems or perforated ducts. Inlet air preheating of 30 to 50 degrees F on a sunny day can be achieved, reducing the heating load for buildings that require heated ventilation air. Annual savings are dependent upon geographical location and local energy costs, but typically range from $2 to $8 per square foot of collector wall. The design is suitable for industrial, commercial, and institutional buildings. Additional energy savings may be achieved by destratifying the ceiling heat while improving the indoor air quality.

Most recently mentioned in EBN 14:8

Solarwall Transpired Solar Collector

Conserval Systems, Inc.
4242 Ridge Lea Rd., #28
Buffalo, NY 14226

Phone: 716-835-4903
Fax: 716-835-4904
www.solarwall.com

Solarwall® is an unglazed (transpired) solar collector that uses perforated sheet metal to preheat ventilation air. Inlet air preheating of 30-50 degrees F on a sunny day can be achieved, reducing the heating load on fresh-air-ventilated commercial and industrial buildings. Savings are dependent upon geographic location and local energy costs. The savings are approximately 2 to 4 therms per ft^2/year. Solarwall offers an optional displacement ventilation system to spread the solar heated fresh air over a wide area inside the building. The design is suited for all types of industrial, commercial, and institutional buildings. Additional energy savings are achieved by destratifying the ceiling heat while improving the indoor air quality.

Most recently mentioned in EBN 5:1, 8:7, 14:8

SunMate Hot Air Solar Panel

Environmental Solar Systems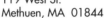
119 West St.
Methuen, MA 01844

Phone: 978-975-1190
Fax: 978-975-1190
www.environmentalsolarsystems.com

Sunmate® is a side-mounted residential solar thermal collector constructed of aluminum, double-sealed glass, and polyisocyanurate insulation. A 100 CFM, 7W fan on an automatic thermostat pulls cool air from the home, channels it through the absorber plate, and circulates hot air back into the home. Sunmate can also be used for fresh air intake in tight houses. One panel heats up to 300 square feet, and panels can be installed in parallel.

Solar Pool Heating Systems

Fafco, Inc.

For full listing, see CSI section 22 51 00 - Swimming Pool Plumbing Systems

Heliocol Solar Pool-Heating Systems

Heliocol

For full listing, see CSI section 22 51 00 - Swimming Pool Plumbing Systems

Gobi Solar Collectors and Helio-Pak Solar Water Heater

Heliodyne, Inc.
4910 Seaport Ave.
Richmond, CA 94804

Phone: 510-237-9614
Fax: 510-237-7018
www.heliodyne.com

Heliodyne is a manufacturer of flat-plate solar collectors and heat-transfer systems for residential and commercial water heating.

Most recently mentioned in EBN 8:7 & 11:4

Solar Collectors

Industrial Solar Technology Corp.
4420 McIntyre St.
Golden, CO 80403

Phone: 303-279-8108
Fax: 303-279-8107
www.industrialsolartech.com

Industrial Solar Technology is a manufacturer of flat plate solar collectors and parabolic-trough concentrating solar collector systems for commercial and industrial water-heating applications, including absorption cooling.

Most recently mentioned in EBN 8:7

Solar Collectors

R&R Services Solar Supply
922 Austin Ln., Bldg. D
Honolulu, HI 96817

Phone: 808-842-0011
Fax: 808-847-4938

R&R Services Solar Supply is a manufacturer of copper-tube/absorber flat-plate collectors. The company packages solar water-heating systems for sale throughout Hawaii.

Most recently mentioned in EBN 8:7

Solar Collectors

Radco Products, Inc.
2877 Industrial Pkwy.
Santa Maria, CA 93455

Toll-free: 800-927-2326
Phone: 805-928-1881
Fax: 805-928-5587
http://radcosolar.com/about.html

Radco Products manufactures glazed flat-plate solar collectors and complete drainback solar water-heating systems for areas with freezing weather conditions. The company also produces a line of unglazed solar pool-heating systems.

Most recently mentioned in EBN 8:7

23 00 00
HVAC

Skyline Solar Thermal Collectors and Systems

SolarRoofs.com Inc.
5840 Gibbons Dr., Ste. G
Carmichael, CA 95608

Toll-free: 888-801-9060
Phone: 916-481-7200
Fax: 916-481-7203
www.solarroofs.com

SolarRoofs.com Inc. manufactures lightweight flat-plate solar water heating systems and collectors. Its Skyline collectors have copper piping and absorber plates with polycarbonate Twinwall glazing. Collectors are available in 26 architectural colors, are SRCC and FSEC certified, and carry an independent structural certification to withstand 150-mph wind. The company offers a variety of systems for different climates, including drain-back and closed-loop with integral PV-powered pump/controller.

Most recently mentioned in EBN 8:7

SunEarth Solar Equipment

SunEarth, Inc.

For full listing, see CSI section 23 56 16 - Packaged Solar Heating Equipment

SOL 25 and Storage Tank

Stiebel Eltron
17 West St.
West Hatfield, MA 01088

Toll-free: 800-582-8423
Phone: 413-247-3380
www.stiebel-eltron-usa.com

Stiebel Eltron manufactures the SOL 25 Plus flat plate solar collectors and SB/SBB Plus storage tanks for solar water-heating systems. The Berlin, Germany based company has manufacturing plants in Holzminden, Germany and Tailand. The solar collector selective absorber surface is chromium oxide, which offers high performance, but carries significant environmental burdens. The storage tanks are insulated with three inches of polyurethane foam and available in four sizes (39 to 109 gallons) and with one or two heat exchangers.

23 00 00
HVAC

Air-Heating Solar Collector

Sunsiaray
4414 N. Washburn Rd.
Davison, MI 48423

Phone: 810-653-3502
Fax: 810-653-9267
www.sunsiaray.com

Sunsiaray Solar Manufacturing produces air-heating solar collectors.

Most recently mentioned in EBN 8:7

ProgressivTube Passive Water Heating Systems

Thermal Conversion Technology
101 Copeland St.
Jacksonville, FL 32204

Phone: 904-358-3720
Fax: 904-358-3728
www.tctsolar.com

Thermal Conversion Technology produces the ProgressivTube® line of integral collector-storage (ICS) systems with 4"-diameter copper pipes in a glass-glazed collector. The collectors are typically for solar preheating of water and are used extensively in Caribbean and Hawaiian hotels. Founded in 1974, the company has sold thousands of the current ProgressiTube® line since its introduction in 1982.

Most recently mentioned in EBN 8:7

Solar Water-Heating Systems

Thermo Dynamics Ltd.

For full listing, see CSI section 23 56 16 - Packaged Solar Heating Equipment

23 56 14
Heating Solar Concentrating Collectors

High-temperature solar thermal systems typically use parabolic reflectors to concentrate the solar energy and heat-transfer fluids other than water.

Solar Collectors

Industrial Solar Technology Corp.

For full listing, see CSI section 23 56 13 - Heating Solar Flat-Plate Collectors

Power Roof

Solargenix Energy, LLC
2101-115 Westinghouse Blvd.
Raleigh, NC 27604

Phone: 919-871-0423
Fax: 919-871-0702
www.solargenix.com

Solargenix Energy's Power Roof™ is a combined heat, power, and cooling system integrating solar hot water, space heating, daylighting, and absorption cooling—both single- and double-effect. (Double-effect absorption chilling uses process heat for part of the energy needed, and is about twice as efficient as single-effect.) The high-temperature version features a roof-integrated solar energy collection system with a fixed reflector

and tracking secondary receiver that operates at temperatures up to 750 degrees F. The mid-temperature version features the non-tracking Integrated Compound Parabolic Concentrator (ICPC) evacuated tube collector that operates to 400 degrees F.

Most recently mentioned in EBN 8:7 & 13:5

Winston Series CPC Collector

Solargenix Energy, LLC

For full listing, see CSI section 23 56 16 - Packaged Solar Heating Equipment

23 56 15
Heating Solar Vacuum-Tube Collectors

Evacuated tubes offer higher efficiencies and better performance in cold weather than conventional flat-plate collectors, though cost is typically higher.

Apricus Evacuated Tube Solar Collectors

Maine Green Building Supply
111 Fox St.
Portland, ME 04101

Phone: 207-780-1500
Fax: 207-780-1510
www.mainegreenbuilding.com

Apricus manufactures evacuated-tube solar collectors in Nanjing, China for worldwide distribution. The borosilicate twin-glass vacuum tubes passively track the sun (because of their round shape). A selective coating on the inner tube provides minimal reflection and maximum solar-radiation absorption, while the vacuum reduces heat losses via conduction and convection. If the vacuum is ever lost, the silver-colored barium layer at the end of the tube, acquired during manufacture, will turn white, allowing the faulty tube to be identified and replaced. The copper heat pipes use a phase change fluid to effect one-way heat flow to the header pipe. Water is intermittently pumped through the header pipe where it absorbs heat. The system has a 10-year limited warranty, and Apricus is ISO 9001 certified.

Sunda Evacuated Tube Solar Collectors

Sun Spot Solar & Heating, Inc.
P.O. Box 55
Delaware Water Gap, PA 18327

Phone: 570-422-1292
Fax: 570-476-5353
www.sssolar.com

Sun Spot Solar offers the Seido line of evacuated tube solar collectors manufactured by Beijing Sunda Solar Energy Technology Co., Ltd. These collectors use an aluminum solar absorber plate mounted in a long glass vacuum tube; the vacuum reduces heat losses via conduction and convection. Heat is transferred from the absorber plate to a small "heat pipe," which acts as a heat-exchanger in a fluid-filled manifold. The fluid in the heating circuit does not flow through the collectors. The vacuum tubes are made with low-iron tempered glass designed to withstand 35mm (1.38 inch) hail. The tubes have a six-year warranty.

Most recently mentioned in EBN 13:2

SunTube Collector

Sun Utility Network, Inc.
4952 Coringa Dr.
Los Angeles, CA 90042

Phone: 323-478-0866
Fax: 323-478-0866
www.sunutility.com

Sun Utility Network is the U.S. distributor of NEG's SunTube evacuated-tube solar water-heating systems. SunTube panels can be used for residential and commercial water heating, space heating and cooling, water pasteurization, and desalination applications.

Most recently mentioned in EBN 8:7

Evacuated Tube Solar Collectors

Thermo Technologies
5560 Sterrett Pl., Ste. 115
Columbia, MD 21044

Phone: 410-997-0778
Fax: 410-997-0779
www.thermotechs.com

Thermo Technologies (formerly Advanced Solar Technologies) is the east-coast U.S. distributor for Thermomax, a European company with manufacturing facilities in Italy, Northern Ireland, and Wales. Thermomax produces an evacuated-tube solar collector system using heat-pipe technology to transfer heat to a manifold. (Heat pipes use a phase-change fluid to effect one-way heat flow, obviating the need for complex controls.) Standard-sized tubes are ganged together to produce any size system from small residential to large commercial and are typically configured into a closed-loop antifreeze system. The selective absorber surface is an environmentally friendly Tinox® titanium nitride oxide coating from Germany. Thermo Technologies also offers balance-of-system components and design services.

Most recently mentioned in EBN 8:7

23 56 16
Packaged Solar Heating Equipment

Packaged Solar Equipment includes 'plug-and-play' systems that include all of the necessary components.

Flat Plate Water Heating Systems

ACR Solar International Corporation
5840 Gibbons Dr., Ste. G
Carmichael, CA 95608

Phone: 916-481-7200
Fax: (916) 481-7203
www.solarroofs.com

The Skylite 10-01 is a lightweight, easy-to-ship solar water heater that weighs only 19 pounds. SolarRoof also offers offers a number of closed- and open-loop kits with DC or AC pumps and all the fittings, including systems for hard freeze climates. The company is known for its Fireball solar water heating products.

ECO-Nomad

Architectural & Community Planning Inc.
261 Albany St.
Winnipeg, MB R3G 2A9 Canada

Phone: 204-831-0216
Fax: 204-837-7518
www.economad.com

The ECO-Nomad™ combined mechanical utility container provides utility services to off-grid locations by creating a self-contained, integrated micro-infrastructure, including potable water storage and purification, biological wastewater treatment, water and space heating, electrical supply, and fire protection. All functions can be remotely monitored. The portable 8' x 8' x 16' utility container can be transported by road, rail, water, or air. Designed for extreme winter conditions, uses include remote residential, tourism, or commercial facilities; temporary mining or logging camps; disaster relief; and remote airports and weather stations.

Architectural Solar-Hydronic System

Dawn Solar Systems, Inc.
183 Route 125, Ste. A-7
Brentwood, NH 03833

Toll-free: 866-338-2018
Phone: 603-642-7899
Fax: 603-642-7897
www.dawnsolar.com

The Dawn Solar System® uses looped hydronic tubing concealed in a one-inch layer between the roof or wall sheathing and the exterior finish material to capture solar heat. The collector system has a 25-year warranty and can be designed as an integrated system to produce heated air, water, and electricity from the same roof or wall area. The system is pre-engineered for each application. In cold climates, a closed-loop glycol system is recommended. The system qualifies for government energy incentives.

Solar Water Heating

EnerWorks Inc.
252 Hamilton Crescent
P.O. Box 9
Dorchester, ON N0L 1G0 Canada

Phone: 519-268-6500
Fax: 519-268-6292
www.enerworks.com

The Solar Hot Water Appliances from EnerWorks provide auxiliary hot water heating for washing, cooking, and space conditioning. These systems utilize low-flow, natural convection for long-term reliability, reduced first cost, and lower operating cost. The system consists of one or more flat-plate solar collector panels, fluid transfer lines, a stainless steel heat transfer module (designed to fit on any new or existing electric storage-type water heater), and a controller. The manufacturer claims average energy savings of 50% for full-year operation in southern Ontario and Northern U.S., and up to 100% for seasonal installations.

Gobi Solar Collectors and Helio-Pak Solar Water Heater

Heliodyne, Inc.

For full listing, see CSI section 23 56 13 - Heating Solar Flat-Plate Collectors

Solar Collectors

R&R Services Solar Supply

For full listing, see CSI section 23 56 13 - Heating Solar Flat-Plate Collectors

Solar Collectors

Radco Products, Inc.

For full listing, see CSI section 23 56 13 - Heating Solar Flat-Plate Collectors

23 00 00
HVAC

Solahart Solar Water Heating Systems

Rheem Water Heating
101 Bell Rd.
Montgomery, AL 36117

Phone: 334 260 1586
Fax: 334 260 1514
www.rheem.com

Solahart's Free Heat series is a closed-circuit thermosiphoning solar water-heating system utilizing a heat-transfer fluid that circulates around a jacketed water tank. The Free Heat series comes with a 10-year warranty in a range of tank sizes and panel configurations. It is designed for use in virtually any climate. Other models, also available in various sizes, have specific design criteria—including the J series for areas with medium to good solar radiation, poor water quality, or frost conditions; the KF series for low to medium solar radiation, poor water quality, or frost or snow conditions; and the L series for frost-free areas with medium to high solar radiation and relatively clean water supplies. The J and KF series have a five-year warranty. The L series has a 10 year warranty. Solahart is a division of Rheem Water Heating.

Most recently mentioned in EBN 14:2

Solar Water Heating Systems

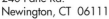

SCHÜCO, LP
240 Pane Rd.
Newington, CT 06111

Toll-free: 877-472-4826
Phone: 860-666-0505
Fax: 860-666-2359
www.schuco-usa.com

Schüco manufactures solar water-heating systems with a controller and pump to circulate a heat-transfer fluid. The system allows for air-purging without accessing the panels. Panels have anodized aluminum hardware and frames. The Solar Thermal Slim Line package is the basic model with two installation options for pitched roofs. The Premium Line has higher system efficiency and a wide range of frame colors and installation options. Schüco also offers custom systems for large installations, apartment buildings, and swimming pools. These products are manufactured in Germany.

23 00 00
HVAC

Renewable Energy Equipment

Solar Energy, Inc.
5191 Shawland Rd.
Jacksonville, FL 32254

Phone: 904-786-6600
Fax: 904-786-1775
www.solarenergy.com

Solar Energy Inc. (SEI) is a manufacturer and distributor of a variety of solar water-heating systems for commercial or residential applications. The turnkey, drainback SUN HoM™ system has one or more roof-integrated flat-plate solar collectors and uses a controller and pump to circulate a heat-transfer fluid. When the pump shuts off, water drains to an insulated reservoir to protect from freezing. Solar Energy also sells other alternative energy systems including PV and wind power.

Winston Series CPC Collector

Solargenix Energy, LLC
2101-115 Westinghouse Blvd.
Raleigh, NC 27604

Phone: 919-871-0423
Fax: 919-871-0702
www.solargenix.com

The Winston Series CPC Collector from Solargenix Energy is a residential and commercial solar water-heating system. The basic system is comprised of 12 small compound parabolic collectors (CPC) which focus light onto absorber tubes through which heat-transfer fluid is piped. One to three collectors are commonly used for residential solar water-heating systems, depending on the size of the hot water storage tank. A roof-integrated thermosiphoning configuration is possible with new construction. The collectors carry a 10-year warranty. The system's heat exchanger, SOLPAC, is also available as a separate item. Coupled with one or more solar collectors, it prepackages the components needed to convert existing electric or gas water heaters into solar water-heating systems.

Most recently mentioned in EBN 13:5 & 13:12

CopperSun

Sun Systems, Inc.
2030 W. Pinnacle Peak Rd.
Phoenix, AZ 85027

Toll-free: 800-777-6657
Phone: 623-869-7652
Fax: 623-869-0891
www.sunsystemsinc.com

Sun Systems manufactures the CopperSun™ integral collector storage (ICS) solar water heater. The unit is designed for integration into a roof, with flush mounting and a flashing kit for roofing right up to the textured-glass cover plate. Systems are available with either a 40- or 50-gallon capacity. The company is primarily pursuing the new-home builder market in the Sun Belt, as the CopperSun system is not appropriate for heavy-freeze climates.

Most recently mentioned in EBN 8:7

SunEarth Solar Equipment

SunEarth, Inc.
8425 Almeria Ave.
Fontana, CA 92335

Phone: 909-434-3100
Fax: 909-434-3101
www.sunearthinc.com

SunEarth, Inc., a manufacturer of solar water-heating equipment since 1978, produces flat-plate solar collectors, ICS and thermosiphon water-heating systems, and ancillary components including residential and commercial racking systems for both solar water heating and PV systems.

Most recently mentioned in EBN 8:7

SunCoil

Taylor Munro Energy Systems Inc.
11-7157 Honeyman St.
Delta, BC V4G 1E2 Canada

Phone: 604-946-4433
Fax: 604-946-3804
www.taylormunro.com

The SunCoil from Taylor Munro Energy Systems is an active solar water heating system for residential or commercial installations. According to the manufacturer, residential SunCoil systems in temperate climates are typically designed to meet 50-60% of the total annual hot water demand, with up to 100% provided during peak summer performance and more supplemental heat needed during the rest of the year. In tropical climates, the SunCoil can provide 80-100% of the hot water demand. Multiple panels can be used to provide institutional water heating for showers and other domestic use, as well as for pools, hatcheries, and process water. The SunCoil system can also be designed for combined water and space heating.

Sunwell

Taylor Munro Energy Systems Inc.
11-7157 Honeyman St.
Delta, BC V4G 1E2 Canada

Phone: 604-946-4433
Fax: 604-946-3804
www.taylormunro.com

The Sunwell three-season batch (or integral collector storage – ICS) solar water heater from Taylor Munro Energy Systems consists of a stainless steel tank and a parabolic reflector inside an insulated, glazed housing. It is most commonly used as a preheater for a conventional water heater. It runs on line water pressure; no additional pump, tank, or heat exchanger is required. According to the manufacturer, the system can provide up to 100% of a family's water heating energy load in non-freezing climates and up to 40% in freezing climates. The unit should not be used during freezing seasons.

Solar Water-Heating Systems

Thermo Dynamics Ltd.
101 Frazee Ave.
Dartmouth, NS B3B-1Z4 Canada

Phone: 902-468-1001
Fax: 902-468-1002
www.thermo-dynamics.com

Thermo Dynamics manufactures a full range of solar water-heating systems with liquid flat-plate, glazed collectors with fused copper tubing and aluminum absorbers. The company also produces the Solar Pump™—a PV-powered pump—and a thermosiphoning heat exchanger.

Most recently mentioned in EBN 8:7

23 56 19
Solar Heating Balance of System Components

These listings include specialized components and materials for solar thermal systems other than the actual panels or collectors.

Solar Hydronic Check Valves, Differential Thermostats

Heliotrope Thermal
4910 Seaport Ave.
Richmond, CA 94804

Phone: 510-237-9614
Fax: 510-237-7018
www.heliotropethermal.com

Heliotrope Thermal offers low-resistance spring/ball brass check valves designed for the high temperatures and pressures of solar domestic hot water systems. The cleanable valves have sweat-union connections, silicone O-rings, and can be Installed on vertical or horizontal lines. Delta-T electronic controllers are differential-temperature thermostats designed to regulate the operation of solar hydronic heating systems by monitoring collector and storage temperatures and automating pumps or blowers appropriately. They can also provide system freeze protection, and high- or low-limit shut-offs. Heliotrope Thermal, like Heliotrope PV, is a successor to Heliotrope General, a branch of Heliodyne, Inc.

Solar Water Storage Tanks

Morley Manufacturing
P.O. Box 1540
Cedar Ridge, CA 95924

Phone: 530-477-6527
Fax: 530-477-0194

Morley manufactures storage tanks used for solar water-heating systems.

Most recently mentioned in EBN 8:7

Winston Series CPC Collector

Solargenix Energy, LLC

For full listing, see CSI section 23 56 16 - Packaged Solar Heating Equipment

Solar Pumping Components

Solarnetix Inc.   **New**
777 Warden Ave.
Toronto, ON M1L4C3 Canada

Phone: 416-699-6746
Fax: 416-699-6746
www.solarnetix.com

Solarnetix is the North American distributor of hydronic heat and solar pumping components made by the German company, Pommerening Armaturenwerk (PAW GmbH & Co. KG). Components range from brass check valves and flow gauges to complete distribution systems designed for the high temperatures and pressures of solar domestic hot water systems. Neatly packaged in insulated wall-mount packs.

SOL 25 and Storage Tank

Stiebel Eltron

For full listing, see CSI section 23 56 13 - Heating Solar Flat-Plate Collectors

Solar Water Storage Tanks

Vaughn Manufacturing Corporation
26 Old Elm St.
P.O. Box 5431
Salisbury, MA 01952

Toll-free: 800-282-8446
Phone: 978-462-6683
Fax: 978-462-4683
www.vaughncorp.com

Vaughn Manufacturing produces stone-lined storage tanks specifically for solar water heating systems. Vaughn tanks have removable copper-finned heat exchangers enabling periodic cleaning of the coil to maintain maximum performance. The tanks—which are lined with centrifugally applied Hydrastone for corrosion protection—come in 65-, 80-, and 115-gallon capacities, and can also be made to custom dimensions.

Viessmann Solar Water Heating System

Viessmann Manufacturing
Company Inc.   **New**
750 McMurray Rd.
Waterloo, ON N2V 2G5 Canada

Toll-free: 800-387-7373
Phone: 519-885-6300
Fax: 519-885-0887
www.viessmann.ca

Viessmann manufactures solar water-heating components which can be purchased separately, or together as part of a fully integrated system package. Components include a number of different collectors and storage tanks, pumps, controllers, and balance-of-system components. Viessmann offers a lower-cost Vitosol 100 flat-plate solar collector and the Vitosol 300 evacuated-tube solar collector. Both hot water tanks, the stainless-steel Vitocell B 300 and the more economical steel Vitocell B 100, use HCFC-free polyurethane insulation and have dual heat exchanger coils that accommodate both solar and conventional-boiler heat input.

23 61 00
Refrigerant Compressors

Look for such advanced qualities as magnetic bearings and high part-load efficiency.

HVACR Compressors

Turbocor
1850 Trans-Canada Hwy.
Dorval, QC H9P2N4 Canada

Phone: 514-421-0523
Fax: 514-421-4277
www.turbocor.com

Turbocor manufactures oil-free compressors utilizing nearly-frictionless magnetic bearings for middle-market water-cooled, evaporatively cooled, and air-cooled HVACR applications. These compressors are optimized for HFC-134a and exceed ASHRAE 90.1 and California Title 24 energy efficiency requirements, particularly under part-load conditions. They weigh about 75% less than traditional units, have 50% less footprint, and operate at 70dBA with very little vibration. These compressors are approximately 40" long and 20" high but have output capacities ranging from 60 to 90 tons. The shipping weight is 300 lbs. Available as OEM equipment or for retrofit, they also work in parallel with existing compressors.

23 00 00
HVAC

23 64 00
Packaged Water Chillers

Products listed here either use ozone-safe refrigerants or have failsafe systems to prevent the escape of refrigerant. (See also 23 23 23 - Refrigerants.) (See feature article EBN Vol. 6, No. 2.)

Broad Absorption Chiller/ Heater

Broad USA, Inc.
401 Hackensack Ave., Ste. 503
Hackensack, NJ 07601

Phone: 201-678-3010
Fax: 201-678-3011
www.broad.com

The Broad absorption chiller/heater offers simultaneous full-load heating, cooling, and domestic hot water. It uses no refrigerants and uses double-effect absorption to provide a coefficient of performance (COP) of 1.34. It is available in sizes ranging from 50 to 2,600 tons of cooling. Note that the units are manufactured in China and shipped to North America.

Evergreen Packaged Chillers

Carrier Corp.
Carrier Parkway
P.O. Box 4808
Syracuse, NY 13221

Toll-free: 800-227-7437
Phone: 315-432-6000
Fax: 315-432-6620
www.carrier.com

The Evergreen® line of air-cooled chillers from Carrier uses chlorine-free R-134A refrigerant. Model 19XR is a rotary chiller with a hermetic centrifugal compressor, and is available from 200 to 1,500 tons. Rotary chiller model 23XRV uses a hermetic screw compressor and is available from 300 to 550 tons. Packaged water-cooled chiller model 30HXC is a screw compressor type in 70 to 265 tons; the similar but condenserless model 30HXA is available in the same tonnage.

23 00 00
HVAC

EarthWise CenTraVac

The Trane Company
3600 Pammel Creek Rd.
La Crosse, WI 54601

Phone: 608-787-2000
Fax: 608-787-2204
www.trane.com

The EarthWise™ CenTraVac is a highly efficient chiller that uses ozone-depleting HCFCs but is designed to keep refrigerant releases below 0.5% per year. This R-123-based chiller was the first commercial building chiller to receive Green Seal certification. An adaptive frequency drive enhances performance when the system is working at part load.

Most recently mentioned in EBN 6:2 & 6:3

23 71 19
Off-Peak Thermal Energy Storage Cooling Systems

Off-peak cooling, or thermal energy storage (TES), is an alternative to conventional chiller operation in commercial buildings. Off-peak electricity is used to provide some or all of a building's cooling requirements by chilling thermal-storage media during times of low electrical demand. Building operating costs are typically lowered through the use of off-peak pricing by the utility company. In new construction, much smaller chillers can often be specified for use in conjunction with the ice storage; the smaller chillers will provide constant full-load operation at their highest efficiency compared to larger units which will run sporadically and at lower efficiencies. Additionally, using primary air that is 10° to 12°F cooler than the usual 55°F requires much less airflow—air handlers, motors, ducts and pumps can often be downsized by 20-40%. These systems can increase total energy use at the site, even while reducing costs and peak demand. Though point-of-use energy savings may not occur, nighttime power generation and distribution by electric utilities may be significantly more efficient than in the daytime, resulting in a potentially significant overall energy savings.

Ice Bank Off-Peak Cooling System

CALMAC Manufacturing Corporation
3-00 Banta Place
Fair Lawn, NJ 07410

Phone: 201-797-1511
Fax: 201-797-1522
www.calmac.com

The Ice Bank® system uses off-peak electricity to make solid blocks of ice in large storage tanks to assist in cooling conditioned spaces and equipment during peak electrical demand periods. Building operating costs are lowered by reducing peak demand, though overall point-of-use electric use can be increased. Smaller chillers can often be specified for use in the system, providing efficient full-load operation; and using 44 degrees F primary air rather than the more usual 55 degrees F requires much less airflow—air handlers, motors, ducts and pumps can often be downsized by 20-40%.

Most recently mentioned in EBN 14:10

Ice Bear Off-Peak Cooling System

Ice Energy, LLC
9351 Eastman Park Dr.
Unit B
Windsor, CO 80550

Phone: 970-545-3630
Fax: 970-545-3634
www.ice-energy.com

The Ice Bear™ from Ice Energy™ is an off-peak thermal storage cooling system appropriate for use with split, mini-split, and packaged air-conditioning systems. It is a commercial product designed to accommodate small to medium-sized commercial buildings of less than 50,000 ft^2. The off-the-shelf system uses a 5-ton condensing unit to provide up to 50 ton-hours of capacity, and uses less than 300 on-peak watts to deliver cooling. The system can be optimized for peak demand reduction, energy conservation, or dehumidification. Installation may be performed by a local HVAC technician.

Most recently mentioned in EBN 14:10 & 14:12

23 72 00
Air-to-Air Energy Recovery Equipment

Heat-Recovery Ventilators (HRVs) and Energy-Recovery Ventilators (ERVs) are mechanical air-exchange systems that can capture up to 90% of the heat content from stale indoor air being exchanged for fresh outside air. These products work by passing the air streams through a heat-exchange core, generally made with multiple aluminum or plastic plates. HRVs capture heat from the outgoing air during heating season to warm the incoming air; and in cooling season, heat from the incoming air is transferred to the outgoing air to help prevent warming the building while providing fresh air. ERVs also provide humidity conditioning using a desiccant wheel or plates made of a permeable material; these help retain indoor moisture during the heating season and exclude it during the cooling season. The efficiency of the heat exchange is dependent on both the equipment and the climate. Most systems are balanced: the same volume of air is exhausted and taken in.

Enthalpy Wheels

Airxchange
85 Longwater Dr.
Rockland, MA 02370

Phone: 781-871-4816
Fax: 781-871-3029
www.airxchange.com

Airxchange makes enthalpy wheels that transfer heat and moisture between incoming and outgoing air streams in buildings. This energy recovery technology reduces heating, cooling, humidification and dehumidification loads. Airxchange wheels are available in a wide range of sizes and are packaged in a variety of mechanical systems, including energy recovery ventilators, accessories for unitary packaged equipment, integrated packages and standard air handlers from OEM manufacturers.

Heat Recovery Ventilators

American Aldes Ventilation Corp.
4537 Northgate Ct.
Sarasota, FL 34234

Toll-free: 800-255-7749
Phone: 941-351-3441
Fax: 941-351-3442
www.americanaldes.com

American Aldes Ventilation offers a wide range of engineered ventilation products, including Heat Recovery Ventilators (HRV) and Energy Recovery Ventilators (ERV). Their residential HRVs are designed for spaces ranging from 1,100 to 8,000 ft². The 200S residential ERV designed for climates with long cooling seasons and moderately cold winters, where the temperature remains above 0 degrees F. Commercial Heat/Energy Recovery Ventilators rated for 450-2900 CFM are also available.

Most recently mentioned in EBN 2:2

Aprilaire Energy Recovery Ventilator

Aprilaire
1015 E. Washington Ave.
P.O. Box 1467
Madison, WI 53701

Toll-free: 800-334-6011
Phone: 608-257-8801
Fax: 608-257-4357
www.aprilaire.com

The Aprilaire Energy Recovery Ventilator (formerly PerfectAire® Fresh Air Exchanger) uses an Energy Max® enthalpic-type air exchanger to recover approximately 77% of the heat in outgoing air and to control moisture, according to the company. Aprilaire also offers a full line of indoor air quality products, such as programmable thermostats, whole-house humidifiers, zoning, and high-efficiency air cleaners.

Energy Recovery Ventilator

BossAire Inc.
2929 West Park Drive
Owatonna, MN 55060

Phone: 507-446-5601
Fax: 507-451-9185
www.bossaire.com

BossAire manufactures ERVs for many sizes of residential buildings and for light commercial and industrial buildings.

Broan Fresh Air Systems

Broan-NuTone LLC
926 W. State St.
P.O. Box 140
Hartford, WI 53027

Toll-free: 800-558-1711
Phone: 262-673-4340
Fax: 262-673-8638
www.broan.com

Broan offers Fresh Air Systems ERVs and HRVs along with appropriate controls for enhancing indoor air quality while maintaining comfort and energy efficiency.

Ventilation Products

Fantech
1712 Northgate Blvd.
Sarasota, FL 34234

Toll-free: 800-747-1762
Phone: 506-743-9500
Fax: 800-487-9915
www.fantech.net

Fantech manufactures ventilation products with energy recovery cores for residential, commercial, and industrial buildings.

Perfect Window Fresh Air Ventilator

Honeywell Home & Building Controls
P.O. Box 524
Minneapolis, MN 55440

Toll-free: 800-328-5111
Phone: 612-951-1000
Fax: 763-954-5138
yourhome.honeywell.com

The Honeywell Perfect Window™ line of Fresh Air Ventilator Systems includes HRVs and ERVs.

Lossnay ERVs

Mitsubishi Electric Sales Canada Inc.
4299 14th Ave.
Markham, ON L3R 0J2

New

Phone: 905-475-7728
Fax: 905-475-5231
www.mitsubishielectric.ca

Mitsubishi Electric Canada, under the Lossnay brand, offers commercial and residential ERVs that can be installed as part of their City Multi product line, or as independently operating units. For light-commercial use, ceiling suspended mounting is available. Mitsubishi Electric also supplies the Lossnay ERV core to RenewAire for their products.

Enerboss HRV/Air Handler

Nu-Air Ventilation Systems
P.O. Box 2758
Windsor, NS B0N 2T0 Canada

Phone: 902-798-2261
Fax: 902-798-2557
www.nu-airventilation.com

The Enerboss integrated HRV/air handler for residential or light-commercial installations couples with a boiler to provide space heating and ventilation. With an optional evaporator coil, the Enerboss will couple with a split system's compressor to also meet cooling loads. A ½-hp ECM motor provides continuous circulating air and ventilation, and provides fresh air to the ERV. An independent exhaust fan serves the HRV. Circulating and ventilating air are filtered separately. The manufacturer claims 69% sensible recovery efficiency in continuous mode, and 71% at high speed. The heat output is 40,000 – 80,000 Btu/hr, and the design air temperature rise is 45°F. Electric draw (heating, 900 – 1150 cfm airflow) is 345 W; circulation draw, at 350 cfm, is 109 W.

Lifebreath Clean Air Furnace

Nutech Brands, Inc.
511 McCormick Blvd.
London, ON N5W 4C8 Canada

Phone: 519-457-1904
Fax: 800-494-4185
www.lifebreath.com

The Clean Air Furnace combines a Heat Recovery Ventilator with an Air Handler. The combination heating system provides constant ventilation and a steady stream of warm air to create a temperature-steady, healthy home environment. The combination heating system is available in hydronic

23 00 00
HVAC

or electric models, and offers up to 90% efficiency. Features include a high-efficiency ECM motor. Add-on cooling capacities range from 2 tons to 5 tons, with heating outputs ranging from 25,000 to 120,000 Btu/H (hydronic), and 17,000 to 75,000 Btu/H (electric).

Lifebreath Heat Recovery Ventilators

Nutech Brands, Inc.
511 McCormick Blvd.
London, ON N5W 4C8 Canada

Phone: 519-457-1904
Fax: 800-494-4185
www.lifebreath.com

Lifebreath residential HRVs range in capacity from 95 to 300 cfm. All have a high-efficiency aluminum heat exchanger core. Heat exchange effectiveness ranges from 80 to 90%, according to the company. Commercial models, designed to be integrated into HVAC systems, range in size from 500 to 2,500 cfm. Nutech also makes a 200 cfm Lifebreath for hot, humid climates that exchanges moisture in the core in addition to heat, reducing dehumidification costs.

RenewAire ERVs

RenewAire
4510 Helgesen Dr.
Madison, WI 53718

Toll-free: 800-627-4499
Phone: 608-221-4499
Fax: 608-221-2824
www.renewaire.com

RenewAire, formerly under the Lossnay name for Mitsubishi Electric, manufactures a full line of commercial and residential ERVs. Among the residential units, the EV 130 is rated at 130 cfm and the EV 200 is rated at 200 cfm with 73% and 76% energy recovery efficiencies, respectively. These units can be installed stand-alone or tied into a furnace.

Pinnacle

SEMCO Incorporated
1800 E. Pointe Dr.
Columbia, MO 65201

Toll-free: 888-473-6264
Phone: 573-443-1481
Fax: 573-443-6921
www.semcoinc.com

Semco's Pinnacle™ Primary Ventilation System controls temperature, ventilation, and humidity simultaneously, while reducing energy loads and providing high quantities of outdoor air. A passive dehumidification wheel that utilizes a desiccant material allows

for the delivery of extremely dry fresh air. This saves energy by allowing the cooling coil to operate closer to its optimum level. The unit includes a total energy recovery wheel, which is used to precondition fresh air using the exhausted building air. This fresh air is then further treated by the cooling coil and passive dehumidification wheel.

UltimateAir RecoupAerator

Stirling Technology, Inc.
178 Mill St.
Athens, OH 45701

Toll-free: 800-535-3448
Phone: 740-594-2277
Fax: 740-592-1499
www.ultimateair.com

The UltimateAir™ RecoupAerator® 200DX ERV system from Stirling Technology has a heat-recovery efficiency of up to 96% and employs a brushless DC, high-efficiency, variable-speed, ECPM motor. The system efficiently delivers 70 ft³ per minute (cfm) using 34 watts to 210 cfm using 200 watts. The low-cfm efficiency is the highest in the industry, owing to the ECPM motor. The system comes with washable MERV 8 filters and a five-year warranty. Optional features include an economizer module; a CO2 sensor that boosts airflow when carbon dioxide levels are elevated; a pressure sensor that reacts to maintain the owner-set indoor pressure; and HEPA (high-efficiency particulate air) filtration (which increases electrical use significantly). A window unit appropriate for single offices and apartments, Model SW-120, is also available.

Most recently mentioned in EBN 13:12 & 14:12

AquaMaster Q100

Vebteck Research

For full listing, see CSI section 23 52 00 - Heating Boilers

AVS Solo and AVS Duo

Venmar Ventilation Inc.
550 Lemire Blvd.
Drummondville, QC J2C 7W9 Canada

Toll-free: 800-567-3855
Phone: 819-477-6226
Fax: 819-475-2660
www.venmar.ca

Previously known as VanEE, Venmar is the leading manufacturer of advanced ventilation equipment. The company manufactures energy-efficient ventilation equipment including enthalpic wheels, HRVs, and ERVs. Venmar's residential products include the AVS Solo, an HRV, and the AVS Duo, an ERV,

meaning that it also reclaims moisture in the air stream. The company offers an extensive line of controls for maintaining comfortable, healthy indoor environments.

23 76 00 Evaporative Air-Cooling Equipment

It takes heat to evaporate moisture, so if a space can tolerate added humidity, direct evaporative cooling is an easy way to convert hot, dry air into cooler, more humid air. In other situations, indirect evaporative cooling may be an option. Evaporative condenser systems use significantly less water than cooling towers and can improve energy efficiency dramatically (particularly in dry climates), since the compressors operate at lower condensing temperatures. (See also 23 81 44 - Heat Pumps, 23 81 43 - Air-Source Unitary Heat Pumps, 23 81 46 - Water-Source Unitary Heat Pumps.)

Coolerado

Coolerado, LLC
4700 W. 60th Ave., Unit 3
Arvada, CO 80003

Phone: 303-375-0878
Fax: 303-375-1693
www.coolerado.com

The Coolerado Cooler is an all-indirect system that, like other evaporative air conditioners, relies on the latent heat of vaporization for cooling. Unlike other systems, the Coolorado does not introduce moisture into the building, and thus can be used in conjunction with conventional compression-cycle air conditioning. The Coolerado R600 delivers four to six tons of cooling with electricity consumption of 1,200 watts—750 watts if specified with an electronically commutated motor (ECM). Water consumption is comparable to or slightly lower than that of direct evaporative coolers—as much as 12 gallons per hour at peak load, but typically averaging about 4 gallons per hour over the cooling season.

Most recently mentioned in EBN 15:12

SolCool V4 Hybrid Air Conditioner

GPM, Inc.

For full listing, see CSI section 23 81 00 - Decentralized Unitary HVAC Equipment

23 00 00
HVAC

Evaporative Condenser Rooftop System

McQuay International
13600 Industrial Park Blvd.
Minneapolis, MN 55441

Toll-free: 800-432-1342
Fax: 763-553-5177
www.mcquay.com

The RoofPak™ evaporative condenser rooftop unit is available in seven sizes, from 75 to 150 tons. Evaporative condenser systems use significantly less water than cooling towers and can improve energy efficiency dramatically (particularly in dry climates); since the compressors operate at lower condensing temperatures, 25-40% less electricity is consumed than in comparable air-cooled units. Some water treatment maintenance is required, and seasonal drainbacks are necessary in freezing climates where rooftop mechanicals are unheated. Theoretical evaporative water consumption is expected to be 1.8 gallons per operating cooling-ton hour; blow-down requirements depend on local water quality but are expected to be 33-50% of theoretical evaporative water consumption.

23 81 00
Decentralized Unitary HVAC Equipment

The two most important issues with compressor-based cooling systems are energy efficiency and potential ozone depletion from refrigerants. Most unitary equipment now uses R-22, an HCFC, as the refrigerant. This refrigerant is slated for phaseout by 2020. A few units use HFC refrigerants, which do not affect the ozone layer but are greenhouse gases that contribute to global warming if released to the atmosphere. Seasonal energy efficiency ratio (SEER) ratings compare cooling capacity (in Btu) to energy inputs (in watts) and are helpful in evaluating central air-conditioner performance. One ton of cooling capacity represents the ability to remove 12,000 Btu of heat per hour. Also consider the moisture-removal capability of air-conditioning equipment. (See also 23 81 44 - Heat Pumps, 23 81 43 - Air-Source Unitary Heat Pumps, 23 81 46 - Water-Source Unitary Heat Pumps.) (See feature articles EBN Vol. 3, No. 3 & Vol. 6, No. 2.)

Allegiance 18

American Standard Heating and Air Conditioning
6200 Troup Hwy.
Tyler, TX 75711

New

Toll-free: 888-556-0125
Phone: 903-581-3499
Fax: 903-581-3280
www.americanstandardair.com

American Standard (the parent company of Trane) offers the Allegiance® 18 Ultra Efficiency Air Conditioner with a variable-speed fan and Dual Duration™ compressors that provide two-stage cooling: a smaller compressor handles most of the work, but on the hottest days a larger compressor takes over. With a SEER rating of up to 18.9, these are among the highest-efficiency central air conditioners available. They are available in 2.5 to 5 tons, and have a ten-year warranty. These units use ozone-depleting R-22 refrigerant.

Infinity Central Air Conditioners

Carrier Corp.
Carrier Parkway
P.O. Box 4808
Syracuse, NY 13221

Toll-free: 800-227-7437
Phone: 315-432-6000
Fax: 315-432-6620
www.carrier.com

The Infinity™ line from Carrier includes the company's most efficient central air conditioner, with SEER ratings from 16 to 21. These 2- to 5-ton, two-speed units use Carrier's Puron refrigerant (R-410a), which is a blend of three different HFCs. Carrier offers a 5-year limited warranty on parts, and a 10-year limited warranty on the compressor.

Most recently mentioned in EBN 4:1, 6:2, 8:1, 13:2

SolCool V4 Hybrid Air Conditioner

GPM, Inc.
525 Amigos Drive, Ste. 5
Redlands, CA 92373

Toll-free: 888-476-5266
Phone: 909-747-0300
Fax: 909-747-0311
www.solcool.net

SolCool V4 is a 24 volt DC HVAC System that uses two DC compressors powered by an internal lithium battery bank offering up to 36 hours of autonomy. It is available in packaged or portable versions that can operate with any DC or US/EU grid power input. The

3-speed DC blower has a top output of 700 CFM that can overcome 1.5 pounds of static pressure. Condensate drains to an onboard holding tank, then pumped to drainage or filtration. The 2' x 2' x 4', 200-pound unit uses R-134A refrigerant and can deliver up to 18,000 Btu, (1.5 tons) of cooling and 12,000 Btus of heat during its two-stage process. In most climates, the manufacturer claims one-quarter the energy consumption of a conventional air conditioning system. DC ceiling fan and light options can be powered directly from the SolCool.

XC21 Air Conditioners

Lennox Industries, Inc.
2100 Lake Park Blvd.
Richardson, TX 75080

Toll-free: 800-953-6669
Phone: 972-497-5000
www.lennox.com

XC21 Air Conditioner uses non-ozone-depleting R410A refrigerant, and with models up to 20.50 SEER, it's one of the highest-rated central air conditioning units available. It carries a 10-year limited compressor warranty, and a 5-year limited warranty on covered components. Though it is non-ozone-depleting, HFC refrigerant R410A is a significant greenhouse gas that, like HCFC, contributes to global warming.

Rheem RASL Prestige Series

Rheem Manufacturing Company
101 Bell Rd.
Montgomery, AL 36117

New

Toll-free: 800-432-8373
Phone: 334-260-1500
www.rheem.com

The RASL Prestige Series from Rheem features ozone-safe R-410A refrigerant and SEER ratings up to 18. The manufacturer uses durable Copeland® Scroll® compressors and on-board safety circuitry to protect against damage cause by improper refrigerant levels. Certain models employ two-speed ECM fan motors. The nominal size is 3 ton (10.5 kW). An on-demand dehumidification terminal can be matched with an optional air handler for greater humidity control. This product is offered with a ten-year warranty.

XL19i Air Conditioners

Trane Residential Systems
6200 Troup Hwy.
Tyler, TX 75707

Phone: 903-581-3200
www.trane.com

23 00 00
HVAC

Trane's 2.5-ton XL19i two-stage air conditioner is a highly efficient unit which, when coupled with an optional air-handler, achieves a SEER rating of up to 19.5. The 3-ton unit, with the optional air-handler, is rated up to SEER 19; the 4- and 5-ton units, similarly enhanced, can deliver 17 and 16.5 SEER, respectively. The XL19i uses R-22 refrigerant. The manufacturer's limited warranty covers compressor, coil, and internal functional parts for 10 years.

Affinity 8T Air Conditioner

York International Corp.
5005 York Dr.
Unitary Products Group
Norman, OK 73069

Toll-free: 877-874-7378
Phone: 405-364-4040
Fax: 405-419-6545
www.yorkupg.com

The Affinity 8T Series line offers up to 18-SEER residential systems in sizes ranging from 2 to 5 tons. The quiet, two-stage design allows improved part-load efficiency; increased demand triggers full capacity. These units are available with R-410A refrigerant. The compressor has a ten-year warranty; the parts warranty is five years.

23 81 44
Heat Pumps

Heat pumps are similar to air conditioners—but in addition to removing heat, they can reverse their cycle to pump heat into a building when needed. Heat pumps use electricity as the energy input; the heat source is the outside air, the ground, or a body of water. Air-source heat pumps use the outdoor air as the heat source or heat sink. Air-source heat pump heating efficiency is measured as the Heating Seasonal Performance Factor (HSPF), which is the ratio of thermal energy output (in Btu) to electrical energy input (in watt-hours) over a heating season. Similarly derived, the cooling performance of air-source heat pumps is typically measured as the seasonal energy efficiency rating (SEER). Ground-source heat pumps utilize the earth's more stable temperatures as the heat source and heat sink; performance is typically measured as the coefficient of performance (COP)—the instantaneous

ratio of energy input in Btus to energy output in Btus. Since the temperatures are usually more moderate underground, geothermal systems typically cost less to operate than conventional heat pumps. Water-source heat pumps are like ground-source heat pumps but use a body of water as the heat source and sink. Some heat pumps can provide water heating in addition to heating and cooling. (See also 23 76 00 - Evaporative Air-Cooling Equipment.) (See feature article EBN Vol. 9, No. 7.)

Heritage Heat Pumps

American Standard Heating and Air Conditioning **New**
6200 Troup Hwy.
Tyler, TX 75711

Toll-free: 888-556-0125
Phone: 903-581-3499
Fax: 903-581-3280
www.americanstandardair.com

American Standard (the parent company of Trane) offers the Heritage® line of heat pumps. They use a variable-speed fan and Dual Duration™ compressors that provide two-stage cooling: a smaller compressor handles most of the work, but on the hottest days a larger compressor takes over. With SEER ratings of up to 18.9, and HSPF ratings up to 9, these are among the highest-efficiency air-sourced heat pumps available. They are available in 1.5 to 5 tons, and have a ten-year warranty. Some units use ozone-depleting R-22 refrigerant; others use ozone-safe R410A.

Quantum Plus 698b Heat Pump

Bryant Heating & Cooling Systems
7310 W. Morris St.
Indianapolis, IN 46231

Toll-free: 800-428-4326
Phone: 317-243-0851
Fax: 315-428-4326
www.bryant.com

Bryant produces the Quantum Plus™ 698b heat pump using non-ozone-depleting Puron™ refrigerant. The heat pump features a quiet fan and pump, two speeds, a SEER rating of 16, HSPF of 8.5, plus a 10-year warranty on the compressor and 5 years on everything else. The 650A heat pump also uses Puron™ refrigerant, has a SEER of 13.0 to 14.5, and the same warranty as the 698b.

Infinity Heat Pumps

Carrier Corp.
Carrier Parkway
P.O. Box 4808
Syracuse, NY 13221

Toll-free: 800-227-7437
Phone: 315-432-6000
Fax: 315-432-6620
www.carrier.com

The Infinity™ line of heat pumps from Carrier has SEER ratings up to 16.5, and up to 8.7 HSPF. These 2- to 5-ton, two-speed units use Carrier's Puron ozone-safe R-410a refrigerant, which is a blend of three different HFCs. Carrier offers a 5-year limited warranty on parts, and a 10-year limited warranty on the compressor.

Ground-Source Heat Pumps

ClimateMaster
7300 S.W. 44th St.
Oklahoma City, OK 73179

Toll-free: 800-299-9747
Phone: 405-745-6000
Fax: 405-745-6058
www.climatemaster.com

ClimateMaster is one of the largest producers of ground-source heat pumps.
Most recently mentioned in EBN 9:7

Ground-Source Heat Pumps

ECONAR Energy Systems Corp.
19230 Evans St.
Elk River, MN 55330

Toll-free: 800-432-6627
Phone: 763-241-3110
Fax: 763-241-3111
www.econar.com

The ColdClimate™ GeoSource® 2000 line of ground-source heat pumps are designed for residential (1 to 6 tons) and commercial (8 to 10 tons) applications. These self-contained units have a 25 degrees F design point for regions with higher numbers of heating degree days per year.

Water-Source Heat Pump

FHP Manufacturing
601 N.W. 65th Ct.
Ft. Lauderdale, FL 33309

Phone: 954-776-5471
Fax: 954-776-5529
www.fhp-mfg.com

The EV and ES Two Stage Series EnviroMiser water-source heat pump is among FHP's most efficient and one of the first ground-source/water-source heat pumps to use the non-ozone-depleting refrigerant R-410a, an HFC mixture.

23 00 00
HVAC

Hallowell All Climate Heat Pump

New

Hallowell International
110 Hildreth St.
Bangor, ME 04401

Phone: 207-990-5600
Fax: 207-990-5602
www.gotohallowell.com

Hallowell's All Climate Heat Pump is a multistage air source heat pump that uses patented Opti-Cycle technology to allow the system to continue its heating performance well below zero degrees without the use of resistance heat backup. Its performance rivals many geothermal heat pumps. The Hallowell heat pump uses non-ozone-depleting refrigerant R-410a and cooling mode operation efficiency is comparable to many dedicated unitary air conditioners.

Most recently mentioned in EBN 13:7, 13:12, 14:10, 15:12

XP19 Heat Pump

Lennox Industries, Inc.
2100 Lake Park Blvd.
Richardson, TX 75080

Toll-free: 800-953-6669
Phone: 972-497-5000
www.lennox.com

The XP19 heat pump has a two-stage operation that saves energy by running at low speed 80% of the time. The XP19 uses non-ozone-depleting R410A refrigerant and at 18.6 SEER (cooling) and 9.3 HSPF (heating), it's one of the highest-rated heat pumps available. It carries a 10-year limited compressor warranty and a 5-year limited warranty on covered components. Though HFC refrigerant R410A is non-ozone-depleting, it, like HCFC, is a significant greenhouse gas that contributes to global warming.

Cold Climate Heat Pump

Nyle Special Products, LLC
P.O. Box 1107
Bangor, ME 04402

Phone: 207-942-2865
Fax: 207-942-2859
www.nyletherm.com

The multiple-stage Cold Climate Heat Pump™ (CCHP) from Nyle Special Products rivals many geothermal heat pumps in performance, achieving an average coefficient of performance (COP) of 2.7. In cooling mode, its seasonal energy efficiency ratio (SEER) is 16, higher than most dedicated unitary air conditioners. Its HSPF is 9.6. The system was designed to take full advantage of the non-ozone-depleting refrigerant R-410a, which can withstand up to 70% higher pressure and has 40% better cooling

capacity than R-22 (which is scheduled to be phased out in the U.S. in 2010).

Most recently mentioned in EBN 13:7, 13:12, 14:10, 15:12

XL Series Heat Pump

Trane Residential Systems
6200 Troup Hwy.
Tyler, TX 75707

Phone: 903-581-3200
www.trane.com

Trane's Weatherton® XL Series of dual-compressor, air-source heat pumps have up to 17.9 SEER (cooling value), and up to 9.05 HSPF (heating value). They are available in 1.5- to 5-ton units. The manufacturer's limited warranty covers compressor, coil, and internal functional parts for 10 years. Some units use ozone-depleting R22 refrigerant; others use R410A.

Ground-Source Heat Pumps

WaterFurnace International, Inc.
9000 Conservation Way
Fort Wayne, IN 46809

Toll-free: 800-222-5667
Phone: 260-478-5667
Fax: 260-478-3029
www.waterfurnace.com

WaterFurnace International manufactures and distributes E Series, Premier, and Versatec commercial, institutional, and residential lines of ground-source geothermal heat pumps for retrofit or new construction. WaterFurnace produces both water-to-air and water-to-water units with 3/4- to 30-ton capacities. E Series line uses R410-A refrigerant that does not deplete the ozone layer. Wholly owned subsidiary LoopMaster, Inc. is an earth loop contractor.

Most recently mentioned in EBN 9:7

Affinity 8T Heat Pump

New

York International Corp.
5005 York Dr.
Unitary Products Group
Norman, OK 73069

Toll-free: 877-874-7378
Phone: 405-364-4040
Fax: 405-419-6545
www.yorkupg.com

The Affinity 8T line of heat pumps from York offers up to 18 SEER (cooling) and 9.4 HSPF (heating) in sizes ranging from 2 to 5 tons. The quiet, two-stage design allows improved part-load efficiency; increased demand triggers full capacity. These units are available with non-ozone-depleting R-410A refrigerant. The compressor has a ten-year warranty; the parts warranty is five years.

23 82 00
Convection Heating and Cooling Units

In highly energy-efficient homes and small commercial buildings, it is often possible to satisfy all heating demands with space heaters rather than a central, distributed heating system. Products listed here include high-efficiency, quiet space heaters.

Space Heaters

Monitor Products, Inc.
P.O. Box 3408
Princeton, NJ 08543

Toll-free: 800-524-1102
Phone: 732-329-0900
Fax: 732-329-0904
www.monitorproducts.com

Monitor space heaters are gas-, LPG-, or kerosene-fired, direct-vented, through-the-wall units with 83% efficiencies.

Energy Saver Ductless Heater

Rinnai
103 International Dr.
Peachtree City, GA 30269

Toll-free: 800-621-9419
Phone: 678-829-1700
Fax: 678-364-8643
www.rinnai.us

The EnergySaver by Rinnai is an 84%-efficient, sealed-combustion space heater. It is 20% more efficient than typical American through-the-wall gas space heaters.

Most recently mentioned in EBN 11:1

Laser Vented Heaters

Toyotomi U.S.A., Inc.
604 Federal Rd.
Brookfield, CT 06804

Phone: 203-775-1909
Fax: 203-775-6330
www.toyotomiusa.com

The four models in the sealed-combustion Laser kerosene heater line from Toyotomi offer heating efficiencies ranging from 90 to 93% (AFUE rating of 87.7%) while providing outputs from 5,200 to 40,000 Btu/hr. The units have heat-circulation fans and require 120-volt AC power, generating a preheating load of 260-280 watts, and a burning load of 42-76 watts. An external fuel tank is usually required. Units feature electronic ignition (no pilot light), setback thermostat, automatic safety shutoff, and power failure recovery. The cabinet stays cool to the touch.

23 00 00
HVAC

Oil Miser Space Heaters

Toyotomi U.S.A., Inc.
604 Federal Rd.
Brookfield, CT 06804

Phone: 203-775-1909
Fax: 203-775-6330
www.toyotomiusa.com

The only oil-fired, sealed-combustion space-heating system in North America, Oil Miser model OM-22 from Toyotomi has an AFUE rating of 90%, with output ranging from 8,000 to 22,000 Btu/hr. An external fuel tank is required (No. 1 or No. 2 fuel oil). The unit has a heat-circulation fan and requires 120-volt AC power for a preheating load of 275 watts and a burning load of 46 watts. Units feature setback thermostat, automatic safety shutoff, and power failure recovery. The cabinet stays cool to the touch.

Most recently mentioned in EBN 13:3

23 83 00
Radiant Heating Units

Products listed here include high-performance panel radiators. (See also 04 57 00 - Masonry Fireplaces.)

Hydronic Panel Radiators

Buderus
50 Wentworth Ave.
Londonderry, NH 03053

Toll-free: 800-283-3787
Phone: 603-552-1100
Fax: 603-584-1681
www.buderus.net

Buderus Solidoflux-N panel radiators deliver hydronic heat and may interfere with furniture placement less than baseboard radiators. Panel radiators are available in heights of 12", 20", and 24" and depths of 2-1/2" and 4". They can be fitted with optional individual thermostats and diverter valves to provide individual zoning. Flexible PEX polyethylene piping can be used in place of copper.

Hydronic Panel Radiators

Runtal North America
187 Neck Rd.
P.O. Box 8278
Ward Hill, MA 01835

Toll-free: 800-526-2621
Phone: 978-373-1666
Fax: 978-372-7140
www.runtalnorthamerica.com

Runtal panel and baseboard radiators are designed to operate at lower temperatures than conventional hydronic radiators (convectors). Therefore, a high percentage of the heat will be delivered through radiation rather than convection. The room's mean radiant temperature may be higher, and the thermostat set point (air temperature) can be kept somewhat lower with comparable comfort. Thus, some energy savings can be achieved. Runtal also manufactures the Omnipanel® radiator for bathrooms, which provides additional radiator area. The company's electric Omnipanel may be justified if its use allows whole-house thermostats to be kept lower. Runtal is a Swiss company.

23 84 00
Humidity Control Equipment

Many of the most significant indoor air quality problems in buildings relate to moisture. While preventing rain penetration, plumbing leaks, wicking of moisture from the soil, and unvented moisture sources are the top priorities, it is sometimes also necessary to remove unwanted moisture from indoor air. Products listed here include high-efficiency dehumidification products.

Sante Fe, Ultra-Aire, and Hi-E Dry Dehumidifiers

Therma-Stor LLC
P.O. Box 8050
Madison, WI 53708

Toll-free: 800-533-7533
Phone: 608-222-5301
Fax: 608-222-1447
www.thermastor.com

Therma-Stor manufactures a range of high-efficiency dehumidifiers for residential and commercial use. Residential products include the Sante Fe and Ultra-Aire APD (air purifying dehumidifier), which provide air filtration in addition to dehumidification. For commercial applications, Therma-Stor offers the Hi-E Dry line of dehumidifiers.

This Space is Available for Your Notes

23 00 00
HVAC

26 00 00 Electrical

PRODUCT LISTINGS

26 01 51
Electrical Component Recycling

Fluorescent and HID lamps and older magnetic ballasts contain hazardous materials that should be disposed of in an environmentally responsible manner. Fluorescent and HID lamps contain mercury, and pre-1970 ballasts contain polychlorinated biphenyls (PCBs). The quantity of mercury in a fluorescent lamp is small (a few grams), while about an ounce of PCB was typically used in every pre-1970 ballast. Both substances are very persistent in the environment, bioaccumulating in animal tissues. Bioaccumulated mercury levels in fish can be 250,000 times as high as in the surrounding environment. Human health risks associated with these toxins include neurological, reproductive, and liver disorders. Recycling services are equipped to recycle and reprocess fluorescent and HID lamps and ballasts safely without releasing these toxins into the environment. Before sending fluorescent lamps and ballasts to out-of-town recycling facilities, check with your local solid-waste agency; many handle lamps and ballast disposal through toxic waste recycling programs. (See feature article EBN Vol. 6, No. 9.)

Fluorescent and HID Lamp Recycling

AERC.com, Inc.
30677 Huntwood Ave.
Hayward, CA 94544

Toll-free: 800-628-3675
Phone: 510-429-1129
Fax: 510-429-1498
www.aercrecycling.com

AERC.com, Inc. recycles spent fluorescent and High Intensity Discharge lamps. Their technology recovers mercury and other metals from the lamps, then segregates the glass, metal end caps, and phosphor powder for further recycling and reuse.

Fluorescent Lamp and Ballast Recycling

Ecolights Northwest
1915 Corgiat Dr.
P.O. Box 94291
Seattle, WA 98124

Phone: 206-343-1247
Fax: 206-343-7445
www.ecolights.com

Ecolights Northwest provides storage/shipping containers, transportation, handling documents, and final recycling for fluorescent and HID lamps and fluorescent ballasts. Ecolights Northwest is sister company to Total Reclaim, Inc., which offers CFC reclamation/recycling, as well as electronic and battery recycling programs.

Fluorescent Lamp and Ballast Recycling

Environmental Light Recyclers, Inc.
2737 Bryan Ave.
Fort Worth, TX 76104

Toll-free: 800-755-4117
Phone: 817-924-9300
Fax: 817-924-9380

Environmental Light Recyclers safely processes used fluorescent and HID lamps and ballasts. ELR handles both PCB ballasts and non-PCB, DEHP-containing magnetic ballasts. Certificates of Recycling are provided to ELR's customers as protection against hazardous materials liabilities.

Fluorescent Lamp and Ballast Recycling

HTR-Group
P.O. Box 185
Lake Ozark, MO 65049

Toll-free: 888-537-4874
Phone: 537-302-7575
Fax: 573-302-7579
www.htr-group.com

HTR-Group is a resource-recovery facility for mercury-containing lamps and for ballasts. The company maintains a fleet of vehicles covering the entire U.S. for material pick up and a 4-acre recycling facility with a processing capacity of 1,500,000 lamps per month. Certificates of Recycle are provided as protection against hazardous materials liabilities. HTR-Group recycles 100% of all lamp parts.

Fluorescent Lamp and Ballast Recycling

Northeast Lamp Recycling, Inc.
250 Main St.
P.O. Box 680
East Windsor, CT 06088

Toll-free: 888-657-5267
Phone: 860-292-1992
Fax: 860-292-1114
www.nlrlamp.com

Northeast Lamp Recycling (NCR) is a licensed hazardous waste transporter operating a fluorescent and HID lamp and ballast recycling facility. NCR separates lamp components of glass, metal, mercury, and phosphor powder for recycling and reuse. Certificates of Recycling are issued as protection against hazardous materials liabilities.

Fluorescent Lamp and Ballast Recycling

Veolia Environmental Services
125 S. 84th St., Ste. 200
Milwaukee, WI 53214

Toll-free: 800-556-5267
Phone: 414-479-7800
Fax: 414-479-7400
veoliaes.com

Veolia Environmental Services (formerly Onyx Electronics Recycling Division), is one of the world's largest recyclers of fluorescent and HID lamps and other items containing toxic and hazardous materials. Packaging and pick-ups are available for some items, including lamps, ballasts, computer and electronic equipment, batteries, and electrical equipment containing PCBs. For prepaid recycling, visit www.onyxpak.com

26 05 00
Common Work Results for Electrical

Penetrations in exterior walls—such as dryer vents and electrical service entrances—are common sources of air infiltration into buildings. Standard electrical boxes, although they don't penetrate the exterior of the building envelope, can be significant sources of

air leakage. Products included here are airtight electrical boxes designed for use in exterior walls.

Air-Vapor Barrier Box

Low Energy Systems Supply Co., Inc.
W. 1330 Happy Hollow Rd.
Campbellsport, WI 53010

Phone: 920-533-8690
Fax: 920-533-3306
www.lessco-airtight.com

Low Energy Systems Supply Co. (LESSCO) manufactures special boxes in which electrical receptacle boxes can be mounted. Caulk sealant is used to seal the wire penetrations into the LESSCO box, and contractor's tape is used to seal box flanges to the air barrier (polyurethane film).

26 09 00
Instrumentation and Control for Electrical Systems

Optimizing lighting systems is a complex task involving daylighting and building design issues, careful lamp and fixture selection, and advanced lighting control. The environmental and financial benefits can be significant. Well-designed systems provide high-quality light where and when it's needed, with reduced energy consumption and maintenance costs. Lighting control systems can be as basic as a bathroom light occupancy sensor or as complex as a whole-building, computer-controlled energy management system that handles lighting, HVAC equipment, and sometimes other functions, such as security. (See feature articles EBN Vol. 8, No. 9, Vol. 8, No. 10, Vol. 12, No. 6.)

Douglas Lighting Controls

Douglas Lighting Controls
4455 Juneau St.
Burnaby, BC V5C 4C4 Canada

Toll-free: 877-873-2797
Phone: 604-873-2797
Fax: 604-873-6939
www.douglaslightingcontrols.com

Douglas Lighting Controls produces centralized switching controls for commercial buildings. Douglas controls use an advanced two-wire latching relay in which low-voltage wiring controls switching. Such inputs as occupancy sensors, photosensors, time clocks, and manual switches can feed into the centralized relay panels.

Occupancy-Based Energy Management

New

Energex Inc.
911-6081 No. 3 Rd.
Three West Centre
Richmond, BC V6Y 2B8 Canada

Toll-free: 866-787-1836
Phone: 604-214-7810
Fax: 604-214-7814
www.energexinc.com

Energex provides sensor-based HVAC and lighting energy management applications for hotels and commercial buildings. Using infrared occupancy sensing with logic-control software, the system switches to "conservation" mode when no occupancy is detected for 30 minutes. Room temperature is restored within five minutes when occupancy occurs. HVAC and lighting costs may be reduced by as much as 45%, according to the manufacturer, while contributing to increased equipment life and noise reduction. Savings are highly dependent on occupancy patterns. A two-year warranty is offered. The Energex technology has been tested and approved by organizations such as BC Hydro, NYSERDA, PG&E, and Quebec Hydro, according to Energex Inc.

LightHAWK-MT

Hubbell Building Automation, Inc.
9601 Dessau Rd., Bldg. 1
Austin, TX 78754

Toll-free: 888-698-3242
Phone: 512-450-1100
Fax: 512-450-1215
www.hubbell-automation.com

The LightHAWK-MT™ occupancy sensor combines passive infrared, ultrasonic, and photocell sensors in one unit to optimize lighting control for energy savings. Hubbell Building Automation, Inc., which was formed by the joining of Mytech Corporation and Unenco, produces a full line of occupancy sensors and controls.

Decora Wall Switch Occupancy Sensors

Leviton Manufacturing Co. Ltd.
59-25 Little Neck Pkwy.
Little Neck, NY 11362

Toll-free: 800-323-8920
Phone: 718-229-4040
Fax: 718-631-6508
www.leviton.com

Decora® Wall Switch Occupancy Sensors are passive infrared sensors that control lighting based upon detected motion. Leviton manufactures wall- and ceiling-mounted, infrared and ultrasonic, commercial and residential occupancy sensors, and lighting control systems.

microWATT and PerSONNA Systems

Lutron Electronics Co., Inc.
7200 Suter Rd.
Coopersburg, PA 18036

Toll-free: 888-588-7661
Phone: 610-282-3800
Fax: 610-282-3090
www.lutron.com

Lutron Electronics is a leading manufacturer of lighting control systems including the microWATT™ and PerSONNA™ product lines. MicroWATT is an automated control system that computes proper light levels based upon daylight intensity, occupant sensors, and timed schedules. MicroWATT is also available in digital web-based format that offers power consumption monitoring, server-based options, etc. PerSONNA is a wireless infrared control system for dimming of electronically ballasted fluorescent fixtures.

Occupancy Sensors

Novitas, Inc.
203 Cooper Circle
Peachtree City, GA 30269

Toll-free: 866-853-4293
Phone: 770-631-2100
Fax: 770-486-2494
www.novitas.com

Novitas manufactures occupancy sensors for many applications of commercial building lighting and HVAC control.

Sensor Switch Occupancy Sensors

Sensor Switch, Inc.
900 Northrop Rd.
Wallingford, CT 06492

Toll-free: 800-727-7483
Phone: 203-265-2842
Fax: 203-269-9621
www.sensorswitch.com

Sensor Switch, Inc. is a leading manufacturer of passive infrared (PIR) and passive dual-technology (PDT) occupancy sensor and photosensor daylighting controls for lighting. Products are available for both commercial and residential applications. PDT combines PIR with sound detection, providing four times the detection reliability, according to the company, and enabling lights to be reactivated by voice if the lights accidentally go out. Sensor Switch also offers a sensor that works on all electrical systems worldwide with a 20-year guaranteed life. Manufactured in the U.S.

Most recently mentioned in EBN 12:6

Starfield Networked Lighting Controls

Starfield Controls, Inc.
1321 W. 121st Ave.
Westminster, CO 80234

Phone: 303-427-1661
Fax: 303-255-0701
www.starfieldcontrols.com

Starfield Controls is the leading U.S. supplier of advanced whole-building digital lighting controls that rely on the recently introduced Digital Addressable Lighting Interface (DALI) protocol for ballasts. The company produces simplified "Bus" wiring for two-wire lighting networks that allow distributed control architecture—eliminating the need for central panels and "home-run" zone wiring.

Most recently mentioned in EBN 12:6

Isolé Plug Load Control

Watt Stopper/Legrand
2800 De La Cruz Blvd.
Santa Clara, CA 95050

Toll-free: 800-879-8585
Phone: 408-988-5331
Fax: 408-988-5373
www.wattstopper.com

The Isolé IDP-3050 Plug Load Control from The Watt Stopper consists of an eight-outlet power strip with surge protection and a passive infra-red (PIR) personal occupancy sensor. The occupancy sensor controls six of the eight outlets and is recommended for computer monitors, task lights, printers, personal electric space heaters, and fans. Computers and fax machines should be plugged into uncontrolled outlets.

Most recently mentioned in EBN 12:6

Occupancy Sensors and Lighting Controls

Watt Stopper/Legrand
2800 De La Cruz Blvd.
Santa Clara, CA 95050

Toll-free: 800-879-8585
Phone: 408-988-5331
Fax: 408-988-5373
www.wattstopper.com

Watt Stopper/Legrand manufactures occupancy sensors and controls for lighting and HVAC equipment in commercial and residential buildings. Products include

automatic wall switches, ceiling- and wall-mount sensors, outdoor motion sensors, and sensors for special applications. They include a range of sensing technologies, such as passive infrared, ultrasonic, and dual technology. In addition, Watt Stopper/Legrand manufactures lighting control panels, daylighting controls, bi-level HID controls, and plug load controls.

26 22 00
Low-Voltage Transformers

Electrical transformers provide voltage matching and conditioning for incoming grid power. Large commercial facilities will typically have 6-10 low-voltage transformers. According to the EPA, transformers waste 60-80 billion kWh each year—the equivalent of nine days of generating capacity in the U.S. A proposed rule from the DOE emphasizes the need to give lifecycle considerations weight; until such a rule is adopted, several states are requiring adherence to the National Electrical Manufacturers Association (NEMA) TP1 efficiency standard for transformers, which considers both core and load losses. Energy Star's voluntary Commercial and Industrial Transformer Program also uses this standard as its starting point. Products included here must exceed the TP1 standard by at least 20%.

Powersmiths T1000 and e-Saver C3 Transformers

Powersmiths International Corp.
8400 Esters Blvd., Ste. 140
Irving, TX 75063

Toll-free: 866-929-0770
Phone: 905-791-1493
Fax: 972-929-0977
www.powersmiths.com

The T1000 is a 3-phase common-core, copper-wound, dry-type transformer that exceeds the Energy Star™ threshold by 20%. Sizes range from 15 to 750 kVa. Internal structural and acoustic treatments reduce operating noise significantly below industry standards. On-site metering options facilitate commissioning. A 25-year warranty is offered. With similar attributes, the e-Saver C3 is a low-voltage distribution transformer that can be use-optimized to take advantage of efficient peak loading. These transformers are built to ISO 14001 standards, demon-

strating the manufacturer's commitment to environmental improvement.

26 27 13
Electricity Metering

Electrical metering equipment provides valuable diagnostic information on building energy loads and usage, from plug loads to whole building energy systems. Some products in this section are also specifically designed to be educational tools.

Brand Digital Power Meter

Brand Electronics
421 Hilton Rd.
Whitefield, ME 04353

Toll-free: 888-433-6600
Phone: 207-549-3401
Fax: 207-549-4568
www.brandelectronics.com

The Brand Digital Power Meter monitors energy usage of 120-volt AC plug loads (up to 1,850 watts). It calculates instantaneous watts, accumulated kWh, and monthly cost. The higher-end models also display peak demand, power factor, and volt-amps, and are capable of datalogging and transferring data to a PC (Win 95/98/XP). Other models are available for multichannel metering, including 240-volt and DC channels. All models measure accurate (+/-2%) wattage—including power factor—by sampling volts and amps at 4 kHz.

Watts up?

Electronic Educational Devices, Inc.
2345 S. Lincoln St.
Denver, CO 80210

Toll-free: 877-928-8701
Phone: 303-282-6410
Fax: 303-282-6411
www.doubleed.com

Watts up? electricity monitors show users the electricity usage of any 120-volt AC load. The monitor displays 16 values including watts, current volts, duty cycle, and dollars and cents based upon a specified electricity rate. The Pro version records this data, and with a PC interface, provides graphs of the collected data over time. Watts up? is an educational tool that is also useful for people planning their off-the-grid energy needs.

26 00 00
Electrical

26 00 00
Electrical

KILL A WATT

P3 International Corporation
132 Nassau St.
New York, NY 10038

Phone: 212-346-7979
Fax: 212-346-9499
www.p3international.com

The Kill A Watt™ energy monitor records appliance electrical consumption by kilowatt-hour within 0.2% accuracy and shows it in a large LCD display by the hour, day, week, month, or up to a year. Also displays volts, amps, watts, hertz, and volt-amps. It is more affordable than most energy-monitoring products on the market.

26 31 00
Photovoltaic Collectors

Photovoltaics (PV) enable the direct conversion of sunlight into electricity. Some PV modules are integrated into building components, such as roofing and wall glazings—these are often referred to as building-integrated photovoltaics (BIPV). Packaged Solar Equipment includes 'plug-and-play' systems that include all of the necessary components. (See also 08 88 26 - Building Integrated Photovoltaic Glazing.) (See feature article EBN Vol. 10, No. 3.)

Sunslates

Atlantis Energy Systems, Inc.

For full listing, see CSI section 07 34 00 - Building Integrated Photovoltaic Roofing

PV Modules

BP Solar
630 Solarex Ct.
Frederick, MD 21703

Phone: 301-698-4200
Fax: 301-698-4201
www.bpsolar.com

BP Solar is one of the world's largest solar electric companies, with manufacturing plants in the U.S., Spain, Australia, and India. They manufacture, design, market, and install a wide range of crystalline silicon solar electric products. The highest percentage of BP Solar's sales are to homeowners, builders, and businesses, and they are the largest supplier to the rural infrastructure market, where solar is the core power source for off-grid communities. In 1999, BP-Amoco

acquired Solarex and folded it into BP's PV Division to form BP Solar.

Most recently mentioned in EBN 3:3, 4:4, 5:2, 5:5, 8:5, 10:3

PV Modules

Evergreen Solar, Inc.
138 Bartlett St.
Marlboro, MA 01752

Phone: 508-357-2221
Fax: 508-229-0747
www.evergreensolar.com

Evergreen Solar is a manufacturer of PV modules and the innovator of the String Ribbon™ method of producing solar cells. This technique uses approximately half the amount of silicon as the industry norm. The company manufactures panels suitable for both grid-tied and off-grid installations and offers a 20-year warranty on all its products. Evergreen products are available through various distributors.

Most recently mentioned in EBN 10:3

PV Modules

First Solar, LLC
4050 E. Cotton Ctr. Blvd., Ste. 6-68
Phoenix, AZ 85040

Phone: 602-414-9300
Fax: 602-414-9400
www.firstsolar.com

First Solar develops and manufactures Cadmium Telluride (CdTe) thin-film photovoltaic modules. First Solar has invested heavily in developing advanced, high-volume manufacturing processes that are considered essential to achieving the low cost required to make solar electricity economically viable across a broad range of applications.

Most recently mentioned in EBN 10:3 & 10:5

PV Systems

Kyocera Solar, Inc.
7812 E. Acoma Dr.
Scottsdale, AZ 85260

Toll-free: 800-223-9580
Phone: 480-948-8003
Fax: 480-483-6431
www.kyocerasolar.com

Kyocera is one of the world's largest manufacturers of polycrystal PV modules.

Most recently mentioned in EBN 8:7 & 13:2

Photovol Glass

MSK Corporation

For full listing, see CSI section 08 88 26 - Building Integrated Photovoltaic Glazing

PowerGuard Interlocking Solar Roof Tiles

PowerLight Corporation

For full listing, see CSI section 07 34 00 - Building Integrated Photovoltaic Roofing

Renewable Energy Equipment

RWE Schott Solar, Inc.

For full listing, see CSI section 01 62 05 - Distributors/Retailers, Renewable Energy Equipment

RWE Schott ASI Solar Glazing

RWE Schott Solar, Inc.

For full listing, see CSI section 08 88 26 - Building Integrated Photovoltaic Glazing

OKASOLAR and OKALUX Insulating Glass Panels

Schott North America, Inc.

For full listing, see CSI section 08 44 00 - Curtain Wall and Glazed Assemblies

Schüco Photovoltaic Modules

New

SCHÜCO, LP
240 Pane Rd.
Newington, CT 06111

Toll-free: 877-472-4826
Phone: 860-666-0505
Fax: 860-666-2359
www.schuco-usa.com

Schüco offers three models of permanently sealed polycrystalline PV modules that are manufactured and tested to meet international quality standards. Model S 125-SP (49.13" x 31.61") has a rated output of 125 W; S 158-SP (62.2" x 31.5") is 158 W; and S 170-SPU (62.2" x 31.5") is 170 W. Schüco provides a 5-year product guarantee, and a performance guarantee of 90% output at 12 years, and 80% at 25 years. These products are manufactured in Germany.

PV Modules

Sharp Electronics Corp. - Solar Systems Division
5901 Bolsa Ave.
Huntington Beach, CA 92647

Toll-free: 800-BE-SHARP
Phone: 630-378-3357
www.sharpusa.com

Sharp Electronics Corporation, a world-wide leader in solar electric technology, offers single-crystal and polycrystalline PV panels. Available modules range from 62 to 208 watts for grid-tied or stand-alone systems. Sharp modules carry a 25-year warranty. Product introductions planned for the future include green, golden brown, and light blue PV cells; triangular modules; AC modules; and thin-film, virtually transparent modules.

PV Modules

Shell Solar
4650 Adohr Ln.
Camarillo, CA 93011

Toll-free: 800-272-6765
Phone: 805-482-6800
Fax: 805-388-6395
www.shell.com/solar/

Shell Solar is one of the world's largest manufacturers of PV modules, producing single-crystal, multi-crystal, and CIS thin-film modules. Shell also offers EarthSafe™ PV kits for residential and commercial installations. These solar electric rooftop kits include mounting hardware, inverter, and 25-year warranty panels. Shell Solar was previously Siemens Solar (and before that Arco Solar) before Shell acquired Siemens in April 2002.

Most recently mentioned in EBN 10:3

Industry Representation

Solar Energy Industries Association
805 15th St. NW, Ste. 510
Washington, DC 20005

Phone: 202-682-0556
Fax: 202-628-7779
www.seia.org

The Solar Energy Industries Association (SEIA) is the national trade association of solar energy manufacturers, dealers, distributors, contractors, and installers. SEIA's primary mission is to expand the use of solar technologies in the global marketplace. Membership exceeds 500 companies providing solar thermal and solar electric products and services.

Blue Link Photovoltaic Systems

Solar Market
25 Limerick Rd.
Arundel, ME 04046

Toll-free: 877-785-0088
www.solarmarket.com

The Blue Link 480 grid-connected photovoltaic system from Solar Market™ is a complete, ground-mounted, plug-and-play unit with a rated power production of 480 watts DC. A steel mounting rack supports the solar panels, inverter, and electrical disconnects; a 25' cable for the intertie is included. Installation takes about 30 minutes. A licensed electrician may be required to connect the unit into a home's load center; check with the local electric utility for any additional requirements or restrictions. The array measures 5' x 8'; the system weighs 140 pounds. The PV panels (manufactured by BP Solar) are guaranteed for 25 years; the balance of the system carries a 5-year warranty.

Solar Turtle

Solar Turtle, Inc.
4901 Cactus Wren Ave.
Tucson, AZ 85746

Phone: 520-883-3356

The Solar Turtle is a photovoltaic power supply and water purification system mostly used for remote cabins and RVs. These systems include 120-watt panels, deep-cycle batteries, an inverter, and General Ecology's SeaGull IV water purification systems. The system can output up to 720 W DC or 2,500 W AC. Most Solar Turtle units include custom features to match customer needs.

UNI-SOLAR PV Shingles and Standing Seam Panels

United Solar Ovonic LLC
For full listing, see CSI section 07 34 00 - Building Integrated Photovoltaic Roofing

---

26 32 13 Microturbines

Microturbines use natural gas, propane, or other fuels to generate electricity on-site. The same principle is used as for large gas turbines at power plants, but microturbines are much smaller and, thus, designed for distributed power production (producing power where it is needed). When combined with cogeneration equipment—heat exchangers that make use of otherwise-wasted thermal energy—the overall efficiency of microturbines can be increased to over 60%. Microturbines have a number of applications, including off-grid generation, utility peak-shaving, emergency back-up power, and combined heat and power (cogeneration) at restaurants, commercial laundries, hospitals, manufacturing plants, and office buildings with dehumidification or absorption cooling systems.

C30, C60 and C65 Microturbine Power Systems

Capstone Turbine Corporation
21211 Nordhoff St.
Chatsworth, CA 91311

Toll-free: 866-422-7786
Phone: 818-734-5300
Fax: 818-734-5320
www.microturbine.com

Capstone's 30, 60kW and 65kW microturbines generate power and heat (when set up for cogeneration) producing very low pollution emissions (<3 ppm NOx). Electrical efficiency is comparable to that of other fossil-fueled power generation (about 27%) but much higher (over 80% in some cases) with combined chilling/heating/power applications. Cost is about twice that of piston engine generators, according to the company, and about one-fifth to one-tenth that of photovoltaic power or fuel cells. Scalable and grid-interconnectable from below 30 kW to 1.2 MW with no external hardware. Introduced in 1998, Capstone had the first microturbine on the market.

Most recently mentioned in EBN 9:10

Warm Air Micro CHP

Climate Energy
93 West St.
Medfield, MA 02052

Phone: 508-359-4500
Fax: 508-359-9755
www.climate-energy.com

Climate Energy's Warm Air Micro CHP is the first residential-sized combined heat and power system in the USA. A low-emission natural gas Honda engine generator produces 1.2 kW of electricity and 11,000 Btu/hr of useful heat, resulting in a combined efficiency of 81%. The generator operates fairly continuously during the heating season, with the waste heat captured and distributed. During periods of high heating demand, the Olsen UltraMax III gas furnace provides 47,000 to 143,000 Btu/hr of additional heat at 95% AFUE efficiency. The system is quieter than a typical warm air furnace, according to the manufacturer. The Climate Energy system is set up to be grid-connected and has an Internet connection for remote monitoring and potential control by the utility company under 'dispatchable load' arrangements. It is also compatible with conventional central air conditioning systems.

Most recently mentioned in EBN 15:9

26 00 00
Electrical

Turbo Alternator

Elliott Energy Systems, Inc.
2901 S.E. Monroe St.
Stuart, FL 34997

Toll-free: 888-687-0876
Phone: 772-219-9449
Fax: 772-219-9448
www.tapower.com

The Turbo Alternator™ TA-100R CHP (Combined Heat and Power) microturbine produces up to 100 kW of high-quality electricity. A "Cogen-Pak" is available from the company to capture waste heat, boosting overall energy efficiency. This cogenerated heat is well suited for centralized building heat, domestic hot water, closed-loop desiccant drying for dehumidification, absorption chiller cooling, or industrial process heat. EESI is a wholly owned subsidiary of the Ebara Corporation of Tokyo, Japan, but manufacturing is done in Florida, where EESI is based.

PowerWorks Ingersoll-Rand Microturbine

Ingersoll-Rand Energy Systems
800-A Beaty St.
Davidson, NC 28036

Toll-free: 877-477-6937
Phone: 704-896-5373
Fax: 704-896-4327
www.irenergysystems.com

Energy Systems Inc., a business of Ingersoll-Rand Company Limited, develops distributed-generation power technologies for prime and peak shaving energy applications to supplement utility grids. These microturbines can use gases produced by wastewater treatment facilities, landfills, and oil and gas production facilities to produce cost-efficient energy on site with comparatively low emissions. A heat-recovery system can provide 100,000 to 400,000 Btu/hour of hot water (nominally at 400 degrees F) for heating, domestic hot water, absorption chilling, desiccant regeneration, or process heat. The MT70 kW and 250 kW models are available. Energy Systems offers comprehensive maintenance, service, and financing programs.

PureComfort 240

UTC Power
195 Governor's Hwy.
South Windsor, CT 06074

Toll-free: 866-900-7693
Phone: 860-727-2200
Fax: 860-727-7922
www.utcpower.com

The PureComfort™ system is the first packaged, building-scale cooling-heating-power (trigen) system to reach the market. Four 60-kW microturbines manufactured by Capstone are coupled with a double-effect absorption chiller from Carrier Corporation and sophisticated controls. The system can provide 240 kW of electricity and either 110 tons of cooling (hot summer day) or 900,000 Btu per hour of hot water (cold winter day). The chiller is 100% ozone-safe and has a coefficient of chiller performance of 1.3, well above the performance of single-effect chillers. The overall efficiency of energy utilization is in the range of 70-80%.

26 32 23
Wind Energy Equipment

Most large wind-power systems are installed in centralized wind farms, with the power fed into electric utility grids. Included here are smaller wind turbines that are more appropriate for individual homes or commercial buildings. Like PV systems, these generators may be designed for use in grid-tied or off-grid applications.

ARE Wind Generators

Abundant Renewable Energy
22700 N.E. Mountain Top Rd.
Newberg, OR 97132

Phone: 503-538-8298
Fax: 503-538-8782
www.abundantRE.com

ARE wind generators are manufactured in Oregon, USA, and distributed worldwide by Abundant Renewable Energy. The ARE110 wind generator is rated at 2,500 watts and is available in 48-volt models for battery-charging applications and in a high-voltage model for grid-connect systems. The ARE442 is rated at 10,000 watts and is available as a grid-connect system.

BWC Excel Wind Turbines

Bergey Windpower Co., Inc.
2200 Industrial Blvd.
Norman, OK 73069

Phone: 405-364-4212
Fax: 405-364-2078
www.bergey.com

Bergey Windpower manufactures three models of wind generators for residential and small-scale commercial applications. The BWC XL.1 is rated at 1,000 watts, the BWC Excel-R is rated at 7,500 watts, and the BWC Excel-S is rated at 10,000 watts.

Fuhrlaender Wind Turbines

Lorax Energy Systems, LLC
4 Airport Rd.
Engineering / Sales Office
Block Island, RI 02807

Phone: 401-466-2883
Fax: 401-466-2909
www.lorax-energy.com

Lorax Energy Systems is the North American distributor for Fuhrlander Wind Turbines manufactured in Germany. The company offers mid-size turbines (30 kW to 2500 kW) for use at such facilities as manufacturing plants, educational institutions, municipal water treatment plants, and farms where the wind power will displace more expensive retail power purchased from a utility. According to the company, wind turbines utilized in this manner provide excellent economics and a very short payback period.

Windstor Wind Turbine

McKenzie Bay International Ltd
37899 Twelve Mile Rd., Ste. 300
Farmington Hills, MI 48331

Phone: 616-940-3800
www.mckenziebay.com

Windstor is a three-bladed, vertical axis wind turbine designed for use on or near the point of use. It is available in 100 kW or 200 kW sizes. Windstor is marketed and installed by Windstor Power Company and produced by Dermond, Inc., both of which are wholly owned subsidiaries of McKenzie Bay International, Ltd. Windstor Power will sell the Windstor, or it will own and operate it on a client's site while providing power to the client at a fixed, guaranteed price.

Wind Turbines

Proven Energy, Ltd.
Wardhead Park
Stewarton, Ayrshire KA3 5LH Scotland, UK

Phone: +44 (0)1560 485 570
Fax: +44 (0)1560 485 580
www.provenenergy.com

Proven Energy, Ltd. manufactures four turbine models, rated at 600, 2,500, 6,000 and 15,000 watts. Proven Energy has three American distributors: Lake Michigan Wind and Sun can be reached by phone at 920-743-0456 and is online at www.windandsun.com; Solar Wind Works can be reached by phone at 530-582-4503 and is online at www.solarwindworks.com; Remote Power Inc. can be reached by phone at 907 457 4299 and is online at www.remotepowerinc.com.

AIR and Whisper Series Wind Turbines

Southwest Windpower
1801 W. Rt. 66
Flagstaff, AZ 86001

Phone: 928-779-9463
Fax: 928-779-1485
www.windenergy.com

Southwest Windpower manufactures 400-, 900-, 1,000- and 3,000-watt wind turbines for on- and off-grid residential and industrial power generation. The 400-watt unit can also be used to power telecommunication stations, and the 1,000-watt unit can be used to pump water.

Skystream 3.7

Southwest Windpower
1801 W. Rt. 66
Flagstaff, AZ 86001

Phone: 928-779-9463
Fax: 928-779-1485
www.windenergy.com

The Skystream 3.7™ is a grid-connected, residential-sized 1.8 kW wind turbine that is designed for quiet operation at low windspeeds. The 12-foot diameter, curved-blade rotor starts producing power at a wind speed of 8 mph and reaches full output at 20 mph. The wind turbine can be mounted on a 35 ft single pole, with towers up to 110 ft available. At an average windspeed of 12 mph, the Skystream 3.7 will produce about 400 kWh per month. The complete installed system costs approximately $7,000 to $10,000, including generator, controls, inverter, and tower.

Urban-Appropriate Wind Turbines

WES Canada
2952 Thompson Rd.
P.O. Box 552
Smithville, ON L0R 2A0 Canada

Phone: 905-957-8791
Fax: 905-957-8789
www.windenergysolutions.ca

WES Canada, in partnership with manufacturer WES Netherlands, offers the Tulipo—a medium-sized, low-noise, low-RPM 2.5 kW wind turbine appropriate for building-integrated urban installations. Larger 80- and 250-kW commercial turbines are also available. These turbines were formerly manufactured under the name Lagerway.

Jacobs 31-20 Wind Turbine

Wind Turbine Industries Corp.
16801 Industrial Cir. SE
Prior Lake, MN 55372

Phone: 952-447-6064
Fax: 952-447-6050
www.windturbine.net

Wind Turbine Industries' Jacobs 31-20 generator is rated at 20,000 watts. Jacobs wind turbines range in size from 10 kW to 20 kW, with rotor sizes ranging from 23 ft. (7m) to 29 ft. (8.8 m). These systems can provide power for a broad range of applications, which include Grid Intertie (utility bill reduction) or off-grid/remote battery charging. Other Jacobs turbines (also known as "Jakes" and made in the 1930s) are no longer manufactured but, due to their exceptional durability, are still widely available as used and rebuilt machines.

26 33 00
Battery Equipment

Lead-acid batteries designed for use in solar applications are included here because of their application. Lead is a toxic heavy metal and should be recycled.

Solaris 3500XP

Alpha Technologies, Inc.

For full listing, see CSI section 26 37 00 - Alternative Energy Balance of Systems Components

GridPoint Connect Backup PV System

GridPoint, Inc.

For full listing, see CSI section 26 37 00 - Alternative Energy Balance of Systems Components

Deep-cycle, Lead-acid Batteries

Surrette Battery Company Limited
1 Station Rd.
P.O. Box 2020
Springhill, NS B0M 1X0 Canada

Toll-free: 800-681-9914
Phone: 902-597-3767
Fax: 800-681-9915
www.surrette.com

Surrette Battery Company Limited manufactures specialty batteries. The deep-cycle, lead-acid batteries for solar applications feature dual containers to withstand rough

handling and prevent acid leakage. These batteries have a ten-year warranty, and an expected life of 15 years. Surrette is the parent company of the Rolls Battery Company in the U.S.

26 00 00
Electrical

26 37 00
Alternative Energy Balance of Systems Components

Inverters convert the direct-current (DC) power produced by the renewable energy system into alternating-current (AC) power needed for most conventional appliances or for feeding site-generated electricity into the power grid. Other power-conditioning equipment, controllers, batteries, and mounting equipment are also included here.

Solaris 3500XP

Alpha Technologies, Inc.
3767 Alpha Way
Bellingham, WA 98226

Phone: 360-647-2360
Fax: 360-671-4936

The Solaris 3500XP system is an integrated 3.5 kW inverter and uninterruptible power supply (UPS) for grid-tied and off-grid photovoltaic applications. The system has a CEC rated efficiency of 91% and the company claims the system maintains its rated output over an operating temperature range of -20 to 50 degrees C. The system is designed to support either 120/240 or 208 VAC output and can include an optional 48-volt DC input for use with a DC generator or additional batteries.

Smart Power M-Series Solar Power Conversion

Beacon Power Corporation
234 Ballardvale St.
Wilmington, MA 01887

Toll-free: 888-938-9112
Phone: 978-694-9121
Fax: 978-694-9127
www.beaconpower.com

Beacon Power Corporation introduced the Smart Power line of inverters in 2003, with inverter technology acquired from Advanced Energy, Inc. (previously of Wilton, New Hampshire). The M-Series is a 4000- or 5000-watt grid connected solar inverter capable of operating during grid outages, providing true sine wave backup power to critical loads. The product includes the charge controller, inverter and switchgear all in one outdoor-rated enclosure. The company claims 90% efficiency at full output and 93% efficiency at 50% output.

Fronius Grid-tied PV Inverters

Fronius USA LLC
5266 Hollister Ave., Ste. 117
Solar Electronics Division
Santa Barbara, CA 93111

Phone: 805-683-2200
Fax: 805-683-2220
www.fronius-USA.com

Fronius manufactures high-efficiency, lightweight, DC-to-AC inverters for residential-scale PV power applications. Most are used for grid-connected applications. The IG line of products has a wide DC-voltage range (150-450 V), and an LCD data display, with a maximum output power ranging from 2.0 to 5.1 kW. The Fronius USA Solar Electronics Division is a branch of the German company Fronius International GmbH.

GridPoint Connect Backup PV System

GridPoint, Inc.
2020 K Street NW, Ste. 550
Washington, D.C. 20006

Phone: 202-903-2100
Fax: 202-903-2101
www.gridpoint.com

GridPoint Connect provides the balance-of-system (everything but the solar panel array) for a grid-connected PV backup power system. Gridpoint Connect combines the electronics, inverter, charge controllers, recyclable batteries, computer, and other needed components, in a single 'plug-and-play' device. This device connects to the main circuit breaker panel, PV array, communication line, and secure load panel (on which critical circuits are placed). The GridPoint Connect system ensures batteries are fully charged and supplies local power needs, feeding excess power to the grid. If the grid is down, the Connect system will power critical loads from the solar array and/or battery pack.

Solar Controllers

Heliotrope PV, LLC
3698 Franklin Blvd.
Eugene, OR 97403

Phone: 541-284-2426
Fax: 541-284-2427
www.heliotrope-pv.com

Heliotrope PV manufacturers electronic charge controllers for PV systems. Though marketed to recreational vehicle users, they are appropriate for any small PV system.

Most recently mentioned in EBN 8:7

SolarDock

McConnell Energy Solutions
1201 N. Market St., Ste. 1605
Wilminton, DE 19801-1149

Phone: 302-504-0124
Fax: 302-428-0723
www.solardock.com

SolarDock™ is a nonpenetrating solar-module mounting system for flat-roof and ground-mount installations. The product is held in place with ballasts and weighs 4 to 6 lbs/ft² to withstand wind speeds of up to 90 mph (for greater protection, more ballast can be used for winds up to 120 mph). The product can be easily moved for routine maintenance or roof replacement. Panels are supported at a 25-degree angle. SolarDock is UL-certified and comes with a 25-year warranty. Made in the USA.

Outback Power System Components

OutBack Power Systems
19009 62nd Ave. NE
Arlington, WA 98223

Phone: 360-435-6030
Fax: 360-435-6019
www.outbackpower.com

Outback Power Systems provides balance-of-system components including inverters, solar charge controllers, communication managers, and a range of other components and accessories for stand-alone, grid-tied, or backup photovoltaic power systems. Outback's FLEXware integration hardware allows horizontal or vertical mounting orientations for locations with limited wall space and can accommodate a wide range of power system sizes.

Sunny Boy Inverters

SMA America, Inc.
12438 Loma Rica Dr.
Grass Valley, CA 95945

Phone: 530-273-4895
Fax: 530-274-7271
www.sma-america.com

SMA America offers 2,500-, 1,800-, and 700-watt inverters designed for residential-scale photovoltaic applications. These German-made inverters carry a 5-year warranty and are being specified by some of the leading PV system designers today. The company also offers a larger, 125 kW inverter, as well as PV control and monitoring equipment.

PV Controllers

Solar Converters Inc.
558 Massey Road, Unit 1
Guelph, ON N1K 1B4 Canada

Phone: 519-824-5272
Fax: 519-823-0325
www.solarconverters.com

Solar Converters Inc. is a designer and manufacturer of highly efficient power control products for the renewable energy field. Included among the products the company has developed are Linear Current Boosters, Battery Equalizers, Power Tracker™ charge controllers with Maximum Power Point Tracking (MPPT), Cathodic Protection Controllers, Generator Starters, Battery Desulphators, Constant Voltage Pump Drivers, Voltage Controlled Switches, Solar Lighting Controllers, DC-DC Converters, and more.

Solectria Grid-tied PV Inverters

Solectria Renewables LLC
360 Merrimack St.
Building 9, 2nd Fl.
Lawrence, MA 01843

Phone: 978-683-9700
Fax: 978-683-9702
www.solren.com

Solectria manufactures a line of high-efficiency DC-to-AC inverters for residential and commercial PV power applications, especially grid-connected systems. The products cover systems from 12-500kW and can include an optional internet-connected data logger and monitoring system. Solectria also manufactures inverters for connected or 'mini-grid' distributed generation with input from fuel cells, batteries, ICE, or heat engines. Solectria also provides engineering services and custom products for any 1-500 kW distributed generation system.

SunEarth Solar Equipment

SunEarth, Inc.

For full listing, see CSI section 23 56 16 - Packaged Solar Heating Equipment

UniRac PV Mounting Systems

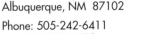

UniRac, Inc.
1411 Broadway Blvd. NE
Albuquerque, NM 87102

Phone: 505-242-6411
Fax: 505-242-6412
www.unirac.com

UniRac produces systems for mounting PV modules. SolarMount® is a system of components for flat and tilted roofs. Solar-

Mount/S-5! is designed for easy installation on standing-seam metal roofs. SunFrame offers building integration, a low-profile and a choice of finishes. PoleTops are ground mounting systems. U-LA is for arrays of 3-kW or more. UniRac recycles all solid waste and purchases recycled materials when available, including 20-25% post-consumer recycled aluminum and 75% recycled steel. In addition, most shipping materials are salvaged or have recycled-content.

Inverters

Xantrex Technology
5916 195th St. NE
Arlington, WA 98223

Toll-free: 888-800-1010
Phone: 360-435-8826
Fax: 360-925-5144
www.xantrex.com

Xantrex Technology, formerly Trace Engineering, manufactures energy-efficient DC-to-AC inverters for residential, commercial, mobile, remote, and emergency applications. These are the most widely used inverters for PV and wind power systems. Inverters specially designed for feeding power into the electric grid are available.

26 51 14
Interior Luminaires

Many innovative, energy-efficient luminaires are available, most of which are primarily relevant to commercial buildings. Environmental characteristics to consider include fluorescent lamp use, effective reflectors, and application-appropriate design. Fluorescent high-bay fixtures can replace conventional HID lighting in gymnasiums, warehouses, and other high-ceiling spaces, offering both direct energy savings and the benefit of instant-on (so they are more likely to be turned off). (See also 08 45 00 - Translucent Wall and Roof Assemblies, 08 61 00 - Roof Windows, 08 62 00 - Unit Skylights, 08 63 00 - Metal-Framed Skylights, 08 62 23 - Tubular Skylights.)

UltraLux T5 High-Bay Fixtures

1st Source Lighting
1730 Industrial Dr.
Auburn, CA 95603

Phone: 530-887-1110
Fax: 530-887-0807
www.1stsourcelight.com

1st Source produces a range of high-bay fixtures for linear T5 lamps and twin-tube (folded) fluorescent lamps. These fixtures are suited to large retail, warehouse, and sporting arena applications, and are an alternative to HID fixtures.

Most recently mentioned in EBN 9:7

Studio A CFL Lighting [New]

American Fluorescent
2345 Ernie Krueger Cir.
Waukegan, IL 60087

Phone: 847-249-5970
Fax: 847-249-2618
www.americanfluorescent.com

American Fluorescent's STUDIO A collections offer decorative and energy-efficient lighting options for kitchen, hallway, and bath. Many of American Fluorescent's lights are Energy Star rated. LED fixtures also available.

CFL Torchieres

Catalina Lighting
18191 N.W. 68th Ave.
Miami, FL 33015

Toll-free: 800-966-7074
Phone: 305-558-4777
Fax: 305-827-3994
www.catalinalighting.com

Catalina Lighting offers energy-efficient, torchiere-style floor lamps that use a single 55-watt fluorescent bulb.

Most recently mentioned in EBN 7:9

High-Bay Fixtures

Crescent-Stonco
2345 Vauxhall Rd.
Union, NJ 07083

Toll-free: 800-334-2212
Phone: 908-964-7000
Fax: 908-964-0968
www.stoncolighting.com

Stonco's T-Bay T-5 and T-8 high-bay fluorescent fixtures replace conventional HID lighting in industrial applications such as large retail areas, warehouses, and sporting arena applications. These fixtures accept multiple suspension methods and have hinged reflectors for ballast service access.

Cast Aluminum Products

Eleek, Inc.
2326 N. Flint Ave.
Portland, OR 97227

Phone: 503-232-5526
Fax: 503-232-5527
www.eleekinc.com

26 00 00
Electrical

Eleek hand-casts architectural items, including tiles, sinks, and indoor and outdoor light fixtures, are made from 100% recycled aluminum (at least 70% post-consumer) finished with a clear, non-reactive, non-toxic, and stainproof powder-coat finish. Custom patinas or colored powdercoats are also available. The sinks require less production energy than porcelain-finished cast iron sinks. (Cast iron melts at 2800 degrees F, while aluminum melts at 1220 F; porcelain finishes must be fired at 1450 F, while powder-coat requires 350 F.) The 5/16"-thick, indoor/outdoor tiles are cast in shapes and sizes designed to fit standard kitchen cabinetry, and can be modified for less usual layouts. Sizes range from 6" x 6" to 12.75" x 17.5"; frontwrap and backsplash sections are available. These products are also available in bronze that is at least 90% recycled (minimum 60% post-consumer). Eleek recommends Teflon®-safe sponges, non-scratching powdered cleansers, or mild liquid soaps for clean-up; knives may cause hairline scratches; protect from heat over 330 degrees F. Eleek's manufacturing principles are defined by The Natural Step.

Frankie Goes Fluorescent, Parallel Universe, Lulu, Flipster and Fibonacci Series

Fire & Water Lighting/David Bergman Architect
241 Eldridge St., Ste. 3R
New York, NY 10002

Phone: 212-475-3106
Fax: 212-677-7291
www.cyberg.com

Most Fire & Water fluorescent lighting fixtures are green both from a materials standpoint and an energy efficiency standpoint. Fibonacci, Flipster, Lulu, and Frankie Goes Fluorescent fixtures use the newest Energy Star pin-based CFL's with replaceable ballasts. Some models can be alternatively ordered with dimmable, integral ballast screw-base CFL's. Frankie Goes Fluorescent ceiling, wall and table fixtures are made of 100% recycled glass (post-consumer content varies) and Environ™, a composite of soy flour and recycled paper. The Lulu series, available in table, floor, wall, and ceiling versions, is made of 50% post-consumer recycled plastic. Fibonacci's shades are made with formaldehyde free, 70-100% post-industrial recycled wood, and process chlorine-free (PCF) paper liners. Flipster's shades are made with up to 40% recycled content resin. Both are available in table, floor, wall, and ceiling models. The Parallel Universe series (floor, table, wall and ceiling) incorporates recycled and sustainable materials, and utilizes pin-based dimmable (dedicated) CFLs.

Most recently mentioned in EBN 8:5

CFL Torchieres

Good Earth Lighting
122 Messner Dr.
Wheeling, IL 60090

Toll-free: 800-291-8838
Phone: 847-808-1133
Fax: 847-808-0838
www.goodearthlighting.com

Good Earth Lighting produces energy-efficient, fluorescent torchiere standing fixtures.

Most recently mentioned in EBN 7:9

T5 High-Bay Fixtures

Holophane Corporation
214 Oakwood Ave.
Newark, OH 43055

Toll-free: 800-448-6646
Phone: 740-345-9631
Fax: 740-349-4426
www.holophane.com

Holophane Corporation produces a series of high-bay fixtures for linear T5 lamps and twin-tube (folded) fluorescent lamps. These fixtures are suited to large retail, warehouse, and sporting arena applications, and are an alternative to HID fixtures.

Most recently mentioned in EBN 9:7

CFL Recessed Downlights

Juno Lighting, Inc.
1300 S. Wolf Rd.
P.O. Box 5065
Des Plaines, IL 60017

Toll-free: 800-367-5866
Phone: 847-827-9880
Fax: 847-827-2925
www.junolighting.com

Juno Lighting manufactures an extensive line of commercial-quality recessed downlights using CFLs. All models have separate ballasts—most electronic—with plug-in twin-tube, quad-tube, or triple-tube CFLs. Fixtures designed for lamp wattages of 13 to 42 are available. Some fixtures have the CFL oriented vertically, others horizontally. Full photometric data are available for all fixtures.

Ergolight

Ledalite Architectural Products, Inc.
19750 - 92A Ave.
Langley, BC V1M 3B2 Canada

Phone: 604-888-6811
Fax: 604-888-2003
www.ledalite.com

Ergolight integrates several energy-efficient and lighting control features into a single luminaire. This fluorescent pendant luminaire houses three T8 lamps, two directed downward and one upward. The dimmable ballast is controlled by an occupancy sensor and a photocell, for daylight-dependent dimming. Ergolight is easily installed onto the dropped-ceiling grid. Individual dimming control is possible through Ergolight software.

Most recently mentioned in EBN 8:9

Hybrid Lighting System

Natural Lighting Co., Inc.

For full listing, see CSI section 08 63 00 - Metal-Framed Skylights

Fluorescent Light Fixtures

Sunpark Electronic Corp.
1850 W. 205th St.
Torrance, CA 90501

Toll-free: 866-478-6775
Phone: 310-320-7880
Fax: 310-320-7875
www.sunpkco.com

Sunpark Electronics produces a wide range of compact-fluorescent and linear-tube fluorescent lamp fixtures, including fluorescent torchieres, ceiling fixtures, recessed downlights, table lamps, floor lamps, outdoor fixtures, and under-counter fixtures. Electronic ballasts are also available.

CFL Fixtures

Technical Consumer Products, Inc.
325 Campus Dr.
Aurora, OH 44202

Toll-free: 800-324-1496
Fax: 330-995-6188
www.tcpi.com

Technical Consumer Products (TCP) produces many types of table and floor lamps, ceiling fixtures, and outdoor and portable fixtures. TCP's electronically ballasted CFL torchieres have a 65-watt T6 lamp configuration and 3-way light levels (30/36/65 W) in polished brass, matte black, glossy white, and brushed steel; average lamp life is 10,000 hours, and average ballast life is 50,000 hours. TCP also produces complete retrofit kits to change an existing recessed-can fixture into an energy-efficient CFL system. The replaceable lamp lasts for 10,000 hours, while the ballast lasts 50,000 hours.

CFL Task Lighting

Waldmann Lighting
9 W. Century Dr.
Wheeling, IL 60090

Toll-free: 800-634-0007
Phone: 847-520-1060
Fax: 847-520-1730
www.waldmannlighting.com

Waldmann Lighting manufactures a complete line of ergonomic lighting fixtures for a number of industries including architectural, office, industrial, electronic, and medical environments. The company's task-lighting fixtures use compact fluorescent lamps and flicker-free electronic ballasts for increased energy efficiency. All lights include a 10-year warranty.

Ethos FS and Spheros S T5 Luminaires

Zumtobel Lighting, Inc.
3300 Rte. 9W
Highand, NY 12528

Toll-free: 800-448-4131
Fax: 845-691-6289
www.zumtobel.us

The Ethos and Spheros S T5 luminaires are 100% uplight hanging-pendant fixtures with integral daylight and occupancy sensors. The integral sensors are standard on these two products and optional on other fixtures from Zumtobel. The 8'-long fixtures come with a remote control to override the automatic switching and dimming, and use the digital addressable lighting interface (DALI) protocol. The Ethos is the higher output design, housing 4 to 6 lamps, while the Spheros S houses 2 to 4 lamps.

26 51 15
Electronic Ballasts

Electronic ballasts for fluorescent lighting are much more energy-efficient than traditional magnetic ballasts, saving as much as 35%. Electronic ballasts are commonly available in new fixtures and for retrofitting existing fixtures. These products are quiet and do not have the characteristic flicker of magnetic ballasts. Additional energy savings are possible with electronic dimming ballasts. Advanced dimming ballasts can now reduce light levels to below 10% of total output. Besides the energy savings that dimming affords, building occupant comfort is enhanced, especially through lessened eye fatigue from reduced com-

puter screen glare. *(See also 26 01 51 - Electrical Component Recycling.) (See feature article EBN Vol. 6, No. 9.)*

Electronic Ballasts

Advance Transformer Co.
10275 W. Higgins Rd.
O'Hare International Ctr.
Rosemont, IL 60018

Toll-free: 800-322-2086
Phone: 847-390-5000
www.advancetransformer.com

Advance Transformer manufactures a wide range of leading-edge energy-efficient ballasts, including electronic, electronic-dimming, and electronic HID and CFL ballasts.

Electronic Ballasts

Howard Industries, Inc.
P.O. Box 1590
Laurel, MS 39441

Toll-free: 800-956-3456
Phone: 601-422-0033
Fax: 601-422-1652
www.howard-ballast.com

Howard Industries manufactures a full range of electronic ballasts.

Just Right Light

JRL Worldwide
23 Spring St.
Morristown, NJ 07960

Toll-free: 877-278-1800
Fax: 973-538-3030
www.jrlworldwide.com

LECS Worldwide's Just Right Light® system makes use of an adjusting (dimmable) electronic ballast that can be programmed to maintain a preset light level. A light sensor, connected via fiber-optic cable to a photosensor inside the ballast, is installed in the fixture to monitor lamp output. The light output is set by the facilities manager with the aid of a light meter and can be readily readjusted. An optional second sensor can be mounted outside the fixture to monitor ambient light levels. This sensor can further boost energy savings by dimming lamp output even more when daylighting is available.

Dimming Electronic Ballasts

Lutron Electronics Co., Inc.
7200 Suter Rd.
Coopersburg, PA 18036

Toll-free: 888-588-7661
Phone: 610-282-3800
Fax: 610-282-3090
www.lutron.com

Lutron's extensive line of dimming electronic ballasts includes products for T12, T8, and T5 HO linear fluorescent lamps and for CFLs. Dimming to 1% available with some products. New products include EcoSystem™, which integrates personal control, daylighting, occupancy sensing, and load shedding.

Electronic Ballasts

Universal Lighting Technologies
26 Century Blvd., Ste. 500
Nashville, TN 37214

Toll-free: 800-BALLAST
Phone: 615-316-5100
Fax: 615-316-5162
www.universalballast.com

Universal Lighting Technologies manufactures a comprehensive line of energy-efficient electronic ballasts and controls.

26 51 16
LED lighting

LEDs (light-emitting diodes) have been improving in light quality and efficacy (lumens of light output per watt of electrical consumption) at a rapid pace. The highest-efficacy LEDs today produce about 50 lumens per watt, more than twice the efficacy of incandescent and halogen lamps. Although fluorescent lamps have higher efficacy than today's LEDs, the ability to more precisely focus LED light output can enable LED luminaires to outperform fluorescents in certain applications. LEDs also have a very long life (30,000 to 50,000 hours) and they are the only common non-incandescent light source that does not rely on mercury vapor.

LED Luminaires from io Lighting

io Lighting
370 Corporate Woods Pkwy.
Vernon Hills, IL 60061

Phone: 847-735-7000
Fax: 847-735-7001
www.iolighting.com

io Lighting is a leading manufacturer of LED luminaires. The company specializes solely in LED lighting and offers a range of luminaires for commercial, industrial, and institutional markets. io Lighting has integrated thermal, optical, and power-design requirements into luminaire designs, producing highly synchronized, modular solutions. One of the company's luminaires won Best of Show at Lightfair in 2004.

Enbryten LED Luminaires

Permlight Products, Inc.
422 W. Sixth St.
Tustin, CA 92780

Phone: 714-508-0729
Fax: 714-508-0920
www.permlight.com

Enbryten™ LED luminaires from Permlight Products use high-efficacy, white LEDs (light-emitting diodes) in a wide variety of luminaire styles. The replaceable LED modules allow easy replacement as needs change, as LED output drops over time, or as LEDs improve in quality and light output. The LEDs currently available in the Enbryten series provide up to 50 lumens per watt. Products are available in pendant, downlight, sconce, and step luminaires for both residential and commercial applications. These luminaires work on standard dimming circuits.

Most recently mentioned in EBN 14:12 & 15:7

Westinghouse NanoLux LED Lamps

Westinghouse Lighting Corporation
12401 McNulty Rd.
Philadelphia, PA 19154

Toll-free: 800-999-2226
Phone: 215-671-2000
Fax: 215-464-4115
www.westinghouselighting.com

Westinghouse Lighting Corporation introduced their NanoLux™ line of decorative LED lamps in 2005. They are available in two sizes: G-19 and S-11 in white, clear, and four colors (blue, red, green, and amber). Lasting up to 100,000 hours and consuming one or three watts, these lamps provide low-output, energy-saving, decorative and accent lighting.

Most recently mentioned in EBN 13:2

26 51 17
Fluorescent Lamps

Fluorescent lamps have long been preferable to incandescent lighting, relative to energy efficiency. New developments with fluorescent technology, including the high-efficacy T5 lamps, have pushed the energy efficiency envelope further. Recently, attention has also been paid to the mercury content of fluorescents and the consequences of mercury releases into the environment. As with all resource use and pollution issues, reduction is the best way to limit the problem. Even with low-mercury lamps, however,

**26 00 00
Electrical**

26 00 00
Electrical

recycling of old lamps remains a high priority. (See also 26 01 51 - Electrical Component Recycling.)

Ecolux Fluorescent Lamps

GE Lighting
1975 Noble Rd., Nela Park
Cleveland, OH 44112

Toll-free: 800-255-1200
Phone: 216-266-2121
Fax: 216-266-2923
www.gelighting.com

Ecolux T12 and T8 fluorescent lamps pass the EPA Toxicity Characteristic Leaching Test (TCLP) because the mercury is not in a leachable form. The Ecolux XL lamps are rated for a 20% longer life than standard T8 lamps.

Most recently mentioned in EBN 11:6

Ecologic Product Line

Osram Sylvania
100 Endicott St.
Danvers, MA 01923

Toll-free: 800-544-4828
Phone: 978-777-1900
Fax: 978-750-2152
www.sylvania.com

Ecologic fluorescent lamps pass the EPA Toxicity Characteristic Leaching Test (TCLP) for mercury leaching. T12, T8, Dulux CFL, and various HID lamps from Osram Sylvania are available with this designation.

Most recently mentioned in EBN 11:6

Pentron T5 Lamps

Osram Sylvania
100 Endicott St.
Danvers, MA 01923

Toll-free: 800-544-4828
Phone: 978-777-1900
Fax: 978-750-2152
www.sylvania.com

Pentron™ T5 lamps by Osram Sylvania have efficacies of 96.4-104.3 lumens/W, depending upon lamp wattage.

Most recently mentioned in EBN 9:7

Panasonic Compact Fluorescent Lamps

Panasonic Consumer Electronics Building Department
Panazip 4A-6
One Panasonic Way
Secaucus, NJ 07094

Toll-free: 866-292-7292
Fax: 847-468-4359
www.panasonic.com

Panasonic manufactures CFLs with integral electronic ballasts, including plug-ins and screw-ins.

Most recently mentioned in EBN 3:2

ALTO Fluorescent Lamps

Philips Lighting Company
200 Franklin Square Dr.
P.O. Box 6800
Somerset, NJ 08875

Toll-free: 800-555-0050
Phone: 732-563-3000
Fax: 732-563-3125
www.lighting.philips.com/nam

Alto™ fluorescent lamps are a low-mercury substitute product for conventional T8 and T12 tubes. The Alto technology reduced the quantity of mercury in the lamps by 66% compared to the 1999 industry average without sacrificing longevity or performance. Philips was the first manufacturer to offer low-mercury fluorescent lamps.

Most recently mentioned in EBN 6:9, 8:11, 11:6, 13:2

SILHOUETTE T5 Lamps

Philips Lighting Company
200 Franklin Square Dr.
P.O. Box 6800
Somerset, NJ 08875

Toll-free: 800-555-0050
Phone: 732-563-3000
Fax: 732-563-3125
www.lighting.philips.com/nam

The Silhouette T5 and Silhouette T5 High Output fluorescents are available in a variety of popular wattages (ranging from 14 to 80 watts), with an average rated life of 20,000 hours. They are particularly suitable for offices, retail stores, hotels, schools, and hospitals, especially where small fixtures are required.

Most recently mentioned in EBN 9:7 & 11:6

---

26 51 19
Compact Fluorescent Lamps

Replacing standard incandescent light bulbs with compact-fluorescent lamps (CFLs) can slash electrical consumption in homes and offices where incandescent lighting is widely used. Most CFLs use roughly one-third as much electricity as incandescent bulbs with comparable output. By more efficiently converting electrical energy into light, CFLs generate less heat—which can reduce cooling

loads, particularly in commercial buildings. In reducing electrical usage, CFLs also reduce associated carbon dioxide, sulfur dioxide, and nitrous oxide emissions. CFL technology continues to evolve; there are many types to choose from, including straight-tube, folded-tube, and twisted-tube. As CFLs have shrunk in size, they have become suitable for most light fixtures that were designed for incandescent light bulbs. Advances in light quality, lamp durability, and dimming technology have also been significant. Most manufacturers offer 15- and 20-watt models; larger lamps are also available. The average life of CFLs is eight to ten times that of incandescent bulbs. (See feature article EBN Vol. 6, No. 9.)

GE CFL and Induction Lamps

GE Lighting
1975 Noble Rd., Nela Park
Cleveland, OH 44112

Toll-free: 800-255-1200
Phone: 216-266-2121
Fax: 216-266-2923
www.gelighting.com

GE Lighting manufactures a full line of CFLs, with and without integral ballasts. Dimmable integral-ballast CFLs are available. The GE Genura lamp is marketed as a compact fluorescent lamp, but is really an induction lamp. The 23-watt Genura offers longer life than standard CFLs (15,000 hours) in an R30 reflector style. The lamp is designed for indoor use and screws into a standard A-type socket and is designed to replace a 65-watt R30 incandescent lamp. Initial output of 1,100 lumens, or 48 lumens per watt, with 25% lumen drop-off over its life. The power factor is relatively low at 0.55 and the total harmonic distortion fairly high at 130%. The lamp should not be used on dimming circuits.

Most recently mentioned in EBN 3:2, 7:2, 11:6

Greenlite Compact Fluorescent Lamps

Greenlite Lighting Corporation USA
10 Corporate Park, Ste. 100
Irvine, CA 92606

Toll-free: 800-930-2111
Phone: 949-261-5300
Fax: 949-261-1798
www.greenliteusa.com

Greenlite manufactures a wide range of compact fluorescent lamps including Dimmable and 3 Way Spirals. The company's 13-watt "Mini" Spiral is nearly comparable in size to a standard incandescent bulb.

26 00 00
Electrical

Compact Fluorescent Lamps

Lights of America
611 Reyes Dr.
Walnut, CA 91789

Toll-free: 800-321-8100
Phone: 909-594-7883
Fax: 909-594-6758
www.lightsofamerica.com

Lights of America manufactures twisted-tube, straight-tube, and other electronic-ballasted fluorescent lamps. Durability concerns have been raised with certain LOA products.

Most recently mentioned in EBN 8:2

Compact Fluorescent Lamps

Link USA International, Inc.
1420 Decision St., Ste. C
Vista, CA 92081

Phone: 760-599-1280
Fax: 760- 599-1291
www.linklights.net

Link USA produces several sizes of compact, spiral, and covered CFLs for indoor/outdoor use.

Most recently mentioned in EBN 8:2

Lumatech Compact Fluorescent Lamps

Lumatech Corporation
2 Marlen Dr.
Hamilton, NJ 08691

Toll-free: 800-932-0637
Phone: 609-689-3122
Fax: 609-689-3091
www.carpenterlighting.com

Lumatech manufactures a variety of CFLs, including the Reflect-A-Star, Microlamp, and new twist lamps. The twist lamps are available from 11 to 32 watts, the latter producing 1900 lumens (the highest output of any twist lamp).

Maxlite Compact Fluorescent Lamps

MaxLite SK America, Inc.
19 Chapin Rd., Bldg. B
Pine Brook, NJ 07058

Toll-free: 800-555-5629
Phone: 973-244-7300
Fax: 973-244-7333
www.maxlite.com

MaxLite SK America manufactures CFLs with integral electronic ballasts.

Compact Fluorescent Lamps

Osram Sylvania
100 Endicott St.
Danvers, MA 01923

Toll-free: 800-544-4828
Phone: 978-777-1900
Fax: 978-750-2152
www.sylvania.com

Osram Sylvania offers a full line of CFLs, both with and without integral ballasts.

Most recently mentioned in EBN 3:2, 6:10, 11:6

Philips Compact Fluorescent Lamps

Philips Lighting Company
200 Franklin Square Dr.
P.O. Box 6800
Somerset, NJ 08875

Toll-free: 800-555-0050
Phone: 732-563-3000
Fax: 732-563-3125
www.lighting.philips.com/nam

Philips Lighting Company produces a full line of CFLs, both with and without integral ballasts, including the Philips Marathon™ line of compact fluorescent bulbs. Lamps in the Marathon line are guaranteed for at least 6,000 hours and are the first CFLs to have the look of standard incandescents. These high-efficacy lamps offer a high color rendering index (CRI) and the energy-saving benefits associated with compact fluorescent technology. Philips introduced CFL lamps.

Most recently mentioned in EBN 3:2, 7:2, 11:6

Twisted-Tube CFLs

Star Lighting Products
11350 Brookpark Rd.
Cleveland, OH 44130

Toll-free: 800-392-3552
Phone: 216-433-7500
Fax: 216-433-7506
www.starlightingproducts.com

Star Lighting Products offers several sizes of compact, twisted-tube CFLs.

Sunpark Twisted-Tube CFLs

Sunpark Electronic Corp.
1850 W. 205th St.
Torrance, CA 90501

Toll-free: 866-478-6775
Phone: 310-320-7880
Fax: 310-320-7875
www.sunpkco.com

Sunpark Electronic Corp. produces several sizes of compact, twisted-tube CFLs.

Most recently mentioned in EBN 8:2

TCP Compact Fluorescent Lamps

Technical Consumer Products, Inc.
325 Campus Dr.
Aurora, OH 44202

Toll-free: 800-324-1496
Fax: 330-995-6188
www.tcpi.com

TCP manufactures a full range of energy-efficient compact fluorescent lamps, such as integral ballast and modular ballast configurations, reflector lamps, spiral- and folded-tube configurations, and candelabra-base lamps.

Compact Fluorescent Lamps

U.S. WAY Lighting
2530 Rt. 176, Unit 4
Prairie Grove, IL 60012

Phone: 773-338-9688
Fax: 847-632-0370
uswaycorp.com

U.S. WAY Lighting offers CFLs in 14 styles and a variety of wattages and color temperatures. Hi-Output up to 300 watts, 21600 lumens, 1,500-watt incandescent equivalent and Hi-Power T5 fixtures and tubes up to 80W, 7000 lumens each. Lamps achieve 95% illumination at start up with full brightness within 3 seconds.

Westinghouse Compact Fluorescent Lamps

Westinghouse Lighting Corporation
12401 McNulty Rd.
Philadelphia, PA 19154

Toll-free: 800-999-2226
Phone: 215-671-2000
Fax: 215-464-4115
www.westinghouselighting.com

Westinghouse Lighting Corporation offers a full line of compact fluorescent lamps (CFLs), including integral-ballast, screw-in and plug-in CFL replacements. The company offers dimming, three-way, photo-sensing, full-spectrum, globe, interior flood, and exterior flood CFLs—most in various sizes and wattages. All Westinghouse CFLs are Energy Star-rated.

Most recently mentioned in EBN 13:2

26 00 00
Electrical

26 51 20
Induction Lamps

Induction lighting offers an extremely long life, fairly high-efficacy, instant-on lighting alternative to incandescent and metal halide lamps. Most products are designed for outdoor applications and hard-to-reach indoor applications. Induction lamps work by using electrical energy to create an alternating magnetic field to induce gas discharge in mercury vapor without the use of electrodes; phosphor coatings convert the UV light into white light, as with fluorescent lamps. Induction lamp systems include a high-frequency generator, a power coupler, and a lamp, so most products can only be used in specialized fixtures. There is moderate lumen depreciation over time. Like fluorescent lamps (including CFLs), induction lamps contain mercury so should be recycled.

GE CFL and Induction Lamps

GE Lighting

For full listing, see CSI section 26 51 19 - Compact Fluorescent Lamps

Osram Sylvania Induction Lighting

Osram Sylvania
100 Endicott St.
Danvers, MA 01923

Toll-free: 800-544-4828
Phone: 978-777-1900
Fax: 978-750-2152
www.sylvania.com

The Endura® induction lamps from Osram (described as "electrodeless fluorescent" lighting by Osram) and the Icetron® lamps from Sylvania offer high efficacy (70-80 lumens per watt) long-life exterior lighting. 70-watt (6,500 lumen), 100-watt (8,000 lumen), and 150-watt (12,000 lumen) products are available in 3500 and 4100°K color temperatures. Lamps are rated for 100,000 hours, have CRI ratings of 80, and offer reliable ignition at temperatures as low as –40°F. Endura and Icetron lamps are warranted for 5 years.

Philips QL Induction Lighting

Philips Lighting Company
200 Franklin Square Dr.
P.O. Box 6800
Somerset, NJ 08875

Toll-free: 800-555-0050
Phone: 732-563-3000
Fax: 732-563-3125
www.lighting.philips.com/nam

The Philips QL induction lamps offer fairly high efficacy (65-70 lumens per watt) lighting for exterior luminaires. 55-watt (3500 lumen) and 85-watt (6000 lumen) products are available for both 120- and 240-volt applications. Lamps are rated for 100,000 hours with a 50% failure rate and 60,000 hours with a 10% failure rate (based on 4,000 burning hours per year), have CRI ratings of 80, are available in three color temperatures (2700, 3000, and 4000°K), and operate at very low temperatures (rated to –13°F). QL lamps are warranted for 5 years.

Most recently mentioned in EBN 11:6

26 52 00
Emergency Lighting

LED signs and emergency lighting use very little energy and have a long life expectancy. Though LED fixtures cost somewhat more than incandescent, they often quickly pay for themselves through reduced energy costs and labor savings.

LED Exit Signs & Emergency Lighting

Chloride Systems

For full listing, see CSI section 26 53 00 - Exit Signs

LED Exit Signs & Emergency Lighting

Cooper Lighting

For full listing, see CSI section 26 53 00 - Exit Signs

LED Exit Signs & Emergency Lighting

Emergi-Lite

For full listing, see CSI section 26 53 00 - Exit Signs

LED Exit Signs & Emergency Lighting

Highlites, Inc.

For full listing, see CSI section 26 53 00 - Exit Signs

LED Signage & Emergency Lighting

Watt-Man L.E.D. Lighting

For full listing, see CSI section 26 53 00 - Exit Signs

26 53 00
Exit Signs

Exit signs are a small, but significant, component of commercial lighting energy use. Older exit signs are still illuminated with two 15- or 20-watt incandescent lamps. In the 1970s and 1980s CFL exit signs began appearing that reduced total electricity use by up to 75%. Today, exit signs and retrofit kits are available that use LEDs (light-emitting diodes) or electroluminescence for illumination. LED exit signs use very little energy (as low as 1.8 W per illuminated face) and are expected to last more than 10 years. Though LED fixtures cost somewhat more than incandescent, they often pay for themselves in less than a year through reduced energy costs and labor savings. The Energy Star program qualifies LED exit signs that use 5 W or less per illuminated face. (See feature article EBN Vol. 15, No. 11.)

LED Exit Signs

Astralite, Inc.
20 Pocono Rd.
Brookfield, CT 06804

Toll-free: 800-832-5483
Phone: 203-775-0172
Fax: 203-775-0797
www.astralite.org

Astralite, formerly a division of a larger firm, has been spun off as a separate company in Connecticut.

Most recently mentioned in EBN 3:3

Xtrabright SP Exit Sign Retrofit Kits

BJI Energy Solutions
30 Vandam St., 5A
New York, NY 10013

Toll-free: 888-733-6374
Phone: 212-675-5312
Fax: 212-253-4248
www.t1lighting.com

T-1® Lighting, a division of BJI Energy Solutions, offers the Xtrabright® SP box exit sign retrofit kit, which uses less than 5 watts to power two T-1 cold cathode lamps. Xtrabright SP retrofit kits are 15 times brighter than LED exit sign retrofit kits and will last 10 years.

LED Exit Signs

Chloride Systems
272 W. Stag Park Service Rd.
Burgaw, NC 28425

Phone: 910-259-1000
Fax: 800-258-8803
www.chloridesys.com

Chloride Systems manufactures a wide range of LED exit signs and other emergency lighting products.

LED Exit Signs

Cooper Lighting
1121 Hwy. 74 S
Peachtree City, GA 30269

Phone: 770-486-4800
Fax: 770-486-4801
www.cooperlighting.com

Cooper Lighting manufactures a wide range of LED exit signs and other emergency lighting products.

LED Exit Signs

Crescent-Stonco
2345 Vauxhall Rd.
Union, NJ 07083

Toll-free: 800-334-2212
Phone: 908-964-7000
Fax: 908-810-4524
www.crescentlighting.com

Crescent manufactures LED exit signs and other emergency lighting products.

LED Exit Signs

Dual-Lite
101 Corporate Dr.
Spartanburg, SC 29303

Phone: 864-599-6000
Fax: 864-699-1428
www.dual-lite.com

Dual-Lite, formerly listed as Hubbell Lighting, produces a wide range of LED exit signs—with over 50 approved Dual-Lite exit sign models listed on documents available through the Energy Star® website.

LED Exit Signs

Emergi-Lite
8155 T&B Blvd.
Memphis, TN 38125

Toll-free: 888-935-3605
Fax: 888-865-1565
www.emergi-lite.com

Emergi-Lite manufactures a wide range of LED exit signs and other emergency lighting products.

LED Exit Signs

Exitronix
1911 West Parkside Lane
Phoenix, AZ 85027

Toll-free: 888-533-3948
Phone: 623-580-3948
Fax: 623-580-8948
www.exitronix.com

Exitronix has been producing LED exit signs since 1985. The company offers both direct-view and edge-lit products in red and green. Retrofit kits are available for older signs.

LED Exit Signs

Gilbert Industries, Inc.
5611 Krueger Dr.
Jonesboro, AR 72401

Toll-free: 800-643-0400
Phone: 870-932-6070
Fax: 870-932-5609
www.gilbertinc.com

Gilbert Industries, Inc. produces a wide range of LED exit signs.

LED Exit Signs

Highlites, Inc.
2142 Thomaston Ave.
Waterbury, CT 06704

Phone: 203-575-2044
Fax: 203-574-3289
www.highliteslighting.com

Highlites, Inc. manufactures a wide range of LED exit signs and other emergency lighting products.

LED Exit Signs

Isolite
31 Waterloo Ave.
Berwyn, PA 19312

Toll-free: 800-888-5483
Phone: 610-647-8200
Fax: 610-296-8953
www.isolite.com

Isolite manufactures a variety of LED exit signs.

LED Exit Signs

Lithonia Lighting
P.O. Box A
Conyers, GA 30012

Phone: 770-922-9000
Fax: 770-483-2635
www.lithonia.com

Lithonia Lighting manufactures a wide range of LED exit signs and other emergency lighting products. Nearly 100 approved Lithonia LED exit signs are listed on documents available on the Energy Star® website.

LED Exit Sign Retrofit Kits

Lumatech Corporation
2 Marlen Dr.
Hamilton, NJ 08691

Toll-free: 800-932-0637
Phone: 609-689-3122
Fax: 609-689-3091
www.carpenterlighting.com

Lumatech manufactures both red and green LED exit sign retrofit kits.

LED Exit Signs

Technical Consumer Products, Inc.
325 Campus Dr.
Aurora, OH 44202

Toll-free: 800-324-1496
Fax: 330-995-6188
www.tcpi.com

TCP manufactures red and green LED exit signs, with or without battery backup, and LED retrofit lamps with 40-diode design. Exit sign lamps have a 5-year warranty.

**26 00 00
Electrical**

LED Signage

Watt-Man L.E.D. Lighting
1 Morton Dr., Ste. 506
Charlottesville, VA 22903

Toll-free: 800-296-3948
Phone: 434-979-6377
Fax: 434-979-6410
www.wattmanledlighting.com

Watt-Man L.E.D. Lighting, formerly a division of Standard Enterprises, Inc., manufactures a wide range of LED lighting fixtures including exit sign retrofit lamps in both red and green, signaling lights for both marine and industrial use, and fixtures for decorative applications.

26 55 00
Special Purpose Lighting

These listings include heavy-duty work lights using high-efficiency compact fluorescent lamps, as well as other efficient solutions for special purpose lighting needs.

SideKick Worklytes

Crescent-Stonco
2345 Vauxhall Rd.
Union, NJ 07083

Toll-free: 800-334-2212
Phone: 908-964-7000
Fax: 908-964-0968
www.stoncolighting.com

Stonco Lighting has introduced a line of portable CFL worklights and cord reels under the name SideKick™. These energy-efficient worklights reduce heat buildup and the risk of contact with hot surfaces. SideKick WorkLytes come in a range of styles for a variety of applications. Included in the series is the Ratchet Lyte™, which ratchets into 8 positions and gives 60-watt light output from a 13-watt quad CFL. Also available is the 13-watt fluorescent Lyte Rover Cordless WorkLyte, which converts any extension cord into a portable light source.

Limelite

EI Products
55 Second St.
Maxwell, TX 78656

Phone: 512-357-2776
Fax: 512-357-2786
www.limelite.com

Limelite® is a lime green electroluminescent exit light with a current draw of 0.2 W.

26 55 33
Hazard Warning Lighting

Signal lighting is intended to alert vehicle operators or pedestrians of hazards and obstructions. Fixtures using grouped LEDs are often sufficient to the task; they use relatively modest amounts of power and the lamps are long-lasting.

Solar LED Hazard Lighting

Carmanah Technologies Corporation
Building 4, 203 Harbour Rd.
Victoria, BC V9A 3S2 Canada

New

Toll-free: 877-722-8877
Phone: 250-380-0052
Fax: 250-380-0062
www.carmanah.com

Carmanah offers solar-powered LED lighting for roadway, industrial, marine, aviation, railway, and other transit applications, including pedestrian and hazard flashers, marine navigation lights, runway lights, and bus shelter lighting kits. Carmanah's Solar LED Lighting Group has more than 100,000 solar-powered LED lighting installations in 110 countries. The company also offers solar power systems and LED illuminated signs.

26 56 00
Exterior Lighting

Outdoor lighting is common around buildings. Incandescent, metal halide, and high-pressure sodium are the most common outdoor lighting options. Environmental issues include lamp efficacy (lumens per watt), luminaire efficiency, controllability of the light source, potential for PV power, and control of light pollution. To control light pollution, full-cutoff luminaires should be specified. (See feature article EBN Vol. 7, No. 8.)

Dark-Sky Compliant CFL Lamps

Bulbrite
145 W. Commercial Ave.
Moonachie, NJ 07074

Toll-free: 800-528-5555
Phone: 201-531-5900
Fax: 800-441-7708
www.bulbrite.com

Bulbrite offers CFL lamps with standard screw bases and integrated hoods that prevent light trespass, complying with light fixture standards of the International Dark Sky Association. These lamps do not require a fixture to control illumination patterns. The 15-watt integral-fixture lamps provide 60 lumens per watt.

Cast Aluminum Products

Eleek, Inc.
For full listing, see CSI section 26 51 14 - Interior Luminaires

Full-Cutoff Luminaires

Gardco Lighting
1611 Clovis Barker Rd.
San Marcos, TX 78666

Toll-free: 800-227-0758
Phone: 512-753-1000
Fax: 512-753-7855
www.sitelighting.com

Gardco Lighting produces a wide range of full-cutoff luminaires for various lamp types.
Most recently mentioned in EBN 7:8

Full-Cutoff Luminaires

Kim Lighting
P.O. Box 60080
City of Industry, CA 91716

Phone: 626-968-5666
Fax: 626-369-2695
www.kimlighting.com

Kim Lighting produces a wide range of full-cutoff luminaires for various lamp types.
Most recently mentioned in EBN 7:8

The GlareBuster

Lighting by Branford
727 Boston Post Rd.
Guilford, CT 06437

Toll-free: 800-548-8714
www.theglarebuster.com

The GlareBuster is a light-pollution-controlling full-cutoff exterior floodlight fixture for residential and light commercial applications. Reduced glare allows better visibility beyond the illumination source, and more focused 100% downlighting decreases light trespass (direct-beam light leaving the property) and light pollution. This product is commonly available at hardware, lighting, and electrical supply stores. The fixture accommodates standard compact fluorescent lamps and other bulb options. The International Dark Sky Association (IDA) has awarded their "Dark Sky Friendly" seal to the GlareBuster.

Solar- or Grid-Powered LED Luminaires

MoonCell, Inc.
P.O. Box 3068
Fredericksburg, VA 22403

Toll-free: 877-396-3142
Phone: 540-429-6155
Fax: 413-403-6100
www.mooncell.com

MoonCell's Solarus45™ outdoor luminaire provides off-grid illumination using solar power. This luminaire is based on MoonCell's Econo-Lum™ fixture, which operates at 90-240VAC using 36 LEDs to provide 900 lumens of white light. The unit has deep-cycle, maintenance free batteries charged by PV modules. The batteries may be pole-mounted or buried. These luminaires are IESNA Type I cutoff fixtures, limiting light pollution. MoonCell has also introduced several grid-connected outdoor light fixtures using LEDs. These products reduce energy consumption by 50-90% compared to conventional lighting technologies, according to the company.

Outdoor Solar Lighting

OkSolar
1 Birch Meadow Dr.
Hadley, MA 01035

Phone: 347-624-5693
Fax: 347-534-9155
www.oksolar.com

OkSolar manufactures solar lighting including fluorescent, low-pressure sodium, and LED lighting for parking lots, walkways, streets, and other outdoor areas. The lights include all components except mounting poles. OkSolar also manufactures multi-LED replacement lamps that can be used in standard lamp sockets.

Sonne Solar-Powered Outdoor Luminaire

Selux Corporation
5 Lumen Ln.
P.O. Box 1060
Highland, NY 12528

Toll-free: 800-735-8927
Phone: 845-691-7723
Fax: 845-691-6749
www.selux.com/usa

Sonne solar-powered Type III full-cutoff luminaires from Selux come equipped with 80-watt or 120-watt solar panels, mounted singly or in pairs on a fully tilting and rotating mount for maximum solar exposure. One or two 12V, 82AH sealed gel batteries power a compact fluorescent lamp rated at 18, 26, 32, or 42 watts, providing initial lumens between 1250 and 3200. A regulator/controller prevents overcharging and backflow; senses and remembers dusk and dawn time; and may be programmed to illuminate during set periods of time relative to sunrise and sunset. A motion detector is optional. Steel parts are hot-dip galvanized; some parts are made with recycled ABS.

Commercial Solar Lighting

SOL Inc.
3210 S.W. 42nd Ave.
Palm City, FL 34990 **New**

Toll-free: 800-959-1329
Phone: 772-286-9461
Fax: 772-286-9616
www.solarlighting.com

SOL Inc. (previously Solar Outdoor Lighting, Inc.) sells a wide range of solar-powered commercial lighting products and systems for signs, streets, parks, security, bus stops, bus shelters, and other applications. The SL Hurricane Series street light is designed to withstand hurricanes. Most products use long-life cold-cathode compact fluorescent lamps (LEDs are available with some products) and provide battery storage for about five days of inclement weather.

SoLed Solar-Powered LED Outdoor Luminaires

SolarOne Solutions
51 Marble St.
Framingham, MA 01702 **New**

Toll-free: 877-527-6461
Phone: 508-620-7652
Fax: 508-620-7650
www.solarone.net

SolarOne® produces Dark-Sky-compliant, solar-powered, LED outdoor lighting systems, including overhead and directional pathway lighting, bus-shelter lighting, and custom and designer systems. Systems typically include solar panels, an adjustable panel-mounting system, LED lamps, battery and enclosure, solar charge controller, and MC2 advanced lighting controls with remote control. A variety of lamp and power packages are available.

Full-Cutoff Luminaires

Sterner Lighting Systems, Inc.
701 Millennium Blvd.
Greenville, SC 29607

Toll-free: 864-678-1000
www.sternerlighting.com

Sterner Lighting produces a wide range of full-cutoff luminaires for various lamp types.
Most recently mentioned in EBN 7:8

SunWize Designer Lighting Systems

SunWize Technologies
1155 Flatbush Rd.
Kingston, NY 12401 **New**

Toll-free: 800-817-6527
Phone: 845-336-0146
Fax: 845-336-0457
www.sunwize.com

The SunWize Designer Lighting Systems for street, security, parking lot, or path lighting include battery packs and all other components except the mounting pole. The luminaires are available with either low-pressure sodium or fluorescent lamps.

Solar Street Lighting

Quality Solar Concepts Inc.
47 Tea Rose Meadow
Rockport , NY 14420 **New**

Phone: 585-278-3773
www.solar4me.com

Quality Solar Concepts manufacturers and distributes photovoltaic-powered outdoor lighting, including street lights, walkway lights, parking lights, and area lights. Fixtures are engineered to be used with either LED or compact fluorescent lamps. Quality Solar Concepts is also distributor for a wide range of other alternative energy components and systems.

This Space is Available for Your Notes

27 00 00 Communications

PRODUCT LISTINGS

27 42 19
Public Information Systems

There can be significant value to interpreting green building features—displaying energy use, or explaining how a daylighting system works, for example. Signs are an excellent application for recycled materials. (See also 10 14 00 - Signage.)

Green Touchscreen   **New**

Quality Attributes Software
614 Billy Sunday Rd., Ste. 500
Ames, IA 50010

Phone: 515-956-1599
Fax: 515-233-3380
www.greentouchscreen.com

Green Touchscreen is an educational tool consisting of web-based kiosks and software that can tie directly into a facility's control system to display real-time building performance data. Green Touchscreen replaces traditional signs and placards with interactive displays of live data using custom graphics and animation. The kiosks can also display maps, directories, events, and other information. Displaying real-time data and comparing current building performance with historical data for that building or a conventional building can educate visitors on the value of building green as well as bringing about changes in building operation to save additional energy.

This Space is Available for Your Notes

**27 00 00
Communications**

This Space is Available for Your Notes

28 00 00 Electronic Safety & Security

PRODUCT LISTINGS

28 30 00
Electronic Detection and Alarm

Alerting building occupants about toxins or contaminants is important in many situations. With some toxins, an immediate warning is needed; with others, long-term exposure is the concern. Detecting water leaks contributes to occupant health by allowing steps to be taken to stop mold before it starts, as well as protecting the health and longevity of the building itself. (See feature article EBN Vol. 7, No. 7.)

Air Check Radon Test

Air Check, Inc.
1936 Butler Bridge Rd.
Fletcher, NC 28732

Toll-free: 800-247-2435
Phone: 828-684-0893
Fax: 828-684-8498
www.radon.com

Air Check offers a series of radon test kits, each designed for different exposure times. The company provides fully certified analysis of mailed-in air samples for as little as $10 per test. Air Check performs same-day tests upon receipt of samples and provides a complete written report describing the results and their implications for indoor air quality.

Optima Portable IEQ Monitoring System

Aircuity, Inc.

For full listing, see CSI section 23 40 13 - Air Quality Monitoring and Assessment

AIRxpert 7000

AIRxpert Systems, Inc.

For full listing, see CSI section 23 40 13 - Air Quality Monitoring and Assessment

H2ORB

New

Aqua One Technologies, Inc.
14726 Golden West, Ste. J
Westminster, CA 92683

Phone: 714-898-7016
Fax: 714-898-7019
www.aquaone.com

The H2Orb is a simple leak-detection system for toilets that includes both bowl and tank sensors. When either sensor detects a flow problem, a wireless signal is sent to the controller which shuts off water flow to the toilet, sounds an alarm, and identifies the problem on its LCD screen. The unit is powered by a battery with a five-year expected life.

Atwood CO Alarm

Atwood Mobile Products
1120 N. Main St.
Elkhart, IN 46514

Phone: 574-264-2131
www.atwoodmobile.com

Atwood Mobile Products' CO alarm is certified by the Canadian Standards Association, which includes specifications for both alarm longevity and time-of-manufacture testing. Atwood uses a patented electrochemical technology to alert building occupants to the presence of carbon monoxide. According to the company, the sensor is more accurate, more energy efficient, and less sensitive to humidity than competing models. A digital display updates CO levels every 30 seconds and indicates battery and sensor conditions. The unit requires 3 AAA batteries. A picture-frame leg allows installation in various locations. The Canadian Standards Association certifies Atwood CO alarms for use in RVs.

Most recently mentioned in EBN 12:7

The Informant

Bacharach, Inc.
621 Hunt Valley Cir.
New Kensington, PA 15068

Toll-free: 800-736-4666
Phone: 724-334-5000
Fax: 724-334-5001
www.bacharach-inc.com

Bacharach's The Informant™ detects refrigerant leaks with a microprocessor-controlled heated-diode sensor. The flashing probe indicates changing gas concentrations, and there is also a bar-graph display. The new Informant 2 detects both refrigerant and combustible gas leaks with the same instrument.

Low Level CO "Health" Monitor

CO-Experts, Div. of G. E. Kerr Companies, Inc.
19299 Katrina Ln.
Eldridge, MO 65463

Toll-free: 888-443-5377
Phone: 417-426-5504
Fax: 417-426-5594
www.coexperts.com

The Low Level (LL) CO Monitor displays carbon monoxide (CO) levels as low as 10 ppm, audible warnings at 25, 35, 50, & 70 ppm with immediate, automatic hush & hush overrides at all levels. Unlike most CO detectors, these monitors (in addition to sensing higher levels) are designed to alert occupants to low levels of CO that may be harmful, but not necessarily fatal, so that corrective measures may be taken. Most CO detectors sound an alarm only after much higher levels are sustained for a protracted period of time. The CO-Experts II Monitors take a CO reading every three seconds, then averages 20 readings, updating the display once a minute, resulting in the most accurate true CO reading ever. The monitor provides 1 ppm resolution. The reasons for diagnostic failure warnings are shown on the display as well as CO exposure data storage timelines, peak, time of peak, duration of CO exposure, and the resulting COHB in the blood stream. If not cleared by owner, the stored data will be retained for 2 years & 8 months. The sensor is fully monitored and provides end of life warning. The unit comes with a 1-year warranty and a 5-year expected lifetime. An annual 1 ppm recalibration service is also available for an additional charge.

Detec Moisture Detection and Monitoring Systems

Detec Systems, LLC
711 St. Helens Ave.
Suite 201
Tacoma, WA 98402

Phone: 253-272-3262
Fax: 253-272-6252
www.detecsystems.com

Detec Systems offers a real-time, automated moisture intrusion monitoring system for building envelopes and roof systems. The detection system uses a proprietary moisture-detection tape with copper conductors and stainless steel probes which can be installed in nearly 100% of the building envelope. Zones of tape are connected to onsite sensor modules that communicate with Detec's central monitoring center. The Detec system is primarily used in commercial, institutional and multi-family/residential buildings. The system can monitor any type of building structure, including wood-frame, non-combustible steel construction, window wall, curtain wall and concrete. The technology was originally developed for the telecom industry, and has been used to monitor cable routes for moisture intrusion since the early '80s.

Most recently mentioned in EBN 14:11

28 00 00
Electronic Safety & Security

Floodstopper Leak Detection and Control

FirstSmart Sensor Corp.
1460 Pandosy St., Ste. 201
Kelowna, BC V1Y 1P3 Canada

Toll-free: 800-660-1522
Phone: 250-763-5694
www.thefloodstopper.com

The Floodstopper™ from FirstSmart Sensor Corporation is designed to stop plumbing overflows on the spot. It uses sensors placed at floor level near toilets, washing machines, and other potential flood sources. These sensors are connected (with wires or via a wireless link) to a central controller and an automatic shutoff valve.

Most recently mentioned in EBN 14:11

Radon Control Equipment

Infiltec Radon Control Supply
108 S. Delphine Ave.
P.O. Box 1125
Waynesboro, VA 22980

Toll-free: 888-349-7236
Phone: 540-943-2776
Fax: 540-932-3025
www.infiltec.com

Infiltec Radon Control distributes and installs radon-control equipment.

Most recently mentioned in EBN 7:7

Nighthawk CO Detector

Kidde Safety
1394 S. Third St.
Mebane, NC 27302

Toll-free: 800-880-6788
Fax: 800-547-2111
www.kidde.com

The Nighthawk CO detector uses electrochemical technology to alert building occupants to the presence of carbon monoxide (CO). The Canadian Standards Association certifies Kidde's Nighthawk CO detectors for use in homes.

Most recently mentioned in EBN 12:7

The Professional Radon Gas Test Kit

Pro-Lab, Inc.
1675 N. Commerce Pkwy.
Weston, FL 33326

Phone: 954-384-4446
www.prolabinc.com

Each EPA-recognized Pro-Lab test kit comes with a pair of radon detectors. The detectors use liquid scintillation technology with silica-gel desiccants, so they require only 96 hours of exposure before they are sealed and sent back to the lab for analysis. Results will be returned within one week; express 2-day analysis is also available. Pro-Lab also offers kits to detect pesticides, molds, carbon monoxide, asbestos, and bacteria in water, paints, dust, and on surfaces.

This Space is Available for Your Notes

31 00 00 Earthwork

PRODUCT LISTINGS

31 35 00
Erosion Protection

While polymer-based products dominate this market, alternatives made from natural fibers are available. These include coir (coconut-husk fiber obtained from coconut oil production) and jute, a fiber commonly used to make twine. The primary advantage of natural-fiber erosion control products is their biodegradability even after vegetation is established. Photodegradable products often fail to break down, as plant growth and other cover prevents light from hitting the material. And unlike polymer-based fabrics, natural-fiber products also absorb moisture and work like a mulch, benefiting seedling establishment. Products listed here are biodegradable. (See also 32 92 13 - Hydro-Mulching.)

Curlex NetFree Erosion-Control Blankets

New

American Excelsior Company
850 Ave. H, E
Arlington, TX 76011

Toll-free: 800-777-7645
Phone: 817-385-3500
Fax: 817-649-7816
www.curlex.com

Curlex® NetFree™ is a 100% biodegradable excelsior erosion control blanket made with softly barbed, interlocking, curled, Great Lakes Aspen excelsior wood fibers (80% >6" long) stitched together with biodegradable thread. These blankets are free from weed seed, chemical additives, tackifiers, and paper products. These netless blankets will not entrap wildlife or pets, tangle in mowing equipment, present future environmental risk, or trip pedestrians. 8' wide X 90' long roll which equals 80 sq. yards of blanket per roll; NetFree™ can be used in low-flow channels up to 1-lb/ft^2 shear stress; recommended for 3:1 maximum slopes. American Excelsior Company has 10 locations in the U.S. and over 100 distributor partners.

Antiwash/Geojute and Geocoir DeKoWe

Belton Industries, Inc.
1205 Hamby Rd.
P.O. Box 127
Belton, SC 29627

Toll-free: 800-845-8753
Phone: 864-338-5711
Fax: 800-851-5049
www.beltonindustries.com

Antiwash®/Geojute® is woven in a 1/2" grid pattern that is suitable for moderate slopes sustaining runoff velocities of up to 8 ft/s. The jute fabric, available in 4'-wide by 225'- or 147'-long rolls, biodegrades in one to two years. Geocoir® DeKoWe®, made from coir, is stronger and more durable than jute geotextiles. This product is available in three different weights: 400, 700, and 900 g/m2; is typically used on steeper slopes; and may last from 4 to 5 years, depending upon the application.

Most recently mentioned in EBN 6:10

BioFence

Environmental Research Corps
15 Mohawk Ave.
East Freetown, MA 02717

Phone: 508-763-5253
Fax: 508-763-8781
www.biofence.com

BioFence™ is a one-piece silt fence made from 100% biodegradable materials. Beech or maple stakes measuring 42" or 48" x 1-1/8" are sewn into 7- to 10-oz., 20-mesh seine weave Hessian Cloth composite stiffened with cornstarch. Aspen wood fiber matting is stitched to the front. This product installs more quickly than conventional silt fence/straw bale combinations and is cost-competitive. Custom fences are available for specific applications.

Slopetame2

Invisible Structures, Inc.
1600 Jackson St., Ste. 310
Golden, CO 80401

Toll-free: 800-233-1510
Phone: 303-233-8383
Fax: 800-233-1522
www.invisiblestructures.com

Slopetame2 is a plastic grid product made from 100% injection-molded recycled HDPE with varying amounts of post-consumer and post-industrial content. Slopetame2 is designed to provide immediate erosion control in permanent installations on weak or eroding slopes by resisting undercutting water and soil movement. It has a geotextile backing.

KoirMat and KoirLog

Nedia Enterprises, Inc.
22187 Vantage Pointe Pl.
Ashburn, VA 20148

Toll-free: 888-725-6999
Phone: 571-223-0200
Fax: 571-223-0202
www.nedia.com

Nedia Enterprises manufactures a full line of primarily coir-based erosion control products. KoirMat™ erosion control matting, made from 100% coir fiber, is suitable for a wide variety of applications. KoirLog™ is a 100% coconut fiber "log" for shoreline and stream channel erosion control applications. KoirLog is available in 12", 16", and 20" diameters and is typically 10' to 20' long.

BioNet Erosion-Control Mats

North American Green
14649 Hwy. 41 N
Evansville, IN 47725

Toll-free: 800-772-2040
Phone: 812-867-6632
Fax: 812-867-0247
www.nagreen.com

North American Green offers 100% biodegradable (as opposed to photodegradable) rolled erosion control blankets, including the netting and thread. The woven net structure reduces the risk of wildlife entrapment and prevents fiber loss. Matrices are agricultural straw or a combination of straw and coir (coconut fiber). Products are available to meet specific applications and functional longevities. 6.7' x 108' rolls cover 80 yd2. North American Green also offers erosion control blankets made with photodegradable polypropylene netting, and blanket pins made of biodegradable PLA plastic. North American Green is a wholly-owned, stand-alone subsidiary of Tensar International Corporation with headquarters in Atlanta, Ga.

Most recently mentioned in EBN 14:12

**31 00 00
Earthwork**

Coir Erosion-Control Products

RoLanka International, Inc.
155 Andrew Dr.
Stockbridge, GA 30281

Toll-free: 800-760-3215
Phone: 770-506-8211
Fax: 770-506-0391
www.rolanka.com

RoLanka manufactures a full line of coir-based products for soil erosion control, sediment control, and streambank stabilization.

Natural-Fiber Erosion-Control Blankets

SI Geosolutions
4109 Industry Dr.
Chattanooga, TN 37416

Toll-free: 800-621-0444
Phone: 423-899-0444
Fax: 423-553-2900
www.fixsoil.com

SI Geosolutions offers natural-fiber erosion control and shoreline stabilization products for many applications.

31 00 00
Earthwork

31 60 00
Special Foundations and Load-Bearing Elements

Conventional foundation excavation can disturb plantings and soil, and cause sediment runoff and erosion. In fragile environments, such as boardwalks and decking in wetlands, and in erosion-prone areas, consider foundation-anchor systems that don't require excavation. (See also 35 50 00 - Marine Construction and Equipment.)

Instant Foundation System

A. B. Chance, Division of Hubbell Power Systems, Inc.
210 N. Allen St.
Centralia, MO 65240

Phone: 573-682-8414
Fax: 573-682-8660
www.abchance.com

A. B. Chance manufactures the Instant Foundation®, a unique screw-anchor foundation system for supporting walkways in ecologically sensitive areas. The steel piers are screwed into the ground or wetland using portable rotary augering equipment, eliminating the need for any excavation or concrete. A. B. Chance also manufactures

galvanized-steel hardware to complete the installations.
Most recently mentioned in EBN 8:10

Diamond Pier

Pin Foundations, Inc.
8607 58th Ave. NW
Gig Harbor, WA 98332

Phone: 253-858-8809
Fax: 253-858-8607
www.pinfoundations.com

Diamond Pier™ DP-100 and DP-50 permit installation of pier foundations with neither excavation nor site-poured concrete. These products provide structural foundation systems for decks, outbuildings, and boardwalks. Held in place with four steel pins driven at angles through the piers and deep into the ground, they are particularly appropriate for frost conditions, fragile ecosystems, heaving soils, or difficult access sites. The company's Butterfly™ and Speed Pile™ systems are no longer offered.
Most recently mentioned in EBN 8:10

This Space is Available for Your Notes

32 00 00 Exterior Improvements

PRODUCT LISTINGS

32 01 90
Operation and Maintenance of Planting

Maintenance products for plantings include such things as soil amendments. Look first to nonchemical, water- and energy-saving landscapes. Use organic fertilizers or fertilizers produced from wastes diverted from landfills. Due to the shipping energy use (and costs), regional sources are generally preferred. (See also 31 35 00 - Erosion Protection & 32 92 00 - Turf and Grasses.) (See feature article EBN Vol. 2, No. 4.)

Cedar Grove Compost

Cedar Grove Composting, Inc.
9010 E. Marginal Way S, Ste. 200
Seattle, WA 98108

Toll-free: 888-832-3008
Phone: 206-832-3000
Fax: 206-832-3030
www.cedar-grove.com

Cedar Grove Composting, Inc. operates the largest independently owned yard waste composting facility in the U.S. The company started by making composted products from a curbside yard-waste collection program in Seattle. Its technology successfully includes pre- and post-consumer food wastes collected in major metropolitan areas.

Premium Compost and Lawn Topdressing

Central Maui Landfill / Maui Eko-Systems
P.O. Box 1065
Puunene, HI 96784

Phone: 808-572-8844
Fax: 808-877-7589

Premium Compost and Lawn Topdressing are soil amendments that are batch-tested by independent labs and certified by the Hawaii Department of Health. These products are available in 1-1/2 ft3 bags, 1 yd³ bulk bags, and in bulk.

EnviroGuard and Promat

Tascon, Inc.
7607 Fairview St.
P.O. Box 41846
Houston, TX 77241

Toll-free: 800-937-1774
Phone: 713-937-0900
Fax: 713-937-1496
www.tasconindustries.com

EnviroGuard™ landscape mulch, manufactured from recycled paper and plant materials, contains no chemical herbicides. It creates a solid layer when surface-applied as a weed block; tilled under, it provides organic matter. PROMAT is a hydro-seeding mulch manufactured from recycled paper.

32 12 00
Flexible Paving

Various materials can be added to or substituted for asphalt in pavement to improve environmental characteristics. Recycled tire rubber is the most common such additive. Though problems occurred in the past when recycled tire rubber was used to constitute 25% of the paving mixture, current mixtures with 18-20% of the material yield promising results. Recycled asphalt shingles have also been processed into flexible pavement components, and some natural-resin binders have been used in some pavement products.

Asphalt Rubber System

International Surfacing Systems
6751 W. Galveston St.
Chandler, AZ 85226

Toll-free: 800-528-4548
Phone: 480-940-9690
Fax: 480-961-0766
www.asphaltrubber.com

International Surfacing manufactures a composite asphalt/rubber hot mix made from ground-down recycled tires. It is often used in road rehabilitation, overlays, and seals. This product uses less material than conventional asphalt and has greater durability. It can also be used as an impermeable membrane.

NaturalPAVE XL Resin Pavement

Soil Stabilization Products Co., Inc.
P.O. Box 2779
Merced, CA 95344

Toll-free: 800-523-9992
Phone: 209-383-3296
Fax: 209-383-7849
www.sspco.com

NaturalPAVE® XL Resin Pavement is a nonpetroleum, durable paving material. Resin Pavement can be constructed in a wide variety of natural colors, depending upon local availability of aggregate materials. Resin Pavement mixtures are appropriate for use in sensitive natural environments, including access to beach, estuary, and riparian areas. Resin Pavement mixtures are cold-applied but installed like hot-mix asphalt pavement mixtures. Paving machines are typically used for placement. When light-colored aggregate materials are selected, Resin Pavement can be constructed that has relatively cool summer surface temperature.

Most recently mentioned in EBN 8:11 & 9:2

32 12 43
Porous Flexible Paving

Flexible porous paving combines the attributes of flexible paving and with the benefits of porous paving. Look for high recycled content and environmentally appropriate binders. (See feature articles EBN Vol. 3, No. 5 & Vol. 13, No. 9.)

Flexi-Pave

KB Industries, Inc.
28100 US Hwy 19 N, Ste. 410
Clearwater, FL 33761

Toll-free: 877-826-8600
Phone: 727-726-2700
Fax: 727-726-2800
www.kbius.com

KB Industries offers Flexi-Pave, a porous paving system made with recycled rubber tires. Poured in place by certified installers, it offers a slip-resistant, impact-absorbing surface that resists damage caused by freeze/thaw and root intrusion. Suitable for parking lots, boat ramps, sidewalks, walkways, handicap ramps, decks, and balconies, it is made with

**32 00 00
Exterior
Improvements**

3/8" nominal recycled rubber granules and 1/2" nominal gravel aggregate, bonded with a proprietary single-component, moisture-cured urethane. The product must be installed over a drainage layer such as crushed stone, or on an existing engineered surface.

Safe Guard Surfacing

Safe Guard Surfacing Corp.

For full listing, see CSI section 32 18 16 - Synthetic Resilient Surfacing

32 13 00
Rigid Paving

Rigid, fluid-installed paving can double as a porous pavement (to provide excellent stormwater drainage) by using specialized formulas of concrete or asphalt that leave the "fines" out so that the cured pavement remains porous. Detailed specifications are available that will help your local concrete and asphalt mixing plants satisfy your needs; with these materials, look for a paving contractor familiar with porous pavement, as the installation is quite different. (See feature articles EBN Vol. 3, No. 5 & Vol. 13, No. 9.)

Rubbersidewalks

Rubbersidewalks, Inc.
2622 W. 157th St.
Gardena, CA 90249

Phone: 310-515-5814
Fax: 310-515-5314
www.rubbersidewalks.com

Rubbersidewalks is a modular sidewalk system made from recycled tires with a polyurethane binder and colorant, and is particularly intended for use near trees. The high-density pavers, anchored together with self-gripping dowels and locked into a restraint chassis, can be removed for root or other maintenance and then reset, eliminating the need for concrete breakout and replacement. The reversible pavers don't expand in hot weather, and they absorb and retain less heat than concrete. The system has been freeze-thaw tested according to ASTM C1026 with good performance characteristics exhibited, and is also ADA compliant for pedestrian and wheeled traffic. While the pavers aren't considered porous themselves, the system provides immediate drainage at the module seams.

StoneyCrete

Stoney Creek Materials, LLC
25 Stoney Creek Cove
P.O. Box 342306
Austin, TX 78734

Phone: 512-261-0821
Fax: 512-261-8709
www.stoneycreekmaterials.com

StoneyCrete™ is a pervious concrete pavement installed by trained and certified contractors. The mix includes a proprietary additive that improves elasticity and strength: 4,000 psi at 28 days. Where available, some of the portland cement in the mix is replaced by fly ash (up to 20%) or blast-furnace slag (up to 40%).

32 14 13
Precast Concrete Unit Paving

Look for high recycled content, such as flyash and alternative aggregates. Consider the use of porous pavers that promote healthy hydrologic balance in the built environment.

Recycled-Glass-Aggregate Concrete Pavers

ECG, Inc.
104 Corporate Dr.
Elizabeth City, NC 27909

Phone: 252-333-1002
Fax: 252-333-1029
www.glass-recycling.com

ECG manufactures commercial-grade pavers with decorative cast patterns using 82% recycled-glass aggregate (principally from post-consumer sources) for such applications as sidewalks, courtyards, and driveways. They may be installed on a concrete sub-base using mortar or grout, or on compacted gravel/sand. Available in eight standard integral colors (custom colors may be ordered), the pavers are 18" x 18" x 2" and weigh 36 lbs. ECG offers a variety of cast-concrete products made with recycled-glass aggregate.

32 14 16
Brick Unit Paving

Recycled bricks are attractive and functional, and can be installed to have drainage voids along the installed edges as porous paving systems. Porous pavement needs to be installed above a "reservoir" of uniform-sized aggregate (for example, 1-1/2" crushed stone). (See feature articles EBN Vol. 3, No. 5 & Vol. 13, No. 9.)

Salvaged Brick

Gavin Historical Bricks
2050 Glendale Rd.
Iowa City, IA 52245

Phone: 319-354-5251
www.historicalbricks.com

Gavin Historical Bricks supplies salvaged bricks and cobblestones recovered from buildings and streets from around the country. Bricks are used in new construction to provide an antique look, as well as for historic restoration projects. Custom brick matching is available. The company also handcuts antique brick into 1/2" floor tile for a variety of applications. Shipping is provided nationwide, though the heavy weight reduces the practicality (and environmental attractiveness) of shipping large quantities long distances.

32 14 44
Porous Unit Paving, Precast Concrete

As the proportion of land covered with impervious surfaces continues to grow, dealing with stormwater in the built environment is increasingly costly, demanding, and important. Natural environments are able to absorb most stormwater loads, maintaining a healthy hydrologic balance. Porous unit pavers made from concrete include open-grid products that can be filled with aggregate or plantings. Solid unit pavers are often used in porous pavement systems, installed to have drainage voids along the installed edges. Porous pavement needs to be installed above a "reservoir" of uniform-sized aggregate (for example, 1-1/2" crushed stone). In addition to infiltrating stormwater, porous paving systems planted with grass also minimize contributions to the urban heat-island effect while providing visually appealing outdoor space. (See also 32 12 43 - Porous Flexible Paving & 32 14 45 - Porous Unit Paving, Plastic.) (See feature articles EBN Vol. 3, No. 5 & Vol. 13, No. 9.)

Bio-Aquifer Storm System

Advanced Pavement Technology
67 Stonehill Rd.
Oswego, IL 60543

Toll-free: 877-551-4200
www.advancedpavement.com

The Bio-Aquifer Storm System (BASS) from Advanced Pavement Technology is an engineered permeable paving system which provides post-construction runoff rates that are the same or better than preconstruction, without the use of detention ponds. The system includes subsurface drainage/detention layers of rocks and aggregate to a minimum depth of 18", topped with concrete porous pavers. The system permits exceptionally heavy vehicle traffic and is not affected by extreme thermal conditions.

Concrete Porous Pavers

Capitol Ornamental Concrete Specialties, Inc.
90 Main St.
P.O. Box 3249
South Amboy, NJ 08879

Toll-free: 800-254-5098
Phone: 732-727-5460
Fax: 732-727-8714
www.capitolconcrete.com

Capitol Ornamental Concrete Specialties offers a number of concrete pavers suitable for porous paving installations, including the Ecologic™ Paver System—an engineered permeable pavement system that uses 4" x 8" and 4" x 4" interlocking concrete pavers installed over an air-entrained soil media.

EP Henry ECO Pavers

EP Henry Corporation
201 Park Ave.
P.O. Box 615
Woodbury, NJ 08096

Toll-free: 800-444-3679
Fax: 856-845-0023
www.ephenry.com

EP Henry manufactures ECO Pavers, permeable interlocking concrete pavers available in blended colors that measure 9" x 6-11/16" x 3-1/8". EP Henry's Monoslabs are an erosion control grid paver measuring 23-1/2" x 15-5/8" x 4-9/16" and have a grid-like configuration with a multilevel surface. Monoslabs are primarily used as a permeable erosion control product. EP Henry's Turf Paver is a lattice-like grid-paver

that measures 23-7/16" x 15-3/4" x 3-1/8" and is commonly used for emergency access lanes. The grid paving systems are typically seeded with grasses.

Most recently mentioned in EBN 13:12

EcoGrid Porous Pavers

Hanover Architectural Products
240 Bender Rd.
Hanover, PA 17331

Toll-free: 800-426-4242
Phone: 717-637-0500
Fax: 717-637-7145
www.hanoverpavers.com

EcoGrid™ Pavers are pervious interlocking concrete paving units which allow moderate vehicle traffic. Each unit is 11-3/4" x 11-3/4" x 4". EcoGrid Pavers contain a percentage of fly ash.

SF-RIMA

Nicolock
640 Muncy Ave.
Lindenhurst, NY 11757

Toll-free: 800-669-9294
Phone: 631-669-0700
Fax: 631-669-0711
www.nicolock.com

Nicolock's environmental paving stones, SF-RIMA™, are made from no-slump concrete with a compressive strength of 8,000 psi. These square pavers (7-3/4" x 7-3/4") can be installed with either wide or narrow spacing, depending upon the orientation of integral spacers. Widely spaced pavers can be seeded with grasses, which may mitigate heat island effects and stormwater runoff. Nicolock has manufacturing facilities in Lindenhurst, NY, Frederick, MD, and North Haven, CT.

Drainstone and Turfstone

Oldcastle Architectural Products Group
375 Northridge Rd., Ste. 250
Atlanta, GA 30350

Toll-free: 800-899-8455
Phone: 770-804-3363
Fax: 770-804-3369
www.belgardhardscapes.com

Drainstone and Turfstone by Belgard are concrete porous paving products. Drainstone has an octagonal pattern (3-1/8" x 4" x 8") that allows water to infiltrate between adjoining pavers. Turfstone is a larger, precast unit covering 2-2/3 ft² each. The 40% open, basketweave pattern supports grass growth in and between the pavers. Both products have a compressive strength greater than 8,000 psi and meet or exceed ASTM tests for water absorption and freeze-thaw stability (C-936 and C-67).

Grasstone I and InfiltraStone

Pavestone Corporation
4835 LBJ Fwy., Ste. 700
Dallas, TX 75244

Phone: 972-404-0400
Fax: 972-404-9200
www.pavestone.com

Grasstone I is an interlocking concrete paver with an open-void lattice design in a figure-8 pattern to accommodate plant growth; it may also be used for permanent erosion control on slopes. InfiltraStone is a brick-shaped concrete paver with quarter-round voids at each corner, and a half-round void on each long edge. Pavestone Corporation has a number of production facilities in several states that can reduce shipping energy use.

UNI Eco-Stone

UNI-Group U.S.A.
4362 Northlake Blvd., Ste. 204
Palm Beach Gardens, FL 33410

Toll-free: 800-872-1864
Phone: 561-626-4666
Fax: 561-627-6403
www.uni-groupusa.org

UNI Eco-Stone® is a 3-1/8"-thick interlocking concrete porous paver that measures approximately 9" long by 5-1/2" at its widest point. These pavers can be installed in running bond, basketweave, and herringbone patterns. UNI-Group U.S.A. licenses over two dozen companies around the country to manufacture these pavers.

32 00 00
Exterior Improvements

32 14 45
Porous Unit Paving, Plastic

Porous paving seeks to combine the load-carrying capacity we expect of paved areas with the water-infiltration qualities of natural ground cover. With plastic porous paving systems, look for recycled content—and avoid systems that can't be easily removed later (such as free fibers that are mixed with the soil) if needs change. These pavers are available in a variety of shapes, sizes, and colors, and some are interlocking. They should be installed above a "reservoir" of uniform-sized aggregate (for example, 1-1/2" crushed stone). In addition to infiltrating stormwater, porous paving systems planted with grass also minimize contributions to the urban heat-island effect while providing visually appealing outdoor space. (See also 32 12 43 - Porous Flexible Paving.) (See feature articles EBN Vol. 3, No. 5 & Vol. 13, No. 9.)

Salvaverde

Geoproducts Corp.
11-110 Jardin Dr.
Concord, ON L4K 4R4 Canada

Toll-free: 877-GEOTUBE
Phone: 905-760-2256
Fax: 905-760-0491
www.geoproductscorp.com

Salvaverde, made from recycled HDPE, is an interlocking modular system for creating vegetated car parking areas, alleys, and walkways. The grid supports vehicle and pedestrian loads (up to 35 tons per square foot), while preventing soil compaction. The hexagonal grid is intended to be installed over a gravel, stone, or rubble drainage layer. The cells may be filled with planting media or aggregate.

MODI Porous Paving Grid

Green Innovations, Ltd
81 Snowhill Crest
Toronto, ON M1S 3T4 Canada

New

Toll-free: 888-725-7524
Phone: 416-725-7524
Fax: 416-283-6273
www.greeninnovations.ca

The modular, reversible MODI Porous Paving Grid from Green Innovations is made from 100% post-consumer HDPE. It can be used to create parking, driving, and nonslip walking surfaces on lawns or sand bases, or to create gravel surfaces. The flexible grid parts, which were designed to be reused, can be individually removed, and may be shaped with a saw or grinding disc. The grids will support heavy trucks, according to the manufacturer. Accessories (made of acetyl resin) include marker plugs and holding rings. The system comes in a dark green color; light grey or light beige are available on request.

GT Tech Panels

GridTech
221 Third St.
Admiral's Gate Tower, Ste. 507
Newport, RI 02840

Toll-free: 800-959-7920
Phone: 401-849-7920
Fax: 401-849-7937
www.gridtech.com

GT Tech Panels are made from 100% recycled HDPE plastic. The reusable interlocking panels are 2" thick and hexagonal in shape. They provide a permeable surface and erosion control for outdoor events, as well as temporary construction roadbeds on fragile soils and wet areas. The surface is designed to be nonskid for convenient handicap access. Large areas can be surfaced quickly with cranes and loading equipment laying preassembled sections.

Netpave 50 and Netpave 25

GridTech
221 Third St.
Admiral's Gate Tower, Ste. 507
Newport, RI 02840

Toll-free: 800-959-7920
Phone: 401-849-7920
Fax: 401-849-7937
www.gridtech.com

GridTech is the North American distributor for Netpave® by Netlon Turf Systems®. Netpave 50 is a system of interlocking pavers made from 100% post-industrial recycled polyethylene from the foil production industry. The pavers, filled with gravel or planted with grass, are suitable for parking lots, driveways, access roads, helipads, and sidewalks. No pins are needed because of a unique lug-and-slot connector design. The pavers are able to adapt as individual units and as a matrix to uneven surfaces, gradients, and differential settlement. Measuring 1 m² and 2" deep, the pavers are lightweight and easy to install. Optional white moldings that clip over the top of the paver cells are available to delineate parking spaces or routes. A similar product, Netpave 25, is a stabilizing system for use on top of existing turf surfaces to protect grassed paths, parking, and other applications from damage and erosion. It will support light traffic on firm ground.

Grasspave2, Gravelpave2, Draincore2

Invisible Structures, Inc.
1600 Jackson St., Ste. 310
Golden, CO 80401

Toll-free: 800-233-1510
Phone: 303-233-8383
Fax: 800-233-1522
www.invisiblestructures.com

Most of Invisible Structures' plastic mat products are made from 100% injection-molded, recycled HDPE with varying amounts of post-consumer and post-industrial content. Some products also have geotextile backings. Grasspave2 and Gravelpave2 are grids that are designed for drive-on, porous paving surfaces of grass or gravel. They are shipped in 9 standard roll sizes. Gravelpave2 comes in 4 standard colors and has a geotextile backing to prevent gravel migration. The tan, gray, and terra cotta Gravelpave2 cannot be guaranteed to be 100% recycled plastic. Draincore2 is a drainage mat designed to be used in conjunction with geotextiles and appropriate soils for effective subsurface drainage of high use outdoor areas. Draincore2 has high compressive strength suitable for heavy traffic.

Most recently mentioned in EBN 3:4 & 3:5

Safety Deck II

Mat Factory, Inc.
760 W. 16th St., Bldg. E
Costa Mesa, CA 92627

Toll-free: 800-628-7626
Phone: 949-645-3122
Fax: 949-645-0966
www.matfactoryinc.com

Safety Deck II is an outdoor surfacing product made from 100% recycled-tire rubber and recycled PVC. It comes in 1"-thick, 20" x 20" interlocking tiles with holes to allow grass to grow through and to facilitate drainage. Safety Deck II creates durable grassed areas that are especially useful for wheelchair-bound people.

TuffTrack and G.P.8. GrassRoad Pavers

NDS
851 N. Harvard Ave.
Lindsay, CA 93247

Toll-free: 800-726-1994
Phone: 559-562-9888
Fax: 559-562-4488
www.ndspro.com

Porous pavers are designed to protect grass areas from compression caused by vehicular and pedestrian traffic. They also act as an effective tool for erosion control. TuffTrack™ and G.P.8.® GrassRoad Pavers® contain up to 50% post-consumer recycled high-impact polypropylene plastic. Rated at 98,500 PSF "empty."

Geoblock

Presto Products Company
670 N. Perkins St.
P.O. Box 2399
Appleton, WI 54912

Toll-free: 800-548-3424
Phone: 920-738-1328
Fax: 920-738-1222
www.prestoproducts.com

The Geoblock® system has a minimum of 50% recycled polyethylene content. The interlocking 20" x 40" x 2" porous paving sections are suitable for high compressive load and turf protection requirements.

Geoweb Porous Paving Systems

Presto Products Company
670 N. Perkins St.
P.O. Box 2399
Appleton, WI 54912

Toll-free: 800-548-3424
Phone: 920-738-1328
Fax: 920-738-1222
www.prestoproducts.com

32 00 00
Exterior Improvements

Geoweb® is a three-dimensional, web-like polyethylene porous paving product for confinement of cohesionless materials such as aggregate infill or aggregate-stabilized turf for high load-support requirements. This product does not contain recycled plastic.

Grassy Pavers

RK Manufacturing, Inc.
222 Market Ridge Rd.
Ridgeland, MS 39157

Toll-free: 800-957-5575
Phone: 601-502-1324
Fax: 601-914-2983
www.rkmfg.com

Grassy™ Pavers are made from UV-sta-bilized, post-consumer recycled-content HDPE. The company claims the dark green plastic-honeycomb grid structure can support 97,500 lbs/ft^2.

Safe Guard Surfacing

Safe Guard Surfacing Corp.

For full listing, see CSI section 32 18 16 - Synthetic Resilient Surfacing

Ecogrid

Terrafirm Solutions Ltd.
1088 Hornby St.
Vancouver, BC V6J 5C2 Canada

New

Toll-free: 888-837-2376
Phone: 604-622-7427
Fax: 604-622-7428
www.terrafirmsolutions.ca

Ecogrid products from Terrafirm Solutions are made from 100% recycled post-con-sumer HDPE. The lock-together trays may be filled with planting medium or gravel. EcoGrid e30 is suitable for moderate vehicle traffic, walkways, and playgrounds. EcoGrid e50 will accommodate heavy vehicle traffic and parking areas. EcoGrid s50 is for slope stabilization. They are available in black, green, and brown, and may also be used for green roof applications to prevent soil com-paction in growing areas while providing a barrier between the roofing membranes and pedestrian traffic.

32 15 00
Aggregate Surfacing

Salvaged and recycled materials, such as brick or glass chunks with soft-ened edges, can be attractive surfacing materials in landscaping applications. Granulated rubber made from recycled

tires can make a durable and highly resilient play environment when ap-plied to a 6" depth; it creates a softer play environment than pea gravel and, unlike wood chips, will not rot or attract insects. Keep these areas separated from other landscaping materials, so that the nonbiodegradable aggregate can later be removed if uses change.

Recycled Glass Aggregates and Powders

American Specialty Glass, Inc.

For full listing, see CSI section 09 66 03 - Terrazzo Flooring Aggregate

RubberStuff

ART (American Rubber Technologies, Inc.)
P.O. Box 6548
Jacksonville, FL 32236

Toll-free: 800-741-5201
Fax: 904-786-1060
www.americanrubber.com

RubberStuff™, made from recycled-tire rub-ber, is a granulated-rubber safety surface for playground applications. The 1/4" rubber granules are usually installed at a 6" depth.

Recycled Glass for Landscaping

Conigliaro Industries, Inc.
701 Waverly St.
Framingham, MA 01702

New

Toll-free: 888-266-4425
Phone: 508-872-9668
Fax: 508-653-6672
www.conigliaro.com

Conigliaro Industries offers "barefoot-friendly" tumbled glass aggregates for decorative, landscape, and construction uses in 1/8" minus and 3/4" minus aggregate sizes. Appropriate for mulch replacement, roadbeds, flowable fills, backfills, and drain-age projects, this aggregate made from 100% recycled glass bottles and plate glass is available in various color blends and in any quantity.

Tire Turf

Continental Turf Systems, Inc.
P.O. Box 389
Continental, OH 45831

Phone: 419-596-4242
Fax: 234-542-2816
www.continentalturf.com

Tire Turf is loose, granulated, 100% post-consumer recycled-tire-rubber ground cover for use in playgrounds, horse arenas, and as a landscaping mulch.

Brick Nuggets

Cunningham Brick Co., Inc.
701 N. Main St.
Lexington, NC 27292

Toll-free: 800-672-6181
Phone: 336-248-8541
Fax: 336-224-0002
www.cunninghambrick.com

Brick Nuggets are crushed waste bricks suit-able for landscaping uses. They are available in 1/2 cubic foot bags.

Recycled Glass for Landscaping

Heritage Glass, Inc.
130 W. 700 S, Bldg. E
Smithfield, UT 84335

Phone: 435-563-5585
Fax: 435-563-5583
www.heritageglass.net

Heritage Glass offers 1/2" to 2" recycled-glass aggregate with dulled edges and a range of colors for exterior and interior landscaping applications. Sources include post-industrial float glass cullet and post-consumer recycled bottle glass. Heritage also provides recycled-glass aggregate for terrazzo applications.

Surfacing

North West Rubber Mats, Ltd.
33850 Industrial Ave.
Abbotsford, BC V2S 7T9 Canada

Toll-free: 800-663-8724
Phone: 604-859-2002
Fax: 604-859-2009
www.northwestrubber.com

North West Rubber produces crumb rubber from used tires in various sizes ranging from 30 mesh to 1/2". Crumb rubber can be used as an ingredient in asphalt mixes, as a play-ground material, and on running tracks.

Granulated Rubber

Rubber Granulators, Inc.
3831 152nd St. NE
Marysville, WA 98271

Phone: 360-658-7754
Fax: 360-653-6430
www.rubbergranulators.com

Rubber Granulators produces granulated rubber made from used tires available in 55-lb. and 2,000-lb. sacks.

32 00 00
Exterior Improvements

Perma-Turf Playground Safety Surface

TIREC Corporation
P.O. Box 604
Mullica Hill, NJ 08062

Phone: 856-478-4491
Fax: 856-478-9786
www.perma-flex1.com

Perma-Turf® Playground Safety Surface is a fiber-reinforced rubber aggregate made from 100% recycled tires with the steel belting removed. Tirec guarantees its products to be 98% free of steel and backs them with a 50-year guarantee. Perma-Flex® High Performance Arena Footing is a similar product made for equestrian arenas.

32 17 13
Parking Bumpers
(Car Stops)

Recycled plastics and rubber can be used for parking stops, diverting material from the waste stream and providing products with lower embodied energy than portland cement-based concrete products. In addition, the lighter weight of plastic parking bumpers (40-50 lbs. versus 250-300 lbs.) reduces transportation energy consumption and cost of shipping. Plastic parking stops are easily installed with 5/8" rebar stakes, and they never need painting. (See also 34 71 13 - Vehicle Barriers, 34 71 19 - Vehicle Delineators, 32 17 14 - Speed Bumps and Humps.) (See feature article EBN Vol. 5, No. 1.)

**32 00 00
Exterior
Improvements**

Aztec Plastic Parking Stops and Bollards

Amazing Recycled Products, Inc.
P.O. Box 312
Denver, CO 80201

Toll-free: 800-241-2174
Phone: 303-699-7693
Fax: 303-699-2102
www.amazingrecycled.com

Amazing Recycled Products manufactures parking stops as well as flat-top, plateau-top, and chamfered-top bollards (also available customized) from recycled HDPE. The parking stops are 6'–8' long and are offered as industrial heavy duty and standard. Custom lengths are also available. Colors include brown, yellow, gray, blue, white and black.

Recycled-Plastic Products

American Recreational Products

For full listing, see CSI section 12 93 43 - Site Seating and Tables, Plastic

Recycled-Plastic Products

American Recycled Plastic, Inc.
1500 Main St.
Palm Bay, FL 32905

Toll-free: 866-674-1525
Phone: 321-674-1525
Fax: 321-674-2365
www.itsrecycled.com

American Recycled Plastic manufactures a range of products from recycled HDPE, including lumber and timbers, car stops, speed bumps and humps, and vehicle barriers. They also offer a wide variety of recycled-HDPE site furnishings, including benches, outdoor tables, waste receptacles, mailboxes, planters, custom wildlife structures, and bicycle racks.

Barco Recycled-Content Products

Barco Products
11 N. Batavia Ave.
Batavia, IL 60510

Toll-free: 800-338-2697
Phone: 630-879-0084
Fax: 630-879-8687
www.barcoproducts.com

Barco Products offers site furnishings, landscape timbers, and traffic devices made with recycled content, including dozens of styles of picnic tables and park benches made with recycled commingled HDPE and LDPE averaging 40% post-consumer, as well as planters and waste receptacles made from recycled HDPE (90 to 100% post-consumer). Landscape Timbers are made from 100% recycled commingled HDPE and LDPE, sized as railroad ties with premolded holes for rebar reinforcement and interlocking edges for stacking stability. Each timber weighs 42 lbs, about half that of most plastic landscape timbers. 100% recycled tire rubber speed bumps and 100% recycled plastic speed bumps are offered, and colored wheel stops made of 95% recycled commingled HDPE and LDPE. Gray wheel stops contain 85% recycled PVC. Bollards are made from 96% recycled commingled LDPE and HDPE (50 to 80% post-industrial).

Bedford Technology Recycled-Plastic Products

Bedford Technology, LLC

For full listing, see CSI section 06 53 13 - Solid Plastic Decking

Power-Stop

C&A, a Tandus Company
311 Smith Industrial Blvd.
P.O. Box 1447
Dalton, GA 30722

Toll-free: 800-248-2878
Phone: 706-259-9711
Fax: 706-259-2179
www.tandus.com

Power-Stop is a parking stop made from C&A's ER3 composite material. This very durable composite is made from post-consumer and post-industrial carpeting and carpet-tile waste that includes PVC backing and nylon face fiber.

Most recently mentioned in EBN 6:6

BetterStop and BetterBump

Curb Appeal Materials, LTD
3824 N. Johnsburg Rd.
McHenry, IL 60050

Phone: 815-344-7926
Fax: 815-344-7960
www.vortexcomposites.com

BetterStop and BetterBump traffic/vehicle control products are made with 100% commingled plastics, including synthetic carpet material, from consumer and industrial sources in a patented cold-extrusion process. The stops are available in yellow, white, blue or gray integral color; the bumps, in black or yellow.

Most recently mentioned in EBN 6:6

Recycled-Rubber Parking Curbs

New

Dinoflex Manufacturing, Ltd.
P.O. Box 3309
Salmon Arm, BC V1E 4S1 Canada

Toll-free: 877-713-1899
Phone: 252-832-7780
Fax: 800-305-2109
www.dinoflex.com

Park-Right Parking Curbs are made from 100% recycled tire rubber. These flexible, lightweight curbs can also be used indoors—mounted on the floor or walls—to prevent damage by forklifts, pallet jacks, dollies, and other plant machinery. They will not warp, crack, chip, or rot.

Car Stops

ECG, Inc.
104 Corporate Dr.
Elizabeth City, NC 27909

Phone: 252-333-1002
Fax: 252-333-1029
www.glass-recycling.com

ECG manufactures DOT Class B fiber- and rebar-reinforced concrete car stops using recycled glass (principally from post-consumer sources) as the aggregate. Normal car stop profiles are 6"h x 8"w x 72" and weigh 180 lbs; low-profile stops are 4"h x 6"w x 72" l and weigh 80 lbs. The mounting holes contain PVC sleeves to prevent freeze/thaw damage caused by standing water. Eight standard integral colors are available; custom colors may be ordered. ECG offers a variety of cast-concrete products made with recycled-glass aggregate.

Recycled-Plastic Parking Stops

Everlast Plastic Lumber
1000 S. 4th St.
Hamburg, PA 19526

Phone: 610-562-8336
Fax: 610-562-8381
www.everlastlumber.com

Everlast parking stops are made with 100% recycled HPDE (80% post-consumer). They are 6-1/2' long, weigh about 40 lbs, and are available in blue, silver-gray, and yellow.

Park-It and Easy Rider

GNR Technologies, Inc.
990 Upton
LaSalle, QC H8R 2T9 Canada

Toll-free: 800-641-4143
Phone: 514-366-6116
Fax: 514-366-6440
www.gnrtech.com

Park-It and Easy Rider are 100% recycled-rubber parking stops and speed bumps, respectively. These durable products are black with reflective yellow tape markings.

Traffic and Parking Delineators and Devices

Inteq Corp.

For full listing, see CSI section 34 71 19 - Vehicle Delineators

Car Stops

Kay Park Recreation Corp.
1301 Pine St.
P.O. Box 477
Janesville, IA 50647

Toll-free: 800-553-2476
Fax: 319-987-2900
www.kaypark.com

Kay Park Recreation's Car Stops are made from 96% post-consumer recycled, commingled plastic.

Parking Stops, Speed Bumps, and Bollards

Litchfield Industries
4 Industrial Dr.
Litchfield, MI 49252

Toll-free: 800-542-5282
Phone: 517-542-2988
Fax: 517-542-3939
www.litchfieldindustries.com

Litchfield Industries manufactures parking stops, speed bumps, and bollards made from 100% post-consumer plastic. Parking stops are 3', 4', or 6' long and are available in yellow, blue, white, gray, and black. Speed bumps are 3', 6', or 9' long and yellow in color.

PlasTEAK Traffic Control Devices

PlasTEAK
3563 Copley Rd.
P.O. Box 4290
Akron, OH 44321

Toll-free: 800-320-1841
Phone: 330-668-2587
Fax: 330-666-0844
www.plasteak.com

PlasTEAK's parking stops, speed humps, and signage are made with 100% post-consumer recycled HDPE. The stops are available in 4', 6', and 8' lengths, as well as 20" wheel chocks, in standard colors yellow, gray, and blue; white, brown, and black are available by special order. Speed humps come in yellow only, in 4', 6', and 9' lengths. A five-year warranty is provided. Signage is available in a wide range of colors and styles.

Car Stops and Speed Bumps

Plastic Recycling of Iowa Falls, Inc.
10252 Hwy. 65
Iowa Falls, IA 50126

Toll-free: 800-338-1438
Phone: 641-648-5073
Fax: 641-648-5074
www.hammersplastic.com

Plastic Recycling of Iowa Falls, formerly Hammer's Plastic Recycling, manufactures yellow, blue, and gray car stops and yellow speed bumps from recycled commingled HDPE, LDPE, LLDPE, and other miscellaneous plastics.

Pilot Rock Site Furnishings

R. J. Thomas Manufacturing Co., Inc.

For full listing, see CSI section 12 93 43 - Site Seating and Tables, Plastic

Parking Stops, Speed Bumps, and Bollards

Recycled Plastic Man, Inc.
P.O. Box 609
Placida, FL 33946

Toll-free: 800-253-7742
Phone: 941-698-1060
Fax: 941-698-1038
www.recycledplasticman.com

Recycled Plastic Man manufactures parking stops, speed bumps, and bollards from post-consumer recycled plastics (primarily HDPE).

32 00 00
Exterior Improvements

Parking Stops and Speed Bumps

The Plastic Lumber Company, Inc.
115 W. Bartges St.
Akron, OH 44311

Toll-free: 800-886-8990
Phone: 330-762-8989
Fax: 330-762-1613
www.plasticlumber.com

The Plastic Lumber Company's Parking Stops of recycled plastic are 3', 4', or 6' in length and come in yellow, white, gray, blue, and black. Bright yellow Speed Bumps are 4', 6', or 9' in length.

Road and Parking Appurtenances

Traffic & Parking Control Co., Inc. (Tapco)
800 Wall St.
Elm Grove, WI 53122

Toll-free: 800-236-0112
Fax: 800-444-0331
www.tapconet.com

TAPCO distributes parking control devices from recycled plastic and rubber, such as wheel stops, bollard covers, speed bumps, and speed humps.

Recycled-Plastic Posts

XPotential Products Inc.
St. Boniface Postal Sta.
P.O. Box 126
Winnipeg, MB R2H 3B4 Canada

Toll-free: 800-863-6619
Phone: 204-224-3933
Fax: 204-224-4678
www.xpotentialproducts.com

XPotential offers parking stops, landscape timbers, and fence posts made with recycled materials, including auto shredder residue as well as HDPE and LDPE plastics. Impact-Curb parking stops are approximately 5-1/4" x 8" in 6' or 8' lengths, and 4" x 6" in 6' or 8' lengths. Interlocking landscape timbers measure 2-1/2" x 3-1/2" x 95" and weigh 36 lbs. each. Impact-Post comes in two sizes (6" x 6" x 8' and 4" x 4" x 8') and is appropriate for landscaping and fencing posts. All the XPotential products come with a limited lifetime warranty.

32 17 14
Speed Bumps and Humps

Recycled plastics and rubber can effectively be used in the manufacture of speed bumps and speed humps. It diverts material from the waste stream, and has lower embodied energy than concrete products. (See feature articles EBN Vol. 5, No. 1 & Vol. 12, No. 3.)

Recycled-Plastic Products

American Recreational Products

For full listing, see CSI section 12 93 43 - Site Seating and Tables, Plastic

Recycled-Plastic Products

American Recycled Plastic, Inc.

For full listing, see CSI section 32 17 13 - Parking Bumpers (Car Stops)

Barco Recycled-Content Products

Barco Products

For full listing, see CSI section 32 17 13 - Parking Bumpers (Car Stops)

Bedford Technology Recycled-Plastic Products

Bedford Technology, LLC

For full listing, see CSI section 06 53 13 - Solid Plastic Decking

BetterStop and BetterBump

Curb Appeal Materials, LTD

For full listing, see CSI section 32 17 13 - Parking Bumpers (Car Stops)

Park-It and Easy Rider

GNR Technologies, Inc.

For full listing, see CSI section 32 17 13 - Parking Bumpers (Car Stops)

Traffic and Parking Delineators and Devices

Inteq Corp.

For full listing, see CSI section 34 71 19 - Vehicle Delineators

Parking Stops, Speed Bumps, and Bollards

Litchfield Industries

For full listing, see CSI section 32 17 13 - Parking Bumpers (Car Stops)

PlasTEAK Traffic Control Devices

PlasTEAK

For full listing, see CSI section 32 17 13 - Parking Bumpers (Car Stops)

Car Stops and Speed Bumps

Plastic Recycling of Iowa Falls, Inc.

For full listing, see CSI section 32 17 13 - Parking Bumpers (Car Stops)

Parking Stops, Speed Bumps, and Bollards

Recycled Plastic Man, Inc.

For full listing, see CSI section 32 17 13 - Parking Bumpers (Car Stops)

Restrictor Speed Humps

Recycled Technology, Inc.
19475 S.W. Teton Ave.
Tualatin, OR 97062

Toll-free: 800-455-6287
Phone: 503-691-5845
Fax: 503-692-9503
www.recycledtech.com

Recycled Technology Restrictor Speed Humps for temporary or permanent installations are made from recycled-tire rubber. They are designed to calm traffic, slowing vehicular speeds to 25 mph.

Speed Bumps

Scientific Developments, Inc.
175 S. Danebo
P.O. Box 2522
Eugene, OR 97402

Toll-free: 800-824-6853
Phone: 541-686-9844
Fax: 541-485-8990
www.sdirubber.com

Scientific Developments Speed Bumps are made from recycled-tire rubber with a UV-stabilized virgin rubber overlay. They are available with very durable, molded-in yellow hypalon stripes.

Parking Stops and Speed Bumps

The Plastic Lumber Company, Inc.

For full listing, see CSI section 32 17 13 - Parking Bumpers (Car Stops)

Road and Parking Appurtenances

Traffic & Parking Control Co., Inc. (Tapco)

For full listing, see CSI section 32 17 13 - Parking Bumpers (Car Stops)

32 17 26
Tactile Warning Surfacing

Look for recycled content (such as flyash and non-quarried aggregate) and exceptional durability.

**32 00 00
Exterior Improvements**

Detectable Warning Pavers

ECG, Inc.
104 Corporate Dr.
Elizabeth City, NC 27909

Phone: 252-333-1002
Fax: 252-333-1029
www.glass-recycling.com

ECG manufactures ADA truncated-dome detectable warning pavers (for such uses as curb ramps and boarding platforms at transit stations). The 12"x12"x2" pavers are made to DOT Class B concrete standards using recycled glass (principally from post-consumer sources) as the aggregate. Ten standard integral colors are available; custom colors may be ordered. Installation considerations include a recommended concrete sub-base of 4 to 8 inches (depending on the anticipated amount of vehicular drive-overs). A one-inch mortar bed is required for installation over cured concrete, or the pavers may be embedded directly in the uncured concrete. The joints and perimeter require grout or sealant. ECG offers a variety of cast-concrete products made with recycled-glass aggregate.

32 18 16
Synthetic Resilient Surfacing

A wide variety of outdoor surfacing products made from recycled plastic or rubber are available. Recycled rubber products made from used automobile tires are durable, resilient, slip-resistant, and water-resistant, and they withstand damage from ice skates, cleats, golf spikes, and heavy traffic. Rubber products may have color integrated into the rubber as flecks or binding matrix, or the color may be incorporated into a thick wear layer. Recycled plastic products are typically available in a number of color choices. They often have an open-weave construction to allow for drainage and a rough texture to enhance slip-resistance. (See also 09 65 00 - Resilient Flooring & 09 65 66 - Resilient Athletic Flooring.)

Child Safe Safety Surface

Child Safe Products, Inc.
645 Broadway
Amityville, NY 11701

Toll-free: 800-434-5616
Phone: 631-841-0363
Fax: 631-841-0562
www.childsafeproducts.com

Child Safe Safety Surface is a poured-in-place recycled-tire rubber playground surface. The product is installed with a 100% recycled cushioning layer topped by a colored EPDM wear layer.

Rubber Playground Tiles and Play Tiles

Dinoflex Manufacturing, Ltd.
P.O. Box 3309
Salmon Arm, BC V1E 4S1 Canada

Toll-free: 877-713-1899
Phone: 252-832-7780
Fax: 800-305-2109
www.dinoflex.com

Rubber Playground Tiles and Play Tiles are formulated from a combination of 100% post-consumer recycled SBR (styrene butadiene rubber), EPDM (ethylene propylene diene monomer) rubber and polyurethane. Colored toppings are made up of either EPDM granules or SBR granules mixed with pigment color. All colored toppings are approximately ½" thick with the SBR granules making up the remainder of the tile.

Play Tiles have an additional custom logo layer. Rubber tiles are used as a playground surface around children's play equipment and comply with ASTM guidelines for shock absorbency.

Vitriturf

Hanover Specialties, Inc.
901 Motor Pkwy.
Hauppauge, NY 11788

Toll-free: 800-777-6596
Phone: 631-231-1300
Fax: 631-231-1329
www.vitriturf.com

Vitriturf is a playground safety surface made from recycled-tire rubber, a proprietary binder, and an EPDM wear layer.

Flexi-Pave and Flex-Path

KB Industries, Inc.
28100 US Hwy. 19 N, Ste. 410
Clearwater, FL 33761

Toll-free: 877-826-8600
Phone: 727-726-2700
Fax: 727-726-2800
www.kbius.com

KB Industries offers Flexi-Pave and Flex-Path, porous paving systems made with recycled rubber tires. Poured in place by certified installers, they offer slip-resistant, impact-absorbing surfaces that resist damage caused by freeze/thaw and root intrusion. Flexi-Pave, suitable for parking lots, boat ramps, sidewalks, trails, and decks, is made with 3/8" nominal recycled rubber granules and

1/2" nominal gravel aggregate, bonded with a proprietary single-component, moisture-cured urethane. The product must be installed over a drainage layer such as crushed stone, or on an existing engineered surface. Flex-Path, suitable as a safety surfacing for use under playground equipment, on walkways, sidewalks, pathways, handicap ramps, and balconies, is made with 3/8" nominal recycled rubber granules and 1/2" nominal gravel aggregate. The product must be installed on an existing engineered surface.

No Fault Safety Surface

No Fault Sport Group
3112 Valley Creek Dr., Ste. C
Baton Rouge, LA 70808

Toll-free: 1-866-637-7678
Phone: 225-215-7760
Fax: 225-291-3821
www.nofault.com

No Fault™ Safety Surface is a porous, poured-in-place product made from recycled-tire rubber mixed with a polyurethane binder for use as a playground surface.

PlayFall

North West Rubber Mats, Ltd.
33850 Industrial Ave.
Abbotsford, BC V2S 7T9 Canada

Toll-free: 800-663-8724
Phone: 604-859-2002
Fax: 604-859-2009
www.northwestrubber.com

PlayFall playground tiles are made from recycled-tire rubber with a synthetic binder. The product comes in 24"-square tiles in 1 3/4", 2 1/2", 3", 3 1/4", and 4 1/4" thicknesses, providing a critical fall height of up to 10'. PlayFall is available in a Basic Series in green, terra cotta, and black; and an EPDM Series and a Planet Series, both of which have a wear layer that contains flecks of EPDM rubber and are available in many colors.

CushionPlay

Playworld Systems
1000 Buffalo Rd.
Lewisburg, PA 17837

Toll-free: 800-233-8404
Phone: 570-522-9800
Fax: 570-522-3030
www.playworldsystems.com

CushionPlay® resilient surfacings are made from 100% recycled-tire rubber for installation under play structures. CushionPlay meets all ADA requirements and exceeds CPSC guidelines for shock absorption, comes with a 5-year warranty, and is available in 4 colors.

32 00 00
Exterior Improvements

Bounce Back

RB Rubber Products, Inc.
904 N.E. Tenth Ave.
McMinnville, OR 97128

Toll-free: 800-525-5530
Phone: 503-472-4691
Fax: 503-434-4455
www.rbrubber.com

Bounce Back Safety Cushions provide fall protection for playgrounds. Bounce Back are 24"-square, smooth-surfaced tiles made from 100% recycled-tire rubber available in black, blue, red, or green and have a waffle-patterned undersurface.

Safe Guard Surfacing

Safe Guard Surfacing Corp.
9 Brandywine Dr.
Deer Park, NY 11729

Toll-free: 800-899-8703
Phone: 631-360-9500
Fax: 631-360-9575
www.safeguardsurfacing.com

Safe Guard Poured-in-Place Surfacing, Tiles, and Mats include recycled-tire rubber. Poured-in-Place Surfacing has a colored EPDM layer that can be customized in free-form designs.

SofTILE KrosLOCK

SofSURFACES, Inc.
4393 Discovery Line
P.O. Box 239
Petrolia, ON N0N 1R0 Canada

Toll-free: 800-263-2363
Phone: 519-882-8799
Fax: 519-882-2697
www.sofsurfaces.com

All SofTILE® KrosLOCK products are made from approximately 90% recycled-tire rubber and polyurethane binder and are used as protective surfaces for playgrounds throughout North America. Recent design changes have enhanced the locking design of SofTILE. Additional design changes include increased density, leading to the highest impact attenuation ratings in the industry, according to the manufacturer. SofSURFACES warrants impact attenuation performance to comply with the latest standards (ASTM F1292-99) for a full 5 years in any weather condition.

SpectraBound Tiles and SpectraPour Surfacing

SpectraTurf, Inc.
500 E. Rincon St.
Corona, CA 92879

Toll-free: 800-875-5788
Phone: 951-736-3579
Fax: 951-734-3630
www.spectraturf.com

SpectraBound Tiles and SpectraPour Surfacing are recycled-tire rubber playground surfacing products.

Playground Surfaces

Surface America, Inc.
P.O. Box 157
Williamsville, NY 14231

Toll-free: 800-999-0555
Phone: 716-632-8413
Fax: 716-632-8324
www.surfam.com

Surface America is a full-service recycled-rubber playground and recreational surfaces company. Poured-in-place, tile, and roll products are offered. The composition of Playbound Tiles and Playbound Poured-in-Place products includes more than 50% recycled rubber.

Playface

Turtle Plastics
7450-A Industrial Pkwy.
Lorain, OH 44053

Toll-free: 800-437-1603
Phone: 440-282-8008
Fax: 440-282-8822
www.turtleplastics.com

Playface playground tiles are made from recycled PVC plastic and rubber. Available in 20 solid colors, the tiles are 3/4" thick, 12" square, with an interlocking, open-weave design and an anti-slip surface. Playface is intended for use over a 4" base layer of granulated recycled rubber.

32 18 23
Athletic Surfacing

Surfacings for outdoor sports courts, fields, and facilities should be durable, appropriate to the activity, and ensure participant safety. High levels of recycled content are possible in many materials. (See also 09 65 66 - Resilient Athletic Flooring.)

Sport Mat Flooring

Dinoflex Manufacturing, Ltd.
P.O. Box 3309
Salmon Arm, BC V1E 4S1 Canada

Toll-free: 877-713-1899
Phone: 252-832-7780
Fax: 800-305-2109
www.dinoflex.com

Sport Mat Flooring is a rubber tile product for use in arenas, fitness centers, golf courses, retail stores, and office buildings. Made from up to 90% recycled-tire rubber with about 10% polyurethane binder, the flooring is available in solid black or with color flecks. As the amount of color flecks increases, the total content of recycled tire rubber decreases. It is made in a square cut or interlocking configuration—the latter is reversible.

Guardian Super Sport and Loktuff

Humane Manufacturing LLC

For full listing, see CSI section 09 65 66 - Resilient Athletic Flooring

EcoRamp

New

KlipTech Composites
2999 John Stevens Way
Hoquiam, WA 98550

Phone: 360-538-9815
Fax: 360-538-1510
www.paperstoneproducts.com

EcoRamp is a rigid composite surfacing with high compressive strength, excellent screw retention, and low water absorption for skate parks and other "extreme sports" facilities. It is made with 50% post-consumer recycled paper bonded with a proprietary water-based resin system using non-petroleum phenols, including cashew nut shell liquid derivatives. The finished product works easily with a triple-chip, carbide-tipped saw blade and carbide-tipped router bits. It has no detectable free formaldehyde and is Class A fire-rated.

Most recently mentioned in EBN 15:4

Ergo Mattas

Mat Factory, Inc.

For full listing, see CSI section 09 65 66 - Resilient Athletic Flooring

**32 00 00
Exterior
Improvements**

Skater's Blend

New

Renew Resources Ltd.
81 Mack Ave.
Toronto, ON M1L 1M5 Canada

Toll-free: 800-439-5028
Phone: 416-335-4040
Fax: 416-335-4039
www.renewresources.com

Renew Resources offers Skater's Blend skate park surfacing material, made of recycled pre-consumer HDPE and wood fiber. The flexible sheets can be worked with standard tools.

32 31 23
Plastic Fences and Gates

Conventional wood fencing—even that made from pressure-treated wood—is prone to degradation and has a short life. This is a good application for recycled plastics because such products are more durable than those made from wood, and the structural requirements are minimal. Recycled-plastic fencing products are significantly greener than virgin-polymer products.

Aeolian Plastic Lumber & Fences

Aeolian Enterprises, Inc.

For full listing, see CSI section 06 53 13 - Solid Plastic Decking

SuperPicket

Curb Appeal Materials, LTD
3824 N. Johnsburg Rd.
McHenry, IL 60050

Phone: 815-344-7926
Fax: 815-344-7960
www.vortexcomposites.com

SuperPicket™ fencing is made with 100% post-consumer recycled materials—nylon carpet waste with some commingled plastic, stabilized with a small amount of carbon black. It's offered as a maintenance-free fencing material that doesn't rot, warp, splinter, split, or harbor insects—at a cost significantly below that of vinyl. The product comes in a charcoal color, and weathers to an aged-cedar gray. It also accepts paints and stains. Most nail guns won't penetrate the dense material; use screws for assembly. Note that this product consists of the pickets only, which are designed to install on standard cedar or treated posts. For fences taller than 4', three rails and decreased post

spacing are recommended due to the weight of the product.
Most recently mentioned in EBN 6:6

Fencing

Inteq Corp.
35800 Glen Dr.
Eastlake, OH 44095

Phone: 440-953-0550
Fax: 440-953-0564
www.4-inteqcorp.com

Inteq manufactures recycled HDPE plastic fencing (10-100% post-consumer content). The capped hollow posts will accept two, three, or four hollow rails. Inteq's fencing products are available in white, gray, weathered (tan), and black. Picket and Privacy fence is also available. Orange safety fence and Snow fence are available in diamond or rectangular shapes and three additional colors.

Recycled-Plastic Landscape Products

Master Mark Plastics
One Master Mark Dr.
P.O. Box 662
Albany, MN 56307

Toll-free: 800-535-4838
Phone: 320-845-2111
Fax: 320-845-7093
www.mastermark.com

Master Mark makes a variety of landscape products, such as lawn edging, lattice, downspout splash blocks, and privacy fencing from recycled HDPE plastic. According to the manufacturer, they currently recycle over 1 billion post-consumer HDPE plastic containers per year, and boast over 50 million feet of quality landscape edging installed every year.

Recycled-Plastic Net Fencing

Masternet Ltd.

New

1236 Cardiff Blvd.
Mississauga, ON L5S 1P6 Canada

Toll-free: 800-216-2536
Phone: 905-795-0005
Fax: 905-795-9293
www.masternetltd.com

Vexar® fencing from Masternet is an extruded plastic netting composed of 97% post-consumer recycled HDPE, 3% color, and ultraviolet (UV) stabilizers. Products include yard fence (an alternative to chain-link) and a lighter-weight border fence; safety, construction, and barrier fences; and drift fences. A number of roll sizes are available. Masternet purchased the Vexar® technology from DuPont Canada in 1993.

PlasTEAK Fencing

PlasTEAK
3563 Copley Rd.
P.O. Box 4290
Akron, OH 44321

Toll-free: 800-320-1841
Phone: 330-668-2587
Fax: 330-666-0844
www.plasteak.com

PlasTEAK fencing, available in more than two dozen styles, is made with 100% post-consumer recycled HDPE.

Recycled-Plastic Posts

XPotential Products Inc.

For full listing, see CSI section 32 17 13 - Parking Bumpers (Car Stops)

32 35 16
Sound Barriers

Sound barriers should have low embodied energy, long useful lives, and be effective at blocking and/or absorbing noise. Look for high recycled content. Graffiti management, freeze-thaw effects, and damage by cars may be considerations. (See also 32 94 16 - Landscape Timbers.)

32 00 00
Exterior Improvements

SmartTie

Curb Appeal Materials, LTD

For full listing, see CSI section 32 94 16 - Landscape Timbers

EverQuiet Wall

New Frontier Industries, Inc.
P.O. Box 1360
Milton, NH 03851

Toll-free: 866-637-7888
Phone: 603-652-7888
www.newfrontierindustries.com

The EverQuiet Wall is a lightweight assembly of snap-together tongue-and-groove plastic "timbers" mounted in H-beams (polyester-fiberglass, steel, or galvanized steel). The maintenance-free 3-1/2" thick x 8" tall hollow boards are made from mixed recycled plastic with a thin, UV-protected PVC wear layer. Total post-consumer content is 95%. The sound transmission class (STC) rating is 42 (slightly better than a 4" concrete block wall). No foundation or footing is required. A variety of colors and simulated wood tones and textures are available. Per the manufacturer, most graffiti will clean by pressure washing with water. This product is re-usable, and comes with a 25-year transferable warranty.

32 80 00
Irrigation

Over half of urban water use in the U.S. is for landscape irrigation. Before researching irrigation systems, consider water-saving landscapes with drought-hardy native plantings to reduce or eliminate water, energy, and chemical use. If irrigation is needed, high-tech, permanent irrigation systems that monitor soil and atmospheric conditions can save a great deal of water simply by not running when irrigation isn't needed. Drip irrigation systems release measured quantities of water directly to the soil surrounding the intended plants instead of spraying an entire area, using water more efficiently and greatly reducing evaporative loss. Look for products with intelligent sensing, long warranties that indicate good durability, and such environmental features as recycled content. Consider integrated systems that re-use water that would otherwise be sent down the drain. (See feature articles EBN Vol. 3, No. 2 & Vol. 4, No. 2.)

**32 00 00
Exterior Improvements**

Graywater Treatment Systems

Clivus Multrum, Inc.

For full listing, see CSI section 22 16 00 - Graywater Systems

Fiskars Soaker Hose and Sprinkler Hose

Fiskars, Inc. - Fiskars Garden Tools
780 Carolina St.
Sauk City, WI 53583

Toll-free: 800-500-4849
Fax: 608-643-4908
www.fiskars.com

Fiskars Soaker Hose and Sprinkler Hose, formerly Moisture Master, are products that contain 65% post-consumer recycled rubber from tires.

WeatherTRAK

HydroPoint Data Systems, Inc.
1726 Corporate Cir.
Petaluma, CA 94954

Toll-free: 800-362-8774
Phone: 707-769-9696
Fax: 707-769-9695
www.weathertrak.com

The WeatherTRAK irrigation control systems (available in commercial and residential models) automatically create watering schedules based on parameters that include plant and soil types, sun exposure, and slope. Each watering zone is subsequently adjusted automatically each day based on analyzed NOAA weather data received from HydroPoint's ET Everywhere™ satellite communications service, which eliminates the need for a standalone weather station by delivering geographically specific weather data. Remote management and monitoring via the internet is available. The system is also compatible with rain sensors that can override watering instructions (i.e., not irrigate if the ground is wet).

Most recently mentioned in EBN 15:12

ReWater System

ReWater Systems, Inc.

For full listing, see CSI section 22 16 00 - Graywater Systems

32 92 00
Turf and Grasses

Lawn maintenance is a major source of air pollution and contaminated runoff from fertilizers and pesticides. Close to 40 million gas-powered mowers are used on the lawns of America. While domestic manufacturers have decreased their products' emissions significantly (as required by EPA regulations), an hour of mowing the lawn with a current gas-powered machine still pollutes about as much as driving a late-model car for 13 hours. Compounding the problem, fertilizer runoff from lawns is one of our most significant non-point-source water pollution problems; also, lawn pesticides are commonly applied at rates up to 20 times that of agricultural pesticides. Landscaping that requires less mowing, fertilizing, and pesticide use has significant environmental advantages. (See also 32 01 90 - Operation and Maintenance of Planting.) (See feature article EBN Vol. 13, No. 4.)

No Mow

Prairie Nursery, Inc.
P.O. Box 306
Westfield, WI 53964

Toll-free: 800-476-9453
Fax: 608-296-2741
www.prairienursery.com

No Mow turfgrass mix consists of six native cool-season fescue varieties for seeding in the northern U.S. and southern Canada. No Mow requires only monthly or annual mowing. These drought-tolerant grasses require minimal irrigation and fertilization, and are appropriate for shady locations. Other prairie wildflowers and grasses for a variety of planting conditions are available.

Most recently mentioned in EBN 8:2 & 13:4

32 92 13
Hydro-Mulching

Hydro-seeding is often the most effective way to sow grass seed over large areas. Cellulose mulch made from recycled newspaper is used as a primary component of hydro-seeding sprays. It prevents erosion, retains soil moisture, and encourages seed germination. There are slight differences among products, but all are similar. (See also 31 35 00 - Erosion Protection.)

A W I Mulch

All-Weather Insulation Co., LLC
19 W. Industry Dr.
Springfield, KY 40069

Phone: 859-336-3651
Fax: 859-336-9631

A W I Mulch contains recycled newspaper.

Applegate Mulch

Applegate Insulation Manufacturing
1000 Highview Dr.
Webberville, MI 48892

Toll-free: 800-627-7536
Phone: 517-521-3545
Fax: 517-521-3597
www.applegateinsulation.com

Applegate mulch is made from recycled paper.

Benovert

Benolec, Ltd.
1451 Nobel St.
Sainte-Julie, QC J3E 1Z4 Canada

Phone: 450-922-2000
Fax: 450-922-4333
www.benolec.com

Benovert hydro-mulch contains recycled newspaper.

EcoSeries Hydromulch

Canfor Panel and Fibre **New**
430 Canfor Ave.
New Westminster, BC V3L 5G2 Canada

Toll-free: 800-363-8873
Phone: 604-521-9650
Fax: 604-521-3179
www.canforpfd.com

A division of Canadian Forest Products Ltd., Canfor's EcoSeries of biodegradable hydromulches are made from long-strand softwood fibers (salvaged from logging operations), with varying amounts of non-toxic binder (guar gum, hydrocolloids) and mineral activators. The EcoAegis, EcoFibre, EcoMatrix, and EcoFlex lines accommodate variations of slope, expected weather conditions, anticipated germination speed, and the erosion susceptibility of the soil. Wood content varies between products from 90% to 100% by weight. The EcoFlex line (which is not available in the U.S. market) contains photodegradable (rather than biodegradable) polypropylene fibers and is not specified here.

Climatizer Hydroseeding Mulch

Climatizer Insulation, Ltd.
120 Claireville Dr.
Etobicoke, ON M9W 5Y3 Canada

Toll-free: 866-871-5495
Phone: 416-798-1235
Fax: 416-798-1311
www.climatizer.com

Climatizer Hydroseeding Mulch contains recycled newspaper.

Fiber Turf

Erie Energy Products, Inc.
1400 Irwin Dr.
Erie, PA 16505

Toll-free: 800-233-1810
Phone: 814-454-2828
Fax: 814-454-2820

Fiber Turf is made from recycled newspaper.

Hydro-Spray

National Fiber
50 Depot St.
Belchertown, MA 01007

Toll-free: 800-282-7711
Phone: 413-283-8747
Fax: 413-283-2462
www.nationalfiber.com

Hydro-Spray hydro-seeding mulch contains a minimum of 90% recycled, over-issue newsprint. According to the manufacturer, it is guaranteed to be clean and free of foreign material.

Nu-Wool HydroGreen

Nu-Wool Co., Inc.
2472 Port Sheldon St.
Jenison, MI 49428

Toll-free: 800-748-0128
Phone: 616-669-0100
Fax: 616-669-2370
www.nuwool.com

Nu-Wool® HydroGreen™ hydroseeding mulch is made from 100% recycled paper fibers and contains an organic dye and wetting agent.

Fibrex

Paul's Insulation
P.O. Box 115
Vergas, MN 56587

Toll-free: 800-627-5190
Phone: 218-342-2800
Fax: 218-342-3050

Fibrex hydro-mulch is made from 100% post-consumer recycled newspaper.

Hydro-Spray Mulch

Profile Products, LLC
750 Lake Cook Rd., Ste. 440
Buffalo Grove, IL 60089

Toll-free: 800-207-6457
Phone: 847-215-1144
Fax: 847-215-0577
www.profileproducts.com

Hydro-Spray Mulch contains recycled newspaper.

EnviroGuard and Promat

Tascon, Inc.

For full listing, see CSI section 32 01 90 - Operation and Maintenance of Planting

Astro-Mulch

Thermo-Kool of Alaska
P.O. Box 230085
Anchorage, AK 99507

Phone: 907-563-3644
Fax: 907-561-2758

Astro-Mulch contains recycled newspaper.

Fiber Mulch

Thermoguard Co.
125 N. Dyer Rd.
Spokane, WA 99212

Toll-free: 800-541-0579
Phone: 509-535-4600
Fax: 509-535-8519
www.service-partners.com

Thermoguard's hydro-mulch contains recycled newspaper.

Natural-Fiber Hydromulch

Verdyol Plant Research Ltd. **New**
5009 Concession 13, R.R. #4
Cookstown, ON L0L 1L0 Canada

Toll-free: 866-250-5592
Phone: 705-458-9601
Fax: 705-458-1047
www.verdyol.ca

Verdyol Plant Research offers hydromulches made with various mixtures of post-consumer recycled newsprint, weed-free natural straw fiber, raw cotton fiber, and vegetable gum carbohydrate stabilizer. Non-toxic liquid and powder tackifiers are also available.

32 00 00
Exterior Improvements

32 93 03
Native Plants and Seeds

Landscaping with native plants adapted to your local climate and not requiring irrigation, fertilizers, or pesticides will result in lower environmental impact than conventional lawns and landscaping with nonnative plantings. Included here are several of the leading suppliers of native seed and seedlings. While these companies can be good sources, you should start by looking for native plant nurseries in your immediate area, as they're likely to have specific genotypes best adapted to your region. (See feature articles EBN Vol. 2, No. 4 & Vol. 4, No. 5.)

Native Plant Supplier

Bitterroot Restoration, Inc.
445 Quast Ln.
Corvallis, MT 59828

Toll-free: 888-892-4991
Phone: 406-961-4991
Fax: 406-961-4626
www.bitterrootrestoration.com

Bitterroot Restoration maintains extensive offerings of native plants appropriate to the western U.S. The company, founded in 1986, provides restoration design and planning services in addition to selling plants. "Plant salvage" is among the services offered—transplanting of plants from land that will be developed. Comprehensive website; catalog available. Locations also in California and Washington.

Most recently mentioned in EBN 10:2

Native Seed and Plant Supplier

Ernst Conservation Seeds
9006 Mercer Pike
Meadville, PA 16335

Toll-free: 800-873-3321
Phone: 814-336-2404
Fax: 814-336-5191
www.ernstseed.com

32 00 00
Exterior
Improvements

Ernst Conservation Seeds is one of the few native seed and plant suppliers in the Northeast. The company was founded in 1963 and specializes in native wildflowers and grasses, legumes, cover crops, bioengineering materials, wetland restoration and wildlife habitat mixes, and naturalized conservation species.

Most recently mentioned in EBN 10:2

Native Seed and Plant Supplier

Ion Exchange, Inc.
1878 Old Mission Dr.
Harpers Ferry, IA 52146

Toll-free: 800-291-2143
Fax: 563-535-7362
www.ionxchange.com

Ion Exchange was founded in 1988 and supplies seedlings and/or seed of more than 250 native grasses and wildflowers. Their selection of grasses, sedges, and rushes is particularly large, with over 40 species—most of which are available in plugs, pots, or seed (by the packet, ounce, or pound). The company has both a printed catalog and an online catalog, which allows searches based on ecosystem, type of plant, and so forth.

Most recently mentioned in EBN 10:2

Native Seed and Plant Supplier

LaFayette Home Nursery, Inc.
RR 1 Box 1A
LaFayette, IL 61449

Phone: 309-995-3311
Fax: 309-995-3909
lafayettenursery.com

One of the oldest suppliers of seed and plants, LaFayette Home Nursery was founded in 1887 and is now run by third- and fourth-generation family members. The company's Prairie Department, which focuses on native plants, was established in 1970.

Most recently mentioned in EBN 10:2

Native Seed and Plant Supplier

Native American Seed
127 N. 16th St.
Junction, TX 76849

Toll-free: 800-728-4043
www.seedsource.com

Serving Texas and the arid Southwest, Native American Seed has a superb website with extensive information, including photos of most of the native plant species they sell. The company, founded in 1974, is committed to supplying seeds that were produced using source seed harvested from sites within the ecoregion being served. In this way, they are able to retain the original genetic integrity of the plants. The parent company is Neiman Environments, Inc., which specializes in large-scale restoration projects of abused, neglected, and/or overgrazed land. The company supplies seed only (from seedlings) from more than 171 species.

Most recently mentioned in EBN 10:2

Native Seed and Plant Supplier

Prairie Nursery, Inc.
P.O. Box 306
Westfield, WI 53964

Toll-free: 800-476-9453
Fax: 608-296-2741
www.prairienursery.com

Founded in 1972, Prairie Nursery's mission is "to preserve native plants and animals by helping people create attractive, non-polluting natural landscapes that can support a diversity of wildlife." The company offers over 100 wildflowers and dozens of grasses, sedges, and bulrushes in seed form, individual plants, or both, as well as many seed mixes and collections of plants for special purposes. Their free, 66-page

catalog and planting guide includes more specific information.

Most recently mentioned in EBN 8:2 & 10:2

Native Seed and Plant Supplier

Prairie Restorations, Inc.
P.O. Box 327
Princeton, MN 55371

Phone: 763-389-4342
Fax: 763-389-4346
www.prairieresto.com

Prairie Restorations supplies native seed and plants for prairie restoration work in the Upper Midwest, offering distribution within a 200-mile radius of their two facilities in Princeton and Hawley, Minnesota—including parts of Wisconsin, Iowa, and the Dakotas. Installation, land management, and consultation services are also available.

Most recently mentioned in EBN 10:2

Native Seed and Plant Supplier

S&S Seeds, Inc.
P.O. Box 1275
Carpinteria, CA 93014

Phone: 805-684-0436
Fax: 805-684-2798
www.ssseeds.com

Founded in 1975, S&S Seeds is a wholesale producer and supplier of more than 900 plant species including wildflowers, native grasses, and erosion-control seed mixes. The company also offers a line of erosion-control products, including EarthGuard, Flexterra, Bonded Fiber Matrices, Greenfix Erosion Control Blankets, and soil stabilizers.

Most recently mentioned in EBN 10:2

Native Seed and Plant Supplier

Taylor Creek Restoration Nurseries
17921 Smith Rd.
Brodhead, WI 53520

Phone: 608-897-8641
Fax: 608-897-8486
www.appliedeco.com

Taylor Creek Restoration Nurseries was founded in the late 1970s as the companion company to Applied Ecological Services, an ecological consulting and restoration contracting firm. Taylor Creek Nurseries offers more than 400 species of native plants that are grown on 300 acres and supplied throughout the Midwest. Seeds, plants, trees and shrubs are available.

Most recently mentioned in EBN 10:2

Native Plant Supplier

The Reveg Edge/Ecoseeds
P.O. Box 361
Redwood City, CA 94064

Phone: 650-325-7333
Fax: 650-325-4056
www.ecoseeds.com/grasses.html

The Reveg Edge, a division of the Redwood City Seed Company, is a unique supplier of native plants in that its plants are custom-grown with seeds supplied by the buyer that were collected from the ecosystem for which the plants are intended. In this way, the established plantings will be appropriate to the intended microclimate. This process allows the company to supply native plants to any place in the United States. The company, founded in 1971, also offers a wide range of hard-to-find and heirloom vegetable, herb, and medicinal plants under the Ecoseeds™ brand name, in addition to in-depth classes and consulting on establishment of native plants.

Most recently mentioned in EBN 10:2

32 94 13
Landscape Edging

Landscape edging products are good applications for recycled plastics and tire-rubber. The material is impervious, resistant to root penetration, will not rot, and structural requirements are minimal.

Lawn Edging, Lattice, and Privacy Fencing

Master Mark Plastics

For full listing, see CSI section 32 31 23 - Plastic Fences and Gates

Lawn Edging and Tree Rings

Phoenix Recycled Products, Inc.
360 W. Church St.
Batesburg, SC 29006

Phone: 803-532-4425
Fax: 803-532-4427
www.permamulch.com

Phoenix Recycled Products fabricates lawn edging and tree rings from recycled tire-rubber. (Tree rings are mats that form a weed barrier around trees.) The manufacturer has certified the following recycled-content levels, by weight: total recovered material 85% typical, 85% guaranteed; post-consumer material 85% typical, 85% guaranteed.

32 94 16
Landscape Timbers

Landscape timbers provide an appropriate use of low-grade, commingled recycled plastics that little else can be produced from. Lighter-weight hollow extrusions, generally made from HDPE, require less energy for shipping. Many manufacturers of recycled plastic lumber also produce landscape timbers. (See also 06 51 13 - Plastic Lumber & 35 50 00 - Marine Construction and Equipment.)

Aztec Recycled-Plastic Lumber

Amazing Recycled Products, Inc.

For full listing, see CSI section 06 53 13 - Solid Plastic Decking

Recycled-Plastic Products

American Recreational Products

For full listing, see CSI section 12 93 43 - Site Seating and Tables, Plastic

Landscape Timbers

American Recycled Plastic, Inc.
1500 Main St.
Palm Bay, FL 32905

Toll-free: 866-674-1525
Phone: 321-674-1525
Fax: 321-674-2365
www.itsrecycled.com

American Recycled Plastic manufactures landscape timbers from recycled HDPE plastic.

Recycled-Plastic Products

American Recycled Plastic, Inc.

For full listing, see CSI section 06 53 13 - Solid Plastic Decking

Barco Recycled-Content Products

Barco Products
11 N. Batavia Ave.
Batavia, IL 60510

Toll-free: 800-338-2697
Phone: 630-879-0084
Fax: 630-879-8687
www.barcoproducts.com

Barco Products offers site furnishings, landscape timbers, and traffic devices made with recycled content, including dozens of styles of picnic tables and park benches made with recycled commingled HDPE and LDPE averaging 40% post-consumer, as well as planters and waste receptacles made from recycled HDPE (90 to 100% post-consumer). Landscape Timbers are made from 100% recycled commingled HDPE and LDPE, sized as railroad ties with premolded holes for rebar reinforcement and interlocking edges for stacking stability. Each timber weighs 42 lbs, about half that of most plastic landscape timbers. 100% recycled tire rubber speed bumps and 100% recycled plastic speed bumps are offered, and colored wheel stops made of 95% recycled commingled HDPE and LDPE. Gray wheel stops contain 85% recycled PVC. Bollards are made from 96% recycled commingled LDPE and HDPE (50 to 80% post-industrial).

Bedford Technology Recycled-Plastic Products

Bedford Technology, LLC

For full listing, see CSI section 06 53 13 - Solid Plastic Decking

SmartTie

Curb Appeal Materials, LTD
3824 N. Johnsburg Rd.
McHenry, IL 60050

Phone: 815-344-7926
Fax: 815-344-7960
www.vortexcomposites.com

32 00 00
Exterior Improvements

SmartTie is made with 100% commingled plastics, including synthetic carpet material, from post-consumer and industrial sources in a patented cold-extrusion process. Colorants can be added for aesthetic effect. The material is more dense than wood, and has a lower burn rate; it doesn't warp or degrade, and is recyclable. It cuts and machines with woodworking tools. SmartTie is available in solid, hollow, and channeled versions in many dimensions. SmartTie can be used to control noise from highways and other sources. The manufacturer indicates that the material is not affected by freeze-thaw cycling.

Most recently mentioned in EBN 6:6

EPS Recycled-Plastic Building Products

Engineered Plastic Systems

For full listing, see CSI section 06 53 13 - Solid Plastic Decking

Site Furnishings and Materials

Inteq Corp.

For full listing, see CSI section 12 93 43 - Site Seating and Tables, Plastic

PlasTEAK Plastic Lumber

PlasTEAK

For full listing, see CSI section 06 53 13 - Solid Plastic Decking

Recycled-Plastic Decking, Docks, and Timbers

Plastic Lumber Yard, LLC

For full listing, see CSI section 06 53 13 - Solid Plastic Decking

The Plastic Lumber Company

The Plastic Lumber Company, Inc.

For full listing, see CSI section 06 53 13 - Solid Plastic Decking

Ecoboard Plastic Lumber

Trelleborg Engineered Products, Inc.

For full listing, see CSI section 06 53 13 - Solid Plastic Decking

32 00 00
Exterior Improvements

Recycled-Plastic Posts

XPotential Products Inc.

For full listing, see CSI section 32 17 13 - Parking Bumpers (Car Stops)

32 94 43
Tree Grates and Guards

Tree grates, guards, and root barriers are good applications for recycled plastic, because of the minimal structural requirements of these products. Tree-ring mats to keep weeds down around trees can be made from recycled-tire rubber.

CP and DWP Root Barrier Panels

Century Products
1144 N. Grove St.
Anaheim, CA 92806

Toll-free: 800-480-8084
Phone: 714-632-7083
Fax: 714-632-5470
www.centuryrootbarrier.com

CP and DWP Series Root Barrier Panels protect hardscape surfaces from uplifting caused by tree roots. The 50% recycled plastic modular panels are flexible and can be separated into 1' sections. DWP Series panels include deep watering channels that efficiently direct irrigation water to the tree's root zone.

Arbor Guard and Universal Barriers

DeepRoot Partners, LP
530 Washington St.
San Francisco, CA 94111

Toll-free: 800-458-7668
Phone: 415-781-9700
Fax: 800-277-7668
www.deeproot.com

DeepRoot Partners manufactures Arbor Guard+ tree trunk protectors. Arbor Guard+ protects young trees from rodent and lawn maintenance equipment damage. The product, made of 50% post-consumer recycled polyethylene, is 9" high and expands to protect 4"-diameter trees—or larger if two or more Arbor Guard+ units are connected. Universal Barriers are designed to protect hard surfaces, such as sidewalks, from uplifting caused by tree roots. The product, made from 50% post-consumer recycled polypropylene (except UB 36-2 and UB 40-2), surrounds the rootball of a young tree and directs the roots downward. DeepRoot Partners also manufactures Linear Barriers for use along a hard surface area instead of around a tree.

Lawn Edging and Tree Rings

Phoenix Recycled Products, Inc.

For full listing, see CSI section 32 94 13 - Landscape Edging

Poly-Grate II Tree Grates

Structural Plastics Corp.
3401 Chief Dr.
Holly, MI 48442

Toll-free: 800-523-6899
Phone: 810-953-9400
Fax: 810-953-9440
www.spcindustrial.com

Structural Plastics manufactures Poly-Grate II Tree Grates from recycled HDPE plastic.

This Space is Available for Your Notes

33 00 00 Utilities

PRODUCT LISTINGS

33 10 05
Rainwater Harvesting Systems and Components

Rainwater harvesting is the practice of collecting and using rainwater, most commonly from roofs. Use of collected rainwater can provide building owners with high-quality soft water for irrigation and potable uses, reduce pressure on water-treatment plants, and reduce stormwater runoff and flooding. To use as potable water, filtration and purification are necessary. (See also 07 71 23 - Gutters and Downspouts & 22 32 00 - Domestic Water Filtration Equipment.) (See feature article EBN Vol. 6, No. 5.)

Smart-Valve Rainwater Diverter

FloTrue International Corp
5516 Yale St.
Metairie, LA 70003

Phone: 504-338-3727
www.flotrue.com

Smart-Valve is a kit that transforms an off-the-shelf pipe fitting into a low-cost first-flush diverter valve for roofwater catchment systems. The amount of water diverted is adjustable.

Rainwater Catchment Systems

Northwest Water Source
P.O. Box 2766
Friday Harbor, WA 98250

Phone: 360-378-8252
Fax: 360-378-8790

Northwest Water Source offers components and equipment as well as design and consulting for both residential and commercial rainwater catchment and harvesting systems. The company imports European rainfall catchment equipment and stormwater infiltration technology from Germany and Holland. Equipment includes European-made stainless steel demand pumping systems that don't require a pressure tank; UV water purification and filtration; and a variety of water storage tanks including above- and below-ground rotationally molded polyethylene and custom-made in-ground units consisting of a polyethylene "endoskeleton" covered by a welded sheet polypropylene.

Rainwater Catchment Components

Rain Harvesting Pty, Ltd
28-34 Reginald St.
Rocklea, Brisbane, QLD 4106 Australia

Phone: +61 7 3248 9600
Fax: +61 7 3248 9699
www.rainharvesting.com

Rain Harvesting Pty Ltd. offers rainwater catchment components including gutter screens, rainheads, first flush diverters, flap valves, filter pits, vermin-proof screens, and overflow valves. A 144-page introductory handbook is also available describing the processes, materials, and uses of rainwater harvesting. Most components offered are made with stainless steel and PVC. No recycled plastic is used in manufacturing these components due to the potential for lead contamination of potable water; only lead-free virgin resins are used. Orders made at their website are drop-shipped from Australia. North American support is provided via the internet and e-mail.

Rainwater Catchment Systems

Rain Man Waterworks
P.O. Box 972
Dripping Springs, TX 78620

Phone: 512-858-7020
www.rainharvester.com

Rain Man Waterworks builds and installs turnkey rainwater catchment systems. The company is also a supplier of components used for rainwater catchment systems.

Most recently mentioned in EBN 6:5

Rainwater Collection and Filtration Systems

Resource Conservation Technology, Inc.
2633 N. Calvert St.
Baltimore, MD 21218   **New**

Toll-free: 800-477-7724
Phone: 410-366-1146
Fax: 410-366-1202
www.conservationtechnology.com

Resource Conservation Technology, Inc. provides residential and commercial rainwater collection, filtration, and storage systems. In a typical installation, water from a building's downspouts is piped underground through a central filter to the storage tanks. System capacities range from hundreds to thousands of gallons, and a system may include additional pumps, controls, and disinfection systems tailored to the application.

Rainwater Harvesting Components

Water Filtration Company
1205 Gilman St.
Marietta, OH 45750

Toll-free: 800-733-6953
Phone: 740-373-6953
www.waterfiltrationcompany.com

Water Filtration Company offers rainwater-catchment parts and accessories. The Filtering Roofwasher installs between the downspout and cistern to remove dirt and debris from water collected from a roof, and can greatly improve the quality of cistern water and significantly increase the time between cistern cleanings. The Filtering Roofwasher is often used in conjunction with Water Filtration's Floating Cistern Filter, which reduces the final filtration loads. Filter elements for the Floating Cistern Filter need replacement approximately every one to two years. Additional filtration or sterilization is usually required for potable water applications.

The Garden Watersaver

Watersaver Products Company
8260 Dalemore Rd.
Richmond, BC V7C 2A8 Canada

Phone: 604-274-6630
Fax: 604-274-6626
www.gardenwatersaver.com

The Garden Watersaver is an automatic rainwater collection system that installs on a downspout from the roof's gutter to divert a percentage of this water to a barrel or other container for later use in a garden or other applications.

33 00 00
Utilities

33 16 00
Water Storage Tanks

Tanks for storing potable water supplies should be drainable, cleanable, and durable.

Vertical Above-Ground Storage Tanks

Holloway Welding & Piping Co.
820 W. Forest Grove Rd.
Allen, TX 75002

Toll-free: 800-548-3134
Phone: 972-562-5033
Fax: 972-562-5035
www.hollowaywp.com

Holloway Welding & Piping supplies storage tanks for use with rainwater catchment systems.

Rainwater Catchment Systems

Northwest Water Source

For full listing, see CSI section 33 10 05 - Rainwater Harvesting Systems and Components

Water Storage Tanks

Norwesco, Inc.
4365 Steiner St.
P.O. Box 439
St. Bonifacius, MN 55375

Phone: 800-328-3420
Fax: 800-874-2371
www.norwesco.com

Norwesco's seamless polyethylene storage tanks range from 12 to 15,000 gallons and are manufactured using resins meeting FDA specifications to ensure safe storage of potable water. Applicable tanks are also NSF-approved. Appropriate for rainwater catchment cisterns.

Rainwater Collection and Filtration Systems

Resource Conservation Technology, Inc.

For full listing, see CSI section 33 10 05 - Rainwater Harvesting Systems and Components

Water Cistern and Storage Tanks

Snyder Industries
4700 Fremont St.
Lincoln, NE 68504

Phone: 402-467-5221
Fax: 402-465-1220
www.snydernet.com

Snyder's NuConCept above- and below-ground water storage tanks are rotationally molded with a variety of polyethylene materials, including FDA- and NSF 61-approved high-density (HDLPE) and cross-linked high-density (XLPE) resins. May be used as rainwater catchment cisterns.

Plastic Cistern Liners

Thompson Plastics Melita
P.O. Box 456
Melita, MB R0M 1L0 Canada

Toll-free: 866-522-3241
Fax: 204-522-3715
www.thompsoncisternliners.com

Thompson cistern liners are made of polyethylene sheeting seam-welded to fit loosely into a round tank or rectangular cavity used to hold liquid, usually water. These liners are appropriate for rainwater storage.

33 30 00
Sanitary Sewerage, Utilities

Conventional on-site wastewater treatment systems—septic tanks and leach fields—typically deliver the nutrients in the wastewater (nitrogen and phosphorous) directly into the groundwater. Various alternative wastewater treatment systems provide some nutrient removal. Some plastic-matrix products incorporate recycled content. Products in this section are appropriate for neighborhoods and large facilities. (See feature article EBN Vol. 3, No. 2.)

Solar Aquatics

Ecological Engineering Associates

For full listing, see CSI section 22 13 00 - Sanitary Sewerage, Facilities

Waterloo Biofilter

Waterloo Biofilter Systems Inc.

For full listing, see CSI section 22 13 00 - Sanitary Sewerage, Facilities

ZeeWeed Wastewater Treatment Systems

New

Zenon Environmental Inc.
3239 Dundas St. W
Oakville, ON L6M 4B2 Canada

Phone: 905-465-3030
Fax: 905-465-3050
www.zenon.com

Zenon offers a number of wastewater treatment options employing immersed-membrane filtration and other technologies for commercial, industrial, and municipal installations. The ZeeWeed® 500 system installs downstream of standard sludge units or septic tanks; hollow-fiber membrane modules are combined to form cassettes in process tanks to deliver high-quality water for reuse within a building or release in biologically sensitive areas. They are also appropriate where standard leach fields cannot be accommodated. The larger ZeeWeed Membrane Bioreactor (MBR) and Tertiary ultrafiltration technology systems provide clarification, aeration, and filtration for biological treatment systems to reduce capital and operating costs while yielding effluent suitable for any discharge or reuse application.

33 42 00
Culverts

Drainage pipes must be durable, and should be made from raw materials that minimize manufacturing and disposal impacts. Products listed here are made from relatively benign raw materials and contain high recycled content.

EcoFirst Drainage Pipe

Hancor, Inc.
401 Olive St.
Findlay, OH 45840

Toll-free: 888-367-7473
Fax: 888-329-7473
www.hancor.com

EcoFirst® Recycled Drainage Pipe is made from 25-75% post-industrial and/or post-consumer recycled HDPE and up to 100% recovered content. It is suitable for such applications as golf courses, parking lots, sports playing fields, pond equalization, and culverts. EcoFirst comes in a range of

33 00 00
Utilities

diameters from 4" to 60", in lengths of 9' 4", 20', and 30', and features a soil tight joint that meets or exceeds the requirements of AASHTO M252, M294 or ASTM F2306. EcoFirst now meets the pipe performance requirements of AASHTO M-294. Use of EcoFirst can increase compliance with EPA Phase II Best Management Practices.

33 44 19
Stormwater Treatment

Hydrocarbons, heavy metals, nutrients, and other pollutants collect on pavement and other impervious surfaces. When it rains, these pollutants can enter stormwater flows and pollute nearby surface waters. Large parking lots and "ultra-urban" areas can benefit from stormwater treatment systems that help remove pollutants (though regular maintenance is critical with such systems). Lower-maintenance "structural practices," such as infiltration trenches, porous pavement, detention ponds, and biofiltration systems, should be used whenever possible. (See feature articles EBN Vol. 3, No. 5 & Vol. 11, No. 2.)

Ultra-Urban Filter with Smart Sponge

AbTech Industries
4110 N. Scottsdale Rd., Ste. 235
Scottsdale, AZ 85251

Toll-free: 800-545-8999
Phone: 480-874-4000
Fax: 480-970-1665
www.abtechindustries.com

The Ultra-Urban® Filter with Smart Sponge® is a stormwater inlet designed to capture trash, sediment, oil, and grease from stormwater before the water enters the storm-drain system. The company offers two basic designs: one to fit drop-in storm drain box-type inlets and the other to fit curb openings. The inserts are made of recycled plastic, and the Smart Sponge filters from a proprietary mix of polymers that absorb hydrocarbons, permanently trapping them, according to the manufacturer. Because the pollutants are permanently absorbed into the filters, they can usually be disposed of as normal solid waste. The sediment trap should be vacuum-cleaned regularly; once the Smart Sponge filter is saturated (estimated within 1-3 years), the whole unit is replaced. Ultra-Urban Filters are available in a variety of sizes that make it possible to retrofit existing storm drains.

Most recently mentioned in EBN 11:2

BaySaver

BaySaver, Inc.
1302 Rising Ridge Rd., Unit 1
Mount Airy, MD 21771

Toll-free: 800-229-7283
Phone: 301-829-6470
Fax: 301-829-3747
www.baysaver.com

The BaySaver® Separation System is comprised of two cylindrical precast concrete tanks. Stormwater flows into one side of the first tank, where coarse sediments settle to the bottom. Hydrocarbons floating on the surface of that tank flow into a second tank, where the floatables remain permanently floating and finer sediments settle. This second tank is "off-line" from the primary flow, so the pollutants are less likely to be re-entrained into the stormwater. The outlet of both tanks is from the midpoint using T-pipes. Both tanks are accessed by manhole for regular cleaning. BaySaver units are available in diameters of 22", 36", 48", and 60" for maximum/optimal flows of 1.1/2.4 to 8.5/21.8 ft³ per second.

Most recently mentioned in EBN 11:2

The SNOUT Stormwater Quality Improvement System

Best Management Products, Inc.
53 Mt. Archer Rd.
Lyme, CT 06371

Toll-free: 800-504-8008
Phone: 410-687-6256
Fax: 410-687-6757
www.bmpinc.com

The SNOUT® is a vented fiberglass-composite hood that acts as an oil-water-debris separator for stormwater. It is installed in sumped inlet structures to remove grit as well as oil and other floatable debris from the stormwater flow entering a storm sewer or outfall. The simple low-cost unit can offer significant reductions in trash, floatable debris, free oils, and suspended solids. The SNOUT is unaffected by corrosive ice-melting chemicals. The hoods are available to cover pipes measuring up to 96" in outside diameter. The product may satisfy requirements of the NPDES Phase II best-management-practice regulations. Flow restrictors, flow deflector plates, and oil-absorbent booms are available accessories for the Snout system.

StormFilter

Contech Stormwater Solutions
12021-B N.E. Airport Way
Portland, OR 97220

Toll-free: 800-925-5240
Phone: 503-522-7592
Fax: 503-258-3172
www.contech-cpi.com

The Stormwater Management StormFilter™ is a proprietary stormwater filtration and pollution-separation system. StormFilter cartridges can be filled with a variety of filtration media to remove selected pollutants, including oil and grease, soluble heavy metals, organics, and soluble nutrients. The product is available in six configurations: precast, high capacity, catch-basin, curb inlet, volume, and down spout. In August 2002, this became the first proprietary stormwater treatment system to be verified by the New Jersey Corporation for Advanced Technology (NJCAT).

Vortechs Stormwater Treatment System

Contech, Inc.
200 Enterprise Dr.
Scarborough, ME 04074

Toll-free: 877-907-8676
Phone: 207-885-9830
Fax: 207-885-9825
www.vortechnics.com

The Vortechs™ Stormwater Treatment System is a hydrodynamic oil/grit separator that has been on the market since 1988—a relatively long time. This rectangular precast concrete tank has a cylindrical inner chamber followed by a baffle. Incoming water swirls around the first chamber, dropping heavier sediments to the bottom. Because the water can pass into the outlet chamber only by passing under a baffle, the floatable pollutants remain in a layer at the top. Following a storm event or as needed, both the accumulated sediment and floating pollutants (especially hydrocarbons) can be vacuumed out. Depending on the model, precast systems can handle stormwater flows from 1.6 to 25 ft³ per second. Larger flows are treated using Vortechs systems that are poured in place. Sediment storage ranges from 0.7 to 7.1 yd³.

Most recently mentioned in EBN 11:2

Salmon Saver Stormwater Filter System

Enviro-Drain, Inc.
12568 33rd Ave. NE
Seattle, WA 98125

Toll-free: 800-820-1953
Phone: 206-363-0316
Fax: 206-362-9354
www.enviro-drain.com

Enviro-Drain stormwater filters are installed below storm sewer grates and can filter out up to 96% of the pollutants in stormwater runoff. The stainless steel units utilize either one, two, or three filtration trays to catch sand, silt, grease, oil, and metals.

33 00 00
Utilities

Howland Swale

Environmental Research Corps
15 Mohawk Ave.
East Freetown, MA 02717

Phone: 508-763-5253
Fax: 508-763-8781
www.biofence.com

Howland Swale™ uses engineered and biological control processes for stormwater mitigation in four major components: a stone-lined siltation trap; a pretreatment marsh; an elongated detention basin with planted sides; and a vegetated takeoff channel for final washing, filtration, and velocity reduction. The design meets or exceeds current EPA requirements for TSS removal.

Storm Water Quality Units

Hancor, Inc.
401 Olive St.
Findlay, OH 45840

Toll-free: 888-367-7473
Fax: 888-329-7473
www.hancor.com

Hancor Storm Water Quality Units are modified sections of HDPE pipe with weir plates at certain locations and heights to remove high percentages of sediment and oils from the first flush of a storm event. Available in 36" through 60" diameters, they can be installed at any point in the subsurface drainage system, and are ideally suited to treat "hot spots" in existing storm water lines. These units are made with virgin HDPE for consistent quality in the high-stress application. (Their EcoFirst drainage pipe is made with recycled HDPE.)

Downstream Defender

Hydro International
94 Hutchins Dr.
Portland, ME 04102

Phone: 207-756-6200
Fax: 207-756-6212
www.hydro-international.biz

The Downstream Defender® is a precast concrete "hydrodynamic vortex separator" that removes sediment through a swirling motion that augments gravity—dropping heavier particles to the bottom and bringing lighter materials to the top. Stormwater enters one side of the cylindrical unit, and treated stormwater flows out the other. A special trap for oil and other floatables allows removal of hydrocarbons. This design, according to the manufacturer, isolates both the collected sediment and floatables, preventing re-entrainment. Standard units are available in 4', 6', 8', and 10' diameters for treating 0.75 to 25 ft³ of water per second.

Most recently mentioned in EBN 11:2

FloGard PLUS

KriStar Enterprises, Inc.
P.O. Box 6419
Santa Rosa, CA 95406

Toll-free: 800-579-8819
Fax: 707-524-8186
www.kristar.com

FloGard® filtration systems are catch basin inserts or hydrodynamic separators for capturing sediment, debris, and hydrocarbons from stormwater before it flows into the storm sewer system. Products are available for rectangular catch basins, curb inlets, and trench drains. Hydrocarbon filtering is provided using special pillows filled with amorphous alumina silicate (Fossil Rock). Filters are easily replaceable.

Most recently mentioned in EBN 11:2

Stormceptor

Rinker Materials / Concrete Pipe Division
6560 Langfield Rd., Bldg. 3
Houston, TX 77092

Toll-free: 800-909-7763
Phone: 832-590-5400
Fax: 832-590-5499
www.rinkerstormceptor.com

Among the most widely recognized oil/grit separators, the Stormceptor® hydrodynamic separator products are manufactured by a number of companies throughout the U.S. and Canada under license to Stormceptor Corporation located in Toronto, Ontario. The Stormceptor units are cylindrical precast concrete structures with a specially designed fiberglass insert which uses gravitational forces to separate sediment and hydrocarbons from stormwater runoff. The product line ranges from the small 4'-diameter, 450-gallon Inlet Stormceptor, designed to serve small areas, to large two-unit (in series) designs up to 16,000 gallons in size. Maintenance to remove trapped pollutants can be achieved by vacuum-equipped trucks without entering the unit.

Most recently mentioned in EBN 11:2

Stormtreat System

StormTreat Systems Inc.
124 Rte 6A
Sandwich, MA 02563

Toll-free: 877-787-6426
Fax: 508-833-1033
www.stormtreat.com

StormTreat™ is a compact treatment system housed in a recycled-polyethylene tank, 9' 6" in diameter by 4' high. Stormwater passes through six sedimentation chambers and a constructed wetland prior to infiltrating into backfilling of 3 to 5 mm washed stone. The

manufacturer claims TSS, fecal coliform bacteria, phosphorus, and petroleum hydrocarbon removal in excess of 90%.

Most recently mentioned in EBN 11:2

33 46 00
Foundation and Slab Drainage

Permanent installations, generally polymeric, that improve drainage around foundations and slabs increase the durability of buildings by enabling water to drain from around the structure. Products listed here have high recycled content or unique properties. (See also 07 14 00 - Fluid-Applied Waterproofing, 07 16 00 - Cementitious and Reactive Waterproofing, 09 97 23 - Concrete and Masonry Coatings.) (See feature article EBN Vol. 3, No. 5.)

Enkadrain 3000 Series

Colbond Inc.
1301 Sand Hill Rd.
P.O. Box 1057
Enka, NC 28728

Toll-free: 800-365-7391
Phone: 828-665-5050
Fax: 828-665-5009
www.colbond-usa.com

Enkadrain® Subsurface Drainage Composite relieves hydrostatic pressure from backfill abutting below-grade structures including foundations and slabs, plaza decks, and retaining walls. It can also be used as a drainage plane for green roofs and roof gardens. It protects waterproofing during and after backfill, and will conform to irregular surfaces and corners. It consists of a post-industrial recycled polypropylene drainage core of fused, entangled filaments and a geocomposite fabric bonded to one or two sides. The entangled filaments are molded into a square waffle pattern. Colbond is currently converting its entire product line to include high levels of recycled content.

Delta-MS and Delta-Dry

Cosella Dörken Products Inc.

For full listing, see CSI section 07 25 00 - Weather Barriers

EcoFirst Drainage Pipe

Hancor, Inc.

For full listing, see CSI section 33 42 00 - Culverts

LowFlow Vertical Drainage System

Polyguard Products, Inc.
3801 S. Business 45
P.O. Box 755
Ennis, TX 75120

Toll-free: 800-541-4994
Phone: 972-875-8421
Fax: 972-875-9425
www.polyguardproducts.com

LowFlow™ is a 100% post-industrial recycled-content plastic geotextile that provides drainage and protection for foundation waterproofing at sites with low transmissivity clay soils.

DrainBoard

Roxul Inc.

For full listing, see CSI section 07 21 13 - Board Insulation

33 49 23
Storm Drainage Water Retention Structures

Stormwater retention products help reduce downstream flooding by detaining or storing the water, and help control pollution by dispersing runoff slowly. Hydrocarbons, heavy metals, nutrients, and other pollutants collect on pavement and other impervious surfaces; when it rains, these pollutants can enter stormwater flows and pollute nearby surface waters. Low-maintenance "structural practices," such as infiltration trenches, porous pavement, detention ponds, and biofiltration systems, should be used whenever possible. (See feature articles EBN Vol. 3, No. 5 & Vol. 11, No. 2.)

Rainstore3

Invisible Structures, Inc.
1600 Jackson St., Ste. 310
Golden, CO 80401

Toll-free: 800-233-1510
Phone: 303-233-8383
Fax: 800-233-1522
www.invisiblestructures.com

Rainstore3 is an underground detention, retention, or water harvesting system used to store stormwater under parking lots, landscaping, or small structures. Its 40"-square, modular structure has cell depths of 4", stackable to 8.2' (25 units high). Assemblies store 250 gal/m³. Rainstore3 is made from 100% recycled HDPE or polypropylene with varying amounts of post-consumer and post-industrial content.

This Space is Available for Your Notes

33 00 00
Utilities

This Space is Available for Your Notes

33 00 00
Utilities

34 00 00 Transportation

PRODUCT LISTINGS

34 71 13
Vehicle Barriers

Recycled plastics and rubber are good choices for the manufacture of roadway markers and vehicle barriers. Recycled plastic diverts material from the waste stream and has lower embodied energy than portland cement-based concrete products; and the lighter weight of plastic bollard-style barriers reduces transportation energy and shipping costs. Products listed here are made of recycled materials. (See feature article EBN Vol. 5, No. 1.)

Aztec Plastic Parking Stops and Bollards

Amazing Recycled Products, Inc.

For full listing, see CSI section 32 17 13 - Parking Bumpers (Car Stops)

Recycled-Plastic Products

American Recycled Plastic, Inc.

For full listing, see CSI section 32 17 13 - Parking Bumpers (Car Stops)

Barco Recycled-Content Products

Barco Products

For full listing, see CSI section 32 17 13 - Parking Bumpers (Car Stops)

Parking Stops, Speed Bumps, and Bollards

Litchfield Industries

For full listing, see CSI section 32 17 13 - Parking Bumpers (Car Stops)

Parking Stops, Speed Bumps, and Bollards

Recycled Plastic Man, Inc.

For full listing, see CSI section 32 17 13 - Parking Bumpers (Car Stops)

Road and Parking Appurtenances

Traffic & Parking Control Co., Inc. (Tapco)

For full listing, see CSI section 32 17 13 - Parking Bumpers (Car Stops)

34 71 19
Vehicle Delineators

Recycled plastics and rubber are good choices for the manufacture of roadway markers and vehicle delineators. Recycled plastic diverts material from the waste stream and has lower embodied energy than portland cement-based concrete products; and the lighter weight of plastic bollard-style barriers reduces transportation energy and shipping costs. Products listed here are made of recycled materials.

FlexStake Highway Safety Products

Flexstake, Inc.
2150 Andrea Ln. #C
Fort Myers, FL 33912

Toll-free: 800-348-9839
Phone: 239-481-3539
Fax: 239-482-3539
www.flexstake.com

FlexStake Highway Safety Products include various traffic delineators and markers made from over 50% post-consumer recycled plastics. Flexstake products will withstand being "mowed-over" by onrushing traffic.

Traffic and Parking Delineators and Devices

Inteq Corp.
35800 Glen Dr.
Eastlake, OH 44095

Phone: 440-953-0550
Fax: 440-953-0564
www.4-inteqcorp.com

Inteq produces a number of traffic and parking accoutrements. Their Parking Stops and Speed Bumps are made from 100% post-consumer recycled HDPE plastic; speed bumps are yellow, and parking stops are yellow, white, gray, black, or blue. They also produce traffic cones and safety delineators with bases of 100% post-consumer rubber or PVC; tops are made from virgin vinyl to maintain proper safety color. Inteq's A-Frame Barricades are made from 100% post-consumer recycled HDPE in 4' to 16' lengths. Highway Barrels are made from virgin LDPE to maintain safety color, but the barrels' ballasts contain recycled truck-tire rubber. The recycled-content levels for Highway Barrels (by weight) is 80-85% post-consumer material. Type I, II, and III Barriers are made from 75% post-consumer recycled HDPE plastic.

Street Smart Traffic Control Units

North West Rubber Mats, Ltd.
33850 Industrial Ave.
Abbotsford, BC V2S 7T9 Canada

Toll-free: 800-663-8724
Phone: 604-859-2002
Fax: 604-859-2009
www.northwestrubber.com

Street Smart Traffic Control Units are portable traffic delineators with 100% recycled-tire rubber bases and bright orange nonrecycled posts.

34 00 00
Transportation

This Space is Available for Your Notes

34 00 00
Transportation

35 00 00 Waterway & Marine Construction

PRODUCT LISTINGS

35 11 13
Signaling Equipment for Waterways

Signal lighting is intended to alert operators of hazards and obstructions. Fixtures using grouped LEDs are often sufficient to the task; they use relatively modest amounts of power and the lamps are long-lasting. Products listed here consume little energy and require little maintenance.

Solar LED Hazard Lighting

Carmanah Technologies Corporation

For full listing, see CSI section 26 55 33 - Hazard Warning Lighting

LED Signage

Watt-Man L.E.D. Lighting

For full listing, see CSI section 26 53 00 - Exit Signs

35 50 00
Marine Construction and Equipment

Treated-wood pilings may introduce hazardous chemicals to marine ecosystems, and their periodic replacement is expensive. Recycled-content plastic pilings are impervious to marine borers and are an appropriate solution for building durable docks and piers. These pilings are usually extruded around steel or fiberglass reinforcing rods and treated with UV inhibitors and antioxidants. While more expensive than wooden pilings, if maintenance and durability are considered, recycled-plastic pilings often have lower life-cycle costs. Docks and other construction in marine environments should avoid all pressure-treated wood in favor of components that are inherently resistant to water and microbial growth. Products listed here are made from recycled plastic, rubber, and fiberglass.

Recycled-Plastic Products

American Recreational Products

For full listing, see CSI section 12 93 43 - Site Seating and Tables, Plastic

PlasTEAK Plastic Paneling

PlasTEAK

For full listing, see CSI section 06 64 00 - Plastic Paneling

Recycled-Plastic Decking, Docks, and Timbers

Plastic Lumber Yard, LLC

For full listing, see CSI section 06 53 13 - Solid Plastic Decking

Marine Pilings and Lumber

Plastic Pilings, Inc.
1485 S. Willow Ave.
Rialto, CA 92376

Phone: 909-874-4080
Fax: 909-874-4860
www.plasticpilings.com

Plastic Pilings manufactures plastic pilings, camels, and structural plastic lumber products for pier and wharf construction. The dimensional plastic lumber ranges from 3" x 6" to 12" x 20" and up to 50' in length. Round sections can be reinforced with a fiberglass tube, steel pipe core, or steel or fiberglass rebar, and are available in diameters from 8" to 36".

Most recently mentioned in EBN 2:4

Recycled-Plastic Lumber Products

Recycled Plastic Man, Inc.
P.O. Box 609
Placida, FL 33946

Toll-free: 800-253-7742
Phone: 941-698-1060
Fax: 941-698-1038
www.recycledplasticman.com

Recycled Plastic Man manufactures extruded plastic lumber and marine-quality pilings from commingled, recycled HDPE in a variety of profiles and colors.

Dock Bumpers and Marine Fenders

Schuyler Rubber Co., Inc.
16901 Woodinville-Redmond Rd.
Woodinville, WA 98072

Toll-free: 800-426-3917
Phone: 425-488-2255
Fax: 425-488-2424
www.schuylerrubber.com

Schuyler Rubber manufactures dock bumpers and marine fenders of recycled bias ply and radial bus and truck tire casings.

SeaPile and SeaTimber

Seaward International, Inc.
3470 Martinsburg Pike
P.O. Box 98
Clearbrook, VA 22624

Toll-free: 800-828-5360
Phone: 540-667-5191
Fax: 540-667-7987
www.seaward.com

Seaward International manufactures SeaPile® and SeaTimber® made from 100% recycled plastic with fiberglass reinforcement, providing an alternative to large pressure-treated marine pilings and timbers. SeaPile and SeaTimber have been U.S. government-approved for structural marine applications and are in widespread use, including at the Summer Street Bridge in Boston. SeaPile and SeaTimber contain UV inhibitors and are impervious to marine borers.

Most recently mentioned in EBN 4:1

Ecoboard Plastic Lumber

Trelleborg Engineered Products, Inc.

For full listing, see CSI section 06 53 13 - Solid Plastic Decking

Trimax

Trimax Building Products, Inc.

For full listing, see CSI section 06 51 13 - Plastic Lumber

35 00 00
Waterway & Marine Construction

This Space is Available for Your Notes

35 00 00
*Waterway
& Marine
Construction*

44 00 00 Pollution Control Equipment

PRODUCT LISTINGS

44 40 00 Water Treatment Equipment

Cooling towers rely on the principle of evaporation to extract heat from water to aid in the cooling of conditioned spaces. This is typically achieved with large heat-transfer areas wetted by recirculating water. The combination of expansive moist areas and recirculating water create an almost ideal environment for bacteria and mold, which build up on the heat-transfer surfaces, reducing their effectiveness. Heat transfer effectiveness is also reduced by scale deposits that form as recirculating water evaporates, leaving behind minerals and other solids. Environment-friendly cooling tower treatment systems based on ozonation or magnetic, electromagnetic, or electrostatic technology, have evolved considerably in recent years. Such systems can reduce and potentially obviate the need for dangerous chemicals, while providing decreased maintenance and reduced blow-down. Magnetic (and electromagnetic) systems are not fully understood, and have a checkered past and present. The systems listed here are from manufacturers with proven track records who have assuaged our concerns about effectiveness and provide the necessary engineering support for a successful system. (See feature articles EBN Vol. 3, No. 2, Vol. 5, No. 4, Vol. 15, No. 4.)

Dolphin Series 2000

Clearwater Systems Corporation
145 Dennison Rd.
P.O. Box 463
Essex, CT 06426

Phone: 860-767-0850
Fax: 860-767-8972
www.clearwater-dolphin.com

The Dolphin non-chemical water treatment system for cooling towers and boilers consists of a transformer panel electrically connected to a PVC-pipe assembly wound with coils that "impart pulsed, high-frequency, electric fields" into the water at 240,000 times per minute. The pulsing electric field induces the coagulation of colloids, creating nucleation sites that encourage calcium carbonate to precipitate as a powder in the bulk solution rather than as lime scale on surfaces—which causes a drop in heat-transfer efficiency and eventual failure. Microorganism control is primarily achieved by encapsulation within the power paratricles or via electroporation of bacteria cell walls. Operating at the saturation point of calcium carbonate, dolphin-equipped systems create a natural, cathodic corrosion inhibiting environment.

Most recently mentioned in EBN 14:4

EnviroTower Cooling Tower Water Treatment System

EnviroTower Inc.   **New**
380 Adelaide St., W
Toronto, ON M5V 1R7 Canada

Toll-free: 877-386-9371
Phone: 416-977-1105
Fax: 416-913-2176
www.envirotower.com

EnviroTower manufactures a non-chemical water treatment system to prevent scale and fouling build-up that can reduce heat-transfer efficiency in cooling towers. The EnviroTower system also controls corrosion and microbiological contamination in the cooling system. The EnviroTower system includes one or more electrostatic conditioners that cause calcium carbonate to precipitate in the bulk solution as free particles, which are then removed with a hydrocyclone separator. The system requires no power to operate, but low levels of ionic zinc and elemental iodine are added as a supplementary disinfectant. Although the EnviroTower company is new, their system is certified by the Canadian Government's Environmental Technology Verification (ETV) program which provides validation and independent verification of performance claims for environmental technologies and has more than 10 years of testing and operation.

Superior Water Conditioner

Superior Manufacturing   **New**
2015 S. Calhoun St.
Division of Magnatech Corporation
Fort Wayne, IN 46802

Toll-free: 800-348-0999
Phone: 260-456-3596
Fax: 260-456-3598
www.superiorwaterconditioners.com

Superior manufactures non-chemical water treatment systems to prevent scale build-up in cooling towers, boilers, and similar applications. Superior systems use a permanent "multiple-pole multiple-field magnet" to encourage calcium carbonate to precipitate as a powder in the bulk solution rather than as calcite scale that can reduce heat-transfer efficiency. Superior has a 40-year track record and was one of three systems found to be effective for scale control in an ASHRAE 2002 research project on non-chemical treatment methods. Superior claims only scale prevention, not bio-film elimination; however the company says that some users have successfully used the system without additional bio-controls.

Clean Streams Ozone Treatment for Cooling Towers

Zentox Corporation
310-G Ed Wright Ln.
Newport News, VA 23606

Phone: 757-369-9870
Fax: 757-369-9871
www.zentox.com

The Clean Streams™ Ozone Systems from Zentox represent the state-of-the-learning-curve in ozonic disinfection for commercial cooling towers. The new generation of these oxidizing biocide systems is highly automated, testing mineral and biological levels hundreds of times per second and reacting accordingly. Energy savings result from decreased biofilm accumulation on heat-transfer surfaces; the film acts as a substrate for accumulating scale, which reduces heat-transfer efficiency. Under the right conditions, treatment chemicals can be entirely withdrawn and blow-down significantly decreased, and the chemical- and pathogen-free blow-down water used for washing, irrigation, or other applications. Ozone systems won't work appropriately when water temperatures exceed 115 degrees F, or in closed systems; hard water or a high organic load from the operating environment can also be an impediment.

This Space is Available for Your Notes

48 00 00 Electrical Power Generation

PRODUCT LISTINGS

48 18 00
Fuel Cell Electrical Power Generation Equipment

Fuel cells offer exciting opportunities for clean, efficient, distributed generation of electricity. Very simply, fuel cells generate power by reversing the common high school chemistry experiment in which electric current is used to split water into hydrogen and oxygen. Fuel cells have been used for decades in space. In buildings, fuel cells can be especially useful for back-up power needs. For lack of a readily available supply of hydrogen, most fuel cells in common use today run on natural gas or some other fossil fuel, which is converted to separate the hydrogen from the other elements, so they are not actually a renewable energy source. (See feature article EBN Vol. 8, No. 4.)

Fuel Cells

Ballard Power Systems
9000 Glenlyon Pkwy.
Burnaby, BC V5J 5J8 Canada

Phone: 604-454-0900
Fax: 604-412-4700
www.ballard.com

Ballard Power Systems is recognized as the world leader in developing, manufacturing, and marketing zero-emission proton-exchange membrane (PEM) fuel cells. Ballard is commercializing fuel cell engines for transportation applications and fuel cell systems for portable and stationary products ranging from 1 to 250 kW. The company is also commercializing electric drives for fuel cell- and battery-powered electric vehicles, power conversion products for fuel cells, and other distributed generation products, and is a Tier 1 automotive supplier of friction materials for power train components.

Most recently mentioned in EBN 8:4

Fuel Cells

IdaTech, LLC
63065 N.E. 18th St.
Bend, OR 97701

Phone: 541-383-3390
Fax: 541-383-3439
www.idatech.com

IdaTech, LLC develops fuel processors and integrated proton exchange membrane (PEM) fuel cell systems for portable, critical backup and remote power applications. IdaTech's core technology is a patented fuel processing technology capable of converting a variety of fuels—including methanol, natural gas and biofuels—into high purity hydrogen, on which the fuel cell solutions operate. The company's products are deployed for backup and critical power, and portable power applications in the 1.5 kW to 15 kW range.

Most recently mentioned in EBN 8:4 & 8:6

Fuel Cells

Plug Power, LLC
968 Albany-Shaker Rd.
Latham, NY 12110

Phone: 518-782-7700
Fax: 518-782-9060
www.plugpower.com

Plug Power has been developing PEM fuel cells to provide reliable on-site energy for stationary residential and light commercial applications. At the end of 2002, Plug Power acquired H-Power Corp., makers of residential, commercial, and transportation-related fuel cells. H-Power was the first to produce very small fuel cells to provide power for specialized uses, such as video equipment.

Most recently mentioned in EBN 8:4

Fuel Cells

UTC Power
195 Governor's Hwy.
South Windsor, CT 06074

Toll-free: 866-900-7693
Phone: 860-727-2200
Fax: 860-727-7922
www.utcpower.com

UTC Power, a unit of United Technologies Corp., manufactures a 200 kW phosphoric acid fuel cell for commercial and institutional buildings. This is the fuel cell used in Four Times Square. UTC was the first company to commercially market fuel cells and has delivered over 250 of their 200 kW model.

Most recently mentioned in EBN 8:4 & 8:11

This Space is Available for Your Notes

48 00 00 Electric Power Generation

This Space is Available for Your Notes

This Space is Available for Your Notes

This Space is Available for Your Notes

This Space is Available for Your Notes

This Space is Available for Your Notes

Index by Product Name

This index is sorted alphabetically by listing title. Use the 6-digit CSI number to the right of each title to find the corresponding product listing. CSI divisions (01 00 00, 02 00 00, etc.) are printed on the thumb tabs at the outer edge of directory pages.

INDEX
*by
Product
Name*

INDEX *by Product Name*

INDEX
by Product Name

INDEX
by
Product
Name

INDEX
by
Product
Name

INDEX *by* **Product Name**

Index by Company Name

This index is sorted alphabetically by company name and then by listing title. Use the 5-digit CSI number to the right of each title to find the corresponding product listing. CSI divisions (01 00 00, 02 00 00, etc.) are printed on the thumb tabs at the outer edge of directory pages.

INDEX
by
Company
Name

INDEX
by
Company
Name

INDEX
by
Company
Name

INDEX
by
Company
Name

INDEX
by
Company
Name

INDEX
by
Company Name

INDEX
by
**Company
Name**

INDEX
by
**Company
Name**

INDEX
by
Company Name

INDEX
by
Company
Name

INDEX
by
**Company
Name**

INDEX *by Company Name*

INDEX
*by
Company
Name*

INDEX
by
Company
Name

INDEX
by
Company
Name

INDEX
*by
Company
Name*

INDEX
by
Company
Name

INDEX
by
Company
Name

About the Authors

Angela Battisto joined BuildingGreen in the spring of 2004 to manage the *GreenSpec®* online database and its product review process. She had previously worked as a programmer for a natural foods distributor in Vermont and enjoyed 20 years in the trades as a woodworker in Boston. Angela was employed as an exhibit builder for the Boston Children's Museum, a staff cabinetmaker for the Museum of Fine Arts, and a wood shop instructor at Massachusetts College of Art. In the early '90s, she also studied interior design at the Boston Architectural Center.

Alex Wilson is president of BuildingGreen, Inc. and serves as executive editor of *Environmental Building News*, a monthly newsletter on environmentally responsible building design and construction, and as coeditor of the *GreenSpec* product directory. Prior to starting his own company in 1985 (now BuildingGreen), he was executive director of the Northeast Sustainable Energy Association for five years; and in the late '70s, he taught workshops on passive solar design and construction in New Mexico. Alex has written about energy-efficient and environmentally responsible design and construction for more than 25 years and is author, coauthor, or editor of several books and manuals, including *Your Green Home* (New Society Publishers, 2006), *Greening Federal Facilities* (U.S. Dept. of Energy, 2nd Edition, 2001), *The Consumer Guide to Home Energy Savings* (ACEEE, 8th edition, 2003) and the Rocky Mountain Institute's comprehensive textbook *Green Development: Integrating Ecology and Real Estate* (John Wiley & Sons, 1998). He has also written hundreds of articles for other publications, including *Fine Homebuilding, Architectural Record, The Construction Specifier, Landscape Architecture,* and *Popular Science*. Alex served on the Board of the U.S. Green Building Council from 2000 to 2005, including two years as Secretary, and he serves as a trustee of the Vermont Chapter of The Nature Conservancy. He is a LEED Accredited Professional.

Nadav Malin is vice president of BuildingGreen, Inc. and serves as editor of *Environmental Building News,* a monthly newsletter on environmentally responsible design and construction, and as coeditor of the *Green-Spec* product directory. He is chair of the Materials and Resources Technical Advisory Group for the U.S. Green Building Council's LEED® Rating System, a LEED Trainer, and a LEED Accredited Professional. He was a principal author of the Applications Reports for the AIA's *Environmental Resource Guide* that compares the environmental value of different building materials in various applications, and he coauthored the chapter on building materials for *Time-Saver Standards*. He has written numerous articles for publications including *Architectural Record* and *The Construction Specifier.* Nadav consults and lectures widely on sustainable design, with a particular focus on green materials. In addition to running LEED training

workshops, he has taught seminars for various USGBC chapters, CSI chapters, state AIA chapters, and private architecture firms. He also serves on the U.S. team for Green Building Challenge, manages the U.S. Department of Energy's High Performance Buildings Database project, and leads the content development team for Web and software resources at BuildingGreen.com.

Mark Piepkorn is an associate editor of *Environmental Building News* and the lead products researcher for *GreenSpec*, publications of BuildingGreen, Inc.; he is also the products editor for *GreenSource*, the USGBC member publication from McGraw Hill with content collaboration from BuildingGreen. A LEED Accredited Professional, his knowledge of conventional and alternative construction methods, materials, and building science—in applications as diverse as underground structures, straw-bale building, and pre-industrial vernaculars, as well as the rehabilitation and remodeling of conventional structures—lends an interesting and important perspective to the understanding of the roles of manufactured products and materials in our built and conditioned environments. Active in the natural building movement, Mark has also been the editor of *The Last Straw,* an international newsletter about straw-bale construction and natural building.

Jennifer Atlee is research director at Building Green, Inc. Through her work with BuildingGreen, Toxics Use Reduction Institute, Massachusetts Institute of Technology, Rocky Mountain Institute, and Demand Management Institute, Jennifer has conducted research and analysis in a variety of sustainability topics including green building, commercial and industrial energy efficiency, electronics recycling, and the economics of toxics use reduction. A primary focus of hers has been developing and clarifying standards to assess the environmental sustainability of products, processes, and organizations. To this end, one of her activities at BuildingGreen is researching and updating product criteria for *GreenSpec*. Jennifer has a dual MS from MIT in Technology Policy and Material Science & Engineering, and a BS in Environmental Science from Brown University.

John Boecker is a cofounder of 7group, a green building consulting firm, and his own architectural practice designing High Performance Green Buildings as a LEED Accredited Professional. He also serves on the U.S. Green Building Council's (USGBC) national LEED Steering Committee, as Chair of the LEED Curriculum & Accreditation Committee, as Chair of the Green Building Association of Central Pennsylvania (an Affiliate of the USGBC), and teaches LEED Advanced Workshops as an appointed LEED Faculty Member with the USGBC. He has practiced architecture in New Haven, Pittsburgh and Los Angeles. In 1999, Mr. Boecker joined a team of six other professionals to create 7goup, A USGBC member and multi-disciplinary consulting group focused on green development and collaboration with developers, architects, engineers, government, and building owners engaged in sustainable projects. Mr. Boecker has designed five LEED Certified buildings, including two of the first 15 buildings nationwide to achieve LEED Certification. He has served as Green Design and LEED Consultant on over 40 additional projects. His design work has been recognized by over 40 design awards, including 25 Awards for Design Excellence from the American Institute of Architects, three Pennsylvania Governor's Awards for Environmental Excellence in 1998, 2001 & 2003, and selection by AIA as one of their nationwide Earth Day 2000 Top Ten. Mr. Boecker taught Architectural Design at Carnegie Mellon University, and now teaches Architectural Design at Harrisburg Area Community College. He also served as the founding Chair of the Pennsylvania AIA Committee on the Environment, and he lectures frequently throughout the U.S. about the benefits of designing High-Performance Green Buildings. Mr. Boecker holds a degree in Architecture from Penn State and a Master of Architecture degree from Yale University.

Scot Horst started Horst, Inc. a sustainable materials consulting firm, where he develops innovative environmental programs relating to materials technologies and testing. This work has ranged from environmental verification of bio-based technologies with the Civil Engineering Research Foundation to extensive work with the cement industry, including a blended cement carbon dioxide offset program with the Climate Trust in Oregon. He helps companies and institutions develop holistic approaches to decision making, and has served as a special advisor to Pennsylvania's Governor's Green Government Council, worked with Princeton University, the University of Pennsylvania, Penn State University, Grand Canyon National Park and many others. Mr. Horst co-founded 7group, a multi-service green building consulting LLC, where he serves as President. As a LEED Accredited Professional he has worked on over 40 LEED projects. Horst currently sits on the LEED Commercial Interiors Core Committee and the Technical Scientific Advisory Committee where he chairs the PVC Task Group. He is a LEED faculty member and, as a partner in 7group, writes credit interpretation rulings and reviews certifications for the U.S. Green Building Council. Horst also serves as Vice President of Athena Institute International, the U.S. non-profit affiliate of the Canadian Athena Sustainable Materials Institute. In this capacity he is involved with a broad range of work related to Life Cycle Assessment (LCA), including the U.S. Life Cycle Inventory Database Project of the National Renewable Energy Laboratory, regional database development and LCA education.

Brian Toevs, P.E., is the founder and president of BETA Engineers, a Harrisburg-area engineering firm specializing in building systems commissioning and a principal of 7group. He has 20 years experience in building systems design and over 5 years commissioning experience, having acted as the commissioning authority for government office buildings, commercial office buildings, hospitals and educational facilities. He also serves as a certification reviewer for LEED submissions.

Marcus B. Sheffer is an energy/environmental consultant with over 20 years of experience. His company, Energy Opportunities, Inc. provides technical consulting services on projects relating to energy management, efficiency and conservation; renewable energy systems, and the environmental impacts of human enterprises. Mr. Sheffer is also a partner in the 7group, a multi-disciplinary team of professionals focused on sustainable development. He is a USGBC Faculty for the LEED Advanced Training. Prior to forming Energy Opportunities in 1993, he was employed by the Pennsylvania Energy Office. Volunteer activities include leadership positions with the Green Building Association of Central PA, AIA PA Committee on the Environment, the Sustainable Energy Fund of Central Eastern PA, and the US Green Building Council. He is a designated by the Association of Energy Engineers as a Certified Energy Manager (CEM). Professional memberships include ASES, ASHRAE, IESNA, and the USGBC. Sheffer earned a Bachelor of Arts degree in Environmental Studies in 1981 and a Master of Science degree in Public Administration in 1986, both from Shippensburg University.

Our Advisory Board:

John Abrams, Chilmark, MA

Bob Berkebile, FAIA, Kansas City, MO

John Boecker, AIA, Harrisburg, PA

Terry Brennan, Rome, NY

Bill Browning, Hon. AIA, Rappahannock, VA

Nancy Clanton, P.E., Boulder, CO

Raymond Cole, Ph.D., Vancouver, BC

David Eisenberg, Tucson, AZ

Drew George, P.E., San Diego, CA

Harry Gordon, FAIA, Washington, DC

John L. Knott, Jr., Dewees Island, SC

Malcolm Lewis, Ph.D., P.E., Irvine, CA

Gail Lindsey, FAIA, Raleigh, NC

Joseph Lstiburek, P.E., Westford, MA

Sandra Mendler, AIA, San Francisco, CA

Greg Norris, Ph.D., N. Berwick, ME

Russell Perry, AIA, Washington, DC

Peter Pfeiffer, FAIA, Austin, TX

Bill Reed, AIA, Arlington, MA

Jonathan Rose, Katonah, NY

Marc Rosenbaum, P.E., Meriden, NH

Michael Totten, Washington, DC

Gail Vittori, Austin, TX

Let BuildingGreen Help You
Build a Greener World.

We've built our reputation on careful fact-finding and impartial analysis to provide you with some of the most highly regarded green building information available.

All of our resources are independently published—not sponsored by any industry or corporation, and carry no advertising—so that we can ensure editorial freedom and avoid bias.

Let BuildingGreen help you spend more of your precious time designing—and a lot less of it digging for information from questionable sources.

In addition to the *GreenSpec® Directory* you have in your hands, our resources include:

Environmental Building News™

One Year: $ 99*
Two Years: $169*
Three Years: $229*

*add $30/yr for delivery
outside US and Canada

"*EBN is the go-to publication for information on green building strategies, product and information. I couldn't do my work without it.*"
—Marcus Sheffer, Partner – 7group

BuildingGreen Suite®

This online resource was developed to keep you informed on the latest developments and trends in the green building field. Our searchable format makes it easy to find green building products for your projects an help you understand the various technologies. We offer a number of pricing options to suite your needs.

"*BuildingGreen Suite is a critical tool for keeping all of us at SmithGroup current in the rapidly evolving world of sustainable design. [Its] digital library of articles and product reviews . . . gives our staff unequaled access to the best unbiased sustainable design information in the business.*"
—Russell Perry, Principal – SmithGroup

For more information or to purchase these or any of the other green building publications that we offer, please visit **www.BuildingGreen.com/promo/GreenSpec** or give us a call at 1-800-861-0954

 **BuildingGreen**   122 Birge Street – Ste. 30 – Brattleboro, Vermont 05101